With love to Alex from Mummy. May, 1949.

Alex D. Shepherd
~~61 London Rd~~
~~Kilmarnock~~
Scotland
27 Gilmour Rd.
Edinburgh 9

STANLEY GIBBONS

PRICED POSTAGE STAMP CATALOGUE

1949

PART 1

BRITISH EMPIRE

(PLUS EGYPT, IRAQ, NEPAL, PALESTINE, TRANSJORDAN)

SECTION A

PERIOD 1840-1936

52nd EDITION.

Reprinted January, 1949

BY APPOINTMENT PHILATELISTS

TO HIS MAJESTY THE KING

STANLEY GIBBONS LTD.

391 STRAND, LONDON, W.C.2

ONLY ADDRESS—NO BRANCHES ANYWHERE

IMPORTANT. All letters to us **containing stamps** (including approval selections returned to us) from countries outside the Sterling Area must be addressed, **" STANLEY GIBBONS LTD., c/o THE BRITISH PHILATELIC ASSOCIATION, LTD., 3 BERNERS ST., LONDON, W.1."** The Sterling Area comprises the British Empire (**except** Canada, Newfoundland and the Anglo-Egyptian Sudan), Burma, Iceland, Iraq and the Faroe Islands. N.B.—Egypt, Palestine and Transjordan are NOT in the Sterling Area.

Please Note

This section of the catalogue lists the stamps of the British Empire and certain other associated countries (see Title Page) issued from 1840 to approximately 1936—the period covered by the reigns of Queen Victoria to King Edward VIII inclusive.

The King George VI and equivalent later issues will be found separately in the

STANLEY GIBBONS
KING GEORGE VI
CATALOGUE

Made and Printed in Great Britain by
William Brendon & Son, Ltd.
(*late of Plymouth*), at Watford

INDEX

INTRODUCTION.

A SUBDIVIDED CATALOGUE

Our object in confining this edition of the bound British Empire Catalogue to the stamps of the reigns of Queen Victoria to King Edward VIII is the simple one of trying to make our limited ration of paper go as far as possible.

Many collectors nowadays are interested solely in the stamps of the present reign and each of these who buys a catalogue which lists all British Empire stamps is not only wasting his own money, but depriving a collector of the older issues of the opportunity of possessing a catalogue of the stamps which interest him. We have therefore issued a separate volume of the stamps of the reign of King George VI which has already attained very wide popularity and we hope that those who want a catalogue of all British Empire stamps will not be greatly inconvenienced by this temporary sub-division of the Catalogue.

We must emphasise that the dividing line which we have adopted is not a rigid one, but is based on common sense and convenience. There seems little object in splitting the lists of a single set between two volumes, just because some were issued a little earlier and some a little later than the first day of the present reign. Whatever division is adopted will, of course, be criticised, but we feel that, on the whole, we have chosen a fair point of cleavage, where any doubt arises.

"FOREIGN" COUNTRIES

For the convenience of collectors who have always included the issues of those countries in a collection of British Empire stamps, we still keep the lists of Egypt, Iraq, Nepal Palestine and Transjordan in this catalogue, though they are now (and some of them have been for years past) "foreign" countries. There seems little object in taking such countries out of Part I and thus compelling many who do not collect the stamps of other foreign countries to buy an additional catalogue.

GENERAL REVISION

During the war years we accumulated a great mass of notes and suggestions from collectors and dealers in regard to this volume, most of which, in normal times, would have been considered from year to year. We have given careful consideration to many of these suggestions and have made a number of improvements in the lists of various countries, though we still have a number of notes left over for further consideration. Our thanks are due to those who have helped us in this way.

Thanks to the kindness of Mr. H. G. Porter, F.R.P.S.L., the well-known specialist in the stamps of the *Nigerias*, we have been able to make a number of improvements in the lists of this group, notably in regard to dates of issue. We have not yet been able to use by any means all the material with which he has very kindly supplied us, but hope to do more work on this section later on.

ORDINARY AND CHALKY PAPERS. We have reinstated, throughout this Catalogue, the letters "O" and "C" to indicate the existence of stamps on ordinary and chalk-surfaced paper, which, for technical reasons, had to be dropped when the type was re-set during the war after its destruction in the "blitz." Many collectors have asked us to provide this information and we are happy to do so.

We have also reinstated, in modified form, the information regarding overprint varieties in the early issues of ***Zanzibar***, but have omitted certain errors previously listed, following the comments made by Sir John Wilson, Bart., in an article published in the *London Philatelist*.

PRICES IN THIS EDITION

No amount of intelligent anticipation will enable a catalogue publisher to keep his prices in line with so buoyant a market as we have at present, especially at a time when it takes many months to get any volume printed and bound.

Prices have, as will be obvious on examination of the lists, been raised sharply in many issues, especially in the early issues of Great Britain and of the more popular British Colonies and Dominions; but there are many rising prices also in the modern issues and among the stamps of the less popular groups, for more and more people are deserting the fiercely-competitive popular areas for countries where collecting is less costly and there is a greater chance of picking up bargains.

With ever-increasing exports of postage stamps, and imports strictly controlled, we can see no reason for any check in the tide of rising values, healthy though such a check would be in shaking out the speculator-collector who is now making the hobby so expensive for the genuine amateur, so far as the scarcer stamps are concerned.

THE NARROWING CIRCLE

With free imports of stamps limited to the sterling area, the circle of countries from which even new issues can be imported is steadily contracting. Since the last edition of this Catalogue was published, Egypt, the Anglo-Egyptian Sudan, Palestine and Transjordan have left the sterling area, so that their stamps can no longer be freely imported, and the process may continue.

We have felt, for some time past, that if the stamp trade in this country is to play its full part in the export drive—and its contribution is already a considerable one—some modification should be made in the present system of controls, in order that dealers wishing to sell stamps abroad should be able to offer their clients complete service, by being allowed to import new issues of all countries under suitable restrictions and by being permitted to strengthen their stocks of obsolete stamps by purchases outside this country.'

As regards new issues, collectors abroad require complete coverage, at least of the British Empire. It is useless for British dealers to tell a collector in New York that they cannot supply new issues of Sudan, Canada and other countries, if he wants a complete new issue service. He is not concerned with British regulations. He wants the stamps, and will cease doing business with Britain and get what he wants through other channels.

Similarly, the dealer who has to rely for replenishment of his stock of the older stamps solely on the British market, which is steadily being drained of material through exports, finds it increasingly difficult to satisfy his overseas clients.

We suggest that exports of postage stamps would be materially increased if the import restrictions were lifted, under proper control, so that a dealer might be permitted to buy stamps abroad to the extent of an agreed proportion of his increased exports.

NEW BRITISH STAMP POLICY

The philatelic world viewed with mixed feelings the announcement that the British Post Office had decided to issue no less than three special sets of postage stamps during 1948—the arrangements made, and the terms in which the new departure in policy was announced, making it clear that the main object was to secure foreign currency by sales of stamps to collectors abroad.

The Silver Wedding of Their Majesties the King and Queen was a most fitting occasion for the issue of special stamps, but good taste should surely have dictated the issue of denominations which would not lay us open to the charge that this happy anniversary was being used for the purpose of raising revenue. As the "set"—if it could be so called—consisted solely of a 2½d. and a £1 stamp, it stood self-condemned.

The issue of a set of stamps in connection with the Olympic Games might well be considered an act of international courtesy, and in this case the denominations chosen were representative and of reasonable face value; but the issue of special stamps to commemorate the liberation of the Channel Islands, to be on general sale only in the Islands and linked, in the official announcement, with the 1948 holiday season, again introduced that nasty flavour of commercialism; not to mention the entirely new complication of stamps issued outside this country, but which have franking power within it.

The reason for all this may probably be found in muddled thinking, coupled with too much reliance on the absurd estimates which have appeared in the press as to the amount of foreign currency which could be raised from special issues of postage stamps, estimates which, by the time these lines are published, will have been proved to be false.

The main reason for dislike of this entirely new orientation of Post Office policy is that, for the first time, it places our country on a level with others—of low repute with philatelists—which issue stamps with the main objective of extracting money from collectors. This fact, unless the policy is quickly reversed, will do great harm to sales of British and British Empire stamps abroad, and the resultant loss will far outweigh any temporary gain accruing from the special British issues of the year.

One thing, at least, the Post Office have succeeded in doing. By issuing a £1 postage stamp, of limited validity, they have created the ideal medium for the illegal transfer of British currency abroad, as no controls which were ever created can stop the circulation of such small pieces of paper.

PHILATELIC SUPPLIES

Owing to paper rationing, the need to increase exports, and the heavy pressure on the printing, binding and manufacturing trades there is still a great shortage of stamp albums, catalogues and accessories. We are doing our utmost to maintain a steady stream of supplies, though the enormous demand absorbs deliveries of most items almost as soon as they reach us.

There seems to be no early prospect of any increase in the paper ration, or any lessening of production difficulties, but we shall continue to do our best to serve collectors.

THE BRITISH PHILATELIC ASSOCIATION

One of the outstanding features of the post-war philatelic world has been the rapid expansion of the British Philatelic Association. During the war the Association was busily engaged in dealing with the many special problems which affected collectors and the stamp trade during that difficult period, but plans were made for the creation of a far wider organisation as soon as conditions permitted.

Now the B.P.A., with an entirely new and democratic constitution, comprises in its scope not only individual collectors and dealers, but philatelic societies and exchange clubs, the interests of each group being cared for by special sub-committees, while the Council of the Association co-ordinates their work and acts as watch-dog for the whole philatelic community.

A number of successful exhibitions have been organised, members have their own very attractive magazine, and numerous special services are available.

The problems and difficulties of the present time are not less urgent than those of the war period, so that the existence of a strong, officially recognised, representative organisation was never more essential than it is to-day. There has never been such a body until now, and never until now, a body worthy of the title of National Philatelic Association.

Those collectors, traders, societies and clubs who realise the need for such an organisation and are prepared to support it, not only in the general interest, but for their own personal benefit, should write for particulars of the British Philatelic Association to The Secretary, B.P.A., Ltd., 3, Berners Street, London, W.1.

DO NOT SEND US STAMPS FROM OVERSEAS, UNLESS—

If you reside outside the United Kingdom and wish to send us stamps, the address to which you write depends on whether or not you live within the "Sterling Area."

The "Sterling Area" comprises the British Empire (*except* Canada, Newfoundland and the Anglo-Egyptian Sudan), Burma, Iceland, Iraq and the Faroe Islands. From any place within this area letters containing stamps can be addressed direct to STANLEY GIBBONS LTD., 391 STRAND, LONDON, W.C.2.

From outside the "Sterling Area" (and we remind you again that the "Sterling Area" does not include Canada, Newfoundland and Sudan, nor Egypt, Palestine and Trans-jordan) all letters containing stamps must be addressed: STANLEY GIBBONS LTD., c/o THE BRITISH PHILATELIC ASSOCIATION LTD., 3 BERNERS ST., LONDON, W.1. This applies to stamps sent us for editorial comment or inspection, to approval selections which you are returning to us and in fact, to any stamps whatsoever, which you wish to send. Failure to address your letter correctly may lead to confiscation of the stamps by the authorities.

We cannot, owing to currency restrictions, buy stamps from anyone resident in countries outside the "Sterling Area."

OUR STAMP-BUYING DEPARTMENT

We are daily buying collections of all kinds, single rarities, covers and quantities of sets and single stamps required for our general stock. We welcome offers of all such items, small or large, and pay cash down for anything we buy.

All communications regarding stamps offered for sale should be addressed to 391, Strand, London. W.C.2. **Please WRITE in the first instance, giving general particulars, before sending stamps.**

Please see notes above *re* sending stamps from non-sterling areas. These must not on any account be sent even through the British Philatelic Association, unless we definitely confirm that permission has been granted.

LANTERN LECTURES AND DISPLAY CARDS. New and revised series of Lantern Lectures and Display Cards of stamps for exhibition are in preparation and we are therefore looking forward to being able to resume our popular loan service. An announcement will be made in *Gibbons' Stamp Monthly* in due course.

PUBLISHERS' TERMS OF SALE, ETC.

GUARANTEE.—Every effort is made to ensure that all stamps sold by us, unless otherwise described, shall be in all respects genuine originals and they are offered for sale as such. If not as described, and if returned to us by the purchaser within six years, we undertake to refund the price paid to us and our liability in respect thereof shall be limited accordingly.

If any stamp is certified as genuine by the Expert Committee of the Royal Philatelic Society, London, or of the British Philatelic Association Ltd., the purchaser shall not be entitled to make any claim against us in respect of any error, omission or mistake in such certificate.

All purchases from us are to be deemed to be subject to the above conditions.

(*N.B. The above form of guarantee is that approved by the Royal Philatelic Society and by the British Philatelic Association Ltd.*)

PRICES AND PRICE ALTERATIONS.—Our prices in this Catalogue are for stamps in fine condition, except in the case of the older "classic" issues which vary greatly in condition. For such issues, our prices are for stamps in good average condition, superb copies being supplied at special prices. *Less perfect copies of those issues in which "condition" varies greatly can be supplied at prices much below those quoted in this Catalogue.* In some issues a range of prices is quoted, but outside this range there are specimens so poor as to be valueless and others so fine as to exceed in value the highest quotation given for normally fine condition.

The prices quoted are those current when the Catalogue was revised, but that is now some months before publication. A number of price alterations are notified each month in *Gibbons' Stamp Monthly*.

We reserve the right to raise or lower the prices quoted in this Catalogue without notice, and we give no guarantee to supply all stamps priced.

Prices for unused stamps are in the left-hand column and those for used in the right. Exceptions in G.B. Controls and South African countries are indicated at the head of the columns.

TERMS.—*Net Cash in advance,* except in the case of clients known to us, or furnishing the usual business references, to whom selections will gladly be sent on approval, on request.

HOW TO REMIT.—Remittances must be made free of costs, preferably by cheque, payable in London, or by Banker's Draft, payable on demand. Cheques should be drawn to the order of "Stanley Gibbons, Ltd.," and crossed "Lloyds Bank, Ltd." Scotch, Irish and Foreign cheques will be sold, and the proceeds only credited to the customer.

Money Orders and Postal Orders should be made payable to "Stanley Gibbons, Ltd.," at the "G.P.O., London," and should be crossed "Lloyds Bank, Ltd."

Coin, Bank of England Notes, or Foreign Bank Notes should be registered. Foreign remittances will be sold and the sender credited with the amount actually received.

Remittances from countries outside the Sterling area must be made by International Money Order or any other method which conforms to the currency restrictions in force in Great Britain. Before remitting by any other method than a Money Order, it is advisable to consult a banker.

Unused, current Empire or Foreign stamps cannot be accepted as remittances. REPLY COUPONS CANNOT BE ACCEPTED.

HOW TO ORDER STAMPS.—In ordering stamps from this Catalogue it is only necessary to give name of country, the number in the left-hand column, and, if there are two sets of price columns, the letter or other indication at the head of the price column indicating the variety desired, and to state if required used or unused. All orders should be written on slips of paper, on one side only, *separately from the letter that accompanies them*; the original order will then be returned with the stamps.

WANT LISTS.—Collectors may confidently send in their lists of wants, and depend on receiving a large proportion of the stamps ordered. If stamps are not in our stock, our world-wide connections often enable us to obtain them elsewhere. All stamps are sent "on approval". Owing to shortage of staff we regret that we cannot at present execute want lists for stamps priced at less than one shilling in this catalogue. These should be bought from our Approval Sheets. Want lists are subject to very considerable delay.

APPROVAL SELECTIONS.—Any portion of our vast stock of stamps can be sent "on approval" to any address in the world. Selections will be arranged to suit the individual requirements of any collector, and when requesting approvals it is particularly desirable that full details should be given of the type of selection required. Arrangements can be made to send selections at regular or irregular intervals, as desired, and there is no obligation to purchase stamps to any particular amount.

APPROVAL SHEETS.—We have a large range of approval sheets, offering a selection of many thousands of different stamps of the less expensive kinds. The quality and value of these sheets have been widely commented on.

APPROVAL BOOKS.—Thousands of our famous approval books are always on hand. Covering the stamps of the whole world, they range in value from a few shillings to hundreds of pounds. Every collector can be sure of receiving attractive and interesting selections if he asks for a Gibbons' Approval Book.

RARITIES.—Special books of rare stamps are available and can be sent on approval to collectors known to us, or furnishing the usual business references.

BRITISH EMPIRE NEW ISSUES.—We are now sending regular selections of British Empire new issues to any address in the world.

We have a well-organised service for this purpose and many hundreds of satisfied collectors are buying their new issues from us in this way. Many limited issues and scarce provisionals have been sent out and regular new issue clients get first choice, where stocks are not sufficient to go round.

Further details will be sent on request.

YOUR FULL AND CLEARLY WRITTEN NAME AND ADDRESS with *every* communication will much oblige.

LETTERS FOR THE EDITOR.—Correspondence on editorial matters connected with this Catalogue should be addressed to the Editor. Orders for stamps, etc., should NOT be sent in the same letters as they will be subjected to delay.

The Editor and Publishers can accept no responsibility for stamps sent by correspondents, though every care will, of course, be taken.

All letters to the Editor must be accompanied by stamped addressed envelope for reply, and where stamps are sent, the necessary amount for registration should be added.

EXAMINATION AND IDENTIFICATION OF STAMPS.—We regret that we cannot give opinions as to the genuineness of stamps, nor do we identify stamps or number them by our Catalogue.

SUPPLEMENTS TO THIS CATALOGUE.—Our magazine, *Gibbons' Stamp Monthly* (price 6s. a year) includes, in addition to articles and features, a monthly illustrated supplement to this Catalogue. We regret that as we are already using our full ration of paper we may not be able to accept new subscriptions immediately, but if this is so, we place customers' names on a waiting list.

OUR ADDRESS—

STANLEY GIBBONS LTD.,
391 STRAND, LONDON, W.C.2.

Telephone: Temple Bar 9707. Telegrams: Philatelic, Rand London.
Cables: Stangib, London. Code: A.B.C. (6th edition).

SHOP DEPARTMENT.—Our retail shop is open at 391 Strand, W.C.2. Hours of business; 9 a.m. to 5.30 p.m. Monday to Friday. (Not open on Saturday.)

De La Rue Dies (Victorian and Georgian).

Types of the General Plates used by Messrs. De La Rue & Co. for printing British Colonial Stamps.

I. VICTORIAN KEY TYPE

Die I

Die II

Die I

1. The ball of decoration on the second point of the Crown appears as a dark mass of lines.
2. Dark vertical shading separates the front hair from the bun.
3. The vertical line of colour outlining the front of the throat stops at the sixth line of shading on the neck.
4. The white space in the coil of the hair above the curl is roughly the shape of a pin's head.

Die II

1. There are very few lines of colour in the ball and it appears almost white.
2. A white vertical strand of hair appears in place of the dark shading.
3. The line stops at the eighth line of shading.
4. The white space is oblong, with a line of colour partially dividing it at the left end.

Plates numbered 1 and 2 are both Die I. Plates 3 and 4 are Die II.

II. GEORGIAN KEY TYPE

Die I

Die II

Die I

A. The second (thick) line below the name of the country is cut slanting, conforming roughly to the shape of the Crown on each side.

B. The labels of solid colour bearing the words "POSTAGE" and "& REVENUE" are square at the inner top corners.

C. There is a projecting "bud" on the outer spiral of the ornament in each of the lower corners.

Die II

A. The second line is cut vertically on each side of the Crown.

B. The labels curve inwards at the top.

C. There is no "bud" in this position.

Unless otherwise stated in the lists, all stamps with wmk. Multiple Crown CA are Die I while those with wmk. Multiple Script CA are Die II.

WATERMARKS.

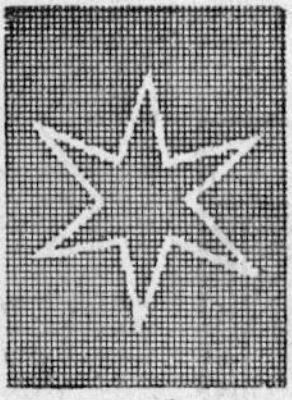

w. 1

w. 2

The watermarks in the stamps printed by Messrs. Perkins Bacon and Co. for various British possessions were (w. **1**) *Large Star*, measuring from 15 to 16 mm. across the star from point to point, and about 27 mm. from centre to centre vertically; (w. **2**) *Small Star* of similar design, but measuring from 12 to 13½ mm. from point to point, and 24 mm. from centre to centre vertically; and (w. **3**) Broad Star, in which the points are broader. The Large Star paper was made for long stamps like Ceylon and St. Helena, the Small Star paper for ordinary size stamps, as Grenada, Barbados, etc.; consequently, when the former was used for the smaller stamps, the watermark only occasionally comes in the centre of the paper, and frequently is so misplaced as to show portions of two stars above and below (this eccentricity will very often determine the watermark when it would be difficult otherwise to test it). The watermarks in the stamps printed by Messrs. De La Rue and Co. for various British possessions—not exclusively used for one colony—are (w. **4**) a Crown over "CC" (Crown Colonies) for the stamps of ordinary size, (w. **5**) for the stamps of larger size, and (w. **6**) a Crown over "CA" (Crown Agents). There is also another (w. **7**) properly described as "CA over Crown." This watermark was specially made for paper on which it was intended to print long fiscal stamps of the size and shape of those (which have been used postally) in Sierra Leone, Western Australia, etc. It occupies twice the space of the ordinary Crown CA watermark. When stamps of normal size are printed on paper with this watermark, the watermark is *sideways*, and it takes a horizontal pair of postage stamps to show the entire watermark.

w. 3

w. 4

w. 5

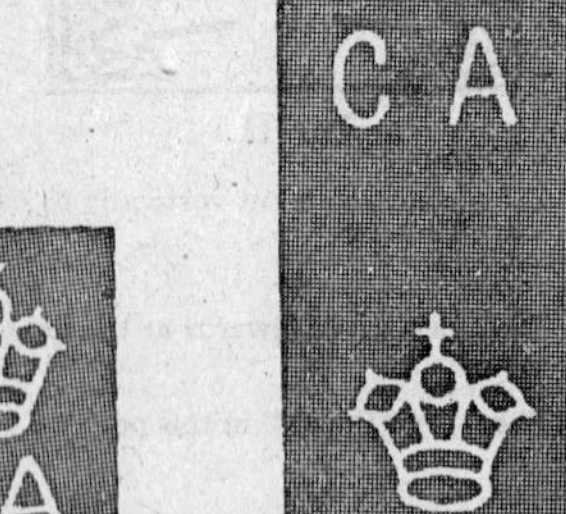

w. 6 w. 7

w. 8

w. 9

In 1904 a new watermark (w. **8**), described as "Multiple Crown CA," was introduced. On stamps of the ordinary size portions of 2 or 3 watermarks appear, and on the large-sized stamps a greater number can be observed.

In 1921 yet another change was made, resulting in what is known as the "Multiple Script CA" watermark, in which the letters are in Script character, while the Crown is of distinctly different shape (Type w. **9**).

w. 10 w. 11

We also illustrate here two watermarks which are found in the stamps of the Australian states, to avoid frequent repetition of them in the text.

NO QUERIES PLEASE

We much regret that as we now have no staff available for the purpose, we cannot answer any queries about stamps, or about the details given in our catalogues.

NOTES

Colonial "Chalky" and Coloured Papers.

"Ordinary" and "Chalk-surfaced" Papers.—It appears that the patent fugitive colours of Messrs. De La Rue and Co. were not found to be quite a sufficient safeguard in the case of stamps used for both postal and fiscal purposes, or that so many different values were used for both purposes that it was impossible to find a sufficient number of different fugitive colours to distinguish them. Consequently the ordinary paper, both for the stamps of Great Britain and for those of the Colonies, was gradually superseded by a *chalk-surfaced* paper, from which it is difficult to remove any form of obliteration without at the same time removing the impression of the stamp.

The majority of the values of the 1902–10 issue of Great Britain, as well as stamps of most of the Colonies, have appeared upon the surfaced paper. The amount of chalk-surfacing is so very variable that in *used* copies it is sometimes impossible to detect it.

From 1907–8 onwards the stamps in "single colours" were, with a few exceptions, printed on unsurfaced or ordinary paper and bicoloured stamps on the surfaced paper, this rule being generally adhered to side by side with the "universal" colour scheme which was then in process of adoption throughout the Crown Agencies.

With a few exceptions we *do not list* the varieties on chalk-surfaced paper separately, but we have indicated the existence of the papers by the letters "**O**" (*ordinary*) and "**C**" (*chalky*) after the description of all stamps where the chalky paper may be found. The two letters together, of course, signify that the stamp exists on both papers. The price quoted is that of the cheaper variety, it in most cases being that on the *chalky* paper.

In some cases also stamps printed on paper watermarked Crown CC, Type w. **5**, or CA over Crown, Type w. **7**, have "chalk-surface." In such cases we have added "**O**" and "**C**" as above, but where no value of the set has appeared on the chalky paper no indication is made.

British Colonial Green and Yellow Papers.—The issue of stamps printed on paper with coloured surface and white back (commonly called "white-backs") necessitated a special method of indicating their existence in the Catalogue lists. Owing to further variations in the Colonial green and yellow papers the lists are now extended, as many of these stamps show one colour on the surface of the paper and another at the back. While there are many variations which will not fall within any hard-and-fast classification, we have adopted the following grouping as being the least likely to cause confusion.

YELLOW PAPER

(*a*) The original *yellow* paper, usually bright in colour.
(*b*) The "*white-backs*."
(*c*) A bright *lemon* paper. Only stamps with the greenish tinge of true lemon have been put in this group, otherwise they belong to Group (*a*). Stamps of Group (*a*) printed in green sometimes make the paper appear *lemon*, and allowance must be made for this.
(*d*) An *orange-buff* paper, with a distinct brownish (coffee) tinge, not to be confused with a muddy yellow belonging to Group (*a*).
(*e*) The *pale yellow* paper, which has a creamy tone.

GREEN PAPER

(*m*) The original *green* paper, varying considerably through shades of bluish and yellowish green.
(*n*) The "*white-backs*."
(*p*) A paper bluish-green on the surface, with "*pale*" or "*olive*" *back*.
(*q*) **Paper with a bright green surface, commonly called "*emerald-surfaced*," with the olive** back of Group (*p*).
(*r*) **The paper with "*emerald back*." As (*q*), but with the bright colour at back and front.**

ABBREVIATIONS USED IN THIS PART

Anniv.	denotes	Anniversary.
B. W. & Co.	,,	Bradbury, Wilkinson & Co.
C	,,	Chalky paper.
Des.	,,	Designer ; designed.
Diag.	,,	Diagonal ; diagonally.
D. L. R. & Co.	,,	De La Rue & Co.
Eng.	,,	Engraver ; engraved.
Fisc.-c.	,,	Fiscally cancelled.
Imp., Imperf.	,,	Imperforate (not Perforated).
Inscr.	,,	Inscribed.
L.	,,	Left.
Litho.	,,	Lithographed.
mm.	,,	Millimetres
O	,,	Ordinary paper.
Opt(d).	,,	Overprint(ed).
P.-c. or Pen.-c	,,	Pen-cancelled.
P, Perf. or Pf.	,,	Perforated.
Percé en arc	,,	Perforated in curves.
Percé en scie	,,	Perforated with a saw-edge.
Photo.	,,	Photogravure.
Pin-Perf.	,,	Perforated without removing any paper.
Ptd.	,,	Printed.
R.	,,	Right.
Recess.	,,	Recess-printed.
Roul.	,,	Rouletted—a broken line of cuts.
S.	,,	SPECIMEN (overprint).
Surch.	,,	Surcharged.
T.	,,	Type.
Typo.	,,	Typographed.
Un.	,,	Unused.
Us.	,,	Used.
W. or Wmk.	,,	Watermark.
W'low & Sons	,,	Waterlow & Sons.
Wmk. s.	,,	Watermark sideways.

† (or * in lists of controls) = does not exist.

— means exists, but price cannot be quoted.

COLOURS. The following and similar abbreviations are in general use throughout the Catalogue where exigencies of space necessitate them :—Bwn., brn. (brown) ; car., carm. (carmine) ; blk. (black) ; grn. (green) ; mar. (marone) ; mve. (mauve) ; orge. (orange) ; pur. (purple) ; sep. (sepia) ; ultram. (ultramarine) ; vio. (violet) ; yell. (yellow).

In the case of stamps printed in two or more colours, the central portion of the design is in the first colour given, unless otherwise stated.

Where stamps are printed from "head" and "duty" plates, the colour of the portions printed from the "duty" plate (e.g. the name of the country and the value, or tablet of value) is usually given second.

COLOURS OF OVERPRINTS AND SURCHARGES. All overprints and surcharges are in black unless otherwise stated, either in the heading or by abbreviations in brackets after the description of the stamp, thus (B.) = blue, (Br.) = brown, (C.) = carmine, (G.) = green, (O.) = orange, (P.) = purple, (R.) = red, (V.) = violet, (Vm.) or (Verm.) = vermilion, (Y.) = yellow.

PERFORATIONS AND WATERMARKS. Stamps not described as "imperf." or "perf." are to be taken as imperforate.

Where no watermark is noted, the stamps are without distinctive watermark.

We do not list inverted watermarks as separate varieties.

STAMPS NOT LISTED in this Catalogue are almost certainly not adhesive postage stamps, but Revenue, Local or other issues outside its scope.

SIMPLIFICATION TABLES

For some years past we have realised that the lists of the early issues of some countries, which were written by specialists for specialists, are too complicated for the average collector and tend to turn him against stamps which are really very interesting.

The *Stanley Gibbons' Simplified Catalogue* has met the need of the collector who requires absolute simplicity, but we have felt that something must be done for the collector who wants to take main varieties of colour, watermark, etc., and who finds, in the more complicated lists of the big *Gibbons' Catalogue*, nothing to guide him as to which these varieties are.

True, the lists, lately revised in this Catalogue (e.g. Austria, Sweden) use small type and tabular statements to indicate varieties of lesser importance, but it will be some years before the whole Catalogue is in this form, in which every collector can find easily the class of varieties which interests him.

Now, therefore, we have introduced at the beginning of each of the more complicated lists a table headed "**SIMPLIFICATION**" which gives the catalogue numbers of the stamps of the earlier issues which the non-specialist collector is likely to need. The general basis is as follows, but common sense has been taken as a guide rather than any rigid rule and each country has been dealt with on its merits.

Plates and Dies. Where differences in plate or die make a clearly appreciable difference in the appearance of the stamp, they are included.

Colours. Where shades are included these are usually so pronounced that they may be regarded as a real difference in colour, clearly apparent to the untrained eye.

Watermarks. All major differences of watermark are included.

Perforations. Stamps imperf. and perf. are regarded as separate varieties. Variations in gauge of perforation are not usually included, though there are exceptions where there is a great difference in the general *appearance* of the perforation.

Errors and Varieties are not included.

The tables are shown as groups of catalogue numbers, main groups or issues being separated by full stops, while the end of a sub-group is indicated by a colon.

HOW TO USE THE TABLES

The catalogue numbers are not placed in catalogue order, but in the order in which we suggest that a straightforward collection might be arranged. **They thus provide a guide to arrangement as well as to simplification.**

Generally speaking, the numbers selected represent the cheapest variety (shade, perf., etc.) but sometimes the stamp which, though not the lowest priced, is likely to be the easiest to obtain. Only one number is given, even though there may be several at the same price. The collector must select his own alternatives.

We particularly urge collectors not to use these tables as a rigid guide, but only as a basis on which to superimpose their own individual ideas. The Simplification Table represents the "middle line." The collector who likes perfs. or shades or errors should amplify the tables for himself, while the "simple lifer" will no doubt cut out many of the shades and other items which we have included.

The whole art of collecting is to please yourself. The catalogue lists and the tables are only guides, each useful in its way, but should not be slavishly followed if full enjoyment is to be gained from the hobby.

GREAT BRITAIN.

GENERAL NOTES.—LINE-ENGRAVED ISSUES.

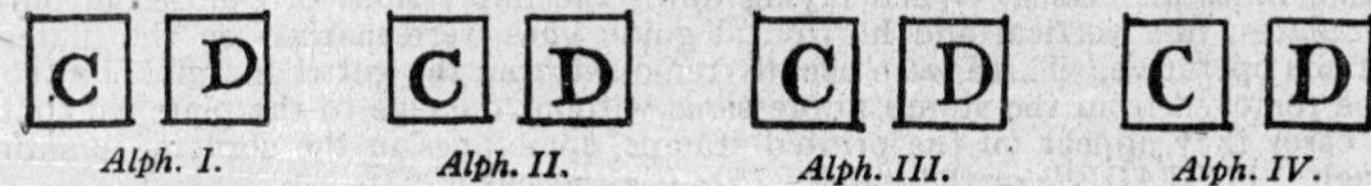

Typical Corner Letters of the four Alphabets.

Alphabets. Four different letterings were used for the corner letters on stamps prior to the issue with letters in all four corners, these being known to collectors as :—

Alphabet I. Used for all plates made from 1840 to the end of 1851. Letters small.

Alphabet II. Plates from 1852 to mid-1855. Letters larger, heavier and broader.

Alphabet III. Plates from mid-1855 to end of period. Letters tall and more slender.

Alphabet IV. 1861. 1d. Die II, Plates 50 and 51 only. Letters were hand-engraved instead of being punched on the plate. They are therefore inconsistent in shape and size.

While the general descriptions and the illustrations of typical letters given above may be of some assistance, only long experience can enable every stamp to be allotted to its particular Alphabet without hesitation, as certain letters in each are similar to those in one of the others.

Blued Paper. The blueing of the paper of the earlier issues is believed to be due to the presence of prussiate of potash in the printing ink, or in the paper, which, under certain conditions, tended to colour the paper when the sheets were damped for printing.

Corner Letters. The corner letters on the early British stamps were intended as a safeguard against forgery, each stamp in the sheet having a different combination of letters. Taking the first 1d. stamp, printed in 20 horizontal rows of 12, as an example, we have lettering as follows :—

Row 1. A A, A B, A C, etc. to A L.
Row 2. B A, B B, B C, etc. to B L.
and so on to
Row 20. T A, T B, T C, etc. to T L.

On the stamps with four corner letters, those in the upper corners are in the reverse positions to those in the lower corners. Thus in a sheet of 240 (12 × 20) we have :—

Row 1. A A / A A, B A / A B, C A / A C etc. to L A / A L
Row 2. A B / B A, B B / B B, C B / B C etc. to L B / B L.
and so on to
Row 20. A T / T A, B T / T B, C T / T C etc. to L T / T L

Dies. (*See illustrations above* No. 17.) The first Die of the 1d. was used for making the original Die of the 2d. which was used for both the No Lines and White Lines issues. In 1855 the 1d. Die I was amended by retouching the head and deepening the lines on a transferred impression of the original. This later version, known to collectors as Die II, was used for making the dies for the 1d. and 2d. with letters in all four corners and also for the 1½d.

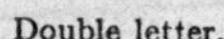

Double letter.

Guide line in corner.

Guide line through value.

NOTE.—*The above illustrations and that illustrating a re-entry, below, show typical examples of the varieties described, but there are numerous stamps showing double letters, guide lines or re-entries of differing importance, intensity and value.*

Double Corner Letters. These are due to the workman placing his letter punch in the wrong position at the first attempt, when lettering the plate, and then correcting the mistake, or to a slight shifting of the punch when struck. If a wrong letter was struck in the first instance, traces of a wrong letter may appear in a corner in addition to the correct one.

Guide Lines and Dots. When laying down the impressions of the design on the early plates, fine vertical and horizontal guide lines were marked on the plates to assist the operative. These were usually removed from the gutter margins, but could not be removed from the stamp impressions without damage to the plate, so that in such cases they appear on the printed stamps, sometimes in the corners, sometimes through " POSTAGE " or the value. (*See illustrations.*)

Guide dots or cuts were similarly made to indicate the spacing of the guide lines. These too sometimes appear on the stamps.

Inverted " S ". The letter " S " in the corner is inverted on Plates 78, 105 and 107 of the 1d. Die I, on S A and S B of Plate 140, on S A of Plate 143, and on most of the stamps of Die II, Plate 5.

Ivory head.

" Ivory Head." The so-called " ivory head " variety (*see illustration*) in which the Queen's Head shows white on the back of the stamp is due to the comparative absence of ink in the head portion of the design, with consequent absence of blueing. (See " Blued Paper " note above.)

Plates. Until the introduction of the stamps with letters in all four corners, the number of the plate was not indicated in the design of the stamp, but was printed on the sheet margin. By long study of identifiable blocks and of the minor variations in the design, coupled with the corner letters, philatelists are now able to allot many of these stamps to their respective plates, though plates with Alphabet II are comparatively little known.

Maltese Cross.

Type of Town postmark.

Type of 1844 postmark.

Postmarks. The so-called " Maltese Cross " design was the first employed for obliterating British postage stamps and was in use from 1840 to 1844. Being hand-cut, the obliterating stamps varied greatly in detail and some distinctive types can be allotted to particular towns or offices. Local types, such as those used at Manchester,

Norwich, Leeds, etc., are keenly sought for. A red ink was first employed but was superseded by black, after some earlier experiments, in February, 1841. Maltese Cross obliterations in other colours are rare.

Obliterators of this type, numbered 1 to 12 in the centre, were used at the London Chief Office in 1843 and 1844.

In 1844 the Maltese Cross design was superseded by numbered obliterators of various types, one of which is illustrated above. This is naturally comparatively scarce on the first 1d. and 2d. stamps. Like the Maltese Cross it is found in various colours, some of which are rare.

Re-cut " R ". On several plates the letter " R " is formed from the letter " P ", the tail having been hand cut. It occurs on the Penny Plate 10 in black and in red and also on Plates 30, 31, 33 ; 58, 83, 86 and 87.

Re-entry.

" Union Jack " re-entry.

Re-entries. Re-entries on the plate show as a doubling of part of the design of the stamp generally at top or bottom. Many re-entries are very slight while others are most marked. (*See illustration.*)

The " *Union Jack" re-entry*, so called owing to the effect of the re-entry on the appearance of the corner stars (*see illustration*) occurs on stamp L K of Plate 75 of the 1d. red, Die I.

M A (M L) T A (T L)

Varieties of the Large Crown Watermark.

I II

Two states of the Large Crown Watermark.

Watermarks. Two watermark varieties, consisting of crowns of entirely different shape, are found in sheets of the Large Crown paper and fall on stamps lettered M A and T A (or M L and T L when the paper is printed on the wrong side). Both varieties are found on the 1d. rose-red of 1857, while the M A (M L) variety comes also on some plates of the 1d. of 1864 (Nos. 43, 44) up to about Plate 96. It has also been found on the 2d. of 1854 (Plate 9). The varieties are believed to be due to the temporary replacement of damaged " bits " of the normal type by others of different shape. (*See illustrations.*)

In 1861 a minor alteration was made in the Large Crown watermark by the removal of the two small vertical strokes, representing *fleurs-de-lis*, which projected upwards from the uppermost of the three horizontal curves at the base of the Crown. Where these strokes are missing from watermarks of stamps before 1861 their absence is due to defective watermark " bits." (*See illustration.*)

QUEEN VICTORIA, 1837–1901.

MULREADY ENVELOPES AND COVERS, which were issued concurrently with the first British adhesive postage stamps, can be supplied as follows :

1d. black

Envelopes:	37/6 *unused* ;	35/0 *used.*
Covers :	37/6 *unused* ;	32/6 *used.*

2d. Blue.

Envelopes :	65s. *unused* ;	£6 *used*
Covers :	65s. *unused* ;	£5 10s *used.*

I.—LINE-ENGRAVED STAMPS.

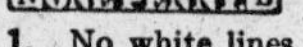
1. No white lines.

2. Small Crown.

(Engraved by Mr. Frederick Heath and printed by Messrs. Perkins Bacon & Co.)

1840 (6 May). *Letters in lower corners. Wmk. Small Crown. T* **2**. *Imperf.*

No.	Type.		Un. s. d.	Used. s. d.
1	1	1d. intense black	£25	70 0
2	,,	1d. black	£22	60 0
3	,,	1d. grey-black (worn plate)	£35	80 0

Varieties. 1d. black.

		Un.	Used.
a.	*On bleuté paper* ..		£5
b.	*Double letter in corner* ..	—	80 0
bb.	*Re-entry* ..	—	80 0
cc.	*Large letters in each corner (I L and J C) (Plate 1b)* ..	—	£9
c.	*Guide line in corner* ..	—	65 0
d.	,, *through value* ..	—	90 0
e.	*Wmk. inverted* ..	—	£8
f.	*Reconstructed plate of 240 stamps* ..	—	£700
g.	*Oblit. red Maltese Cross* ..	—	60 0
h.	*Oblit. black Maltese Cross* ..	—	60 0
i.	,, *blue* ,, ..	—	£35
k.	,, *magenta* ,, ..	—	£25
m.	,, *yellow* ,, ..		
n.	*Number (1 to 12) in Maltese Cross from*	—	£26
o.	*Town oblit. in black* ..	—	£25
p.	*Town oblit. in yellow* ..	—	£45
q.	*Penny Post oblit. in black* ..	—	£15
r.	*Oblit. of 1844 in black* ..	—	£12

NOTES. The 1d. stamp in black was printed from Plates 1 to 11. Plate 1 was printed from in two states (known to collectors as 1*a* and 1*b*), the latter being the result of extensive repairs.

The so-called "Royal reprint" of the 1d. black was made in 1864, from Plate 66, Die II, on paper with Large Crown watermark, inverted. A printing was also made in carmine, on paper with the same watermark, normal.

4	1	2d. deep full blue (no white lines) ..	£80	95 0
5	,,	2d. blue (,, ,,) ..	£80	80 0
6	,,	2d. pale blue (,, ,,) ..	£125	£12

For 1d. black with "VR" in upper corners see No. 601 following the Postage Dues.

Varieties. 2d. blue.

		Un.	Used.
a.	*Double letter in corner* ..	—	£16
aa.	*Re-entry* ..	—	£16
b.	*Guide line in corner* ..	—	£5
c.	,, *through value* ..	—	£12
d.	*Wmk. inverted* ..	—	£20
e.	*Oblit. red Maltese Cross* ..	—	80 0
f.	,, *black* ,, ..	—	80 0
g.	*Oblit. blue Maltese Cross* ..	—	£25
h.	,, *magenta* ,, ..	—	£30
i.	,, *number (1 to 12) in Maltese Cross from* ..	—	£25
k.	,, *of towns in black* ..	—	£15
l.	,, *of 1844 in black* ..	—	£8
m.	,, ,, *blue* ..	—	£26

NOTE. The 2d. stamps without white lines below "POSTAGE" and above the value were printed from Plates 1 and 2.

1841 (10 February). *Wmk. T* **2**. *Paper more or less blued. Imperf.*

7	1	1d. deep orange-brown (paper quite white) ..	£40	45 0
8	,,	1d. red-brown ..	45 0	1 6
8*a*	,,	1d. red-brown on very blue paper ..	80 0	3 0
9	,,	1d. pale red-brown (worn plate) ..	95 0	4 0
10	,,	1d. deep red-brown ..	50 0	5 0
11	,,	1d. lake-red ..	70 0	12 6
12	,,	1d. orange-brown ..	£8	22 6

Error. No letter "A" *in right lower corner.* (*Stamp* B (A), *Plate* 77.)

12*a* 1 1d. red-brown .. .. ..

Varieties. 1d. red-brown, etc.

		Un.	Used.
aa.	*Re-entry* ..	—	35 0
b.	*Double letter in corner* ..	—	35 0
ba.	,, *star* (*Plate* 75) "*Union Jack*" *re-entry* (see page 3) ..	—	£12
c.	*Guide line in upper right corner* ..	—	6 6
d.	,, *through value* ..	—	35 0
e.	*Thick outer frame to stamp* ..	—	12 6
f.	*Ivory head* ..	—	6 6
g.	*Wmk. inverted* ..	—	17 6
h.	*Oblit. red Maltese Cross* ..	—	£25
i.	,, *black* ,, ..	—	1 6
k.	,, *blue* ,, ..	—	30 0
m.	*Oblit. No.* 1 *in Maltese Cross* ..	—	10 0
	,, ,, 2 ,, ..	—	7 0
	,, ,, 3 ,, ..	—	12 6
	,, ,, 4 ,, ..	—	25 0
	,, ,, 5 ,, ..	—	10 0
	Oblit. No. 6 *in Maltese Cross* ..	—	7 6
	,, ,, 7 ,, ..	—	7 6
	,, ,, 8 ,, ..	—	7 6
	,, ,, 9 ,, ..	—	7 6
	,, ,, 10 ,, ..	—	8 0
	,, ,, 11 ,, ..	—	10 0
	,, ,, 12 ,, ..	—	17 6
n.	*Oblit. of Penny Post* ..	—	55 0
o.	*Oblit. of towns in black* ..	—	35 0
p.	,, ,, ,, *blue* ..	—	£6
q.	,, ,, ,, *green* ..		
r.	,, ,, ,, *yellow* ..		
s.	*Oblit. of* 1844 *in blue* ..	—	12 6
t.	,, ,, ,, *red* ..	—	£25
u.	,, ,, ,, *green* ..	—	60 0
v.	,, ,, ,, *violet* ..		
w.	*Left-corner letter* "s" *inverted* ..	—	70 0

NOTES. Plates 1, 2, 5, and 8 to 11 of those used for printing the 1d. black were also used for the earlier printings of the 1d. in red and are therefore known to collectors as the " black plates."

The error " No letter A in right corner " was due to the omission to insert this letter on stamp B A of Plate 77. The error was discovered some months after the plate was registered and was then corrected.

Stamps with thick outer frame to the design are from plates on which the frame-lines have been strengthened or recut, particularly Plates 76 and 90.

There are innumerable variations in the colour and shade of the 1d. " red " and those given in the above list represent colour groups each covering a wide range.

For " Union Jack re-entry ", " Inverted S " etc., see General Notes above.

3. White lines added.

13	3	2d. pale blue (13 March, 1841)	£12	15 0
14	"	2d. blue	£12	10 0
15	"	2d. deep full blue	£15	25 0

Varieties. 2d. blue.

a.	*Guide line in corner*	—	12 6	*Oblit. No. 4 in Maltese Cross*	—	27 6
b.	" *through value*	—	20 0	" " 5 " "	—	32 6
bb.	*Double letter in corner*	—	60 0	" " 6 " "	—	30 0
bc.	*Re-entry*	—	80 0	" " 7 " "	—	30 0
c.	*Ivory head*	—	17 6	" " 8 " "	—	35 0
d.	*Wmk. inverted*	—	70 0	" " 9 " "	—	55 0
e.	*Oblit. red Maltese Cross*	—	£35	" " 10 " "	—	£5
f.	*Oblit. black* "	—	10 0	" " 11 " "	—	90 0
g.	" *blue* "	—	80 0	" " 12 " "	—	25 0
i.	*Oblit. No. 1 in Maltese Cross*	—	35 0	k. *Oblit. of 1844 in black*	—	10 0
	" " 2 " "	—	35 0	l. " " " *blue*	—	50 0
	" " 3 " "	—	30 0	m. " " " *red*		
				n. " " " *green*		

NOTE. The 2d. stamp with white lines was printed from Plates 3 and 4.

1841 (April). *Trial printing (unissued) on Dickinson silk-thread paper.*

16 1 1d. red-brown (Plate 11) £50

Eight sheets were printed on this paper, six being gummed. Specimens known are without gum.

1848. *Rouletted 12, by Henry Archer.*

16*a* 1 1d. red-brown (Plates 70, 71) £75

1850. *P 16, by Henry Archer.*

16*b* 1 1d. red-brown (from Plates 90, 92–101 and 105. Also Pl. 8, unused only) .. £25 £28

* The used price is for stamp on cover with dated postmark. Stamps off cover, 90s. each.

1853. *Government Trial Perforations.*

16*c* 1 1d. red-brown (*perf.* 16) (*on cover*) .. ..

16*d* " 1d. " (*perf.* 14) £100

NOTES. Although the various trials of machines for rouletting and perforating were unofficial, Archer had the consent of the authorities in making his experiments, and sheets so experimented upon were afterwards put in use by the Post Office.

As Archer ended his experiments in 1850 and plates with corner letters of Alphabet II did not come into issue until 1852, perforated stamps with corner letters of Alphabet I may safely be assumed to be Archer productions, if genuine.

The Government trial perforations were done on Napier machines in 1853. As Alphabet II was by that time in use, the trials can only be distinguished from the perforated stamps listed below by being dated prior to January 28th, 1854, the date when the perforated stamps were officially issued.

Die I.

Die II.

Die I is the original die, used from 1840 to 1855. The features of the portrait are lightly shaded and consequently lack emphasis.

Die II is Die I retouched by Mr. William Humphrys in which the lines of the features have been deepened and appear stronger.

The eye is deeply shaded and made more lifelike. The nostril and lips are more clearly defined, the latter appearing much thicker. A strong downward stroke of colour marks the corner of the mouth. There is a deep indentation of colour between lower lip and chin. The band running from the back of the ear to the chignon has a bolder horizontal line below it than in Die I.

4. Large Crown.

1854–57. *Paper more or less blued.* (i.) *Wmk. Small Crown, T* **2**. *P* 16.

17	1	1d. red-brown (Die I) (February, 1854)	50 0	2 6
18	,,	1d. yellowish brown (Die I)	60 0	5 0
19	3	2d. deep blue (Plate 4) (13 March, 1854)	£30	15 0
20	,,	2d. pale blue (Plate 4)	£30	40 0
20a	,,	2d. blue (Plate 5) (28 August, 1855)	£80	£12
21	1	1d. red-brown (Die II) (6 March, 1855)	65 0	10 0
		a. Imperf.		

(ii.) *Wmk. Small Crown, T* **2**. *P* 14.

22	1	1d. red-brown (Die I) (January, 1855)	£12	25 0
23	3	2d. blue (Plate 4) (4 March, 1855)	£45	27 6
23a	,,	2d. blue (Plate 5) (16 July, 1855)	£55	45 0
24	1	1d. red-brown (Die II) (28 February, 1855)	75 0	12 6
24a	,,	1d. deep red-brown (very blue paper) (Die II)	95 0	25 0
25	,,	1d. orange-brown (Die II)	£18	90 0

(iii.) *Wmk. Large Crown, T* **4**. *P* 16.

26	1	1d. red-brown (Die II) (18 August, 1855)	£28	27 6
27	3	2d. blue (Plate 5) (20 July, 1855)	£130	£8
		a. Imperf. (Plate 5)		

(iv.) *Wmk. Large Crown, T* **4**. *P* 14.

29	1	1d. red-brown (Die II) (15 May, 1855)	27 6	1 0
		a. Imperf.	£30	
30	1	1d. brick-red (Die II)	30 0	5 0
31	,,	1d. plum (Die II) (February, 1857)	£8	20 0
32	,,	1d. brown-rose (Die II)	37 6	7 0
33	,,	1d. orange-brown (Die II) (March, 1857)	£10	25 0
34	3	2d. blue (Plate 5) (20 July, 1855)	£9	10 0
35	,,	2d. blue (Plate 6) (2 July, 1857)	£9	10 6

1856–58. *Paper no longer blued.* (i.) *Wmk. Large Crown, T* **4**. *P* 16.

36	1	1d. rose-red (Die II) (29 December, 1857)	£18	12 6
36a	3	2d. blue (Plate 6) (11 February, 1858)	£90	40 0

(ii.) (Die II) *Wmk. Large Crown, T* **4**. *P* 14.

37	1	1d. red-brown (November, 1856)	65 0	15 0
38	,,	1d. pale red (9 April, 1857)	30 0	5 0
		a. Imperf.		
39	,,	1d. pale rose	25 0	3 0
40	,,	1d. rose-red (July, 1857)	9 0	0 4
		a. Imperf.	£25	£28
41	1	1d. deep rose-red (August, 1857)	10 0	0 8

1861. *Letters engraved on plate instead of punched* (Alphabet IV).

42	1	1d. rose-red (Die II) (Plates 50 and 51)	75 0	7 6
		a. Imperf.		

NOTES. 1d. The numbering of the 1d. plates recommenced at 1 on the introduction of Die II. Corner letters of Alphabet III appear on Plate 22 and onwards.

As an experiment, the corner letters were engraved by hand on Plates 50 and 51 in 1856, instead of being punched (Alphabet IV), but punching was again resorted to on Plate 52 and onwards. Plates 50 and 51 were not put into use until 1861.

The variety "Inverted S in corner" is found on stamps S D to S L of the 1d. Die II, Plate 5.

2d. Plate 4 of the 2d. had corner letters of Alphabet I, Plate 5 Alphabet II and Plate 6 Alphabet III. In Plate 6 the white lines are thinner than before.

In both values varieties may be found as described in the preceding issues—ivory heads, inverted watermarks, re-entries, and double letters in corners.

The change of perforation from 16 to 14 was decided upon late in 1854 owing to the fact that the closer holes of the former gauge tended to cause the sheets of stamps to break up when handled, but for a time both gauges were in concurrent use. Owing to faulty alignment of the impressions on the plates and to shrinkage of the paper when damped, badly perforated stamps are plentiful in the line-engraved issues.

☞ All following stamps of Queen Victoria are *P* 14, unless otherwise stated.

5

6

Showing position of the plate number on the 1*d. and* 2*d. values.*

1858-64. *Letters in all four corners. Wmk. Large Crown, T* **4.** *Die II* (1*d. and* 2*d.*)

			Un.	Used.
43	5	1d. rose-red (1 April, 1864)	2 6	0 2
44	,,	1d. lake-red	2 6	0 2

Plate No.	Un. s. d.	Used. s. d.	Plate No.	Un. s. d.	Used. s. d.	Plate No.	Un. s. d.	Used. s. d.	Plate No.	Un. s. d.	Used. s. d.
71.	6 0	0 6	110.	7 6	0 6	150.	4 0	0 4	188.	8 0	0 4
72.	6 0	0 6	111.	6 6	0 6	151.	10 6	0 6	189.	10 0	0 6
73.	7 6	0 6	112.	20 0	0 8	152.	5 0	0 2	190.	3 0	0 4
74.	8 0	0 8	113.	6 6	0 6	153.	15 0	4 0	191.	2 6	0 6
76.	10 0	0 8	114.	8 0	0 8	154.	7 6	0 6	192.	2 6	0 4
77.	£450	£300	115.	30 0	0 6	155.	8 0	0 4	193.	2 6	0 4
78.	3 6	0 4	116.	12 6	0 6	156.	6 6	0 6	194.	6 0	0 6
79.	3 9	0 6	117.	2 6	0 4	157.	6 0	0 4	195.	7 6	0 6
80.	8 6	0 6	118.	3 0	0 6	158.	3 6	0 4	196.	3 6	0 6
81.	22 6	0 6	119.	3 9	0 4	159.	5 0	0 6	197.	10 0	0 4
82.	15 0	0 8	120.	2 6	0 2	160.	3 6	0 6	198.	3 6	0 2
83.	£9	7 6	121.	3 6	0 4	161.	12 6	0 6	199.	3 6	0 4
84.	4 0	0 6	122.	3 0	0 2	162.	7 6	0 6	200.	4 6	0 4
85.	6 6	0 8	123.	3 0	0 6	163.	6 0	0 6	201.	3 0	0 6
86.	15 0	0 6	124.	3 0	0 6	164.	5 0	0 4	202.	4 0	0 6
87.	3 0	0 8	125.	5 0	0 6	165.	4 6	0 4	203.	4 0	0 4
88.	70 0	4 0	127.	5 0	0 4	166.	5 6	0 6	204.	6 0	0 2
89.	6 0	0 6	129.	4 6	0 6	167.	3 6	0 4	205.	6 6	0 2
90.	15 0	0 6	130.	4 0	0 6	168.	6 0	0 4	206.	5 0	0 2
91.	3 9	0 6	131.	3 6	0 6	169.	7 0	0 6	207.	3 6	0 4
92.	8 0	0 6	132.	70 0	7 6	170.	5 0	0 4	208.	8 0	0 2
93.	9 0	0 6	133.	60 0	3 0	171.	3 6	0 4	209.	10 0	0 2
94.	12 6	0 6	134.	3 6	0 8	172.	4 0	0 6	210.	12 6	0 4
95.	10 0	0 6	135.	4 0	0 6	173.	3 6	0 6	211.	15 0	3 6
96.	17 6	0 8	136.	6 0	0 6	174.	3 0	0 2	212.	6 0	0 6
97.	10 0	0 6	137.	7 6	0 8	175.	3 6	0 4	213.	6 0	0 4
98.	6 6	0 6	138.	4 0	0 6	176.	6 0	0 4	214.	6 0	0 4
99.	10 0	0 6	139.	4 0	0 8	177.	3 0	0 6	215.	7 6	0 4
100.	6 0	0 6	140.	2 6	0 2	178.	7 6	0 4	216.	6 9	0 8
101.	12 6	0 6	141.	7 6	0 9	179.	6 0	0 6	217.	7 6	2 6
102.	7 6	0 6	142.	10 6	0 6	180.	10 0	0 6	218.	6 0	2 6
103.	5 0	0 6	143.	10 0	0 6	181.	6 6	0 4	219.	15 0	12 0
104.	17 6	2 6	144.	12 0	0 6	182.	6 0	0 6	220.	3 6	2 6
105.	30 0	1 9	145.	3 6	0 6	183.	4 6	0 2	221.	12 0	5 0
106.	10 0	0 8	146.	4 6	0 6	184.	2 6	0 8	222.	12 0	5 0
107.	15 0	0 6	147.	4 6	0 4	185.	6 6	0 4	223.	15 0	12 6
108.	22 6	0 6	148.	3 0	0 4	186.	4 6	0 8	224.	15 0	10 0
109.	30 0	0 6	149.	8 0	0 4	187.	5 0	0 4	225.	£15	80 0

Variety. Imperf. Issued at Cardiff (Plate 116).

			Un.	Used.
44*b*	5	1d. rose-red (18.1.70)	—	£60

The following plate numbers are also known imperf. and used :—79, 81, 86, 88, 90, 91, 92, 93, 97, 100, 101, 102, 103, 104, 105, 107, 108, 109, 112, 114, 117, 120, 121, 122, 136, 142, 146, 148, 158, 162 64, 171, 174 and 191.

NOTES. The numbering of this series of plates follows after that of the previous 1d. stamp, last printed from Plate 68.

Plates 69, 70, 75, 126 and 128 were prepared for this issue but rejected owing to defects, and stamps from these plates do not exist, so that specimens which appear to be from these plates (like many of those which optimistic collectors believe to be from Plate 77) bear other plate numbers. Owing to faulty engraving or printing it is not always easy to identify the plate number. Plate 77 was also rejected but some stamps printed from it were used. One specimen is in the Tapling Collection and six or seven others are known. Plates 226 to 228 were made but not used.

Specimens from most of the plates are known with inverted watermark. The variety of watermark described in the General Notes occurs on stamp M A (or M L) on plates up to about 96.

Re-entries in this issue are few, the best being on stamps M K and T K of Plate 71 and on S L and T L, Plate 83.

45	6	2d. blue (thick lines) (July, 1858)	27 6	1 6
		a. Imperf. (Plate 9)		

Plate No.	Un. s. d.	Used. s. d.	Plate No.	Un. s. d.	Used. s. d.
7.	£8	4 6	9.	27 6	1 6
8.	£9	3 6	12.	£5	15 0

46	6	2d. blue (thin lines) (1 July, 1869)	35 0	3 6
47	,,	2d. deep blue (thin lines)	35 0	3 6
		a. Imperf. (Plate 13)		

Plate No.	Un. s. d.	Used. s. d.
13.	35 0	3 6
14.	50 0	6 6
15.	40 0	6 6

NOTES. Plates 10 and 11 were prepared but rejected. Plates 13 to 15 were laid down from a new roller impression on which the white lines were thinner.

There are some marked re-entries, particularly on Plates 7 and 12.

Stamps with inverted watermark may be found and the M A (M L) watermark variety (see General Notes) is known on Plate 9.

Though the paper is normally white, some printings showed blueing and stamps showing the "ivory head" may therefore be found.

7

9

Showing the plate number (20).

1870 (1 Oct.). *Wmk. T 9, extending over three stamps.*

48	7	½d. rose-red	6 0	1 3
49	,,	½d. rose	6 0	1 3

Plate No.	Un. s. d.	Used. s. d.	Plate No.	Un. s. d.	Used. s. d.	Plate No.	Un. s. d.	Used. s. d.	Plate No.	Un. s. d.	Used. s. d.
1.	25 0	6 0	6.	6	1 6	11.	6 0	1 3	15.	7 6	2 0
3.	10 6	2 0	8.	40 0	12 6	12.	10 6	1 3	19.	35 0	3 6
4.	10 6	1 6	9.	£16	65 0	13.	6 6	1 3	20.	15 0	3 0
5.	8 6	1 3	10.	7 6	1 3	14.	8 6	1 3			

The following plate numbers are known imperf. and used: 1, 4, 5, 6, 8 and 14.

NOTES. The ½d. was printed in sheets of 480 (24 × 20) so that the check letters run from $\frac{\text{A A}}{\text{A A}}$ to $\frac{\text{X T}}{\text{T X}}$.

Plates 2, 7, 16, 17 and 18 were not completed while Plates 21 and 22, though made, were not used.

Owing to the method of perforating, the outer side of stamps in either the A or X row (i.e. the left or right sides of the sheet) is imperf.

Stamps may be found with watermark inverted or reversed, or without watermark, the latter due to misplacement of the paper when printing.

8

1870 (1 Oct.). *Wmk. T* **4.**

51	8	1½d. rose-red	45 0	8 0
52	,,	1½d. lake-red	45 0	8 0
		a. Imperf. (Plate 1 and 3)	£40	
		Error of lettering. **OP–PC** *for* **CP–PC** (*Plate* 1.		
53	8	1½d. rose-red	£150	£30

Plate No.	Un. s. d.	Used. s. d.
(1)	55 0	10 0
3	45 0	8 0

NOTES. Owing to a proposed change in the postal rates, 1½d. stamps were first printed in 1860, in rosy mauve, No. 53*a*, but the change was not approved and the greater part of the stock was destroyed.

In 1870 a 1½d. stamp was required and was issued in rose-red.

Plate 1 did not have the plate number in the design of the stamps, but on stamps from Plate 3 the number will be found in the curved pattern a little above the lower corner letter at each side.

Plate 2 was defective and was not used.

The error of lettering O P–P C on Plate 1 was apparently not noticed by the printers and therefore not corrected. It was not noted by collectors until 1894.

Imperf. stamps are known from both plates.

1860. *Prepared for use but not issued ; blued paper.*

53*a* 8 1½d. rosy mauve (Plate 1) £25

One example of the error **OP-PC** is known in this colour.

II.—EMBOSSED STAMPS.

10 11 12

13 Showing position of die number.

(Primary die engraved at the Royal Mint by Mr. William Wyon. Stamps printed at Somerset House.)

1847–54. *Imperf.* (For paper and wmk. see footnote.)

54	**10**	1s. pale green (11 September, 1847) ..	£35	50 0
55	„	1s. green ..	£35	50 0
56	„	1s. deep green	£45	£8
		Die 1. **1847** ..	£35	50 0
		Die 2. **1854** ..	£35	50 0
57	**11**	10d. brown (6 November, 1848) ..	£25	£8
		Die 1. **1848** ..	—	£20
		No die number ..	—	—
		Die 2. **1850** ..	£25	£8
		Die 3. **1853** ..	£25	£8
		Die 4. **1854** ..	£25	£10
58	**12**	6d. mauve (1 March, 1854) ..	£28	65 0
59	„	6d. dull lilac ..	£30	60 0
60	„	6d. purple ..	£40	60 0
61	„	6d. violet ..	£30	85 0

NOTES. The 1s. and 10d. are on " Dickinson " paper with silk threads. The 6d. is on paper watermarked V R in single-lined letters, Type **13,** which may be found in four ways—upright, inverted, upright reversed, and inverted reversed ; none are scarce.

The die numbers are indicated on the base of the bust. Only Die 1 (1 WW) of the 6d. was used for the adhesive stamps. The 10d. is from Die 1 (W.W.1 on stamps), and Dies 2 to 4 (2 W.W., 3 W.W., 4 W.W.) but the number and letters on stamps from Die 1 are seldom clear and many specimens are known without any trace of them. That they are from Die 1 is proved by the existence of blocks showing stamps with and without the die number. The 1s. is from Dies 1 and 2 (W.W. 1, W.W. 2).

The normal arrangement of the silk threads in the paper was in pairs running down each vertical row of the sheet, the space between the threads of each pair being approximately 5 mm. and between pairs of threads 20 mm. Varieties due to misplacement of the paper in printing show a single thread on the first stamp from the sheet margin and two threads 20 mm. apart on the other stamps of the row. Faulty manufacture is the cause of stamps with a single thread in the middle.

Through bad spacing of the impressions, which were hand-struck, all values may be found with two impressions more or less overlapping. Owing to the small margin allowed for variation of spacing, specimens with good margins on all sides are not common.

Double impressions are known of all values.

Later printings of the 6d. had the gum tinted green to enable the printer to distinguish the gummed side of the paper.

GENERAL NOTES.—SURFACE-PRINTED ISSUES.

" Abnormals." The majority of the great rarities in the surface-printed group of issues are the so-called " abnormals," whose existence is due to the practice of printing six sheets from every plate as soon as made, one of which was kept for record purposes at Somerset House, while the others were perforated and usually issued. If such plates were not used for general production or if, before they came into full use, a change of watermark or colour took place, the six sheets originally printed would differ from the main issue in plate, colour or watermark and, if issued, would be extremely rare.

The abnormal stamps of this class listed in this Catalogue and distinguished by a star (*) are:—

3d. Plate 3 (with white dots). 4d. vermilion, Plate 16. 4d. sage-green, Plate 17. 6d. mauve, Plate 10. 6d. pale chestnut, Plate 12. 6d. pale buff, Plate 13. 9d., Plate 3 (hair lines). 9d., Plate 5. 10d., Plate 2. 1s., Plate 3 (Plate No. 2). 1s. green, Plate 14. 2s. blue, Plate 3.

Those which may have been issued, but of which no specimens are known, are 2½d. wmk. Anchor, Plates 4 and 5 ; 3d. wmk. Emblems, Plate 5 ; 3d. wmk. Spray, Plate 21 ; 6d. grey, wmk. Spray, Plate 18 ; 8d. orange, Plate 2 ; 1s. wmk. Emblems, Plate 5 ; 5s. wmk. Maltese Cross, Plate 4.

The 10d. Plate 1, wmk. Emblems, is sometimes reckoned among the abnormals, but was probably an error, due to the use of the wrong paper.

Corner Letters. With the exception of the 4d., 6d. and 1s. of 1855–57, the ½d., 1½d., 2d. and 5d. of 1880, the 1d. lilac of 1881 and the £5 (which had letters in lower corners only, and in the reverse order to the normal), all the surface-printed stamps issued prior to 1887 had letters in all four corners, as in the later line-engraved stamps. The arrangement is the same, the letters running in sequence right across and down the sheets, whether these were divided into panes or not. The corner letters existing naturally depend on the number of stamps in the sheet and their arrangement.

Plate Numbers. All stamps from No. 75 to No. 163 bear in their designs either the plate number or, in one or two earlier instances, some other indication by which one plate can be distinguished from another. With the aid of these and of the corner letters it is thus possible to " reconstruct " a sheet of stamps from any plate of any issue or denomination—a task undertaken by many collectors.

Wing Margins. As the vertical gutters (spaces) between the panes, into which sheets of stamps of most values were divided until the introduction of the Imperial Crown watermark, were perforated through the centre with a single row of holes, instead of each vertical row of stamps on the inner side of the panes having its own line of perforation as is now usual, a proportion of the stamps in each sheet have what is called a " wing margin " about 5 mm. wide on one or other side. Though actually scarcer than the normally perforated stamps (and of course essential to completing plates), such stamps were in the past unpopular with collectors and in consequence have often been cut down and re-perforated. A knowledge of the lettering on the stamps which had the wing margin will enable the collector to guard against these fakes.

III.—SURFACE-PRINTED STAMPS.

(Printed by Messrs. De La Rue & Co.)

14

15. Small.

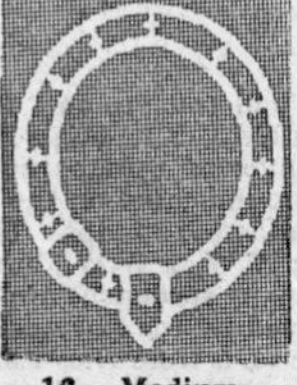

16. Medium.

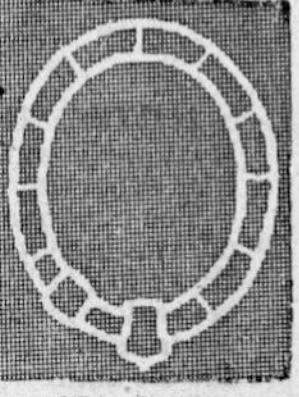

17. Large.

1855–57. (i.) *On blue safety paper.* (1855–56.) (*a*) *Wmk. Small Garter, T* **15.**

62	14	4d. deep carmine (31.7.55)	£45	65 0
63	„	4d. pale carmine	£40	65 0

(*b*) *Wmk. Medium Garter, T* **16.**

64	14	4d. deep carmine (25.2.56)	£50	£5
65	„	4d. pale carmine	£50	£5

(ii.) *On white paper.* (1856–57.) (*a*) *Wmk. Small Garter, T* **15.**

65a	14	4d. rose-carmine	£180	£15

(b) Wmk. Medium Garter, T 16.

No.	Type	Description	Unused	Used
66	14	4d. rose-carmine (September, '56)	£30	40 0
		a. Thick paper	£45	90 0
		b. Azure paper		

(c) Wmk. Large Garter, T 17.

No.	Type	Description	Unused	Used
67	14	4d. rose-carmine (January, '57)	£25	15 0
68	,,	4d. rose	£17	12 6
		a. Azure paper	£50	£30

(iii.) *On thick white paper. Wmk. Large Garter, T 17.*

No.	Type	Description	Unused	Used
68b	14	4d. rose-carmine	£35	65 0

18 19 20 20*a*. Error.

Wmk. Emblems, T 20.

No.	Type	Description	Unused	Used
69	18	6d. deep lilac (21 October, 1856)	£10	20 0
70	,,	6d. pale lilac	£7	12 6
		a. Azure paper	£70	£8
		b. Thick paper	—	75 0
71	19	1s. deep green (1 November, 1856)	£32	75 0
72	,,	1s. green	£20	40 0
73	,,	1s. pale green	£15	40 0
		a. Azure paper	—	£22
		b. Thick paper	—	£8

21 22 23 24 25. Plate 2.

A. White dots added. B. Hair lines.

1862. *A small uncoloured letter in each corner, the 4d. wmk. Large Garter, T 17, the others Emblems, T 20.*

No.	Type	Description	Unused	Used
75	21	3d. deep carmine-rose (Plate 2) (1 May, 1862)	£25	85 0
76	,,	3d. bright carmine-rose	£9	40 0
77	,,	3d. pale carmine-rose	£9	40 0
		a. Error. Wmk., three roses and shamrock (Type 20a)	—	£25
		b. Thick paper	—	£10
78	,,	3d. rose (with white dots, Type A, Plate 3) (August, '62)	*	£120
79	22	4d. bright red (Plate 3) (15 January, 1862)	£10	12 6
80	,,	4d. pale red	£8	10 6
81	,,	4d. bright red (Hair lines, Plate 4) (Type B) (16 October, '63)	£9	12 6
82	,,	4d. pale red (Hair lines, Plate 4) (Type B)	£8	12 6
		a. Imperf. (Plate 4)	£18	
83	23	6d. deep lilac (Plate 3) (1 December, 1862)	£9	12 6
84	,,	6d. lilac	£9	12 6
		a. Azure paper	—	£35
		b. Thick paper	—	80 0
85	,,	6d. lilac (Hair lines, Plate 4) (20 April, '64)	£10	30 0
		a. Imperf.	£15	
		b. On azure paper		
86	24	9d. bistre (Plate 2) (15 January, 1862)	£10	60 0
87	,,	9d. straw	£10	60 0
		a. On azure paper	—	£140
		b. Thick paper	—	£12
88	24	9d. straw (Hair lines, Plate 3) (May, '62)	£275	£120
89	25	1s. deep green (Plate No. 1 = Plate 2) (1 December, 1862)	£30	40 0

90	25	1s. green (Plate No. 1 = Plate 2)	£15	35 0
		a. "K" in lower left corner in white circle ..	—	£18
		b. On azure paper		
		c. Thick paper	—	£9
91	,,	1s. deep green (Plate No. 2 = Plate 3)	£350	*
		a. Imperf.	£30	

NOTES. The 3d., as T **21**, but with network background in the spandrels, which is found overprinted "SPECIMEN", was never issued.

The plates of this issue may be distinguished as follows :—

3d. Plate 2. No white dots. Plate 3. White dots as Illustration A.
4d. Plate 3. No hair lines. Roman I next to lower corner letters. Plate 4. Hair lines in corners. (Illustration B.) Roman II.
6d. Plate 3. No hair lines. Plate 4. Hair lines in corners.
9d. Plate 2. No hair lines. Plate 3. Hair lines in corners. Beware of faked lines.
1s. Plate 2. Numbered 1 on stamps. Plate 3. Numbered 2 on stamps and with hair lines. Of Plate 3 only one pane of 20 was perforated and the stamp was never issued.

The variety "K" in circle, found on stamps lettered K D, is due to the K plug not being driven home when the plate was being lettered, so that there was a slight circular indentation which appeared as an uncoloured line on the stamps.

The 9d. on azure paper (No. 87a) is very rare, only one specimen being known. There is also only one known unused copy of the "K" in circle variety.

The watermark variety "three roses and a shamrock" illustrated in Type **20a** was evidently due to the substitution of an extra rose for the thistle in a faulty watermark bit. It is found on stamp T A of Plates 2 and 4 of the 3d., Plates 5 and 6 of the 6d., Plate 4 of the 9d. and Plate 4 of the 1s.

26 27 28

29 30 31

1865–67. *Large uncoloured corner letters. Wmk. Large Garter, (4d.); others Emblems.*

92	26	3d. rose (Plate No. 4) (1 March, 1865)	£9	27 6
		a. Error. Wmk., three roses and shamrock (Type 20a) ..	—	£20
		b. Thick paper	—	50 0
93	27	4d. dull vermilion (4 July, 1865)	60 0	10 6
94	,,	4d. vermilion	60 0	10 6
95	,,	4d. deep vermilion	60 0	10 6
		a. Imperf. (Plates 11, 12)	£18	

Plate No.	Year	Unused	Used	Plate No.	Year	Unused	Used
Plate No. 7 ..	1865 ..	95 0	15 0	Plate No. 11 ..	1869 ..	60 0	10 6
,, ,, 8 ..	1866 ..	85 0	12 6	,, ,, 12 ..	1870 ..	60 0	10 6
,, ,, 9 ..	1867 ..	70 0	10 6	,, ,, 13 ..	1872 ..	80 0	12 6
,, ,, 10 ..	1868 ..	90 0	16 0	,, ,, 14 ..	1873 ..	60 0	10 6

96	28	6d. deep lilac (with hyphen) (1 April, 1865)	£7	10 6
97	,,	6d. lilac (with hyphen)	£5	10 6
		a. Thick paper	£18	45 0
		b. Stamp doubly printed (Plate 6)	—	£120
		c. Error. Wmk., three roses and shamrock (Plates 5, 6) (Type 20a) ..	—	£25

Plate No. 5 ..	1865 ..	£5	10 6	Plate No. 6 ..	1867 ..	£35	27 6

98	29	9d. straw (1 December, 1865)	£30	£15
		a. Thick paper		
		b. Error. Wmk., three roses and shamrock (Plate 4) (Type 20a) ..	—	£45

Plate No. 4 ..	1865 ..	£30	£15	Plate No. 5 ..	1866 ..	£350	*

99	30	10d. red-brown (Plate No. 1) (11.11.67)	*	£450
101	31	1s. green (Plate No. 4) (February, 1865)	£5	17 6
		a. Error. Wmk., three roses and shamrock (Type 20a) ..	—	£30
		b. Thick paper	—	£8

NOTES ON 1865-67 ISSUE. From mid-1867 to about the end of 1871 4d. stamps of this issue appeared generally with watermark inverted.

The 10d. stamps, No. 99, were printed in *error* on paper wmkd. "Emblems" instead of on paper wmkd. "Spray."

32

33

34

1867–80. *Wmk. Spray of Rose, T* **33.**

No.	Type	Description	Unused	Used
102	**26**	3d. deep rose (12 July, 1867)	60 0	8 6
103	,,	3d. rose	55 0	8 0
		a. Imperf. (Plates 5, 6, 8, 10)		

Plate	Year	Unused	Used	Plate	Year	Unused	Used
Plate No. 4	**1867**	£9	20 0	Plate No. 8	**1872**	70 0	8 6
,, ,, 5	**1868**	60 0	8 6	,, ,, 9	,,	75 0	15 0
,, ,, 6	**1870**	55 0	8 6	,, ,, 10	**1873**	75 0	20 0
,, ,, 7	**1871**	70 0	8 0				

No.	Type	Description	Unused	Used
104	**28**	6d. lilac (with hyphen between "SIX PENCE") (Plate No. 6) (21 June, '67)	£8	10 6
105	,,	6d. deep lilac (with hyphen between "SIX PENCE") (Plate No. 6)	£8	17 6
106	,,	6d. purple (with hyphen between "SIX PENCE") (Plate No. 6)	£8	27 6
107	,,	6d. bright violet (with hyphen) (Plate No. 6) (22 July, '68)	£8	20 0
108	,,	6d. dull violet (Plate No. 8) (without hyphen) (13 March, 1869)	90 0	15 0
109	,,	6d. mauve (without hyphen)	90 0	15 0
		a. Imperf. (Plate Nos. 8 and 9)	£20	£25

Plate	Year	Shade	Unused	Used
Plate No. 8	**1869**	mauve	90 0	15 0
,, ,, 9	**1870**	mauve	90 0	15 0
,, ,, 10	**1869**	mauve	*	£600

No.	Type	Description	Unused	Used
110	**29**	9d. straw (Plate No. 4) (3 October, 1867)	£9	60 0
111	,,	9d. pale straw (Plate No. 4)	£9	55 0
		a. Imperf. (Plate 4)	£25	
112	**30**	10d. red-brown (1 July, 1867)	£12	75 0
113	,,	10d. pale red-brown	£12	90 0
114	,,	10d. deep red-brown	£25	75 0
		a. Imperf. (Plate 1)		

Plate	Year	Unused	Used	Plate	Year	Unused	Used
Plate No. 1	**1867**	£12	75 0	Plate No. 2	**1867**	*	£175

No.	Type	Description	Unused	Used
115	**31**	1s. deep green (7 August, 1867)	£8	5 0
117	,,	1s. pale green	70 0	5 0
		a. Imperf. between (pair) (Plate 7)		
		b. Imperf. (Plate 4)	£20	

Plate	Year	Unused	Used	Plate	Year	Unused	Used
Plate No. 4	**1867**	70 0	13 6	Plate No. 6	**1872**	£9	5 0
,, ,, 5	**1871**	£8	5 0	,, ,, 7	**1873**	£10	15 0

No.	Type	Description	Unused	Used
118	**32**	2s. dull blue (1 July, 1867)	£18	35 0
119	,,	2s. deep blue	£20	40 0
		a. Imperf. (Plate 1)		
120	**32**	2s. pale blue	£15	45 0
120a	,,	2s. cobalt	—	£15
120b	,,	2s. milky blue	£45	£8

Plate	Year	Unused	Used
Plate No. 1	**1867**	£15	45 0
,, ,, 3	**1868**	*	£300

No.	Type	Description	Unused	Used
121	**32**	2s. brown (Plate No. 1) (27 February, 1880)	£50	£25

1872–73. *Type* **34.** *Uncoloured letters in corners. Wmk. Spray, T* **33.**

No.	Type	Description	Unused	Used
122	**34**	6d. deep chestnut (12 April, 1872)	£9	10 6
123	,,	6d. chestnut (23 May, 1872)	95 0	10 6
124	,,	6d. pale buff (23 November, 1872)	£6	90 0

Plate	Year	Shade	Unused	Used
Plate No. 11	**1872**	deep chestnut	£9	10 6
,, ,, 11	,,	chestnut	95 0	10 6
,, ,, 11	,,	pale buff	95 0	40 0
,, ,, 12	,,	pale chestnut ‡	*	£75
,, ,, 12	,,	pale buff	£12	80 0

(‡) The price quoted is for the true pale chestnut shade which is very rare.

No.	Type	Description	Unused	Used
125	**34**	6d. grey (Plate No. 12) (24 June, 1873)	90 0	27 6
		a. Imperf.		

35

36

37

38

39

40

1867–83. *Uncoloured letters in corners.*

(i.) *Wmk. Maltese Cross, T* **39**. *P* 15½ × 15.

126	35	5s. rose (1 July, 1867)	£25	60 0
127	„	5s. pale rose	£25	60 0

Plate No. 1 ..	1867 ..	£25	60 0
„ „ 2 ..	1874 ..	£28	95 0

128	36	10s. greenish grey (Plate No. 1) (26 September, 1878)	£125	£20
129	37	£1 brown-lilac (Plate No. 1) (26 September, 1878)	£200	£25

(ii) *Wmk. Anchor, T* **40**. *P* 14. *Blued paper.*

130	35	5s. rose (Plate No. 4) (30 November, 1882)	£50	£15
131	36	10s. grey-green (Plate No. 1) (February, 1883)	£225	£28
132	37	£1 brown-lilac (Plate No. 1) (December, 1882)	£300	£40
133	38	£5 orange (Plate No. 1) (21 March, 1882)	£30c	£50

(iii.) *Same wmk. and perf. White paper.*

134	35	5s. rose (Plate No. 4)	£70	£20
135	36	10s. greenish grey (Plate No. 1)	£225	£30
136	37	£1 brown-lilac (Plate No. 1)	£400	£45
137	38	£5 orange (Plate No. 1)	£45	£30

41

42

43

44

45

46

47

48

1873-80. *Large coloured letters in the corners.*

(i.) *Wmk. Anchor, T* **47.**

138 **41** 2½d. rosy mauve (*blued* paper) (1 July, 1875) 90 0 30 0
139 „ 2½d. rosy mauve (*white* paper) 50 0 10 6

Plate	Paper	Year	Unused	Used
Plate No. 1	(*blued* paper)	**1875**	90 0	30 0
„ „ 1	(*white* paper)	„	50 0	10 6
„ „ 2	(*blued* paper)	„	£80	£15
„ „ 2	(*white* paper)	„	50 0	10 6
„ „ 3	(*white* paper)	„	£8	15 0
„ „ 3	(*blued* paper)	„	—	£25

Error of Lettering **L H—F L** for **L H—H L** (*Plate No.* 2).

140 **41** 2½d. rosy mauve .. .. — £30

(ii.) *Wmk. Orb, T* **48.**

141 **41** 2½d. rosy mauve (31 May, 1876) 40 0 8 0

Plate	Year	Unused	Used
Plate No. 3	**1876**	£12	17 6
„ „ 4	„	55 0	15 0
„ „ 5	„	50 0	8 0
„ „ 6	„	42 6	8 0
„ „ 7	**1877**	45 0	8 6
„ „ 8	„	50 0	8 0
„ „ 9	„	40 0	10 6
„ „ 10	**1878**	60 0	10 6
Plate No. 11	**1878**	45 0	8 6
„ „ 12	„	45 0	8 6
„ „ 13	„	40 0	8 0
„ „ 14	**1879**	40 0	8 0
„ „ 15	„	42 6	8 0
„ „ 16	„	40 0	10 0
„ „ 17	**1880**	75 0	50 0

142 **41** 2½d. blue (5 February, 1880) 30 0 8 0

Plate	Year	Unused	Used
Plate No. 17	**1880**	30 0	8 0
„ „ 18	„	50 0	8 0
Plate No. 19	**1880**	30 0	8 0
„ „ 20	„	30 0	8 0

(iii.) *Wmk. Spray, T* **33.**

143 **42** 3d. rose (5 July, 1873) 40 0 12 0
144 „ 3d. pale rose 40 0 12 0

Plate	Year	Unused	Used
Plate No. 11	**1873**	50 0	16 6
„ „ 12	„	75 0	17 6
„ „ 14	**1874**	75 0	12 0
„ „ 15	„	55 0	12 6
„ „ 16	**1875**	60 0	15 0
Plate No. 17	**1875**	55 0	12 0
„ „ 18	„	45 0	12 6
„ „ 19	**1876**	40 0	12 6
„ „ 20	**1879**	50 0	25 0

145 **43** 6d. pale buff (Plate No. 13) (15 March, 1873) .. .. .. * £100
146 „ 6d. deep grey (31 March, 1873) 45 0 8 6
147 „ 6d. grey 35 0 8 6

Plate	Year	Unused	Used
Plate No. 13	**1874**	45 0	8 6
„ „ 14	**1875**	45 0	8 6
„ „ 15	**1876**	35 0	8 6
Plate No. 16	**1878**	35 0	8 6
„ „ 17	**1880**	45 0	20 0

148 **44** 1s. deep green (1 September, 1873) 95 0 20 0
150 „ 1s. pale green 50 0 15 0

Plate	Year	Unused	Used
Plate No. 8	**1873**	95 0	20 0
„ „ 9	**1874**	95 0	22 6
„ „ 10	„	95 0	22 6
„ „ 11	**1875**	95 0	20 0
Plate No. 12	**1875**	60 0	15 0
„ „ 13	**1877**	50 0	15 0
„ „ 14	**1876**	*	£600

151 **44** 1s. orange-brown (Plate No. 13) (14 October, 1880) £10 55 0

(iv.) *Wmk. Large Garter, T* 17.

152 **45** 4d. vermilion (1 March, 1876) £10 60 0

Plate	Year	Unused	Used
Plate No. 15	**1876**	£10	60 0
„ „ 16	**1874**	*	£500

153 **45** 4d. sage-green (12 March, 1877) 50 0 30 0
a. Imperf. (Plate No. 15) £12

Plate	Year	Unused	Used
Plate No. 15	**1877**	60 0	35 0
„ „ 16	„	50 0	30 0
„ „ 17	„	*	£175

154 **45** 4d. grey-brown (Plate No. 17) (15 August, 1880) 85 0 45 0
156 **46** 8d. orange (Plate No. 1) (11 September, 1876) 90 0 42 6

1876 (July). *Prepared for use but not issued.*

156*a* **46** 8d. purple-brown (Plate No. 1) £25

49

3d

50

1880-83. ***Wmk. Imperial Crown, T* 49.**

157	**41**	2½d. blue (23 March, 1881)	17 6	3 6
		Imperf. (Plate No. 23)		
		Plate No. 21 .. **1881** .. 45 0 8 0		
		„ „ 22 .. „ .. 17 6 3 6		
		„ „ 23 .. „ .. 20 0 3 6		
158	**42**	3d. rose (February, 1881)	35 0	12 6
		Plate No. 20 .. **1881** .. 50 0 20 0		
		„ „ 21 .. „ .. 35 0 12 6		
159	**42**	3d. lilac (*carmine* surcharge—*T* **50**) (Plate No. 21) (1 January, 1883)	40 0	20 0
160	**45**	4d. grey-brown (10 December, 1880)	30 0	8 6
		Plate No. 17 .. **1880** .. 30 0 8 6		
		„ „ 18 .. **1882** .. 30 0 8 6		
161	**43**	6d. grey (1 January, 1881)	35 0	15 0
		Plate No. 17 .. **1881** .. 37 6 15 0		
		„ „ 18 .. **1882** .. 35 0 17 6		
162	**43**	6d. lilac (*carmine* surcharge—as *T* **50**) (Plate No. 18) (1 January, 1883)	35 0	17 6
		a. One stop only under " d "	£35	£10
		b. Dots slanting	£22	£6
163	**44**	1s. orange-brown (29 May, 1881)	50 0	20 0
		a. Imperf.		
		Plate No. 13 .. **1881** .. 50 0 20 0		
		„ „ 14 .. **1881** .. 50 0 20 0		

The 1s. Plates 13 and 14 are known in purple, but were not issued thus. They come from the Souvenir Album prepared for members of the " Stamp Committee of 1884."

52 53 54 55 56

1880-81. ***Wmk. Imperial Crown, T* 49.**

164	**52**	½d. deep green (14 October, 1880)	4 0	0 10
		a. Imperf.		
165	**52**	½d. pale green	4 0	0 10
166	**53**	1d. Venetian red (1 January, 1880)	1 6	0 4
		a. Imperf.	90 0	
167	**54**	1½d. Venetian red (14 October, 1880)	15 0	10 0
168	**55**	2d. pale rose (8 December, 1880)	40 0	15 0
168*a*	„	2d. deep rose	30 0	15 0
169	**56**	5d. indigo (15 March, 1881)	45 0	10 6

A

57

B

1881. ***Wmk. Imperial Crown, T* 49.** *a*) 14 *dots in each corner, Type* A (12 *July*).

170	**57**	1d. lilac	15 0	1 6
171	„	1d. pale lilac	12 0	1 6

(*b*) 16 *dots in each corner, Type* B (12 *December*).

172	**57**	1d. lilac	0 4	0 1
172*a*	„	1d., bluish lilac	80 0	15 0
		b. Blued paper	£35	
173	„	1d. deep purple	0 4	0 1
		a. Printed both sides	£20	†
		b. Frame broken at bottom	£15	£15
		c. Printed on gummed side	£9	†
		d. Imperf. three sides (pair)	£40	†
174	„	1d. mauve	0 4	0 1
		a. Imperf.	40 0	

1d. stamps with the words " PEARS' SOAP " printed on back in *orange, blue,* or *mauve,* price 17s. 6d.

The variety " frame broken at bottom " shows a white space just inside the bottom frame-line, from between the " N " and " E " of " ONE " to below the first " N " of " PENNY " breaking the pearls and cutting into the lower part of the oval below " PEN ".

58

59

60

1883–84. *Coloured letters in the corners. Wmk. Anchor,* **T 40.**

(i.) *Blued paper.*

175	**58**	2s. 6d. lilac (2 July, 1883)	£15	90 0
176	**59**	5s. rose (1 April, 1884)	£75	£15
177	**60**	10s. ultramarine (1 April, 1884)	£150	£35
177*a*	,,	10s. cobalt (May, 1884)	£175	£40

(ii.) *White paper.*

178	**58**	2s. 6d. lilac	50 0	25 0
179	,,	2s. 6d. deep lilac	40 0	15 0
180	**59**	5s. rose	£7	17 6
181	,,	5s. crimson	45 0	17 6
182	**60**	10s. cobalt	£175	£25
183	,,	10s. ultramarine	95 0	40 0
183*a*	,,	10s. pale ultramarine	95 0	40 0

61

1884 (1 April). *Wmk.* 3 *Imperial Crowns,* **T 49.**

185	**61**	£1 brown-lilac	£80	£20

1888 (1 Feb.). *Wmk.* 3 *Orbs,* *T* **48.**

186	**61**	£1 brown-lilac	£150	£30

62

63

64

65

66

1883 (1 Aug.) (9d.) *or* **1884** (1 April) (*others*). *Wmk. Imperial Crown,* **T 49.**

187	**52**	$\frac{1}{2}$d. slate-blue	3 0	0 6
188	**62**	1$\frac{1}{2}$d. lilac	12 6	8 6
189	**63**	2d. lilac	30 0	15 0
		Imperf.		

190	64	2½d. lilac	10	6	3	0
191	65	3d. lilac	20	0	8	6
192	66	4d. dull green	50	0	27	6
193	62	5d. dull green	40	0	22	6
194	63	6d. dull green	35	0	17	6
195	64	9d. dull green (1 August, 1883)	80	0	70	0
196	65	1s. dull green	70	0	40	0

The above prices are for stamps in the true dull green colour. Stamps which have been soaked, causing the colour to run, are almost valueless.

Stamps of the above set and No. 180 are also found perf. 12; these are official perforations, but were never issued. A second variety of the 5d. is known with a line instead of a stop under the "d" in the value; this was never issued and is therefore only known *unused*.

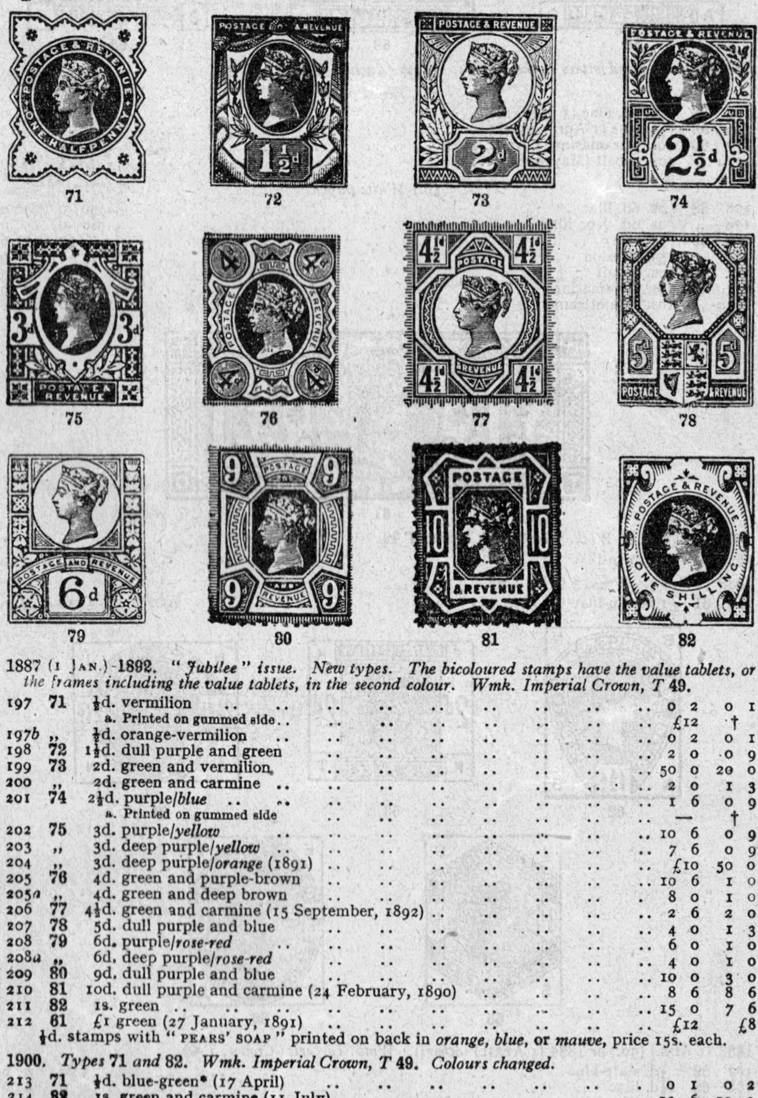

71 72 73 74 75 76 77 78 79 80 81 82

1887 (1 Jan.)-1892. "*Jubilee*" *issue. New types. The bicoloured stamps have the value tablets, or the frames including the value tablets, in the second colour. Wmk. Imperial Crown, T* 49.

197	71	½d. vermilion	0	2	0	1
		a. Printed on gummed side	£12		†	
197*b*	,,	½d. orange-vermilion	0	2	0	1
198	72	1½d. dull purple and green	2	0	0	9
199	73	2d. green and vermilion	50	0	20	0
200	,,	2d. green and carmine	2	0	1	3
201	74	2½d. purple/*blue*	1	6	0	9
		a. Printed on gummed side	—		†	
202	75	3d. purple/*yellow*	10	6	0	9
203	,,	3d. deep purple/*yellow*	7	6	0	9
204	,,	3d. deep purple/*orange* (1891)	£10		50	0
205	76	4d. green and purple-brown	10	6	1	0
205*a*	,,	4d. green and deep brown	8	0	1	0
206	77	4½d. green and carmine (15 September, 1892)	2	6	2	0
207	78	5d. dull purple and blue	4	0	1	3
208	79	6d. purple/*rose-red*	6	0	1	0
208*a*	,,	6d. deep purple/*rose-red*	4	0	1	0
209	80	9d. dull purple and blue	10	0	3	0
210	81	10d. dull purple and carmine (24 February, 1890)	8	6	8	6
211	82	1s. green	15	0	7	6
212	61	£1 green (27 January, 1891)	£12		£8	

½d. stamps with "PEARS' SOAP" printed on back in *orange, blue,* or *mauve*, price 15s. each.

1900. *Types* 71 *and* 82. *Wmk. Imperial Crown, T* 49. *Colours changed.*

213	71	½d. blue-green* (17 April)	0	1	0	2
214	82	1s. green and carmine (11 July)	12	6	10	0

* The ½d. No. 213, in bright blue, is a colour changeling.

KING EDWARD VII., 1901 (22 JAN.)–1910 (6 MAY).

83 84 85 86 87 88 89 90 91 92 93 94 95 96 97 97a

1902–10 (1 JAN.). *T* **83** (*½d., 1d. and 6d.*) *to* **97**. *Printed by Messrs. De La Rue & Co. Wmks. Imperial Crown* (*½d. to 1s.*) ; *Anchor* (*2s. 6d. to 10s.*) ; *Three Crowns* (*£1*). *P* 14.

O = " Ordinary " paper. C = Chalk-surfaced paper.

215	½d. dull blue-green, O (1 January, 1902)	0	4	0	1
216	½d. blue-green, O	0	6	0	1
217	½d. pale yellow-green, O (26 November, 1904)	0	3	0	1
218	½d. yellow-green, O	0	3	0	1
	a. Stamp from booklet with cross attached (pair)	30	0	35	0
	b. Doubly printed (bottom row on one pane) (Control H9)				
219	1d. scarlet, O (1 January, 1902)	0	4	0	1

No.	Description	Unused	Used
220	1d. bright scarlet, O	0 4	0 1
	a. Imperf	£50	
221	1½d. dull purple and yellow-green, O (21 March, 1902)	4 0	0 8
222	1½d. slate-purple and yellow-green, O	8 6	0 9
223	1½d. dull purple and green, C (September, 1905)	6 0	0 5
224	1½d. slate-purple and green, C	2 6	0 5
225	2d. yellow-green and carmine, O (25 March, 1902)	8 0	1 3
226	2d. grey-green and carmine, O (March, 1903)	10 6	1 3
227	2d. green and carmine, C (September, 1905)	4 0	1 3
228	2d. deep green and carmine, C (July, 1910)	3 0	1 3
229	2d. pale blue-green and carmine, C	8 6	1 0
230	2½d. deep bright blue, O (1 January, 1902)	2 0	0 5
231	2½d. pale bright blue, O	2 0	0 5
232	3d. dull purple/*orange-yellow*, O (20 March, 1902)	8 6	0 9
233	3d. dull purple/*orange*, C (March, 1906)	35 0	2 6
233*a*	3d. dull purple/*lemon*, C	40 0	2 6
234	3d. purple/*yellow*, C	2 6	0 6
235	4d. pale green and grey-brown, O (27 March, 1902)	12 6	1 0
236	4d. green and chocolate-brown, O	12 6	1 0
237	4d. green and chocolate-brown, C (January, 1906)	6 0	0 9
238	4d. deep green and chocolate-brown, C	6 0	0 8
239	4d. brown-orange, O (1 November, 1909)	15 0	5 0
240	4d. pale orange, O (December, 1909)	3 6	1 3
241	4d. orange-red, O (December, 1910)	3 6	1 3
242	5d. purple and blue, O (14 May, 1902)	10 6	1 6
243	5d. dull purple and blue, C	7 6	1 6
244	5d. slate-purple and blue, C (May, 1906)	4 6	1 6
245	6d. pale dull purple, O (1 January, 1902)	8 0	1 0
246	6d. dull purple, O	6 6	0 6
247	6d. reddish purple, C (October, 1905)	6 6	0 8
248	6d. dull purple, C	3 6	0 8
249	7d. grey-black, O (4 May, 1910)	4 6	2 6
249*a*	7d. deep grey-black, O	12 6	2 6
250	9d. dull purple and blue, O (7 April, 1902)	15 0	3 6
251	9d. slate-purple and blue, O	10 0	3 6
252	9d. dull purple and pale blue, C (29 June, 1905)	10 6	4 6
253	9d. slate-purple and bright blue, C	6 6	3 6
254	10d. dull purple and carmine, O (3 July, 1902)	20 0	5 0
	a. No cross on crown	£17	
255	10d. dull purple and carmine, C (September, 1905)	10 0	4 0
	a. No cross on crown	£10	
256	10d. dull purple and scarlet, C (September, 1910)	30 0	10 6
	a. No cross on crown	£17	
257	1s. green and carmine, O (24 March, 1902)	12 6	2 6
258	1s. green and carmine, C (September, 1905)	27 6	2 6
259	1s. green and scarlet, C (1910)	8 0	3 6
260	2s. 6d. dull purple, O (5 April, 1902)	55 0	15 0
261	2s. 6d. reddish purple, C (October, 1905)	50 0	17 6
262	2s. 6d. dull purple, C	45 0	17 6
263	5s. carmine, O (5 April, 1902)	65 0	17 6
264	5s. deep carmine, O	£5	25 0
265	10s. ultramarine, O (5 April, 1902)	£8	60 0
266	£1 green, O (16 June, 1902)	£12	£6

1910 (May). *T 97a. Prepared for use, but not issued.*

266*a* 2d. Tyrian plum

One copy of this stamp is known used, but it was never issued to the public.

To distinguish De La Rue printings from the provisional printings of the same values made either by Messrs. Harrison & Sons or at Somerset House, the following hints may be helpful. The 6*d.* is the only value *on chalk-surfaced paper,* printed by De La Rue and also at Somerset House. The latter printing can be distinguished by the shade and impression.

Of the stamps *on ordinary paper,* the De La Rue impressions are usually clearer and of a higher finish than those of the other printers. The shades are markedly different except in some printings of the 4*d.*, 6*d.*, and 7*d.*, and in the 5*s.*, 10*s.*, and £1. With a little experience the collector should have no difficulty in allotting mint specimens of any value to their respective printings.

1911. *Printed by Messrs. Harrison & Sons. "Ordinary" paper. Wmk. Imp. Crown.* (*a*) *P* 14.

No.	Description	Unused	Used
267	½d. dull yellow-green (3 May, 1911)	1 6	0 8
268	½d. dull green	1 9	0 8
269	½d. deep dull green	2 0	0 10
270	½d. pale green	2 0	0 10
	a. From booklet, with cross attached (pair)	70 0	75 0
	b. Wmk. sideways		
271	½d. bright green (very clear printing) (June, 1911)	60 0	40 0
272	1d. rose-red (May, 1911)	2 0	1 0
	a. No wmk.	£17	
273	1d. deep rose-red	2 0	1 3
274	1d. rose-carmine	30 0	6 6
275	1d. aniline pink (Aug. 1911)	£12	80 0
276	2½d. bright blue (July, 1911)	7 6	5 0
277	3d. dull purple/*yellow* (Sept. 1911)	17 6	22 6
278	4d. bright orange (July, 1911)	7 6	4 6

(*b*) *P* 15×14.

No.	Description	Unused	Used
279	½d. pale green (October, 1911)	3 6	5 0
280	1d. rose-red (October, 1911)	9 6	7 6
281	1d. rose-carmine	2 9	2 0
282	1d. pale rose-carmine	2 6	2 3
283	2½d. bright blue (October, 1911)	2 9	0 10
284	2½d. blue	4 0	0 10
285	3d. dull purple/*lemon* (September, 19..	2 6	1 0
285*a*	3d. grey/*lemon*	£50	
286	4d. bright orange (November, 1911)	3 0	1 0

1911–12. *Printed at Somerset House. Ordinary paper, unless marked* (C) (*=chalk-surfaced paper.*) *Wmks. as* 1902–10. *P* 14.

No.	Description	Unused	Used
287	1½d. dull reddish purple and yellow-green (13 July, 1911)	10 0	5 0
288	1½d. purple and green	2 6	1 3
289	1½d. slate-purple and green (September, 1912)	6 6	2 0
290	2d. dull green and red (August, 1911)	5 0	2 9
291	2d. dull green and carmine (December, 1911)	2 6	1 9
292	2d. grey-green and carmine (1912)	2 0	1 9
293	5d. purple and bright blue (August, 1911)	2 0	1 9
294	5d. dull purple and bright blue	2 6	1 9
295	6d. bright plum (November, 1911)	10 6	12 6
296	6d. bright magenta, C	£50	
297	6d. dull purple	3 6	1 3
298	6d. pale reddish purple	3 0	1 9
299	6d. deep plum	10 6	5 6
300	6d. blackish purple (November, 1912)	10 0	3 0
301	6d. dull purple, C (October, 1913)	3 6	3 0
302	6d. pale dull purple, C	7 6	3 6
303	6d. deep plum, C	8 6	6 0
	a. No cross on crown (*various shades*) *From*	£9	£5
305	7d. slate-grey (August, 1912)	5 0	2 6
306	9d. pale reddish purple and pale blue (July, 1911)	22 6	10 6
307	9d. purple and bright blue (October, 1911)	5 6	3 6
308	9d. blackish purple and bright blue (October, 1912)	20 0	10 6
309	10d. dull purple and scarlet (9 October, 1911)	20 0	8 6
310	10d. dull purple and aniline pink (October, 1911)	£12	£8
311	10d. dull purple and carmine (May, 1912)	8 6	6 0
312	1s. deep green and scarlet (19 July, 1911)	30 0	7 6
313	1s. green and scarlet (October, 1911)	25 0	6 6
314	1s. green and carmine (April, 1912)	5 0	2 0
315	2s. 6d. dull purple (September, 1911)	95 0	20 0
316	2s. 6d. reddish purple (1912)	40 0	20 0
317	2s. 6d. blackish purple (1912)	55 0	27 6
318	5s. carmine (February, 1912)	60 0	20 0
319	10s. bright ultramarine (January, 1912)	£8	95 0
320	£1 deep green (September, 1911)	£12	£5

KING GEORGE V., 1910 (6 MAY)–1936 (20 JAN.).

WATERMARK VARIETIES.
For note *re* watermark varieties see after No. 429.

NOTE. *T* **98** *to* **102** *were typographed by Harrison & Sons, with the exception of certain preliminary printings, referred to in the footnote below No.* 343.

98

99

A B

A

B

1911–12. *T* **98** *and* **99**. *Wmk. Imperial Crown, T* **49**. *P* 15×14.

No.	Description	Unused	Used
321	½d. pale yellow-green (Die A) (June, 1911)	2 0	0 9
322	½d. yellow-green (Die A)	1 9	0 9
323	½d. bluish green (Die A)	8 6	5 0
	a. Error. Perf. 14	—	£25
324	½d. yellow-green (Die B)	2 0	0 9
325	½d. green (Die B)	1 0	0 9
326	½d. bluish green (Die B)	10 0	5 0
327	1d. deep rose-red (Die A) (June, 1911)	3 0	1 0
	a. Error. Perf. 14		
	b. Experimental ptg. chalk-surfaced paper (Control A.11)	£8	
328	1d. carmine (Die A)	3 6	1 9
	a. No Cross on Crown	£20	
329	1d. carmine (Die B)	1 9	0 6

330	1d. pale carmine (Die B)	1 9	0 6
	a. No Cross on Crown	£14	£14
331	1d. rose-pink (Die B)	22 6	10 6
332	1d. scarlet (Die B) (June, 1912)	10 6	5 0
333	1d. aniline scarlet (Die B)	£8	90 0

Die A (in the case of each value) is the original and Die B the altered Die.

HALFPENNY.—In Die A of the ½d. the three upper scales on the body of the right-hand dolphin form a triangle, while in Die B the uppermost of the three is incomplete.

PENNY.—In Die A the second line of shading on the ribbon to right of the Crown is long, extending right across the wreath. In Die B the shading on the ribbon consists of short broken lines.

100

1912 (AUG.). *T* **98** *and* **99.** *(Dies B.) Wmk. Royal Cypher ("Simple"), T* **100.** *P* 15×14.

334	½d. pale green	3 0	3 6
335	½d. green	2 0	3 0
336	1d. scarlet	2 0	2 6
337	1d. bright scarlet	2 6	2 6

101

102

1912 (1 JAN.). *T* **101** *and* **102.** *Wmk. Imperial Crown, T* **49.** *P* 15×14.

338	½d. deep green	7 6	3 0
339	½d. green	0 9	0 3
340	½d. yellow-green	0 9	0 3
	a. No Cross on Crown	45 0	20 0
341	1d. bright scarlet	0 6	0 2
	a. No Cross on Crown	17 6	10 6
342	1d. scarlet	0 6	0 2
343	1d. aniline scarlet	£8	90 0

HALFPENNY.—In T **98** the ornament between the dolphin's heads has two thin lines of colour to the left of the centre, where it breaks the rim of the medallion. In T **101** it has one thick line.

PENNY.—In T **99** the body of the lion is white (unshaded). In T **102** it is shaded all over.

A preliminary printing, from the plates of the 1d. (both types), was made at Somerset House before the plates were handed over to Messrs. Harrison & Sons, but these can only be distinguished with certainty when the control is attached, this being lettered "A. 11," "B. 11," or "B. 12," whereas the Harrison control lacks the period after the letter. The ½d. and 1d. wmk. **T 103**, with period after the letter, were also printed at Somerset House.

1912 (AUG.). *Types* **101** *and* **102.** *Wmk. Royal Cypher ("Simple"), T* **100.** *P* 15×14.

344	½d. green	1 0	0 6
	a. No Cross on Crown	£8	75 0
345	1d. scarlet	1 0	0 6
	a. No Cross on Crown	50 0	20 0

103

1912 (DEC.). *Types* **101** *and* **102.** *Wmk. Royal Cypher ("Multiple"), T* **103.** *P* 15×14.

346	½d. green	0 9	0 9
	a. No Cross on Crown	£12	90 0
	b. Imperf.	£5	
347	½d. bright green	3 0	1 0
348	½d. pale green	0 9	1 0
349	1d. bright scarlet	1 9	1 0
350	1d. scarlet	1 0	1 0
	a. No Cross on Crown	60 0	25 0
	b. Imperf.	85 0	
	c. Wmk. sideways	85 0	60 0
	d. Wmk. sideways. No Cross Crown	£35	

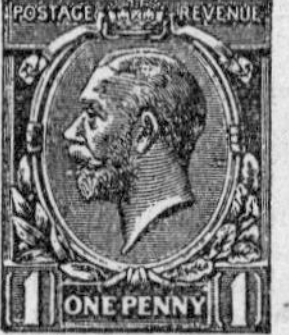

104

105

106

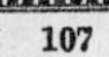

107

108

DIE I.

DIE II.

2d. Die I.—Inner frame-line at top and sides close to solid of background. *Four* complete lines of shading between top of head and oval frame-line White line round "TWOPENCE" thin.

Die II.—Inner frame-line further from solid of background. *Three* lines between top of head and oval. White line round "TWOPENCE" thicker.

(Typo. by Messrs. Harrison & Sons, except the 6d. printed by the Stamping Department of the Board of Inland Revenue, Somerset House. The latter also made printings of other values which can only be distinguished by the "controls," *q.v.*)

1912–22. *T* **104** *to* **108.** *Wmk. Royal Cypher, T* **100.** *P* 15×14.

No.	Type	Description	Unused	Used
351	105	½d. green (Jan. 1913)	0 3	0 2
		a. Doubly printed (Control G.15) ..		
352	,,	½d. bright green	0 3	0 2
353	,,	½d. deep green	1 6	0 3
354	,,	½d. yellow-green	2 0	0 3
355	,,	½d. bright yellow-(Cyprus) green	£15	
356	,,	½d. blue-green	15 0	4 0
357	104	1d. bright scarlet (Oct., 1912)	0 3	0 3
		a. "Q" for "O" in "ONE"	75 0	85 0
358	,,	1d. scarlet	0 3	0 2
359	,,	1d. pale rose-red	1 0	0 2
360	,,	1d. carmine-red	5 0	3 0
361	,,	1d. scarlet-vermilion	17 6	4 6
		a. Printed on back	—	†
362	105	1½d. red-brn. (Oct., 1912	0 6	0 2
		a. Error "PENCF"	60 0	65 0
363	,,	1½d. chocolate-brown	0 10	0 6
		a. Thick paper without wmk.	90 0	
364	,,	1½d. chestnut	2 0	0 3
		a. Error "PENCF"	35 0	40 0
365	,,	1½d. yellow-brown	4 0	0 9
366	106	2d. orange-yellow (Die I.) (Aug., 1912)	2 6	1 9
367	,,	2d. reddish orange (Die I.) (Nov., 1913)	1 0	0 2
368	,,	2d. orange (Die I.)	1 0	0 2
369	,,	2d. bright oran. (Die I.)	1 9	0 2
370	,,	2d. orange (Die II.) (Sept., 1921)	2 0	1 3
371	104	2½d. bright ultramarine (Oct., 1912)	1 0	0 2
372	,,	2½d. blue	1 0	0 2
373	,,	2½d. Prussian blue	50 0	35 0
374	106	3d. reddish violet (Oct., 1912)	2 9	0 4
375	,,	3d. violet	1 6	0 3
376	,,	3d. bluish violet (Nov., 1913)	1 9	0 2
377	,,	3d. pale bluish violet	2 0	0 2
378	,,	4d. deep grey-green (Jan., 1913)	10 0	0 8
379	,,	4d. grey-green	1 6	0 2
380	,,	4d. pale grey-green	3 6	0 2
381	107	5d. brown (June, 1913)	2 9	0 2
382	,,	5d. yellow-brown	2 9	0 2
		a. Without watermark	£12	£12
383	,,	5d. bistre-brown	6 0	1 6
384	,,	6d. dull pur., C (Aug., 1913)	10 0	8 6
385	,,	6d. reddish pur., C	2 6	0 3
		a. Perf. 14 (1921)	7 6	8 6
386	,,	6d. deep reddish pur., C	2 6	0 2
387	,,	7d. pale olive (Aug., '13)	8 0	3 0
388	,,	7d. deep olive	10 0	3 0
389	,,	7d. sage-green	12 6	4 0
390	,,	8d. black/*yellow* (Aug., 1913)	8 6	4 6
391	,,	8d. black/*yellow-buff* (*granite*) (May, 1917)	9 0	5 0
392	108	9d. agate (June, 1913)	10 0	1 6
393	,,	9d. deep agate	12 0	1 6
393a	108	9d. olive-green (Sept., 1922)	10 0	4 0
393b	,,	9d. pale olive-green	12 6	5 0
394	,,	10d. turquoise-blue (Aug. 1913)	8 0	5 0
395	,,	1s. pale bistre-brown (Aug., 1913)	7 6	1 3
396	,,	1s. olive-bistre	9 0	1 3

For the 2d., T **106**, bisected, see "Channel Islands."

1913 (Aug.). *T* **105** *and* **104.** *Wmk. Royal Cypher ("Multiple"), T* **103.** *P* 15×14.

No.	Description	Unused	Used
397	½d. bright green	25 0	30 0
398	1d. dull scarlet	20 0	25 0

Both these stamps were originally issued in rolls only. Subsequently sheets were found, so that horizontal pairs and blocks are known but are of considerable rarity.

109

110

A

T **109.** (A. *Background around portrait consists of horizontal lines.*) *Recess. Wmk. Single Cypher, T* **110.** *P* 11×12.

1913 (July). *Printed by Waterlow Bros. & Layton.*

No.	Description	Unused	Used
399	2s. 6d. deep sepia-brown	90 0	25 0
400	2s. 6d. sepia-brown	85 0	22 6
	a. Re-entry	£45	£30
401	5s. rose-carmine	95 0	22 6
402	10s. indigo-blue	£10	£6
403	£1 green	£30	£16
404	£1 dull blue-green	£28	£16

1915 (Dec.)–**1918.** *Printed by De La Rue & Co.*

No.	Description	Unused	Used
405	2s. 6d. deep brown	55 0	25 0
406	2s. 6d. chestnut-brown	60 0	30 0
407	2s. 6d. brown	45 0	22 6
408	2s. 6d. grey-brown	40 0	22 6
	a. Re-entry	£30	£15
409	5s. bright carmine	85 0	30 0
410	5s. pale carmine	85 0	30 0
411	10s. deep bright blue	£16	£8
412	10s. blue	£10	80 0
413	10s. pale blue	£12	80 0

1918 (Dec.)–**1930.** *Printed by Bradbury, Wilkinson & Co., Ltd.*

No.	Description	Unused	Used
413a	2s. 6d. brown	32 6	12 6
414	2s. 6d. chocolate-brown	27 6	12 6

415	2s. 6d. red-brown	30 0	10 6
415a	2s. 6d. pale brown ('30) ..	30 0	8 6
	b. Re-entry	£30	£16
416	5s. rose-red	45 0	12 6
417	10s. dull grey-blue	60 0	20 0

For (1934) re-engraved Waterlow printings, see Nos. 450/2.

In the De La Rue printings the gum is usually patchy and yellowish, and the colour of the stamp, particularly in the 5s., tends to show through the back.

The distinguishing characteristics of the Bradbury printings are as follows:—The paper appears whiter owing to use generally of a pure white gum. The holes of the perforation are larger.

In the majority of copies of the Bradbury printings a minute coloured dot appears in the margin just above the middle of the upper frame-line.

A further test for the Bradbury printings is the size: the stamps printed by Waterlow and De La Rue being almost invariably 22 mm. high, while those printed by Bradbury, Wilkinson measure between 22¾ and 23 mm.

111

(Typographed by Waterlow & Sons, Ltd. (all values except 6d.) and later, 1934–5, by Harrison & Sons, Ltd. (all values). Until 1934 the 6d. was printed at Somerset House where a printing of the 1½d. was also made in 1926 (see No. C 152). Printings by Harrison & Sons, Ltd., in 1934–35 can be identified, when in mint condition, by the fact that the gum shows a streaky appearance vertically, the Waterlow gum being uniformly applied.)

1924 (April)–**1926.** *T* **104,** *etc.* *W* **111.** *P* 15×14.

418	½d. green	0 4	0 1
	a. Wmk. sideways	2 6	2 0
	b. Doubly printed (control U34)		
419	1d. scarlet	0 4	0 1
	a. Wmk. sideways	2 0	2 6
420	1½d. chestnut	0 10	0 1
	a. Tête-bêche (pair)	£16	
	b. Wmk. sideways	4 0	2 6
	c. Printed on the gummed side.	£10	
421	2d. orange (Die II.) ..	1 6	0 1
	a. No wmk...	£5	
	b. Wmk. sideways	3 6	2 6
422	2½d. blue	2 6	0 1
	a. No wmk.	£6	
423	3d. violet	3 0	0 1
424	4d. grey-green	3 6	0 1
	a. Printed on the gummed side.	—	†
425	5d. yellow-brown	4 0	0 2
426	6d. purple, C	4 6	0 10
426a	6d. purple, O (1926) ..	4 0	0 3
427	9d. olive-green	6 6	2 0
428	10d. turquoise-blue ..	8 0	4 0
429	1s. bistre	8 6	2 6

There are numerous shades in this issue.

The 6d. on both chalky and ordinary papers was printed by both Somerset House and Harrison. The Harrison printings have streaky gum, differ slightly in shade, and that on chalky paper is printed in a highly fugitive ink. The prices quoted are for the commoner (Harrison) printing in each case.

WATERMARK VARIETIES.

☛ Many *modern* British stamps exist without watermark owing to misplacement of the paper, and with either inverted, reversed, or inverted and reversed watermarks. A proportion of the low value stamps issued in booklets have the wmk. inverted in the normal course of printing. We do not list such wmk. varieties separately, but a number are always in stock. The 1½d. and 5d. 1912–22, and 2d. and 2½d. 1924–26, listed here, are from *whole* sheets without wmk.

The ½d., 1d., 1½d., 2d. and 2½d. values with *watermark sideways* are from stamp rolls used in automatic machines. We now list these.

112

(Des. H. Nelson. Recess. Waterlow & Sons, Ltd.)

1924–25. *British Empire Exhibition stamps.* *T* **112.** *W* **111.** *P* 14.

	(a) 23.4.24. *Dated* "1924."		
430	1d. scarlet	2 0	2 0
431	1½d. brown	2 6	2 6
	(b) 9.5.25. *Dated* "1925."		
432	1d. scarlet	6 6	6 6
433	1½d. brown	20 0	20 0

113

114

115

116

117

(Typographed by Messrs. Waterlow & Sons, Ltd., from plates made at the Royal Mint, except T **116**, recess-printed by Messrs. Bradbury, Wilkinson & Co., Ltd., from die and plate of their own manufacture. T **113** and **115** were designed by Mr. F. W. Farleigh, T **114** by Mr. E. Linzell, and T **116** by Mr. Harold Nelson.)

1929 (10 May). *Ninth Congress of the Universal Postal Union. W* **111.** *P* 15×14.

434	**113**	½d. yellow-green	0	4	0	2
		a. Wmk. sideways	2	6	3	0
435	**114**	1d. scarlet	0	8	0	4
		a. Wmk. sideways	3	0	3	6
436	,,	1½d. purple-brown	1	0	0	2
		a. Wmk. sideways	3	0	3	6
437	**115**	2½d. blue	6	6	3	6

W **117.** *P* 12.

438	**116**	£1 black	£12	£8

118

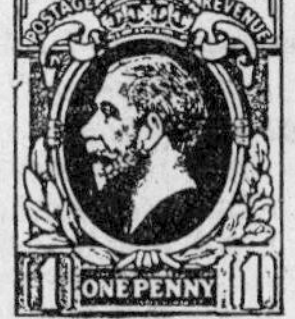

119

120

121

122

(Photo. Harrison & Sons.)

934-36. *W* **111.** *P* 15×14.

39	**118**	½d. green (19.11.34)	0	4	0	2
		a. Wmk. sideways	0	6	0	9
440	**119**	1d. scarlet (24.9.34)	0	6	0	2
		a. Imperf. (pair)				
		b. Printed on the gummed side				
		c. Wmk. sideways	1	0	1	0
441	**118**	1½d. red-brown (20.8.34)	0	10	0	2
		a. Imperf. (pair)	£60			
		b. Imperf. between (pair)				
		c. Wmk. sideways	1	3	1	3
442	**120**	2d. orange (21.1.35)	1	6	0	2
		a. Imperf. (pair)				
		b. Wmk. sideways	1	9	2	0
443	**119**	2½d. ultramarine (18.3.35)	2	0	0	3
444	**120**	3d. violet (18.3.35)	2	6	0	3
445	,,	4d. deep grey-green (2.12.35)	3	6	0	3
446	**121**	5d. yell.-brn. (17.2.36)	4	0	0	6
447	**122**	9d. deep olive-green (2.12.35)	7	0	2	6
448	,,	10d. turquoise-blue (24.2.36)	8	0	2	6
449	,,	1s. bistre-brown (24.2.36)	9	0	1	0

Owing to the need for wider space for the perforations the size of the designs of the ½d., 1d., 1½d. and 2d. has been several times reduced.

There are also numerous minor variations, due to the photographic element in the process, which have no importance. We do not separate the various sizes in our stock and regret that we cannot execute orders for them.

For No. 442 bisected, see "Channel Islands" in King George VI catalogue.

B

(Recess. Waterlow & Sons.)

1934 (Oct.). *T* **109** (*re-engraved*). (B. *Background around portrait consists of horizontal and diagonal lines.*) *W* **110.** *P* 11×12.

450	**109**	2s. 6d. chocolate	20	0	4	0
451	,,	5s. bright rose-red	40	0	10	0
452	,,	10s. indigo	60	0	12	6

There are numerous other minor differences in the design of this issue.

123

(Des. B. Freedman. Photo. Harrison & Sons.)

1935 (7 May). *Silver Jubilee. W* **111.** *P* 15×14.

453	**123**	½d. green	0	6	0	2
454	,,	1d. scarlet	1	0	0	3
455	,,	1½d. red-brown	1	3	0	2
456	,,	2½d. blue	3	0	1	9
456*a*	,,	2½d. Prussian blue	£100			

The 1½d. and 2½d. values differ from T **123** in the emblem in the panel at right.

KING EDWARD VIII, 20.1.36–11.12.36.

124

125

(Photo. Harrison & Sons, Ltd.)

1936 *W* **125.** *P* 15×14.

457	124	½d. green (1.9.36) ..	0	2	0	2
458	„	1d. scarlet (14.9.36) ..	0	4	0	2
459	„	1½d. red-brown (1.9.36) ..	0	6	0	2
460	„	2½d. ultramarine (1.9.36)	1	0	0	10

POSTAGE DUE STAMPS.

D1

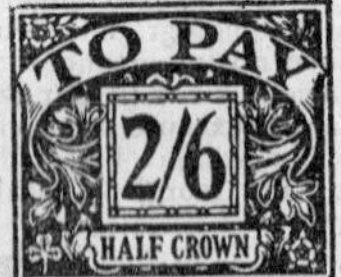

D2

1914–23. *Wmk. Royal Cypher, sideways ("Simple"), T* **100.** *P* 14×15.

D 1	D1	½d. emerald	0	4	0	5
D 2	„	1d. carmine	0	5	0	3
D 3	„	1d. pale carmine ..	0	9	0	3
D 3a	„	1½d. chestnut (1923) ..	12	6	7	6
D 4	„	2d. agate..	0	10	0	5
D 5	„	3d. violet (1918) ..	1	9	0	6
D 6	„	3d. dull violet	1	9	0	6
D 7	„	4d. dull grey-green (1921)	2	9	0	8
D 8	„	5d. bistre-brown ..	2	0	0	5
D 9	„	1s. bright blue (1915) ..	6	0	0	5
D10	„	1s. deep bright blue ..	6	0	0	5

The ½d., 1d., 2d., and 5d. were printed by Messrs. Harrison & Sons and also (early trial printings) at Somerset House, the 1s. at the latter place only. The printings are not easily distinguishable except by the control.

The 1d. is known bisected and used to make up 1½d. rate on understamped letters from Ceylon (1921).

1924. *As* 1914–23, *but thick chalk-surfaced paper*

D10a	D1	1d. carmine	1	6	1	0

(Typo. Waterlow & Sons, Ltd.)

1924–31. *W* **111,** *sideways. P* 14×15.

D10b	D1	½d. emerald	0	4	0	5
D11	„	1d. carmine	0	4	0	3
D12	„	1½d. chestnut	27	6	27	6
D13	„	2d. agate	0	6	0	3
D14	„	3d. dull violet	1	0	0	8
		a. Printed on gummed side	£6		†	
D15	„	4d. dull grey-green ..	1	3	0	10
D16	„	5d. bistre-brown ('31) ..	2	0	1	9
D17	„	1s. bright blue.. ..	3	0	1	0
D18	D2	2s. 6d. purple/*yellow* ..	8	6	1	6

(Typo. Harrison & Sons, Ltd.)

1936–37. *W* **125** (E 8 R). *P* 14×15.

D19	D1	½d. emerald (June, '37)	0	3	0	5
D20	„	1d. carmine (May, '37) ..	0	4	0	6
D21	„	2d. agate (May, '37) ..	0	7	0	8
D22	„	3d. dull violet (Mar., '37)	0	9	0	9
D23	D1	4d. dull grey-grn. (Dec., '36)	0	10	1	0
D24	„	5d. bistre-brn. (Nov., '36)	1	0	1	3
D24a	„	5d. yellow-brown ('37) ..	2	6	2	0
D25	„	1s. bright blue (Dec., '36)	2	6	1	6
D26	D2	2s. 6d. pur./*yell.* (5.37) ..	6	0	2	6

OFFICIAL STAMPS.

In 1840 the 1d. black (Type **1**), with "V R" in the upper corners, was prepared for official use, but never issued for postal purposes. Obliterated specimens are those which were used for experimental trials of obliterating inks, or those that passed the post by oversight.

O1

Prepared for use but not issued.

"V" "R." in upper corners. Imperf.

601	O1	1d. black	£60

1. INLAND REVENUE.

I.R. I. R.

OFFICIAL (151) OFFICIAL (152)

Overprinted with T **151** *(on the lower values) or* **152** *(on the 5s., 10s., and £1), in black.*

1882–1901. *Stamps of Queen Victoria.*

Issues of **1880–81.**

O 1	½d. green (28.10.82) ..	5	0	1	3
O 3	1d. lilac (27.9.82)	0	6	0	2
	a. Optd. in blue-black ..	50	0	9	0
O 4	6d. grey (30.10.82)	20	0	3	0

Controls. 1d. A *to* X.

Issues of **1884–88.**

O 5	½d. slate-blue (8.5.85) ..	3	0	1	0
O 6	2½d. lilac (12.3.85)	42	6	32	6
O 7	1s. green (12.3.85)	£8		80	0
O 8	5s. rose (12.3.85)	£18		£14	
	a. Raised stop after "R" ..	£30		£18	
	b. Optd. in blue-black ..				
O 9	5s. rose (*blued* paper) (12.3.85)	£35		£22	
O 9a	10s. cobalt (12.3.85) ..	£38		£26	
O 10	10s. ultramarine (12.3.85) ..	£20		£15	
	a. Raised stop after "R" ..	£35		£18	
	b. Optd. in blue-black ..				
O 10c	10s. ultram. (*blued* paper) ..	—		£38	
O 11	£1 brn.-lilac (wmk. Crns.) (12.3.85)	£350		£300	
O 12	£1 brn.-lil. (wmk. Orbs) ('90)	£275		£250	

Issues of **1887–92.**

O 13	½d. vermilion (21.1.88) ..	0	6	0	1
	a. Without "I. R." ..				
	b. Opt. double (imperf.) ..	£27			
O 14	1s. green (15.3.89)	28	0	8	0
O 15	2½d. purple/*blue* (20.10.91) ..	20	0	1	0
O 16	£1 green (13.4.92)	£35		£12	
	a. No stop after "R" ..	—		£80	

Controls. ½d. A *to* Q.

Nos. O 3, O 13, O 14, and O 16 may be found with two varieties of overprint, viz. 1887 printings, *thin* letters, and 1894 printings, *thicker* letters.

Issues of **1887** *and* **1900.**

O 17 ½d. blue-green (April, '01) 4 6 1 0
O 18 6d. pur./*rose-red* (14.6.01) .. 75 0 12 0
O 19 1s. grn. & carm. (Dec., '01) £15 90 0

Controls. ½d. R.

1902–4. *Stamps of King Edward VII.*

O 20 ½d. deep green, O (4.2.02) 4 0 1 6
O 21 1d. scarlet, O (4.2.02) .. 1 9 0 4
O 22 2½d. bright blue, O (19.2.02) £9 35 0
O 23 6d. dull purple, O (14.5.04)
O 24 1s. green & car., O (29.4.02) £15 45 0
O 25 5s. carmine, O (29.4.02) £150 £75
a. Raised stop after "R" .. £250 £100
O 26 10s. ultram., O (29.4.02) ..£2000 £1500
a. Raised stop after "R" ..£2250 £1800
O 27 £1 green, O (29.4.02) .. £450 £175

Controls. ½d. A *and* B, *continuous.*
1d. A *and* B, *continuous.*

2. OFFICE OF WORKS.

O. W.
OFFICIAL
(153)

Overprinted with T **153**, *in black.*
Stamps of Queen Victoria.

1896.

O 31 ½d. vermilion (24.3.96) .. 22 6 12 0
O 32 1d. lilac (24.3.96) 22 6 8 0

1901.

O 33 ½d. blue-green (5.11.01) .. 40 0 22 6

Controls. ½d. verm. O
½d. green R
1d. U

1902.

O 34 5d. purple & blue (29.4.02) 72 6 52 6
O 35 10d. purple & carm. (28.5.02) 90 0 80 0

1902. *Stamps of King Edward VII.*

O 36 ½d. deep green, O (11.2.02) 35 0 4 6
O 37 1d. scarlet, O (11.2.02) .. 27 6 3 0
O 38 2d. green & car., O (29.3.02) 70 0 10 0
O 39 2½d. bright blue, O (20.3.02) 90 0 30 0
O 40 10d. pur. & car., O (18.5.02) £25 £12

Controls. ½d. A *and* B, *continuous.*
1d. A *and* B, *continuous.*

3. ARMY.

ARMY
OFFICIAL
(154)

ARMY
OFFICIAL
(155)

Overprinted with T **154** (*½d. and* 1d.) *or* **155** (*2½d. and 6d.*) *in black.*

Stamps of Queen Victoria.

1896 (1 Sept.).

O 41 ½d. vermilion 0 4 0 2
O 42 1d. lilac 0 4 0 2
O 43 2½d. purple/*blue* 0 10 0 8

Errors. "OFFICIAI" *for* "OFFICIAL".

O 44 ½d. vermilion 22 6 17 6
O 45 1d. lilac 18 0 14 0

Controls. ½d. O, P, Q
1d. U, V, W, X

1900–1.

O 46 ½d. blue-green (April, 1900) 0 5 0 2
O 47 6d. pur./*rose-red* (7.11.01) .. 2 6 3 6

Controls. ½d. R.

1902. *Stamps of King Edward VII overprinted with T* **154**, *in black.*

O 48 ½d. deep green, O (11.2.02) 0 5 0 2
O 49 1d. scarlet, O (11.2.02) .. 0 5 0 3
a. Without "ARMY" ..
O 50 6d. dull purple, O (23.8.02) 4 0 4 0

Controls. ½d. A *and* B, *continuous.*
1d. A *and* B, *continuous.*

ARMY
OFFICIAL
(156)

1903. *Overprinted with T* **156**, *in black.*

O 52 6d. dull pur., O (Sept., '03) £10 £5

4. GOVERNMENT PARCELS.

GOVT
PARCELS
(157)

Overprinted with T **157**, *in black.*
Stamps of Queen Victoria.

1883–86.

O 61 1½d. lilac (30.4.86) 32 6 8 0
a. No dot under "T" .. — £6
b. Dot to left of "T" ..
O 62 6d. green (30.4.86) .. £7 35 0
O 63 9d. green (1.8.83) 45 0 45 0
O 64 1s. brown (Pl. 13) (1.7.83) 47 6 17 6
a. No dot under "T" .. — 95 0
b. Dot to left of "T" ..
O 64c 1s. brown (Pl. 14) (1.7.83) £7 25 0
d. No dot under "T" — £9

1887–90.

O 65 1½d. purple & grn. (29.10.87) 4 6 0 8
a. No dot under "T" .. 62 6 8 6
b. Dot to right of "T" .. 42 6 4 0
c. Dot to left of "T" .. 42 6 4 0
O 66 6d. pur./*rose-red* (19.12.87) 8 6 0 8
a. No dot under "T" .. 85 0 32 6
b. Dot to right of "T" .. — 42 6
c. Dot to left of "T" .. — 15 0
O 67 9d. purple & blue (21.8.88) 17 6 1 6
O 68 1s. green (25.3.90) 12 0 2 0
a. No dot under "T" .. — 37 6
b. Dot to right of "T" .. — 47 6
c. Dot to left of "T" .. — 32 6
d. Optd. in blue-black ..

1891–1900.

O 69 1d. lilac (June, '97) .. 3 6 0 5
a. No dot under "T" .. 52 6 11 0
b. Dot to left of "T" .. 57 6 15 0
O 70 2d. green & carm. (24.10.91) 6 0 1 3
a. No dot under "T" .. 62 0 16 6
b. Dot to left of "T" .. 52 6 18 6
O 71 4½d. grn. & carm. (Sept., 1892) 32 6 7 6
O 72 1s. grn. & carm. (Nov., '00) 27 6 14 0

Error. Overprint inverted.

O 73 1d. lilac £45 £30
a. Dot to left of "T" ..

Controls. 1d. W *and* X

1902. *Stamps of King Edward VII.*

O 74 1d. scarlet, O (30.10.02) .. 11 6 2 0
O 75 2d. green & car., O (29.4.02) 14 0 2 0
O 76 6d. dull purple, O (19.2.02) 10 0 2 0
O 77 9d. pur. & blue, O (28.8.02) 30 0 7 6
O 78 1s. grn. & car., O (17.12.02) 45 0 20 0

Controls. 1d. A, *continuous.*

5. BOARD OF EDUCATION.

BOARD

OF

EDUCATION

(158)

Overprinted with T 158, in black.

1902 (19 Feb.). *Stamps of Queen Victoria.*

O 81	5d. purple and blue ..	£8	40 0
O 82	1s. green and carmine ..	£25	£10

1902–4. *Stamps of King Edward VII.*

O 83	½d. deep green, O (19.2.02)	25 0	2 6
O 84	1d. scarlet, O (19.2.02) ..	20 0	1 6
O 85	2½d. bright blue, O (19.2.02)	£7	30 0
O 86	5d. pur. and blue, O (6.2.04)	£28	£23
O 87	1s. grn. & car., O (23.12.02)	£600	£450

Controls. ½d. A *and* B, *continuous.*
1d. B, *continuous.*

6. ROYAL HOUSEHOLD.

R.H.

OFFICIAL

(159)

1902. *Stamps of King Edward VII overprinted with T* **159**, *in black.*

O 91	½d. deep grn., O (29.4.02) ..	42 6	37 6
O 92	1d. scarlet, O (11.2.02) ..	35 0	22 6

Controls. ½d. *an* 1d. A, *continuous.*

7. ADMIRALTY.

ADMIRALTY OFFICIAL (160) ADMIRALTY OFFICIAL (161)

1903 (12 Mar.). *Stamps of King Edward VII overprinted with T* **160**, *in black.*

O 101	½d. deep green, O ..	7 6	2 6
O 102	1d. scarlet, O	3 0	0 4
O 103	1½d. purple and green, O ..	40 0	17 6
O 104	2d. green and carmine, O	25 0	9 0
O 105	2½d. bright blue, O ..	27 6	22 6
O 106	3d. purple/*yellow*, O ..	22 6	10 0

1903 (May (½d.) *and* Sept.). *Stamps of King Edward VII overprinted with T* **161**, *in black.*

O 107	½d. deep green, O	3 6	2 0
O 108	1d. scarlet, O	3 0	0 6
O 109	1½d. purple and green, O ..	95 0	35 0
O 110	2d. green and carmine, O	£10	90 0
O 111	2½d. bright blue, O ..	£15	£9
O 112	3d. purple/*yellow*, O ..	£6	20 0

Controls. Overprint, T **160**.
½d. A *and* B, *continuous.*
1d. A *and* B, *continuous.*
Overprint, T **161**.
½d. *and* 1d. B, *continuous.*

Stamps of various values, perforated with a Crown and initials ("H.M.O.W.", "O.W.", or "B.T."), have been used for official purposes, but we do not catalogue this class of stamp.

CONTROL LETTERS.

PRICES quoted for Nos. C 1 to C 759*m* and for Postage Due controls are for mint single copies, except where pairs, etc., are mentioned. Pairs, strips, or blocks, with control, can be supplied at the prices quoted plus the catalogue price of the extra stamps.

MARGINS. There are two varieties of control, one in which the vertical perforation does not cross the margin of the sheet on which the control appears ("margin imperf.") and the other in which it does ("margin perf."), that we list and price these varieties separately, the price columns being headed I (=Imperf.) and P (=Perf.) respectively. Partially perf. margins are regarded as imperf. * Indicates that the particular variety of margin does not exist with the control indicated. A dash (—) means 'exists but price cannot be quoted."

Perf. margin.

Imperf. margin.

QUEEN VICTORIA.

I. ½*d. vermilion.*

(*a*) *Without "Jubilee Line."*†

			I.	P.
C 1	½d. *no control, corner pair*		*	£6
C 2	½d. A	..	*	20 0
C 3	½d. B	..	*	55 0
C 4	½d. C	..	*	30 0
C 5	½d. D	..	*	30 0
C 6	½d. E	.	*	£14

(*b*) *With "Jubilee Line."*

			I.	P.
C 7	½d. B	..	*	—
C 8	½d. C	..	—	17 6
C 9	½d. D	..	—	16 6
C 10	½d. E	..	—	4 0
C 11	½d. F	..	—	3 6
C 12	½d. G	..	£10	7 6
C 13	½d. H	..	5 0	3 6
C 14	½d. I	..	3 6	0 6
C 15	½d. J	..	42 6	1 9
C 16	½d. K	..	35 0	3 6
C 17	½d. L	..	30 0	2 6
C 18	½d. M	..	1 0	0 8
C 19	½d. N	..	0 10	0 6
C 20	½d. O	..	0 10	0 8
C 21	½d. P	..	0 4	2 6
C 22	½d. Q	..	0 4	0 8

II. ½*d. green. With line.*

			I.	P.
C 23	½d. R	..	0 4	1 3

III. 1d. *lilac.*

(a) Without "Jubilee Line."

		I.	P.
	1d. *none, corner pair* ..	*	£12
C 25	1d. A ..	*	£14
C 26	1d. B ..	*	42 6
C 27	1d. C ..	*	85 0
C 28	1d. D ..	*	22 6
C 29	1d. E ..	*	20 0
C 30	1d. F ..	*	20 0
C 31	1d. G ..	*	10 0
C 32	1d. H ..	*	17 6
C 33	1d. I ..	*	65 0
C 34	1d. J ..	*	40 0

(b) With "Jubilee Line."

		I.	P.
C 35	1d. G ..	*	17 6
C 36	1d. H ..	*	12 6
C 37	1d. I ..	*	7 6
C 38	1d. J ..	*	3 6
C 39	1d. K ..	—	4 0
C 40	1d. L ..	15 0	2 6
C 41	1d. M ..	12 0	3 6
C 42	1d. N ..	7 6	0 8
C 43	1d. O ..	3 6	0 6
C 44	1d. O over N	£35	£45
C 45	1d. P ..	50 0	1 0
C 46	1d. Q ..	12 6	1 3
C 47	1d. R ..	12 0	1 6
C 48	1d. S ..	1 6	0 8
C 49	1d. T ..	1 0	0 8
C 50	1d. U ..	0 8	0 8
C 51	1d. V ..	0 8	0 8
C 52	1d. W ..	0 8	0 8
C 53	1d. X ..	0 8	4 0

The "Jubilee Line" is the coloured line extending round the pane outside the stamps.

When this line is unbroken, as shown in illustration of ½d. vermilion (P) above, it is described as "*continuous,*" but when broken into lengths corresponding with the size of the stamps, as shown above (D 4), it is termed "*Co-extensive.*"

KING EDWARD VII.

De La Rue & Co.

With "Continuous Line."

(i.) ½*d. blue-green.*

		I.	P.
C 54	½d. A ..	1 6	1 9
C 55	½d. B ..	1 0	3 0
C 56	½d. C ..	3 0	35 0
C 57	½d. C 4 ..	1 3	42 6
C 58	½d. D 4 ..	1 6	£15

(ii.) ½*d. yellow-green.*

		I.	P.
C 59	½d. D 4 ..	50 0	—

With "Co-extensive Line."

(i.) ½*d. blue-green.*

		I.	P.
C 60	½d. B ..	75 0	*
C 61	½d. C ..	6 0	—
C 62	½d. C 4 ..	4 0	—
C 63	½d. D 4 ..	1 0	£12

(ii.) ½*d. yellow-green.*

		I.	P.
C 64	½d. D 4 ..	0 10	£8
C 65	½d. D 5 ..	1 3	80 0
C 66	½d. E 5 ..	0 6	7 6
C 67	½d. E 6 ..	1 9	—
C 68	½d. F 6 ..	1 0	3 0
C 69	½d. F 7 ..	5 0	6 0
C 70	½d. G 7 ..	1 3	1 3
C 71	½d. G 8 ..	2 0	2 9
C 72	½d. H 8 ..	2 0	2 0
C 73	½d. H 9 ..	2 6	3 6
C 74	½d. I 9 ..	0 8	0 8
C 75	½d. I 10 ..	1 6	1 9
C 76	½d. J 10 ..	0 8	0 8

Harrison & Sons. *(a) P* 14.

		I.	P.
C 77	½d. A 11 ..	4 0	2 0

(b) P 15×14.

		I.	P.
C 78	½d. A 11 ..	7 6	8 6

De La Rue & Co.

With "Continuous Line."

		I.	P.
C 79	1d. A ..	0 8	6 0
C 80	1d. B ..	0 6	15 0
C 81	1d. C ..	2 6	47 6
C 82	1d. C 4 ..	1 9	18 6
C 83	1d. D 4 ..	1 3	47 6
C 84	1d. D 5 ..	57 6	—

With "Co-extensive Line."

		I.	P.
C 85	1d. C ..	4 0	£14
C 86	1d. C 4 ..	4 0	£14
C 87	1d. D 4 ..	0 8	£12
C 88	1d. D 5 ..	1 3	£25
C 89	1d. E 5 ..	0 8	1 0
C 90	1d. E 6 ..	1 6	£14
C 91	1d. F 6 ..	0 8	0 10
C 92	1d. F 7 ..	4 0	4 0
C 93	1d. G 7 ..	0 8	0 10
C 94	1d. G 8 ..	1 6	1 6
C 95	1d. H 8 ..	0 6	0 6
C 96	1d. H 9 ..	1 3	1 3
C 97	1d. I 9 ..	0 6	0 8
C 98	1d. I 10 ..	1 0	1 0
C 99	1d. J 10 ..	0 8	0 8

Harrison & Sons. *P* 14.

		I.	P.
C 100	1d. A 11 (c)	50 0	—
C 100*a*	1d. A 11 (w)	5 0	3 0

(c) "close" and (w) "wide spacing" refer to the distance between the figures which is respectively 1 mm. and 1½ mm.

P 15×14.

		I.	P.
C 101	1d. A11 (c)	3 0	3 0

Somerset House.

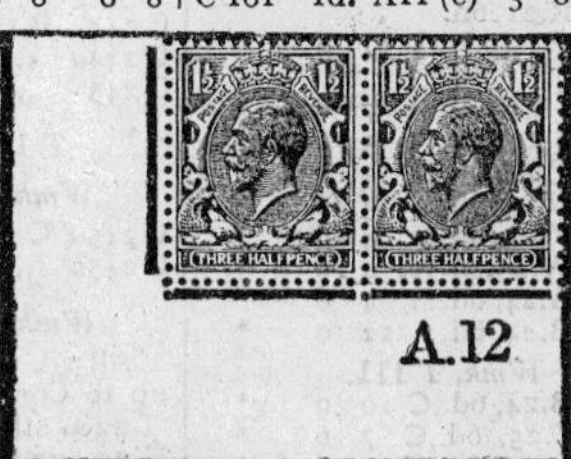

Somerset House.

Harrison.

KING GEORGE V.

Printed at Somerset House.
With full stop after letter.

T **99.** *Wmk. Crown.*

		I.	P.
102	A.11, Die A, 1d. ..	70 0	75 0

Deepened Die.

		I.	P.
C 103	A.11, Die B, 1d. ..	4 0	4 0

T **102.** *Wmk. Crown.*

		I.	P.
C 104	B.11, 1d.	15 0	14 0
C 104*a*	B.12, ½d.		
C 105	B.12, 1d.	7 6	7 6

Wmk. "GvR," *T* **103.**

		I.	P.
C 105*a*	B.12, ½d.	£40	£40
C 105*b*	B.12, 1d.	£30	£45

T **104** *to* **108.**

Wmk. "GvR," *T* **100** (*all* 6*d. P* 15 × 14 *unless otherwise* *stated*). (c) *and* (w) *refer to close and wide spacing.*

		I.	P.
C 106	A. 12, 1½d. (w)	2 0	75 0
C 106a	„ 1½d. (c)	3 0	—
C 107	„ 2½d. ..	2 0	£22
C 108	„ 3d. (w)	3 6	£14
C 108a	„ 3d. (c)	4 6	10 0
C 109	B.13, ½d...	0 9	£15
C 110	„ 3d...	3 6	5 0
C 111	„ 4d...	2 6	80 0
C 112	„ 5d...	4 0	10 0
C 113	„ 9d...	15 0	*
C 114	C.13, 2d...	3 6	2 0
C 115	„ 3d...	5 6	52 6
C 116	„ 6d. pur.	22 6	12 6
C 117	„ 6d. br. pur.	3 6	3 0
C 118	„ 7d...	10 0	*
C 119	„ 8d...	10 6	*
C 120	C.13, 10d.	12 0	£30
C 121	„ 1s...	9 0	75 0
C 122	D.14 6d.	3 6	*
C 123	E.14, 6d..	4 0	5 0
C 124	F.15, 6d...	10 0	£22
C 126	G.15, 6d...	3 0	*
C 127	H.16, 6d...	3 0	*
C 128	I.16, 6d...	3 0	*
C 129	J.17, 6d...	3 0	*
C 130	„ 2½d...	£15	*
C 131	K.17, 6d...	3 0	*
C 132	L.18, 6d...	3 0	55 0
	a. No stop after letter	4 6	*
C 133	M.18, 6d...	3 0	*
C 134	N.19, 6d...	3 0	60 0
C 135	O.19, 6d...	3 0	*
C 136	P.20, 6d...	3 0	*
C 137	Q.20, 6d. (15×14)	5 6	*
C 138	„ 6d. (p. 14)	8 6	*
C 139	R.21, 6d. (p. 14)	17 6	*
C 140	„ 6d. (15×14)	7 6	*
C 141	S.21, 6d...	3 6	65 0
C 142	T.22, 6d...	3 6	85 0
C 143	U.22, 6d...	3 6	*
C 144	V.23, 6d...	4 6	*
C 145	W.23, 6d...	4 6	*
C 146	A.24, 6d...	4 6	*
C 147	B.24, 6d...	12 0	*

Wmk. T **111.**

		I.	P.
C 148	B.24, 6d.,C	10 0	*
C 149	C.25, 6d.,C	7 6	*
C 150	D.25, 6d.,C	7 6	*
C 151	D.25, 6d.,O	37 6	*
C 152	E.26, 1½d.	£25	*
C 153	„ 6d.,O	5 0	—
C 154	F.26, 6d.,O	5 0	*
C 155	G.27, 6d.,O	5 0	*
C 156	H.27, 6d.,O	5 0	*
C 157	I.28, 6d.,O	6 0	17 6
C 158	J.28, 6d.,O	5 0	20 0
C 159	K.29, 6d.,O	5 0	*
C 160	L.29, 6d.,O	5 0	*
C 161	M.30, 6d.,O	5 0	*
C 162	N.30, 6d.,O	5 0	*
C 163	O.31, 6d.,O	5 0	*
C 164	P.31, 6d.,O	5 0	*
C 165	Q.32, 6d.,O	5 0	*
C 166	R.32, 6d.,O	5 0	*
C 167	S.33, 6d.,O	6 0	*
C 168	T.33, 6d.,O	5 0	*

For later 6d. controls, see **C 753, etc.**

Harrison & Sons.

Without stop after letter.

T 98 *and* **99.** *Wmk. Crown.*

		I.	P.
C 231	A 11 (w) ½d. **Die A** ..	6 6	4 6
C 231a	A 11 (c) ½d. Die A		
C 232	A 11 (w) 1d. Die A ..	7 6	4 0
C 232a	A 11 (c) 1d. Die A ..	40 0	£9
C 233	A 11 (w) ½d. Die B ..	4 6	2 0
C 233a	A 11 (c) ½d. Die B ..	3 6	2 6
C 234	A 11 (w) 1d. Die B ..	40 0	—
C 234a	A 11 (c) 1d. Die B ..	2 0	2 0

(c) "close" and (w) "wide" refer to the space between the figures. (1 mm. and 1½ mm. respectively.)

T 101 *and* **102.** (*a*) *Wmk. Crown.*

		I.	P.
C 235	B 11, ½d.	1 6	2 6
C 236	„ 1d.	1 0	1 6
C 237	B 12 (c) ½d.	1 0	1 0
C 237a	„ (w) ½d.	4 6	3 6
C 238	„ (c) 1d.	0 8	0 8
C 238a	„ (w) 1d.	0 8	0 8

(c) "close" and (w) "wide" refer to the space between "B" and the serif of "1." (4½ mm. and 6 mm. respectively.)

Error. Complete lower row of sheet.

		I.	P.
C 239	None ½d. 12 stamps	50 0	*

(*b*) *Wmk.* "GvR," *T* **100.**

		I.	P.
C 240	B 12(c) ½d.	1 6	1 6
C 240a	„ (w) ½d.	1 6	1 6
C 241	„ (w) 1d.	1 6	1 6
C 242	B13, ½d.	1 6	1 6
C 243	„ 1d. ..	1 6	2 0

(*c*) *Wmk.* "GvR," *T* **103.**

		I.	P.
C 244	B 12(c) ½d.	1 3	1 6
C 244a	„ (w) ½d.	1 6	1 0
C 245	„ 1d. ..	1 6	3 0

T **104/8** *and* **113/5.**

Wmk. "GvR," *T* **103.**

		I.	P.
C 245a	C 13, ½d.	£40	—
C 245b	„ 1d.	£40	*

Wmk. "GvR," *T* **100.**

All 2d. stamps are Die I only, up to Control R 21; thence to T 22 as stated in brackets; from U 22 onwards, Die II only.

The 9d. is in agate to Control S 22; from T 22 it is in olive-green.

		I.	P.
C 246	C 12, 1d.	0 6	0 6
C 247	None, 2d. *left corner pair*	30 0	30 0
C 248	C 13, ½d.	0 4	0 4
C 249	„ 1d.	0 4	0 4
C 250	„ 1½d.	1 0	1 0
C 251	„ 2½d.	1 6	1 6
C 252	„ 3d. v.	3 6	3 6
C 253	„ 3d. bl. v.	2 6	2 6
C 254	„ 4d.	2 0	2 0
C 255	„ 7d.	10 0	10 0
C 256	C 14, ½d.	1 3	1 3
C 257	„ 1d.	0 8	0 8
C 258	„ 2d.	2 6	2 0
C 259	„ 2½d.	1 6	1 6
C 260	„ 5d.	3 6	4 0
C 261	D 14, ½d.	0 4	0 4
C 262	„ 1d.	0 4	0 4
C 263	„ 1½d.	1 0	1 0
C 264	„ 2d.	1 6	1 6
C 265	„ 2½d.	17 6	17 6
C 266	D 14 3d.	2 0	4 0
C 267	„ 4d.	2 6	2 6
C 268	„ 5d.	3 6	3 6
C 269	„ 7d.	12 6	12 6
C 270	„ 8d.	10 0	10 0
C 271	„ 10d.	10 0	10 0
C 272	„ 1s.	8 6	8 6
C 273	E 14, ½d	0 4	0 4
C 274	„ 1d.	0 5	0 4
C 275	„ 2½d.	1 6	1 6
C 276	„ 3d.	2 0	2 0
C 277	„ 9d.	*	15 0
C 278	„ 1s.	£30	£30
C 279	F 15, ½d.	0 4	0 4
C 280	„ 1d.	0 4	0 4
C 281	„ 1½d.	3 6	1 9
C 282	„ 2d.	1 6	3 0
C 284	„ 3d.	2 0	2 0
C 285	„ 4d.	2 0	2 6
C 286	„ 5d.	5 0	5 6
C 287	„ 7d.	17 6	12 0
C 288	„ 8d.	10 0	11 0
C 289	„ 9d.	20 0	60 0
C 290	„ 10d.	20 0	25 6
C 291	„ 1s.	8 6	9 4
C 292	G 15, ½d.	0 4	0 4
C 293	„ 1d.	0 4	0 0
C 294	„ 1½d.	1 0	1 3
C 295	„ 2d.	1 3	1 6
C 296	„ 2½d.	1 6	1 0
C 297	„ 3d.	10 0	2 0
C 298	„ 4d.	2 0	2 6
C 299	„ 5d.	3 6	6 0
C 300	„ 7d.	10 0	10 0
C 301	„ 8d.	10 0	10 6
C 302	„ 9d.	12 6	12 0
C 303	„ 10d.	30 0	40 6
C 304	„ 1s.	8 6	8 0
C 305	H 16, ½d.	0 4	0 16
C 306	„ 1d.	0 4	0 3
C 307	„ 1½d.	1 0	1 5
C 308	„ 2d.	1 6	£16
C 309	„ 2½d.	1 6	1 0
C 310	„ 3d.	3 0	10 0
C 311	„ 4d.	4 0	50 0
C 312	„ 5d.	3 6	4 0
C 313	„ 7d.	10 0	10 0
C 314	„ 8d.	10 0	10 0
C 315	„ 9d.	13 6	12 6
C 316	„ 10d.	15 0	40 0
C 317	„ 1s.	8 6	17 6
C 318	I 16, ½d.	0 4	0 6
C 319	„ 1d.	0 7	0 7
C 321	„ 2d.	2 0	20 0
C 322	„ 2½d.	1 6	3 0
C 323	„ 3d.	4 0	2 0
C 324	„ 4d.	2 0	7 6
C 325	„ 5d.	5 6	5 6
C 327	„ 8d.	10 0	10 0
C 328	„ 9d.	12 6	60 0
C 329	„ 10d.	10 0	20 0
C 330	„ 1s.	8 6	20 0
C 331	J 17, ½d.	0 4	0 4
C 332	„ 1d.	0 4	0 4
C 333	„ 1½d.	1 0	1 3
C 334	„ 2d.	1 6	3 0
C 335	„ 2½d.	1 9	3 0
C 336	„ 3d.	2 0	4 6
C 337	„ 4d.	2 0	3 6
C 338	„ 5d.	3 6	4 0
C 339	„ 7d.	10 0	11 0
C 340	„ 8d.	10 0	10 0
	a. Granite paper	10 0	10 0
C 341	J 17, 9d.	12 6	12 6
C 342	„ 10d.	30 0	10 0
C 343	„ 1s.	8 6	15 0
C 344	K 17, ½d.	0 9	1 0
C 345	„ 1d.	0 6	0 9
C 347	„ 2d.	1 6	22 6
C 348	„ 2½d.	1 6	£6
C 350	„ 4d.	2 0	£6
C 351	„ 5d.	3 6	8 6

			I.	P.
C 352	K 17,	9d.	12 6	15 0
C 353	„	1s.	8 6	85 0
C 354	K 18,	½d.	0 6	0 7
C 355	„	1d.	0 6	0 8
C 356	„	1½d.	12 6	12 6
	a. "18" only ("K" omitted)		£20	£25
C 357	K 18,	4d.	2 0	2 3
C 358	„	8d.	£7	10 0
C 359	„	9d.	10 0	12 6
C 360	„	10d.	50 0	10 0

L 18

Letter and figures with serifs.

			I.	P.
C 361	L 18,	½d.	0 6	0 6
C 362	„	1d.	0 7	0 7
C 363	„	1½d.	0 8	0 9
C 364	„	2d.	1 3	2 6
C 365	„	2½d.	1 6	1 6
C 366	„	3d.	2 0	2 0
C 368	„	5d.	3 3	3 3
C 370	„	7d.	10 0	£7
C 371	„	9d.	12 6	12 6
C 372	„	1s.	9 6	8 6
C 373	M 18,	½d.	0 6	0 6
C 374	„	1d.	0 7	0 7
	a. "M" only ("18" omitted)		£40	—
C 375	M 18,	1½d.	0 9	0 9
C 377	„	2½d.	8 0	7 6
C 378	„	3d.	2 0	2 3
C 379	„	4d.	2 0	2 0
C 384	M 19,	½d.	0 7	0 6
C 385	„	1d.	0 7	0 8
C 386	„	1½d.	0 9	0 8
C 387	„	2d.	3 6	8 6
C 388	„	2½d.	10 0	6 0
C 389	„	10d.	10 0	15 0
C 390	„	1s.	9 0	8 6
C 391	N 19,	½d.	0 6	0 8
C 392	„	1d.	0 6	0 8
C 393	„	1½d.	0 9	0 9
C 394	„	2d.	1 6	10 0
C 395	„	2½d.	2 6	2 0
C 396	„	3d.	2 0	2 0
C 397	„	4d.	2 0	2 6
C 398	„	5d.	3 6	3 6
C 399	„	9d.	12 6	12 6
C 401	„	1s.	8 6	8 6
C 402	O 19,	½d.	0 9	1 0
C 403	„	1d.	0 7	0 9
C 404	„	1½d.	1 0	0 9
C 405	„	2d.	2 0	£5
C 406	„	2½d.	4 0	4 6
C 406a	„	5d.	5 6	4 6
C 407	„	9d.	12 6	12 6
C 408	„	10d.	10 0	11 0
C 409	„	1s.	10 0	8 6
C 410	O 20,	½d.	0 6	0 6
C 411	„	1d.	0 9	0 9
C 412	„	1½d.	0 9	0 8
C 413	„	2d.	1 3	1 3
C 414	„	2½d.	1 6	1 6
C 415	„	3d.	2 0	2 0
C 416	„	4d.	2 0	2 6
C 417	„	9d.	12 6	12 6
C 418	„	1s.	10 0	8 6
C 419	P 20,	½d.	0 6	0 4
C 420	„	1d.	0 6	0 8
C 421	„	2d.	1 6	1 6
C 422	„	2½d.	2 0	1 6
C 423	„	3d.	2 6	2 6
C 424	„	9d.	12 6	12 6
C 425	„	1s.	8 6	8 6
C 426	Q 20,	½d.	0 6	0 6
C 427	„	1d.	0 6	0 6
C 428	„	1½d.	1 6	1 6
C 429	„	2d.	1 3	1 3
C 430	„	9d.	12 6	12 6

			I.	P.
C 431	Q 20,	1s.	8 6	8 6
C 432	Q 21,	½d.	0 4	0 4
C 433	„	1d.	0 6	0 6
C 434	„	1½d.	0 9	0 9
C 435	„	2d.	1 3	1 6
C 436	„	2½d.	1 9	1 6
C 437	„	3d.	2 0	2 0
C 438	„	4d.	7 6	6 0
C 439	„	5d.	3 6	4 0
C 440	„	10d.	10 0	11 0
C 441	R 21,	½d.	0 4	0 4
C 442	„	1d.	0 4	0 4
C 443	„	2d.	1 4	1 4
C 444	„	2½d.	1 9	1 6
C 445	„	3d.	3 0	3 0
C 446	„	4d.	2 0	2 0
C 447	„	5d.	4 0	3 6
C 448	„	9d.	12 6	12 6
C 449	„	1s.	8 6	8 6
C 450	S 21,	½d.	0 7	0 7
C 451	„	1d.	0 7	0 7
C 453	„	2d. (I)	1 6	1 6
C 454	„	2d. (II)	3 6	3 6
C 455	„	2½d.	1 6	1 6
C 456	„	3d.	2 0	2 0
C 457	„	4d.	25 0	7 6
C 458	„	5d.	3 6	5 0
C 459	„	9d.	12 6	12 6
C 460	„	10d.	10 0	10 0
C 461	„	1s.	8 6	8 6
C 462	S 22,	½d.	0 4	0 4
C 463	„	1d.	0 4	0 4
C 465	„	2d. (I)	1 6	1 6
C 466	„	2d. (II)	3 0	2 6
C 467	„	2½d.	1 6	1 9
C 468	„	3d.	2 0	2 0
C 469	„	4d.	3 6	10 0
C 470	„	5d.	7 6	£6
C 471	„	9d.	25 0	12 6
C 472	„	10d.	50 0	10 0
C 473	„	1s.	8 6	10 0
C 474	T 22,	½d.	0 4	0 4
C 475	„	1d.	0 4	0 4
C 476	„	1½d.	0 9	0 9
C 477	„	2d. (I)	2 3	1 6
C 478	„	2d. (II)	2 6	3 3
C 479	„	2½d.	1 6	1 6
C 480	„	3d.	2 6	2 0
C 481	„	4d.	2 6	2 0
C 482	„	5d.	7 6	7 6
C 483	„	9d.	20 0	20 0
C 484	„	10d.	11 0	10 0
C 485	„	1s.	8 6	8 6
C 486	U 22,	½d.	0 6	0 6
C 487	„	1d.	0 8	0 6
C 488	„	1½d.	0 9	0 9
C 489	„	2d.	4 0	2 6
C 490	„	3d.	2 3	2 0
C 491	„	4d.	12 0	15 0
C 492	„	1s.	8 6	10 0
C 493	U 23,	½d.	0 4	0 4
C 494	„	1d.	0 6	0 6
C 495	„	1½d.	0 8	0 10
C 496	„	2d.	2 3	2 3
C 497	„	2½d.	3 6	3 6
C 498	„	3d.	2 6	5 0
C 499	„	4d.	25 0	2 6
C 500	„	5d.	3 6	3 6
C 501	„	9d.	15 0	15 0
C 502	„	10d.	10 0	10 0
C 503	„	1s.	10 0	8 6
C 504	V 23,	½d.	0 4	0 4
C 505	„	1d.	0 4	0 4
C 506	„	1½d.	0 9	0 9
C 507	„	2d.	4 6	4 0
C 508	„	2½d.	1 4	1 4
C 509	„	3d.	2 0	2 0
C 510	„	4d.	2 0	2 0
C 511	„	5d.	3 6	3 6
C 512	„	9d.	15 0	15 0
C 513	„	1s.	8 6	10 0
C 514	W 23,	½d.	1 4	1 4
C 515	„	1d.	2 0	1 6

			I.	P.
C 516	W 23,	1½d.	1 0	0 9
C 517	„	2d.	3 0	2 6
C 518	„	3d.	3 0	3 6
C 519	W 24,	½d.	12 6	12 6
C 520	„	1d.	10 0	10 0
C 521	„	1½d.	20 0	20 0
C 522	„	2d.	20 0	25 0

A 24

Without stop. Smaller thick letters and figures, with serifs. Wmk. "GvR" *T* **111.**

(*a*) Typo. Waterlow & Sons.

			I.	P.
C 523	A 24,	½d.	0 6	4 6
C 524	„	1d.	1 0	35 0
C 525	„	1½d.	1 0	5 0
C 526	„	2d.	2 0	*
C 527	„	5d.	5 0	6 6
C 528	„	9d.	12 0	10 0
C 529	„	10d.	40 0	10 0
C 530	„	1s.	10 0	35 0
C 531	B 24,	½d.	0 6	40 0
C 532	„	1d.	0 6	50 0
C 533	„	1½d.	1 0	£8
C 534	„	2d.	2 0	£5
C 535	„	2½d.	3 0	*
C 536	„	3d.	4 0	*
C 537	„	4d.	4 6	*
C 538	„	1s.	10 0	*
C 539	C 25,	½d.	0 6	60 0
C 540	„	1d.	0 6	20 0
C 541	„	1½d.	1 0	—
C 542	„	2d.	2 0	*
C 543	„	2½d.	3 0	*
C 544	„	3d.	4 0	*
C 545	„	4d.	4 6	*
C 546	„	5d.	5 0	*
C 547	„	9d.	12 6	*
C 548	D 25,	½d.	0 6	*
C 549	„	1d.	4 0	*
C 550	„	1½d.	1 0	*
C 551	„	2d.	2 0	*
C 552	„	2½d.	3 0	*
C 553	„	3d.	4 0	*
C 554	„	10d.	17 6	*
C 555	„	1s.	10 0	*
C 556	E 26,	½d.	0 6	*
C 557	„	1d.	0 8	*
C 558	„	1½d.	1 0	*
C 559	„	2d.	2 0	*
C 560	„	2½d.	3 0	*
C 561	„	3d.	4 0	*
C 562	„	4d.	4 0	*
C 563	F 26,	½d.	0 6	80 0
C 564	„	1d.	0 6	*
C 565	„	1½d.	1 0	60 0
C 566	„	2d.	2 0	*
C 570	„	5d.	5 0	*
C 571	„	9d.	15 0	*
C 572	„	10d.	17 6	*
C 573	„	1s.	10 0	*
C 574	G 27,	½d.	0 8	35 0
C 575	„	1d.	0 6	*
C 576	„	1½d.	1 0	*
C 577	„	2d.	2 0	*
C 578	„	2½d.	3 0	*
C 579	„	3d.	4 0	£7
C 580	„	4d.	4 6	*
C 583	„	10d.	10 0	*
C 584	H 27,	½d.	0 6	40 0
C 585	„	1d.	0 6	*
C 586	„	1½d.	1 0	60 0
C 587	„	2d.	2 0	*
C 588	„	2½d.	8 6	*
C 589	„	5d.	7 6	*
C 590	„	1s.	12 6	*
C 591	I 28,	½d.	0 8	*
C 592	„	1d.	0 9	

No.	Control	Value	I.	P.
C 593	I 28,	1½d.	1 0	£8
C 594	,,	2d.	2 0	£8
C 595	,,	2½d.	3 0	*
C 596	,,	3d.	6 0	*
C 597	,,	4d.	4 6	*
C 598	,,	5d.	6 0	*
C 599	,,	9d.	12 6	*
C 600	,,	1s.	10 0	*
C 601	J 28,	½d.	0 8	*
C 602	,,	1d.	0 6	*
C 603	,,	1½d.	1 0	*
C 604	,,	2d.	2 0	*
C 609	,,	9d.	12 6	*
C 610	,,	10d.	15 0	*
C 611	,,	1s.	10 0	*
C 612	K 29,	½d.	0 6	*
C 613	,,	1d.	0 6	*
C 614	,,	1½d.	1 0	£7
C 615	,,	2d.	2 0	*
C 616	,,	2½d.	3 6	*
C 617	,,	3d.	4 0	*
C 618	,,	4d.	4 6	*
C 619	,,	5d.	5 0	*
C 622	,,	1s.	11 0	*
C 623	,,	½d.113	1 0	*
C 624	,,	1d.114	1 6	*
C 625	,,	1½d. ,,	1 6	*
C 626	,,	2½d.115	8 6	*
C 627	L 29,	½d.113	3 6	*
C 628	,,	1d.114	4 6	—
C 629	,,	1½d. ,,	5 6	*
C 630	,,	2½d.115	10 0	*
C 631	,,	½d.	0 6	40 0
C 632	,,	1d.	1 0	£6
C 633	,,	1½d.	1 0	*
C 634	,,	2d.	2 0	*
C 638	,,	5d.	5 0	*
C 639	,,	9d.	12 6	*
C 640	,,	10d.	22 6	*
C 641	,,	1s.	10 0	*
C 642	M 30,	½d.	0 6	*
C 643	,,	1d.	0 6	*
C 644	,,	1½d.	1 0	*
C 645	,,	2d.	2 0	*
C 646	,,	2½d.	3 0	*
C 647	,,	3d.	4 0	*
C 648	,,	4d.	4 6	*
C 649	,,	5d.	15 0	*
C 653	N 30,	½d.	0 6	*
C 654	,,	1d.	6 0	*
C 655	,,	1½d.	1 0	—
C 656	,,	2d.	2 0	*
C 657	,,	2½d.	3 6	*
C 658	,,	3d.	4 0	*
C 661	N 30,	9d.	12 6	*
C 663	,,	1s.	10 0	*
C 664	O 31,	½d.	0 6	—
C 665	,,	1d.	0 7	—
C 666	,,	1½d.	1 0	*
C 667	,,	2d.	2 0	*
C 668	,,	2½d.	£40	*
C 670	,,	4d.	4 6	*
C 671	,,	5d.	8 6	*
C 673	,,	10d.	25 0	*
C 675	P 31,	½d.	0 6	*
C 676	,,	1d.	0 7	*
C 677	,,	1½d.	1 0	*
C 678	,,	2d.	2 0	*
C 680	,,	3d.	4 0	*
C 683	,,	9d.	12 6	*
C 685	,,	1s.	10 0	*
C 686	Q 32,	½d.	0 6	*
C 687	,,	1d.	0 7	*
C 688	,,	1½d.	1 0	*
C 689	,,	2d.	2 0	*
C 690	,,	2½d.	4 0	*
C 692	,,	4d.	4 6	*
C 693	,,	5d.	17 6	*
C 695	,,	10d.	65 0	*
C 697	R 32,	½d.	0 6	*
C 698	,,	1d.	4 6	*
C 699	,,	1½d.	1 0	*
C 700	,,	2d.	2 0	*
C 701	,,	2½d.	4 6	*
C 702	,,	3d.	4 0	*
C 703	,,	4d.	5 0	*
C 705	,,	9d.	12 6	*
C 707	,,	1s.	22 6	*
C 708	S 33,	½d.	0 6	*
C 709	,,	1d.	0 7	*
C 710	,,	1½d.	1 0	*
C 711	,,	2d.	2 0	*
C 712	,,	2½d.	10 0	*
C 713	,,	3d.	6 0	*
C 715	,,	5d.	5 6	*
C 717	,,	10d.	15 0	*
C 718	,,	1s.	15 0	*
C 719	T 33,	½d.	0 6	*
C 720	,,	1d.	0 7	*
C 721	,,	1½d.	1 0	*
C 722	,,	2d.	2 0	*
C 723	,,	2½d.	3 0	*
C 724	,,	3d.	4 0	*
C 725	,,	4d.	4 6	*
C 726	,,	5d.	£30	*
C 727	,,	9d.	12 6	*
C 730	U 34,	½d.	2 0	*
C 731	,,	1d.	3 6	*
C 732	U 34,	1½d.	1 6	*
C 737	,,	5d.	6 0	*
C 739	,,	10d.	20 0	*
C 740	,,	1s.	12 6	*

(b) Typo. Harrison & Sons.

No.	Control	Value	I.	P.
C 741	U 34,	½d.	5 0	*
C 742	,,	1d.	8 6	*
C 743	,,	1½d.	5 0	*
C 743a	,,	2d. (smooth gum)	7 6	*
C 744	U 34,	2d. (streaky gum)	4 6	*
C 745	V 34,	½d.	0 6	20 0
C 746	,,	1d.	1 6	20 0
C 747	,,	1½d.	2 6	—
C 748	,,	2d.	3 0	—
C 749	,,	2½d.	25 0	*
C 750	,,	3d.	4 0	*
C 751	,,	4d.	7 6	*
C 752	,,	5d.	8 6	*
C 753	,,	6d.,O	6 0	*
C 754	,,	9d.	10 0	*
C 754a	,,	10d.	30 0	*
C 755	,,	1s.	12 6	£7
C 756	W35,	2½d.	10 0	32 6
C 756a	,,	4d.	14 0	*
C 757	,,	6d.,O	10 0	12 6
C 758	,,	9d.	11 0	*
C 758a	,,	10d.	15 0	*
C 759	,,	1s.	10 0	
C 759a	X 35,	4d.	5 0	—
C 759b	,,	5d.	8 0	*
C 759c	,,	6d.,O	5 0	12 6
C 759d	,,	9d.	12 6	17 6
C 759e	,,	1s.,	10 0	*
C 759f	Y 36,	6d.,O	6 0	*
C 759g	Y 36,	6d.,C	£8	*
C 759h	Z 36,	6d.,O	6 0	*
C 759i	Z 36,	6d.,C	7 0	*
C 759j	A 37,	6d.,O	6 0	*
C 759k	B 37,	6d.,C	8 6	—
C 759l	C 38,	6d.,O	6 0	*
C 759m	D 38,	6d.,O	6 0	7 6

Harrison printings with U 34 control can in some cases be distinguished from Waterlow printings with the same control by their vertically streaky gum.

T123 (*Jubilee*). **W 111.** "*Fractional*" *control in left-hand margin.*

No.	Control	Value	I.	P.
C 760	W 35,	½d.	5 0	*

Photo. Harrison & Sons.

PHOTOGRAVURE CONTROLS

With the exception of Nos. C 764 and C 765, the controls on sheets of the photogravure printings by Harrison are "fractional" (letter above numeral) and in the left-hand margin. (See illustration.)

The normal position of the fractional controls is beside the third stamp from the bottom of the sheet, but the V 34 control on the ½d., 1d., and 1½d. is found only beside the *second* stamp from the bottom.

Cylinder numbers. The small coloured numbers on the sheet margins of this printing indicate the cylinder from which the sheet was printed. **We do not list these separately, but selections can be sent on request.**

PRICES. These fractional controls are best collected in blocks, to show the control, cylinder number and both left and bottom margins.

Our prices quoted below are therefore for blocks of four of the ½d., 1d. and 1½d. V 34 and for vertical blocks of six of the Silver Jubilee stamps and all numbers from C 771 onwards. Where strips, pairs or singles are in stock, they will be supplied at the prices quoted, less an allowance for the reduced number of stamps.

The letters I (Imperf.) and P (Perf.) refer to the *left-hand* margins in all fractional controls and NOT to the *bottom* margins.

No.	Control	Value	I.	P.
C 761	W 35,	1d.	8 6	*
C 762	"	1½d.	8 6	*
C 763	"	2½d.	25 0	*

The King George V photogravure controls from the 3d. value upwards were issued successively with bars below control; below and to left; below, to left and to right; and finally all round the control as shown in the accompanying illustration. These represent different control periods and are just as important as the changes in control letters and numbers, but are listed in small type for convenience.

Photo. Harrison & Sons.

T 118 to 122. W 111.

(a) *Control below second stamp in bottom row.*

No.	Control	Value	I.	P.
C 764	U 34,	1½d.	30 0	35 0
C 765	V 34,	1½d.	10 0	10 0

(b) "*Fractional*" *control* (*letter above numeral*) *in left-hand margin.*

No.	Control	Value	I.	P.
C 767	V 34,	½d.	2 6	5 0
C 768	"	1d.	3 6	4 0
C 769	"	1½d.	4 6	5 0
C 770	"	2d.	20 0	35 0
C 771	W 35,	½d.	3 6	10 0
C 772	"	1d.	75 0	*
C 773	"	1½d.	6 0	10 6
C 774	"	2d.	10 0	—
C 775	"	2½d.	15 0	50 0
C 776	"	3d.	17 6	17 6
C 777	"	4d.	—	25 0
C 778	X 35,	½d.	2 6	12 6
C 779	"	1d.	3 6	17 6
C 780	"	1½d.	6 0	60 0
C 781	"	2d.	10 0	*
C 782	"	3d.	20 0	*
C 783	"	4d.	25 0	£5
C 783a	"	5d.	£20	*
C 784	"	9d.	50 0	*
	a. Bar —		50 0	*
	b. Bars ⌊		52 6	*
	c. Bars ⌊⌋		50 0	*
	d. Bars □		50 0	*
C 785	Y 36,	½d.	2 6	—
C 786	"	1d.	3 6	30 0
C 787	"	1½d.	6 0	35 0
C 788	"	2d.	10 0	40 0
C 789	"	2½d.	15 0	£5
C 790	"	3d.	20 0	75 0
C 791	"	4d.	25 0	*
	a. Bar —		25 0	*
	b. Bars ⌊		25 0	*
	c. Bars ⌊⌋		25 0	*
	d. Bars □		25 0	*
C 792	Y 36,	5d.	30 0	£7
C 795	"	10d.	55 0	*
	a. Bar —		57 6	*
	b. Bars ⌊		57 6	*
	c. Bars ⌊⌋		57 6	*
	d. Bars □		57 6	*
C 796	Y 36,	1s.	60 0	*
C 797	Z 36,	½d.	3 6	*
C 798	"	1½d.	5 0	60 0
C 799	"	2d.	10 0	40 0
C 800	"	3d.	17 6	75 0
	a. Bar —		17 6	—
	b. Bars ⌊		20 0	*
C 801	Z 36,	5d.	32 6	*
	a. Bars —		32 6	£7
	b. Bars ⌊		30 0	*
	c. Bars ⌊⌋		30 0	*
	d. Bars □		30 0	*
C 802	Z 36,	1s.	62 6	*
	a. Bar —		60 0	*
	b. Bars ⌊		62 6	*
	c. Bars ⌊⌋		62 6	*
	d. Bars □		60 0	*
C 803	A 37,	2d.	12 6	*

KING EDWARD VIII.

Photo. Harrison & Sons.

T 124. W 125.

No.	Control	Value	I.	P.
C 804	A 36,	½d.	1 6	35 0
C 805	"	1d.	2 6	£8
C 806	"	1½d.	3 0	40 0
C 807	"	2½d.	7 6	*
	a. Bar —		6 6	*
C 808	A 37,	½d.	1 6	*
C 809	"	1d.	5 6	*
C 810	"	1½d.	3 0	*

POSTAGE DUE STAMPS.

☞ (Prices are for single stamp with control attached. The letters "I" and "P" refer to the bottom margins, in all Postage Due Controls.)

Somerset House. Wmk. "GvR," **T 100.**

Stop after letter.

No.	Control	Value	I.	P.
CD 1	D.14	½d.	*	10 0
CD 2	"	1d.	*	10 0
CD 3	"	2d.	*	15 0
CD 4	"	5d.	*	17 6
CD 5	F.15,	1s.	*	18 6
CD 6	O.19,	1s.	*	30 0
CD 7	S.21,	1s.	*	30 0
CD 8	V.23,	1s.	17 6	*

Harrison & Sons. *Wmk.* "GvR," **T 100.**

No stop after letter.

No.	Control	Value	I.	P.
CD 21	D 14,	½d.	2 0	2 0
CD 22	"	1d.	3 6	3 6
CD 23	"	2d.	5 0	4 0
CD 24	"	5d.	10 0	£12
CD 25	E 14,	1d.	5 0	1 9
CD 26	G 15,	1d	3 6	20 0
CD 27	H 16,	2d.	4 6	4 6
CD 28	I 16,	½d.	5 6	5 6
CD 29	"	1d.	2 6	6 6
CD 30	"	2d.	4 0	10 0
CD 31	K 17,	1d.	2 6	2 6
CD 32	"	2d.	12 6	2 6
CD 33	L 18,	3d.	3 0	12 6
CD 34	N 19,	½d.	2 0	3 6
CD 35	"	1d.	2 6	2 6
CD 37	O 19,	2d.	3 6	5 0
CD 38	O 20,	3d.	2 6	2 6
CD 39	P 20,	1d.	2 0	*
CD 40	"	2d.	1 6	7 6
CD 41	Q 20,	1d.	12 6	*
CD 42	"	4d.	6 0	6 0
CD 43	Q 21,	1d.	12 6	20 0
CD 44	R 21,	½d.	3 6	8 6
CD 45	"	1d.	1 9	5 6
CD 46	"	2d.	3 0	12 6
CD 47	S 21,	1d.	3 6	3 6
CD 48	S 22,	½d.	*	2 6
CD 49	"	1d.	3 0	3 0
CD 51	T 22,	1d.	3 6	2 6
CD 52	"	3d.	5 0	3 0
CD 53	U 22,	½d.	2 6	15 0
CD 54	"	1½d.	17 6	*
CD 55	U 23,	1d.	2 6	2 6
CD 56	"	1½d.	17 6	*
CD 57	"	2d.	25 0	2 6
CD 60	V 23,	1½d.	17 6	17 6
CD 61	"	3d.	3 6	3 6
CD 62	W 23,	½d.	10 0	12 6
CD 63	"	3d.	8 6	20 0

Waterlow & Sons.

(a) **W 100.** *Thick chalk-surfaced paper.*

No.	Control	Value	I.	P.
CD 64	B 24,	1d	12 6	*
CD 65	C 25,	1d.	3 6	*

(b) **W 111.**

No.	Control	Value	I.	P.
CD 66	A 24,	2d.	3 6	*
CD 67	"	4d.	45 0	*
CD 68	"	1s.	£35	*
CD 68a	B 24,	½d.	*	2 0
CD 69	"	1d.	15 0	*
CD 70	"	1½d.	50 0	*
CD 71	"	3d.	3 0	*
CD 72	"	4d.	8 6	*
CD 73	"	1s.	22 6	*
CD 74	"	2s. 6d.	30 0	*
CD 76	C 25,	2d.	2 0	*
CD 77	"	1s.	15 0	*
CD 78	D 25,	3d.	7 6	*
CD 79	E 26,	2d.	3 6	*
CD 80	"	3d.	5 0	*
CD 81	"	4d.	12 6	*
CD 82	"	1s	—	32 6
CD 83	F 26,	½d.	2 0	*
CD 84	"	1d.	1 6	7 6
CD 85	"	2d.	2 0	*
CD 86	"	3d.	5 0	*
CD 87	"	4d.	8 6	*
CD 88	"	1s.	10 0	*
CD 89	G 27,	3d.	2 0	*
CD 90	"	1s.	11 6	*
CD 91	H 27,	2d.	50 0	*
CD 92	"	3d.	*	20 0
CD 93	"	2s. 6d.	40 0	*
CD 94	I 28,	½d.	1 6	*
CD 95	"	1d.	1 6	*
CD 96	"	2d.	2 0	*
CD 97	"	3d.	2 0	*
CD 98	"	4d.	*	20 0
CD 99	"	1s.	10 0	*
CD 100		2s. 6d.	45 0	*
CD 101	K 29,	½d.	*	2 0
CD 102	"	1d.	1 6	40 0
CD 103	"	2d.	3 0	*
CD 104	"	3d.	2 0	*
CD 105	"	4d.	6 0	*
CD 106	"	1s.	7 6	*
CD 107	"	2s. 6d.	40 0	—
CD 108	L 29,	½d.	2 0	*
CD 109	"	1d.	1 6	*
CD 110	"	2d.	2 0	*
CD 111	"	3d.	2 0	*
CD 112	"	4d.	6 0	*
CD 114	"	2s. 6d.	40 0	*
CD 115	M 30,	½d.	2 0	*
CD 117	"	2d.	2 0	*
CD 120	"	1s.	22 6	*
CD 123	N 30,	1d.	1 6	*
CD 125	"	3d.	2 0	*
CD 126	"	4d.	5 0	*
CD 127	"	5d.	6 0	*
CD 128	"	2s. 6d.	65 0	*
CD 129	O 31,	½d.	3 6	*
CD 130	"	1d.	3 6	*
CD 131	"	2d.	3 6	*
CD 132	"	3d.	1 6	*
CD 133	"	5d.	3 0	*
CD 134	"	1s.	22 6	*
CD 135	"	2s. 6d.	55 0	*
CD 136	P 31,	½d.	1 0	*
CD 137	"	2d.	1 6	*
CD 138	Q 32,	½d.	1 0	*
CD 139	"	1d.	1 3	*
CD 140	"	2d.	4 0	*
CD 141	"	3d.	1 6	*
CD 142	"	4d.	4 0	*
CD 143	"	5d.	5 0	*
CD 144	"	1s.	5 0	*
CD 145	"	2s. 6d.	25 0	*
CD 146	R 32,	2d.	4 0	*
CD 147	"	3d.	4 6	*
CD 148	"	4d.	6 6	*
CD 149	"	1s.	5 0	*
CD 150	"	2s. 6d.	10 0	*
CD 151	S 33,	½d.	1 0	*
CD 152	"	1d.	2 0	—
CD 154	"	5d.	30 0	*
CD 155	"	1s.	25 0	*
CD 156	"	2s. 6d.	40 0	*
CD 157	T 33,	2d.	50 0	*
CD 158	"	3d.	2 6	*

			I.	P.
CD 159	T 33,	4d.	£12	*
CD 160	U 34,	½d.	20 0	*
CD 161	,,	1d.	37 6	37 6
CD 162	,,	5d.	60 0	*
CD 163	,,	1s.	50 0	*
CD 164	,,	2s. 6d.	85 0	*
Harrison & Sons.	(a) W 111.			
CD 165	U 34,	½d.	4 6	*
CD 166	V 34,	2d.	40 0	*
CD 167	,,	4d.	35 0	*
CD 167a	,,	2s. 6d.	80 0	*
CD 168	W 35,	½d.	4 0	*
CD 169	W 35,	1d.	20 0	*
CD 170	,,	3d.	20 0	*
CD 170a	,,	5d.	10 0	*
CD 171	,,	1s.	37 6	*
CD 171a	X 35,	2d.	3 6	*
CD 171b	,,	4d.	30 0	*
CD 172	,,	1s.	40 0	*
CD 173	,,	2s. 6d.	70 0	*
CD 174	Y 36,	½d.	2 6	*
CD 175	,,	1d.	3 6	*
CD 176	,,	2d.	5 0	*
CD 177	,,	3d.	7 6	12 6
CD 178	Z36,	2s. 6d.	40 0	*
	(b) W 125.			
CD 179	A 36,	4d.	3 6	*
CD 180	,,	5d.	6 6	*
CD 181	,,	1s.	12 6	*
CD 182	A 37,	½d.	1 9	*
CD 183	,,	1d.	2 3	*
CD 184	,,	2d.	2 6	*
CD 185	,,	3d.	3 6	*
CD 186	,,	5d.	12 6	*
CD 187	,,	2s. 6d.	35 0	*
CD 188	C38,	2s. 6d.	25 0	*

POSTAL FISCALS.

AUTHORIZED FOR POSTAL USE 1ST JUNE, 1881.
ONE PENNY VALUES. SURFACE-PRINTED. P 15½×15.
(Printed by Messrs. De La Rue & Co.)

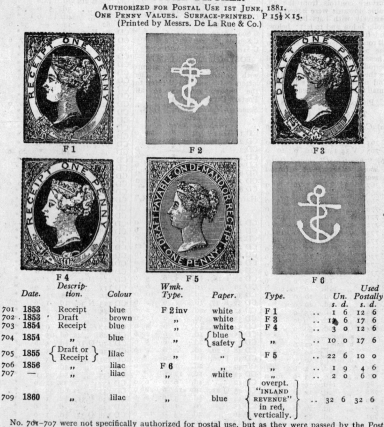

F 1

F 2

F 3

F 4

F 5

F 6

No.	Date.	Description.	Colour	Wmk. Type.	Paper.	Type.		Un. s. d.	Used Postally s. d.
701	1853	Receipt	blue	F 2 inv	white	F 1	..	1 6	12 6
702	1853	Draft	brown	,,	white	F 3	..	17 6	17 6
703	1854	Receipt	blue	,,	white	F 4	..	3 0	12 6
704	1854	,,	blue	,,	blue safety	,,	..	10 0	17 6
705	1855	Draft or Receipt	lilac	,,	,,	F 5	..	22 6	10 0
706	1856	,,	lilac	F 6	,,	,,	..	1 9	4 6
707	—	,,	lilac	,,	white	,,	..	2 0	6 0
709	1860	,,	lilac	,,	blue	overpt. "INLAND REVENUE" in red, vertically.	..	32 6	32 6

No. 701–707 were not specifically authorized for postal use, but as they were passed by the Post Office without question in 1881, they are given here. Nos. 709–756 only were authorized by Acts of Parliament. No. 702 exists *tête-bêche*.

F 7

F 8

F 9

No.	Date.	Descrip-tion.	Colour.	Wmk. Type.	Paper.	Type.	Un. s. d.	Used Postally s. d.
710	1860	{ Inland Revenue }	lilac	F 6	white	F 7	2 6	5 0
711	—	„	lilac	„	blue	„	2 6	5 0
712	1864	„	lilac	40, 16 mm. high	bluish	„	1 9	4 0
713	—	„	lilac	„	white	„	3 6	3 6
713a	1867	„	lilac	40, 18 mm. high	bluish	„	6 6	3 6
713b	—	„	lilac	„	white	„		

First Type. (a) "Inland Revenue." Second Type. (b) Small rectangular. Third Type. (c)*

P 14.

No.	Date.	Type.	Colour.	Wmk. Type.	Paper.		Un. s. d.	Used Postally s. d.
714	1867	F 8	lilac	Anchor, 47	white	.. .. ..	5 0	6 0
715	1867	„	lilac	„	bluish	.. .. ..	5 0	6 0
716	1868	F 9 (a)	lilac	„	white	.. .. ..	0 8	2 3
717	1871	„ „	lilac	„	bluish	.. .. ..	1 3	2 3
718	1877	„ (b)	lilac	„	white	.. .. ..	1 3	4 0
719	1877	„ „	lilac	„	bluish	.. .. ..	2 6	5 0
720	1879	„ (c)	lilac	„	white	.. .. ..	1 0	2 9
721	1878	„ „	lilac	„	bluish	.. .. ..	3 6	2 6
722	1881	„ „	lilac	Orb, 48	white	.. .. ..	1 0	1 0
723	1881	„ „	lilac	„	bluish	.. .. ..	1 3	1 9

* In a the corner ornaments are small; in b they are larger and in c still larger.

F 10

F 13

INLAND
REVENUE
(I)

INLAND
REVENUE
(II)

Embossed. *T* F **10** *and similar types. Optd.* "inland revenue."
(Made at Somerset House by the Inland Revenue Authorities.)

1883 (1 Jan.).

No.	Die		Value	Colour	Paper	Perf.	Un.	Used
724	Die C	1860	3d.	pink	blue paper	imperf.	30 0	50 0
724a	„ D	„	3d.	pink	blue paper	„	£9	
724b	„ C	„	3d.	pink	blue paper	perf. 12½		
724c	„ D	„	3d.	pink	blue paper	„		
725	„ T	„	6d.	pink	blue paper	imperf.	£24	
725a	„ U	„	6d.	pink	blue paper	„	90 0	80 0
726	„ K	„	2s.	pink	blue paper	„	£12	£9

724aa. *Tête-bêche* pair of No. 724. £30.

1860–82. *T* F **13,** *and similar types with crown in design, optd.* "inland revenue."
A. "inland revenue" *T* I. Blue *paper*. *No wmk.* *Imperf.* (1860–70.)
B. *Ditto.* *Ditto.* *Perf.* 12½ (1861–73.)
C. "inland revenue" *T* II. White *paper*. *Wmk. Anchor.* *Perf.* 12½. (1874.)

No.		A. Un.	A. Used	B. Un.	B. Used	C. Un.	C. Used
727	2d. pink (Die A)	70 0	90 0	£7	£5	–	£8
728	9d. pink (Die C)	£8	–	£8	£8	–	–
729	1s. pink (Die E)	–	£6	£5	95 0	†	
730	1s. pink (Die F)	70 0	70 0	£5	95 0	£5	£6
	a. Tête-bêche (pair)	£7		†		†	
731	2s. 6d. pink (Die N)	–	–	†		†	
732	2s. 6d. pink (Die O)	30 0	30 0	35 0	35 0	–	£8

D. "inland revenue" Type I. Blue *or* white *paper*. *Wmk. Anchor.* *P* 12½. (1875–80.)
E. *Ditto.* Blue *paper*. *Wmk. Orbs.* *P* 12½. (1882.)

No.		D. Un.	D. Used	E. Un.	E. Used
733	2d. vermilion (Die A)	£6	80 0	–	–
734	9d. vermilion (Die C)	£6	£6	–	–
735	1s. vermilion (Die E)	50 0	40 0	–	–
736	1s. vermilion (Die F)	70 0	50 0	†	
737	2s. 6d. vermilion (Die O)	80 0	70 0	£12	£8

F 17

F 18

SURFACE-PRINTED STAMPS.
(Printed by Messrs. De La Rue & Co.)
T **F 17** *and* **18,** *bluish to white paper.*

No.		*Wmk. Type.*	*Perf.*	Date		
747	3d. lilac	F 6	15½ × 15	(1860)	£7	60 0
748	3d. lilac	**40,** 16 mm. high	„	(1864)	40 0	30 0
749	3d. lilac	**40,** 18 mm. „	„	(1867)	15 0	20 0
750	3d. lilac	**40,** 18 mm. „	14	(1881)	£10	£10
751	3d. lilac	**40,** 20 mm. „	14	(1881)	£6	40 0
752	6d. lilac	F 6	15½ × 15	(1860)	8 6	18 6
753	6d. lilac	*W* **40,** 16 mm. high	*P* 15½ × 15	(1864)	7 0	18 6
754	6d. lilac	„ **40,** 18 mm. „	„	(1867)	4 0	10 0
755	6d. lilac	„ **40,** 18 mm. „	14	(1881)	40 0	50 0
756	6d. lilac	„ **40,** 20 mm. „	14	(1881)	30 0	60 0

TELEGRAPH STAMPS.

Owing to shortage of paper these issues, not being of general interest, are temporarily omitted from this Catalogue. They were last included in 1941 (47th Edn.).

BRITISH STAMPS USED ABROAD.

STAMPS OF GREAT BRITAIN OBLITERATED WITH ONE OF THE FOLLOWING TYPES :—

I. Horizontal oval.

(1)

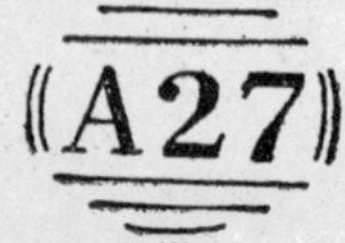

(2)

(3)

(4)

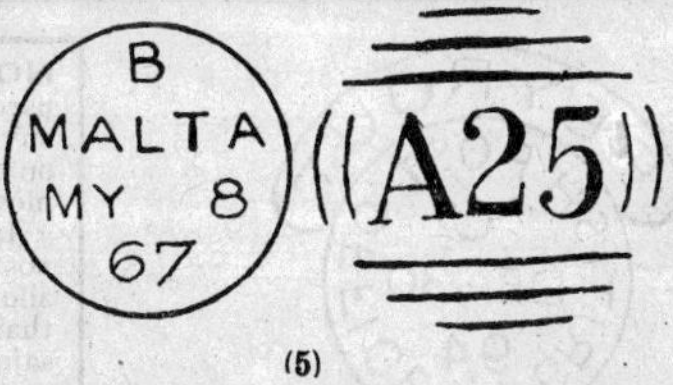

(5)

(6)

(7)

II. Vertical oval.

(8)  (9)  (10)  (11)

(12)

(13)

(14)

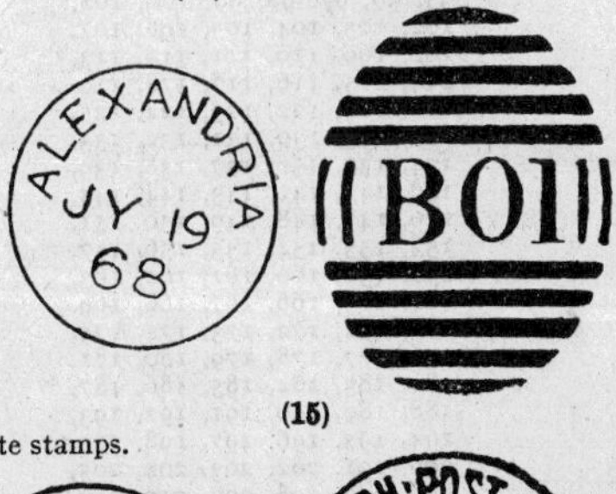

(15)

III. Circular date stamps.

(16)

(17)

(18)

(19)

(20)

NOTE.—Prices quoted for British stamps used abroad are for single stamps not on envelopes unless otherwise stated. Stamps on envelopes are worth considerably more in most instances.

In many instances obliterators allotted to post offices abroad were, at a later date, re-allotted to post offices at home. Later issues than those included in our lists can therefore safely be regarded as *not* "used abroad."

I.

Used in British Possessions in Europe.

MALTA.

1857–85.

"**M**" *Obliteration, T* **1.**

No.	Description	s.	d.
z 1	1d. red-brown, Die I, *wmk.* Small Crown, *perf.* 16	65	0
z 1*a*	1d. red-brown, Die II (1855), *wmk.* Small Crown, *perf.* 14	80	0
z 2	1d. red-brown, Die II (1855), *wmk.* Large Crown, *perf.* 14	62	6
z 3	1d. rose-red (1857), *wmk.* Large Crown, *perf.* 14	6	0
z 3*a*	2d. blue (1841)	£6	
z 4	2d. blue (1855), *wmk.* Large Crown, *perf.* 14 (Plates 5, 6)	15	0
z 5	2d. blue (1858), *wmk.* Large Crown, *perf.* 16 (Plate 6)	90	0
z 6	2d. blue (1858) (Plate No. 7)	15	0
z 7	4d. rose (1857)	15	0
z 8	6d. violet (1854)		
z 9	6d. lilac (1856)	15	0
z 10	6d. lilac (1856) (blued *paper*)		
z 11	1s. green (1856)	45	0

"**A25**" *Obliteration as T* **1, 2, 5, 6, 8** *or* **11.**

No.	Description	s.	d.
z 12	½d. rose-red (1870–79) .. *From* Plate Nos. 4, 5, 6, 8, 9, 10, 11, 12, 13, 14, 15, 19, 20.	10	0
z 13	1d. red-brown (1841), *imperf.*		
z 14	1d. red-brown (1855), *wmk.* Large Crown, *perf.* 14		
z 15	1d. rose-red (1857), *wmk.* Large Crown, *perf.* 14	3	6
z 16	1d. rose-red (1864–79) .. *From* Plate Nos. 71, 72, 73, 74, 76, 78, 79, 80, 81, 82, 83, 84, 85, 86, 87, 88, 89, 90, 91, 92, 93, 94, 95, 96, 97, 98, 99, 100, 101, 102, 103, 104, 105, 106, 107, 108, 109, 110, 111, 112, 113, 114, 115, 116, 117, 118, 119, 120, 121, 122, 123, 124, 125, 127, 129, 130, 131, 132, 133, 134, 135, 136, 137, 138, 139, 140, 141, 142, 143, 144, 145, 146, 147, 148, 149, 150, 151, 152, 153, 154, 155, 156, 157, 158, 159, 160, 161, 162, 163, 164, 165, 166, 167, 168, 169, 170, 171, 172, 173, 174, 175, 176, 177, 178, 179, 180, 181, 182, 183, 184, 185, 186, 187, 188, 189, 190, 191, 192, 193, 194, 195, 196, 197, 198, 199, 200, 201, 202, 203, 204, 205, 206, 207, 208, 209, 210, 212, 213, 214, 215, 216, 217, 218, 219, 220, 221, 223, 224.	7	6
z 17	1½d. lake-red (1870–79) (Plate 3)		
z 17*a*	2d. blue (1841), *imperf.*		
z 17*b*	2d. blue (1855), *wmk.* Large Crown, *perf.* 14	35	0
z 18	2d. blue (1858–69) .. *From* Plate Nos. 7, 8, 9, 12, 13, 14, 15.	8	6
z 19	2½d. rosy mauve (1875) (blued *paper*) (Plate Nos. 1, 2) .. *From*	37	6
z 20	2½d. rosy mauve (1875–76) .. *From* Plate Nos. 1, 2, 3.	12	0
z 21	2½d. rosy mauve (*Error of Lettering*)		
z 22	2½d. rosy mauve (1876–79) .. *From* Plate Nos. 3, 4, 5, 6, 7, 8, 9, 10, 11, 12, 13, 14, 15, 16, 17.	10	0
z 23	2½d. blue (1880–81) .. *From* Plate Nos. 17, 18, 19 20.	9	0
z 24	2½d. blue (1881) .. *From* Plate Nos. 21, 22, 23.	4	0
z 25	3d. carmine-rose (1862)	45	0
z 26	3d. rose (1865) (Plate No. 4)	30	0
z 27	3d. rose (1867–73) .. *From* Plate Nos. 4, 5, 6, 7, 8, 9, 10.	10	0
z 28	3d. rose (1873–76) .. *From* Plate Nos. 11, 12, 14, 15, 16, 17, 18, 19, 20.	15	0
z 29	3d. rose (1881) (Plate Nos. 20, 21)		
z 30	3d. lilac (1883) (3d. *on* 3d.)		
z 31	4d. rose (1857)	15	0
z 32	4d. red (1862) (Plates 3, 4) *From*	15	0
z 33	4d. vermilion (1865–73) .. „ Plate Nos. 7, 8, 9, 10, 11, 12, 13, 14.	12	6
z 34	4d. vermilion (1876) (Plate No. 15)	65	0
z 35	4d. sage-green (1877) Plate Nos. 15, 16	35	0
z 36	4d. grey-brown (1880) (Plate No. 17)	60	0
z 37	4d. grey-brown (1881) Plate Nos. 17, 18.	12	6
z 37*a*	6d. violet (1854)		
z 38	6d. lilac (1856)	16	0
z 39	6d. lilac (1862) (Plates 3, 4) *From*	17	6
z 40	6d. lilac (1865–67) .. „ Plate Nos. 5, 6.	12	6
z 41	6d. lilac (1867) (Plate No. 6)	30	0
z 42	6d. violet (1867–70) .. *From* Plate Nos. 6, 8, 9.	12	6
z 43	6d. buff (1872–73) .. *From* Plate Nos. 11, 12.	45	0
z 44	6d. chestnut (1872) (Plate No. 11)	12	6
z 45	6d. grey (1873) (Plate No. 12)	35	0
z 46	6d. grey (1874–80) .. *From* Plate Nos. 13, 14, 15, 16, 17.	15	0
z 47	6d. grey (1881–82) Plate Nos. 17, 18	32	6
z 48	6d. lilac (1883) (6d. *on* 6d.)	30	0
z 49	8d. orange (1876)	60	0
z 50	9d. straw (1862)	90	0
z 51	9d. bistre (1862)		
z 52	10d. red-brown (1867)	£6	
z 52*a*	1s. (1847), embossed		
z 53	1s. green (1856)	45	0
z 54	1s. green (1862)	45	0
z 55	1s. green ("K" *variety*)		
z 56	1s. green (1865) (Plate No. 4)	22	6
z 57	1s. green (1867–73) .. *From* Plates Nos. 4, 5, 6, 7.	8	0
z 58	1s. green (1873–77) .. *From* Plate Nos. 8, 9, 10, 11, 12, 13.	20	0
z 59	1s. orange-brown (1880) Plate No. 13	60	0
z 60	1s. orange-brown (1881) .. *From* Plate Nos. 13, 14.	25	0
z 61	2s. blue (*shades*) (1867)	42	6
z 62	2s. brown (1880)		
z 63	5s. rose (1867–74) .. *From* Plate Nos, 1, 2.	70	0

z 64 5s. rose (1882) (Plate No. 4), blue *paper* .. ..
z 65 5s. rose (1882) (Plate No. 4), white *paper* .. ..
z 66 10s. grey-green (1878) .. .. ..

1880.

z 67 ½d. deep green 3 0
z 68 ½d. pale green 3 0
z 69 1d. Venetian red 2 6
z 69a 1½d. Venetian red .. ..
z 70 2d. pale rose 22 6
z 71 2d. deep rose 25 0
z 72 5d. indigo 15 0

1881.

z 73 1d. lilac (14 *dots*) 10 0
z 74 1d. lilac (16 ,,) 3 6

1883-4.

z 75–z 79 ½d. slate blue; 1½d., 2d., 2½d., 3d. .. .. *From* 5 0
z 80–z 83a 4d., 5d., 6d., 9d., 1s. .. ,, 32 6
z 84 5s. rose (blued *paper*) ..
z 85 5s. rose (white ,,) ..

POSTAL FISCALS.

z 86 1d. lilac (1871), *wmk.* Anchor ..
z 86a 1d. lilac (1881) ,, Orb .. ..

GIBRALTAR.

1857.

"G" *Obliteration as T* 1.

z 87 1d. red-brown (1855), Die II, *wmk.* Small Crown, *perf.* 16.
z 88 1d. red-brown (1855), Die II, *wmk.* Small Crown, *perf.* 14 ..
z 89 1d. red-brown (1855), Die II, *wmk.* Large Crown, *perf.* 14. .. 35 0
z 90 1d. rose-red (1857), Die II, *wmk.* Large Crown, *perf.* 14 .. 20 0
z 91 2d. blue (1855), *wmk.* Small Crown, *perf.* 14 .. .. ..
z 92 2d. blue (1855–58), *wmk.* Large Crown, *perf.* 16 .. .. £5
z 93 2d. blue (1855), *wmk.* Large Crown, *perf.* 14 (Plate Nos. 5, 6) .. 15 0
z 94 2d. blue (1858) (Plate No. 7) ..
z 95 4d. rose (1857) 25 0
z 96 6d. lilac (1856) 15 0
z 96a 6d. lilac (1856) (blued *paper*) ..
z 97 1s. green (1856) 45 0
z 97a 1s. green (blued *paper*) .. ..

"**A26**" *Obliteration as T* 2, 5, 11 *or* 14.

z 98 ½d. rose-red (1870–79) .. *From* 15 0
Plate Nos. 4, 5, 6, 8, 10, 11, 12, 13, 14, 15, 19, 20.
z 99 1d. red-brown (1855), *wmk.* Large Crown, *perf.* 14 .. ..
z 100 1d. rose-red (1857), *wmk.* Large Crown, *perf.* 14 .. .. 12 6
z 101 1d. rose-red (1864–79) .. *From* 10 0
Plate Nos. 71, 72, 73, 74, 76, 78, 79, 80, 81, 82, 83, 84, 85, 86, 87, 88, 89, 90, 91, 92, 93, 94, 95, 96, 97, 98, 99, 100, 101, 102, 103, 104, 106, 107, 108, 109, 110, 111, 112, 113, 114, 115, 116, 117, 118, 119, 120, 121, 122, 123, 124, 125, 127, 129, 130, 131, 132, 133, 134, 136, 137, 138, 139, 140, 142, 143, 144, 145, 146, 147, 148, 149, 150, 151, 152, 153, 154, 155, 156, 157, 158, 159, 160, 161, 162, 163, 164, 165, 166, 167, 168, 169, 170, 171, 172, 173, 174, 175, 176, 177, 178, 179, 180, 181, 182, 183, 184, 185, 186, 187, 188, 189, 190, 191, 192, 193, 194, 195, 196, 197, 198, 199, 200, 201, 202, 203, 204, 205, 206, 207, 208, 209, 210, 211, 212, 213, 214, 215, 216, 217, 218, 219, 220, 221, 222, 223, 224, 225.
z 102 1½d. lake-red (1870–74) (Plate No. 3)
z 103 2d. blue (1855), *wmk.* Large Crown, *perf.* 14 (Plate No. 6) .. ..
z 104 2d. blue (1858–69) .. *From* 6 6
Plate Nos. 7, 8, 9, 12, 13, 14, 15.
z 105 2½d. rosy mauve (1875) (blued *paper*)
Plate Nos. 1, 2 .. *From* 37 6
z 106 2½d. rosy mauve (1875–76) ,, 10 0
Plate Nos. 1, 2, 3.
z 107 2½d. rosy mauve (*Error of Lettering*)
z 108 2½d. rosy mauve (1876–79) *From* 9 0
Plate Nos. 3, 4, 5, 6, 7, 8, 9, 10, 11, 12, 13, 14, 15, 16, 17.
z 109 2½d. blue (1880–81) .. *From* 9 0
Plate Nos. 17, 18, 19, 20.
z 110 2½d. blue (1881) .. .. *From* 4 6
Plate Nos. 21, 22, 23.
z 111 3d. carmine-rose (1862) 45 0
z 112 3d. rose (1865) (Plate No. 4) .. 35 0
z 113 3d. rose (1867–73) .. *From* 12 6
Plate Nos. 4, 5, 6, 7, 8, 9, 10.
z 114 3d. rose (1873–76) .. *From* 22 6
Plate Nos. 11, 12, 14, 15, 16, 17, 18, 19, 20.
z 115 3d. rose (1881) (Plate Nos. 20, 21)
z 116 3d. lilac (1883) (3d. *on* 3d.) ..
z 117 4d. rose (1857) 22 6
z 118 4d. red (1862) (Plates 3, 4) *From* 20 0
z 119 4d. vermilion (1865–73) 15 0
Plate Nos 7, 8, 9, 10, 11 12 13, 14.
z 120 4d. vermilion (1876) (Plate No. 15)
z 121 4d. sage-green (1877) 62 6
Plate Nos. 15, 16.
z 122 4d. grey-brown (1880) (Plate No. 17) .. ..
z 123 4d. grey-brown (1881–82) .. *From* 22 6
Plate Nos. 17, 18.
z 124 6d. lilac (1856) 15 0
z 125 6d. lilac (1862) (Plates 3, 4) *From* 17 6
z 126 6d. lilac (1865–67) .. .. ,, 15 0
Plate Nos. 5, 6.
z 127 6d. lilac (1867) (Plate No. 6) .. 15 0
z 128 6d. violet (1867–70) .. *From* 12 6
Plate Nos. 6, 8, 9.
z 129 6d. buff (1872–73) .. *From* 40 0
Plate Nos. 11, 12.
z 130 6d. chestnut (1872) (Plate No. 11) 12 6
z 131 6d. grey (1873) (Plate No. 12) .. 32 6
z 132 6d. grey (1874–80) .. *From* 12 6
Plate Nos. 13, 14, 15, 16, 17.
z 133 6d. grey (1881) (Plates 17, 18)
z 134 6d. lilac (1883) .. .. ..
z 135 8d. orange (1876) .. .. ..
z 136 9d. bistre (1862) .. .. ..
z 137 9d. straw (1862) .. .. ..
z 138 9d. straw (1865) .. .. ..
z 139 9d. straw (1867) 75 0
z 140 10d. red-brown (1867) 80 0
z 141 1s. green (1856) 40 0
z 142 1s. green (1862) 42 6
z 143 1s. green (1862) ("K" *variety*) ..
z 144 1s. green (1865) (Plate No. 4) .. 22 6
z 145 1s. green (1867–73) .. *From* 10 0
Plate Nos. 4, 5, 6, 7.
z 146 1s. green (1873–77) .. *From* 22 6
Plate Nos. 8, 9, 10, 11, 12, 13.
z 146a 1s. orange-brown (1880) .. ..
z 147 1s. orange-brown (1881) 40 0
Plate Nos. 13 and 14.
z 148 2s. blue (1867) 65 0
z 149 5s. rose (1867) (Plate No. 1) ..

1880.

z 150 ½d. deep green 5 0
z 151 ½d. pale green 5 0
z 152 1d. Venetian red 2 0
z 153 1½d. Venetian red .. .. ..
z 154 2d. pale rose 27 6
z 155 2d. deep rose .. .. ..
z 156 5d. indigo .. ..

1881.

z 157 1d. lilac (14 *dots*) 8 6
z 158 1d. lilac (16 *dots*) 3 0

1884.

z 159–62 ½d. slate-blue; 2d., 2½d., 3d. *From* 3 0
z 163–64 4d., 6d. .. .. .. „ 42 6

1887.

z 165–68 ½d., 1½d., 2d., 2½d. .. *From* 7 6

1902.

z 169–72 ½d. deep blue-green; ½d. pale yellow-green; 1d. scarlet; 2½d. blue .. *From* 6 6

POSTAL FISCAL.

z 173 1d. lilac (1881), *wmk.* Orb ..

VARIOUS TOWNS IN CYPRUS.

LARNACA.

"**942**" *Obliteration as T* **9**.

1878 *to* **1881.**

z 176 ½d. rose-red (1870–79) .. *From* 25 0
Plate Nos. 11, 12, 13, 14, 15, 19, 20.
z 177 1d. rose-red (1864–79) .. *From* 20 0
Plate Nos. 146, 170, 171, 174, 176, 177, 179, 183, 184, 187, 188, 190, 191, 192, 193, 194, 195, 196, 197, 198, 199, 200, 201, 202, 203, 204, 206, 207, 209, 210, 212, 213, 215, 217, 218, 220, 221, 222, 225.
z 178 2d. blue (1858–69) 37 6
Plate Nos. 14, 15.
z 179 2½d. rosy mauve (1876–79) *From* 20 0
Plate Nos. 5, 6, 8, 10, 11, 12, 13, 14, 15, 16, 17.
z 180 2½d. blue (1880–81)
Plate Nos. 17, 19, 20.
z 181 2½d. blue (1881) (Plate No. 21) ..
z 182 4d. sage-green (1877) 80 0
Plate Nos. 15, 16.
z 183 6d. grey (1874–76) 80 0
Plate Nos. 15, 16.
z 183*a* 8d. orange (1876) .. ..
z 184 1s. green (1873–77) .. ..
Plate Nos. 12, 13.

NIKOSIA.

"**969.**" *Obliteration as T* **9**.

1878 *to* **1881.**

z 185 ½d. rose-red (1870–79) .. ..
Plate Nos. 13, 15.
z 186 1d. rose-red (1864–79) .. *From* 25 0
Plate Nos. 81, 170, 171, 192, 202, 203, 206, 207, 218, 221.
z 187 2d. blue (1858–69) (Plate No. 15)
z 188 4d. sage-green (1877) (Plate No. 16)
z 189 2½d. rosy mauve (1876–79) *From* 25 0
Plate Nos. 10, 11, 12, 13, 14, 15, 16.
z 190 2½d. blue (1881) (Plate No. 20) ..

KYRENIA.

"**974.**" *Obliteration as T* **9**.

1878 *to* **1880.**

z 190*a* ½d. rose-red (1870–79) (Plate No. 1)
z 191 1d. rose-red (1864–79) .. *From* 55 0
Plate Nos. 168, 171, 206, 207, 209, 220.
z 192 2d. blue (1858–69) (Plate No. 15)
z 193 2½d. rosy mauve (1876–79)
Plate No. 14.

LIMASOL.

"**975.**" *Obliteration as T* **9**.

1878 *to* **1880.**

194 ½d. rose-red (1870–79)
Plate Nos. 13, 15, 19

z 195 1d. rose-red (1864–79) .. *From* 30 0
Plate Nos. 146, 171, 179, 184, 202, 206, 218, 222, 225.
z 196 1½d. lake-red (1870–74) (Plate 3) ..
z 197 2d. blue (1858–69) (Plate No. 15)
z 198 2½d. rosy mauve (1876–79) *From* 25 0
Plate Nos. 12, 13, 14, 15.
z 198*a* 2½d. blue (1880) (Plate No. 19)
z 198*b* 4d. green (Plate No. 16) .. ..

PAPHO (BAFFO).

"**981.**" *Obliteration as T* **9**.

1878 *to* **1881.**

z 199 1d. rose-red (1864–79) .. *From* 30 0
Plate Nos. 204, 206.
z 200 2d. blue (1858–69) (Plate No. 15)
z 201 2½d. rosy mauve (1876–79)
Plate No. 15. ..

FAMAGUSTA

"**982.**' *Obliteration as T* **9**.

1878 *to* **1881.**

z 202 ½d. rose-red (1870–79)
Plate No. 13. ..
z 203 1d. rose-red (1864–79) 40 0
Plate No. 145.
z 204 2d. blue (1858–69)
Plate Nos. 13, 14, 15. ..
z 205 1s. orange-brown (1881)
Plate No. 14.

POLYMEDIA.

"**D47.**" *Obliteration as T* **8**.

1878 *to* **1880.**

z 206 1d. rose-red (1864–79) .. *From* 40 0
Plate Nos. 85, 109, 110, 118, 175, 205, 206, 208, 209.
z 207 2d. blue (1858–69) (Plate No. 15)

ARMY HEADQUARTERS' CAMP (CYPRUS).

"**D48.**" *Obliteration as T* **8**.

1878 *to* **1880.**

z 208 1d. rose-red (1864–79) .. *From* 30 0
Plate Nos. 95, 102, 105, 115, 118, 123, 171, 174, 205, 214.
z 209 2d. blue (1858–69) (Plate No. 15)

II.

British Offices in Turkish Empire.

CONSTANTINOPLE.

"**C**" *Obliteration or circular postmarks as T* **1**, **10**, *or* **19**.

1857.

z 210 ½d. rose red (1870–79) .. *From* 27 6
Plate Nos. 6, 10. 11, 12, 14, 15, 20.
z 211 1d. red-brown (1854), Die I, *wmk.* Small Crown, *perf.* 16
z 211*a* 1d. red-brown, *wmk.* Large Crown, *perf.* 14.. .. .. .. 37 6
z 212 1d. rose-red (1857).. .. .. 12 6
z 213 1d. rose-red (1864–79) .. *From* 8 0
Plate Nos, 71, 72, 73, 74, 76, 78, 79, 80, 81, 83, 85, 87, 89, 90, 92, 93, 94, 95, 96, 101, 102, 105, 106, 108, 109, 110, 113, 116, 118, 119, 120, 121, 122, 123, 124, 125, 127, 129, 130, 131, 134, 135, 136, 137, 138, 140, 141, 143, 144, 146, 147, 148, 149, 150, 151, 152, 155, 156, 157, 158, 159, 161, 162, 164, 166, 167, 170, 171, 173, 174, 175, 176, 177, 178, 179, 181, 183, 184, 186, 187, 189, 190, 191, 193, 194, 195, 196, 198, 200, 201, 203, 204, 207, 208, 210, 212, 214, 215, 216, 222, 224.

z 214 1½d. rose-red (1870) (Plate 1) ..
z 215 2d. blue (1858–69) .. *From* 10 0
Plate Nos. 8, 9, 12, 13, 14, 15.
z 216 2½d. rosy mauve (1875–76) (blued *paper*) (Plate Nos. 1, 2) *From* 40 0
z 217 2½d. rosy mauve (1875–76) .. 12 6
Plate Nos. 1, 2, 3.
z 218 2½d. rosy mauve (*Error of Lettering*)
z 219 2½d. rosy mauve (1876–79) *From* 10 0
Plate Nos. 3, 4, 5, 6, 7, 8, 9, 10, 11, 12, 13, 14, 15, 16, 17.
z 220 2½d. blue (1880–81) .. *From* 9 0
Plate Nos. 17, 18, 19, 20.
z 221 2½d. blue (1881) .. .. „ 4 6
Plate Nos. 21, 22, 23.
z 222 3d. rose (1867–73) .. „ 12 0
Plate Nos. 4, 5, 6, 7, 8, 9, 10.
z 223 3d. rose (1873–76) 22 6
Plates 15, 16, 17, 18, 19.
z 224 3d. rose (1881) (Plate No. 21) ..
z 225 4d. rose (1857) 15 0
z 226 4d. red (1862) (Plates 3, 4) *From* 15 0
z 227 4d. vermilion (1865–73) .. „ 12 6
Plate Nos. 7, 8, 9, 10, 11, 12, 13, 14.
z 228 4d. vermilion (1876) (Plate No. 15)
z 229 4d. sage-green (1877) 42 6
Plate Nos. 15, 16.
z 230 4d. grey-brown (1880) .. ..
z 231 4d. grey-brown (1881) .. *From* 32 6
Plate Nos. 17, 18.
z 232 6d. lilac (1856) 15 0
z 233 6d. lilac (1862) (Plates 3, 4) .. 17 6
z 234 6d. lilac (1865–67) .. *From* 12 6
Plate Nos. 5, 6.
z 235 6d. lilac (1867) (Plate No. 6) .. 15 0
z 236 6d. violet (1867–70) .. *From* 12 6
Plate Nos. 6, 8, 9.
z 237 6d. buff (1872–73) .. „ 45 0
Plate Nos. 11, 12.
z 238 6d. chestnut (1872) (Plate No 11) 15 0
z 239 6d. grey (1873) (Plate No. 12) .. 40 0
z 240 6d. grey (1874–76) .. *From* 27 6
Plate Nos. 13, 14, 15, 16.
z 241 6d. grey (1881–82) .. „ 35 0
Plate Nos. 17, 18.
z 242 6d. lilac (1883) (Plate No. 18) .. 50 0
z 243 8d. orange (1876) .. ..
z 244 10d. red-brown (1867) .. £5
z 245 1s. green (1856) 40 0
z 246 1s. green (1862) 37 6
z 247 1s. green (1862) (" K " *variety*) ..
z 248 1s. green (1865) (Plate No. 4) 22 6
z 249 1s. green (1867–73) .. *From* 10 0
Plate Nos. 4, 5, 6, 7.
z 250 1s. green (1873–77) .. *From* 25 0
Plate Nos. 8, 9, 10, 11, 12, 13.
z 251 1s. orange-brown (1880) .. 75 0
Plate No. 13.
z 252 1s. orange-brown (1881) .. *From* 32 6
Plate Nos. 13, 14.
z 253 2s. blue (1867) 45 0
z 254 5s. rose (1867–74) .. *From* 65 0
Plate Nos. 1, 2.
z 255 5s. rose (1882) (white *paper*) ..
z 256 5s. rose (1882) (blued *paper*) ..

1880.

z 257 ½d. deep green 4 0
z 258 ½d. pale green 3 6
z 259 1d. Venetian red 5 0
z 260 2d. pale rose 22 6
z 261 2d. deep rose 25 0

1881.

z 262 1d. lilac (14 *dots*) .. .. ..
z 263 1d. lilac (16 *dots*) 4 0

1883 *to* 1884.

z 264 ½d. slate 12 6
z 265–68 1½d., 2d., 2½d., 3d. .. *From* 4 0
z 269–72 4d., 5d., 9d., 1s. .. „ 37 6
z 273 2s. 6d. lilac (blued *paper*) ..
z 274 2s. 6d. lilac (white *paper*) .. 42 6
z 275 5s. rose (blued *paper*) .. ..
z 276 5s. rose (white *paper*) .. ..

1887.

z 276*a–l* ½d., 1½d., 2d., 2½d., 3d., 4d., 4½d., 5d., 6d., 9d., 10d., 1s *From* 5 0

1900.

z 277–77*a* ½d., 1s. .. .. .. *From* 5 0

1902.

z 278–90*c* ½d., 1d., 1½d., 2d., 2½d., 3d., 4d., 4d. orange, 5d., 6d., 7d., 9d., 10d., 1s., 2s. 6d., 5s. *From* 2 6

1911–14.

z 290*d–h* ½d. (No. 339), 1d. (No. 330), ½d. (No. 351), 2½d., 3d. .. *From* 3 6

SALONICA.

Office opened in 1900 ; *circular postmark as* T **19.**

z 290*i* 1887, ½d. vermilion .. ..
z 291 1900, ½d. green .. .. ..
z 292 1902, ½d. deep green .. ..
z 293 1902, ½d. pale green .. ..
z 293*a* 1902, 1d. scarlet .. ..
z 293*b* 1887, 6d. purple/*red* ..
z 293*c* 1900, 1s. green and carmine ..
z 293*d* 1902, 1s. green and carmine ..

1911.

z 293*e* ½d. (*T* **98**) .. .. ..
z 293*f* 1d. (*T* **99**) .. .. ..

1912–13.

z 293*g* ½d. (*T* **105**) .. .. ..
z 293*h* 1d. (*T* **104**) .. .. ..
z 293*i* 7d. (*T* **107**) .. .. ..

STAMBOUL (CONSTANTINOPLE).

" S " *Obliteration as T* **10.**

1884.

z 294 ½d. slate .. .. ..
z 295 2½d. lilac .. .. ..
z 296 5d. green .. .. ..

1887.

z 296*a* ½d. vermilion 37 6

1911.

z 296*b* ½d. (*T* **98**) .. .. ..

Circular postmark as T **18.**

z 298 1d. lilac (1881) 25 0
z 299 2½d. lilac (1884) .. ..
z 300 5d. green (1884) .. ..

1887.

z 301–301*k* ½d., 1½d., 2d., 2½d., 3d., 4d., 4½d., 5d., 6d., 9d., 10d., 1s. *From* 12 6

1900.

z 302 ½d. 22 6
z 303 1s. .. ..

1902–10.

z 304–15*d* ½d., 1d., 1½d., 2d., 2½d., 3d. 4d., 4d. orange, 5d., 6d. 7d., 9d., 10d., 1s., 2s. 6d., 5s. .. .. .. *From* 9 0

1911–13.

z 316–29*d* ½d. (Type **101**), 1d. (Type **99**), ½d. (Type **105**), 1d. (Type **104**), 1½d., 2d., 2½d., 3d., 4d., 5d., 6d., 7d., 8d., 9d., 10d., 1s., 2s. 6d., 5s. *From* 6 6

ALEXANDRIA (EGYPT).

" B01." *Obliteration as T* **2, 8, 12** *or* **15.**

1860 *to* 1879.

z 330 ½d. rose-red (1870–79) .. *From* 30 0
Plate Nos. 5, 6, 8, 10, 13, 20.
z 331 1d. rose-red (1857) 15 0
z 332 1d. rose-red (1864–79) .. *From* 10 0
Plate Nos. 71, 72, 73, 74, 76, 78, 79, 80, 81, 82, 83, 84, 85, 86,

87, 88, 89, 90, 91, 92, 93, 94, 95, 96, 97, 98, 99, 101, 102, 103, 104, 106, 107, 109, 110, 111, 112, 113, 114, 115, 117, 118, 119, 120, 121, 122, 123, 125, 127, 129, 130, 131, 133, 134, 136, 137, 138, 139, 140, 142, 143, 144, 145, 146, 147, 148, 149, 154, 156, 157, 158, 159, 160, 162, 163, 165, 168, 169, 170, 171, 172, 174, 175, 177, 179, 180, 181, 182, 183, 188, 190, 198, 200, 203, 210, 220.

z 333 2d. blue (1858–69) .. *From* 10 0
Plate Nos. 7, 8, 9, 13, 14, 15.
z 334 2½d. rosy mauve (1875) (blued *paper*)
Plate Nos. 1, 2 .. *From* 37 6
z 335 2½d. rosy mauve (1875–6) .. „ 12 6
Plate Nos. 1, 2, 3.
z 336 2½d. rosy mauve (*Error of Lettering*)
z 337 2½d. rosy mauve (1876–79) .. *From* 10 0
Plate Nos. 3, 4, 5, 6, 7, 8, 9.
z 338 3d. rose (1862) 50 0
z 339 3d. rose (1865) (Plate No. 4) .. 40 0
z 340 3d. rose (1867–73) .. .. *From* 12 6
Plate Nos. 4, 5, 6, 7, 8, 9.
z 341 3d. rose (1873–76) .. .. *From* 25 0
Plate Nos. 11, 12, 14, 16, 18, 19.
z 342 4d. rose (1857) 50 0
z 343 4d. red (1862) (Plates 3, 4) *From* 32 6
z 344 4d. vermilion (1865–73) .. „ 12 6
Plate Nos. 7, 8, 9, 10, 11, 12, 13, 14.
z 345 4d. vermilion (1876) (Plate No. 15) £5
z 346 4d. sage-green (1877) 50 0
Plate No. 15.
z 347 6d. lilac (1856) 22 6
z 348 6d. lilac (1862) (Plates 3, 4) *From* 15 0
z 349 6d. lilac (1865–67) .. „ 12 6
Plate No. 5, 6.
z 350 6d. lilac (1867) (Plate No. 6) .. 15 0
z 351 6d. violet (1867–70) .. *From* 12 6
Plate Nos. 6, 8, 9.
a. Imperf. (Plate No. 8) .. ..
z 352 6d. buff (1872–73) .. .. *From* 42 6
Plate Nos. 11, 12.
z 353 6d. chestnut (1872) (Plate No. 11) 17 6
z 354 6d. grey (1873) (Plate No. 12) .. 32 6
z 355 6d. grey (1874–76) .. *From* 10 6
Plate Nos. 13, 14, 15.
z 356 9d. straw (1862) £5
z 357 9d. bistre (1862) .. ..
z 358 9d. straw (1867) .. ..
z 359 10d. red-brown (1867) £6
z 360 1s. green (1856) 40 0
z 361 1s. green (1862) 40 0
z 361*a* 1s. green (1862) ("K" *variety*) ..
z 362 1s. green (1865) (Plate No. 4) .. 25 0
z 363 1s. green (1867–73) .. *From* 8 0
Plate Nos. 4, 5, 6, 7.
z 364 1s. green (1873–77) .. *From* 17 6
Plate Nos. 8, 9, 10, 11, 12, 13.
z 365 2s. blue (1867) 45 0
z 366 5s. rose (1867–74) .. .. *From* 70 0
Plate Nos. 1, 2.

1880.

z 366*a* ½d. green .. ..

PORT SAID.

Stamps issued after 1877 can be found with the Egyptian cancellation "Port Said," but these are on letters posted from British ships.

SUEZ (EGYPT).

"B02." *Obliteration as T* **2, 8, 12** *or* **15.**

1860 *to* 1879.

z 367 ½d. rose-red (1870–79) .. ..
Plate Nos. 10, 11, 12, 13, 14.
z 368 1d. rose-red (1857) 16 0
z 369 1d. rose-red (1864–79) .. *From* 12 6
Plate Nos. 74, 79, 80, 83, 86, 91, 94, 96, 97, 101, 106, 113, 120, 121, 122, 129, 131, 134, 137, 140, 145, 148, 149, 150, 154, 156, 158, 162, 163, 164, 165, 174, 176, 177, 179, 180, 181, 182, 186, 187, 189, 190, 205.
z 370 2d. blue (1858–69) .. *From* 32 6
Plate Nos. 9, 13, 14, 15.
z 371 2½d. rosy mauve (1875) (blued *paper*) 32 6
Plate No. 1.
z 372 2½d. rosy mauve (1875–76) *From* 12 6
Plate Nos. 1, 2, 3.
z 373 2½d. rosy mauve (*Error of Lettering*)
z 374 2½d. rosy mauve (1876–79) *From* 10 6
Plate Nos. 3, 4, 5, 6, 7, 8, 9.
z 375 3d. rose (1862) 52 6
z 376 3d. rose (1865) (Plate No. 4) .. 45 0
z 377 3d. rose (1867–73) .. ..
Plate Nos. 5, 6, 7, 8.
z 378 3d. rose (1873–76) .. .. *From* 45 0
Plate Nos. 12, 16.
z 379 4d. rose (1857) 60 0
z 380 4d. red (1862) (Plates 3, 4) .. 50 0
z 381 4d. vermilion (1865–73) .. *From* 15 0
Plate Nos. 7, 8, 9, 10, 11, 12, 13, 14.
z 382 4d. vermilion (1876) (Plate No. 15)
z 383 4d. sage-green (1877) (Plate No. 15) 40 0
z 384 6d. lilac (1856) 27 6
z 385 6d. lilac (1862) (Plates 3, 4) *From* 22 6
z 386 6d. lilac (1865–67) .. *From* 15 0
Plate Nos. 5, 6.
z 387 6d. lilac (1867) (Plate Nos 6) .. 15 0
z 388 6d. violet (1867–70) .. *From* 12 6
Plate Nos. 6, 8, 9.
z 389 6d. buff (1872–73) .. .. *From* 42 6
Plate Nos. 11, 12.
z 390 6d. chestnut (1872) (Plate No. 11) 17 6
z 391 6d. grey (1873) (Plate No. 12) .. 27 6
z 392 6d. grey (1874–76) .. *From* 22 6
Plate Nos. 13, 14, 15, 16.
z 393 8d. orange (1876) .. .. ..
z 394 9d. straw (1862) 90 0
z 395 9d. bistre (1862) .. ..
z 396 9d. straw (1867) .. ..
z 397 10d. red-brown (1867) £6
z 398 1s. green (1856) 70 0
z 399 1s. green (1862) 40 0
z 400 1s. green (1862), ("K" *variety*) ..
z 401 1s. green (1865) (Plate No. 4) .. 22 6
z 402 1s. green (1867–73) .. *From* 12 6
Plate Nos. 4, 5, 6, 7.
z 403 1s. green (1873–77) .. *From* 27 6
Plate Nos. 8, 9, 10, 11, 12.
z 404 2s. blue (1867) 60 0
z 405 5s. rose (1867–74) .. *From* 85 0
Plate Nos. 1, 2.

1880.

z 405*a* ½d. green .. .. ..

SMYRNA.

"F87" *Obliteration or circular postmark as T* **8, 16, 18** *or* **19.**

1872.

z 406 ½d. rose-red (1870–79) .. *From* 30 0
Plate Nos. 11, 12, 13, 14, 15.
z 407 1d. rose-red (1864–79) .. *From* 10 0
Plate Nos. 120, 124, 134, 137, 138, 139, 140, 142, 143, 145, 146, 148, 149, 150, 151, 152, 153, 155, 156, 157, 158, 159, 160, 161, 162, 163, 164, 166, 167, 168, 169, 170, 171, 172, 173, 174, 175, 176, 177, 178, 183, 184, 185, 186, 187, 188, 191, 193, 195, 196, 198, 200, 204, 210.
z 408 1½d. lake-red (1870–74) (Plates 1, 3)
z 409 2d. blue (1858) *wmk.* Large Crown, *perf.* 16 .. .. ..
z 410 2d. blue (1858–69) .. *From* 17 6
Plate Nos. 13, 14, 15.
z 411 2½d. rosy mauve (1875) (blued *paper*) 35 0
Plate No. 1.

No.	Description	s.	d.
z 412	2½d. rosy mauve (1875–76) *From*	12	6
	Plate Nos. 1, 2, 3.		
z 413	2½d. rosy mauve (*Error of Lettering*)		
z 414	2½d. rosy mauve (1876–79) *From*	8	6
	Plate Nos. 3, 4, 5, 6, 7, 8, 9, 10, 11, 12, 13, 14, 15, 16, 17.		
z 415	2½d. blue (1880–81) .. *From*	12	6
	Plate Nos. 17, 18, 19, 20.		
z 416	2½d. blue (1881)	6	0
	Plate Nos. 21, 22, 23.		
z 417	3d. rose (1867–73)	45	0
	Plate Nos. 5, 7, 9, 10.		
z 418	3d. rose (1873–76) (Plate No. 14)		
z 419	4d. vermilion (1865–73)	15	0
	Plate Nos. 12, 13, 14.		
z 420	4d. vermilion (1876) (Plate No. 15)		
z 421	4d. sage-green (1877)	50	0
	Plate Nos. 15, 16.		
z 422	4d. grey-brn. (1880) (Plate No. 17)		
z 423	4d. grey-brn. (1881–82) .. *From*	30	0
	Plate Nos. 17, 18.		
z 424	6d. buff (1872–73) .. .. *From*	40	0
	Plate Nos. 11, 12.		
z 425	6d. chestnut (1872) (Plate No. 11)		
z 426	6d. grey (1873) (Plate No. 12) ..		
z 427	6d. grey (1874–80) .. *From*	12	6
	Plate Nos. 13, 14, 15, 16, 17.		
z 428	6d. grey (1881–82)		
	Plate Nos. 17, 18.		
z 429	6d. lilac (1883)		
z 430	9d. straw (1867)		
z 431	10d. red-brown (1867)	£5	
z 432	1s. green (1867–73) (Plate No. 7)		
z 433	1s. green (1873–77) .. *From*	55	0
	Plate Nos. 8, 9, 10, 11, 12, 13.		
z 434	1s. orange-brown (1880)		
	Plate No. 13		
z 434*a*	1s. orange (1881) (Plate Nos. 13, 14)		
z 435	5s. rose (1867–74) (Plate No. 2) ..		
1880.			
z 436	½d. deep green	12	0
z 437	½d. pale green	12	0
z 438	1d. Venetian red	22	6
z 439	1½d. Venetian red	22	6
z 440	2d. pale rose	50	0
z 441	2d. deep rose	50	0
z 442	5d. indigo	37	6
1881.			
z 443	1d. lilac (16 *dots*)	7	6
1884.			
z 444	½d. slate-blue	20	0
z 445–6	2d., 2½d. .. .. *From*	5	0
z 447–9	4d., 5d., 1s. .. .. *From*	37	6
1887.			
z 450–7*a*	½d., 1½d., 2d., 2½d., 3d., 4d., 5d., 6d., 1s. .. .. *From*	5	0
1900.			
z 458–9	½d., 1s. .. .. .. *From*	7	6
1902–10.			
z 460–71*b*	½d., 1d., 1½d., 2d., 2½d., 3d., 4d., 5d., 6d., 7d., 9d., 10d., 1s., 2s. 6d. .. .. *From*	6	6
1911–23.			
z 472–86	½d., 1d., 1½d., 2d., 2½d., 3d., 4d., 5d., 6d., 7d., 8d., 9d., 10d., 1s., 2s. 6d. .. *From*	5	0

BEYROUT (LEVANT).

"**G06.**" *Obliteration or circular postmark as* **T 8, 19** *or* **20.**

No.	Description	s.	d.
1873.			
z 487	½d. rose-red (1870–79) .. *From*	25	0
	Plate Nos. 12, 13, 14, 19, 20.		
z 488	1d. rose-red (1864–79) .. *From*	20	0
	Plate Nos. 107, 118, 140, 145, 148, 155, 157, 162, 167, 177, 179, 180, 184, 185, 195, 200, 204, 213.		
z 489	1½d. lake-red (1870–74) (Plate 3) ..		
z 490	2d. blue (1858–69) .. *From*	27	6
	Plate Nos. 13, 14, 15.		
z 491	2½d. rosy mauve (1875) (blued *paper*)	35	0
	Plate No. 1.		
z 492	2½d. rosy mauve (1875–76) *From*	12	6
	Plate Nos. 1, 2, 3.		
z 493	2½d. rosy mauve (1876–79) *From*	10	0
	Plate Nos. 3, 4, 5, 6, 7, 8, 9, 10, 11, 12, 13, 14, 15, 16, 17.		
z 494	2½d. blue (1880–81) .. *From*	10	0
	Plate Nos. 17, 18, 19, 20.		
z 495	2½d. blue (1881) .. .. *From*	12	6
	Plate Nos. 21, 22, 23.		
z 496	3d. rose (1867–73) (Plate No. 10)		
z 497	3d. rose (1873–76)		
	Plate Nos. 12, 15, 19.		
z 498	3d. rose (1881) (Plate Nos. 20, 21)		
z 499	4d., vermilion (1865–73) .. *From*	45	0
	Plate Nos. 11, 12, 13, 14.		
z 500	4d. vermilion (1876) (Plate No. 15)		
z 501	4d. sage-green (1877)		
	Plate Nos. 15, 16).		
z 502	4d. grey-brn. (1880) (Plate No. 17)		
z 503	4d. grey-brown (1881)		
	Plate Nos. 17, 18.		
z 504	6d. buff (1872–73) .. .. *From*	35	
	Plate Nos. 11, 12.		
z 505	6d. chestnut (1872) (Plate No. 11)	25	0
z 506	6d. grey (1873) (Plate No. 12) ..		
z 507	6d. grey (1874–80) .. *From*	40	0
	Plate Nos. 13, 14, 15, 16, 17.		
z 507*a*	8d. orange (1876)		
z 508	10d. red-brown (1867)	£5	
z 509	1s. green (1867–73)	50	0
	Plate Nos. 6, 7.		
z 510	1s. green (1873–77) .. *From*	30	0
	Plate Nos. 8, 9, 10, 12, 13.		
z 511	1s. orge.-brn. (1880) (Plate No. 13)		
z 512	1s. orange-brown (1881)	65	0
	Plate Nos. 13, 14.		
z 513	2s. blue (1867)	45	0
z 514	5s. rose (1867) (Plate Nos. 1, 2) ..		
1880.			
z 515	½d. deep green	6	0
z 516	½d. pale green	6	0
z 517	1d. Venetian-red	8	0
z 518	1½d. Venetian-red	12	6
z 519	2d. pale rose	22	6
z 520	2d. deep rose	25	0
z 521	5d. indigo	20	0
1881.			
z 522	1d. lilac (14 *dots*)		
z 523	1d. lilac (16 *dots*)		
1884.			
z 524–529*a*	½d., 1½d., 2d., 2½d., 4d., 5d., 1s. .. .. *From*	8	0
1887.			
z 530–7*a*	½d., 1½d., 2d., 2½d., 3d., 4½d., 5d., 6d., 1s. .. *From*	5	0
1900.			
z 538–9	½d., 1s. .. .. *From*	7	6
1902–12.			
z 540–5	½d., 1d., 2½d., 5d., 10d., 1s. *From*	3	6
1912–13.			
z 545*a*–*b*	½d., 1d. (*T* **105, 104**)		

POSTAL FISCALS.

No.	Description	s.	d.
z 546	1d. lilac (*wmk.* Anchor)		
z 547	1d. lilac (*wmk.* Orb)		

III.

British West Indies.

VARIOUS TOWNS IN JAMAICA.

British stamps were issued to several District post offices between 8 May, 1858, and 1 March, 1859 (i.e. before the Obliterators A 27–A 78 were issued). These can only be distinguished (off the cover) when they have the Town's date-stamp on them. They are worth about double the price of those with an obliteration number.

KINGSTON

"A01." *Obliteration as T* **2.**

1858 (8 May)–**1860** (24 Aug.).

		Single stamp.	Stamp on cover.
J 1	1d. rose-red, *perf.* 16 (No. 36)	—	—
J 2	1d. rose-red, *perf.* 14 (No. 40)	17 6	25 0
J 3	4d. rose-carmine (No. 67)	17 6	30 0
J 4	4d. rose .. (No. 68)	17 6	30 0
J 5	6d. lilac (No. 70)	15 0	25 0
J 6	1s. green .. (No. 72)	70 0	£8

"A01." *Obliteration as T* **7.**

1859 (26 May)–**1860** (24 Aug.).

		Single stamp.	Stamp on cover.
J 7	1d. rose-red, *perf.* 14 (No. 40)	20 0	30 0
J 8	4d. rose-carmine (No. 67)	17 6	30 0
J 9	4d. rose (No. 68)	17 6	30 0
J 10	6d. lilac (No. 70)	17 6	27 6
J 11	1s. green (No. 72)	£5	£14

"A01." *Obliteration as T* **3.**

1859 (26 May)–**1860** (24 Aug.).

		Single stamp.	Stamp on cover.
J 12	1d. rose-red, *perf.* 14 (No. 40)	35 0	55 0
J 13	4d. rose-carmine (No. 67)	30 0	50 0
J 14	4d. rose (No. 68)	30 0	50 0
J 15	6d. lilac (No. 70)	27 6	50 0
J 16	1s. green (No. 72)		

Note :—For **A02**, etc., see after **A78.**

"A27" *to* **"A78."** *Obliterations as T* **2.**

1859 (1 Mar.)–**1860** (24 Aug.).

A27. ALEXANDRIA.

		Single stamp.	Stamp on cover.
J 17	1d. rose-red, *perf.* 14 (No. 40)		
J 18	4d. rose-carmine (or rose) (Nos. 67 and 68) ..	£12	£22
J 19	6d. lilac (No. 70)		

A28. ANNOTTO BAY.

		Single stamp.	Stamp on cover.
J 20	1d. rose-red	90 0	£7
J 21	4d. rose-carmine (or rose) ..	70 0	£7
J 22	6d. lilac	80 0	£8

A29. BATH.

		Single stamp.	Stamp on cover.
J 23	1d. rose-red	£6	£8
J 24	4d. rose-carmine (or rose) ..	75 0	£8
J 25	6d. lilac		

A30. BLACK RIVER.

		Single stamp.	Stamp on cover.
J 26	1d. rose-red	45 0	65 0
J 27	4d. rose-carmine (or rose) ..	45 0	85 0
J 28	6d. lilac	40 0	65 0

A31. BROWN'S TOWN.

		Single stamp.	Stamp on cover.
J 29	1d. rose-red	£6	£8
J 30	4d. rose-carmine (or rose) ..	85 0	£9
J 31	6d. lilac	80 0	£8

A32. BUFF BAY.

		Single stamp.	Stamp on cover.
J 32	1d. rose-red	85 0	£7
J 33	4d. rose-carmine (or rose) ..	65 0	£7
J 34	6d. lilac	80 0	£8

A33. CHAPELTON.

		Single stamp.	Stamp on cover.
J 35	1d. rose-red		
J 36	4d. rose-carmine (or rose) ..	80 0	£8
J 37	6d. lilac	90 0	£9

A34. CLAREMONT.

		Single stamp.	Stamp on cover.
J 38	1d rose-red	£8	£10
J 39	4d. rose-carmine (or rose) ..	90 0	£10
J 40	6d. lilac	£7	£12

A35. CLARENDON.

(Near Four Paths.)

		Single stamp.	Stamp on cover.
41	1d. rose-red	£7	£9
42	4d. rose-carmine (or rose) ..	75 0	£9
43	6d. lilac	95 0	£10

A36. DRY HARBOUR.

		Single stamp.	Stamp on cover.
J 44	1d. rose-red	£9	£11
J 45	4d. rose-carmine (or rose) ..	£7	£11
J 46	6d. lilac	£8	£14

A37. DUNCANS.

		Single stamp.	Stamp on cover.
J 47	1d. rose-red		
J 48	4d. rose-carmine (or rose) ..	90 0	£10
J 49	6d. lilac	80 0	£9

A38. EWARTON.

		Single stamp.	Stamp on cover.
J 50	1d. rose-red		
J 51	4d. rose-carmine (or rose) ..		
J 52	6d. lilac		

A39. FALMOUTH.

		Single stamp.	Stamp on cover.
J 53	1d. rose-red	37 6	55 0
J 54	4d. rose-carmine (or rose) ..	45 0	90 0
J 55	6d. lilac	40 0	65 0
J 56	1s. green (No. 72)	£14	£25

A40. FLINT RIVER.

(Near Hopewell.)

		Single stamp.	Stamp on cover.
J 57	1d. rose-red	£7	£9
J 58	4d. rose-carmine (or rose) ..	80 0	£9
J 59	6d. lilac	90 0	£10
J 60	1s. green (No. 72)	—	—

A41. GAYLE.

		Single stamp.	Stamp on cover.
J 61	1d. rose-red	£7	£9
J 62	4d. rose-carmine (or rose) ..	90 0	£10
J 63	6d. lilac	80 0	£9
J 64	1s. green (No. 72)	£16	£30

A42. GOLDEN SPRING.

(Near Stony Hill.)

		Single stamp.	Stamp on cover.
J 65	1d. rose-red		
J 66	4d. rose-carmine (or rose) ..		
J 67	6d. lilac	£12	£22
J 68	1s. green (No. 72)	£22	£45

A43. GORDON TOWN.

		Single stamp.	Stamp on cover.
J 69	1d. rose-red		
J 70	4d. rose-carmine (or rose) ..		
J 71	6d. lilac	£12	£22

A44. GOSHEN.

(Near Santa Cruz.)

		Single stamp.	Stamp on cover.
J 72	1d. rose-red	35 0	55 0
J 73	4d. rose-carmine (or rose) ..	55 0	£7
J 74	6d. lilac	40 0	55 0

A45. GRANGE HILL.

		Single stamp.	Stamp on cover.
J 75	1d. rose-red	85 0	£7
J 76	4d. rose-carmine (or rose) ..	65 0	£7
J 77	6d. lilac	80 0	£8
J 77*a*	1s. green (No. 72)		

A46. GREEN ISLAND.

		Single stamp.	Stamp on cover.
J 78	1d. rose-red	£6	£9
J 79	4d. rose-carmine (or rose) ..	75 0	£9
J 80	6d. lilac	90 0	£10
J 81	1s. green (No. 72)	£18	£34

A47. HIGHGATE.

		Single stamp.	Stamp on cover.
J 82	1d. rose-red	45 0	65 0
J 83	4d. rose-carmine (or rose) ..	65 0	£7
J 84	6d. lilac	85 0	£8

A48. HOPE BAY.

		Single stamp.	Stamp on cover.
J 85	1d. rose-red		
J 86	4d. rose-carmine (or rose) ..	90 0	£10
J 87	6d. lilac	£7	£12

A49. LILLIPUT.

(Near Balaclava.)

		Single stamp.	Stamp on cover.
J 88	1d. rose-red	45 0	65 0
J 89	4d. rose-carmine (or rose) ..	65 0	£8
J 90	6d. lilac	42 6	65 0

A50. LITTLE RIVER.

A50 was sent out for use at Little River, but no specimen has yet been found used on British stamps.

A51. LUCEA.

No.	Stamp	Single stamp.	Stamp on cover.
J 91	1d. rose-red	65 0	85 0
J 92	4d. rose-carmine (or rose) ..	35 0	55 0
J 93	6d. lilac	55 0	75 0

A52. MANCHIONEAL.

No.	Stamp	Single stamp.	Stamp on cover.
J 94	1d. rose-red	£6	£9
J 95	4d. rose-carmine (or rose) ..	85 0	£9
J 96	6d. lilac		

A53. MANDEVILLE.

No.	Stamp	Single stamp.	Stamp on cover.
J 97	1d. rose-red	85 0	£8
J 98	4d. rose-carmine (or rose) ..	65 0	£8
J 99	6d. lilac	75 0	£9

A54. MAY HILL.

(Near SPUR TREE.)

No.	Stamp	Single stamp.	Stamp on cover.
J 100	1d. rose-red	45 0	70 0
J 101	4d. rose-carmine (or rose)	45 0	90 0
J 102	6d. lilac	40 0	80 0

A55. MILE GULLY.

No.	Stamp	Single stamp.	Stamp on cover.
J 103	1d. rose-red	85 0	£8
J 104	4d. rose-carmine (or rose)	85 0	£9
J 105	6d. lilac	70 0	£8

A56. MONEAGUE.

No.	Stamp	Single stamp.	Stamp on cover.
J 106	1d. rose-red	£7	£9
J 107	4d. rose-carmine (or rose)	80 0	£9
J 108	6d. lilac	90 0	£10

A57. MONTEGO BAY.

No.	Stamp	Single stamp.	Stamp on cover.
J 109	1d. rose-red	45 0	70 0
J 110	4d. rose-carmine (or rose)	25 0	40 0
J 111	6d. lilac	35 0	90 0
J 112	1s. green (No. 72) ..	£12	£22

A58. MONTPELIER.

No.	Stamp	Single stamp.	Stamp on cover.
J 113	1d. rose-red		
J 114	4d. rose-carmine (or rose)		
J 115	6d. lilac		

A59. MORANT BAY.

No.	Stamp	Single stamp.	Stamp on cover.
J 116	1d. rose-red	90 0	£8
J 117	4d. rose-carmine (or rose)	70 0	£8
J 118	6d. lilac	80 0	£9

A60. OCHO RIOS.

No.	Stamp	Single stamp.	Stamp on cover.
J 119	1d. rose-red		
J 120	4d. rose-carmine (or rose)	80 0	£9
J 121	6d. lilac	90 0	£10

A61. OLD HARBOUR.

No.	Stamp	Single stamp.	Stamp on cover.
J 122	1d. rose-red	90 0	£8
J 123	4d. rose-carmine (or rose)	70 0	£8
J 124	6d. lilac	80 0	£9

A62. PLANTAIN GARDEN RIVER.

(Now called GOLDEN GROVE.)

No.	Stamp	Single stamp.	Stamp on cover.
J 125	1d. rose-red	60 0	80 0
J 126	4d. rose-carmine (or rose)	70 0	£8
J 127	6d. lilac	80 0	£9

A63. PEAR TREE GROVE.

No.	Stamp	Single stamp.	Stamp on cover.
J 128	1d. rose-red		
J 129	4d. rose-carmine (or rose)		
J 130	6d. lilac	£12	£22

A64. PORT ANTONIO.

No.	Stamp	Single stamp.	Stamp on cover.
J 131	1d. rose-red	90 0	£8
J 132	4d. rose-carmine (or rose)	90 0	£9
J 133	6d. lilac	70 0	£8

A65. PORT MORANT.

No.	Stamp	Single stamp.	Stamp on cover.
J 134	1d. rose-red	90 0	£8
J 135	4d. rose-carmine (or rose)	70 0	£8
J 136	6d. lilac	80 0	£9

A66. PORT MARIA.

No.	Stamp	Single stamp.	Stamp on cover.
J 137	1d. rose-red	£7	£9
J 138	4d. rose-carmine (or rose)	80 0	£9
J 139	6d. lilac	90 0	£10

A67. PORT ROYAL.

No.	Stamp	Single stamp.	Stamp on cover.
J 140	1d. rose-red	£8	£10
J 141	4d. rose-carmine (or rose)		
J 142	6d. lilac	£7	£12

A68. PORUS.

No.	Stamp	Single stamp.	Stamp on cover.
J 143	1d. rose-red	70 0	90 0
J 144	4d. rose-carmine (or rose)	70 0	£8
J 145	6d. lilac	90 0	£10

A69. RAMBLE.

No.	Stamp	Single stamp.	Stamp on cover.
J 146	1d. rose-red	70 0	£7
J 147	4d. rose-carmine (or rose) (Nos. 67 and 68) ..	90 0	£9
J 148	4d. rose-carmine on thick glazed paper (No. 68b)	£12	£22
J 149	6d. lilac	£7	£10

A70. RIO BUENO.

No.	Stamp	Single stamp.	Stamp on cover.
J 150	1d. rose-red	60 0	85 0
J 151	4d. rose-carmine (or rose)	80 0	£9
J 152	6d. lilac	70 0	£8

A71. RODNEY HALL.

(Now called LINSTEAD.)

No.	Stamp	Single stamp.	Stamp on cover.
J 153	1d. rose-red	90 0	£8
J 154	4d. rose-carmine (or rose)	70 0	£8
J 155	6d. lilac	80 0	£9

A72. SAINT DAVID.

(Now called YALLAHS.)

No.	Stamp	Single stamp.	Stamp on cover.
J 156	1d. rose-red	£7	£9
J 157	4d. rose-carmine (or rose)	90 0	£9
J 158	6d. lilac		

A73. ST. ANN'S BAY.

No.	Stamp	Single stamp.	Stamp on cover.
J 159	1d. rose-red	60 0	85 0
J 160	4d. rose-carmine (or rose)	80 0	£9
J 161	6d. lilac	70 0	£8

A74. SALT GUT.

(Near ORACABESSA.)

No.	Stamp	Single stamp.	Stamp on cover.
J 162	1d. rose-red	90 0	£8
J 163	4d. rose-carmine (or rose)	90 0	£9
J 164	6d. lilac	70 0	£8

A75. SAVANNA-LA-MAR.

No.	Stamp	Single stamp.	Stamp on cover.
J 165	1d. rose-red	50 0	75 0
J 166	4d. rose-carmine (or rose)	27 6	45 0
J 167	6d. lilac	70 0	£9
J 168	1s. green (No. 72) ..	£14	£26

A76. SPANISH TOWN.

No.	Stamp	Single stamp.	Stamp on cover.
J 169	1d. rose-red	50 0	75 0
J 170	4d. rose-carmine (or rose)	50 0	95 0
J 171	6d. lilac	70 0	£8
J 172	1s. green (No. 72) ..	£12	£22

A77. STEWART TOWN.

No.	Stamp	Single stamp.	Stamp on cover.
J 173	1d. rose-red		
J 174	4d. rose-carmine (or rose)	£7	£10
J 175	6d. lilac	£8	£14

A78. VERE.

(Now called ALLEY.)

No.	Stamp	Single stamp.	Stamp on cover.
J 176	1d. rose-red	90 0	£7
J 177	4d. rose-carmine (or rose)	70 0	£7
J 178	6d. lilac	80 0	£9
J 179	1s. green (No. 72) ..	£14	£26

The use of British stamps in JAMAICA after August, 1860, was unauthorised by the P.M.G. of Great Britain. For full details see the *JAMAICA* handbook.

OTHER TOWNS IN THE WEST INDIES.

"**A02**" *to* "**A15**" *and* "**A18.**" *Obliterations as T 2.*

A02. ST. JOHN'S (ANTIGUA).

No.	Stamp	Single stamp.
z 553	1d. rose-red (1857)	55 0
z 553a	2d. blue (Plate No. 6)	
z 554	2d. blue (1858) (Plate Nos. 7, 8, 9)	£5
z 555	4d. rose (1857)	45 0

556 6d. lilac (1856) 30 0
557 1s. green (1856) £8

A03. GEORGETOWN *or* DEMERARA (BRITISH GUIANA).

z 558 1d. rose-red (1857) 50 0
z 559 4d. rose (1857) 37 6
z 560 6d. lilac (1856) 25 0
z 561 1s. green (1856) £8

A04. NEW AMSTERDAM *or* BERBICE (BRITISH GUIANA).

z 562 1d. rose-red (1857) .. .. ..
z 563 2d. blue (1858) (Plate Nos. 7, 8)
z 564 4d. rose (1857) .. .. ..
z 565 6d. lilac (1856) 52 6
z 566 1s. green (1856) .. .. ..

A05. NASSAU (BAHAMAS).

z 567 1d. rose-red (1857) 75 0
z 568 2d. blue (1858) (Plate Nos. 7, 8) 75 0
z 569 4d. rose (1857) 90 0
z 570 6d. lilac (1856) 75 0
z 571 1s. green (1856) .. .. ..
z 571a 1s. green (1862) .. .. ..

A06. BRITISH HONDURAS.

z 572 1d. rose-red (1857) .. .. ..
z 573 4d. rose (1857) 52 6
z 574 6d. lilac (1856) 42 6
z 575 1s. green (1856) .. .. ..

A07. DOMINICA.

z 576 1d. rose-red (1857) .. .. ..
z 577 4d. rose (1857) 70 0
z 578 6d. lilac (1856) 52 6
z 579 1s. green .. ..

A08. MONTSERRAT.

z 580 1d. rose-red (1857) .. .. ..
z 581 4d. rose (1857) .. .. ..
z 582 6d. lilac (1856) .. .. ..
z 583 1s. green (1856) .. .. ..

A09. NEVIS.

z 584 1d. rose-red (1857) £5
z 585 2d. blue (1858) (Plate Nos. 7, 8)
z 586 4d. rose (1857) .. .. ..
z 587 6d. lilac (1856) 50 0
z 588 1s. green (1856) .. .. ..

A10. KINGSTOWN (ST. VINCENT).

z 589 1d. rose-red (1857) .. .. ..
z 590 2d. blue (1855) .. .. ..
z 591 4d. rose (1857) 80 0
z 592 6d. lilac (1856) 60 0
z 593 9d. straw (1862) .. .. ..
z 594 1s. green (1856) .. .. ..

A11. CASTRIES (ST. LUCIA).

z 595 1d. rose-red (1857) .. .. ..
z 596 2d. blue (1855) .. .. ..
z 597 4d. rose (1857) £6
z 598 6d. lilac (1856) 45 0
z 599 1s. green (1856) £18

A12. BASSE-TERRE (ST. CHRISTOPHER).

z 600 1d. rose-red (1857) .. .. ..
z 601 4d. rose (1857) .. .. ..
z 602 6d. lilac (1856) 42 6
z 603 1s. green (1856) .. .. ..

A13. TORTOLA.

z 604 1d. rose-red (1857) 80 0
z 605 6d. lilac (1856) .. .. ..
z 606 1s. green (1856) .. .. ..

A14. SCARBOROUGH (TOBAGO).

z 607 1d. rose-red (1857) .. ..
z 608 4d. rose (1857) 50 0
z 609 6d. lilac (1856) 37 6
z 610 1s. green (1856) .. .. ..

A15. ST. GEORGE (GRENADA).

z 611 1d. rose-red (1857) .. ..
z 612 2d. blue (1858) (Plate No. 7) ..
z 613 4d. rose (1857) .. .. ..
z 614 6d. lilac (1856) 40 0
z 615 1s. green (1856) .. .. ..

A18. ENGLISH HARBOUR (ANTIGUA)

z 616 6d. lilac .. ..

IV.

VARIOUS FOREIGN TOWNS IN SOUTH AND CENTRAL AMERICA AND THE WEST INDIES.

BUENOS AYRES (ARGENTINA).
"**B32.**" *Obliteration as T* 2, 12 *or* 13.

1860 *to* **1873.**

z 736 1d. rose-red (1857) .. .. ..
z 737 1d. rose-red (1864) .. .. *From* 30 0
Plate Nos. 71, 72. 73, 74, 79, 85, 87, 90, 92, 94, 95, 96, 97, 103, 104, 110, 117, 118, 119, 120, 130, 131, 135, 139, 140, 144, 145, 147, 149, 150, 151, 155, 159, 163.
z 738 2d. blue (1858–69) .. *From* 55 0
Plate Nos. 8, 9, 12, 13, 14.
z 739 3d. carmine-rose (1862) .. 55 0
z 740 3d. rose (1865) (Plate No. 4) .. 55 0
z 741 3d. rose (1867–73) .. .. *From* 30 0
Plate Nos. 4, 5, 6, 7, 8, 9, 10.
z 742 4d. rose (1857) 55 0
z 743 4d. red (1862) (Plate Nos. 3, 4) .. 85 0
z 744 4d. vermilion (1865–73) .. *From* 20 0
Plate Nos. 7, 8, 9, 10, 11, 12, 13.
z 745 6d. lilac (1856) 40 0
z 746 6d. lilac (1862) (Plate Nos. 3, 4) ..
z 747 6d. lilac (1865–67) .. *From* 40 0
Plate Nos. 5, 6.
z 748 6d. lilac (1867) (Plate No. 6) .. 30 0
z 749 6d. violet (1867–70) .. *From* 25 0
Plate Nos. 6, 8, 9.
z 750 6d. buff (1872) (Plate No. 11) .. 45 0
z 751 6d. chestnut (1872) (Plate No. 11) 55 0
z 752 9d. bistre (1862) .. .. ..
z 753 9d. straw (1862) £6
z 754 9d. straw (1865) £12
z 755 9d. straw (1867) 85 0
z 756 10d. red-brown (1867) 80 0
z 757 1s. green (1856) 60 0
z 758 1s. green (1862) 32 6
z 759 1s. green (1865) 22 6
z 760 1s. green (1867) .. .. *From* 17 6
Plate Nos. 4, 5, 6, 7.
z 760a 1s. grn. (1873–77) (Plate Nos. 8, 9)
z 761 2s. blue (1867) 70 0
z 762 5s. rose (1867) (Plate No. 1) .. £5

MONTEVIDEO (URUGUAY).
"**C28.**" *Obliteration as T* 4 *or* 12.

1862 *to* **1872.**

z 763 1d. rose-red (1864) .. .. ..
Plate Nos. 72, 75.
z 764 2d. blue (1858–69) (Plate Nos. 9, 13) 85 0
z 764a 3d. rose (1865) (Plate No. 4) ..
z 765 3d. rose (1867–71) (Plate Nos. 5, 7)
z 766 4d. rose (1857) .. .. ..
z 766a 4d. red (1862) (Plate 4) .. ..
z 767 4d. vermilion (1865–70) .. *From* 60 0
Plate Nos. 7, 8, 9, 11, 12.
z 768 6d. lilac (1856) .. .. ..
z 769 6d. lilac (1865–67) (Plate Nos. 5, 6) 70 0
z 770 6d. lilac (1867) .. .. ..
z 771 6d. violet (1867–70) .. *From* 70 0
Plate Nos. 8, 9.
z 772 6d. buff (1872) .. .. ..
z 773 6d. chestnut (1872) .. ..
z 774 9d. straw (1862) .. .. ..
z 775 9d. straw (1865) .. .. ..
z 776 9d. straw (1867) .. .. ..
z 777 10d. red-brown (1867) £6
z 778 1s. green (1862) 70 0
z 779 1s. green (1865) 50 0

z 780 1s. green (1867–73) (Plate Nos. 4, 5) 50 0
z 781 2s. blue (1867) £6
z 782 5s. rose (1867) (Plate No. 1) ..

VALPARAISO (CHILE).

"C30." *Obliteration as T* 12, 14 *or* 17..

1865 *to* 1881..

z 783 ½d. rose-red (Plate Nos. 6, 11, 12)
z 783*a* 1d. rose-red (1864–79) .. *From* 25 0
Plate Nos. 85, 91, 123, 140, 149, 152, 157, 162, 167, 175, 178, 181, 185, 186, 187, 189, 190, 195, 197, 198, 200, 201, 207, 209, 210, 211, 212, 214, 215, 217.
z 784 1½d. lake-red (1870–74) .. ..
Plate Nos. 1 and 3.
z 785 2d. blue (1858–69) 55 0
Plate Nos. 9, 13, 14, 15.
z 785*a* 2½d. rosy mauve (Plate No. 4) ..
z 785*b* 3d. rose (1862) .. .. ..
z 785*c* 3d. rose (1865) (Plate No. 4) ..
z 786 3d. rose (1867–73) .. .. *From* 25 0
Plate Nos. 5, 6, 7, 8, 9, 10.
z 787 3d. rose (1873–76) .. .. *From* 25 0
Plate Nos. 11, 12, 14, 16, 17, 18.
z 788 4d. vermilion (1865–73) .. *From* 20 0
Plate Nos. 10, 11, 12, 13, 14.
z 789 4d. vermilion (1876) (Plate No. 15)
z 790 4d. sage-green (1877) .. *From* 50 0
Plate Nos. 15, 16.
z 791 4d. grey-brown (1880)(PlateNo.17)
z 792 6d. lilac (1862) (Plate 4) 45 0
z 793 6d. lilac (1865)(Plate Nos. 5, 6) ..
z 794 6d. lilac (1867) (Plate No. 6) ..
z 795 6d. violet (1867–70) 25 0
Plate Nos. 6, 8, 9.
z 796 6d. buff (1872–73) .. .. *From* 45 0
Plate Nos. 11, 12.
z 797 6d. chestnut (1872) (Plate No. 11). 30 0
z 798 6d. grey (1873) (Plate No. 12) .. 32 6
z 799 6d. grey (1874–80) .. *From* 17 6
Plate Nos. 13, 14, 15, 16, 17.
z 800 6d. grey (1881) (Plate No. 17) ..
z 801 8d. orange (1876) .. .. ..
z 802 9d. straw (1862) .. .. ..
z 803 9d. straw (1865) .. .. ..
z 804 9d. straw (1867) 55 0
z 805 10d. red-brown (1867) 95 0
z 805*a* 1s. green (1865) (Plate No. 4) ..
z 806 1s. green (1867–73) .. *From* 25 0
Plate Nos. 4, 5, 6, 7.
z 807 1s. green (1873–77) .. *From* 18 6
Plate Nos. 8, 9, 10, 11, 12, 13.
z 808 1s. orange-brown (1880) .. ..
z 809 2s. blue (1867) 50 0
z 810 2s. brown (1880) .. .. ..
z 811 5s. rose (1867–74) .. .. *From* 80 0
Plate Nos. 1, 2.
z 812 10s. grey-grn. (1878) (*wmk.* Cross) ..
z 813 20s. brown-vio. (1878) (*wmk.* Cross)

1880.

z 814 1d. Venetian red .. ..

ARICA (PERU).

"C36." *Obliteration as T* 4, 12 *or* 14.

1865 *to* 1879.

z 815 ½d. rose-red (1870–79) .. *From* 55 0
Plate Nos. 5, 10, 11, 13
z 816 1d. rose-red (1864–79) .. *From* 37 6
Plate Nos. 102, 139, 163.
z 817 1½d. lake-red (1870–74) (Plate No. 3)
z 818 3d. rose (1873–76) .. .. *From* 55 0
Plate Nos. 11, 12, 17, 19.
z 819 4d. vermilion (1865–73) .. *From* 45 0
Plate Nos. 10, 11, 13, 14.
z 820 4d. vermilion (1876) (Plate No. 15)
z 821 4d. sage-green (1877) 60 0
Plate Nos. 15, 16.
z 822 6d. lilac (1862) (Plate 4) .. ..
z 823 6d. violet (1867–70) 35 0
Plate Nos. 6, 8, 9.
z 824 6d. buff (1872) (Plate No. 11) .. 60 0
z 825 6d. chestnut (1872) (Plate No. 11)
z 825*a* 6d. grey (1873) (Plate No. 12) .. 50 0
z 826 6d. grey (1874–76) .. *From* 42 6
Plate Nos. 13, 14, 15, 16.
z 827 8d. orange (1876) .. .. ..
z 828 9d. straw (1862) .. .. ..
z 828*a* 9d. straw (1867) 60 0
z 829 10d. red-brown (1867) .. ..
z 830 1s. green (1862) .. .. ..
z 830*a* 1s. green (1865) .. .. ..
z 831 1s. green (1867–73) .. *From* 37 6
Plate Nos. 4, 5, 6, 7.
z 832 1s. green (1873–77) .. *From* 37 6
Plate Nos. 8, 10, 11, 12, 13.
z 833 2s. blue (1867) 90 0
z 834 5s. rose (1867–74) (Plate Nos. 1, 2)

CALDERA (CHILE)

"C37." *Obliteration as T* 4.

1865 *to* 1881.

z 835 1d. rose-red (1864–79) .. *From* 35 0
Plate Nos. 71, 88, 90, 95, 195.
z 836 1½d. lake-red (1870–74) (Plate No. 3)
z 837 2d. blue (1858–69) (Plate No. 9) . 45 0
z 838 3d. rose (1865) .. .. ..
z 839 3d. rose (1867–73) (Plate Nos. 5, 7)
z 840 3d. rose (1873–76) .. .. *From* 47 6
Plate Nos. 11, 12, 16, 17, 18, 19.
z 841 4d. red (1862) (Plate 4) .. ..
z 842 4d. vermilion (1865–73) .. *From* 37 6
Plate Nos. 8, 12, 13, 14.
z 843 4d. sage-green (1877) (Plate No. 16)
z 843*a* 6d. lilac (1862) (Plate 4) .. ..
z 844 6d. lilac (1865–67) (Plate No. 6) ..
z 845 6d. violet (1867–70) .. *From* 32 6
Plate Nos. 6, 8, 9.
z 846 6d. buff (1872) (Plate No. 11) ..
z 847 6d. chestnut (1872) .. ..
z 848 6d. grey (1873) .. .. ..
z 849 6d. grey (1874–80) .. *From* 37 6
Plate Nos. 13, 14, 15, 16, 17.
z 850 8d. orange (1876) .. .. ..
z 851 9d. straw (1867) .. .. ..
z 852 10d. red-brown (1867) 70 0
z 853 1s. green (1867–73) .. *From* 37 6
Plate Nos. 4, 5, 6.
z 854 1s. green (1873–77) .. *From* 37 6
Plate Nos. 8, 10, 11, 12, 13.
z 855 2s. blue (1867) .. .. ..
z 856 2s. brown (1880) .. .. ..
z 857 5s. rose (1867–74) (Plate No. 2) ..

COBIJA (BOLIVIA).

"C39." *Obliteration as T* 4, 8 *or* 12.

1865 *to* 1878.

z 857*a* 1d. rose-red (Plate Nos. 93, 95) ..
z 858 2d. blue (1858–69) (Plate No. 14)
z 859 3d. rose (1867–73) (Plate No. 6) ..
z 860 3d. rose (1873–76) (Plate No. 16) .
z 861 6d. buff (1872) (Plate No. 11) ..
z 862 6d. grey (1874–76) .. ..
Plate Nos. 13, 14, 15, 16.
z 863 1s. green (1867–73) (Plate No. 5)
z 864 1s. green (1873–77) .. ..
Plate Nos. 10, 11, 12.
z 865 2s. blue (1867) .. .. ..
z 866 5s. rose (1867–74) (Plate No. 2) ..

COQUIMBO (CHILE).

"C40." *Obliteration as T* 4.

1865 *to* 1881.

z 867 1d. rose-red (1857) .. .. ..
z 867*a* 1d. rose-red (1864–79) (Pl. No. 204)
z 868 2d. blue (1858–69) (Plate Nos. 9, 14)
z 869 3d. rose (1865) .. .. ..
z 869*a* 3d. rose (1872) (Plate No. 8) ..
z 870 3d. rose (1873 76) .. .. *From* 45 0
Plate Nos. 18, 19.
z 870*a* 4d. red (1862) (Plate 4) .. ..
z 871 4d. vermil. (1865–73) (Plate No. 14)

z 872 4d. sage-green (1877) .. ..
Plate Nos. 15, 16
z 873 6d. lilac (1862) (Plate 4) .. ..
z 873a 6d. lilac (Plate 6) .. .. ..
z 874 6d. violet (1867–70) .. *From* 47 6
Plate Nos. 6, 8, 9.
z 875 6d. buff (1872–73) .. .. *From* 57 6
Plate Nos. 11, 12.
z 876 6d. chestnut (1872) .. ..
z 877 6d. grey (1873) 42 6
z 878 6d. grey (1874–76) .. *From* 32 6
Plate Nos. 13, 14, 15, 16.
z 878a 9d. straw (1862) .. .. ..
z 879 9d. straw (1867) 75 0
z 880 10d. red-brown (1867) .. ..
z 881 1s. green (1865) 50 0
z 882 1s. green (1867–73) 45 0
Plate Nos. 4, 5, 6.
z 883 1s. green (1873–77) .. *From* 37 6
Plate Nos. 8, 10, 11, 12, 13.
z 884 2s. blue (1867) 60 0
z 885 2s. brown (1880) .. .. ..
z 886 5s. rose (1867–74) (Plate Nos. 1, 2)

IQUIQUE (*then in* PERU).

"**D87.**" *Obliteration as T* **12.**

1868 *to* **1878.**

z 886a ½d. rose (Plate No. 6) .. ..
z 887 2d. blue (1858–69) (Plate Nos. 9, 13)
z 888 3d. rose (1867–73) .. *From* 80 0
Plate Nos. 5, 6, 7, 8, 9.
z 889 3d. rose (1873–76) .. ..
Plate Nos. 18, 19.
z 890 4d. vermilion (1865–73) .. ..
Plate Nos. 12, 13.
z 890a 4d. sage-green (1877) (Plate 15) ..
z 890b 6d. mauve (1869) (Plate No. 9) ..
z 891 6d. buff (1872–73) .. .. ..
Plate Nos. 11, 12.
z 892 6d. grey (1873) (Plate No. 12) ..
z 893 6d. grey (1874–76) .. ..
Plate Nos. 13, 14, 15, 16.
z 893a 8d. orange (1876) .. .. ..
z 894 9d. straw (1867) .. .. ..
z 895 10d. red-brown (1867) .. ..
z 896 1s. green (1867–73) .. *From* 70 0
Plate Nos. 4, 6.
z 897 1s. green (1873–77) .. ..
Plate Nos. 8, 10, 11, 12, 13.
z 898 2s. blue (1867) .. .. ..

CALLAO (PERU).

"**C38.**" *Obliteration as T* **4, 12** *or* **14.**

1865 *to* **1879.**

z 899 ½d. rose-red (1870–79) .. *From* 35 0
Plate Nos. 5, 6, 10, 11, 12, 13.
z 900 1d. rose-red (1864–79) 20 0
Plate Nos. 88, 93, 97, 127, 130, 137, 140, 141, 143, 144, 145, 148, 149, 156, 160, 163, 172, 175, 180, 193, 195, 198, 200, 201, 206, 209.
z 901 1½d. lake-red (1870–74) (Plate No. 3)
z 902 2d. blue (1858–69) .. *From* 27 6
Plate Nos. 9, 12, 13, 14, 15.
z 903 3d. rose (1862) .. .. ..
z 903a 3d. rose (1865) (Plate 4) 40 0
z 904 3d. rose (1867–73) .. .. *From* 27 6
Plate Nos. 5, 6, 7, 8, 9, 10.
z 905 3d. rose (1873–76) .. .. *From* 20 0
Plate Nos. 11, 12, 14, 15, 16, 17, 18, 19.
z 906 4d. red (1862) (Plates 3, 4) ..
z 907 4d. vermilion (1865–73) 20 0
Plate Nos. 8, 10, 11, 12, 13, 14.
z 908 4d. vermilion (1876) (Plate No. 15) 72 6
z 909 4d. sage-green (1877) 47 6
Plate Nos. 15, 16.
z 910 6d. lilac (1862) (Plates 3, 4) ..
z 911 6d. lilac (1867) .. .. ..
z 912 6d. violet (1867–70) .. *From* 22 6
Plate Nos. 6, 8, 9.
z 913 6d. buff (1872–73) .. .. *From* 37 6
Plate Nos. 11, 12.
z 914 6d. chestnut (1872) 22 6
z 915 6d. grey (1873) 25 0
z 916 6d. grey (1874–80) .. *From* 17 6
Plate Nos. 13, 14, 15, 16, 17.
z 917 6d. grey (1882) (Plate No. 18) ..
z 918 8d. orange (1876) .. .. ..
z 918a 9d. straw (1862) .. .. ..
z 919 9d. straw (1865) .. .. ..
z 920 9d. straw (1867) 75 0
z 921 10d. red-brown (1867) 87 6
z 922 1s. green (1865) .. .. ..
z 923 1s. green (1867–73) .. *From* 22 6
Plate Nos. 4, 5, 6, 7.
z 924 1s. green (1873–77) .. *From* 20 0
Plate Nos. 8, 9, 10, 11, 12, 13.
z 925 2s. blue (1867) 35 0
z 926 5s. rose (1867–74) .. .. *From* 60 0
Plate Nos. 1, 2.

ISLAY (PERU).

"**C42.**" *Obliteration as T* **4.**

1865 *to* **1879.**

z 927 1d. rose-red (1864–79) .. *From* 42 6
Plate Nos. 78, 84, 87, 88, 96, 103.
z 928 1½d. lake-red (1870–74) (Plate No. 3)
z 929 2d. blue (1858–69) 35 0
Plate Nos. 9, 15.
z 930 3d. rose (1865) .. .. ..
z 931 3d. rose (1867–73) .. .. ..
Plate Nos. 4, 5, 6, 10.
z 932 4d. red (1862) (Plates 3, 4) ..
z 933 4d. vermilion (1867–73) .. *From* 32 6
Plate Nos. 9, 10, 11, 12, 13.
z 934 4d. vermilion (1876) .. ..
z 935 4d. sage-green (1877) .. ..
Plate Nos. 15, 16.
z 936 6d. lilac (1862) (Plates 3, 4) ..
z 937 6d. lilac (1865) (Plate No. 5) .. 35 0
z 938 6d. violet (1867–70) .. *From* 35 0
Plate Nos. 6, 8, 9.
z 938a 6d. buff (1873) (Plate No. 12) ..
z 939 6d. grey (1873) (Plate No. 12) ..
z 940 6d. grey (1874–76) .. *From* 35 0
Plate Nos. 13, 14, 15.
z 941 9d. straw (1867) 70 0
z 942 10d. red-brown (1867) .. ..
z 943 1s. green (1865) .. .. ..
z 944 1s. green (1867–73) .. *From* 55 0
Plate Nos. 4, 5, 6, 7.
z 945 1s. green (1873–77) .. *From* 55 0
Plate Nos. 10, 12, 13.
z 946 2s. blue (1867) .. .. ..
z 947 5s. rose (1867) (Plate No. 1) ..

PAYTA (PERU).

"**C43.**" *Obliteration as T* **4.**

1865 *to* **1879.**

z 948 2d. blue (1858–69) (Plate Nos. 9, 14)
z 949 3d. rose (1867–73) (Plate Nos. 5, 6)
z 949a 3d. rose (1876) (Plate Nos. 17, 19)
z 950 4d. vermilion (1865–73) .. *From* 40 0
Plate Nos. 10, 11, 12, 13, 14.
z 951 4d. sage-green (1877) (Plate No. 15)
z 952 6d. lilac (1862) (Plate No. 3) ..
z 953 6d. lilac (1867) (Plate No. 6) ..
z 954 6d. violet (1867–70) .. ..
Plate Nos. 6, 8, 9.
z 955 6d. buff (1872–73) .. .. *From* 55 0
Plate Nos. 11, 12.
z 955a 6d. chestnut (Plate No. 11) ..
z 956 6d. grey (1873) .. .. ..
z 957 6d. grey (1874–76) .. .. ..
Plate Nos. 13, 14, 15.
z 958 10d. red-brown (1867) .. ..
z 959 1s. green (1865) .. .. ..
z 960 1s. green (1867–73) (Plate No. 4)
z 961 1s. green (1873–77) .. ..
Plate Nos. 8, 9, 10, 13.
z 962 2s. blue (1867) .. .. ..
z 963 5s. rose (1867) (Plate No. 1) ..

PISCO (PERU).

"D74." *Obliteration as T* **12.**

1868 *to* **1870.**

z 963*a* 1d. rose-red (1864–79) (Plate No. 137)
z 963*b* 2d. blue (1858–69) (Plate No. 9)
z 964 4d. vermilion (1865–73) .. ..
Plate Nos. 10, 12, 13.
z 965 6d. grey (1874–76) (Plate No. 13)
z 965*a* 1s. green (1867) (Plate No. 4) ..
z965*b* 1s. green (1875) (Plate No. 12) ..
z966 2s. blue (1867) .. .. ..

PANAMA (COLOMBIA).

"C35." *Obliterations as T* **4, 11** *or* **14.**

1865 *to* **1884.**

z 967 ½d. rose-red (1870–79) .. ..
Plate Nos. 10, 11, 12, 13, 14, 15.
z 968 1d. rose-red (1864–79) .. *From* 15 0
Plate Nos. 72, 76, 85, 88, 95, 101, 114, 124, 138, 139, 159, 168, 171, 172, 174, 177, 179, 184, 189, 191, 192, 193, 200, 203, 204, 205, 207, 208, 209, 210, 211, 213, 214, 215.
z 969 1½d. lake-red (1870–74) (Plate No. 3) 35 0
z 970 2d. blue (1858–69) .. *From* 25 0
Plate Nos. 9, 12, 13, 14, 15.
z 971 2½d. rosy mauve (1875–78) ..
Plate Nos. 1, 12.
z 972 2½d. blue (1881) (Plate Nos. 22, 23)
z 972*a* 3d. carmine-red (1862) .. ..
z 973 3d. rose (1865) (Plate No. 4) ..
z 974 3d. rose (1867–73) .. .. *From* 25 0
Plate Nos. 4, 5, 6, 7, 8, 9.
z 975 3d. rose (1873–76) .. .. *From* 20 0
Plate Nos. 14, 15, 16, 17, 18, 19, 20.
z 976 3d. rose (1881) (Plate Nos. 20, 21)
z 977 4d. red (1862) (Plate 4) .. ..
z 978 4d. vermilion (1865–73) .. *From* 17 6
Plate Nos. 7, 9, 10, 11, 12, 13, 14.
z 979 4d. vermilion (1876) (Plate No. 15) £5
z 980 4d. sage-green (1877) 35 0
Plate Nos. 15, 16.
z 981 4d. grey-brown (1881) .. *From* 35 0
Plate Nos. 17, 18.
z 982 6d. lilac (1862) (Plates 3, 4) *From* 30 0
z 983 6d. lilac (1865–67) .. *From* 25 0
Plate Nos. 5, 6.
z 984 6d. lilac (1867) (Plate No. 6) ..
z 985 6d. violet (1867–70) 25 0
Plate Nos. 6, 8, 9.
z 986 6d. buff (1872–73) .. .. *From* 45 0
Plate Nos. 11, 12.
z 987 6d. chestnut (Plate No. 11) .. 45 0
z 988 6d. grey (1873) (Plate No. 12) .. 45 0
z 989 6d. grey (1875–80) .. *From* 37 6
Plate Nos. 13, 14, 15, 16, 17.
z 990 6d. grey (1881) (Plate No. 17) ..
z 991 8d. orange (1876) .. .. ..
z 992 9d. straw (1867) 80 0
z 993 10d. red-brown (1867) .. ..
z 994 1s. green (1865) (Plate No. 4) .. 25 0
z 995 1s. green (1867–73) .. *From* 20 0
Plate Nos. 4, 5, 6, 7.
z 996 1s. green (1873–77) .. *From* 20 0
Plate Nos. 8, 9, 10, 11, 12, 13.
z 997 1s. orange-brown (1880) 75 0
z 998 1s. orge.-brn. (1881) (Plate No. 13) 55 0
z 999 2s. blue (1867) 45 0
z 1000 2s. brown (1880) .. .. ..
z 1001 5s. rose (1867–74) .. .. *From* 70 0
Plate Nos. 1, 2.

1880.

z 1001*a* 1d. Venetian red 12 6
z 1002 2d. rose 35 0
z 1003 5d. indigo 37 6

1881.

z 1004 1d. lilac (14 *dots*) .. .. ..
z 1005 1d. lilac (16 *dots*) 18 6

1884.

z 1006–z 1010 1½d., 2d., 2½d., 4d., 5d. *Fr.* 20 0

1887–92.

z 1010*a* 2d. green and vermilion .. ..

CARTAGENA (COLOMBIA).

"C56." *Obliterations as T* **4** *or* **13.**

1865 *to* **1881.**

z 1010*b* 1d. rose-red (1864) (Plate No. 87)
z 1011 2d. blue (1858–69) .. *From* 45 0
Plate Nos. 9, 14.
z 1011*a* 3d. "*Emblems*" (1865) (Plate No. 4)
z 1012 3d. rose (1865–68) .. ..
Plate Nos. 4, 5.
z 1013 4d. vermilion (1865–73) .. *From* 35 0
Plate Nos. 7, 8, 9, 10, 11, 12, 13, 14.
z 1014 4d. vermilion (1876) .. ..
z 1014*a* 4d. sage-green 70 0
Plate Nos. 15, 16.
z 1015 6d. lilac (1865–67) (Plate Nos. 5, 6)
z 1016 6d. vio. (1867–70) (Plate Nos. 6, 8)
z 1017 6d. grey (1873) .. .. ..
z 1018 6d. grey (1874–76) .. *From* 45 0
Plate Nos. 13, 15.
z 1019 8d. orange (1876) .. .. ..
z 1019*a* 9d. straw (1865) .. .. ..
z 1020 1s. green (1865) .. .. ..
z 1021 1s. green (1867–73) .. ..
Plate Nos. 4, 5, 7.
z 1022 1s. green (1873–77) .. ..
Plate Nos. 9, 10, 11, 12, 13.
z 1023 1s. orange-brown (1880) .. ..
z 1023*a* 2s. blue (1867) .. .. ..
z 1024 5s. rose (1867) (Plate No. 1) ..

"C65" *error for* **"C56."**

1870 *to* **1881.**

z 1025 2d. blue (1858–69) (Plate No. 9) 50 0
z 1026 3d. rose (1873–76) (Plate No. 19)
z 1027 4d. vermilion (1865–73) .. *From* 35 0
Plate Nos. 7, 9, 11, 12, 13, 14.
z 1028 4d. vermilion (1876) (Plate No. 15)
z 1029 4d. sage-green (1877) .. *From* 55 0
Plate Nos. 15, 16.
z 1030 6d. violet (1867–70) (Plate No. 6)
z 1030*a* 6d. grey (Plate Nos. 12, 13) ..
z 1030*b* 8d. orange (1876) .. .. ..
z 1031 1s. green (1865) (Plate No. 4) ..
z 1032 1s. green (1867) (Plate Nos. 4, 7) 45 0
z 1033 1s. green (1873–77) .. *From* 35 0
Plate Nos. 11, 12, 13.
z 1033*a* 1s. orange-brown (1880) .. ..
z 1033*b* 2s. brown (1880) .. .. ..
z 1034 5s. rose (1867) (Plate No. 1) ..

SANTA MARTHA (COLOMBIA).

"C62." *Obliteration as T* **4.**

1865 *to* **1881.**

z 1035 1d. rose-red (1864–79) .. ..
Plate No. 106.
z 1036 2d. blue (1858–69) (Plate No. 9)
z 1037 4d. vermilion (1865–73) .. *From* 45 0
Plate Nos. 7, 8, 9, 11, 12, 13, 14.
z 1037*a* 6d. lilac (Plate No. 5) .. ..
z 1037*b* 6d. grey (1873) (Plate No. 12) ..
z 1038 6d. grey (1874–76) (Plate No. 14)
z 1039 1s. green (1865) (Plate No. 4) .. 65 0
z 1040 1s. green (1867–73) 65 0
Plate Nos. 5, 7.
z 1041 1s. green (1873–77) (Plate No. 8)

ASPINWALL, COLON (COLOMBIA).

"E88." *Obliteration as T* **12.**

1870 *to* **1881.**

z 1042 1d. rose-red (1864–79) .. *From* 30 0
Plate Nos. 107, 121, 122, 123, 125, 127, 130, 136, 142, 150, 151, 152, 153, 156, 157, 158, 160, 171, 174, 176, 178, 184, 187, 194, 201, 209, 213, 214, 217.

z 1042a 1d. Venetian red (1880) .. ..
z 1043 1½d. lake-red (1870–74) .. ..
Plate No. 3.
z 1044 2d. blue (1858–69) 55 0
Plate Nos. [illegible], 15.
z 1045 3d. rose (1867–73) (Plate No. 9) .
z 1046 3d. rose (1873–76) 40 0
Plate Nos. 12, 16, 18, 19, 20.
z 1047 4d. vermilion (1865–73) .. *From* 20 0
Plate Nos. 10, 11, 12, 13, 14.
z 1048 4d. vermilion (1876) (Plate No. 15)
z 1049 4d. sage-green (1877) 32 6
Plate Nos. 15, 16.
z 1050 4d. grey-brown (1880) £6
Plate No. 17.
z 1051 4d. grey-brown (1881) .. ..
Plate No. 17.
z 1052 6d. violet (1867–70) .. ..
Plate Nos. 6, 8, 9.
z 1052a 6d. buff (1872) (Plate No. 11) ..
z 1053 6d. chestnut (1872) (Plate No. 11)
z 1054 6d. grey (1873) (Plate No. 12) ..
z 1055 6d. grey (1874–76) .. *From* 37 6
Plate Nos. 13, 14, 15, 16, 17.
z 1056 9d. straw (1867) .. ..
z 1057 1s. green (1867–73) 35 0
Plate Nos. 4, 5, 6, 7.
z 1058 1s. green (1873–77) .. *From* 35 0
Plate Nos. 8, 9, 10, 11, 12, 13.
z 1059 1s. orange-brown (1880).. ..
Plate No. 13.
z 1060 1s. orange-brown (1881).. ..
Plate No. 13.
z 1061 2s. blue (1867) .. ..
z 1061a 5s. rose (1867) (Plate Nos. 1, 2) .

SAVANILLA (COLOMBIA).

"**F69.**" *Obliteration as T* 12.

1872 *to* **1881.**

z 1062 ½d. rose-red (1870–79) 32 6
Plate No. 6.
z 1063 1d. rose-red (1864–79) 52 6
Plate Nos. 122, 171.
z 1064 1½d. lake-red (1870–74) .. ..
Plate No. 3.
z 1065 3d. rose (1867–73) (Plate No. 7) .
z 1066 3d. rose (1873–76) (Plate No. 20)
z 1067 4d. vermilion (1865–73) 27 6
Plate Nos. 12, 13, 14.
z 1068 4d. vermilion (1876) (Plate No. 15)
z 1069 4d. sage-green (1877) 55 0
Plate Nos. 15, 16.
z 1070 4d. grey-brn. (1880) (Plate No. 17)
z 1071 4d. grey-brn. (1881) (Plate No. 17)
z 1072 6d. buff (1872) (Plate No. 11) ..
z 1072a 8d. orange (1876) .. ..
z 1073 1s. green (1867–73) (Plate No. 5). 45 0
z 1074 1s. green (1873–77) .. ..
Plate Nos. 12, 13.
z 1075 1s. orange-brown (1880).. ..
z 1076 2s. blue (1867) .. ..
z 1077 5s. rose (1867–74) (Plate No. 2)..

GUAYAQUIL (ECUADOR).

"**C41.**" *Obliteration as T* 4.

1865 *to* **1880.**

z 1078 ½d. rose-red (1870–79) .. ..
Plate No. 6.
z 1079 1d. rose-red (1857) .. ..
z 1080 1d. rose-red (1864–79) 27 6
Plate Nos. 74, 85, 92, 94, 110, 115, 133, 145, 166, 174.
z 1081 1½d. lake-red (1870–74) .. ..
Plate No. 3.
z 1082 2d. blue (1858–69) .. *From* 32 6
Plate Nos. 9, 13, 14.
z 1083 3d. rose (1865) 35 0
z 1084 3d. rose (1867–73) .. *From* 32 6
Plate Nos. 6, 7, 9, 10.
z 1085 3d. rose (1873–76) .. *From* 32 6
Plate Nos. 11, 16, 17, 18, 19.
z 1086 4d. red (1862) (Plates 3, 4) ..
z 1087 4d. vermilion (1865–73) .. *From* 25 0
Plate Nos. 7, 8, 9, 10, 11, 12, 13, 14.
z 1088 4d. vermilion (1876) .. ..
z 1089 4d. sage-green (1877) .. ..
Plate Nos. 15, 16.
z 1090 6d. lilac (1862) (Plate 4) ..
z 1091 6d. lilac (1865–67) 30 0
Plate Nos. 5, 6.
z 1092 6d. lilac (1867) (Plate No. 6) ..
z 1093 6d. violet (1867–70) .. *From* 30 0
Plate Nos. 6, 8, 9.
z 1094 6d. buff (1872–73) .. ..
Plate Nos. 11, 12.
z 1095 6d. chestnut (1872) .. ..
z 1096 6d. grey (1873) .. ..
z 1097 6d. grey (1874–76) .. *From* 27 6
Plate Nos. 13, 14, 15, 16.
z 1098 8d. orange (1876) .. ..
z 1098a 9d. straw (1867) 90 0
z 1099 10d. red-brown (1867) £5
z 1100 1s. green (1865) 27 6
z 1101 1s. green (1867–73) .. *From* 17 6
Plate Nos. 4, 5, 6, 7.
z 1102 1s. green (1873–77) .. *From* 22 6
Plate Nos. 8, 9, 10, 11, 12, 13.
z 1103 2s. blue (1867) 55 0
z 1104 2s. brown (1880) .. ..
z 1105 5s. rose (1867–74) .. *From* 90 0
Plate Nos. 1, 2.

GREYTOWN (NICARAGUA).

"**C57.**" *Obliteration as T* **4, 12** *or* **14.**

1865 *to* **1882.**

z 1106 ½d. rose-red (1870–79) .. ..
Plate No. 11.
z 1107 1½d. lake-red (1870–74) 35 0
Plate No. 3.
z 1108 2d. blue (1858–69) (Plate Nos. 9, 14)
z 1109 3d. rose (1873–76) .. ..
Plate Nos. 19, 20.
z 1110 3d. rose (1881) (Plate No. 20) ..
z 1111 4d. vermilion (1865–73) .. *From* 27 6
Plate Nos. 8, 10, 11, 12, 13, 14.
z 1112 4d. vermilion (1876) (Plate No. 15)
z 1113 4d. sage-green (1877) 35 0
Plate Nos. 15, 16.
z 1114 4d. grey-brown (1880) 62 6
Plate No. 17.
z 1115 4d. grey-brown (1881) 37 6
Plate No. 17.
z 1116 6d. grey (1874–76) .. ..
Plate Nos. 14, 15, 16.
z 1117 8d. orange (1876) .. ..
z 1118 1s. green (1867–73) .. ..
Plate Nos. 6, 7.
z 1119 1s. green (1873–77) 32 6
Plate Nos. 8, 12, 13.
z 1120 1s. orange-brown (1880).. .. 65 0
Plate No. 13.
z 1121 1s. orange-brown (1881).. .. 45 0
Plate No. 13.
z 1122 2s. blue (1867) 65 0
z 1123 2s. brown (1880) .. ..
z 1124 5s. rose (1867–74) (Plate Nos. 1, 2) £5

1880.

z 1125 1d. Venetian red .. .. ..
z 1126 1½d. Venetian red .. .. ..

TAMPICO (MEXICO).

"**C63.**" *Obliteration as T* **4.**

1865 *to* **1876.**

z 1127 1d. rose-red (1864–79) .. ..
Plate Nos. 81, 89, 103, 117, 139, 147.
z 1128 2d. blue (1858–69) .. ..
Plate Nos. 9, 14.
z 1129 4d. vermilion (1865–73) .. *From* 80 0
Plate Nos. 7, 8, 10, 11, 12, 13, 14.
z 1130 1s. green (1867–73) .. ..
Plate Nos. 4, 5, 7.
z 1130a 2s. blue (1867) .. ..

VERA CRUZ (MEXICO).

"**C64.**" *Obliteration as T* **4.**

1865 *to* **1874.**

z 1131 3d. rose (1867–71) .. ..
Plate Nos. 6, 7.
z 1132 6d. grey (1874–76) .. ..
Plate Nos. 13, 15.
z 1133 1s. green (1865) (Plate No. 4) ..
z 1134 1s. green (1867–73) .. ..
Plate Nos. 4, 7.
z 1134a 1s. green (1873–77) (Plate No. 8)

LA GUAYRA (VENEZUELA).

"**C60.**" *Obliteration or circular postmark as T* **4** *or* **16.**

1865 *to* **1880.**

z 1135 1d. rose-red (1864–79) .. *From* 27 6
Plate Nos. 92, 96, 111, 113, 115, 131, 138, 145, 177, 178, 180, 196.
z 1136 1½d. lake-red (1870–74) (Plate 3) .
z 1137 2d. blue (1858–69) (Plate No. 14)
z 1138 3d. rose (1873–76) .. ..
Plate Nos. 14, 15, 17, 18, 19.
z 1139 4d. vermilion (1865–73) .. *From* 20 0
Plate Nos. 11, 12, 13, 14.
z 1140 4d. vermilion (1876) (Plate No. 15)
z 1141 4d. sage-green (1877) 37 6
Plate Nos. 15, 16.
z 1142 6d. lilac (1865) (Plate No. 5)
z 1143 6d. violet (1867–70) (Plate No. 8)
z 1144 6d. buff (1872–73) .. ..
Plate Nos. 11, 12.
z 1145 6d. grey (1873) (Plate No. 12) .. 55 0
z 1146 6d. grey (1874–76) .. ..
Plate Nos. 13, 16.
z 1146a 8d. orange .. .. ..
z 1147 10d. red-brown (1867) .. ..
z 1147a 1s. green (1865) (Plate No. 4) ..
z 1148 1s. green (1873) (Plate No. 7) ..
z 1149 1s. green (1873–77) .. *From* 35 0
Plate Nos. 8, 9, 10, 11, 12, 13.
z 1150 2s. blue (1867) .. .. ..
z 1151 5s. rose (1867–74) (Plate Nos. 1, 2)

CIUDAD BOLIVAR OR ANGOSTURA (VENEZUELA).

"**D22.**" *Obliteration or circular postmark as T* **12** *or* **17.**

1868 *to* **1880.**

z 1152 1d. rose-red (1864–79) 42 6
Plate No. 133.
z 1153 3d. rose (1867–73) (Plate No. 5) .
z 1154 4d. vermilion (1865–73) .. ..
Plate Nos. 9, 12, 14.
z 1155 4d. sage-green (1877) .. ..
Plate Nos. 15, 16.
z 1155a 10d. red-brown (1867) .. ..
z 1156 1s. green (1867–73) .. ..
Plate Nos. 4, 5, 7.
z 1157 1s. green (1873–77) 75 0
Plate Nos. 10, 12, 13.
z 1158 2s. blue (1867) .. .. ..
z 1158a 5s. rose (Plate Nos. 1, 2) ..

BAHIA (BRAZIL).

"**C81.**" *Obliteration as T* **12.**

1866 *to* **1874.**

z 1159 1d. rose-red (1864) .. *From* 27 6
Plate Nos. 90, 108, 113, 117, 135, 147.
z 1160 1½d. lake-red (1870–74) (Plate 3) .
z 1161 2d. blue (1858–69) .. ..
Plate Nos. 9, 12, 13, 14.
z 1162 3d. rose (1865) (Plate No. 4) ..
z 1163 3d. rose (1867–73) .. ..
Plate Nos. 4, 8, 9, 10, 11.
z 1164 4d. vermilion (1865–73) .. *From* 25 0
Plate Nos. 9, 11 12, 13.
z 1164a 6d. lilac (1865–67) (Plate No. 5) ..
z 1165 6d. lilac (1867) (Plate Nos. 6, 9) *From* 30 0
z 1166 6d. violet (1867–70) .. *From* 35 0
Plate Nos. 6, 8.
z 1166a 6d. buff (1872–73) .. *From* 50 0
Plate Nos. 11, 12.
z 1167 6d. chestnut (1872) (Plate No. 11)
z 1168 6d. grey (1873) (Plate No. 12) ..
z 1169 6d. grey (1874–76) (Plate No. 13)
z 1170 9d. straw (1865) .. .. ..
z 1170a 9d. straw (1867) .. .. ..
z 1171 1s. green (1865) (Plate No. 4) .. 30 0
z 1172 1s. green (1867–73) .. *From* 35 0
Plate Nos. 4, 5, 6, 7.
z 1173 1s. green (1873–77) .. *From* 35 0
Plate Nos. 8, 9, 12.
z 1174 2s. blue (1867) 70 0
z 1175 5s. rose (1867) (Plate No. 1) ..

PERNAMBUCO (BRAZIL).

"**C82.**" *Obliteration as T* **14.**

1866 *to* **1874.**

z 1176 1d. rose-red (1864) .. *From* 32 6
Plate Nos. 85, 108, 111, 130, 132, 149, 160, 198.
z 1177 2d. blue (1858–69) .. *From* 45 0
Plate Nos. 9, 12, 13, 14.
z 1178 3d. rose (1867–73) .. ..
Plate Nos 4, 5, 6, 10.
z 1178a 3d. rose (1873–77) (Plate No. 11).
z 1179 4d. vermilion (1865–73) .. *From* 30 0
Plate Nos. 9, 10, 11, 12, 13, 14.
z 1180 6d. lilac (1865–67)(Plate Nos. 5, 6)
z 1181 6d. lilac (1867) (Plate No. 6) ..
z 1182 6d. violet (1867–70) .. *From* 40 0
Plate Nos. 8, 9.
z 1183 6d. buff (1872–73) .. ..
Plate Nos. 11, 12.
z 1184 6d. chestnut (1872) (Plate No. 11)
z 1185 6d. grey (1873) (Plate No. 12) ..
z 1186 9d. straw (1865) .. .. ..
z 1187 9d. straw (1867) .. .. ..
z 1188 10d. red-brown (1867) .. ..
z 1189 1s. green (1865) (Plate No. 4) ..
z 1190 1s. green (1867–73) .. ..
Plate Nos. 4, 5, 6, 7.
z 1191 2s. blue (1867) .. .. ..
z 1192 5s. rose (1867–74)(Plate Nos. 1, 2)

RIO DE JANEIRO (BRAZIL).

"**C83.**" *Obliteration as T* **12.**

866 *to* **1874.**

z 1193 1d. rose-red (1857) £5
z 1194 1d. rose-red (1864) .. *From* 30 0
Plate Nos. 71, 117, 123, 132, 134, 135, 159, 166, 200, 207, 209.
z 1195 2d. blue (1858–69) .. *From* 35 0
Plate Nos. 9, 12, 13, 14.
z 1196 3d. rose (1867–73) .. *From* 35 0
Plate Nos. 5, 6, 7, 8.
z 1197 3d. rose (1873–77) .. ..
Plate Nos. 11, 17.
z 1198 4d. vermilion (1865–73) .. *From* 25 0
Plate Nos, 8, 9, 10, 11, 12, 13, 14.
z 1199 4d. vermilion (1876)(Plate No. 15)
z 1200 6d. lilac (1867) 32 6
z 1201 6d. violet (1867–70) .. *From* 27 6
Plate Nos. 6, 8, 9.
z 1202 6d. buff (1872) (Plate No. 11) ..
z 1203 6d. chestnut (1872) (Plate No. 11)
z 1204 6d. grey (1873) (Plate No. 12) ..
z 1205 9d. straw (1865) .. ..
z 1206 9d. straw (1867) .. ..
z 1207 10d. red-brown (1867) .. ..
z 1208 1s. green (1865) (Plate No. 4) .. 30 0
z 1209 1s. green (1867–73) .. *From* 22 6
Plate Nos. 4, 5, 6, 7.
z 1210 1s. green (1873–77) 35 0
Plate Nos. 8, 9, 12, 13.
z 1211 2s. blue (1867) 50 0
z 1212 5s. rose (1867–74) .. *From* 90
Plate Nos. 1, 2.

1880.

z 1212a 1d. Venetian red .. .. ..

JACMEL (HAYTI).

"C59." *Obliteration as T* **4.**

1865 *to* **1881.**

z 1213 ½d. rose-red (1870–79) .. *From* 35 0
Plate Nos. 4, 5, 6, 10, 11, 12, 15.
z 1213a ½d. green (1880) .. .. ..
z 1214 1d. rose-red (1864–79) .. *From* 30 0
Plate Nos. 87, 95, 122, 136, 137, 139, 150, 152, 156, 157, 159, 160, 166, 171, 181, 186, 187, 192, 194, 200.
z 1215 1½d. lake-red (1870–74) (Plate 3) . 40 0
z 1216 2d. blue (1858–69) 40 0
Plate Nos. 9, 13, 14, 15.
z 1217 3d. rose (1867–73) .. *From* 35 0
Plate Nos. 5, 6, 8, 9, 10.
z 1218 3d. rose (1873–76) 35 0
Plate Nos. 11, 12, 14, 16, 17, 18, 19.
z 1218a 4d. red (*hair lines*) .. ..
z 1219 4d. vermilion (1865–73) .. *From* 22 6
Plate Nos. 7, 8, 9, 10, 11, 12, 13, 14.
z 1220 4d. vermilion (1876)(Plate No. 15)
z 1221 4d. sage-green (1877) 40 0
Plate Nos. 15, 16.
z 1222 4d. grey-brn. (1880)(Plate No. 17) 75 0
z 1223 4d. grey-brn. (1881)(Plate No. 17) 35 0
z 1224 6d. lilac (1867) (Plate No. 6) .. 35 0
z 1225 6d. vio. (1867–70)(Plate Nos. 8, 9) 35 0
z 1226 6d. buff (1872–73) .. ..
Plate Nos. 11, 12.
z 1227 6d. chestnut (1872) (Plate No. 11)
z 1228 6d. grey (1873) (Plate No. 12) ..
z 1229 6d. grey (1874–76) .. *From* 35 0
Plate Nos. 13, 14, 16.
z 1230 8d. orange (1876) .. ..
z 1230a 9d. straw (1862) .. .. ..
z 1231 9d. straw (1867) .. .. ..
z 1232 10d. red-brown (1867) .. ..
z 1233 1s. green (1865) (PlateNo. 4) .. 25 0
z 1234 1s. green (1867–73) .. *From* 20 0
Plate Nos. 4, 5, 6, 7.
z 1235 1s. green (1873–77) .. *From* 30 0
Plate Nos. 8, 9, 10, 11, 12, 13.
z 1236 1s. orange-brown (1880) .. ..
Plate No. 13.
z 1237 2s. blue (1867) 60 0
z 1238 2s. brown (1880) .. .. ..
z 1239 5s. rose (1867–74) .. *From* 90 0
Plate Nos. 1, 2. .. ..

1880.

z 1240 1d. Venetian red 35 0
z 1241 1½d. Venetian red 40 0
z 1242 2d. rose 55 0

PORT-AU-PRINCE (HAYTI).

"E53." *Obliteration as T* **11, 12** *or* **14.**

1869 *to* **1881.**

z 1243 ½d. rose-red (1870–79) .. *From* 27 6
Plate Nos. 5, 6, 10, 11, 12, 13.
z 1244 1d. rose-red (1864–79) .. *From* 20 0
Plate Nos. 87, 154, 167, 171, 174, 183, 193, 199, 202, 206, 209, 210, 218.
z 1245 1½d. lake-red (1870–74) (Plate 3) . 35 0
z 1246 2d. blue (1855–69) .. ..
Plate Nos. 14, 15.
z 1247 2½d. rosy mauve (1876–79) ..
Plate Nos. 3, 9.
z 1248 3d. rose (1873–76) 40 0
Plate Nos. 17, 20.
z 1249 4d. vermilion (1865–73) .. *From* 25 0
Plate Nos. 11, 12, 13, 14.
z 1250 4d. vermilion (1876)(Plate No. 15)
z 1251 4d. sage-green (1877) 37 6
Plate Nos. 15, 16.
z 1252 4d. grey-brn. (1880)(Plate No. 17) 80 0
z 1253 4d. grey-brn. (1881)(Plate No. 17) 55 0
z 1254 6d. grey (1874–76) (Plate No. 15)
z 1255 8d. orange (1876) .. ..
z 1256 1s. green (1867–73) .. *From* 30 0
Plate Nos. 4, 5, 6, 7.
z 1257 1s. green (1873–77) .. *From* 30 0
Plate Nos. 9, 10, 11, 12, 13.
z 1258 1s. orge.-brn. (1880)(Plate No. 13) 80 0
z 1259 1s. orge.-brn. (1881)(Plate No. 13)
z 1260 2s. blue (1867) .. .. ..
z 1261 2s. brown (1880) .. .. ..
z 1262 5s. rose (1867–74) .. ..
Plate Nos. 1, 2.
z 1262a 10s. grey-green (1878) .. ..

1880.

z 1263 ½d. green .. ..
z 1264 1d. Venetian red 25 0
z 1265 1½d. Venetian red 27 6

PORTO PLATA (DOMINICAN REPUBLIC)

"C86." *Obliteration or circular postmark as T* **8, 12** *or* **17.**

1867 *to* **1879.**

z 1266 ½d. rose-red (1870–79) .. *From* 47 6
Plate Nos. 10, 12, 14.
z 1267 1d. rose-red (1864–79) .. *From* 32 6
Plate Nos. 123, 130, 136, 146, 178, 199, 217.
z 1268 1½d. lake-red (1870–74) .. ..
Plate No. 3.
z 1269 2d. blue (1858–69) (Plate No. 15). 45 0
z 1270 2½d. rosy mauve (1876–79) ..
Plate No. 14.
z 1270a 3d. rose (1873–76) (Plate No. 18)
z 1270b 4d. vermilion (1873) (Plate No. 14)
z 1271 4d. vermilion (1876) (Plate No. 15)
z 1272 4d. sage-green (1877) .. ..
Plate No. 15.
z 1272a 6d. violet (1867–70) (Plate No. 8)
z 1273 6d. grey (1874–76) (Plate No. 15)
z 1274 1s. green (1867–73) *From* 55 0
Plate Nos. 4, 7.
z 1275 1s. green (1873–77) .. *From* 40 0
Plate Nos. 11, 12, 13.
z 1276 2s. blue (1867) .. ..

SAN DOMINGO (DOMINICAN REP.)

"C87." *Obliteration or circular postmark as T* **12** *or* **17.**

1867 *or* **1879.**

z 1277 ½d. rose-red (1870–79) .. *From* 37 6
Plate Nos. 10, 11, 13.
z 1278 1d. rose-red (1864–79) .. *From* 25 0
Plate Nos. 146, 171, 173, 174, 178, 186, 190, 220.
z 1279 1½d. lake-red (1870–74) 47 6
Plate No. 3.
z 1280 2d. blue (1858–69) (Plate No. 13)
z 1281 4d. vermilion (1865–73) .. *From* 40 0
Plate Nos. 11, 12, 14.
z 1282 4d. vermilion (1876)(Plate No. 15)
z 1283 9d. straw (1867) .. .. ..
z 1284 1s. green (1867) (Plate No. 4) ..
z 1285 1s. green (1873–77) .. *From* 35 0
Plate Nos. 10, 11, 12, 13.

ST. THOMAS (D.W.I.).

"C51." *Obliteration as T* **4, 12** *or* **14.**

1865 *to* **1879.**

z 1286 ½d. rose-red (1870–79) 32 6
Plate Nos. 5, 6, 8, 10, 11, 12.
z 1286a 1d. rose-red (1857) .. ..
z 1287 1d. rose-red (1864–79) .. *From* 12 6
Plate Nos. 71, 72, 79, 81, 84, 85, 86, 88, 89, 90, 93, 94, 95, 96, 97, 98, 100, 101, 102, 105, 106, 107, 110, 112, 113, 114, 117, 118, 119, 120, 121, 122, 123, 124, 125, 127, 129, 130, 131, 133, 134, 136, 137, 138, 139, 140, 141, 142, 144, 145, 146, 147, 148, 149, 150.

151, 152, 154, 155, 156, 157, 158, 159, 160, 161, 162, 163, 164, 165, 166, 167, 169, 170, 171, 172, 173, 174, 175, 176, 177, 178, 179, 180, 182, 186, 189, 190, 197.

z 1288 1½d. lake-red (1870–74) 30 0
Plate No. 3.

z 1289 2d. blue (1858–69) .. *From* 20 0
Plate Nos. 9, 12, 13, 14, 15.

z 1290 3d. rose (1865) (Plate No. 4) .. 60 0

z 1291 3d. rose (1867–73) .. *From* 35 0
Plate Nos. 4, 5, 6, 7, 8, 9, 10.

z 1291*a* 3d. rose (1867–73) .. *From* 37 6
Plate Nos. 11, 12, 14, 15, 16, 17, 18, 19.

z 1292 4d. red (1862) (Plates 3, 4) ..

z 1293 4d. vermilion (1865–73) .. *From* 17 6
Plate Nos. 7, 8, 9, 10, 11, 12, 13, 14.

z 1294 4d. verm. (1876) (Plate No. 15) 80 0

z 1295 4d. sage-green (1877) .. *From* 30 0
Plate Nos. 15, 16.

z 1295*a* 4d. grey-brn. (1880) (Plate No. 17) 70 0

z 1296 6d. lilac (1862) (Plate 4) ..

z 1297 6d. lilac (1865–67) .. *From* 17 6
Plate Nos. 5, 6.

z 1298 6d. lilac (1867) (Plate No. 6) .. 20 0

z 1299 6d. violet (1867–70) .. *From* 17 6
Plate Nos. 6, 8, 9.

z 1300 6d. buff (1872–73) .. *From* 40 0
Plate Nos. 11, 12.

z 1301 6d. chestnut (1872) (Plate No. 11)

z 1302 6d. grey (1873) (Plate No. 12) .. 27 6

z 1303 6d. grey (1874–76) 15 0
Plate Nos. 13, 14, 15, 16.

z 1304 8d. orange (1876) 80 0

z 1305 9d. straw (1862) .. .. ..

z 1306 9d. bistre (1862) 75 0

z 1307 9d. straw (1865) £14

z 1308 9d. straw (1867) 50 0

z 1309 10d. red-brown (1867) 80 0

z 1310 1s. green (1865) 25 0

z 1311 1s. green (1867–73) .. *From* 10 0
Plate Nos. 4, 5, 6, 7.

z 1312 1s. green (1873–77) .. *From* 20 0
Plate Nos. 8, 9, 10, 11, 12, 13.

z 1313 2s. blue (1867) 50 0

z 1314 5s. rose (1867–74) .. *From* 80 0
Plate Nos. 1, 2.

SPANISH MAIL PACKET ST. THOMAS.

"D26." *Obliteration as T* **12.**

1868 *to* **1879** (?).

z 1315 1d. rose-red (1864) .. ..
Plate Nos. 98, 125.

z 1316 4d. vermilion (1865–73) .. ..
Plate Nos. 9, 11.

z 1317 6d. violet (1867–70) (Plate No. 8)

HAVANA (CUBA).

"C58." *Obliteration as T* **4** *or* **14.**

1867 *to* **1877.**

z 1318 ½d. rose-red (1870) (Plate No. 12)

z 1319 1d. rose-red (1864) .. ..
Plate Nos. 98, 124, 174.

z 1320 2d. blue (1858–69) .. ..
Plate Nos. 9, 14, 15.

z 1321 3d. rose (1867–76) .. ..
Plate Nos. 4, 19.

z 1322 4d. vermilion (1865–73) .. *From* 35 0
Plate Nos. 7, 10, 11, 12, 13, 14.

z 1323 4d. verm. (1876) (Plate No. 15)

z 1323*a* 4d. grey (1880) (Plate No. 17) ..

z 1324 6d. grey (1874–76) .. ..
Plate Nos. 15, 16.

z 1325 8d. orange (1876) .. ..

z 1325*a* 9d. straw (1867) .. .. ..

z 1326 10d. red-brown (1867) .. ..

z 1327 1s. green (1865) (Plate No. 4) ..

z 1328 1s. green (1867–73) .. *From* 40 0
Plate Nos. 4, 5, 7.

z 1329 1s. green (1873–77) .. *From* 30 0
Plate Nos. 10, 12, 13.

z 1330 2s. blue (1867) .. ..

z 1331 5s. rose (1867–74)(Plate Nos. 1, 2)

ST. IAGO DE CUBA.

"C88." *Obliteration as T* **14.**

1866 *to* **1877.**

z 1332 1d. rose-red (1864) .. *From* 27 6
Plate Nos. 100, 105, 106, 109, 120, 123, 146, 171, 208.

z 1333 1½d. lake-red (1870–74) .. ..
Plate No. 3.

z 1334 2d. blue (1858–69) .. ..
Plate Nos. 9, 12, 13, 14.

z 1334*a* 3d. rose (1867) (Plate No. 5) ..

z 1335 4d. vermilion (1865–73) .. *From* 35 0
Plate Nos. 9, 10, 12, 13, 14.

z 1336 4d. verm. (1876) (Plate No. 15)

z 1337 6d. vio. (1867–70) .. .. *From* 55 0
Plate Nos. 8, 9.

z 1337*a* 6d. buff (Plate No. 11) .. ..

z 1338 10d. red-brown (1867) .. ..

z 1339 1s. green (1867–73) .. ..
Plate Nos. 4, 5, 6.

z 1340 1s. green (1873–77) .. ..
Plate Nos. 9, 10, 12, 13.

z 1341 2s. blue (1867) .. .. ..

PORTO RICO.

"C61." *Obliteration as T* **4, 8** *or* **14.**

1865 *to* **1877.**

z 1342 ½d. rose-red (1870) .. *From* 32 6
Plate Nos. 5, 10, 15.

z 1343 1d. rose-red (1857) .. ..

z 1344 1d. rose-red (1864) .. *From* 12 6
Plate Nos. 73, 81, 84, 90, 100, 107, 124, 127, 130, 138, 140, 146, 149, 153, 156, 159, 160, 163, 169, 171, 172, 173, 175, 182, 186.

z 1345 1½d. lake-red (1870–74) .. ..
Plates 1, 3.

z 1346 2d. blue (1858–69) .. *From* 20 0
Plate Nos. 9, 13, 14.

z 1347 3d. rose (1865) (Plate No. 4) .. 30 0

z 1348 3d. rose (1867–73) .. *From* 27 6
Plate Nos. 5, 6, 7, 8, 9, 10.

z 1349 3d. rose (1873–76) .. *From* 20 0
Plate Nos. 11, 12, 14, 15, 16, 17, 18.

z 1350 4d. vermilion (1865–73) .. *From* 15 0
Plate Nos. 7, 8, 9, 10, 11, 12, 13, 14.

z 1351 4d. verm. (1876) (Plate No. 15)

z 1352 6d. lilac (1865–67) .. *From* 20 0
Plate Nos. 5, 6.

z 1353 6d. lilac (1867) (Plate No. 6) .. 20 0

z 1354 6d. violet (1867–70) .. *From* 20 0
Plate Nos. 6, 8, 9.

z 1355 6d. buff (1872) 40 0
Plate Nos. 11, 12.

z 1356 6d. chestnut (1872) (Plate No. 11) 35 0

z 1357 6d. grey (1873) (Plate No. 12) ..

z 1358 6d. grey (1874–76) .. *From* 15 0
Plate Nos. 13, 14, 15.

z 1359 9d. straw (1865) £15

z 1360 9d. straw (1867) 65 0

z 1361 10d. red-brown (1867) 85 0

z 1362 1s. green (1865) (Plate No. 4) .. 20 0

z 1363 1s. green (1867–73) .. *From* 15 0
Plate Nos. 4, 5, 6, 7.

z 1364 1s. green (1873–77) .. *From* 20 0
Plate Nos. 8, 9, 10, 11, 12, 13.

z 1365 2s. blue (1867) 50 0

z 1366 5s. rose (1867) .. .. *From* 80 0
Plate Nos. 1, 2.

ARROYO (PORTO RICO).

"F83." *Obliteration or circular postmark at T* **8** *or* **17.**

1872 *to* **1877.**

z 1366*a* ½d. rose-red (Plate No. 5) .. 50 0

z 1367 1d. rose-red (1864) 47 6
Plate Nos. 156, 174, 175.
z 1367a 1½d. lake-red (1870) (Plate No. 1)
z 1368 2d. blue (1858-69) (Plate No. 14)
z 1369 3d. rose (1867-73) .. ..
Plate Nos. 7, 10.
z 1370 3d. rose (1873-76) .. ..
Plate Nos. 12, 14.
z 1371 4d. vermilion (1865-73) 45 0
Plate Nos. 12, 13, 14.
z 1372 4d. verm. (1876) (Plate No. 15)
z 1373 6d. grey (1874-76) .. ..
Plate Nos. 13, 14.
z 1374 9d. straw (1867) .. .. ..
z 1375 10d. red-brown (1867) .. ..
z 1376 1s. green (1865) (Plate No. 4) ..
z 1377 1s. green (1867-73) 40 0
Plate Nos. 4, 5, 6, 7.
z 1378 1s. green (1873-77) 35 0
Plate Nos. 8, 9, 10, 11, 12.
z 1379 2s. blue (1867) .. .. ..
z 1379a 5s. rose (1867-74) (Plate No. 2)

AGUADILLA (PORTO RICO).

"**F84.**" *Obliteration or circular postmark as T* **8** *or* **17**.

1873 *to* **1877.**

z 1380 1d. rose-red (1864) 40 0
Plate Nos. 122, 156.
z 1381 2d. blue (1858-69) (Plate No. 14)
z 1382 3d. rose (1867-73) .. ..
Plate Nos. 8, 9.
z 1383 3d. rose (1873-76) (Plate No. 12)
z 1384 4d. vermilion (1865-73) 25 0
Plate Nos. 12, 13, 14.
z 1385 4d. verm. (1876) (Plate No. 15)
z 1386 6d. grey (1874-76) .. ..
Plate Nos. 13, 14.
z 1387 9d. straw (1867) .. .. ..
z 1388 10d. red-brown (1867) .. ..
z 1389 1s. green (1867-73) .. *From* 25 0
Plate Nos. 4, 5, 6, 7.
z 1390 1s. green (1873-77) .. *From* 25 0
Plate Nos. 8, 9, 10, 11, 12.
z 1390a 2s. blue .. ..

MAYAGUEZ (PORTO RICO).

"**F85.**" *Obliteration or circular postmark as T* **8** *or* **17**.

1873 *to* **1877.**

z 1391 ½d. rose-red (1870) .. *From* 40 0
Plate Nos. 4, 5, 6, 8, 10, 11.
z 1392 1d. rose-red (1864) 30 0
Plate Nos. 120, 122, 124, 134, 137, 140, 149, 150, 151, 154, 155, 156, 160, 167, 171, 174, 176, 178, 180, 182, 185, 186, 189.
z 1393 1½d. lake-red (1870-74) ..
Plate Nos. 1, 3.
z 1394 2d. blue (1858-69) 25 0
Plate Nos. 13, 14.
z 1395 3d. rose (1867-73) .. ..
Plate Nos. 7, 8, 9.
z 1396 3d. rose (1873-76) 25 0
Plate Nos. 11, 12, 14, 16, 17, 18, 19.
z 1397 4d. vermilion (1865-73) 20 0
Plate Nos. 11, 12, 13, 14.
z 1398 4d. verm. (1876) (Plate No. 15)
z 1398a 6d. mauve (1870) (Plate No. 9)
z 1399 6d. buff (1872) (Plate No. 11) ..
z 1400 6d. chestnut (1872) (Plate No. 11)
z 1401 6d. grey (1873) (Plate No. 12) ..
z 1402 6d. grey (1874-76) .. ..
Plate Nos. 13, 14, 15.
z 1403 8d. orange (1876) .. .. ..
z 1404 9d. straw (1867) .. .. ..
z 1405 10d. red-brown (1867) .. ..
z 1406 1s. green (1867-73) 25 0
Plate Nos. 4, 5, 6, 7.
z 1407 1s. green (1873-77) .. *From* 25 0
Plate Nos. 8, 9, 10, 11, 12.
z 1408 2s. blue (1867) .. .. ..
z 1409 5s. rose (1867-74) (Plate No. 2)

PONCE (PORTO RICO).

"**F88.**" *Obliteration or circular postmark as T* **8** *or* **17**.

1873 *to* **1877.**

z 1409a ½d. rose-red (1870) 40 0
Plate Nos. 5, 12.
z 1410 1d. rose-red (1864) .. *From* 25 0
Plate Nos. 121, 122, 123, 146 148, 156, 157, 158, 160, 167, 171, 174, 175, 187.
z 1411 1½d. lake-red (1870-74) .. ..
Plate No. 3.
z 1412 2d. blue (1858-69) .. ..
Plate Nos. 13, 14.
z 1413 3d. rose (1867-73) (Plate No. 9)
z 1414 3d. rose (1873-76) 35 0
Plate Nos. 17, 18, 19, 20.
z 1415 4d. vermilion (1865-73) .. *From* 15 0
Plate Nos. 8, 9, 12, 13, 14.
z 1416 4d. verm. (1876) (Plate No. 15)
z 1417 4d. sage-green (1877) .. ..
Plate Nos. 14, 16.
z 1418 6d. buff (1872-73) .. ..
Plate Nos. 11, 12.
z 1419 6d. chestnut (1872) (Plate No. 11) 37 6
z 1420 6d. grey (1873) (Plate No. 12) ..
z 1421 6d. grey (1874-76) .. *From* 27 6
Plate Nos. 13, 14, 15, 16, 17.
z 1422 10d. red-brown (1867) .. ..
z 1423 1s. green (1867-73) 40 0
Plate Nos. 6, 7.
z 1424 1s. green (1873-77) .. *From* 40 0
Plate Nos. 8, 9, 10, 11 12, 13.
z 1425 2s. blue (1867) .. .. ..
z 1426 5s. rose (1867-74) (Plate Nos. 1, 2)

NAGUABO (PORTO RICO).

"**582.**" *Obliteration as T* **9**.

1875 *to* **1877.**

z 1428 ½d. rose-red (1870-79) .. ..
Plate Nos. 12, 14.
z 1429 1d. rose-red (1864-79) .. ..
Plate No. 165.
z 1430 3d. rose (1873-76) (Plate No. 18).
z 1430a 4d. vermilion (1873-76) ..
Plate Nos. 14, 15.
z 1431 6d. grey (1874-76) (Plate No. 15)
z 1432 9d. straw (1867) .. .. ..
z 1432a 10d. red-brown (1867) .. ..
z 1432b 1s. green (Plate Nos. 11, 12) ..

V.

Miscellaneous.

FERNANDO POO.

"**247.**" *Obliteration as T* **9**.

1874 *to* **1877.**

z 1432c 4d. vermilion (1865-72) ..
Plate No. 14.
z 1432d 6d. grey (1874-76) .. ..
Plate Nos. 13, 14, 15, 16.

MAURITIUS.

"**B53.**" *Obliteration as T* **4**.

z 1526 1d. rose-red (1857) .. ..
z 1527 1d. rose-red (1864) .. ..
Plate Nos. 85, 153, 170, 187.
z 1527a 4d. verm. (1865) (Plate No. 10) ..
z 1527b 6d. lilac (1862) (Plate No. 3) ..
z 1528 6d. lilac (1867) (Plate No. 6) ..
z 1529 6d. violet (1867-70) 80 0
Plate Nos. 6, 8, 9.
z 1529a 6d. chestnut (1872)(Plate No. 11)
z 1530 1s. green (1865) (Plate No. 4) .. £5
z 1531 1s. green (1867) (Plate No. 4) ..

HONG KONG.

"**B62.**" *Obliteration as T* **4.**

18(?) to 1870.

z 1535 6d. lilac (1862) (Plate No. 3) ..
z 1536 6d. lilac (1865–67) .. ..
Plate Nos. 5, 6, 16.

SEYCHELLES.

"**B64.**" *Obliteration as T* **2.**

1858 to 1860.

z 1537 6d. lilac (1862) (Plate No. 3) ..

ASCENSION.

Circular postmarks of various sizes as *T* **16** or oval Registration postmark.

1867–1922.

z 1543 1d. red-brown (1855) ..
z 1543*a* 1d. rose-red (1864) .. ..
Plate Nos. 122, 138, 154, 155, 157, 160, 168.
z 1544–52*b* ½d., 1d., 1½d., 2d., 2½d., 3d., 4d., 5d., 6d., 9d., 1s. (1881–87) .. .. *From* 15 0
z 1553–*a* ½d., 1s. (1900) .. ..
z 1554–54*p* ½d., 1d., 1½d., 2d., 2½d., 3d., 4d., 5d., 6d., 7d., 9d., 10d., 1s., 2s. 6d., 5s., 10s., £1 (1902–11) .. .. *From* 15 0
z 1555 ½d. (No. 325) .. .. ..
z 1556 ½d. (No. 339) .. ..
z 1557–67*e* ½d., 1d., 1½d., 2d., 2½d., 3d., 4d., 5d., 6d., 7d., 8d., 9d., 10d., 1s., 2s. 6d., 5s., (1911–22) .. .. *From* 10 0

MAIL BOAT OBLITERATIONS.

For many years it was supposed that obliterations numbered A **80** to A **99**, B **03**, B **12**, B **56**, B **57** and C **79** were used at Naval Stations abroad (the whereabouts of which were not known), owing to the fact that they are almost invariably found on sailors' letters.

It has now been definitely established that these obliterations were allotted to mail boats and they are therefore omitted from this Catalogue.

VI.

ARMY FIELD OFFICES.

CRIMEA.

1854 to 1857.

Crown between Stars.

z 1569 1d. red-brown (1841), *imperf.* .. £6
z 1570 1d. red-brown (1854), Die I, *wmk.* Small Crown, *perf.* 16 .. 90 0
z 1571 1d. red-brown (1855), Die II, *wmk.* Small Crown, *perf.* 16 .. 90 0
z 1572 1d. red-brown (1855), Die II, Small Crown, *perf.* 14 ..
z 1572*a* 2d. blue, Small Crown, *perf.* 16 .. Plate No. 4 .. .. ..
z 1572*b* 1s. green (1847) .. .. ..

Star between Cyphers.

z 1573 1d. red-brown (1841), *imperf.* .. £22
z 1574 1d. red-brown (1854), Die I, *wmk.* Small Crown, *perf.* 16 .. 30 0
z 1575 1d. red-brown (1855), Die II, *wmk.* Small Crown, *perf.* 16 .. 30 0
z 1576 1d. red-brown (1855), Die I, *wmk.* Small Crown, *perf.* 14 .. 55 0
z 1577 1d. red-brown (1855), Die II, *wmk.* Small Crown, *perf.* 14 .. 35 0
z 1577*a* 1d. red-brown (1855), Die II, *wmk.* Large Crown, *perf.* 16 ..
z 1578 1d. red-brown (1855), Die II, *wmk.* Large Crown, *perf.* 14 .. 30 0
z 1579 2d. blue (1841), *imperf.* ..
z 1580 2d. blue (1854), *wmk.* Small Crown, *perf.* 16 .. .. .. £6
z 1581 2d. blue (1855), *wmk.* Small Crown, *perf.* 14 .. .. .. £7
z 1582 2d. blue (1855), *wmk.* Large Crown, *perf.* 16 .. .. .. £9
z 1583 2d. blue (1855), *wmk.* Large Crown, *perf.* 14 .. .. .. £5
z 1584 4d. rose (1857) .. .. ..
z 1585 6d. violet (1854) £30
z 1586 1s. green (1847) .. .. ..

EGYPT.

1882 to 1885.

z 1586*a* ½d. rose-red (Plate No. 20) ..
z 1586*b* ½d. green (1880) .. ..
z 1587 1d. lilac (1881) 85 0
z 1588 2½d. blue (1881) (Plate Nos. 22, 23) 65 0
z 1589 2½d. lilac (1884) 80 0
z 1589*a* 5d. green (1884) .. .. ..

SOUTH AFRICAN WAR.

1900 to 1902.

z 1590–1601*b* ½d., 1d., 1½d., 2d., 2½d., 3d., 4d., 4½d., 5d., 6d., 9d., 10d., 1s., 5s. (1881–92) *From* 4 0
z 1602–3 ½d., 1s. (1900) .. *From* 7 6

z 1604–15 ½d., 1d., 1½d., 2d., 2½d., 3d., 4d., 5d., 6d., 9d., 10d., 1s. (1902) .. *From* 6 6

Many types of postmark exist besides those shown

ARMY OFFICIAL.

z 1616 ½d. vermilion .. .. ..
z 1617 ½d. green .. ..
z 1618 1d. lilac .. ..
z 1619 6d. purple/*red* .. .. ..

VII.

Various Towns on the Niger Coast and River.

THE ROYAL NIGER COMPANY
CHARTERED & LIMITED.
7- AUG. 98
POST OFFICE
AKASSA.

THE ROYAL NIGER COMPANY,
CHARTERED & LIMITED.
4 NOV. 1889
POST OFFICE,
AKASSA.

AKASSA.

1895 *to* 1899.

z 1620 ½d. vermilion 12 6
z 1621 1d. lilac 6 6
z 1622 2d. green and vermilion .. ..
z 1623 2½d. purple/*blue* 8 6
z 1624 3d. purple/*yellow* 52 6
z 1625 4d. green and brown 42 6
z 1626 4½d. green and carmine 70 0
z 1627 5d. dull purple and blue .. 22 6
z 1628 6d. deep purple/*red* 52 6
z 1629 9d. dull purple and blue .. 65 0
z 1630 10d. dull purple and carmine .. 37 6
z 1631 2s. 6d. deep lilac 55 0

ABUTSHI.

1899.

z 1632 ½d. vermilion .. ..
z 1633 1d. lilac .. ..
z 1633*a* 2½d. purple/*blue* .. ..
z 1633*b* 5d. dull purple and blue ..
z 1633*c* 10d. dull purple and carmine ..
z 1633*d* 2s. 6d. deep lilac .. ..

BURUTU.

1897 *to* 1899.

z 1634 ½d. vermilion 8 6
z 1635 1d. lilac 4 6
z 1636 2d. green and vermilion .. ..
z 1637 2½d. purple/*blue* 6 6
z 1638 3d. purple/*yellow* .. .. ..
z 1639 4d. green and brown .. ..
z 1640 4½d. green and carmine .. ..
z 1641 5d. dull purple and blue .. 27 6
z 1642 6d. deep purple/*red* .. ..
z 1643 9d. dull purple and blue ..
z 1644 10d. dull purple and carmine .. 37 6
z 1645 2s. 6d. deep lilac 52 6

LOKOJA.

1899 *to* 1900.

z 1646 ½d. vermilion 35 0
z 1647 1d. lilac 25 0
z 1648 2½d. purple/*blue* 55 0
z 1649 5d. dull purple and blue ..
z 1649*a* 10d. dull purple and carmine ..

BONNY RIVER.

1892.

z 1649*b* 2½d. purple/*blue* (1887) .. ..
z 1650 6d. purple/*red* (1887) .. ..

FORCADOS RIVER.

1894.

z 1650*a* 1d. lilac .. .. ..
z 1651 5d. dull purple and blue (1887) .. .. ..
z 1652 10d. dull purple and carm. (1890) .. .. ..

OLD CALABAR.

z 1653 ½d. vermilion .. ..
z 1654 1d. lilac .. ..
z 1655 1½d. dull purple and green

ANTIGUA.

1

(Recess. Perkins Bacon & Co.)

3 (Die I)

(Typo. De La Rue & Co.)

T 1.

1862 (Aug.). *No watermark.* (*a*) *Rough perf* 14 *to* 16.

1 6d. blue-green £12 £9

(*b*) *P* 11 *to* 12.

2 6d. blue-green £125

(*c*) *P* 14 *to* 16×11 *to* 13.

3 6d. blue-green £55

Nos. 2 and 3 have not been found *used.*

1863 (Jan.)—**1867.** *Wmk. Small Star, T* w 2.

(*a*) *Rough perf.* 14 *to* 16.

5 1d. rosy mauve 32 6 17 6
6 1d. dull rose (1864) 35 0 17 6
7 1d. vermilion (1867) 32 6 16 0
a. Imperf. between (pair) ..

No.	Description	Unused		Used	
8	6d. green	70	0	32	6
8a	6d. dark green	60	0	20	0
9	6d. yellow-green	£50		40	0

(b) *Perf. compound of* 11, 12 *and* 14 *to* 16.

No.	Description	Unused	Used
9a	1d. rosy mauve		

This stamp is not known used.

Varieties. Imperf.

No.	Description	Unused	Used
10	1d. rosy mauve	—	£25
11	6d. green	—	£22
12	6d. yellow-green	—	£35

(Printed by Messrs. De La Rue & Co.)

Wmk. Crown CC.

1872. (a) *P* 12½.

No.	Description	Unused		Used	
13	1d. lake	20	0	15	0
14	1d. scarlet	70	0	25	0
15	6d. blue-green	£10		12	6

1876. (b) *P* 14.

No.	Description	Unused		Used	
16	1d. lake	27	6	12	6
	a. Bisected (½d.)	—		£6	
17	1d. lake-rose	27	6	12	6
18	6d. blue-green	70	0	15	0

1879. *T* **3.** *Wmk. Crown CC. P* 14

No.	Description	Unused		Used	
19	2½d. red-brown	£12		95	0
	a. "2" in "2½" with slanting foot	—		£30	
20	4d. blue	80	0	17	6

1882. *T* **3.** *Wmk. Crown CA. P* 14.

No.	Description	Unused		Used	
21	½d. dull green	3	0	3	6
22	2½d. red-brown	55	0	22	6
	a. "2" in "2½" with slanting foot	£25		£16	
23	4d. blue	70	0	15	0

1884. *T* **1.** *Wmk. Crown CA. P* 12.

No.	Description	Unused		Used	
24	1d. carmine-red	22	6	8	0

The 1d. scarlet is a colour changeling.

1884–86. *T* **1** (*1d. and 6d.*) *and* **3.** *Wmk. Crown CA. P* 14.

No.	Description	Unused		Used	
25	1d. carmine-red	2	6	3	0
26	1d. rose	17	6	7	6
27	2½d. ultramarine	8	0	9	0
	a. "2" in "2½" with slanting foot	40	0	45	0
28	4d. chestnut	5	0	6	0
29	6d. deep green	27	6	30	0
30	1s. mauve	90	0	95	0

Most of the 1d. and 6d. stamps are perforated by a line machine, but we have had blocks of both values perforated by a comb machine of the same gauge.

The variety No. 27a is the 1st stamp of the 3rd and 7th rows of the sheet.

The stamps for Antigua were temporarily superseded by the general issue for Leeward Islands on 31st October, 1890, but the stamps following were or are in concurrent use with the stamps inscribed "LEEWARD ISLANDS."

4 5

(Typo. De La Rue & Co.)

1903–9. *T* **4** *and* **5** (5s.). *Wmk. Crown CC. P* 14.

No.	Description	Unused		Used	
31	½d. grey-black & grey-grn., O	2	0	2	6
32	1d. grey-black & rose-red., O	3	6	2	6
	a. Blue paper (1903)	55	0	60	0
33	2d. dull purple & brown, O ..	8	6	10	0
34	2½d. grey-black & blue, OC ..	10	6	12	0
35	3d. grey-grn. & orange-brn., O	10	6	12	6
36	6d. purple and black, O ..	22	6	22	6
37	1s. blue and dull purple, OC	30	0	30	0
38	2s. grey-grn. & pale violet, O	35	0	40	0
39	2s. 6d. grey-black & pur., O	30	0	32	6
40	5s. grey-green and vio., OC ..	75	0	80	0

1908–12. *T* **4.** *Wmk. Mult. Crown CA. P* 14.

No.	Description	Unused		Used	
42	½d. green, O	3	0	3	0
43	1d. red, O	3	0	3	0
43a	2d. dull pur. & brn., C (1912)	5	0	6	0
44	2½d. ultramarine, O	10	6	12	6
44a	2½d. blue, O	7	6	8	6
45	3d. grey-green and orange-brown, C (1912) ..	7	6	8	6
46	6d. purple & blk., C (1911)	10	6	12	6
47	1s. blue and dull purple, C ..	10	6	10	6
48	2s. grey-grn. & vio., C (1912)	60	0	60	0

1913. *As T* **5,** *but portrait of King George V. Wmk. Mult. Crown CA. P* 14.

No.	Description	Unused		Used	
49	5s. grey-green & violet, C ..	60	0	60	0

1915–17. *T* **4.** *Colour changed. Wmk. Mult. Crown CA. P* 14.

No.	Description	Unused		Used	
50	½d. blue-green O (1917) ..	1	6	1	9
51	1d. scarlet O (5.8.15)	2	6	3	0

WAR STAMP

(7)

1916 (Sept.). *No.* 42 *overprinted in London with T* **7.** (a) *In black.*

No.	Description	Unused		Used	
52	½d. deep green	0	4	0	6

(b) *In red* (1 Oct., 1917).

No.	Description	Unused		Used	
53	½d. deep green	0	4	0	6

1918. *T* **4,** *overprinted with T* **7,** *in black. Wmk. Mult. Crown CA. P* 14.

No.	Description	Unused		Used	
54	1½d. orange	1	0	1	0

8

(Typo. De La Rue & Co.)

1921–29. *T* **8.** *P* 14.

(a) *Wmk. Mult. Crown CA.*

No.	Description	Unused		Used	
55	3d. purple/*pale yellow*, C ..	3	6	4	0
56	4d. grey-black and red/*pale yellow*, C (Jan., '22) ..	5	0	6	0
57	1s. black/*emerald*, C	10	0	10	6
58	2s. purple and blue/*blue*, C ..	20	0	25	0
59	2s. 6d. black and red/*blue*, C ..	20	0	22	6
60	5s. green and red/*pale yellow*, C (Jan., '22)	40	0	45	0
61	£1 purple & black/*red*, C ('22)	£10		£12	

(b) *Wmk. Mult. Script CA.*

No.	Description	Unused		Used	
62	½d. dull green, O	0	4	0	4
63	1d. carmine-red, O	2	0	1	0
64	1d. bright scarlet, O ('29) ..	0	6	0	6
65	1d. bright violet, O	3	0	0	6
66	1d. mauve, O	1	3	1	3
67	1½d. dull orange, O ('22) ..	8	0	9	0
68	1½d. carmine-red, O ('26) ..	1	3	1	3
69	1½d. pale red-brown, O ('29)	1	0	1	0
70	2d. grey, O	1	3	1	6
71	2½d. bright blue, O	7	0	8	0
72	2½d. ultramarine, O ('27) ..	2	0	2	6
73	2½d. orange-yellow, O	2	6	3	6
74	3d. purple/*pale yellow*, C ('25)	2	3	2	6
75	6d. dull and bright purple, C	3	6	4	0
76	1s. black/*emerald*, C ('29) ..	8	0	8	6
77	2s. pur. & blue/*blue*, C ('27) ..	22	6	25	0

78	2s. 6d. blk. & red/*blue*, C ('27)	20	0	22	6
79	3s. green and violet, C ('22)..	27	6	30	0
80	4s. grey-black & red, C ('22)..	35	0	38	0

9. Old Dockyard, English Harbour.   **12.** Sir Thomas Warner's vessel.

10. Government House, St. John's.

11. Nelson's *Victory*

(Des. and recess Waterlow & Sons, except 5s. des. by Mrs. J. Goodwin.)

1932 (27 JAN.). *Tercentenary issue. Dated* 1632–1932. *Wmk. Mult. Script CA. P* 12½.

81	**9**	½d. green	2	6	3	0
82	,,	1d. scarlet	3	0	3	6
83	,,	1½d. brown	8	0	10	0
84	**10**	2d. grey	16	0	17	6
85	,,	2½d. deep blue	17	6	20	0
86	,,	3d. orange	22	6	25	0
87	**11**	6d. violet	25	0	27	6
88	,,	1s. olive-green	45	0	50	0
89	,,	2s. 6d. claret	£5		£6	
90	**12**	5s. black and chocolate ..	£18		£20	

13

(Recess. De La Rue & Co.)

1935 (6 MAY). *Silver Jubilee. Wmk. Mult. Script CA. P* 13½ × 14.

91	**13**	1d. deep blue and carmine	0	8	0	10
92	,,	1½d. ultramarine and grey ..	1	3	1	6
93	,,	2½d. brown and deep blue ..	9	0	10	0
94	,,	1s. slate and purple ..	18	0	20	0

ASCENSION.

ASCENSION

(1)

1922. *T* **14** *and* **15** *of St. Helena, optd. with T* **1**.

(*a*) *Wmk. Mult. Script CA.*

	½d. black and green	2	0	2	6
	1d. green	6	0	7	6
3	1½d rose-scarlet	10	0	10	6
4	2d. black and grey	12	0	12	6
5	3d. bright blue	15	0	16	0
6	8d. black and dull purple ..	35	0	40	0
7	2s. black and blue/*blue* ..	60	0	70	0
8	3s. black and violet	80	0	£5	

(*b*) *Wmk. Mult. Crown CA*

9	1s. black/*green* (R.)	30	0	32	

2. Badge of St. Helena.

(Typo. De La Rue & Co.)

1924–33. *T* **2.** *Wmk. Mult. Script CA. P* 14.

10	½d. grey-black and black, C ..	2	0	2	6
11	1d. grey-blk. & dp. bl.-grn., C	2	6	4	0
11*a*	1d. grey-black & bright blue-green, C ('33)	10	6	12	6
12	1½d. rose-red, C	4	0	4	6
13	2d. grey-black and grey, C ..	4	6	5	0
14	3d. blue, C	6	0	6	0
15	4d. grey-blk. & blk./*yellow*, C	25	0	27	6
15*a*	5d. purple & olive-green, C ..	8	0	10	0
16	6d. grey-blk. & bright pur., C	90	0	£6	
17	8d. grey-blk. & bright vio., C	10	6	12	0
18	1s. grey-black and brown, C	20	0	22	6
19	2s. grey-black & blue/*blue*, C	35	0	40	0
20	3s. grey-blk. & blk./*blue*, C ..	70	0	80	0

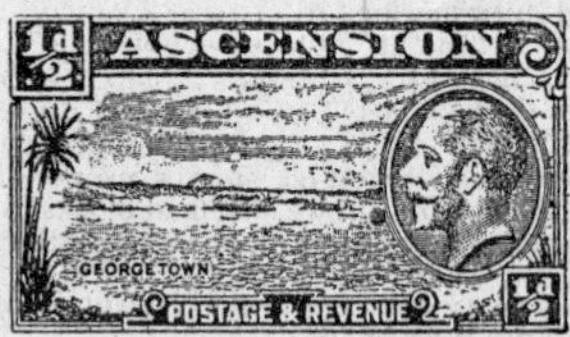

3. Georgetown.

4. Ascension Island.

5. The Pier.

6. Long Beach.

7. Three Sisters.

8. Sooty Tern and Wideawake Fair.

9. Green Mountain.

T **5** *to* **9** *are same size as T* **3**.

(Des. and recess. De La Rue & Co.)

1934 (2 JULY). *Wmk. Mult. Script CA. P* 14.

21	**3**	½d. black and violet ..	0	4	0	8
22	**4**	1d. black and emerald ..	0	9	0	10
23	**5**	1½d. black and scarlet ..	1	0	1	3
24	**4**	2d. black and orange ..	1	3	1	6

25	6	3d. black and ultramarine	1	6	2	0
26	7	5d. black and blue	4	0	5	0
27	4	8d. black and sepia ..	6	0	7	6
28	8	1s. black and carmine ..	12	6	15	0
29	4	2s. 6d. black & bright pur.	22	6	25	0
30	9	5s. black and brown ..	35	0	37	6

1935 (6 May). *Silver Jubilee. As T* **13** *of Antigua, inscr.* " ASCENSION ". *Recess. W'low & Sons. Wmk. Mult. Script CA. P* 11×12.

31	1½d. deep blue and scarlet ..	6	0	6	6
32	2d. ultramarine and grey ..	10	0	12	0
33	5d. green and indigo	25	0	27	6
34	1s. slate and purple	85	0	90	0

AUSTRALIA.

1

2

(Des. B. Young. Typo. Govt. Stamp Printing Office, Melbourne, by J. B. Cooke.)

1913 (Jan.). *T* **1**. *W* **2**. *P* 12.

1	½d. green	0	8	0	3
2	1d. red	0	6	0	1
	a. Wmk. sideways	90	0	45	0
2b	1d. carmine	0	8	0	1
3	2d. grey	6	0	0	8
4	2½d. indigo	6	0	1	0
5	3d. olive (Feb.)	7	0	1	0
5a	3d. yellow-olive	10	0	1	3
6	4d. orange (Feb.)	20	0	4	0
7	4d. orange-yellow	20	0	12	0
8	5d. chestnut	15	0	7	6
9	6d. ultramarine	8	6	1	6
10	9d. violet (Feb.)	20	0	5	0
11	1s. emerald	22	6	1	6
11a	1s. blue-green	22	6	2	0
12	2s. brown	37	6	15	0
	a. Double print ..				
13	5s. grey and yellow (Mar.) ..	90	0	50	0
14	10s. grey and pink (Mar.) ..	£6		50	0
15	£1 brown and blue (Mar.) ..	£16		£9	
16	£2 black and rose (April) ..	£26		£15	

Inverted watermarks are met with in some values in this and subsequent issues.

3

4. Kookaburra

(Recess. T. S. Harrison, Melbourne.)

1913 (Dec.)–**1914**. *T* **3** *and* **4**. *No wmk. P* 11.

17	1d. red (Dec., 1913)	2	0	1	9
	a. Imperf. between (pair) ..	£20			
18	1d. pale rose-red	2	0	2	0
	a. Imperf. between (pair) ..	£20			
19	6d. claret (Aug., 1914) ..	20	0	20	0

printings from Plate 1 were in the shade . 18.

5

1914–15. *T* **1**. *W* **5**. *P* 12.

20	2d. grey	10	6	1	3
21	2½d. indigo (1915)	10	6	4	0
23	6d. ultramarine (1915) ..	17	6	4	0
23a	6d. bright blue (1915) ..	37	6	20	0
24	9d. violet (1915)	25	0	5	0
25	1s. blue-green (1915) ..	25	0	3	6
26	2s. brown (Aug., 1915) ..	55	0	17	6
27	5s. grey and yellow (1915) ..	90	0	37	6
	a. Yellow portion doubly printed	—		£25	

The watermark in this issue is often misplaced as the paper was intended to be used for stamps of the Georgian type.

Die II

5a

Die III

(Dies engraved by Messrs. Perkins Bacon & Co. Stamps typographed by J. B. Cooke until 1918, then by T. S. Harrison, Commonwealth Stamp Printers, Melbourne.)

1914–21. *T* **5a**. *W* **5**. *P* 14.

29	½d. bright green (Jan., 1915)	0	8	0	2
29a	½d. yellow-green	0	9	0	2
29b	½d. green (1916)	0	8	0	2
	c. Fraction at right thinner ..	£20		£20	
30	1d. carm.-red (I) (July 1914)	0	8	0	2
	a. Top of crown missing ..	55	0	25	0
31	1d. pale carmine (I)	0	6	0	1
31a	1d. carm.-pink (I) (Jan., '18)	22	6	6	6
31b	1d. rose-red (I) (Mar., '18) ..	12	6	5	0
31c	1d. carm. (aniline) (I) (1921)	6	6	4	6
31d	1d. carmine-red (II)	20	0	4	6
	e. Top of crown missing ..	60	0	25	0
32	4d. orange (Jan., 1915) ..	6	0	1	3
33	4d. yellow-orange	7	6	2	0
33a	4d. pale orange-yellow ..	20	0	8	6
33b	4d. lemon-yellow (1916) ..	17	6	8	0
33c	4d. dull orange	12	0	2	0
	d. Line through "FOUR PENCE" (all shades) .. *From*	65	0	30	0
34	5d. brown (Feb., 1915) ..	9	0	1	9
34a	5d. yellow-brown (1920) ..	10	6	3	0

The variety No. 29c was caused by the insertion of a new fraction in a defective electro.

Of the two Dies of the 1d., Die II was intended for stamped stationery. A number of clichés made from it were, however, inserted in certain of the plates used for postage stamps. It may be distinguished from Die I by the white upward projection to right of base of figure " 1 " in the shield containing value at left as shown in the illustration.

The varieties 30a and 31e are from two clichés

one from each die, which were inserted in one plate in replacement of two damaged clichés.

The 5d. is known printed on the gummed side of the paper.

Two separate machines were used for the 14 perforation, one an old single line, converted to that gauge, the other a new comb-machine. The former was used only for early printings of the 1d. and 5d.

6

(Typographed by J. B. Cooke, T. S. Harrison, A. J. Mullett, or J. Ash.)

1915–28. *T* **1.** *W* **6** (*narrow Crown*). *P* 12

No.	Description	Unused	Used
35	2d. grey	5 0	0 3
35*a*	2d. silver-grey (*shiny paper*)	5 6	0 5
36	2½d. indigo	6 0	0 6
	a. "1" of fraction omitted ..	£35	£30
36*b*	2½d. deep blue (1921).. ..	6 0	0 9
37	3d. yellow-olive	6 6	0 6
37*a*	3d. olive-green (1917) ..	6 0	0 6
38	6d. ultramarine	10 0	0 8
38*a*	6d. dull blue	10 6	1 9
38*b*	6d. bright ultramarine (1922)	7 6	0 6
	c. Leg of Kangaroo broken ..	£5	85 0
39	9d. violet (1916)	10 6	1 6
39*a*	9d. bright violet	8 6	1 0
40	1s. blue-green (1916) ..	6 6	1 0
	a. Watermark sideways (1927)..	25 0	25 0
41	2s. brown (1916)	20 0	2 6
	a. Imperf. three sides	£50	
41*b*	2s. red-brown	30 0	6 0
42	5s. grey and yellow (1916) ..	40 0	15 0
42*a*	5s. grey and orange (1920)	40 0	10 6
42*b*	5s. grey & pale yellow (1928)	35 0	10 6
42*c*	5s. grey and deep yellow ..	42 6	15 0
43	10s. grey and pink (1917) ..	95 0	35 0
43*a*	10s. grey & bt. aniline pink	85 0	30 0
43*b*	10s. grey & p. anil. pink ('28)	85 0	30 0
44	£1 choc. & dull blue (1916) ..	£15	75 0
45	£1 chestnut and brt. blue (17)	£17	£8
45*a*	£1 bistre-brn. & bright blue	£10	75 0
46	£2 grey and crimson (1920)	£15	£8
46*a*	£2 black and rose	£15	£8
46*b*	£2 pur.-blk. & pale rose (1924)	£15	£8

Two dies exist in some values, but the differences are not very marked. The 5s., 10s., and £1 are known with watermark sideways.

1916–18. *T* **5a.** *W* **5.** *Rough paper, locally gummed.* *P* 14.

No.	Description	Unused	Used
47	1d. scarlet (I) (Dec., 1916) ..	4 0	1 6
48	1d. deep red (I)	3 0	1 0
49	1d. rose-red (I) (1918) ..	4 0	1 6
	a. Top of crown missing	35 0	10 6
49*b*	1d. rosine (I)	22 6	10 0
50	1d. rose-red (II)	30 0	5 0
50*a*	1d. rosine (II)	70 0	35 0
50*b*	5d. bright chestnut (Perf. "O.S.") (1918)	£15	30 0

1918 (June). *T* **5a,** *printed from a new plate* (Die III) *on white unsurfaced paper, locally gummed.* *W* **5.** *P* 14.

No.	Description	Unused	Used
50*c*	1d. rose-red (III)	4 0	4 0
50*d*	1d. rose-carmine (III) ..	3 0	2 0
	e. Printed both sides	£12	

Die III. In 1918 a printing (in sheets of 120) was made on paper prepared for printing War Savings Stamps, with wmk. T **5.** A special plate was made for this printing, differing in detail from those previously used. The shading round the head is even; the solid background of the words "ONE PENNY" is bounded at each end by a *white* vertical line; and there is a horizontal white line cutting the vertical shading lines at left on the King's neck.

6*a*

(Typographed by J. B. Cooke or T. S. Harrison.)

1918–19. *T* **5a.** *W* **6a** (*Mult.*). *P* 14.

No.	Description	Unused	Used
51	½d. green (*shades*)	0 6	0 1
	a. Fraction at right thinner ..	25 0	10 6
51*b*	1d. carmine-pink (I)	22 6	12 6
52	1d. deep red (I)	85 0	65 0
53	1d. carmine (I) (Dec., 1919) ..	2 0	1 3
54	1½d. black-brown (Jan., 1919)	1 9	0 6
	a. Very thin paper (March, 1919).	7 6	3 6
55	1½d. red-brown (April, 1919) ..	1 9	0 4
56	1½d. chocolate	2 6	0 6

Of the above, No. 51 was printed by Cooke and by Harrison, Nos. 51*b* and 52 by Cooke, and Nos. 53 to 56 by Harrison. Nos. 51*b* and 52 have rather yellowish gum, that of No. 53 being pure white.

1918 (Nov.)–**1919.** *T* **5a.** *W* **5.** *P* 14.

No.	Description	Unused	Used
57	1½d. black-brown (Nov., 1918)	1 6	0 4
58	1½d. red-brown (June, 1919)..	2 6	0 4
59	1½d. chocolate	2 0	0 4

1920–23. *T* **5a.** *W* **5.** *P* 14.

No.	Description	Unused	Used
60	1½d. bright red-brown (1922) ..	4 0	1 0
61	2d. dull orange (Sept., 1920)	4 0	0 2
62	2d. brown-orange	5 0	0 2
63	4d. violet (June, 1921) ..	5 0	1 3
	a. Line through "FOUR PENCE"	£30	£22
	b. "FOUR PENCE" in thinner letters	£6	55 0
64	1s. 4d. pale blue (Dec., 1920)	12 6	7 6
65	1s. 4d. dull greenish blue (1923)	15 0	6 6
65*a*	1s. 4d. bright turquoise ..	£7	80 0

1922–23. *T* **5a.** *Colours changed.* *W* **5.** *P* 14.

No.	Description	Unused	Used
66	½d. orange (Nov., 1923) ..	0 8	0 3
67	1d. violet (*shades*)	1 9	0 3
	a. Imperf. three sides	£30	
68	1d. red-violet	1 9	0 4
69	1½d. green (Mar., 1923) ..	1 9	0 3
70	2d. bright rose-scarlet ..	1 9	0 2
71	2d. dull rose-scarlet	1 9	0 2
72	4d. ultramarine	6 6	1 0
	a. "FOUR PENCE" in thinner letters	65 0	35 0

The variety of Nos. 63 and 72 with "FOUR PENCE" thinner, was caused by the correction of a defective cliché (No. 6, 2nd row, right-hand pane), which showed a line running through these words.

(Typographed by T. S. Harrison or A. J. Mullett.)

1923–24. *T* **1.** *W* **6.** *P* 12.

No.	Description	Unused	Used
73	6d. chestnut (Dec., 1923) ..	3 6	0 8
	a. Leg of Kangaroo broken ..	25 0	25 0
74	2s. marone (May, 1924) ..	10 6	2 6
75	£1 grey (May, 1924)	90 0	60 0

1924. *T* **5a.** *P* 14. (*a*) *W* **5.**

No.	Description	Unused	Used
76	1d. sage-green	0 8	0 1
77	1½d. scarlet (*shades*)	0 6	0 1
	a. Very thin paper	15 0	10 0
	b. "HALEPENCE"	6 0	6 0
	c. "RAL" of "AUSTRALIA" thin	5 0	5 0
	d. Curved "1" and thin fraction at left	5 0	5 0
78	2d. red-brown	2 6	0 8
78*a*	2d. bright red-brn. (*aniline*)	6 0	1 6
79	3d. dull ultramarine	3 6	0 2
80	4d. olive-yellow	6 6	1 9
81	4½d. violet	8 0	1 9

(*b*) *W* **6a.**

No.	Description	Unused	Used
82	1d. sage-green	1 3	0 10

(*c*) *No wmk.*

No.	Description	Unused	Used
83	1d. sage-green	1 3	1 0
84	1½d. scarlet	2 0	1 3

In the thin semi-transparent paper of Nos. 54*a* and 77*a* the watermark is almost indistinguishable Nos. 77*b*, 77*c*, and 77*d* are due to retouching. In No. 77*c* the letters "RAL" differ markedly from the normal. There is a white stroke cutting the oval frame-line above the "L", and the right-hand outer line of the Crown does not cut the white frame-line above the "A". No. 77*b* is immediately above No. 77*c* in the sheet, so that the varieties may be had *se-tenant*.

I.

II.

(Typographed by A. J. Mullett or J. Ash.)

1926–30. *T* **5a.** *W* **7.** (*a*) *P* 14.

No.	Description	Unused	Used
85	½d. orange	0 8	0 8
86	1d. sage-green	0 8	0 1
87	1½d. scarlet	0 8	0 1
88	1½d. golden scarlet	1 3	0 1
89	2d. red-brown	6 6	1 6
90	3d. dull ultramarine	3 6	0 9
91	4d. yellow-olive	4 6	1 3
92	4½d. violet	6 0	1 0
93	1s. 4d. pale greenish blue	12 6	10 0

(*b*) *P* 13½ × 12½.

No.	Description	Unused	Used
94	½d. orange	0 6	0 2
95	1d. sage-green (Die I)	0 6	0 1
96	1d. sage-green (Die II)	6 6	4 0
97	1½d. scarlet	0 8	0 1
98	1½d. golden scarlet	0 8	0 2
98*a*	1½d. red-brown (16.9.30)	1 0	0 8
99	2d. red-brown	2 6	0 10
99*a*	2d. golden scarlet (Die I)	1 0	0 1
99*b*	2d. golden scarlet (Die II)	1 0	0 1
	e. No. wmk.	£8	
100	3d. dull ultramarine (Die I)	2 6	0 2
101	3d. deep ultram. (Die II)	2 6	0 2
102	4d. yellow-olive	4 0	0 4
103	4½d. violet	6 6	1 0
103*a*	5d. orange-brown ('30)	4 6	0 10
104	1s. 4d. turquoise	10 0	3 6

Dies I and II.

1d. For the differences between Dies I and II of this value, see note after No. 34*a*.

2d. *a.* Height of frame. D I, 25.6 mm. D II, 25.1 mm. *b.* The lettering and figures of value in Die I are not so bold as in Die II.

3d. Die II has bolder letters and figures than Die I, as shown in illustrations above.

5d. Nos. 103*a* and 130 are from a new die having a broader figure "5" with flat top. Nos. 34, 34*a*, and 50*b* are from the old die.

The 1½d. with watermark T **7** is from steel plates made from a new die. Nos. 88 and 98 are the Ash printings, the ink of which is shiny.

Owing to defective manufacture, part of a sheet of the 2d. (Die II) escaped unwatermarked; while the watermark in other parts of the same sheet was faint or normal.

8. Parliament House, Canberra.

(Des. R. A. Harrison. Die eng. by Waterlow & Sons. Plates and printing by J. Ash.)

1927 (9 May). *Opening of Parliament House Canberra.* *T* **8.** *No wmk.* *P* 11.

No.	Description	Unused	Used
105	1½d. brownish lake	1 0	0 4
	a. Imperf. between (vert. pair)	£25	

1928 (29 Oct.). *Melbourne Philatelic Exhibition As T* **4.** *No wmk.* *P* 11.

No.	Description	Unused	Used
106	3d. blue	4 6	4 6

Special sheets of 60 stamps, divided into 15 blocks of 4 (5 × 3) and separated by wide gutters perforated down the middle, were printed and sold at the Exhibition. Block of 4, *unused*, 17s. 6d.

(Typographed by J. Ash.)

1929–30. *T* **1.** *W* **7.** *P* 12.

No.	Description	Unused	Used
107	6d. chestnut	4 0	0 6
108	9d. violet	8 0	0 8
109	1s. blue-green	8 6	0 6
110	2s. marone	12 6	0 10
111	5s. grey and yellow	40 0	15 0
112	10s. grey and pink	85 0	45 0
114	£2 black and rose ('30)	£12	£9

9

(Designed by R. A. Harrison and H. Herbert. Recess-printed by J. Ash.)

1929 (20 May). *Air stamp.* *T* **9.** *No wmk.* *P* 11.

No.	Description	Unused	Used
115	3d. green	2 0	1 6

10

(Des. by Pitt Morrison. Recess. J. Ash.)

1929 (28 Sept.). *Centenary of Western Australia. T* **10.** *No wmk. P* 11.

116	1½d. dull scarlet	1	6	0	6
	a. Re-entry ("T" of "AUSTRALIA" clearly double)	50	0	50	0

11. Capt. Chas. Sturt.

(Recess-printed by John Ash.)

1930 (2 June). *Centenary of Exploration of the River Murray by Capt. Sturt. T* **11.** *No wmk. P* 11.

117	1½d. scarlet	1	6	0	8
118	3d. blue	4	6	2	6

No. 117 with manuscript overprint "2d. paid P M L H I" was issued by the Postmaster of Lord Howe Island during a shortage of 2d. stamps. This provisional is not recognised by the Australian postal authorities.

TWO

PENCE

(12)

1930 (1 Aug.). *T* **5a** *surch. as T* **12.** *W* **7.** *P* 13½ × 12½.

119	2d. on 1½d. golden scarlet ..	1	0	0	4
120	5d. on 4½d. violet	5	0	2	0

No. 120 is from a redrawn die in which the words "FOURPENCE HALFPENNY" are noticeably thicker than in the original die and the figure "4" has square instead of tapering ends.

Stamps from the redrawn die without the surcharge were printed but not issued thus. A few stamps, *cancelled to order*, were included in sets supplied by the post office.

13. The 'Southern Cross" above hemispheres.
ecess-printed by John Ash.)

1931 (19 Mar.). *Kingsford Smith's flights. No wmk. P* 11.

(*a*) *Postage stamps. Inscribed* "POSTAGE" *at each side.*

121	**13**	2d. rose-red	1	6	0	4
122	,,	3d. blue	3	0	1	9

(*b*) *Air stamp. Inscribed* "AIR MAIL SERVICE" *at sides.*

123	**13**	6d. violet	6	6	6	6
		a. Re-entry ("FO" of "KINGSFORD" and "LD" of "WORLD" double) ..	50	0	50	0

15

(Typographed by John Ash.)

1931–36. *W* **15.**

(*a*) *T* **5a.** *P* 13½ × 12½.

124	½d. orange	0	4	0	4
125	1d. green (Die I)	0	6	0	1
126	1½d. red-brown ('36)	2	6	2	6
127	2d. golden scarlet (Die II) ..	1	0	0	1
128	3d. ultramarine (Die II) ..	1	9	0	9
129	4d. yellow-olive	2	0	0	9
130	5d. orange-brown	2	0	0	9
131	1s. 4d. turquoise	6	6	2	6

(*b*) *T* **1.** *P* 12.

132	6d. chestnut	3	0	2	6
133	9d. violet	4	0	0	4
134	2s. marone ('35)	6	0	1	9
135	5s. grey and yellow	30	0	10	0
136	10s. grey and pink	50	0	20	0
137	£1 grey ('35)	95	0	45	0
138	£2 black and rose ('34) ..	£8		90	0

For re-engraved type of No. 134, see No. 212 in King George VI Catalogue.

(Recess-printed by John Ash.)

1931 (4 Nov.). *Air stamp. As T* **13** *but inscr.* "AIR MAIL SERVICE" *in bottom tablet. No wmk. P* 11.

139	6d. sepia	3	0	3	0

17. Lyre-bird.

(Recess-printed by John Ash.)

1932 (15 Feb.). *T* **17.** *No wmk. P* 11.

140	1s. green	3	6	0	4

18. Sydney Harbour Bridge.
(Printed by John Ash.)

1932 (14 MAR.). *T* **18.**

(*a*) *Recess-printed. No wmk. P* 11

141	2d. scarlet	1 3	0 4
142	3d. blue	2 0	1 3
143	5s. blue-green	£8	£7

(*b*) *Typographed. W* **15.** *P* $10\frac{1}{2} \times 11$.

144	2d. scarlet	1 0	0 2

19. Kookaburra.

(Typographed by John Ash.)

1932 (1 JUNE). *T* **19.** *W* **15.** *P* $13\frac{1}{2} \times 12\frac{1}{2}$.

146	6d. red-brown	1 9	0 2

20. Melbourne and R. Yarra.

1934 (2 JULY). *Centenary of Victoria.* *W* **15.**

			I. P $10\frac{1}{2}$.		II. P $11\frac{1}{2}$.	
147	**20**	2d. orange-vermil.	1 3	1 0	1 6	0 4
148	,,	3d. blue ..	2 0	1 0	2 6	1 6
149	,,	1s. black ..	10 0	9 0	10 0	10 0

21. Merino Sheep.

1934 (1 NOV.). *MacArthur Centenary.* *W* **15.** *P* $11\frac{1}{2}$.

150	**21**	2d. carmine-red	1 0	0 1
151	,,	3d. blue	3 6	1 6
152	,,	9d. bright purple	15 0	15 0

There are two distinct types of the 2d., in one of which the hill in the background shows shading varying from light to dark (as in our illustration) while in the other the shading is almost uniformly dark. The latter is understood to be due to a reworking of the original die and the making of more deeply engraved plates from it.

22. Hermes.

1934 (1 DEC.). *No wmk. P* 11.

153	**22**	1s. 6d. dull purple ..	3 0	1 0

For similar stamp with wmk., p. $13\frac{1}{2} \times 14$, see No. 153*a* in King George VI Catalogue.

23. Cenotaph, Whitehall. **24.** King George V on "Anzac."

935 (18 MAR.). *20th Anniv. of "Anzac" landing at Gallipoli.* *W* **15.** *P* $13\frac{1}{2} \times 12\frac{1}{2}$ *or* 11 (1s.).

154	**23**	2d. scarlet	1 0	0 2
155	,,	1s. black (*chalk-surfaced*) ..	15 0	15 0

1935 (2 MAY). *Silver Jubilee. Chalk-surfaced paper.* *W* **15.** *P* $11\frac{1}{2}$.

156	**24**	2d. scarlet	0 5	0 2
157	,,	3d. blue	3 0	2 6
158	,,	2s. bright violet	22 6	22 6

25. Amphitrite and Telephone Cable.

1936 (1 APR.). *Opening of Submarine Telephone Communication to Tasmania.* *W* **15.** *P* $11\frac{1}{2}$.

159	**25**	2d. scarlet	0 6	0 2
160	,,	3d. blue	2 0	1 3

26. Site of Adelaide, 1836; Old Gum Tree, Glenelg; King William St., Adelaide.

1936 (3 AUG.). *Centenary of South Australia* *W* **15.** *P* $11\frac{1}{2}$.

161	**26**	2d. carmine	0 6	0 1
162	,,	3d. blue	2 0	1 0
163	,,	1s. green	8 6	6 6

POSTAGE DUE STAMPS.

D 1

D 2

(Ptd. at Govt. Printing Office, Sydney.)

1902. *Type* D **1**, *design of the similar stamps of New South Wales* (*T* **120**), *with the letters at foot removed. Chalk-surfaced paper. Wmk.* D **2**.

(*a*) *P* 11½, 12.

D 1	½d. emerald-green	1 3	1 6
D 2	1d. emerald-green	1 9	1 6
D 3	2d. emerald-green	1 9	1 9
D 4	3d. emerald-green	1 9	1 9
D 5	4d. emerald-green	2 0	1 9
D 6	6d. emerald-green	2 0	1 9
D 7	8d. emerald-green	4 6	4 0
D 8	5s. emerald-green	17 6	12 6

(*b*) *P* 11½, 12, *compound with* 11.

D 9	1d. emerald-green	6 0	3 0
D 10	2d. emerald-green	7 6	6 0
D 11	4d. emerald-green	80 0	80 0

(*c*) *P* 11.

D 12	1d. emerald-green	27 6	16 6

Stamps may be found showing portions of the letters " N S W " at foot.

D 3

D 4

1902–04. *Type* D **3**, *space at foot filled in. Chalky paper. Wmk.* D **2**. (*a*) *P* 11½, 12.

D 13	1d. emerald-green	12 6	4 0
D 14	2d. emerald-green	15 0	5 0
D 15	3d. emerald-green	25 0	5 0
D 16	4d. emerald-green		
D 17	5d. emerald-green	1 6	1 6
D 18	10d. emerald-green	3 6	2 0
D 19	1s. emerald-green	3 0	1 0
D 20	2s. emerald-green	6 0	2 0
D 21	5s. emerald-green	110 0	30 0

(*b*) *P* 11½, 12, *compound with* 11.

D 22	½d. emerald-green	1 6	0 6
D 23	1d. emerald-green	0 9	0 2
D 24	2d. emerald-green	1 6	0 4
D 25	3d. emerald-green	2 0	0 6
D 26	4d. emerald-green	3 0	0 9
D 27	5d. emerald-green	3 0	1 3
D 28	6d. emerald-green	2 6	2 6
D 29	8d. emerald-green	4 0	1 9
D 30	10d. emerald-green	5 0	2 6
D 31	1s. emerald-green ..	5 0	2 6
D 32	2s. emerald-green	17 6	5 0
D 33	5s. emerald-green	15 0	1 6

(*c*) *P* 11.

D 34	½d. emerald-green	15 0	7 6
D 35	1d. emerald-green	4 6	2 0
D 36	2d. emerald-green	4 0	1 9
D 37	3d. emerald-green	2 6	1 6
D 38	4d. emerald-green	3 0	1 3
D 39	5d. emerald-green	7 6	1 3
D 40	6d. emerald-green	4 0	2 0
D 41	1s. emerald-green	15 0	4 6
D 42	5s. emerald-green	50 0	7 6
D 43	10s. emerald-green	£12	£12
D 44	20s. emerald-green	£20	£20

1906–8. *Type* D **3**. *Chalky paper. Wmk. Crown and single-lined* A, *Type* D **4**.

(*a*) *P* 11½, 12, *compound with* 11.

D 45	½d. emerald-green (1907) ..	0 5	0 4
D 46	1d. emerald-green	0 8	0 2
D 47	2d. emerald-green	1 0	0 2
D 48	3d. emerald-green	3 0	1 3
D 49	4d. emerald-green (1907) ..	4 0	0 7
D 50	6d. emerald-green (1908) ..	3 6	0 8

(*b*) *P* 11.

D 51	1d. emerald-green	8 6	6 0
D 52	4d. emerald-green	20 0	15 0

1907. *Type* D **3**. *Chalky paper. Wmk. Crown and double-lined A, Type* w. **11**. *P* 11½, 12, *compound with* 11.

D 53	½d. emerald-green	1 3	0 9
D 54	1d. emerald-green	1 6	0 9
D 55	2d. emerald-green	4 0	1 6
D 56	4d. emerald-green	5 0	3 0
D 57	6d. emerald-green	6 0	4 0

D 6

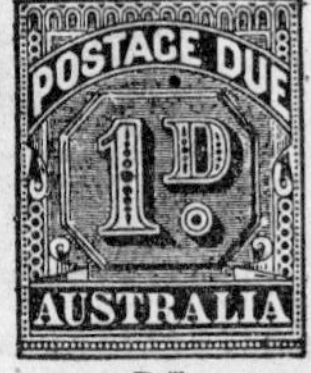

D 7

1908–9. *Type* D **6**. *Stroke after figure of value. Chalky paper. Wmk. Type* D **4**. (*a*) *P* 11½, 12, *compound with* 11.

D 58	1s. emerald-green (1909) ..	4 0	2 0
D 59	5s. emerald-green	15 0	4 0

(*b*) *P* 11.

D 60	2s. emerald-green	55 0	55 0
D 61	10s. emerald-green	£10	£10
D 62	20s. emerald-green	£18	£18

(Typo. by J. B. Cooke, Melbourne.)

1909 (July)–**1911.** *Type* D 7. *Wmk. Crown over A, Type* w. **11**.

(*a*) *P* 12 × 12½ (*comb.*) *or* 12½ (*line*).

D 63	½d. rosine and yellow-green	0 4	0 3
D 64	1d. rosine and yellow-green	0 8	0 2
D 65	2d. rosine and yellow-green	0 9	0 2
D 66	3d. rosine and yellow-green	0 10	0 5
D 67	4d. rosine and yellow-green	1 0	0 4
D 68	6d. rosine and yellow-green	1 3	0 6
D 69	1s. rosine and yellow-green	2 0	0 3
D 70	2s. rosine and yellow-green	5 0	1 9
D 71	5s. rosine and yellow-green	8 6	2 6
D 72	10s. rosine and yellow-green	32 6	20 0
D 73	£1 rosine and yellow-green	65 0	30 0

Of the 1d. and 2d., two Dies exist differing in the detail of the value-tablet or figure. Subsequent issues are all from the second Dies.

(*b*) *P* 11.

D 74 1d. rose & yellow-grn. (1911) 80 0 60 0
D 75 6d. rose & yellow-grn. .. £10 £10

The 1d. of this printing is distinguishable from No. D 78 by the colours, the green being very yellow and the rose having less of a carmine tone. The paper is thicker and slightly toned, that of No. D 78 being pure white, the gum is thick and yellowish, No. D 78 having thin white gum.

1912–23. *Type* D **7.** *Thin paper. White gum. Wmk. Type* w. **11.** (*a*) *P* 12½ (1912).

D 76 ½d. scarlet and pale yell.-grn. 1 3 0 6

(*b*) *P* 11 (1913–15).

D 77 ½d. rosine and apple-green . 3 0 1 3
D 78 1d. rosine and apple-green . 0 4 0 4

(*c*) *P* 14 (1915–23).

D 79 1d. scar. & pale yell.-grn. .. 0 8 0 6
D 80 2d. scar. & pale yell.-grn. .. 0 6 0 6
D 81 1s. scar. & pale yell.-grn.('23) 1 9 2 0
D 82 10s. scar. & pale yell.-grn.('21) 30 0 30 0
D 83 £1 scar. & pale yell.-grn.('21) 60 0 60 0

Although printed by Cooke in 1914, the three higher values were not issued until some years later.

1916. *Type* D **7.** *Wmk. Type* w. **11.** *P* 14.

D 84 ½d. rosine and yellow-green 5 0 1 6
D 85 1d. rosine and yellow-green 5 0 1 9

(Typo. by T. S. Harrison, Melbourne.)

1918–21. *Type* D **7.** *Wmk. Type* w. **11.** *P* 14.

D 86 ½d. carm. & apple-grn. .. 0 6 0 3
D 87 1d. carm. & apple-grn. .. 0 6 0 3
D 88 2d. carm. & apple-grn. .. 1 0 0 6
D 89 3d. carm. & apple-grn.(1919) 1 6 1 0
D 90 4d. carm. & apple-grn.(1920) 1 6 1 0

Nos. D 77, D 78 and D 90 exist with wmk. sideways.

(Typo. by T. S. Harrison, A. J. Mullett and John Ash.)

1918–30. *Type* D **7.** *W* **6.** (*a*) *P* 14.

D 91 ½d. carmine & yellow-green 0 3 0 3
D 92 1d. carmine & yellow-green 0 4 0 3
D 93 1½d. car. & yell.-grn. (16.3.25) 0 4 0 4
D 94 2d. carmine & yellow-green 0 6 0 4
D 95 3d. carmine & yellow-green 0 9 0 3
D 96 4d. carmine & yellow-green 1 3 0 9
D 97 6d. carmine & yellow-green 1 3 1 0

P 11.

D 98 4d. carmine & yellow-green 0 9 0 2

(Typo. by John Ash.)

1931–36. *Type* D **7.** *W* **15.** (*a*) *P* 14.

D 100 1d. carmine & yellow-green 0 9 0 4
D 102 2d. carmine & yellow-green 0 9 0 4

(*b*) *P* 11.

D 105 ½d. carm. & yellow-grn. ('34) 0 3 0 3
D 106 1d. carm. & yellow-grn. 0 4 0 3
D 107 2d. carm. & yellow-grn. 0 6 0 5
D 108 3d. carm. & yellow-grn. ('36) 1 0 1 0
D 109 4d. carm. & yellow-grn. ('34) 1 0 1 0
D 110 6d. carm. & yellow-grn. ('36) 3 6 3 6
D 111 1s. carm. & yellow-grn. ('34) 3 0 3 6

For stamps similar to Type D **7**, but with recess-printed frame, see King George VI Catalogue.

OFFICIAL STAMPS.

Postage stamps perforated "O S" in either large or small letters were used for official purposes. We do not list such varieties separately, but can supply when in stock.

O S

O 1

1931 (4 May). *Overprinted with T* O **1.**

O 1 **13** 2d. rose-red 12 6 7 6
O 2 „ 3d. blue 25 0 15 0

1931 (17 Nov.). *Air. No.* 139 *optd. with T*

O 3 6d. sepia 1 9 1 0

1932–33. *Overprinted as T* O **1.**

(*a*) *W* **7.** (i.) *P* 13½ × 12½.

O 4 **5a** 2d. golden scarlet .. 0 6 0 4
O 5 „ 4d. yellow-olive (Jan. '32) 2 0 0 6

(ii.) *P* 12.

O 6 **1** 6d. chestnut 4 6 3 6

(*b*) *W* **15.** (i.) *P.* 13½ × 12½.

O 7 **5a** ½d. orange 0 9 0 6
O 8 „ 1d. sage-green (Feb. '32) 0 5 0 1
O 9 „ 2d. golden scarlet (10.2.32) 0 9 0 1
O 10 „ 3d. ultramarine (Mar. '33) 1 3 0 9
O 11 „ 5d. orange-brown .. 1 9 1 6

(ii.) *P* 12.

O 13 **1** 6d. chestnut 2 6 2 0

(*c*) *Recess-printed. No wmk. P* 11.

O 16 **18** 2d. scarlet 1 0 0 6
O 17 „ 3d. blue 3 0 2 6
O 18 **17** 1s. green 3 6 2 6

Issues of specially overprinted Official stamps became obsolete in 1933 when the various States reverted to the use of stamps with perforated initials.

BAHAMAS.

1 2

(Engraved and printed by Perkins Bacon & Co.)

T **1.** *No watermark.*

1859 (10 June). *Imperf.* (*a*) *Thick paper.*

1 1d. dull lake £30 £25

(*b*) *Thin paper.*

2 1d. lake (*Pen-canc.* 5s.) .. 25 0 £12

Collectors are warned against false postmarks upon the remainder stamps of 1d., imperf., on thin paper, and also against purchasing specimens of No. 2 on the thickest of the thin paper, as the scarce No. 1, which differs in colour as well as in paper.

1860 (Oct.). *Clean-cut perf.* 14 *to* 16.

3 1d. lake £35 £20

1861 (June). *T* **1** (1d.) *and* **2** (4d. *and* 6d.). *No wmk.*

(*a*) *Rough perf.* 14 *to* 16.

4 1d. lake £15 80 0
5 4d. dull rose (Dec., 1861 .. £38 £12
a. Imperf. between (pair) ..
6 6d. grey-lilac (Dec., 1861) .. — £12
6a 6d. pale dull lilac £40 £12

(*b*) *P* 11 *to* 12.

7 1d. lake £50

This stamp has only been seen unused.

(Printed by Messrs. De La Rue and Co.)

1862. *T* 1 *and* 2. *No wmk.* (*a*) *P* 11½, 12.

8 1d. carmine-lake £15 90 0
9 1d. lake £16 £5
10 4d. dull rose £80 £12
11 6d. lavender-grey £85 £15

(*b*) *P* 11½, 12, *compound with* 11.

12 1d. carmine-lake £30 £22
13 1d. lake
14 4d. dull rose — £35
15 6d. lavender-grey — £40

(*c*) *P* 13.

16 1d. lake £14 55 0
17 1d. brown-lake £12 50 0
18 4d. dull rose £65 £10
19 6d. lavender-grey — £8
19*a* 6d. lilac £60 £15

3

1863-80. *T* 1, 2 *and* 3 (1*s*.). *Wmk. Crown CC.*

(*a*) *P* 12½.

20 1d. brown-lake 32 6 35 0
21 1d. carmine-lake 27 6 30 0
22 1d. carmine-lake (aniline) 40 0 35 0
23 1d. rose-red 20 0 20 0
24 1d. red 18 6 18 6
25 1d. vermilion 25 0 28 0
26 4d. dull rose 75 0 30 0
27 4d. bright rose 60 0 25 0
28 4d. brownish rose £6 27 6
28*a* 6d. lilac
29 6d. bright lilac 60 0 30 0
30 6d. deep violet (*Pen-c.* 3/6) 40 0 25 0
31 6d. violet (aniline) 65 0 35 0
32 1s. green (1869 ?) £32 65 0

(*b*) *P* 14.

33 1d. scarlet-vermilion 15 0 15 0
34 1d. scarlet (aniline) £30 75 0
35 4d. bright rose £12 30 0
36 4d. dull rose £12 27 6
37 4d. rose-lake £15 35 0
38 1s. dark green (1863) 30 0 15 0
39 1s. green (thick paper) (1880 ?) 10 0 7 6

1882 (March). *T* 1, 2 *and* 3. *Wmk. Crown CA.*

(*a*) *P* 12.

40 1d. scarlet-vermilion 12 6 12 6
41 4d. rose £8 30 0

(*b*) *P* 14.

42 1d. scarlet-vermilion 95 0 27 6
43 4d. rose £25 40 0
44 1s. green 15 0 15 0

FOURPENCE

(4)

1883. *No.* 30 *surcharged with T* 4, *in black.*

45 4d. on 6d. deep violet £18 £12

Variety. Surcharge inverted.

46 4d. on 6d. deep violet £80 £70

The surcharge is also found placed diagonally and in various other positions.

5

(Typo. De La Rue & Co.)

1884-98. *T* 5 (1*s*. *T* 3). *Wmk. Crown CA. P* 14.

47 1d. pale rose 10 0 7 6
48 1d. carmine-rose 5 0 1 9
49 1d. bright carmine (aniline) 4 6 2 6
50 2½d. dull blue 22 6 15 0
51 2½d. blue 12 6 7 6
52 2½d. ultramarine 6 0 3 6
53 4d. deep yellow 7 6 7 6
54 6d. mauve 7 6 8 0
55 1s. blue-green (1898) 16 0 17 6
56 5s. sage-green 50 0 47 6
57 £1 Venetian red £7 £6

6. Queen's Staircase, Nassau.

(Recess. De La Rue & Co.)

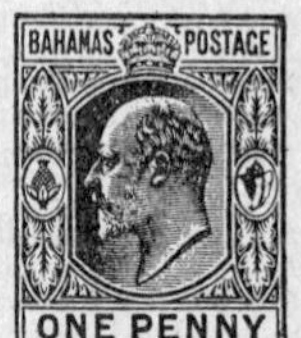

7

(Typo. De La Rue & Co.)

1901-10. *T* 6. *Centre in first colour. P* 14.

(*a*) *Wmk. Crown CC.* (Sept., 1901.)

58 1d. black and red 2 6 2 6

(*b*) *Wmk. Mult. Crown CA* (1910).

59 1d. black and red 3 0 2 0

For later shades, see Nos. 93, 94.

1902 (Dec.). *T* 7. *Wmk. Crown CA. P* 14.

60 1d. carmine 5 0 3 0
61 2½d. ultramarine 12 6 8 6
62 4d. orange 10 6 10 6
63 4d. deep yellow 12 0 12 0
64 6d. brown 18 0 18 0
65 1s. grey-black and carmine 25 0 27 6
66 1s. brownish grey & carmine 22 6 25 0
67 5s. dull purple and blue 60 0 65 0
68 £1 green and black £12 £12

1903. *T* 6. *Wmk. Crown CC. P* 14.

69 5d. black and orange 15 0 17 6
70 2s. black and blue 22 6 25 0
71 3s. black and green 27 6 30 0

1906-11. *T* 7. *Wmk. Mult. Crown CA. P* 14.

72 ½d. pale green 2 6 1 9
73 1d. carmine-rose 4 0 1 3
74 2½d. ultramarine (1907) 8 0 8 0
75 6d. bistre-brown (1911) 12 6 15 0

1.1.17.

(8) (9)

(Typo. De La Rue and Co.)

1912–19. *T* 8. *Wmk. Mult. Crown CA. P* 14.

76 ½d. green, O 0 4 0 6
77 ½d. yellow-green, O 0 10 0 9
78 1d. carmine (aniline), O .. 1 0 0 6
79 1d. deep rose, O 2 0 1 0
80 1d. rose, O 2 0 1 6
81 2d. grey, O (1919) 2 6
82 2½d. ultramarine, O 6 0 6 6
83 2½d. deep dull blue, O 6 6 7 0
84 4d. orange-yellow, O 6 0 7 0
85 4d. yellow, O 5 0 6 0
86 6d. bistre-brown, O 4 6 5 0
87 1s. grey-blk. and carmine, C .. 8 6 10 0
88 1s. jet-black and carmine, C 10 0 12 0
89 5s. dull purple and blue, C .. 37 6 40 0
90 5s. pale dull pur. & dp. blue, C 37 6 40 0
91 £1 dull green and black, C .. £10 £12
92 £1 green and black, C .. £10 £12

1916–19. *T* 6. *Wmk. Mult. Crown CA. P* 14.

93 1d. grey-black and scarlet .. 1 3 1 3
94 1d. grey-black and deep carmine-red (1919) 2 9 2 6
95 3d. purp./*orange* (*thin*) (1917) 8 6 10 0
96 3d. reddish purp./*yellow* (*thick*) (1919) 6 6 7 0
97 5d. black and mauve (1917) .. 3 0 3 6
98 2s. black and blue .. 22 6 25 0
99 3s. black and green (1917) .. 25 0 27 6

1917 (18 May). *No.* 59 *overprinted with T* 9.

100 1d. black and red (R.) .. 0 6 0 6
a. Lon stroke to "7" in "17" 6 0 8 6

The above stamps were to have been on sale on 1st January, 1917, but owing to delay in shipment they were not issued till May, 1917.

WAR TAX

(10)

1918 (21 Feb.). *T* 8 *and* 6 (3*d*.) *overprinted locally at Nassau with T* 10, *in black.*

101 ½d. green 3 6 4 6
a. Double £8 £10
b. Inverted £6
102 1d. carmine 1 6 2 0
a. Double £8 £10
b. Inverted £5
103 3d. purple/*yellow* 3 0 3 0
a. Inverted £6 £8
b. Double £6 £6
104 1s. grey-black and carmine .. 35 0 45 0
a. Double £15

1918 (June). *T* 6. *Wmk. Mult. Crown CA. Overprinted with T* 10.

105 1d. black and red 3 0 4 0
a. Double overprint, one inverted £20
b. Overprint double £35
c. Overprint inverted £35 £35

One sheet of No. 105 has been seen in which the top row of stamps is normal, and the other four rows consist of double overprint—one normal and the other inverted (=No. 105a.)

This stamp was only on sale for ten days.

WAR TAX WAR TAX

(11) (12)

1918 (June). *T* 8 *and* 6 (3*d*.) *overprinted in London with T* 11 *and* 12 (3*d*.), *in black or red* (1*s*.).

106 ½d. green 0 2 0 3
107 1d. carmine 0 2 0 4
108 3d. purple/*yellow* 0 9 1 6
109 1s. grey-black and carmine 2 0 3 6

1919. *T* 6, *colour changed. Wmk. Mult. Crown CA. P* 14.

110 3d. black and brown .. 2 9 3 3

1919. *No.* 110 *overprinted with T* 12.

111 3d. black and brown .. 1 0 1 6

WAR WAR

WAR CHARITY

3.6.18. TAX TAX

(13) (14) (15)

1919 (Jan.). *No.* 59 *overprinted with T* 13.

112 1d. black and red (R.) .. 0 4 0 4
a. Overprint double .. £35

The date is that originally fixed for the issue of the stamp. The year 1918 was also the bicentenary of the appointment of the first Royal governor.

1919 (14 July). *T* 8 *overprinted with T* 14, *in black* (1*d*.) *or red* (½*d. and* 1*s*.).

113 ½d. green 0 1 0 2
114 1d. carmine 0 2 0 4
115 1s. grey-black and carmine 2 0 2 6

No. 110 *overprinted with T* 15, *in black.*

116 3d. black and brown .. 0 9 1 0

16

(Recess. De La Rue & Co.)

1920 (1 Mar.). *Peace Celebration issue, T* 16. *Wmk. Mult. Crown CA. P* 14.

117 ½d. green 2 0 2 6
118 1d. carmine 3 6 4 0
119 2d. slate-grey 10 0 10 6
120 3d. deep brown 15 0 17 6
121 1s. deep myrtle-green .. 40 0 45 0

1921–29. *Wmk. Mult. Script CA.* P 14.

122 **6** 1d. grey and rose-red (29.3.21) 1 0 1 3
122*a* ,, 5d. black and purple ('29) 3 6 4 0
123 ,, 2s. black and blue ('22) 17 6 20 0
123*a* ,, 3s. black and green ('24) 25 0 27 6

124 **8** ½d. green, O ('24) .. 0 2 0 3
125 ,, 1d. carmine, O (8.9.21) .. 0 6 0 3
125*a* ,, 2d. grey, O (1927) .. 1 3 1 6
126 ,, 2½d. ultramarine, O ('22) 1 9 1 9
127 ,, 4d. orange-yellow, O ('24) 3 0 3 0
128 ,, 6d. bistre-brown, O ('22) 4 6 5 0
129 ,, 1s. black & carm., C ('26) 7 6 7 6
130 ,, 5s. dull pur. & bl., C ('24) 27 6 30 0
131 ,, £1 green & black, C ('26) £6 £7

17

18

(T **17/8.** Recess. Bradbury, Wilkinson & Co.)

1930 (2 Jan.). *Tercentenary of the Colony.* **T 17** *Wmk. Mult. Script CA.* P 12.

132 1d. black and scarlet .. 4 0 4 6
133 3d. black and deep brown .. 6 0 6 6
134 5d. black and deep purple .. 12 6 15 0
135 2s. black and deep blue .. 45 0 52 6
136 3s. black and green 70 0 80 0

1931. *T* **18.** *Wmk. Mult. Script CA.* P 12.

137 2s. black and deep blue .. 2 8 3 0
138 3s. black and green .. 4 0 4 6

1931–37. *T* **8.** *New values. Wmk. Mult. Script CA.* P 14.

139 1½d. red-brown, O ('34) .. 0 8 0 9
140 3d. pur./*pale yellow*, C ('31) 2 0 2 0
a. Purple/orange-yellow, C ('37) 8 6 12 6

1935 (6 May). *Silver Jubilee. As T* **13** *of Antigua, inscr.* "BAHAMAS". *Recess. D.L.R. & Co. Wmk. Mult. Script CA.* P 13½×14.

141 1½d. deep blue and carmine 1 6 2 0
142 2½d. brown and deep blue .. 4 0 5 0
143 6d. light blue and olive-green 10 0 10 6
144 1s. slate and purple .. 17 6 20 0

19. Flamingoes in flight.

(Recess. Waterlow & Sons.)

1935 (June). *Wmk. Mult. Script CA.* P 12½.

145 **19** 8d. ultramarine and scarlet 12 6 15 0

SPECIAL DELIVERY STAMPS.

SPECIAL
DELIVERY
(S 1)

1916–17. *T* **6.** *Wmk. Crown CC. Overprinted locally with T* S **1**, *in black.*

253 5d. black and orange .. 65 0 70 0
a. Overprint double £10
b. Overprint double, one inverted £20 £30
c. Overprint inverted £30
d. Pair, one without opt. .. £80 £80
253*e* 5d. grey-black & bright oran. (Mar.. 1917) 27 6 35 0

These two stamps were on sale in Canada, at Ottawa, Toronto, Westmount and Winnipeg, to facilitate commercial correspondence between the two countries. Nos. 254 and 255 were used in the Bahamas only.

SPECIAL DELIVERY (S 2) SPECIAL DELIVERY (S 3)

1917 (2 July). *T* **6** (*wmk. Mult. Crown CA*) *overprinted in London with T* S **2**, *in black.*

254 5d. black and orange .. 4 0 6 0

1918. *T* **6** *overprinted with T* S **3**, *in red.*

255 5d. black and mauve .. 1 6 3 0

BAHRAIN.

BAHRAIN (1) BAHRAIN (2)

1933 (10 Aug.)–**1934.** *Stamps of India* (*King George V*). *Wmk. Mult. Star, T* **69.** P 14.

(*a*) *Optd. with T* **1.**

1 **55** 3 p. slate ('34) 0 3 0 3
2 **56** ½ a. green 0 6 0 3
3 **80** 9 p. deep green 0 8 0 6
4 **57** 1 a. chocolate 0 8 0 4
5 **82** 1 a. 3 p. mauve 0 8 0 10
6 **70** 2 a. vermilion 0 10 1 3
7 **62** 3 a. blue 3 0 4 0
8 **83** 3 a. 6 p. ultramarine .. 2 9 3 0
9 **71** 4 a. sage-green 4 0 4 6
10 **65** 8 a. reddish purple .. 4 0 4 0
11 **66** 12 a. claret 4 6 5 0

(*b*) *Overprinted with T* **2.**

12 **67** 1 r. chocolate and green .. 8 0 8 6
13 ,, 2 r. carmine and orange .. 12 6 12 6
14 ,, 5 r. ultramarine & purple .. 30 0 35 0

1934–37. *Types and colours changed. Stamps of India (King George V) optd. with T* **1**. *Wmk. Mult. Star, T* **69**. *P* 14.

No.	Type	Description	Unused	Used
15	79	½ a. green ('35)	0 4	0 3
16	81	1 a. chocolate ('35)	0 8	0 4
17	59	2 a. vermilion ('35).. ..	5 0	3 6
17a	,,	2 a. verm. ('37) (*small die*)	3 0	3 6
18	62	3 a. carmine	1 3	1 3
19	63	4 a. sage-green ('35) ..	2 0	2 0

BARBADOS.

— SIMPLIFICATION (see p. xii.) —

Nos. 1 to 84.

2, 7, 4, 9, 4a, 5, 11, 12a. 13, 14.
20, 21, 24, 25, 29, 31, 35.
43, 65, 66, 45, 46, 61.
56, 52, 63, 49, 50, 54, 64.
72, 74, 75, 68, 76, 77, 79, 81, 82.

1

2

(Eng. and printed by Perkins Bacon & Co.)

T **1**. *No wmk. Imperf.*

1852 (15 April)–**1855**. *Paper blued.*

No.	Description	Unused	Used
1	(½d.) yellow-green ..	£40	50 0 *to* £10
2	(½d.) deep green ..	75 0	60 0 *to* £12
3	(1d.) blue ..	20 0	15 0 *to* 40 0
4	(1d.) deep blue ..	20 0	15 0 *to* 40 0
4a	(2d.) greyish slate ..	£10	
	b. Bisected (1d.) ..	—	£35
5	(4d.) brnsh. red (1855)	45 0	40 0 *to* £12

It has now been proved that the stamp in greyish slate was intended for issue as a 2d. stamp. As its use for this rate was extremely limited it was officially bisected and used for the penny rate in August and September, 1854.

Prepared for use, but not issued.

No.	Description	Unused
5a	(No value), slate-blue ..	30 0
5b	(No value), slate	90 0

Apart from the shade, which is distinctly paler, No. 4a can be distinguished from No. 5b by the smooth even gum, the gum of No. 5b being yellow and patchy, giving a mottled appearance to the back of the stamp. No. 5a also has the latter gum.

1856–57. *White paper.*

No.	Description	Unused	Used
7	(½d.) yellow-green ..	£25	25 0 *to* 80 0
8	(½d.) green ..	75 0	25 0 *to* 80 0
9	(1d.) pale blue ..	50 0	12 6 *to* 30 0
10	(1d.) deep blue ..	20 0	12 6 *to* 30 0

1858. *T* **2**. *Imperf.*

No.	Description	Unused	Used
11	6d. pale rose-red ..	£45	35 0 *to* £9
11a	6d. deep rose-red ..	£35	40 0 *to* £10
12	1s. brown-black ..	£12	20 0 *to* 75 0
12a	1s. black	95 0	20 0 *to* 75 0

1860. *T* **1**.

(*a*) *Pin-perf.* 14.

No.	Description	Unused	Used
13	(½d.) yellow-green	£48	£12
14	(1d.) pale blue	£48	65 0
15	(1d.) deep blue	£40	65 0

(*b*) *Pin-perf.* 12½.

No.	Description	Unused	Used
16	(½d.) yellow-green	£85	£12
16a	(1d.) blue	—	£24

1861. *T* **1**. *Clean-cut perf.* 14 *to* 16.

No.	Description	Unused	Used
17	(½d.) deep green	50 0	25 0
18	(1d.) pale blue	£45	50 0
19	(1d.) blue	£55	50 0
	a. Bisected (½d.)	—	£30

1861–70. *Rough perf.* 14 *to* 16.

T **1**.

No.	Description	Unused	Used
20	(½d.) deep green	20 0	20 0
21	(½d.) green	17 6	20 0
21a	(½d.) blue-green	—	£10
	b. Imperf.		
22	(½d.) grass-green	22 6	25 0
	a. Imperf.		
23	(1d.) blue (1861)	45 0	10 6
	a. Imperf.	£12	
24	(1d.) deep blue	30 0	10 6
	a. Bisected diagonally (½d.) ..	—	£25
25	(4d.) dull rose-red (1861) ..	85 0	45 0
	a. Imperf.	£18	
26	(4d.) dull brown-red (1865) ..	£5	45 0
	a. Imperf.	£20	
27	(4d.) lake-rose (1868).. ..	95 0	50 0
	a. Imperf.		
28	(4d.) dull vermilion (1869) ..	£15	80 0
	aa. Imperf.	£25	

Variety. *P* 11 *to* 12.

No.	Description	Unused
28a	(½d.) green	£150
28b	(1d.) blue	£35

These stamps are only known unused.

T **2**.

No.	Description	Unused	Used
29	6d. rose-red (1861)	£12	20 0
30	6d. orange-red (1864) ..	95 0	20 0
31	6d. bright orange-verm. (1868)	80 0	18 0
32	6d. dull orange-verm. (1870) ..	80 0	18 0
	a. Imperf.	£5	
33	6d. orange (1870) ..	80 0	27 6
34	1s. brown-black (1863) ..	45 0	20 0
35	1s. black (1866)	30 0	12 6

Error of colour.

No.	Description	Unused
37	1s. blue	£400

T **1** *and* **2** (*6d. and* 1s.).

1870. *Wmk. Large Star, T* w. **1**. *Rough perf.* 14 *to* 16.

No.	Description	Unused	Used
43	(½d.) green	70 0	22 6
	a. Imperf.		
43b	(½d.) yellow-green	—	70 0
44	(1d.) blue	£45	37 6
	a. Blue paper	—	60 0
45	(4d) dull vermilion	£35	75 0
46	6d. orange-vermilion ..	£30	35 0
47	1s. black	£12	30 0

1871. *Wmk. Small Star, T* w. **2**. *Rough perf.* 14 *to* 16.

No.	Description	Unused	Used
48	(1d) blue	80 0	12 6
49	(4d) dull rose-red	£40	60 0
50	6d. orange-vermilion	£20	30 0
51	1s. black	£8	30 0

1872. *Wmk. Small Star, T* w. **2**.

(*a*) *Clean-cut perf.* 14½ *to* 15½.

No.	Description	Unused	Used
52	(1d.) blue	£5	8 6
	a. Bisected diagonally (½d.) ..		
53	6d. orange-vermilion	£25	40 0
54	1s. black	95 0	22 6

(*b*) *P* 11 *to* 13 × 14½ *to* 15½.

No.	Description	Unused	Used
56	(½d.) green	£10	30 0
57	(4d.) dull vermilion	£15	80 0

1873. *Wmk. Large Star, T w.* **1.** *Clean-cut perf.* 14½ *to* 15½.

58	(½d.) green	£9	40 0
59	(4d.) dull rose-red	£30	90 0
60	6d. orange-vermilion	£20	45 0
	a. Imperf. between (horiz. pair)		
61	1s. black	80 0	27 6

Variety. Imperf.

62	6d. orange-vermilion	£5	

Two used specimens have been seen. It seems probable therefore that the stamp was issued.

Date? *No wmk. Clean-cut perf.* 14½ *to* 15½.

62*a*	(½d.) pale green	—	£100

1873 (June). *T* **2.** *Wmk. Small Star, T w.* **2** (*two points upwards*). *P.* 14.

63	3d. brown-purple	£8	80 0

3

1873. *T* **3.** *Wmk. Small Star, T w.* **2.** *P* 15½×15.

64	5s. dull rose	£30	£15

1874 (May). *T* **2.** *Wmk. Large Star, T w.* **1.**

(*a*) *Perf.* 14.

65	½d. deep green	25 0	15 0
66	1d. deep blue	35 0	8 0

(*b*) *Clean-cut perf.* 14½ *to* 15½.

66*a*	1d. deep blue		

(*c*) *Imperf.*

66*b*	1d. deep blue		

(Printed by Messrs. De La Rue and Co.)

1875–78. *T* **2.** *Wmk. Crown CC* (*sideways on 6d. and 1s.*). (*a*) *P* 12½.

67	½d. bright green	25 0	7 6
68	4d. deep red	£9	35 0
69	6d. bright yellow (aniline)	£30	45 0
70	6d. chrome-yellow	£25	50 0
71	1s. violet (aniline)	£12	40 0

(*b*) *P* 14.

72	½d. bright green (1876)	12 6	3 6
73	1d. dull blue	35 0	3 6
	a. Bisected (½d.)	—	£10
74	1d. grey-blue	35 0	3 0
75	3d. mauve-lilac (1878)	70 0	45 0
76	4d. red (1878)	80 0	22 6
77	4d. carmine	85 0	10 6
78	4d. crimson-lake	£8	12 6
79	6d. chrome-yellow (1876)	60 0	10 6
80	6d. yellow	80 0	12 6
80*a*	6d. bright yellow (aniline)	£35	
81	1s. purple (1876)	70 0	12 6
82	1s. violet (aniline)	£75	27 6
83	1s. dull mauve	£8	12 6
	a. Bisected (6d.)	—	£75

Variety. Perf. 14×12½.

84	4d. red	£100	

Very few specimens of No. 84 have been found unused. One used specimen is known.

1D. (A) 1D. (B) 1D. (C)

1878 (March). *No.* 64, *with lower label removed, divided vertically, and each half surcharged in black.*

(A) *Large numeral* "1", 7 *mm. high with curved serif, and large letter* "D", 2¾ *mm. high.*

86	1d. on half 5s. dull rose	£75	£30
	a. Unsevered pair	£300	£80

(B) *As last, but numeral with straight serif.*

87	1d. on half 5s. dull rose	—	£50

(C) *Smaller numeral* "1", 6 *mm. high, and smaller* "D", 2½ *mm. high.*

88	1d. on half 5s. dull rose	—	£50

Both types of the surcharge are found reading upwards as well as downwards, and there are minor varieties of the type.

4

(Typo. De La Rue.)

1882–86. *T* **4.** *Wmk. Crown CA. P* 14.

89	½d. dull green (1882)	2 0	1 0
90	½d. green	1 3	0 6
91	1d. rose (1882)	10 0	2 0
	a. Bisected (½d.)	—	60 0
92	1d. carmine	6 6	0 6
93	2½d. ultramarine (1882)	12 6	1 9
94	2½d. deep blue	17 6	2 0
95	3d. pale mauve (1885)	50 0	30 0
96	3d. purple	10 6	10 6
97	4d. grey (1882)	50 0	12 6
98	4d. pale brown (1885)	6 0	3 6
99	4d. deep brown	4 6	3 0
100	6d. olive-black (1886)	22 6	25 0
102	1s. chestnut (1886)	25 0	25 0
103	5s. bistre (1886)	£8	£8

HALF-PENNY

(5)

1892. *Provisional. No.* 99 *surcharged with T* **5.**

104	½d. on 4d. deep brown	1 6	1 6
	a. No hyphen	9 0	9 0

Variety. Surcharge double, one red, one black.

106	½d. on 4d. deep brown	£35	£35
	a. No hyphen	£100	£100

6. Seal of Colony.

(Typo. De La Rue.)

1892–99. Type **6.** *Wmk. Crown CA. P* 14.

107	½d. slate-grey & carm. (1896)	0 4	0 2
108	½d. dull green	0 6	0 1
109	1d. carmine	0 9	0 2
109*a*	2d. slate-blk. & orge. (1899)	7 6	8 6
110	2½d. ultramarine	3 6	1 0
111	5d. grey-olive	10 0	10 0
112	6d. mauve and carmine	12 6	12 6
113	8d. orange and ultramarine	10 6	10 6
114	10d. dull blue-grn. & carmine	17 6	17 6
115	2s. 6d. blue-black & orange	40 0	40 0

7

(Typo. De La Rue.

8. Monument to Nelson.

(Des. G. Goodman. Recess. De La Rue.)

1897–98. *Jubilee issue.* *T* **7.** *Value in second colour. Wmk. Crown CC. P* 14.

(*a*) *White paper* (1897.)

No.	Description	s.	d.	s.	d.
116	¼d. grey and carmine	1	0	1	0
117	½d. dull green	1	6	1	3
118	1d. rose	3	6	2	6
119	2½d. ultramarine	8	6	5	0
120	5d. olive-brown	20	0	20	0
121	6d. mauve and carmine	25	0	30	0
122	8d. orange and ultramarine	25	0	30	0
123	10d. blue-green and carmine	40	0	42	6
124	2s. 6d. blue-black and orange	42	6	42	6

(*b*) *Paper blued* (1898).

No.	Description	s.	d.	s.	d.
125	¼d. grey and carmine	15	0	15	0
126	½d. dull green	22	6	25	0
127	1d. carmine	35	0	30	0
128	2½d. ultramarine	30	0	27	6
129	5d. olive-brown	£9		£9	
130	6d. mauve and carmine	60	0	60	0
131	8d. orange and ultramarine	70	0	70	0
132	10d. dull green and carmine	85	0	90	0
133	2s. 6d. blue-black and orange	60	0	65	0

1903. *T* **6.** *Wmk. Crown CA. P* 14.

No.	Description	s.	d.	s.	d.
134	2s. 6d. violet and green	55	0	55	0

1904–5. *T* **6.** *Wmk. Mult. Crown CA. P* 14.

No.	Description	s.	d.	s.	d.
135	¼d. slate-grey and carmine	0	6	0	4
136	½d. dull green	1	9	0	4
137	1d. carmine	2	6	0	4
139	2½d. blue	8	6	1	6
141	6d. mauve and carmine	25	0	27	6
142	8d. orange and ultramarine	30	0	27	6
144	2s. 6d. violet and green	55	0	55	0

1906. *Nelson Centenary.* *T* **8.** *Wmk. Crown CC. P* 14.

No.	Description	s.	d.	s.	d.
145	¼d. black and grey	2	6	3	0
146	½d. black and pale green	3	0	2	6
147	1d. black and red	3	6	2	0
148	2d. black and yellow	15	0	17	6
149	2½d. black and bright blue	15	0	17	6
150	6d. black and mauve	27	6	27	6
151	1s. black and rose	35	0	40	0

Two sets may be made of the above: one on thick, opaque, creamy white paper; the other on thin, rather transparent, bluish white paper.

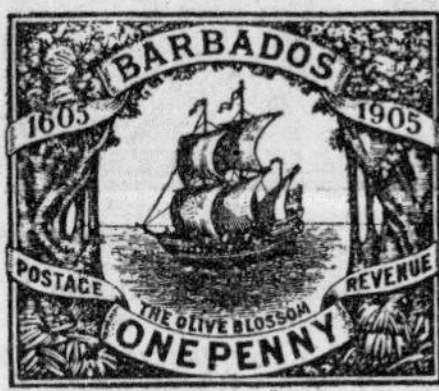

9

(Des. Lady Carter. Recess. De La Rue.)

1906 (15 Aug.). *Tercentenary of annexation. T* **9,** *sea and clouds in second colour, corners in third colour. Wmk. Multiple Crown CA* (*sideways*). *P* 14.

No.	Description	s.	d.	s.	d.
152	1d. black, blue, and green	5	0	4	6

Kingston
Relief
Fund.
1d.

(10)

1907 (25 Jan.). *No.* 109*a surcharged with T* **10,** *in red.*

No.	Description	s.	d.	s.	d.
153	1d. on 2d. slate-black & oran.	4	6	5	0

Varieties. (i.) *No stop after* " 1d ".

No.	Description	s.	d.	s.	d.
154	1d. on 2d. slate-black & oran	25	0	27	6

(ii.) *Surcharge inverted.* **1907** (25 Feb.).

No.	Description	s.	d.	s.	d.
155	1d. on 2d. slate-black & oran.	6	6	6	6
156	1d. on 2d. slate-black & oran. (i.)	27	6	30	0

(iii.) *Surcharge double.*

No.	Description	s.	d.	s.	d.
157	1d. on 2d. slate-black & oran.	£50			

(iv.) *Surcharge double, both inverted.*

No.	Description	s.	d.	s.	d.
157*a*	1d. on 2d. slate-black & oran.	£45			

(v.) *Surcharge tête-bêche* (*pair*).

No.	Description	s.	d.	s.	d.
157*b*	1d. on 2d. slate-black & oran.	£65			

The above stamp was sold for 2d., of which 1d. was retained for postal revenue, and the other 1d. given to a fund for the relief of the sufferers by the earthquake in Jamaica.

1907 (6 July). *T* **8.** *Wmk. Mult. Crown CA. P* 14.

No.	Description	s.	d.	s.	d.
158	¼d. black and grey	2	6	3	0
161	2d. black and yellow	17	6	17	6
162	2½d. black and bright blue	17	6	17	6
162*a*	2½d. black and indigo	£15		£15	

1909–10. *T* **6.** *Wmk. Mult. Crown CA. P* 14.

No.	Description	s.	d.	s.	d.
163	¼d. brown	0	10	0	4
164	½d. blue-green	1	9	0	3
165	1d. red	1	6	0	3
166	2d. greyish slate	7	6	8	6
167	2½d. bright blue ('10)	8	6	2	0
168	6d. dull and bright purple ('10)	17	6	17	6
169	1s. black/*green* ('10)	22	6	22	6

11

12

13

(Typo. De La Rue.)

14

(Recess. De La Rue.)

1912 (23 JULY–13 AUG.). *T* **11, 12** (*3d. to 6d.*), *and* **13** (*1s. to 3s.*). *Wmk. Mult. Crown CA. P* 14.

No.	Description	Unused	Used
170	¼d. brown (23 July)	0 6	0 6
170*a*	¼d. pale brown	0 6	0 6
171	½d. green (23 July) ..	1 0	1 0
172	1d. red	2 0	0 6
172*a*	1d. scarlet	4 6	0 9
173	2d. greyish slate	10 6	12 0
174	2½d. bright blue	7 6	3 0
175	3d. purple/*yellow*	9 0	10 6
176	4d. red and black/*yellow* ..	12 0	12 6
177	6d. purple and dull purple	17 6	17 6
178	1s. black/*green*	27 6	30 0
179	2s. blue and purple/*blue* ..	70 0	80 0
180	3s. violet and green ..	£5	£6

1916 (16 JUNE)–**1920**. *T* **14**. *Wmk. Mult. Crown CA. P* 14.

No.	Description	Unused	Used
181	¼d. deep brown	0 9	0 6
182	¼d. chestnut-brn. (Apl., 1918)	0 8	0 6
183	¼d. sepia-brown (Nov., 1918)	0 10	0 8
184	½d. green	1 0	0 6
185	½d. deep green (Apl., 1918)	1 0	0 6
186	½d. pale green (Oct., 1918) ..	1 6	1 0
187	1d. deep red	4 0	1 3
187*a*	1d. bright carmine-red ..	0 9	0 6
188	1d. pale car.-red (July, 1917)	1 6	0 6
189	2d. grey	8 6	10 0
190	2½d. ultramarine	4 6	4 6
191	3d. purple/*yellow* (*thin*) ..	8 6	10 0
191*a*	3d. deep purp./*yell.* (*thick*) ('20)	12 6	12 6
192	4d. red/*yellow* (*thin*) ..	8 0	9 0
193	6d. purple	8 0	9 0
194	1s. black/*green*	17 6	18 6
195	2s. purple/*blue*	35 0	37 6
196	3s. deep violet	£6	£7

WAR TAX

(15)

1917 (10 OCT.). *T* **11** *overprinted in London with T* **15**, *in black.*

No.	Description	Unused	Used
197	1d. bright red	0 3	0 3
	Thicker bluish paper (*April*, 1918).		
198	1d. pale red	0 3	0 2

1918 (18 FEB.). *T* **14**. *Colours changed. Wmk. Mult. Crown CA. P* 14.

No.	Description	Unused	Used
199	4d. black and red	4 6	5 0
200	3s. green and deep violet ..	60 0	70 0
200*a*	3s. green and bright violet ..	£20	£22

The centres of these are from a new die having no circular border line.

16 17

(Recess. De La Rue.)

1920 (9 SEPT.). *Victory issue. T* **16** *and* **17** (1/– *to* 3/–). *Centres in black except* 2½*d.* (*indigo*). *Wmk. Mult. Crown CA. P* 14.

No.	Description	Unused	Used
201	¼d. bistre-brown	1 0	1 3
202	½d. bright yellow-green ..	1 6	1 6
203	1d. vermilion	1 9	1 3
204	2d. grey	6 6	7 6
205	2½d. ultramarine	9 0	10 6
206	3d. purple	8 6	10 0
207	4d. blue-green	8 6	10 0
208	6d. brown-orange	10 0	12 0
209	1s. bright green	20 0	22 6
210	2s. brown	30 0	35 0
211	3s. dull orange	47 6	55 0

1921 (22 AUG.). *T* **16**. *Wmk. Mult. Script CA. P* 14.

No.	Description	Unused	Used
212	1d. black and vermilion ..	3 0	2 0

18 19

(Recess. De La Rue.)

1921 (14 Nov.)–**1924** *T* **18**. *P* 14.

No.	Description	Unused	Used
	(*a*) *Wmk. Mult. Crown CA.*		
213	3d. purple/*pale yellow* ..	4 0	4 6
214	4d. red /*pale yellow*	5 0	6 0
215	1s. black/*emerald*	22 6	25 0
	(*b*) *Wmk. Mult. Script CA.*		
217	¼d. brown	0 6	0 6
219	½d. green	0 8	0 8
220	1d. red	0 8	0 3
220*a*	1d. bright rose-carmine ..	1 6	0 4
221	2d. grey	2 0	1 9
222	2½d. ultramarine	3 6	3 6
225	6d. reddish purple	8 6	10 6
226	1s. black/*emerald* (18.9.24) ..	45 0	47 6
227	2s. purple/*blue*	35 0	40 0
228	3s. deep violet	45 0	50 0

1925–35. *T* **19**. *Wmk. Mult. Script CA.* (I.) *P* 14. (II.) *P* 13½ × 12½ ('32.)

No.	Description	I. Unused	I. Used	II. Unused	II. Used
229	¼d. brown ..	0 2	0 3	†	
230	½d. green ..	0 3	0 1	0 3	0 1
231	1d. scarlet ..	0 6	0 1	0 10	0 3
231*a*	1½d. orange ..	1 0	0 4	0 10	0 4
232	2d. grey ..	1 0	1 3	†	
233	2½d. blue ..	3 0	1 9	†	
233*a*	2½d. bt. ultram.	1 0	0 10	2 0	2 6
234	3d. pur/*p. yell*...	2 0	1 9	†	
234*a*	3d. reddish pur./*yellow* ('35) ..	1 9	2 0	†	
235	4d. red/*p. yell.* ..	3 0	3 6	†	
236	6d. purple ..	5 0	5 0	†	
237	1s. blk./*emerald*	10 6	10 6	10 6	10 6
237*a*	1s. brownish blk./*bt. yell-grn.* ..	8 6	8 6	†	
238	2s. purple/*blue* ..	22 6	22 6	†	
238*a*	2s. 6d. car./*blue*	22 6	22 6	†	
239	3s. deep violet ..	50 0	55 0	†	

20. King Charles I and King George V.

(Recess. Bradbury, Wilkinson & Co.)

1927 (17 FEB.). *Tercentenary of Settlement of Barbados. T* **20**. *Wmk. Mult. Script CA. P* 12½.

No.	Description	Unused	Used
240	1d. carmine	2 6	2 6

1935 (6 MAY). *Silver Jubilee. As T* **13** *of Antigua, inscr.* " BARBADOS ". *Recess. W'low & Sons. Wmk. Mult. Script CA. P* 11×12.

241	1d. deep blue and scarlet ..	0	9	1	0
242	1½d. ultramarine and grey	1	0	1	3
243	2½d. brown and deep blue ..	8	6	10	0
244	1s. slate and purple	20	0	22	6

POSTAGE DUE STAMPS.

D 1

(Typographed by De La Rue & Co.)

1934-47. *Wmk. Mult. Script CA. P* 14.

D 1	D 1	½d. green (10.2.35) ..	0	1	0	4
D 2	,,	1d. black (2.1.34) ..	0	2	0	4
		a. Bisected (½d.) ..	—		£15	
D3	,,	3d. carmine (13.3.47) ..	0	5		

The use of the bisected 1d. stamp was officially authorised pending the arrival of supplies of the ½d. Some of the specimens we have seen had the value " ½d " written across the half stamp in red ink.

BARBUDA.

BARBUDA
(1)

1922 (13 JULY). *T* **10** *to* **12** *of Leeward Islands overprinted with T* **1**, *in black or red* (1s. *and* 4s.). (*All are Die II.*)

(*a*) *Wmk. Mult. Script CA*

1	½d. deep green, O	1	3	1	6
2	1d. bright scarlet, O	2	6	3	6
3	2d. slate-grey, O	4	0	5	0
4	2½d. bright blue, O	4	0	5	0
5	6d. dull and bright purple, C	8	6	10	0
6	2s. purple & blue/*blue*, C ..	22	6	25	0
7	3s. bright green and violet, C	30	0	35	0
8	4s. black and red, C ..	37	6	45	0

(*b*) *Wmk. Mult. Crown CA.*

9	3d. dull pur./*pale yellow*, C ..	3	6	4	0
10	1s. black/*emerald*, C	8	6	10	6
11	5s. grn. & red/*pale yellow*, C	45	0	50	0

BASUTOLAND.

1. King George V, Crocodile and Mountains.

(Recess. Waterlow & Sons Ltd.)

1933 (1 DEC.). *Wmk. Mult. Script CA. P* 12½.

1	1	½d. emerald	0	4	0	4
2	,,	1d. scarlet	0	6	0	6
3	,,	2d. bright purple ..	1	0	1	3
4	,,	3d. bright blue ..	2	0	2	6
5	,,	4d. grey	4	6	5	0
6	,,	6d. orange-yellow ..	6	0	6	6
7	,,	1s. red-orange ..	12	6	15	0
8	,,	2s. 6d. sepia	25	0	27	6
9	,,	5s. violet	40	0	42	6
10	,,	10s. olive-green ..	65	0	70	0

1935 (4 MAY). *Silver Jubilee. As T* **13** *of Antigua, inscribed* " BASUTOLAND ". *Recess. D. L. R. & Co. Wmk. Mult. Script CA. P* 13½×14.

11	1d. deep blue and carmine ..	0	8	0	10
12	2d. ultramarine and grey ..	3	6	4	0
13	3d. brown and deep blue ..	5	0	6	0
14	6d. slate and purple	7	6	8	6

OFFICIAL STAMPS.

1934 (4 MAY). *Optd.* " OFFICIAL ".

O 1 1 ½d. emerald .. ..
O 2 ,, 1d. scarlet .. ..
O 3 ,, 2d. bright purple .. ..
O 4 ,, 6d. orange-yellow .. ..

Collectors are advised to buy these stamps only from reliable sources. They were not sold to the public.

POSTAGE DUE STAMPS.

D 1

(Typographed by De La Rue & Co.)

1933 (1 DEC.). *Wmk. Mult. Script CA. P* 14.

D 1	D 1	1d. carmine	1	3	1	9
		a. Scarlet	0	2	0	4
D 2	,,	2d. violet	0	3	0	4

BATUM.

BRITISH OCCUPATION.

1

БАТУМ. ОБ.

Руб 10 Руб
(2)

1919. *T* 1. *Lithographed. Imperf.*

1	5 kop. green	0	6	1	0
2	10 kop. ultramarine	0	6	1	0
3	50 kop. yellow	0	4	0	6
4	1 rbl. chocolate	0	6	0	9
5	3 rbls. violet	1	6	2	6
6	5 rbls. brown	2	6	3	6

Russian stamps, Arms types, surch. with T **2**.

7	10 rbls. on 1 k. orange (*imperf.*)	12	6	12	6
8	10 rbls. on 3 k. red (*imperf.*) ..	7	6	7	6
9	10 rbls. on 5 k. dull pur. (*perf.*)	£6		£6	
10	10 rbls. on 10 on 7 k. dull blue (*perf.*)	£5		£5	

БАТУМ ОБЛАС.
P 10 P.
BRITISH
OCCUPATION
(3)

БАТУМЪ
BRITISH
P. 15 P.
OCCUPATION
ОБЛ.
(4)

1919. *Russian stamps, Arms types, surcharged with T* **3** *or* **4**, *in black. Imperf.*

11	10 rbls. on 3 k. red	7	6	7	6
12	15 rbls. on 1 k. orange ..	15	0	15	0
	a. Surcharge in red	15	0	15	0
	b. Surcharge in violet	15	0	15	0

BRITISH
OCCUPATION
(5)

БАТУМ.ОБЛ
P.50P.
BRITISH
OCCUPATION
(6)

1919. *T* **1**, *colours changed and new values, optd. with T* **5**.

13	5 k. yellow-green	1	6	2	0
14	10 k. bright blue	1	6	2	0
15	25 k. orange-yellow	1	0	1	6
16	1 rbl. pale blue	0	9	1	0
17	2 rbls. pink	0	6	0	9
18	3 rbls. bright violet	0	9	1	0
19	5 rbls. brown	1	0	1	6
	a. "COUPATION"	50	0	60	0
20	7 rbls. brownish red	1	6	2	0

1920. *Russian stamps, Arms types, surcharged as T* **6**, *in black* (Bk.) *or blue* (B.).

(*a*) *Perf.*

21	25 r. on 5 k. dull purple (Bk.)	10	0	10	0
22	25 r. on 5 k. dull purple (B.)	10	0	10	0
23	25 r. on 10 on 7 k. blue (Bk.)	25	0	25	0
24	25 r. on 10 on 7 k. blue (B.)	15	0	15	0
25	25 r. on 20 on 14 k. red and blue (Bk.)	25	0	25	0
26	25 r. on 20 on 14 k. red and blue (B.)	20	0	20	0
27	25 r. on 25 k. purp. & green (B.)	25	0	25	0
28	25 r. on 25 k. pur. & grn. (Bk.)	30	0	30	0
29	25 r. on 50 k. grn. & pur. (Bk.)	10	0	10	0
30	25 r. on 50 k. grn. & pur. (B.)	25	0	25	0
31	50 r. on 2 k. green (Bk.) ..	30	0	30	0
32	50 r. on 3 k. red (Bk.) ..	30	0	30	0
33	50 r. on 4 k. rose (Bk.) ..	30	0	30	0
34	50 r. on 5 k. dull purple (Bk.)	25	0	25	0

(*b*) *Imperf.*

35	50 r. on 2 k. green (Bk.) ..	£5	£5
36	50 r. on 3 k. red (Bk.) ..	£5	£5
37	50 r. on 5 k. dull purple (Bk.)	£10	£10

Stamp of Romanov issue, as T **25** *of Russia, surcharged with T* **6**.

38	50 r. on 4 k. rose-carmine (B.)	35	0	35	0

Stamps of Russia, Arms types, surcharged as T **3**, *in black or carmine.* (*a*) *Imperf.*

39	50 r. on 1 k. orange	£6	£6
40	50 r. on 2 k. green	£10	£8

(*b*) *Perf.*

41	50 r. on 2 k. green	£10		£10	
42	50 r. on 3 k. red	£8		£8	
43	50 r. on 4 k. rose	£8		£8	
44	50 r. on 5 k. dull purple ..	£6		£5	
44a	50 r. on 10 k. deep blue (C.)	£10		£10	
45	50 r. on 15 k. ultram. & purple	80	0	80	0

РУБ 25 ЛЕЙ
25 РУБ. 25
(7)

R.50R.
BRITISH
OCCUPATION
РУБ.
(8)

1920. *Nos.* 13 *and* 15 *surcharged with T* **7**, *in black or blue* (B.)

46	25 r. on 5 k. yellow-green ..	10	0	10	0
47	25 r. on 5 k. yellow-green (B.)	15	0	15	0
48	25 r. on 25 k. orange-yellow	10	0	10	0
49	25 r. on 25 k. orange-yell. (B.)	30	0	30	0

1920. *No.* 3 *surcharged with T* **8**, *in black or blue* (B.)

50	50 r. on 50 k. yellow	10	0	10	0
51	50 r. on 50 k. yellow (B.) ..	25	0	25	0

1920 (June). *T* **1** *overprinted with T* **5**, *in black. Colours changed and new values. Imperf.*

A. *Normal.* B. *Variety.* "BPITISH."

		A.				B.			
52	1 r. chestnut	0	1	0	3	7	6	10	0
53	2 r. pale blue	0	1	0	3	7	6	10	0
54	3 r. pink	0	2	0	4	7	6	10	0
55	5 r. black-brn.	0	2	0	4	7	6	10	0
56	7 r. yellow	0	3	0	6	7	6	10	0
57	10 r. myrtle-grn.	0	4	0	9	15	0	20	0
58	15 r. violet	0	6	1	0	15	0	20	0
59	25 r. scarlet	1	0	1	9	25	0	30	0
60	50 r. deep blue	1	6	2	6	30	0	40	0

BECHUANALAND.

(A) BRITISH BECHUANALAND.

British
Bechuanaland
(1)

BRITISH
BECHUANALAND
(2)

1886 (Feb.). *Stamps of Cape of Good Hope* ("*Hope*" *seated*) *overprinted with T* **1**. *Wmk. Crown CA or CC.*

1	6	½d. slate (R.) (wmk. CA) ..	8	0	9	0
		a. Opt. double, in red and in black	£10			
2	„	3d. claret (wmk. CA) ..	12	0	12	6
3	„	4d. blue (wmk. CC)	20	0	20	0

Wmk. Anchor (*Cape, T* **13**).

4	6	½d. grey-black	3	6	4	6
		a. Error "ritish"	£8		£8	
5	„	1d. pale rose-red	10	0	10	0
		a. Error "ritish"	£22			
		b. Overprint double				
6	„	2d. bistre	15	0	10	0
		a. Error "ritish"	£35			
7	4	6d. purple	37	6	35	0
8	„	1s. green	£6		70	0
		a. Error "ritish"	£110			

Overprints with stop after "Bechuanaland" are forged.

1887 (Oct.). *Stamp of Gt. Britain optd. with T* **2.**

9 **71** ½d. vermilion 0 4 0 6
a. Overprint double .. ..

3

(Typo. De La Rue & Co.)

1887. "*Unappropriated dies*" *inscribed as shown. P* 13½, 14.

(*a*) *Wmk. Orb* (G.B. *T* **48**).

10 **3** 1d. lilac and black 3 6 4 0
11 „ 2d. lilac and black 12 6 4 0
a. Pale dull lilac and black .. 12 6 6 6
12 „ 3d. lilac and black 3 0 3 6
a. Pale reddish lilac and black .. 6 0 7 6
13 „ 4d. lilac and black 12 6 10 0
14 „ 6d. lilac and black 20 0 10 0

4

5

(*b*) *Wmk. Script* " V R " *sideways, reading up.*

15 **4** 1s. green and black .. 7 6 4 6
16 „ 2s. green and black .. 15 0 15 0
17 „ 2s. 6d. green and black .. 17 6 17 6
18 „ 5s. green and black .. 40 0 40 0
19 „ 10s. green and black .. 50 0 52 6

(*c*) *Wmk. two orbs, sideways.*

20 **5** £1 lilac and black £8 £7
21 „ £5 lilac and black £28 £12

Several values of the above series are known on blued paper. No. 11*a* is the first printing of the 2d. (on safety paper ?) and has a faded appearance.

1d. (6) 1s. (7)

1888 (7 Aug.). *Surcharged as T* **6** *or* **7.**

22 **3** 1d. on 1d. lilac and blk. (Bk.) 7 6 7 6
a. Surcharge double .. ..
23 „ 2d. on 2d. lilac and blk. (R.) 10 0 10 0
a. Pale dull lilac and black .. 17 6 17 6
b. Curved foot to "2" .. £10 £10
24 „ 2d. on 2d. lilac and blk. (G.) — £20
25 „ 4d. on 4d. lilac and blk. (R.) 75 0 75 0
26 „ 6d. on 6d. lilac and blk. (Bk.) 40 0 17 6
27 „ 6d. on 6d. lilac and blk. (B.) — £45
28 **4** 1s. on 1s. grn. and blk. (Bk.) 65 0 32 6

One Half-Penny (8)   British Bechuanaland. (9)   British Bechuanaland (10)

1888 (Dec.). *No.* 12*a surcharged with T* **8.**

29 **3** ½d. on 3d. pale reddish lilac and black 85 0 90 0

1889. *T* **6** *of Cape of Good Hope* (*wmk. Anchor*) *overprinted with T* **9.**

30 ½d. slate (G.) 4 6 5 6
a. Overprint double £6
b. Overprint double, one inverted £15
c. Overprint double, one vertical £15
d. As Var. c, se-tenant with stamp without overprint .. £35
e. "British" omitted .. ..

1891 (Nov.). *T* **6** *of Cape of Good Hope* (*wmk. Anchor*), *overprinted with T* **10**, *reading upwards.*

31 1d. rose-red 7 6 8 0
a. No dots to "i" of "British" £5 £5
b. "British" omitted .. .. — £5
32 2d. bistre 3 0 3 6
a. No stop after "Bechuanaland" £6 £6

BRITISH

BRITISH BECHUANALAND (11)   BECHUANALAND (12)

1891 (Dec.)–1894. *Stamps of Great Britain overprinted with T* **11.**

33 **57** 1d. lilac 0 8 0 9
34 **73** 2d. green and carmine .. 3 0 1 3
35 **76** 4d. green and purple-brown 2 6 2 6
36 **79** 6d. purple/*rose-red* 3 0 3 6
37 **82** 1s. green (July, 1894) .. 6 6 7 0

1893–95. *As Nos.* 31 *and* 32, *but T* **10** *reads downwards.*

38 1d. rose-red (1893) 3 6 3 6
a. "British" omitted £6
b. No dots to letters "i" in "British" 50 0 50 0
39 2d. bistre (1895) 3 6 3 6
a. Overprint double £30 £25
b. "British" omitted £6
c. No dots to letters "i" in "British" 50 0 50 0

1897. *T* **6** *of Cape of Good Hope* (*wmk. Anchor*), *overprinted as T* **12.** (*First measurement given is distance between lines of overprint: the second the length of the word* "BECHUANALAND.")

40 ½d. yell.-grn. (13 mm./16 mm.) 1 6 2 6
41 ½d. yell.-grn. (10½ mm./15 mm.) 3 6 5 0
42 ½d. yell.-grn. (13½ mm./15 mm.) 7 6 7 6

(B) BECHUANALAND PROTECTORATE.

Protectorate (13)   Protectorate (14)

Protectorate (15)

1888 (Aug.). *No. 9 overprinted.*

43 **13** ½d. vermilion 2 0 3 0
a. "Protectorate" double .. £5
44 **14** ½d. vermilion 30 0 40 0
a. "Protectorate" inverted .. 30 0 40 0
b. "Portectorate" for "Protectorate" inverted ..
c. "Protectorate" double .. 40 0
d. "Protectorate" double and inverted £15
45 **15** ½d. vermilion 40 0 55 0
a. "Protectorate" double .. £10
b. "Protectorrte" for "Protectorate" .. ..

Protectorate
1d
(16)

1888 (Aug.). *Nos.* 10 *to* 19 *surcharged* (*or overprinted* "Protectorate" *only as T* **16**.

46 **3** 1d. on 1d. lilac and black .. 3 6 4 6
a. Small figure "1" .. £8 £8
47 " 2d. on 2d. lilac and black .. 15 0 15 0
b. Curved foot to "2" .. £8 £8
48 " 3d. on 3d. pale reddish lilac and black 60 0 60 0
49 " 4d. on 4d. lilac and black .. 80 0 80 0
50 " 6d. on 6d. lilac and black .. 25 0 22 6
51 **4** 1s. green and black .. 45 0 22 6
a. First "o" of "Protectorate" omitted £15 £15
52 " 2s. green and black .. £8 £8
a. First "o" of "Protectorate" omitted £45
53 " 2s. 6d. green and black .. £10 £12
a. First "o" of "Protectorate" omitted £50
54 " 5s. green and black .. £15 £17
a. First "o" of "Protectorate" omitted £50
55 " 10s. green and black .. £35 £40
a. First "o" of "Protectorate" omitted £100

No. 25 (*red* "4d.") *overprinted with T* **13**.

56 **3** 4d. on 4d. lilac and black .. 32 6 32 6

Bechuanaland

Protectorate.
(17)

1889. *T* **6** *of Cape of Good Hope* (*wmk. Anchor*), *overprinted with T* **17**.

57 ½d. slate (G.) 2 6 3 6
a. Overprint double £6
b. "Bechuanaland" omitted .. £15

Protectorate

Fourpence
(18)

No. 9 surcharged with T **18**.

58 4d. on ½d. vermilion 7 6 6 6

BECHUANALAND PROTECTORATE
(19)

BECHUANALAND PROTECTORATE
(20)

1897 (Oct.)–**1902.** *Stamps of Great Britain* (*Queen Victoria*) *overprinted with T* **19**.

59 **71** ½d. vermilion 0 8 0 8
60 " ½d. blue-green (25.2.02) .. 0 10 1 0
61 **57** 1d. lilac 1 3 0 10
62 **73** 2d. green and carmine .. 1 6 1 3
63 **75** 3d. purple/*yell.* (Dec. '97) .. 3 6 3 6
64 **76** 4d. green and purple-brown 6 6 6 0
65 **79** 6d. purple/*rose-red* 6 0 6 0

1904–13. *Stamps of Great Britain* (*King Edward VII*) *overprinted with T* **20**.

66 **83** ½d. blue-green (Mar. '06) 1 0 1 3
67 " ½d. yellow-green (Nov. '08) 1 3 1 3
68 " 1d. scarlet (Apr. '05) .. 1 6 0 6
69 **86** 2½d. ultramarine (29.11.04) 4 6 5 0
a. Stop after "P" in "PROTECTORATE." £12
70 **93** 1s. green & scarlet (1912) 10 0 12 0
71 " 1s. green & carmine (1913) 7 0 7 6

Nos. 70 and 71 are the Somerset House printings.

1912 (Sept.). *T* **102** *of Great Britain* (*King George V, wmk. Crown*) *optd. with T* **20**.

72 1d. scarlet 0 10 1 0
a. No cross on crown .. ..

BECHUANALAND PROTECTORATE
(21)

1914–24. *Stamps of Great Britain* (*King George V*) *overprinted.*

(*a*) *With T* **20** (*wmk. Script Cypher, T* **100**).

73 **105** ½d. green 0 4 0 6
74 **104** 1d. scarlet 0 6 0 6
75 **105** 1½d. red-brown 0 8 0 9
76 **106** 2d. red-orange (Die I) .. 1 9 1 6
77 " 2d. orange (Die II) (1924) 4 0 2 6
78 **104** 2½d. ultramarine 1 0 1 3
79 **106** 3d. blue-violet 2 0 2 6
80 " 4d. slate-green 2 0 2 6
81 **107** 6d. dull purple, C .. 3 0 3 6
82 **108** 1s. bistre-brown .. 5 0 5 6

(*b*) *With T* **21**. (*Wmk. T* **110**.)

(i.) *Waterlow printings.* (1914.)

83 **109** 2s. 6d. deep sepia-brown 25 0 27 6
a. Re-entry £20
84 " 5s. rose-carmine 30 0 32 6

(ii.) *De La Rue printings.* (1916–20.)

85 **109** 2s. 6d. grey-brown (1916) 15 0 17 6
86 " 2s. 6d. deep brown (1920) 25 0 27 6
87 " 5s. bright carmine (1920) 65 0 70 0

(iii.) *Bradbury Wilkinson printings.* (1920–23.)

88 **109** 2s. 6d. chocolate-brown .. 15 0 17 6
89 " 5s. rose-red 30 0 27 6
90 " 5s. deep carmine 32 6 35 0

A 1d., King George V, Type **2** of South Africa, overprinted "Bechuanaland Protectorate", was issued for a short period in 1922 as a **Revenue stamp.**

1925–27. *As* 1914–24, *but W* **111** (*block letters*).

91 **105** ½d. green 0 8 0 8
92 **104** 1d. scarlet 0 10 0 8
93 **106** 2d. orange (Die II) .. 1 9 1 6
94 " 3d. violet 2 0 2 6
95 " 4d. grey-green 2 6 2 9
96 **107** 6d. purple, C 5 0 6 0
97 " 6d. purple, O 4 6 5 0
98 **108** 1s. bistre-brown 7 6 8 0

22. King George V, Baobab Tree and Cattle drinking.

(Des. from photograph by Resident Commissioner, Ngamiland. Recess. Waterlow & Sons.)

1932 (12 Dec.). *Wmk. Mult. Script CA. P* 12½.

99	**22**	½d. green	0	4	0	6
100	,,	1d. scarlet	0	8	0	8
101	,,	2d. brown	1	3	1	6
102	,,	3d. ultramarine	2	0	2	6
103	,,	4d. orange	3	0	4	0
104	,,	6d. purple	4	6	5	0
105	,,	1s. black and olive-green	8	0	9	0
106	,,	2s. black and orange ..	15	0	17	6
107	,,	2s. 6d. black and scarlet	20	0	22	6
108	,,	3s. black and purple ..	25	0	27	6
109	,,	5s. black and ultramarine	40	0	45	0
110	,,	10s. black and brown ..	80	0	95	0

1935 (4 May). *Silver Jubilee. As T* **13** *of Antigua, inscribed* " BECHUANALAND PROTECTORATE ". *Recess. B. W. & Co. Wmk. Mult. Script CA. P* 11 × 12.

111	1d. deep blue and scarlet ..	0	6	0	8
112	2d. ultramarine & grey-black	2	6	3	0
113	3d. brown and deep blue ..	4	0	4	6
114	6d. slate and purple ..	5	0	6	0

All values exist with " double flagstaff " variety.

POSTAGE DUE STAMPS.

BECHUANALAND PROTECTORATE
(D 1)

BECHUANALAND
PROTECTORATE
(D 2)

1926. *T* D 1 *of Great Britain, overprinted with T* D **1** *or* D **2** (2d.).

D 1	½d. emerald (No. D 10*b*) ..	0	6	0	10
D 2	1d. carmine (No. D 10*a*) ..	0	8	1	0
D 3	2d. agate (No. D 13) ..	1	0	1	6

D 3

(Typographed by De La Rue & Co.)

1932 (12 Dec.). *Wmk. Mult. Script CA. P* 14.

D 4	D **3**	½d. sage-green	0	1	0	2
D 5	,,	1d. carmine	0	2	0	4
D 6	,,	2d. violet	0	3	0	5

POSTAL FISCAL.

Bechuanaland

Protectorate
(F 1)

1910. *Stamp of Transvaal (King Edward VII, wmk. Mult. Crown CA), optd. with T* F **1**.

F1 6d. black and orange, C (B.) 40 0 45 0

This provisional was issued for fiscal purposes, but a few were allowed to be used for postage.

BERMUDA.

1*
Postmaster's Stamp.

1848. *T* **1***. *Prepared and issued by Mr. W. B. Perot, Postmaster of Hamilton.*

O1	1d. black .. .. .. —	£700
O2	1d. red/*white* .. .. .. —	£600
O3	1d. red/*blue*	

1

2

3

4

5

(Typo. De La Rue.)

1865 (Sept.)–**1873.** *T* **1** *to* **5.** *Wmk. Crown CC.*

(*a*) *P* 14.

1	1d. rose-red (13 Sept., '65) ..	15 0	5 0
2	1d. pale rose	17 6	5 0
3	2d. dull blue (14 Mar., '66) ..	30 0	12 6
4	2d. bright blue	32 6	10 6
5	3d. yellow-buff (10 Mar., '73)	70 0	40 0
5*a*	3d. orange	60 0	37 6
6	6d. dull purple (13 Sept., '65)	70 0	22 6
7	6d. dull mauve	7 6	7 6
8	1s. green (13 Sept., '65) ..	30 0	17 6

(*b*) *Imperf.*

9	1d. rose-red	£175	£100

(*c*) *P* 14×12½.

10	3d. yellow-buff	50 0	30 0
10*a*	6d. bright mauve	8 0	9 0
11	1s. green	10 0	12 6
	a. Vert. strip of 3, two stamps imperf. horizontally ..	£85	£75

Though probably manufactured shortly after 1875, the stamps with the above perforation were not issued until some time later, the 3d. being discovered in 1886, the 1s. in 1894, and the 6d. not until 1903.

THREE PENCE (6) THREE PENCE (6*a*)

THREE PENCE (7)

1874 (2 Mar.). *Nos.* 1 *and* 8 *surcharged diagonally in black.*

(*a*) *In fancy capitals, T* **6.** (" P " *and* " R " *different type.*)

12	3d. on 1d. rose-red	£60	
13	3d. on 1s. green	£15	£12

(*b*) *In fancy capitals, T* **6*a*.** (" P " *same type as* " R").

13*a*	3d. on 1d. rose-red		
13*b*	3d. on 1s. green	£30	£30

(*c*) *In Roman capitals, T* **7.** (19 May, '74.)

14	3d. on 1s. green	£17	£12

The 3d. on 1d. is now believed to be an essay.

One Penny. (8)

1873 (April)–**1875.** *Nos.* 4, 5, *and* 8 *surcharged with T* **8**, *in black.*

15	1d. on 2d. bright blue ..	£15	£10
	a. No stop after " Penny " ..		
16	1d. on 3d. yellow-buff ..	£8	£10
17	1d. on 1s. green (11 Mar., '75)	75 0	70 0
	a. Surcharge inverted	—	£130
	b. No stop after " Penny " ..		

9

10

(Typo. De La Rue.)

1880 (23 March). *T* **9** *and* **10.** *Wmk. Crown CC. P* 14.

19	½d. stone	3 6	3 0
20	4d. orange-red	2 6	2 6

11

ONE FARTHING (12)

(Typo. De La Rue.)

1884–93. *Wmk. Crown CA. P* 14.

21	**9**	½d. dull green (1892) ..	1 0	0 10
21*a*	„	½d. deep grey-green ..	0 10	0 10
22	**1**	1d. dull rose (April, '84) ..	30 0	7 6
23	„	1d. rose-red	10 6	5 0
24	„	1d. carmine-rose (1886) ..	5 0	0 4
24*a*	„	1d. aniline carmine ..	2 6	0 4
25	**2**	2d. blue (Dec., '86) ..	10 6	7 6
26	„	2d. aniline purple (1893) ..	8 0	6 6
26*a*	„	2d. brown-purple (1898) ..	6 6	3 0
27	**11**	2½d. deep ultram. (10.11.84)	5 0	2 0
27*a*	„	2½d. pale ultram. ..	4 0	2 0
28	**3**	3d. grey (1886) ..	5 0	4 0
29	**5**	1s. yellow-brown (1893) ..	12 6	10 0
29*a*	„	1s. olive-brown	10 0	10 0

1901. *T* **5.** *Wmk. Crown CA. P* 14. *Surcharged with T* **12**, *in black.*

30	½d. on 1s. dull grey	0 4	0 6
30*a*	½d. on 1s. bluish grey ..	0 2	0 4

13. Dry Dock.

(Typo. De La Rue.)

1902–3. *T* **13.** *Wmk. Crown CA. P* 14.

31	½d. black and green (1903) ..	5 0	4 0
32	1d. brown and carmine ..	2 0	1 0
33	3d. magenta and sage-green ..	6 0	6 6

1904. *T* **10.** *Wmk. Crown CA. P* 14.

34	4d. orange-brown	15 0	17 6

1906–9. *T* **13.** *Wmk. Mult. Crown CA. P* 14.

34*a*	½d. brown and violet (1908) ..	1 0	1 0
35	½d. black and green	4 0	3 0
36	1d. brown and carmine ..	5 0	0 10
37	2d. grey and orange (1907) ..	8 6	10 0
38	2½d. brown and ultramarine ..	10 0	10 0
39	4d. blue and chocolate (1909)	6 6	6 6

1908–10. *T* **13.** *Wmk. Mult. Crown CA. P* 14.

41	½d. green (1909)	10 0	8 0
42	1d. red	3 0	1 0
43	2½d. blue (1910)	12 6	10 6

14

15

(Recess. De La Rue.)

1910–19. *T* **14.** *Wmk. Mult. Crown CA. P* 14.

No.	Description				
44	½d. brown	0	4	0	5
44*a*	½d. pale brown	0	9	0	9
45	½d. green (1910)	0	6	0	6
45*a*	½d. deep green	3	6	3	6
46	1d. red (1910)	1	0	0	1
46*a*	1d. rose-red	2	0	0	1
46*b*	1d. carmine	2	6	0	6
47	2d. grey	4	0	4	0
48	2½d. blue	3	6	3	0
49	3d. purple/*yellow*	5	0	5	6
49*a*	4d. red/*yellow*	7	6	8	0
50	6d. purple	8	0	8	0
50*a*	6d. pale claret	7	6	7	6
51	1s. black/*green*	10	0	10	0
51*a*	1s. jet-black/*olive*	7	6	7	6

(Typo. De La Rue.)

1918 (MAY)–**1921.** *T* **15.** *Wmk. Mult. Crown CA. P* 14.

No.	Description				
51*b*	2s. pur. & blue/*blue*, C (1921)	15	0	17	6
52	2s. 6d. black & red/*blue*, C	25	0	27	6
52*a*	4s. black & carm., C (1921)	30	0	35	0
53	5s. green and red/*yellow*, C	25	0	27	6
54	10s. green and red/*green*, C	95	0	£5	
55	£1 purple and black/*red*, C	£6		£7	

Beware of cleaned copies of the 10s. with faked postmarks.

WAR TAX
(16)

1918 (4 MAY). *Nos.* 46 *and* 46*a overprinted locally with T* **16**, *in black.*

No.	Description				
56	1d. red	0	6	0	8
57	1d. rose-red	0	3	0	6

WAR TAX
(17)

1920 (MARCH). *No.* 46 *overprinted with T* **17.**

No.	Description				
58	1d. red	0	4	0	4

Tercentenary of Establishment of Representative Institutions.

1st Issue.

18

(Designed by the Governor. Typo. De La Rue.)

1920 (11 NOV.)–**1921.** *T* **18.** *P* 14.

(*a*) *Wmk. Mult. Crown CA* (JAN., 1921).

No.	Description				
59	¼d. brown, O	2	0	2	6
60	½d. green, O	3	0	3	6
61	2d. grey, O	12	6	15	0
62	3d. dull & dp. pur./*pale yell.*, C	17	6	20	0
63	4d. black & red/*pale yell.*, C	17	6	20	0
64	1s. black/*blue-green*, C	45	0	50	0

(*b*) *Wmk. Mult. Script CA.*

No.	Description				
65	1d. carmine, O (11.11.20)	5	0	3	6
66	2½d. bright blue, O (11.11.20)	15	0	17	6
67	6d. dull & brt. purple, C ('21)	20	0	22	6

2nd Issue.

19

(Des. H. J. Dale. Recess. De La Rue.)

1921 (MAY). *T* **19.** *P* 14.

(*a*) *Wmk. Mult. Crown CA.*

No.	Description				
68	2d. slate-grey	10	6	12	6
69	2½d. bright ultramarine	15	0	15	0
70	3d. purple/*pale yellow*	12	6	15	0
71	4d. red/*pale yellow*	15	0	17	6
72	6d. purple	22	6	25	0
73	1s. black/*green*	40	0	45	0

(*b*) *Wmk. Mult. Script CA.*

No.	Description				
74	¼d. brown	2	0	2	6
75	½d. green	4	0	4	6
76	1d. deep carmine	5	0	5	6

Type I Type II Type I Type II

1922–35. *T* **14** (*to* 1s.) *and* **15.** *Wmk. Mult. Script CA. P* 14.

No.	Description				
76*a*	¼d. brown (July, '28)	0	2	0	3
77	½d. green (Oct., '22)	0	2	0	3
78	1d. scarlet (I) (29.1.23)	1	9	0	2
78*a*	1d. carmine (I)	5	0	0	6
79	1d. carmine (II)	0	8	0	3
79*a*	1d. carmine-lake ('35) (II)	0	4	0	1
79*b*	1½d. red-brown (28.3.34)	1	3	0	8
80	2d. grey (Dec., '23)	1	9	2	0
81	2½d. sage-green (20.1.23)	3	6	3	6
82	2½d. ultramarine (I) (Oct., '26)	7	6	2	6
82*a*	2½d. ultramarine (II) (1932)	2	0	2	6
83	3d. ultramarine (Dec., '24)	7	6	8	0
84	3d. purple/*yellow* (Oct., '26)	2	6	1	9
85	4d. red/*yellow* (Aug., '24)	3	0	1	9
86	6d. purple (Aug., '24)	5	0	4	0
87	1s. black/*emerald* (Oct., '27)	10	0	10	6
87*a*	1s. brownish blk./*bright emerald* ('35)	45	0	55	0
88	2s. purple & bright blue/*blue*, C (Sept., '27)	17	6	20	0
89	2s. 6d. black and red/*blue*, C (April '27)	25	0	27	6
89*a*	2s. 6d., blk. & orge.-ver./*blue*, C ('30)	80	0	90	0
89*b*	2s. 6d. black & vermilion/*blue*, C, ('30)	17	6	20	0
92	10s. green & red/*emerald*, C (Dec. '24)	90	0	£5	
93	12s. 6d. grey & orge, C ('32)	£8		£10	

1d. In Type II a strong line completes the scroll at top left which in Type I is very weak. There are two plates of Type I differing slightly in the shape of "1d" and in the spacing of marginal jubilee lines. Type II is without jubilee lines.

2½d. Type I: Short, thick figures, especially the "1"; small "d". Type II: Figures taller and thinner; "d" larger.

No. 89*a*, which is from an early printing, is a much paler vermilion than the vermilion shades of subsequent printings.

1935 (6 MAY). *Silver Jubilee. As T* **13** *of Antigua, inscr.* "BERMUDA". *Recess. W'low. & Sons. Wmk. Mult. Script CA.* P 11×12.

No.	Description				
94	1d. deep blue and scarlet	0	10	1	0
95	1½d. ultramarine and grey	1	3	1	6
96	2½d. brown and deep blue	8	6	10	0
97	1s. slate and purple	17	6	20	0

20. Hamilton Harbour.

21. South Shore, near Spanish Rock.

22. The " Lucie." 23. Grape Bay, Paget Parish.

24. Point House, Warwick Parish (*Horizontal*).

25. House at Par-la-Ville, Hamilton (*Vertical*).

(Recess. Bradbury, Wilkinson & Co.)

1936 (14 Apr.). *Wmk. Mult. Script CA.* *P* 12.

98	**20**	½d. bright green	0	1	0	1
99	**21**	1d. black and scarlet ..	0	6	0	2
100	,,	1½d. black and chocolate ..	0	8	0	8
101	**22**	2d. black and pale blue ..	1	6	1	6
102	**23**	2½d. light and deep blue ..	1	6	1	6
103	**24**	3d. black and scarlet ..	3	0	3	0
104	**25**	6d. carmine-rose and violet	0	8	0	9
105	**23**	1s. green	6	0	7	6
106	**20**	1s. 6d. brown	2	0	2	6

BRITISH CENTRAL AFRICA.

See NYASALAND PROTECTORATE.

BRITISH COLUMBIA & VANCOUVER ISLAND.

1

(Typo. De La Rue & Co.)

1860. *T* **1.** *No wmk.* *Imperf.*

1	2½d. pale dull red	£35	

1860. *T* **1.** *No wmk.* *P* 14.

2	2½d. deep reddish rose ..	95	0	85	0
3	2½d. pale reddish rose	95	0	85	0

From June 20, 1864, to Nov. 1, 1865, the 2½d. was sold for 3d., and did duty as a 3d. provisional. No. 1 was never actually issued.

VANCOUVER ISLAND.

2 3

(Typo. De La Rue & Co.)

1865 (19 Sept.). *T* **2** *and* **3.** *Wmk. Crown CC.*
(*a*) *Imperf.*

11	5 c. rose	£450	£250
12	10 c. blue	£50	£35

Medium or poor copies of Nos. 11 and 12 can be supplied at much lower prices, when in stock.

(*b*) *P* 14.

13	5 c. rose	95	0	95	0
14	10 c. blue	95	0	95	0

BRITISH COLUMBIA.

4

(Typo. De La Rue & Co.)

1865 (1 Nov.)–**1867.** *T* **4.** *Wmk. Crown CC.* *P* 14.

21	3d. deep blue (1865)	27	6	30	0
22	3d. pale blue (1867)	25	0	27	6

On 19 Nov., 1866, British Columbia and Vancouver Island were consolidated as one territory, called British Columbia, after which date the current stamps of each colony were distributed and used throughout the combined territory.

Though bearing the names of both colonies the 2½d. of 1860 was mainly used for inland postage in British Columbia.

TWO CENTS (5) **5.CENTS.5** (6)

1868–71. *T* **4** *in various colours.* *Wmk. Crown CC.* *Surch. as T* **5** *or* **6.** *Colour of surcharge given in brackets.*

(*a*) *P* 12½.

23	5 c. red (*black*)	(Mar., '69)	£15	£15
24	10 c. lake (*blue*) ..	(Mar., '69)	£15	£14
25	25 c. yellow (*violet*)	(Mar., '69)	£12	£12
26	50 c. mauve (*red*)	(Mar., '69)	£14	£10
27	1 dol. green (*green*)	(Mar., '69)	£25	£30

(*b*) *P* 14.

28	2 c. brown (*black*)	(Jan., '68)	25	0	25	0
29	5 c. pale red (*black*)	(May, '69)	55	0	52	6
30	10 c. lake (*blue*) ..	.. ..	£18			
31	25 c. yellow (*violet*)	(July, '69)	50	0	45	0
32	50 c. mauve (*red*)	(Feb., '71)	£10			
33	1 dol. green (*green*)	.. ..	£30			

Nos. 30 and 33 were not issued.

The stamps of British Columbia were withdrawn from use on July 20, 1871, on the admittance of the Colony into the Dominion of Canada.

BRITISH EAST AFRICA.

I. Company's Administration.

BRITISH
EAST AFRICA
COMPANY

HALF ANNA
(1)

BRITISH
EAST AFRICA
COMPANY

1 ANNA
(2)

(Surcharged by De La Rue & Co.)

1890 (May). *Stamps of Great Britain (Queen Victoria). Surch. as T* **1** *or* **2** (1 a. *and* 4 a.).

1	**57**	½ a. on 1d. dull purple	.. 65 0	65 0
		a. "HALF" *for* "HALF"	.. £38	
2	**73**	1 a. on 2d. green and carm.	£8	95 0
3	**78**	4 a. on 5d. dull pur. & blue	£6	85 0

3

4

(Lithographed by Bradbury, Wilkinson & Co.)

1890 (Oct.)–**1894**. *P* 14½.

4	**3**	½ a. deep brown	1 6	1 9
		a. Pale brown	0 9	1 0
		b. Imperf.	20 0	12 6
		c. Imperf. between (pair) ..	12 6	12 6
5	„	1 a. blue-green	1 6	2 0
		a. Deep blue-green	1 0	2 0
		b. Imperf.	—	20 0
6	„	2 a. vermilion	1 9	3 0
		a. Imperf.	20 0	20 0
7	„	2½ a. black/*buff*	6 6	6 6
		a. Black/yellow	3 0	3 6
		b. Imperf.	20 0	20 0
		c. Imperf. between (pair) ..	15 0	12 6
8	„	3 a. black/*dull red*	6 0	7 0
		a. Black/bright red	1 9	3 0
		b. Imperf.	20 0	17 6
		c. Imperf. between (pair) ..	15 0	15 0
9	„	4 a. yellow-brown	2 0	4 0
		a. Imperf.	25 0	25 0
10	„	4 a. grey (*imperf.*)	65 0	65 0
11	„	4½ a. dull violet	10 0	10 0
		a. Purple	2 0	
		b. Imperf.	25 0	25 0
		c. Imperf. between (pair) ..	30 0	30 0
12	„	8 a. bright blue	2 6	3 0
		a. Imperf.	40 0	30 0
13	„	8 a. grey	40 0	42 6
14	„	1 r. carmine	2 6	6 0
		a. Imperf.	60 0	35 0
15	„	1 r. grey	42 6	42 6
16	**4**	2 r. brick-red	5 0	8 0
17	„	3 r. slate-purple	6 0	8 0
18	„	4 r. ultramarine	7 6	12 0
19	„	5 r. grey-green	7 6	14 0

Note.—For the 5 a. and 7½ a. in *T* **3**, see Nos. 29 and 30.

The entire sheet of each value of the above is watermarked "PURE LINEN WOVE BANK" and "W. C. S. & Co." in a monogram, the trademark of the makers Messrs. William Collins Sons & Co., but the ½ a., 1 a., 2½ a., 3 a. and 4½ a. were also printed on paper without watermark. Single specimens cannot always be distinguished.

The paper of Nos. 7, 7a, 8 and 8a. is coloured on the surface only.

1891. *Provisionals.*

(*a*) *New value handstamped in dull violet, and with MS. initials in black.*

20	**3**	"½ anna" on 2 a. vermilion ("A.D.") (Jan.) ..	£35	£10
		a. "½ Anna" double ..	—	£18
21	„	"1 anna" on 4 a. brown ("A.B.") (Feb.) ..	£65	£15

(*b*) *Both value and initials in MS., in black.*

22	**3**	"½ anna" on 2 a. vermilion ("A.B.") (Jan.) ..	—	£8
		a. Error: "½ Annas" ("A.B.")	—	£22
23	„	"½ anna" on 2 a. vermilion ("A.D.")	—	£8
		a. Error: "½ annas" ..	—	£15
24	„	"½ anna" on 3 a. black/*dull red* ("A.B.") (May) ..	£40	£15
25	„	"1 anna" on 3 a. black/*dull red* ("V.H.M.") (June)	—	£10
26	„	"1 anna" on 4 a. brown ("A.B.") (April) ..	£25	£8

A.D. = Andrew Dick, representative of the Company in Mombasa.

A.B. = Archibald Brown, cashier of the Company.

V.H.M. = Victor H. Mackenzie, bank manager in Mombasa.

5
ANNAS.
(5)

(Surcharged by Bradbury, Wilkinson & Co.)

1894 (1 Nov.). *Surcharged as T* **5**.

27	**3**	5 a. on 8 a. bright blue ..	35 0	35 0
28	„	7½ a. on 1 r. carmine ..	35 0	35 0

1894 (Dec.). *No wmk. P* 14½.

29	**3**	5 a. black/*grey-blue*	1 0	10 0
30	„	7½ a. black	1 3	12 6

These two stamps have "LD" after "COMPANY" in the inscription.

The paper of No. 29 is coloured on the surface only.

1895 (22 Feb.). *Surcharged with value and initials ("T.E.C.R.") in MS.*

31	**3**	"½ anna" on 3 a. blk./*dull red*	30 0	25 0
32	„	"1 anna" on 3 a. blk./*dull red*	£20	£16

T.E.C.R. = T. E. C. Remington, postmaster.

II. Imperial Administration.

British
East
Africa
(6)

(Handstamped at Mombasa.)

1895 (1 July). *Overprinted with T* **6**.

33	**3**	½ a. dull brown	20 0	12 6
		a. Deep brown	20 0	12 6
34	„	1 a. blue-green	32 6	35 0
		a. Deep blue-green	32 6	32 6
		b. Overprint double ..	70 0	
35	„	2 a. vermilion	52 6	45 0
36	„	2½ a. black/*yellow*	45 0	25 0
		a. Overprint double	—	80 0
37	„	3 a. black/*dull red*	20 0	18 6
38	„	4 a. yellow-brown	15 0	16 0
		a. Overprint double	—	75 0

39	3	4½ a. dull violet	60 0	45 0
		a. Purple	110 0	90 0
40	„	5 a. black/*grey-blue* ..	110 0	85 0
41	„	7½ a. black	42 6	42 6
		a. Overprint double	£6	
42	„	8 a. bright blue	35 0	30 0
		a. Overprint double	£6	
		b. Overprint inverted ..	£30	
43	„	1 r. carmine	22 6	20 0
		a. Overprint double	£8	
44	4	2 r. brick-red	90 0	95 0
45	„	3 r. deep purple	65 0	65 0
46	„	4 r. ultramarine	65 0	67 6
		a. Overprint double	£7	
47	„	5 r. grey-green	£5	95 0

2½

(7)

(Surcharged locally.)

1895 (Oct.). *No.* 39 *surcharged with T* 7.

48	3	2½ on 4½ a. dull violet (R.) ..	55 0	50 0

British East Africa (8)   British East Africa (9)

(Overprinted at the offices of a Zanzibar newspaper.)

1895 (Nov.). *Stamps of India* (*Queen Victoria overprinted with T* 8 *or* 9 (2 *r. to* 5 *r.*).

49	23	½ a. deep green	1 6	1 0
		a. "British" for "British"	£24	
		b. "Brltish" for "British"	20 0	
		c. "Afrlca" for "Africa"	25 0	
50	25	1 a. plum	3 0	2 0
		a. "British" for "British"	£30	
		b. "Brltish" for "British"	20 0	
		c. "Afrlca" for "Africa"	30 0	
51	26	1½ a. sepia	3 0	2 6
		a. "Brltish" for "British"	25 0	
		b. "Afrlca" for "Africa"	30 0	
52	27	2 a. ultramarine	3 6	2 6
		a. "British" for "British"	£30	
		b. "Brltish" for "British"	25 0	
		c. "Afrlca" for "Africa"	25 0	25 0
53	36	2½ a. green	3 6	3 6
		a. "Biitish" for "British"	£40	
		b. "Bpitish" for "British"	£40	
		c. "British" for "British"	—	£30
		d. "Eas" for "East" ..	£10	
		e. "Brltish" for "British"	30 0	30 0
		f. "Afrlca" for "Africa"	25 0	
54	28	3 a. brown-orange ..	6 0	6 0
		a. "Brltish" for "British"	25 0	25 0
		b. "Afrlca" for "Africa"	30 0	
55	29	4 a. olive-green	8 0	9 0
		a. Slate-green	7 0	7 0
		b. "Brltish" for "British"	25 0	25 0
		c. "Afrlca" for "Africa"	30 0	
56	21	6 a. pale brown	7 6	7 6
		a. "Brltish" for "British"	90 0	
		b. "Afrlca" for "Africa"	42 6	
57	31	8 a. dull mauve	22 6	22 6
		a. "Brltish" for "British"	40 0	
		b. "Afrlca" for "Africa"	80 0	
		c. Magenta	9 6	10 6
		ca. "Easv" for "East" ..	—	£35
58	32	12 a. purple/*red*	9 6	9 6
		a. "Brltish" for "British"	45 0	45 0
		b. "Afrlca" for "Africa"	70 0	
59	33	1 r. slate	25 0	27 6
60	37	1 r. green and carmine ..	20 0	17 6
		a. "Easv" for "East" ..	£40	
		b. "Brltish" for "British"	50 0	
		c. "Afrlca" for "Africa"	60 0	
		d. Opt. double, one sideways	65 0	
61	38	2 r. carmine and yell.-brn.	35 0	40 0
62	„	3 r. brown and green	42 6	42 6
63	„	5 r. ultramarine and violet	52 6	57 6
		a. Overprint double.. ..	£45	

The relative positions of the three lines of the overprint vary considerably.

There are numbers of less important varieties, such as inverted "s" in "British", wide and narrow "B", and inverted "V" for "A" in "Africa".

The 2, 3, and 5 r. normally overprinted in larger type than the lower values, are also known with the smaller overprint; but these last were—as far as we know—*not issued* for postal purposes.

2½

(10)

(Surcharged locally.)

1895 (Dec.). *No.* 51 *surcharged with T* 10 *in bright red.*

64	26	2½ on 1½ a. sepia	20 0	17 6
		a. Inverted "1" in fraction ..	£6	

No. 51 also exists surcharged with *T* 12, 13 and 14 in *brown-red*. These stamps were sent to the Postal Union authorities at Berne, but were never issued to the public.

11

(Recess-printed by De La Rue & Co.)

1896 (19 May)–**1903**. *Wmk. Crown CA.* *P* 14.

65	11	½ a. yellow-green	0 6	0 6
66	„	1 a. carmine-red	1 3	0 4
		a. Bright rose-red	1 3	0 4
		b. Rosine (1903)	5 0	3 6
67	„	2 a. chocolate	2 9	2 0
68	„	2½ a. deep blue	2 6	1 9
		a. Violet-blue	2 0	1 6
69	„	3 a. grey	4 0	3 6
70	„	4 a. deep green	4 0	3 6
71	„	4½ a. orange-yellow ..	4 6	3 6
72	„	5 a. yellow-bistre ..	5 0	4 0
73	„	7½ a. mauve..	6 0	6 0
74	„	8 a. grey-olive	6 0	5 0
75	„	1 r. pale dull blue.. ..	22 6	22 6
		a. Ultramarine	18 6	18 6
76	„	2 r. orange	22 0	22 0
77	„	3 r. deep violet	27 6	27 6
78	„	4 r. carmine-lake	27 6	27 6
79	„	5 r. sepia	32 6	32 6

1897 (Jan.). *Stamps of Zanzibar* (1896 *issue*) *overprinted with T* 8. *Wmk. Single Rosette.*

80	13	½ a. green and red ..	20 0	22 6
81	„	1 a. indigo and red ..	30 0	30 0
82	„	2 a. red-brown and red ..	20 0	22 6
83	„	4½ a. orange and red ..	20 0	20 0
84	„	5 a. bistre and red ..	20 0	20 0
85	„	7½ a. mauve and red ..	20 0	22 6

An overprint similar to *T* 8, but with stop after "Africa," is known in *red* on the 1 a. and in *black* on the other values. These were made for purposes of official record, but were apparently not issued to the public.

Stamps of Zanzibar with watermark "Multiple Rosettes" and overprinted with *T* 8 are forgeries.

2½	2½	2½
(12)	(13)	(14)

(Surcharged locally.)

1897 (Jan.). *Stamps of Zanzibar* (1896 *issue*) *optd. with T* 8 *and further surch. with T* 12, 13, *or* 14, *in red.*

No.	Type	Description				
86	12	2½ on 1 a. indigo and red ..	32	6	32	6
		a. "2" over "1" for "½" ..	£25			
87	13	2½ on 1 a. indigo and red ..	62	6	45	0
88	14	2½ on 1 a. indigo and red ..	37	6	37	6
89	12	2½ on 3 a. grey and red ..	22	0	22	0
		a. "2" over "1" for "½" ..				
90	13	2½ on 3 a. grey and red ..	35	0	35	0
91	14	2½ on 3 a. grey and red ..	32	6	32	6

Both the notes after No. 85 apply to this issue also.

15

(Recess-printed by De La Rue & Co.)

1897 (Nov.). *Wmk. Crown CC.* *P* 14.

No.	Type	Description				
92	15	1 r. dull blue	18	6	18	6
		a. Bright ultramarine ..	20	0	20	0
93	„	2 r. orange	35	0	35	0
94	„	3 r. deep violet	45	0	45	0
95	„	4 r. carmine	£5		£5	
96	„	5 r. deep sepia	80	0	80	0
97	„	10 r. yellow-bistre	£7		£7	
98	„	20 r. pale green	£16		£16	
99	„	50 r. mauve	£45		£40	

In 1903 stamps inscribed "British East Africa" were superseded by those inscribed "East Africa and Uganda Protectorate". (*See* Kenya, Uganda and Tanganyika.)

BRITISH GUIANA.

SIMPLIFICATION (see p. xii)

Nos. 1 to 115.
1, 8, 4, 6. 9, 10. 11, 20, 21. 24, 26. 29, 40, 41, 51, 58, 60, 62, 47, 49, 64. 85, 88, 90, 94, 74, 95, 99, 103, 105.

Nos. 116 to 125.
Take cheapest stamp of each value, ignoring types.

1

(Set up and printed at the office of the *Royal Gazette*, Georgetown, British Guiana.)

1850 (1 July). *T* 1. *Type-set. Black impression. Medium wove paper.*

Prices are for—(a) Cut square, (b) Cut round.

No.	Description	*a* *Used.*	*b* *Used.*
1	2 c. *rose* (1851)	—	£2500
2	4 c. *orange*	£1000	£200
3	4 c. *lemon-yellow*	£1100	£250
4	8 c. *green*	£900	£150
5	12 c. *blue*	£200	£75
6	12 c. *indigo*	£350	£70
7	12 c. *pale blue*	£500	£90
	a. "2" of "12" with straight foot		
	Pelure paper.		
8	4 c. *pale yellow*	£1000	£200

These stamps were initialled by the postmaster, or the Post Office clerks, before they were issued. The initials are—E. T. E. D(alton), E. D. W(ight), J. B. S(mith), H. A. K(illikelley), and W. H. L(ortimer). There are several types of each value.

2

(Lithographed by Messrs. Waterlow & Sons.)

1852 (Jan.). *T* 2. *Surface-coloured paper.*

No.	Description	Un.	Used
9	1 c. black/*magenta*	£400*	£150*
10	4 c. black/*deep blue*	£500*	£175*

There are two varieties of type for each value. Reprints of both stamps were made in 1865; they are printed on thicker paper and perforated 12½, but specimens are frequently seen with the perforation removed. (*Price* 20*s., either value.*)

*** NOTE.**—*Prices for Nos.* 9 *and* 10 *are for fine copies. Poor to medium specimens can be supplied when in stock at from one-tenth of above prices.*

3

(Dies engraved and stamps lithographed by Messrs. Waterlow & Sons.)

1853. *T* 3. *Imperf.*

No.	Description		
11	1 c. vermilion	£75	£40

This 1 c. is known in *reddish brown*; this is probably a proof.

5 ONE CENT 5	ONE CENT
A	B
5 ONE CENT 3	3 ONE CENT 3
C	D

1858–59. *Fresh lithographic transfers with varying labels of value, as illustrated.*

White line above value.

A. "o" in "ONE" large and 1 mm. from left corner.

B. "o" in "ONE" small and ¾ mm. from left corner.

C. "o" in "ONE" small and ¾ mm. from left corner. "N" and "T" in "CENT" widely spaced.

D. Letters "ONE" close together, "o" 1¼ mm. from left corner.

12	1 c. dull red (A)	—	£40
13	1 c. brownish red (A) ..	—	£50
14	1 c. dull red (B)	£100	£40
15	1 c. brownish red (B) ..	—	£45
16	1 c. dull red (C)	£85	£45
17	1 c. dull red (D)		

NOTE.—*These prices are for fine copies with four margins. Medium specimens can be supplied at much lower rates.*

4

5

1853–60. *T* **4.** *Imperf.*

18	4 c. deep blue (1853)	£60	£35
19	4 c. blue (1856 ?)	£50	£30
20	4 c. pale blue (1859)	£45	£28

Retouched varieties.

20*a*	4 c. deep blue	£90	£50
20*b*	4 c. pale blue	£80	£40

NOTE *after* No. 17 *also applies here.*

These stamps are generally found with a white line or traces of it above the label of value and lower corner figures. In some stamps on the sheet this line is missing, owing to having been retouched, and in these cases a line of colour usually appears in its place.

The 1 c. and 4 c. stamps were reprinted in 1865 from fresh transfers of five varieties. These are on *thin* paper and perf. 12½.

1860. *T* **5.** *Figures in corners framed. Imperf.*

21	4 c. blue	£60	£25

6

(Set up and printed at the office of the *Official Gazette* by Baum and Dallas, Georgetown.)

1856 (FEB.). *T* **6.** *Type-set. Surface-coloured paper.*

23	1 c. black/*magenta*	
24	4 c. black/*magenta* .. *used*	£80 *to* £350
24*a*	4 c. black/*rose-carmine* ..	
26	**4 c. black/*blue*** .. ***used***	£500 *to* £1250

1856 (AUG.). *Paper coloured through.*

27	4 c. black/*deep blue*	—	£2500

These stamps, like those of the first issue, were initialled before being issued. There are eight types of each. The initials are—E.T.E.D., E.D.W., C.A.W(atson), and W.H.L. No. 23 is the *rarest* stamp known.

7

(Dies engraved and stamps lithographed by Messrs. Waterlow & Sons.)

1860. *T* **7.** *Tablets of value as illustrated Thick paper. P* 12.

29	1 c. pale rose	£45		£10	
30	2 c. deep orange	60	0	20	0
31	2 c. pale orange	60	0	20	0
32	4 c. deep blue	£10		37	6
33	4 c. blue	£9		37	6
34	8 c. brownish rose	£12		55	0
35	8 c. pink	£10		45	0
36	12 c. lilac	£18		35	0
37	12 c. grey-lilac	£12		30	0
38	24 c. deep green	£45		70	0
39	24 c. green	£40		70	0

The 1 c. was reprinted in 1865 on *thin* paper, P 12½–13, and in a different shade. *Price* 7s. 6d.

The 12 c. in both shades is frequently found surcharged with a large "5d." in *red*; this is to denote the proportion of postage repayable by the colony to Great Britain for oversea letters.

1861. *T* **7.** *Colour changed.*

40	1 c. reddish brown	£10		90	0

1862. *T* **7.** *Thin paper. P* 12.

41	1 c. brown	£15		£10	
42	1 c. black	40	0	22	6
43	2 c. orange	35	0	15	0
44	4 c. blue	60	0	22	6
45	4 c. pale blue	40	0	15	0
46	8 c. pink	60	0	37	6
47	12 c. dull purple	55	0	17	6
48	12 c. purple	57	6	20	0
49	12 c. lilac	80	0	22	6
50	24 c. green	£25		60	0

1863. *T* **7.** *Thin paper. P* 12½–13.

51	1 c. black	12	6	17	6
52	2 c. orange	30	0	17	6
53	4 c. blue	35	0	18	0
54	8 c. pink	85	0	50	0
55	12 c. brownish lilac	£15		50	0
56	24 c. green	£18		50	0

Specimens are found on *pelure* paper.

1863. *T* 7. *Medium paper.* *P* 12½–13.

No.	Description	Unused		Used	
57	1 c. black	25	0	15	0
58	2 c. deep orange	22	6	12	6
59	2 c. orange	25	0	12	6
60	4 c. greyish blue	32	6	15	0
61	4 c. blue	35	0	15	0
62	8 c. pink	95	0	25	0
63	12 c. brownish lilac	£8		60	0
64	24 c. green	95	0	35	0
65	24 c. deep green	£10		40	0

1866. *T* 7. *P* 10.

No.	Description	Unused		Used	
65*a*	12 c. grey-lilac	£10		27	6

8 9

G H

I K

New transfers for the 1 c., 2 c., 8 c., and 12 c., with the spaces between values and the word "CENTS" about 1 mm.

1863–64. *T* 8 *and* 9 (6 *c.*, 24 *c.*, *and* 48 *c.*). *Medium paper.* *P* 12½–13.

No.	Description	Unused		Used	
66	1 c. black	12	6	7	6
67	2 c. orange-red	22	6	7	6
68	2 c. orange	17	6	6	0
69	6 c. blue	50	0	30	0
70	6 c. greenish blue	50	0	35	0
71	6 c. deep blue	45	0	40	0
72	6 c. milky blue	60	0	40	0
73	8 c. pink	70	0	17	6
74	8 c. carmine	75	0	17	6
75	12 c. grey-lilac	£12		17	6
76	12 c. brownish purple ..	£15		17	6
77	24 c. green (*perf.* 12)	£8		22	6
78	24 c. yellow-green (*perf.* 12) ..	65	0	22	6
79	24 c. yellow-grn. (*perf.* 12½–13)	70	0	20	0
80	24 c. green (*perf.* 12½–13) ..	70	0	17	6
81	24 c. blue-green (*perf.* 12½–13)	£5		20	0
82	48 c. pale red	80	0	35	0
83	48 c. deep red	80	0	35	0
84	48 c. carmine-rose	£8		35	0

There is no 4 c. value of this issue, that of the previous issue being used concurrently.

There is a variety of the 6 c. with stop before "VICISSIM".

Varieties of most of the values of issues of 1863–64 and 1866 are to be found on both very thin and thick papers.

1866. *T* 8 *and* 9. *P* 10.

No.	Description	Unused		Used	
85	1 c. black	8	6	6	0
86	1 c. grey-black	10	0	8	6
87	2 c. orange	15	0	5	0
88	2 c. reddish orange ..	15	0	5	0
89	4 c. slate-blue	35	0	10	0
90	4 c. blue	35	0	8	6
91	4 c. pale blue	40	0	10	0
92	6 c. milky blue	90	0	25	0
93	6 c. ultramarine	90	0	25	0
94	6 c. dull blue	90	0	25	0
95	8 c. pink	70	0	17	6
96	8 c. brownish pink	85	0	20	0
96*a*	8 c. carmine	85	0	22	6
97	12 c. pale lilac	£8		27	6
98	12 c. grey-lilac	85	0	25	0
99	12 c. brownish grey	75	0	15	0
100	12 c. lilac	75	0	15	0
101	24 c. dark green	£8		17	6
102	24 c. bluish green	—		12	6
103	24 c. yellow-green	90	0	10	6
104	48 c. crimson	£10		35	0
105	48 c. red	£9		35	0

1875. *T* 8 *and* 9. *P* 15.

No.	Description	Unused		Used	
106	1 c. black	15	0	10	6
107	2 c. orange-red	70	0	12	6
108	2 c. orange	65	0	12	6
109	4 c. bright blue	£10		85	0
111	6 c. ultramarine	£12		60	0
112	8 c. deep rose	90	0	45	0
113	12 c. lilac	£15		37	6
114	24 c. yellow-green	£18		30	0
115	24 c. deep green	£18		30	0

There is a variety of the 48 c. *with* stop after "P" in "PETIMUSQUE."

The 6 c., 24 c., and 48 c. are known *imperf.*, but in this state are probably proofs.

1862 (Oct.). *Type-set and printed by Mr. George Melville at the office of the "Royal Gazette," Georgetown. Black on coloured paper.*

Rouletted 6.

10

NOTE.

Prices for stamps of this 1862 issue are for good average copies. Superb copies with roulettes on all sides are worth considerably more.

No.	Type	Description	Unused	Used
116	**10**	1 c. *rose* (12 *in sheet*) ..	£45	£20
		a. Unsigned	£10	
		b. "1" for "I" in "BRITISH"	—	£30
		c. Wrong ornament on left ..	—	£30
117	**10**	2 c. *yellow* (12 *in sheet*) ..	£50	£15
		a. Unsigned	£12	
		b. "1" for "I" in "BRITISH"	—	£30

11

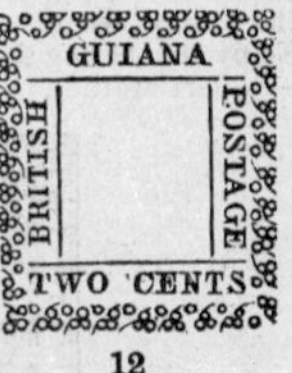

12

No.	Type	Description	Unused	Used
118	**11**	1 c. *rose* (8 *in sheet*) ..	£55	£20
		a. Unsigned	£12	
		b. "1" for "I" in "BRITISH"	—	£35
		c. "1" for "I" in "GUIANA"	—	£35
		d. Italic "S" in "POSTAGE"	—	£30
		e. Narrow "T" in "CENTS"	—	£30
		f. Wrong ornament in top frame	—	£30
		g. Wrong ornament in left frame	—	£30
119	**11**	2 c. *yellow* (8 *in sheet*) ..	£75	£20
		a. Unsigned	£12	
		b. "1" for "I" in "BRITISH"	—	£30
		c. "1" for "I" in "GUIANA"	—	£30
		d. Italic "S" in "POSTAGE"	—	£30
		e. "C" for "O" in "TWO" and narrow "T" in "CENTS"	—	£30
		f. Wrong ornament in top frame..	—	£28
		g. Italic "T" in "TWO" ..	—	£28

120 **12** 1 c. *rose* (4 *in sheet*) .. £90 £40
 a. Unsigned £25
 b. "1" for "I" in "GUIANA" — £45
 c. "o" for "o" in "POSTAGE" — £45

121 **12** 2 c. *yellow* (4 *in sheet*) .. £120 £40
 a. Unsigned .. ..
 b. "1" for "I" in "GUIANA" — £45
 c. "o" for "o" in "POSTAGE" .. — £45

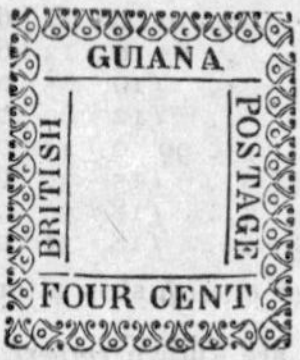

13

14

122 **13** 4 c. *blue* (10 *in sheet*) .. £40 £25
 a. Unsigned
 b. Ornament omitted on right — £35

123 **14** 4 c. *blue* (6 *in sheet*) .. £55 £30
 a. Unsigned £25

15

124 **15** 4 c. *blue* (6 *in sheet*) .. £55 £30
 a. Unsigned .. ..
 b. "1" for "I" in "BRITISH" — £40

As T **15**, *but with four thin inner lines.*

125 – 4 c. *blue* (2 *in sheet*) .. £150 £100
 a. Unsigned .. ..

There are in all 24 varieties of type of each value. Many of these types are in stock, and can be sent on approval to advanced collectors. The stamps were initialled in the centre before use by the Acting Receiver-General of the colony —Robert Mather.

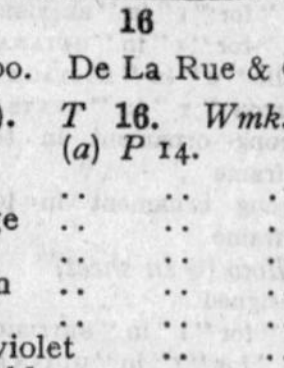

16

(Typo. De La Rue & Co.)

1876 (1 July). *T* **16**. *Wmk. Crown CC*

(*a*) *P* 14.

126	1 c. slate	.. 3	0		0	8
127	2 c. orange	.. 10	0		0	8
128	4 c. blue	.. 25	0		10	0
129	6 c. brown	.. 22	6		10	6
130	8 c. rose	.. 25	0		6	6
131	12 c. pale violet	.. 25	0		7	6
132	24 c. emerald-green	.. 22	6		8	6
133	48 c. red-brown	.. 30	0		17	6
134	96 c. olive-bistre	.. £25			£12	

(*b*) *P* 12½.

135 4 c. blue .. £35 £15

(*c*) *Perf. compound of* 14 × 12½

136 1 c. slate .. — £15

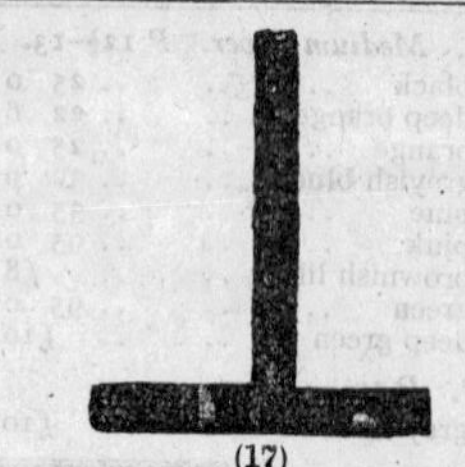

(17)

1878. *Various stamps with bars ruled in ink, in black.*

A. *On ordinary issues.*

With two horizontal bars.

137 (1 c.) on 6 c. brown (No. 129) 17 6 16 0

6 Nov. *With horizontal and vertical bars, T* **17**.

138 (1 c.) on 6 c. ultram. (No. 93) 70 0 40 0
139 (1 c.) on 6 c. brown (No. 129) 85 0 35 0

B. Nov. *On stamps overprinted* "OFFICIAL".

Horizontal bar across "OFFICIAL".

140 1 c. black (No. 501) .. 40 0 37 6
141 1 c. slate (No. 506) .. 45 0 20 0
142 2 c. orange (No. 507) .. 60 0 15 0

With two horizontal bars and one vertical.

144 (1 c.) on 4 c. blue (No. 508) 40 0 30 0
145 (1 c.) on 6 c. brown (No. 509) 80 0 40 0
146 (2 c.) on 8 c. rose (No. 503) 85 0 65 0

23 Nov. *With one horizontal bar and one vertical.*

148 (2 c.) on 8 c. rose (No. 510) £6 30 0

1 (18) 1 (19) 2 (20) 2 (21)

1881 (Dec.). *Various stamps with bar ruled in ink obliterating original value, and surcharged with figure, in black.*

A. *On ordinary issues.*

149 **18** 1 on 48 c. red (No. 105) .. 15 0 12 6
150 **19** 1 on 96 c. ol.-bis. (No. 134) 5 0 5 6

The obliterating bar is found 1, 2½, or 4 mm. wide.

151 **20** 2 on 96 c. ol.-bis. (No. 134) 7 6 10 0
152 **21** 2 on 96 c. ol.-bis. (No. 134) 12 6 17 6

The obliterating bar is found 1 or 3 mm. wide

B. *On stamps overprinted* "OFFICIAL".

1
OFFICIAL
(22)

As T **22**.

153 1 on 12 c. brownish purple (No. 504) 20 0 20 0
154 1 on 48 c. red-brown (*as* No. 133) 22 6 22 6

2
OFFICIAL
(23)

2
OFFICIAL
(24)

Nos. 131 *and* 132 *surcharged as T* **23** *or* **24**.

155 **23** 2 on 12 c. pale violet .. 55 0 55 0
156 **24** on 12 c. pale violet .. 25 0 22 6

157	23	2 on 24 c. emerald-green ..	60 0	62 6
158	24	2 on 24 c. emerald-green ..	30 0	25 0

Varieties. Surcharge double.

159	24	2 on 12 c. pale violet ..	£30
160	„	2 on 24 c. emerald-green ..	£35

2

OFFICIAL

(25)

Surcharged as T 25.

161	2 on 24 c. green (No. 505) ..	45 0	45 0

The obliterating bar is found 1, 2, or 3 mm. wide.

26 27

(Set up and printed by Messrs. Baldwin & Co., of Georgetown.)

1882. *Black impression. P 12. With the word* "SPECIMEN" *perforated across the stamp diagonally.*

162	26	1 c. *magenta*	17 6	17 6
		a. Imperf. between (pair) ..		
163	26	2 c. *yellow*	18 0	17 6
164	27	1 c. *magenta*	17 6	15 0
165	„	2 c. *yellow*	17 6	17 0
		a. Bisected diagonally (1 c.)		

The word "SPECIMEN" was perforated across the stamp to prevent fraud. The stamps being type-set, this "control" was used to render fraud on the P.O. more difficult.

These stamps were arranged on the sheet in six rows of two in a row, or in three rows of four. In every sheet of the 1 c. one stamp has a "1" with a foot, and in every sheet of the 2 c. are four stamps with the "2" smaller than that shown in T 26.

Without "SPECIMEN."

166	26	1 c. *magenta*	80 0	65 0
167	„	2 c. *yellow*	85 0	85 0
168	27	1 c. *magenta*	80 0	65 0
169	„	2 c. *yellow*	85 0	85 0

(Engraved and printed by De La Rue & Co.)

1882 (May). *T 16. Wmk. Crown CA. P 14.*

170	1 c. slate	3 6	0 6
171	2 c. orange	10 0	0 8
172	4 c. blue	17 6	6 0
173	6 c. brown	10 0	6 0
174	8 c. rose	20 0	3 0

INLAND 4 CENTS (*a*)

2 CENTS REVENUE (28) 4 CENTS (*b*)

1888–89. *T 16 (without value in lower label) overprinted* "INLAND REVENUE", *and surcharged with value as T 28, in black. Two types of* "4", *as (a) and (b). Wmk. Crown CA. P 14.*

175	1 c. dull purple	2 6	2 6
176	2 c. dull purple	3 0	2 6
177	3 c. dull purple	2 6	2 6
178	4 c. dull purple (*a*)	2 6	2 6
179	6 c. dull purple	3 0	3 0
180	8 c. dull purple	3 0	2 0
181	10 c. dull purple	7 0	6 0
182	20 c. dull purple	10 0	10 0
183	40 c. dull purple	17 6	17 6
184	72 c. dull purple	17 6	17 6
185	1 dol. green	£8	£8
186	2 dol. green	£6	130 0
187	3 dol. green	50 0	52 6
188	4 dol. green (*a*)	£8	£9
189	5 dol. green	75 0	80 0

Varieties. Larger figure 4, as (b).

190	4 c. dull purple	7 6	7 6
191	4 dol. green	£15	£18

2

(29)

1889 (July). *No. 176 surcharged locally with a figure* "2", *in addition, as T 29 in red.*

192	"2" on 2 c. dull purple ..	3 0	2 0

The varieties with figure "2" *inverted* or *double-printed* were of private manufacture, emanating from a postal employee in Demerara.

30

(Typo. De La Rue & Co.)

1889 (Sept.)–1890. *T 30. Wmk. Crown CA P 14.*

193	1 c. dull pur. & slate-grey	2 0	0 8
194	2 c. dull pur. & orange ..	1 0	0 2
195	4 c. dull pur. & ultramarine	5 0	3 6
196	4 c. dull pur. & cobalt ..	7 6	6 6
197	6 c. dull pur. & brown ..	10 0	8 6
198	6 c. dull pur. & marone ..	8 0	7 6
199	8 c. dull pur. & rose (1890)	5 6	5 0
200	12 c. dull pur. & bright pur.	7 6	4 0
200*a*	12 c. dull pur. & mauve ..	6 0	5 0
201	24 c. dull pur. & green ..	7 6	7 6
202	48 c. dull pur. & orange-red	18 0	17 6
203	72 c. dull pur. & red-brown	20 0	20 0
204	72 c. dull pur. & yellow-brn.	22 6	20 0
205	96 c. dull pur. & carmine ..	27 6	25 0
206	96 c. dull pur. & rosine ..	25 0	23 0

INLAND One Cent ~~1 DOLLAR~~ REVENUE

(31)

1890 (15 July). *Stamps of* 1888–89 *surcharged locally* " One Cent ", *in red, as in T* **31**.

No.	Description	Unused	Used
207	1 c. on 1 dol. (No. 185) ..	2 0	1 9
208	1 c. on 2 dol. (No. 186) ..	1 6	1 9
209	1 c. on 3 dol. (No. 187) ..	1 9	1 6
210	1 c. on 4 dol. (No. 188) ..	4 0	5 0

Varieties. (i.) *With larger figure* 4. *Var.* (*b*).

No.	Description	Unused	Used
211	1 c. on 4 dol. (No. 191) ..	8 0	12 6

(ii.) *Surcharge double.*

No.	Description	Unused	Used
212	1 c. on 1 dol. (No. 185) ..	—	90 0
212*a*	1 c. on 2 dol. (No. 186)		
212*b*	1 c. on 3 dol. (No. 187) ..	80 0	
212*c*	1 c. on 4 dol. (No. 188) ..	£7	

1890 (Dec.)–**1891.** *T* **30**. *Wmk. Crown CA. P* 14.

No.	Description	Unused	Used
213	1 c. sea-green (1891) ..	0 8	0 2
214	5 c. ultramarine (1891) ..	4 0	0 10
215	8 c. dull pur. & greenish blk.	7 6	7 6

32. Mount Roraima.

33. Kaieteur Falls.

(Recess. De La Rue and Co.)

1898. *Jubilee issue. Dated* 1897. *Centre in first colour. Wmk. Crown CC. P* 14.

No.	Type	Description	Unused	Used
216	**32**	1 c. blue-black & carmine	3 0	2 0
217	**33**	2 c. brown and indigo ..	3 0	2 0
		a. Imperf. between (pair) ..		
218	**33**	2 c. brown and blue ..	2 6	2 0
219	**32**	5 c. green and sepia ..	5 0	4 6
		a. Imperf. between (pair) ..		
220	**33**	10 c. blue-blk. & orge.-red	17 6	17 6
221	**32**	15 c. red-brown and blue	15 0	15 0

The 1 c. was afterwards retouched, the lines of shading on the mountains in the background being strengthened, and along the ridge distinct from each other, whereas, in the original, they are more or less blurred. In the retouched die the shading of the sky is not so pronounced as in the original.

TWO CENTS.

(34)

1899. *Surcharged with T* **34** *in black.*

No.	Description	Unused	Used
222	2 c. on 5 c. (No. 219) ..	2 0	2 6
223	2 c. on 10 c. (No. 220) ..	3 0	3 6
224	2 c. on 15 c. (No. 221) ..	2 0	2 6

Varieties.

(i.) *No stop after* " cents ". (*No.* 53 *on sheet in* 225/6 *and No.* 50 *on sheet in* 227.)

No.	Description	Unused	Used
225	2 c. on 5 c.	30 0	30 0
226	2 c. on 10 c.	30 0	30 0
227	2 c. on 15 c.	22 6	25 0

(ii.) " gents " *for* " cents ". (*No.* 55 *on sheet.*)

No.	Description	Unused	Used
228	2 c. on 10 c.	35 0	37 6

(iii.) *Surcharge double.*

No.	Description	Unused	Used
229	2 c. on 15 c.	£15	

(iv.) *Surcharge double, one without stop after* " cents ".

No.	Description	Unused	Used
230	2 c. on 15 c. ..	£80	

(v.) *Surcharge inverted*

No.	Description	Unused	Used
231	2 c. on 10 c.	£20	
232	2 c. on 15 c.	£25	

1900–7. *T* **30**. *Wmk. Crown CA. P* 14.

No.	Description	Unused	Used
233	1 c. grey-green ('07) ..	2 0	0 6
234	2 c. dull purple and carmine	1 9	0 6
235	2 c. dull purple & black/*red*	1 3	0 3
236	6 c. grey-blk. & ultram. ('02)	12 6	10 0
237	48 c. grey & purple-brn. ('01)	27 6	30 0
238	48 c. brownish grey & brn. ('07)	25 0	25 0
239	60 c. green and rosine ('03) ..	70 0	75 0

The 1 c. of this date is a reissue in non-fugitive ink.

1905–7. *T* **30**. *Wmk. Multiple Crown CA. P* 14.

No.	Description	Unused	Used
240	1 c. grey-green, OC	2 0	0 2
241	2 c. purple & black/*red*, OC	0 10	0 2
242	4 c. dull pur. & ultram., OC	10 0	8 6
243	5 c. dull pur. & blue/*blue*, OC	9 0	8 6
244	6 c. grey-blk. & ultram., OC	10 6	12 6
245	12 c. dull & bright pur., OC ..	17 6	10 6
246	24 c. dull pur. & grn., OC ('06)	8 0	8 6
247	48 c. grey & pur.-brown, OC	12 6	12 6
248	60 c. green and rosine, OC ..	22 6	25 0
249	72 c. pur. & orge.-brn., C ('07)	25 0	27 6
250	96 c. blk. & ver./*yell.*, C ('06) ..	30 0	35 0

35

POSTAGE AND REVENUE

(36)

1905. *T* **35**. " revenue " *and value in second colour. Wmk. Multiple Crown CA. Overprinted with T* **36**, *in black. P* 14.

No.	Description	Unused	Used
251	$2.40, green and violet, C ..	£10	£10

1907–10. *T* **30**. *Colours changed. Wmk. Mult. Crown CA. P* 14.

No.	Description	Unused	Used
252	1 c. blue-green, O ('10) ..	0 8	0 2
253	2 c. rose-red, O	1 3	0 2
254	4 c. brown and purple, O ..	3 0	3 0
255	5 c. ultramarine, O	4 0	2 6
256	6 c. grey and black, O ..	4 6	4 6
257	12 c. orange and mauve, O ..	6 0	6 6

1910. *T* **30** *redrawn. Wmk. Mult. Crown CA. P* 14.

No.	Description	Unused	Used
258	2 c. rose-red, O	1 0	0 3

In this redrawn type the flag at the maintruck is close to the mast, whereas in the former type it appears to be flying loose from halyards. There are two background lines above the value " 2 cents " instead of three and the " s " is further away from the end of the tablet.

37

War Tax

(38)

(Typo. De La Rue & Co.)

1913–21. *T* **37.** *Wmk. Mult. Crown CA. P* 14.

No.	Description	Unused	Used
259	1 c. yellow-green, O ..	0 6	0 1
259*a*	1 c. blue-green, O (1917) ..	0 6	0 1
260	2 c. carmine, O	1 0	0 1
260*a*	2 c. scarlet, O (1916) ..	0 8	0 1
261	4 c. brown & bright pur., C	3 6	1 0
261*a*	4 c. deep brown & purple, C	3 6	1 0
262	5 c. bright blue, O ..	3 0	2 6
263	6 c. grey and black, O ..	3 6	2 6
264	12 c. orange and violet, C ..	4 6	3 0
265	24 c. dull purple & green, C ..	6 6	6 6
266	48 c. grey & purple-brown, C	10 6	12 0
267	60 c. green and rosine, C ..	15 0	17 6
268	72 c. purple & orge.-brown, C	22 6	22 6
269	96 c. blk. & ver./*yell.*, C (1915)	25 0	27 6
	a. White back (1913) ..	30 0	32 6
	b. On lemon (1916) ..	32 6	35 0
	c. On pale yellow (1921) ..	27 6	30 0

1918 (4 Jan.). *No.* 260*a overprinted with T* 38.

No.	Description	Unused	Used
271	2 c. scarlet	0 4	0 4

The relative positions of the words "WAR" and "TAX" vary considerably in the sheet.

1921–27. *T* 37. *Wmk. Mult. Script CA. P* 14.

No.	Description	Unused	Used
272	1 c. green, O	0 4	0 2
273	2 c. rose-carmine, O ..	0 6	0 2
274	4 c. brown & bright pur., O	0 8	0 6
275	12 c. orange and violet, O ..	4 0	2 0
276	24 c. dull purple & green, C	5 0	4 6
277	48 c. black & purple, C ('26)	10 0	10 6
278	60 c. green and rosine, C ('26)	12 0	12 6
279	72 c. dull pur. & orge.-brn., C	12 0	12 6
280	96 c. blk. & red/*yell.*, C ('27)	25 0	27 6

1922–23. *T* 37. *Colours changed. Wmk. Mult Script CA. P* 14.

No.	Description	Unused	Used
281	2 c. bright violet, O ..	0 6	0 1
282	6 c. bright blue, O	1 6	1 0

39 Ploughing a Rice Field.

40. Indian shooting fish. **41.** Kaieteur Falls.

42. Public buildings, Georgetown.

(Recess-printed by Waterlow & Sons, Ltd.)

1931 (21 July). *Centenary of County Union. T* **39** *to* **42.** *Script wmk. P* 12½.

No.	Type	Description	Unused	Used
283	**39**	1 c. emerald-green ..	2 0	2 0
284	**40**	2 c. brown	2 6	1 0
285	**41**	4 c. carmine	10 0	7 6
286	**42**	6 c. blue	20 0	17 6
287	**41**	$1 violet	55 0	60 0

43. Ploughing a Rice Field.

44. Gold Mining.
45. Shooting Logs over Falls (*horiz.*).
46. Stabroek Market (*horiz.*).
47. Sugar Canes in Punts (*horiz.*).
48. Forest Road (*horiz.*).

49. Victoria Regia Lilies.
50. Mount Roraima (*horiz.*).
51. Sir Walter Raleigh and his son (*vert.*)
52. Botanical Gardens (*horiz.*).

(Recess. Waterlow & Sons, Ltd.)

1934. *Types as* **40** (2 *c.*) *and* **41** (4 *c. and* 50 *c.*) *but without dates at top of frame* and T* **43** *to* **52.** *Wmk. Mult. Script CA. P* 12½.

No.	Type	Description	Unused	Used
288	**43**	1 c. green	0 4	0 2
289	**40***	2 c. red-brown	0 4	0 2
290	**44**	3 c. scarlet	0 3	0 5
291	**41***	4 c. slate-violet ..	1 0	0 8
		a. Imperf. between (vert. pair)		
292	**45**	6 c. deep ultramarine ..	2 0	2 0
293	**46**	12 c. vermilion	0 8	0 6
294	**47**	24 c. purple	8 0	8 0
295	**48**	48 c. black	15 0	15 0
296	**41***	50 c. green	15 0	16 0
297	**49**	60 c. red-brown	18 6	22 6
298	**50**	72 c. purple	12 6	12 6
299	**51**	96 c. black	40 0	45 0
300	**52**	$1 bright violet ..	42 6	47 6

For 3 c. p. 12½×13½, see King George VI Catalogue.

1935 (6 May). *Silver Jubilee. As T* **13** *of Antigua, inscribed* "BRITISH GUIANA". *Recess. D.L.R. & Co. Wmk. Mult. Script CA P* 13½×14.

No.	Description	Unused	Used
301	2 c. ultramarine and grey ..	0 6	0 6
302	6 c. brown and deep blue ..	4 6	3 6
303	12 c. green and indigo ..	8 6	8 0
304	24 c. slate and purple ..	10 6	12 6

OFFICIAL STAMPS.

OFFICIAL (O 1) **OFFICIAL** (O 2)

1875. *T* 7, 8, *and* 9 *overprinted. P* 10.

No.	Type	Description	Unused	Used
501	O 1	1 c. black (R.)	12 6	10 6
		a. Imperf. between (pair)		

502 O 2 2 c. orange 60 0 10 0
503 „ 8 c. rose £7 70 0
504 „ 12 c. brownish purple .. £20 £10
505 „ 24 c. green £10 75 0

Two types of the word "OFFICIAL" are found on each value of this issue. On the 1 c. the word is either 16 or 17 mm. long. On the other values the chief difference is in the shape and position of the letter "o" in "OFFICIAL". In one case the "o" is upright, in the other it slants to the left.

1877. *T* **16** (*Wmk. CC*) *overprinted. P* 14.

506 O 2 1 c. slate £6 55 0
a. Imperf. between (vert. pair)
507 O 2 2 c. orange 30 0 10 0
508 „ 4 c. blue 45 0 20 0
509 „ 6 c. brown £50 £10
510 „ 8 c. rose £50 £8

Prepared for use but not issued.

511 O 2 12 c. pale violet £30
512 „ 24 c. green £40

These stamps should only be purchased with a responsible guarantee, as there are many good forgeries of the word "OFFICIAL".

BRITISH HONDURAS.

1

(Typo. De La Rue & Co.)

T 1 (*various frames*).

1866 (JAN.). *No wmk. P* 14.

1 1d. pale blue 30 0 35 0
a. Imperf. between (pair) ..
2 1d. blue 30 0 35 0
3 6d. rose 80 0 65 0
4 1s. green 90 0 55 0

1872–79. *Wmk. Crown CC.* (*a*) *P* 12½.

5 1d. pale blue 22 6 20 0
6 1d. deep blue 25 0 22 6
7 3d. red-brown 60 0 52 6
8 3d. chocolate 65 0 52 6
9 6d. rose 90 0 45 0
9*a* 6d. bright rose-carmine — 45 0
10 1s. green £9 35 0
10*a* 1s. deep green £12 37 6
b. Imperf. between (pair)

(*b*) *P* 14.

11 1d. pale blue 42 6 42 6
12 1d. blue 35 0 35 0
a. Imperf. between (pair) .. £45
13 3d. chestnut 52 6 45 0
14 4d. mauve (1879) .. 55 0 35 0
15 6d. rose £12 £10
16 1s. green 65 0 35 0
a. Imperf. between (pair)

1882–87. *Wmk. Crown CA. P* 14.

17 1d. blue (1884) 25 0 20 0
18 1d. rose (1884) 17 6 17 6
a. Bisected diagonally (½d.)
19 1d. carmine 17 6 12 0
20 4d. mauve (1882) .. 30 0 8 6
21 6d. yellow (1885) .. £12 £12
22 1s. grey (1887) £18 £12

2
CENTS
(2)

1888 (1 JAN.)–**1889.** *Stamps of* 1872–87 *surcharged as T* **2**, *in black.*

(*a*) *P* 12½. *Wmk. Crown CC.*

23 2 c. on 6d. rose 90 0 £5
24 3 c. on 3d. chocolate £300 £120

Collectors are warned against very dangerous forgeries of these surcharges.

(*b*) *P* 14.

25 2 c. on 1d. rose (CA) 12 6 15 0
a. Bisected diagonally (1 c.) .. — 32 6
26 2 c. on 6d. rose (CC) 60 0 60 0
a. Bisected diagonally (1 c.) .. — £8
b. Slanting "2" with curved foot £25
27 3 c. on 3d. red-brown (CC) 65 0 55 0
28 10 c. on 4d. mauve (CA) .. 25 0 25 0
29 20 c. on 6d. yellow (CA) .. 20 0 20 0
30 50 c. on 1s. grey (CA) £30 £30

Varieties. (i.) *Surcharge inverted.*

31 2 c. on 1d. rose £90 £70

(ii.) *Surcharge double.*

32 2 c. on 1d. rose £70 £70

Error of surcharge.

33 5 c. on 1s. grey £250

TWO
(3)

No. 30 *surcharged with T* **3**.

34 "TWO", in *black*, on 50 c. .. £400 £300
35 "TWO", in *red*, on 50 c. .. 32 6 35 0
a. Bisected (1 c.) .. .. — 52 6
36 "TWO", in *black* & in *red*, on 50 c. £350

2
CENTS
(4)

T 1. *Wmk. Crown CA. Surcharged as T* **4**, *in black. P* 14.

37 2 c. on 1d. carmine 0 6 1 0
a. Bisected diagonally (1 c.) .. — 10 0
38 3 c. on 3d. red-brown .. 1 0 1 6
39 10 c. on 4d. mauve .. 3 0 2 6
a. Surcharge double ..
40 20 c. on 6d. yellow (1889) .. 6 0 7 6
41 50 c. on 1s. grey 22 6 22 6

6
~~10~~
CENTS
(5)

1891. *No.* 39 *surch. with new value, as in T* 5

43 6 in *red*, on 10 c. 2 6 2 6
44 6 in *black*, on 10 c. 1 9 2 9

Varieties. (*a*) "6" *and bar inverted.*

45 6 in *red*, on 10 c. £25 £25
46 6 in *black*, on 10 c. £175 £40

(*b*) "6" *only inverted.*

46*a* 6 in *red*, on 10 c. .. .. — £150
46*b* 6 in *black*, on 10 c. .. .. — £150

Of variety (*b*) only six copies of each can exist, as one of each of these errors came in the first six sheets, and the mistake was then corrected. Of variety (*a*) more copies exist, but we have no details.

1891. *T* 1 *surcharged as T* **4** *in black. Wmk. Crown CA. P* 14.

47 6 c. on 3d. ultramarine .. 3 6 4 0

1 CENT (6)

FIVE (7)

15 (7a)

1891. *T 1 surch. with T 6. Wmk. Crown CA. P 14.*

48 1 c. on 1d. dull green .. 1 0 1 3

1891. *Surcharged with T 7 or 7a.*

49 "FIVE" in *blk.* on 3 c. (No. 38) 1 9 3 0
- a. Wide space between "I" and "V" of "FIVE" .. 27 6
- b. "FIVE" and bar double .. £15

50 15 in *red*, on 6 c. (No. 47) .. 5 0 6 0
- a. Surcharge double .. ..

8  9

10  11

(Typo. De La Rue & Co.)

1891–98. *Wmk. Crown CA. P 14.*

51 8 1 c. dull green 1 0 1 0
52 ,, 2 c. carmine-rose 1 3 0 10
53 ,, 3 c. brown 4 0 3 6
54 ,, 5 c. ultramarine (1895) .. 8 6 4 0
55 ,, 6 c. ultramarine 4 6 4 6
56 9 10 c. mauve and green (1895) 17 6 15 0
57 ,, 12 c. pale mauve and green 8 6 9 0
58 ,, 12 c. violet and green .. 10 6 12 0
59 ,, 24 c. yellow and blue .. 12 0 12 6
60 ,, 24 c. orange and blue .. 15 0 15 0
61 ,, 25 c. red-brn. & grn (1898) 35 0 35 0
62 10 50 c. green and carmine .. 20 0 22 6
63 11 $1 green and carmine .. 25 0 40 0
64 ,, $2 green and ultramarine .. 60 0 75 0
65 ,, $5 green and black .. £15 £15

1899. *Various stamps overprinted* "REVENUE," *in black.* (a) *Overprint* 12 *mm. long.*

66 5 c. (No. 54) 2 6 3 0
67 10 c. (No. 56) 6 0 7 6
68 25 c. (No. 61) 6 0 7 6
69 50 c. (No. 41) 95 0 £6

Errors. (i.) "BEVENUE."

70 5 c. (No. 54) 35 0 45 0
71 10 c. (No. 56) £15
72 25 c. (No. 61) 90 0 £5
73 50 c. (No. 41) £100

(ii.) "REVENU."

73*a* 10 c. (No. 56) £25

Two minor varieties, a small "U" and a tall, narrow "U," are found in the word "REVENUE."

(*b*) *Overprint* 11 *mm. long.*

74 5 c. (No. 54) 5 0 5 6
75 10 c. (No. 56) 10 0 12 6
76 25 c. (No. 61) 6 6 7 6
77 50 c. (No. 41) 90 0 95 0

There is a minor variety with narrow "U" in "REVENUE."

1900–1. *Wmk. Crown CA. P 14.*

78 11 5 c. grey-black and ultramarine/*blue* 4 0 4 0
79 10 10 c. dull purple and green (1901) 4 6 5 0

14

15

(Typo. De La Rue & Co.)

1902–4. *Wmk. Crown CA. P 14.*

80 14 1 c. grey-grn. & grn. (1904) 7 6 8 6
81 ,, 2 c. purple & black/*red* .. 3 0 1 6
82 ,, 5 c. grey-black & blue/*blue* 4 6 4 6
83 15 20 c. dull & bright pur. (1904) 12 6 15 0

1905. *Wmk. Mult. Crown CA. P 14.*

84 14 1 c. grey-green & grn., OC 2 0 2 6
85 ,, 2 c. purple & black/*red*, OC 2 0 1 9
86 ,, 5 c. grey-black & blue/*blue*, C 4 0 4 6

1907. *Wmk. Mult. Crown CA. P 14.*

87 15 10 c. dull pur. & emer.-grn., C 6 0 7 6
89 ,, 25 c. dull pur. & orge., C .. 15 0 17 6
90 ,, 50 c. grey-grn. & carm., C 22 6 25 0
91 14 $1 grey-grn. & carm., C 30 0 35 0
92 ,, $2 grey-green & blue, C 60 0 65 0
93 ,, $5 grey-green & black, C £15 £16

1908–10. *Wmk. Mult. Crown CA. P 14.*

95 14 1 c. blue-green, O .. 2 6 1 6
96 ,, 2 c. carmine, O (1908) .. 2 0 0 9
97 ,, 5 c. ultramarine, O .. 5 0 4 0
100 15 25 c. black/*green*, C .. 17 6 20 0

16

17

(Typo. De La Rue & Co.)

1913–21. *Wmk. Mult. Crown CA. P 14.*

101 16 1 c. blue-green, O .. 0 6 0 4
101*a* ,, 1 c. yellow-green, O .. 0 8 0 3
102 ,, 2 c. red, O .. 0 9 0 3
102*a* ,, 2 c. bright scar., O ('16) 0 8 0 3
102*b* ,, 2 c. scarlet, O (1917) .. 0 8 0 4
103 ,, 3 c. orange, O (1917) .. 1 3 1 0
104 ,, 5 c. bright blue, O .. 3 0 3 6
105 17 10 c. dull purple and yellow-green, C 8 0 8 6
105*a* ,, 10 c. dull pur. & brt. grn., C 6 0 6 6
106 ,, 25 c. black/*green*, C .. 7 0 8 6
- *a. On blue-green, olive back* (1917) 10 6 11 0
- *b. On emerald back* (1921) .. 7 0 7 6

107 17 50 c. pur. & blue/*blue*, C 15 0 15 0
108 16 $1 black and carm., C 27 6 30 0
109 ,, $2 purple and green, C 70 0 75 0
110 ,, $5 pur. & black/*red*, C £8 £9

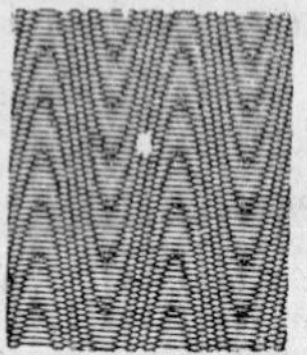

(18)

1915. *Optd. with T* **18** *in violet.*

111	**16**	1 c. green	6 0	6 6
111*a*	,,	1 c. yellow-green ..	4 0	4 6
112	,,	2 c. scarlet	2 6	2 6
113	,,	5 c. bright blue	2 6	2 6

These were part of a consignment shipped early in the war, and were thus overprinted, so that in case of seizure by the enemy they could be distinguished and rendered invalid.

WAR (19) WAR (20)

1916. *No.* 111. *Optd. locally with T* **19**.

114	**16**	1 c. green	0 4	0 6
		a. Overprint inverted ..	65 0	70 0

1917. *Optd. with T* **19**.

116	**16**	1 c. yellow-green	0 6	0 8
117	,,	1 c. blue-green	0 4	0 6
118	,,	3 c. orange	1 3	1 6
		a. Overprint double ..	£15	

1918. *Optd. with T* **20**.

119	**16**	1 c. blue-green/*bluish* ..	0 2	0 3
119*a*	,,	1 c. yellow-green ..	0 3	0 4
120	,,	3 c. orange	0 4	0 6

21

(Recess. De La Rue & Co.)

1921. *Peace Commemorative.* *T* **21**. *Wmk. Mult. Crown CA. P* 14.

121		2 c. rose-red	4 0	3 0

T **21**, *but without words* "PEACE." *Wmk. Mult. Script CA. P* 14.

122		4 c. slate	5 0	4 6

1922. *Wmk. Mult. Script CA. P* 14.

123	**16**	1 c. green, O	0 4	0 4

22

BELIZE
RELIEF FUND
PLUS
3 CENTS
(23)

(Typo. De La Rue & Co.)

1922–33. *P* 14. (*a*) *Wmk. Mult. Crown CA.*

124	**22**	25 c. black/*emerald*, C ..	25 0	30 0
125	,,	$5 purple & black/*red*, C	95 0	£6

(*b*) *Wmk. Mult. Script CA.*

126	**22**	1 c. green, O (1929) ..	0 3	0 4
127	,,	2 c. brown, O	0 6	0 6
128	,,	2 c. rose-carmine, O (1927)	0 4	0 6
128*a*	,,	3 c. orange, O (1933) ..	0 6	0 8
129	,,	4 c. grey, O (1929) ..	0 8	0 8
130	,,	5 c. ultramarine, O (1922)	1 0	1 0
131	,,	5 c. milky blue, O (1923)	5 0	5 0
132	,,	10 c. dull pur. & sage-grn., C	3 0	3 0
133	,,	25 c. black/*emerald*, C ..	7 6	8 0
134	,,	50 c. pur. & blue/*blue*, C ..	12 6	15 0
136	,,	$1 black and scarlet, C	20 0	22 6
137	,,	$2 yell.-grn. & brt. pur., C	55 0	57 6

1932. *Belize Relief Fund. T* **22** *surcharged as T* **23**. *Wmk. Mult. Script CA. P* 14.

138	**22**	1 c.+1 c. green, O ..	1 3	2 0
139	,,	2 c.+2 c. rose-carmine, O	1 6	2 6
140	,,	3 c.+3 c. orange, O ..	2 6	3 6
141	,,	4 c.+4 c. grey, O (R.) ..	6 0	7 6
142	,,	5 c.+5 c. ultramarine, O	7 6	8 0

1935 (6 May). *Silver Jubilee. As T* **13** *of Antigua, inscribed* "BRITISH HONDURAS". *Recess. B.W. & Co. Wmk. Mult. Script CA. P* 11×12.

143		3 c. ultramarine & grey-black	1 0	1 3
144		4 c. green and indigo ..	2 6	2 9
145		5 c. brown and deep blue ..	4 0	4 6
146		25 c. slate and purple ..	8 6	10 6

The 3 c., 4 c. and 25 c. exist with "double flagstaff."

POSTAGE DUE STAMPS.

D 1

(Typo. De La Rue & Co.)

1923. *Wmk. Mult. Script CA. P* 14.

D 1	**D 1**	1 c. black..	0 2	0 3
D 2	,,	2 c. black..	0 3	0 4
D 3	,,	4 c. black..	0 4	0 5

BRITISH LEVANT.

80 PARAS (1) 4 PIASTRES (2)

12 PIASTRES (3)

Stamps of Great Britain (Queen Victoria) surcharged as T **1** *to* **3**.

1885 (1 April).

1	**64**	40 par. on 2½d. lilac ..	6 6	3 6
2	**62**	80 par. on 5d. green ..	15 0	4 6
3	**58**	12 pi. on 2s. 6d. lilac (on *bluish*)	£5	75 0
		a. On paper deeply blued ..	£12	£6
		b. On white paper	17 6	7 6

1887–96.

4	**74**	40 par. on 2½d. purple/*blue*	1 6	0 2
		a. Surcharge double ..	£65	£55
5	**78**	80 par. on 5d. pur. and blue	7 6	1 0
		a. Small "0" in "80" ..	35 0	20 0
6	**81**	4 pi. on 10d. purple and carmine (1896)	7 6	6 0
		a. Large, wide "4"	15 0	15 0

1893 (25 Feb.). *Roughly handstamped at Constantinople, as T* **1**.

7	71	40 par. on ½d. vermilion ..	£6	60 0

This provisional was in use five days only. As fraudulent copies were made with the original handstamp, this stamp should only be purchased from undoubted sources. (Price of genuine stamp, used on envelope, from £5.)

1902–5. *Stamps of Great Britain* (*King Edward VII*) *surcharged as T* **1** *to* **3**.

8	86	40 par. on 2½d. brt. blue, O (6.2.02) ..	3 6	0 4
9	89	80 par. on 5d. pur. & blue, O (5.6.02) ..	3 6	4 0
		a. Small "0" in "80" ..	65 0	30 0
10	92	4 pi. on 10d. purple and carmine, O (6.9.02) ..	4 6	4 0
		a. No cross on crown ..	40 0	40 0
		b. Chalky paper	6 0	6 0
		ba. Chalky. No cross on crown	50 0	50 0
11	94	12 pi. on 2s. 6d. dull pur., O (29.8.03)	15 0	12 6
		a. *Reddish purple (chalky)* ..	15 0	12 6
12	95	24 pi. on 5s. car., O (1905)	22 6	22 6

LEVANT
(4)

1905. *Stamps of King Edward VII optd. with T* **4**.

13	83	½d. pale yellow-green, O ..	0 8	0 6
14	,,	1d. scarlet, O	1 9	1 3
15	84	1½d. dull pur. & yell.-grn., O	4 0	4 6
		a. Chalky paper	4 6	4 0
16	85	2d. grey-green & carm., O	4 0	4 6
		a. *Green and carmine (chalky)*	1 9	2 0
17	86	2½d. bright blue, O ..	12 6	12 6
18	87	3d. purple/*yellow*, O ..	8 6	10 0
19	88	4d. green & choc.-brn., O	10 0	12 6
20	89	5d. purple and blue, O ..	12 6	12 6
21	83	6d. dull purple, O	12 6	12 6
22	93	1s. green and carmine, O	12 6	12 6
		a. Chalky paper	15 0	17 6

1 PIASTRE
(5)

1906. *Surcharged in* "PIASTRES" *instead of* "PARAS" *as T* **5** *and* **2**.

23	86	1 pi. on 2½d. bright blue, O	2 0	0 6
24	89	2 pi. on 5d. pur. & blue, O	3 6	3 0
		a. Chalky paper	4 0	2 0

1 Piastre
(6)

1906 (2 July). *Issued at Beirut.* No. 16 *surcharged with T* **6**.

25	85	1 pi. on 2d. grn. & carm., O	£35	£25

1 PIASTRE 10 PARAS
(7)

1909 (Nov.–Dec.). *Stamps of King Edward VII surcharged as T* **1** (30 *par.*), **7**, *and* **2** (5 *pi.*).

26	84	30 par. on 1½d. dull pur. and green, C	3 0	3 0
27	87	1 pi. 10 par. on 3d. purple/*yellow*, C	12 6	15 0
28	88	1 pi. 30 par. on 4d. green & chocolate-brown, C ..	10 6	12 0
29	,,	1 pi. 30 par. on 4d. orge., O (16.12.09)	18 0	18 0
30	83	2 pi. 20 par. on 6d. reddish purple, C	16 0	17 6
31	93	5 pi. on 1s. grn. & carm., C	8 6	8 6

1¾ PIASTRE
(8)

4 Normal "4." 4 "Pointed "4."

1910 (Feb.) *Stamps of King Edward VII surcharged as T* **8**.

32	87	1¼ pi. on 3d. purple/*yell.*, C	1 0	1 6
33	88	1¾ pi. on 4d. orange, O ..	1 9	2 0
		a. Thin, pointed "4" in fraction	6 0	7 6
34	83	2½ pi. on 6d. reddish pur., C	2 0	2 6

1 PIASTRE (9) **1 PIASTRE** (10)

1911. *Stamps of King Edward VII* (*new printings by Messrs. Harrison and Sons, Ltd., or at Somerset House*) *surch. or optd.*

(*a*) *Surcharged with T* **5**.

35	86	1 pi. on 2½d. brt. blue (*perf.* 14)	1 6	1 6
36	,,	1 pi. on 2½d. brt. blue (*perf.* 15×14)	2 0	0 6

(*b*) *Surcharged with T* **9**.

37	86	1 pi. on 2½d. brt. blue (*perf* 15×14)	1 9	0 6

(*c*) *Surcharged with T* **10**.

38	86	1 pi. on 2½d. brt. blue (*perf.* 15×14)	1 6	0 4

Type differences. In T **5** the letters are tall and narrow and the space enclosed by the upper part of the "A" is small.

In T **9** the opening of the "A" is similar, but the letters are shorter and broader, the "P" and the "E" being particularly noticeable.

In T **10** the letters are short and broad, but the "A" is thin and open.

(*d*) *Surcharged as T* **1** *to* **3**.

39	84	30 par. on 1½d. dull reddish purple and yellow-green	2 0	1 3
		a. *Slate-purple and green* ..	1 3	1 6
40	89	2 pi. on 5d. pur. & brt. blue	1 9	2 0
41	92	4 pi. on 10d. dull purple and scarlet	10 6	10 0
		a. *Dull purple and carmine* ..	8 0	8 6
42	93	5 pi. on 1s. grn. & carmine	6 6	6 6
43	94	12 pi. on 2s. 6d. deep reddish purple	27 6	27 6
		a. *Dull purple (greyish)* ..	15 0	15 0
		b. *Pale reddish purple* ..	17 6	20 0
44	95	24 pi. on 5s. carmine ..	20 0	20 0

(*e*) *Overprinted with T* **4**.

45	83	½d. yellow-green (*perf.* 14)	3 0	4 0

Stamps of King George V optd. with T **4**.

(*a*) **1911** (Sept.). *Dies A. Wmk. Crown.*

46	98	½d. yellow-green (No. 322)	1 3	1 3
47	99	1d. deep rose-red (No. 327)	0 10	1 0

(*b*) **1912** (Mar.). *Redrawn types. Wmk. Crown.*

48	101	½d. green (No. 339) ..	0 4	0 6
49	102	1d. scarlet (No. 342) ..	0 6	0 8

(*c*) **1913** (July). *New types. Wmk. Royal Cypher.*

50	105	½d. green (No. 351) ..	0 8	0 8
51	104	1d. scarlet (No. 358) ..	0 8	0 8

These two stamps were reissued in 1919.

For other values of this series with "LEVANT" overprint see Nos. 68 to 74.

1913–14. *Stamps of King George V, wmk. Royal Cypher, surcharged as T* **1** (30 *par.*). **10** (1 *pi.*), **8** *or* **2** (4 *and* 5 *pi.*).

52	105	30 par. on 1½d. red-brown	1 6	1 9
53	104	1 pi. on 2½d. bright blue	1 0	0 8
54	106	1¼ pi. on 3d. violet ..	2 6	2 9
55	,,	1¾ pi. on 4d. grey-green ..	4 6	5 0
		a. Thin, pointed "4" in fraction	37 6	37 6
56	108	4 pi. on 10d. turquoise-blue	10 0	10 6
57	,,	5 pi. on 1s. bistre-brown ..	15 0	17 6

D*

1½ PIASTRES (11) **15 PIASTRES** (12)

1921. *Stamps of King George V, wmk. Royal Cypher, surcharged as T* **1** (30 *par.*), **11** *and* **12** (15 *and* 18¾ *pi.*).

58 **105** 30 par. on ½d. green .. 0 3 0 3
59 **104** 1½ pi. on 1d. scarlet .. 0 3 0 3
60 „ 3¾ pi. on 2½d. blue .. 0 6 0 6
61 **106** 4½ pi. on 3d. blue-violet .. 0 8 0 10
62 **107** 7½ pi. on 5d. yellow-brown 0 9 0 6
63 **108** 15 pi. on 10d. turquoise-blue 1 6 1 6
64 „ 18¾ pi. on 1s. bistre-brown 2 0 2 0

45 PIASTRES (13)

1921. *Stamps of King George V (Bradbury-Wilkinson printing), surcharged as T* **13.**

65 **109** 45 pi. on 2s. 6d. chocolate-brown 8 0 8 6
66 „ 90 pi. on 5s. rose-red .. 12 6 9 0
67 „ 180 pi. on 10s. dull grey-blue 20 0 10 0

1921. *Stamps of King George V optd. as T* **4.**

68 **106** 2d. red-orange (Die I) .. 0 10 1 0
69 „ 3d. blue-violet 1 0 1 3
70 „ 4d. grey-green 1 6 1 9
71 **107** 5d. yellow-brown 1 9 2 0
72 „ 6d. reddish purple, C .. 2 0 2 6
73 **108** 1s. bistre-brown 3 0 2 0
74 **109** 2s. 6d. chocolate-brown .. 8 6 8 6

On No. 74 the letters of the overprint are shorter, being only 3 mm. high.

The British P.O.'s in the Turkish Empire were closed in 1914. The 1921 issues were in use during the British Occupation after the War.

SPECIAL ISSUE FOR SALONICA.

Levant (S 1)

1916 (End of Feb. *to* 9 March). *Stamps of King George V, wmk. Royal Cypher, overprinted with T* S **1.**

S 1 **105** ½d. green 22 6 55 0
a. Overprint double £35 £35
b. Overprint omitted (in vertical pair, with normal) £20 £25
S 2 **104** 1d. scarlet 22 6 65 0
a. Overprint double £35 £33
S 3 **106** 2d. red-orange (Die I) .. £12 £14
S 4 „ 3d. blue-violet .. £6 £8
a. Overprint double ..
S 5 „ 4d. grey-green .. £12 £15
S 6 **107** 6d. reddish purple .. 55 0 75 0
a. Overprint omitted (in vertical pair, with normal) £25 £35
S 7 **108** 9d. agate £28 £35
a. Overprint double .. £120 £100
S 8 „ 1s. bistre-brown £25 £28

Collectors are warned against forgeries of these overprints, which are freely offered. These stamps should only be purchased from well-known firms with a guarantee that the overprints are genuine.

For full details of these issues see handbook *Long Island and Salonica*, by Fred. J. Melville, price 6d., postage 2d. extra.

BRITISH NEW GUINEA.

See **PAPUA.**

BRITISH P.O.'s IN CRETE.

British Sphere of Administration. (Candia.)

During the provisional Joint Administration by France, Great Britain, Italy, and Russia.

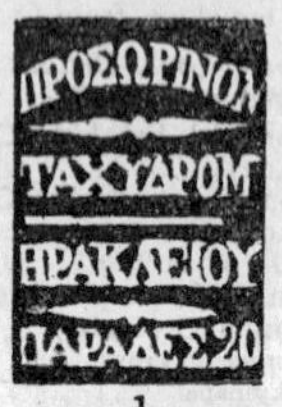

1

1898 (25 Nov.). *Handstruck locally. Imperf.*

1 **1** 20 par. bright violet £6 £6

2

1898 (3 Dec.). *Lithographed by M. Grundmann Athens. P* 11½.

2 **2** 10 par. blue 1 6 1 6
3 „ 20 par. green 1 6 1 6

1899. *P* 11½.

4 **2** 10 par. brown 3 0 3 0
5 „ 20 par. rose 2 6 2 6

Varieties. Imperf.

6 **2** 10 par. brown 22 6
7 „ 10 par. blue 22 6
8 „ 20 par. green.. .. .. 22 6
9 „ 20 rose .. ..

BRITISH SOLOMON IS. PROTECTORATE.

1

(Lithographed by W. E. Smith & Co., Sydney.)

1907 (14 Feb.). *No wmk. P* 11.

1 **1** ½d. ultramarine 6 6 7 6
2 „ 1d. rose-carmine 12 6 15 0
3 „ 2d. indigo 12 6 15 0
a. Imperf. betw. (horiz. pair) ..
4 „ 2½d. orange-yellow 17 6 20 0
a. Imperf. betw. (vert. pair) .. £30
b. Imperf. betw. (horiz. pair) .. £35

No.	Type	Description	Unused	Used
5	1	5d. emerald-green	22 6	25 0
6	„	6d. chocolate	30 0	27 6
		a. Imperf. betw. (vert. pair) ..	£30	
		b. Imperf. betw. (horiz. pair) ..		
	„	1s. bright purple	35 0	40 0

Three types exist of the ½d. and 2½d., and six each of the other values, differing in minor details. Prices for strips, showing all types, on application.

2

(Recess. De La Rue & Co.)

1908 (1 Nov.)–**1911.** *Wmk. Mult. Crown CA sideways. P* 14.

No.	Type	Description	Unused	Used
8	2	½d. green	2 0	2 6
9	„	1d. red	2 6	2 9
10	„	2d. greyish slate	3 0	3 6
11	„	2½d. ultramarine	6 0	6 6
11*a*	„	4d. red/*yell.* (Mar., 1911) ..	7 6	8 0
12	„	5d. olive	9 0	10 6
13	„	6d. claret	9 6	10 6
14	„	1s. black,*green*	17 6	18 0
15	„	2s. purple/*blue* (Mar., 1910)	22 6	25 0
16	„	2s. 6d. red/*blue* (Mar., 1910)	40 0	45 0
17	„	5s. green/*yell.* (Mar., 1910)	50 0	55 0

The ½d. and 1d. were issued in 1913 on rather thinner paper and with brownish gum.

3

4

(T **3** and **4.** Typo. De La Rue & Co.)

1913. *Inscribed* "POSTAGE," "POSTAGE." *Wmk. Multiple Crown CA. P* 14.

No.	Type	Description	Unused	Used
18	3	½d. green (1 April)	0 9	1 0
19	„	1d. red (1 April) ..	4 6	5 0
20	„	3d. purple/*yell.* (27 Feb.) ..	6 0	6 6
		a. On orange-buff	5 0	6 0
21	„	11d. dull purple & scarlet (27 Feb.)	8 6	10 6

1914–23. *Inscribed* "POSTAGE," "REVENUE." *Wmk. Mult. Crown CA. P* 14.

No.	Type	Description	Unused	Used
22	4	½d. green, O	0 9	1 0
23	„	½d. yellow-green, O (1917)	0 6	0 9
24	„	1d. carmine-red, O ..	1 0	1 0
25	„	1d. scarlet, O (1917) ..	1 0	1 3
26	„	2d. grey, O	3 6	4 0
27	„	2½d. ultramarine, O ..	1 0	1 6
28	„	3d. pur./*p. yell.*. C (Jan., '23)	35 0	40 0
29	„	4d. black & red/*yellow*. C ..	3 6	4 0
30	„	5d. dull pur. & olive-grn., C	4 6	6 0
31	„	5d. brn.-pur. & olive-grn., C	3 6	4 6
32	„	6d. dull & bright purple, C	3 6	4 6
33	„	1s. black/*green*, C	8 6	9 6
		a. On blue-green, olive back ..	7 6	9 6
34	„	2s. purple & blue/*blue*, C ..	10 6	12 0
35	„	2s. 6d. black & red/*blue*, C	15 0	16 0
36	„	5s. green & red/*yellow*, C ..	32 6	35 0
		a. On orange-buff (1920) ..	52 6	55 0
37	4	10s. green and red/*green*, C	65 0	65 0
38	„	£1 purple and black/*red*, C	£8	£8

A number of varieties in the coloured papers are known, but most of these are due to climate and are not indicative of separate printings.

1922–31. *Wmk. Mult. Script CA. P* 14.

No.	Type	Description	Unused	Used
39	4	½d. green, O (Oct., 1922)	0 4	0 4
40	„	1d. scarlet, O (Aug., 1923)	1 3	1 6
41	„	1d. dull violet, O (1927) ..	0 8	0 8
42	3	1½d. bright scar., O (1924)	1 3	1 3
43	4	2d. slate-grey, O (Apr., '23)	1 6	1 9
44	„	3d. pale ultram., O (Nov. '23)	2 0	2 3
45	„	4d. blk. & red/*yell.*, C ('27)	2 6	3 0
45*a*	„	4½d. red-brown, O ('31) ..	3 0	4 0
46	„	5d. dull pur. & olive.-grn., C	6 6	7 6
47	„	6d. dull & bright purple, C	6 6	7 0
48	„	1s. black/*emerald*, C ..	7 0	8 0
49	„	2s. pur. & blue/*blue*, C ('27)	10 6	12 6
50	„	2s. 6d. black & red/*blue*, C	15 0	16 0
51	„	5s. grn. & red/*pale yell.*, C	20 0	22 6
52	„	10s. grn. & red/*emer.*, C ('25)	£5	£6

1935 (6 May). *Silver Jubilee. As T* **13** *of Antigua, inscribed* "BRITISH SOLOMON ISLANDS". *Recess. D.L.R. & Co. Wmk. Mult. Script CA. P* 13½ × 14.

No.	Description	Unused	Used
53	1½d. deep blue and carmine ..	1 3	1 9
54	3d. brown and deep blue	10 6	12 6
55	6d. light blue and olive-green	12 6	15 0
56	1s. slate and purple	17 6	22 6

BRITISH SOMALILAND.

(SOMALILAND PROTECTORATE)

BRITISH
SOMALILAND

(1)

1903. *Stamps of India* (*Queen's Head*) *overprinted with T* **1**, *in black, at top of stamp.*

No.	Description	Unused	Used
1	½ a. green	1 3	1 6
2	1 a. carmine	1 6	1 6
3	2 a. pale violet	1 6	1 9
4	2½ a. ultramarine	2 6	3 0
5	3 a. brown-orange	2 0	3 0
6	4 a. slate-green	2 6	3 0
7	6 a. pale brown	3 6	4 6
8	8 a. dull mauve	4 0	5 0
9	12 a. purple/*red*	5 0	6 6
10	1 r. green and carmine ..	6 0	7 6
11	2 r. carmine & yellow-brown	22 6	27 6
12	3 r. brown and green ..	25 0	30 0
13	5 r. ultramarine and violet ..	37 6	42 6

Varieties. (i.) "BRIT SH" *for* "BRITISH."

No.	Description	Unused	Used
14	½ a. green	30 0	
15	1 a. carmine	42 6	
16	2 a. pale violet	70 0	
16*a*	2½ a. ultramarine	£14	
17	3 a. brown-orange	£16	

(ii.) *Overprint inverted.*

No.	Description	Unused	Used
17*a*	12 a. purple/*red*	—	£35
17*b*	3 r. brown and green ..	£20	

1903. *Stamps of India* (*Queen's Head*) *overprinted with T* **1**, *in black, at bottom of stamp.*

No.	Description	Unused	Used
18	2½ a. blue	1 6	2 6
19	6 a. pale brown	3 6	5 0
20	12 a. purple/*red*	6 6	7 6
21	1 r. green and carmine ..	7 6	10 0
22	2 r. carmine & yellow-brown	15 0	20 0
23	3 r. brown and green	20 0	25 0
24	5 r. ultramarine and violet ..	27 6	37 6

1903. *Stamps of India (King's Head) overprinted with T* **1**, *in black, at bottom of stamp.*

No.	Description		Unused	Used
25	½ a. green	.. .. ..	0 10	0 8
26	1 a. carmine	.. .. ..	1 0	1 3
27	2 a. mauve	.. .. ..	3 0	4 0
28	3 a. orange-brown	.. ..	3 6	4 0
29	4 a. olive-green	.. ..	5 0	6 0
30	8 a. magenta	.. .. ..	5 0	6 0

Varieties. "BRIT SH" *for* "BRITISH."

No.	Description		Unused	Used
30*a*	½ a. green	.. .. ..		
31	1 a. carmine	.. .. ..	65 0	
31*a*	2 a. mauve	.. .. ..		

2

3

(Typo. De La Rue & Co.)

1904. *Wmk. Crown CA. P* 14.

No.	Type	Description	Unused	Used
32	**2**	½ a. dull green and green ..	0 8	1 0
33	,,	1 a. grey-black and red ..	4 0	5 0
34	,,	2 a. dull and bright purple ..	4 0	5 6
35	,,	2½ a. bright blue	6 0	7 6
36	,,	3 a. chocolate & grey-green	7 6	8 0
37	,,	4 a. green and black ..	7 0	7 6
38	,,	6 a. green and violet ..	10 0	10 6
39	,,	8 a. grey-black and pale blue	10 0	10 6
40	,,	12 a. grey-black & orange-buff	15 0	17 6

Wmk. Crown CC. P 14.

No.	Type	Description	Unused	Used
41	**3**	1 r. green	17 6	20 0
42	,,	2 r. dull and bright purple ..	20 0	22 6
43	,,	3 r. green and black	22 6	25 0
44	,,	5 r. grey-black and red ..	30 0	37 6

1905–6. *Wmk. Mult. Crown CA. P* 14.

No.	Type	Description	Unused	Used
45	**2**	½ a. dull green and grn., O	0 10	1 3
46	,,	1 a. grey-black & red, OC	1 9	1 9
47	,,	2 a. dull and brt. pur., OC	3 0	3 6
48	,,	2½ a. bright blue, O ..	5 6	6 6
49	,,	3 a. chocolate and grey-grn., OC	5 6	6 6
50	,,	4 a. green and black, OC ..	4 0	5 0
51	,,	6 a. green and violet, OC ..	5 0	6 0
52	,,	8 a. grey-blk. & pale blue, O	7 6	8 6
52*a*	,,	8 a. black and blue, C ..	8 6	9 6
53	,,	12 a. grey-black and orange-buff, OC	8 0	9 0

1909. *Wmk. Mult. Crown CA. P* 14.

No.	Type	Description	Unused	Used
58	**2**	½ a. bluish green, O ..	3 6	4 6
59	,,	1 a. red, O	3 6	4 6

4

5

(Typo. De La Rue & Co.)

1912 (Dec.)–**1919.** *Wmk. Mult. Crown CA. P* 14.

No.	Type	Description	Unused	Used
60	**4**	½ a. green, O	0 6	0 8
61	,,	1 a. red, O	1 0	1 3
61*a*	**4**	1 a. scarlet, O (1917) ..	1 6	1 9
62	,,	2 a. dull & bright pur., C ..	7 6	8 0
62*a*	,,	2 a. dull pur. & violet-pur., C (1919)	8 0	8 6
63	,,	2½ a. bright blue, O ..	2 9	3 0
64	,,	3 a. choc. & grey-grn., C ..	2 6	3 0
65	,,	4 a. grn. & blk., C (1913)	2 9	3 6
66	,,	6 a. green and violet, C ..	3 6	3 9
67	,,	8 a. grey-blk. & pale blue, C	4 6	5 0
68	,,	12 a. grey-black and orange-buff, C	6 0	7 6
69	**5**	1 r. green, C	6 6	8 0
70	,,	2 r. dull pur. & pur., C ('19)	15 0	16 6
71	,,	3 r. green & blk., C (1919)	25 0	27 6
72	,,	5 r. blk. & scar., C (1910)	30 0	32 6

1921. *Wmk. Mult. Script CA. P* 14.

No.	Type	Description	Unused	Used
73	**4**	½ a. blue-green, O	0 6	0 6
74	,,	1 a. carmine-red, O ..	0 8	0 8
75	,,	2 a. dull & bright pur., C ..	1 0	1 0
76	,,	2½ a. bright blue, O ..	1 3	1 6
77	,,	3 a. chocolate & green, C ..	1 6	2 0
78	,,	4 a. green and black, C ..	1 9	2 0
79	,,	6 a. green and violet, C ..	2 6	3 0
80	,,	8 a. grey-blk. & pale blue, C	3 0	3 6
81	,,	12 a. grey-blk. & orge.-buff, C	5 0	6 0
82	**5**	1 r. dull green, C	7 6	8 6
83	,,	2 r. dull purple & purple, C	10 0	12 6
84	,,	3 r. dull green & black, C ..	17 6	20 0
85	,,	5 r. black and scarlet, C ..	25 0	30 0

1935 (6 May). *Silver Jubilee. As T* **13** *of Antigua, inscribed* "SOMALILAND PROTECTORATE". *Recess W'low. & Sons. Wmk. Mult. Script CA. P* 11 × 12.

No.	Description		Unused	Used
86	1 a. deep blue and scarlet	..	1 0	1 6
87	2 a. ultramarine and grey	..	5 0	7 6
88	3 a. brown and deep blue	..	7 6	12 6
89	1 r. slate and purple ..	..	20 0	30 0

OFFICIAL STAMPS.

.SERVICE

BRITISH

SOMALILAND

(O 1)

BRITISH
SOMALILAND

(O 2)

1903. *Stamps of India overprinted.*

(i) *Official stamps of* 1883–1900, *Queen's Head, with Type* O **1** (*wider spaced on* 1 r.).

No.	Description		Unused	Used
O 1	½ a. green	.. .. ..	1 9	2 0
O 2	1 a. carmine	.. .. ..	1 9	2 0
O 3	2 a. pale violet	.. ..	2 0	3 0
O 4	8 a. dull mauve	.. ..	17 6	20 0
O 5	1 r. green and carmine	..	17 6	20 0

Varieties exist on all values in which "BRITISH" measures 11 mm., and the 8 a. is known without stop after "M" in "H.M.S."

(ii) *Postage stamps of* 1902, *King's Head, with Type* O **2**.

No.	Description		Unused	Used
O 6	½ a. green	.. .. ..	0 8	
O 7	1 a. carmine	.. .. ..	0 8	
O 8	2 a. pale violet	.. .. ..	0 10	
O 9	8 a. magenta	.. .. ..	16 6	

Varieties. "BRIT SH" *for* "BRITISH."

No.	Description		Unused	Used
O 10	½ a. green	.. .. ..	25 0	
O 11	1 a. carmine	.. .. ..	35 0	
O 12	2 a. pale violet	.. .. ..	70 0	
O 13	8 a. magenta	.. .. ..		

Other varieties exist in which the second "E" of "SERVICE" is out of alignment, and also in which the word is in a different fount, measuring 11½ mm.

O.H.M.S.

(O 3)

1904. *T* **2**, *wmk. Crown CA, P* 14, *overprinted with Type* O **3**, *in black.*

No.	Description	Unused s.	d.	Used s.	d.
O 14	½ a. dull green and green ..	8	6	10	0
	a. No stop after "M" ..				
O 15	1 a. grey-black and carmine.	15	0	15	0
	a. No stop after "M" ..				
O 16	2 a. dull and bright purple..	70	0	70	0
	a. No stop after "M" ..				
O 17	8 a. grey-black and pale blue	50	0	50	0
	a. No stop after "M" ..				

T **2**, *wmk. Mult. Crown CA, P* 14, *optd. with Type* O **3**, *in black.*

No.	Description	Unused s.	d.	Used s.	d.
O 18	2 a. dull & bright pur., O	50	0	52	6
	a. No stop after "M" ..				

T **3**, *wmk. Crown CC, P* 14, *optd. as Type* O **3**.

No.	Description	Unused		Used	
O 19	1 r. green	£8		£9	

Of the above stamps it is doubtful if Nos. O 6 to O 13 were ever issued. Of No. O 19 we have had three used copies on a portion of an official envelope. Another stamp—viz. the 1 r. *green and carmine* (*Queen's Head*)—exists overprinted with Type O **2**, but it was never issued for use. (*Price* 15s. *un.*)

BRITISH SOUTH AFRICA COMPANY.

See **RHODESIA.**

BRUNEI.

BRUNEI.
(1)

BRUNEI. **BRUNEI.**

TWO CENTS. **25 CENTS.**

(2) (3)

1906. *Stamps of Labuan, T* **42** (*Nos.* 116*a, etc.*), *overprinted with T* **1**, *or surcharged as T* **2** (*the* 25 *c. T* **3**), *in red.*

No.	Description	Unused s.	d.	Used s.	d.
1	1 c. black and purple.. ..	17	6	20	0
2	2 c. on 3 c. black and sepia ..	8	6	10	0
	a. "BRUNEI" double	£90			
3	2 c. on 8 c. black & vermilion	16	6	17	6
4	3 c. black and sepia	16	6	17	6
5	4 c. on 12 c. black and yellow	6	6	7	0
6	5 c. on 16 c. green and brown	9	0	10	6
7	8 c. black and vermilion ..	7	6	8	6
8	10 c. on 16 c. green and brown	8	6	8	6
9	25 c. on 16 c. green and brown	25	0	27	6
10	30 c. on 16 c. green and brown	22	6	25	0
11	50 c. on 16 c. green and brown	30	0	32	6
12	1 dol. on 8 c. black & verm. ..	45	0	50	0

Error. Overprinted in black.

No.	Description	Unused		Used	
13	1 c. black and purple ..	£50		£35	

4. View on Brunei River.
(Recess. De La Rue & Co.)

1907. *Wmk. Mult. Crown CA. P* 14.

No.	Type	Description	Unused s.	d.	Used s.	d.
14	**4**	1 c. grey-blk. and pale grn.	2	6	3	6
15	„	2 c. grey-blk. and scarlet..	3	6	4	0
16	„	3 c. grey-blk. and chocolate	7	6	8	0
17	„	4 c. grey-blk. and mauve..	7	6	8	0
		a. Grey black and reddish-purple	30	0	20	0
18	„	5 c. grey-blk. and blue ..	18	6	20	0
19	„	8 c. grey-blk. and orange..	12	6	15	0
20	„	10 c. grey-blk. and deep grn.	7	6	8	6
21	„	25 c. pale blue and ochre-brn	12	6	15	0
22	„	30 c. violet and black ..	12	6	15	0
23	„	50 c. green and deep brown	17	6	18	0
24	„	$1 red and grey	35	0	37	6

3c THREE CENTS 3c

I

3c THREE CENTS 3c

II

I. *Double plate.* Lowest line of shading on water is dotted.

II. *Single plate.* Dotted line of shading removed.

Stamps printed in two colours are as I.

1908–24. *Colours changed. Wmk. Mult. Crown CA. P* 14.

No.	Type	Description	Unused s.	d.	Used s.	d.
24*a*	**4**	1 c. green (I)	3	6	4	0
25	„	1 c. green (II)	1	3	1	0
26	„	2 c. black and brown (1911)	1	3	1	6
27	„	3 c. scarlet (I)	2	0	1	9
27*a*	„	3 c. scarlet (II)	8	0	6	0
28	„	4 c. claret (II) (1912) ..	1	6	1	3
29	„	5 c. black and orange ..	3	6	4	0
31	„	8 c. blue and indigo-blue..	5	0	6	0
33	„	10 c. purple/*yell.* (II) (1912)	4	0	4	0
		a. On pale yellow (1924) ..	2	6	2	6
34	„	25 c. deep lilac (II) (1912)	4	0	4	6
35	„	30 c. pur. & orge.-yell. (1912)	4	0	5	0
36	„	50 c. black/*green* (II) (1912)	17	6	20	0
		a. On blue-green	10	0	10	0
37	„	$1 black & red/*blue* (1912)	12	6	12	6
38	„	$5 carmine/*green* (I) ..	35	0	37	6
39	„	$25 black/*red* (I)	£12		£12	

The 10 c. on *yellow*, with apparent *white* back, is due to climatic change, not separate printing. We have seen other values in apparent shade variations due to the same cause. There are several marked retouches, notably in the clouds of the central design in some of the values printed at two operations.

1916. *Colours changed. Wmk. Mult. Crown CA. P* 14.

No.	Type	Description	Unused s.	d.	Used s.	d.
40	**4**	5 c. orange (II)	2	0	1	6
41	„	8 c. ultramarine (II) ..	3	0	3	6

MALAYA-
BORNEO
EXHIBITION,
1922.
(5)

1922. *Optd. with T* **5**, *in black.*

No.	Type	Description	Unused s.	d.	Used s.	d.
42	**4**	1 c. green (II)	3	0	3	6
43	„	2 c. black and brown ..	3	6	3	6
44	„	3 c. scarlet (II)	3	6	4	0
45	„	4 c. claret (II)	4	6	5	0
46	„	5 c. orange (II)	4	6	5	0
47	„	10 c. purple/*yellow* (II) ..	6	6	7	6
48	„	25 c. purple (II)	12	6	12	6
49	„	50 c. black/*blue-green* (II) ..	20	0	22	6
50	„	$1 black and red/*blue* ..	22	6	25	0

6. View of Brunei Town.
(Recess. De La Rue & Co.)

1924-37. *Wmk. Mult. Script CA. P* 14.

No.	Type	Description	Unused	Used
51	4	1 c. black (II) (1926)	0 4	0 6
52	„	2 c. brown (II)	2 6	2 6
52*a*	„	2 c. green (II) ('33)	0 6	0 6
53	„	3 c. green (II)	2 0	2 6
54	„	4 c. marone (II)	4 6	4 0
55	„	4 c. orange (II) (1929) ..	1 6	1 6
56	„	5 c. orange-yellow (II) ..	3 0	3 0
57	„	5 c. grey (II) ('31) ..	3 0	3 0
57*a*	„	5 c. chocolate (II) ('33) ..	1 6	1 6
58	6	6 c. black	0 3	0 4
59	„	6 c. scarlet ('31)	1 6	1 9
60	4	8 c. ultram. (II) ('27) ..	4 6	4 6
60*a*	„	8 c. grey-black (II) ('33)	2 0	2 0
60*b*	„	10 c. purple/*yell.* (II) ('37)	3 0	3 6
61	6	12 c. blue	3 6	4 0
		a. Pale greenish-blue	6 0	7 6
62	4	25 c. slate-purple (II) ('31)	4 6	5 0
63	„	30 c. pur. & orge.-yell. (I) ('31)	5 0	5 0
64	„	50 c. black/*emer.* (II) ('31)	7 6	8 0
65	„	$1 blk. & red/*blue* (I) ('31)	15 0	17 6

BUSHIRE.
(BRITISH OCCUPATION.)

BUSHIRE
Under British
Occupation.
(1)

1915 (15 Aug.). *Portrait stamps of Iran,* 1911–13, *overprinted with T* 1, *in black.*

No.	Description	Unused	Used
1	1 ch. orange and green ..	15 0	15 0
	a. No stop	50 0	50 0
2	2 ch. sepia and carmine ..	15 0	15 0
	a. No stop	50 0	50 0
3	3 ch. green and grey	17 6	17 6
	a. No stop	65 0	65 0
4	5 ch. carmine and brown ..	£7	£7
5	6 ch. lake and green	20 0	20 0
	a. No stop	65 0	65 0
6	9 ch. indigo-lilac and brown ..	20 0	20 0
	a. No stop	60 0	60 0
7	10 ch. brown and carmine ..	20 0	20 0
	a. No stop	80 0	80 0
8	12 ch. blue and green	30 0	30 0
	a. No stop	90 0	90 0
9	24 ch. green and purple ..	32 6	32 6
	a. No stop	90 0	90 0
10	1 kr. carmine and blue ..	30 0	30 0
	a. Double overprint		
	b. No stop	90 0	90 0
11	2 kr. claret and green ..	80 0	80 0
	a. No stop	£12	
12	3 kr. black and lilac	£5	£5
	a. No stop	£13	
13	5 kr. blue and red	60 0	60 0
	a. No stop	£8	
14	10 kr. rose and sepia	50 0	50 0
	a. No stop	£6	

1915 (Sept.). *Coronation issue of Iran, overprinted with T* 1, *in black.*

No.	Description	Unused	Used
15	1 ch. deep blue and carmine..	£20	£20
16	2 ch. carmine and deep blue..	£250	
17	3 ch. deep green	£30	£30
18	5 ch. vermilion	£200	£200
19	6 ch. carmine and green ..	£160	£160
20	9 ch. deep violet and brown ..	£30	£30
21	10 ch. brown and deep green ..	£40	£40
22	12 ch. ultramarine	£50	£50
23	24 ch. sepia and brown ..	£22	£25
24	1 kr. black, brown, and silver	£20	£22
25	2 kr. carmine, slate, and silver	£30	£22
26	3 kr. sepia, dull lilac, and silver	£30	£30
27	5 kr. slate, sepia, and silver ..	£25	£25
	a. Overprint inverted		
28	1 t. black, violet, and gold ..	£20	£20
29	3 t. red, crimson, and gold ..	£120	

Bushire, a seaport town of Iran, was occupied by the British on August 8th, 1915.

CAMEROONS.
(BRITISH OCCUPATION.)

(A)

(B)

The above are the types of German Colonial stamps that have been surcharged.

C. E. F.

1d.

(1)

C. E. F.

1s.

(2)

1915. *Stamps of the German Colonial issues of* 1900 *and* 1906–7 (5, 10, 20 *pf. and* 5 *m.*), *Types* A *and* B, *surcharged as T* 1 *and* 2.

No.	Description	Unused	Used
1	½d. on 3 pf. (B.)	2 6	3 0
2	½d. on 5 pf. (B.)	1 0	1 3
	a. Double surcharge	£30	£10
	b. Black surcharge	7 6	8 6
3	1d. on 10 pf. (B.)	1 0	1 6
	a. Thin serif and foot to "1" ..	40 0	50 0
	b. Double surcharge	£6	
	c. Double surcharge with thin serif and foot to "1"		
	d. "1d." double, but "C.E.F." not double	£100	
	e. Black surcharge	7 6	
	f. Black surcharge with thin serif and foot to "1"	50 0	
	g. "C.E.F." omitted		
4	2d. on 20 pf.	2 0	2 6
5	2½d. on 25 pf.	4 0	4 6
	a. Double surcharge	£100	
6	3d. on 30 pf.	4 0	4 6
7	4d. on 40 pf.	4 0	4 6
	a. Shorter "4"		
8	6d. on 50 pf.	4 0	4 6
9	8d. on 80 pf.	4 0	4 6
10	1s. on 1 m.	42 6	50 0
	a. "s" inverted	£16	£20
11	2s. on 2 m.	42 6	50 0
	a. "s" inverted	£16	£20
12	3s. on 3 m.	42 6	50 0
	a. "s" inverted	£16	£20
	b. Double surcharge	£120	
	c. Double surcharge and "s" inverted		
13	5s. on 5 m.	42 6	50 0
	a. "s" inverted	£16	£20

The letters "C. E. F." signify "Cameroons Expeditionary Force."

CANADA.

SIMPLIFICATION (see p. xii)

Nos. 1 to 45.

1a, 2, 4.
23, 6, 12, 13, 22, 20c: 25, 26, 27a.
29, 44, 31, 33, 34, 38, 39, 42.

Nos. 46 to 76 and 113-114.

53, 55, 75, 56, 57, 58, 70, 59, 60, 61, 63 (113), 64 (114), 67.

Nos. 77 to 112 and 117 to 120.

101, 77, 80, 82, 83, 105, 106, 87, 107, 88, 109, 117, 118, 120, 89, 112.

COLONY OF CANADA.

1. Beaver.

(Designed by Sir Sanford Fleming.)

2. Prince Albert.

3.

(Engraved and printed by Messrs. Rawdon Wright, Hatch and Edson, New York.)

1851. *T 1 to 3. Imperf. Laid paper.*

		Un.	*Used.*
1	3d. red (23 April) ..	£175	60 0 *to* £20
1a	3d. orange-vermilion ..	£175	60 0 *to* £20
	b. Major re-entry*	—	£30
2	6d. slate-violet (15 May)	£125	£8 *to* £30
3	6d. brown-purple ..	£150	£8 *to* £30
	a. Bisected (3d.)	..	
4	12d. black (14 June) ..	£950	£300 *to* £800

* There are a number of re-entries on the plate of the 3d. and these occur in this stamp on all papers. The major-re-entry listed above shows a prominent line through the top of the letters "EE PEN."

1852–57. *T 1 to 3. Imperf.*

A. *Thin wove paper.*

6	3d. red	£30	30 0 *to* 95 0
7	3d. deep red	£30	30 0 *to* £8
7a	3d. scarlet-vermilion ..	£45	40 0 *to* £10
8	6d. slate-violet ..	£160	£12 *to* £55
9	6d. greenish grey ..	£185	£20 *to* £70
9a	12d. black	—	£600 *to* £1000

B. *Medium hard wove paper.*

10	3d. red	£20	30 0 *to* 80 0
11	3d. deep red	£20	30 0 *to* 80 0
11a	3d. brown-red	£25	35 0 *to* £8
12	6d. slate-violet ..	£150	£8 £40
	a. Bisected (3d).	..	
13	6d. greenish grey ..	£155	£10 *to* £40
14	6d. brownish grey ..	£155	£10 *to* £40
14a	12d. black	..	

C. *Thick hard wove paper.*

		Un.	*Used.*
15	3d. red	£30	60 0 *to* £15
	a. Bisected ..	..	
16	6d. grey-lilac	£250	£20 *to* £75

D. *Very thick soft wove paper.*

17	6d. purple (reddish) ..	£300	£25 *to* £85
	a. Bisected (3d.)	..	

1857. E. *Thin soft ribbed paper.*

18	3d. red	£55	£16

F. *Thin soft brittle wove paper.*

19	3d. red	—	£20

4. Jacques Cartier.

(Engraved & printed by Messrs. Rawdon, Wright, Hatch and Edson, New York.)

1855 (JAN.). *T 4. Imperf.*

A. *Thin wove paper.*

		Un.	*Used.*
20	10d. bright blue	£110	£5 *to* £30
20a	10d. dull blue ..	£110	£5 *to* £30

B. *Medium wove paper, semi-transparent.*

20b	10d. bright blue	£120	£5 *to* £30
20c	10d. Prussian blue	£130	£5 *to* £30

1857. C. *Stout hard wove paper.*

21	10d. blue ..	£150	£12 *to* £40

There are a number of re-entries in the 10d. stamps.

These stamps may be divided into "wide" and "narrow," due to the shrinkage of the paper, which is wetted before printing, and which contracts unevenly when drying. Stamps in extreme width measure from 17 mm. wide up to 18 mm., the narrower ones being the commoner.

5

6

1857 (2 JUNE). *T 5. Imperf.*

22	7½d. pale yellow-green	£120	£12 *to* £50
22a	7½d. deep yellow-green	£150	£15 *to* £60

There are several re-entries in these stamps.

The same remarks apply to this stamp as to the 10d. blue. The width varies less, being generally 18 to 18½ mm.

1857 (1 AUG.). *T 6. Imperf.*

A. *Stout hard wove paper.*

		Un.	*Used.*
23	½d. deep rose	£18	50 0 *to* £10

B. *Thin soft ribbed paper.*

24	½d. deep rose (*horizontal*)	£42	£30
24a	½d. deep rose (*vertical*)	—	£35

1858–59. *T* **6, 1** *and* **2.**

A. *Stout wove paper.* *P* 12.

No.	Description	Unused	Used
25	½d. deep rose	£25	£15
25a	½d. lilac-rose	—	£20
26	3d. red	£25	£10
27	6d. brownish grey	£90	£50
27a	6d. slate-violet	£85	£45

The 3d. is known perf. 14, and also *percé en scie* 13, both these being unofficial, but used at the date of issue.

7

8. Beaver

9 Prince Albert.

10

11. Jacques Cartier.

(Recess. American Bank Note Co.)

On 1st May, 1858, Messrs. Rawdon, Wright, Hatch, and Edson altered the name of their firm to " The American Bank Note Co.," and the " imprint " on sheets of the following stamps has the new title of the firm with " New York " added.

1859 (1 JULY). *T* **7** *to* **11.** *P* 12.

No.	Description	Unused	Used
29	1 c. pale rose (to rose-red) ..	55 0	25 0
30	1 c. deep rose (to carm.-rose) ..	62 6	30 0
	a. Imperf.	£25	
	b. Imperf. × perf.		
	c. Laid paper		
31	5 c. pale red	70 0	12 6
32	5 c. deep red	70 0	12 6
	a. Re-entry*	—	£20
	b. Imperf.	£20	
	c. Bisected (2½ c.)		
33	10 c. black-brown	£120	£30
	a. Bisected (5 c.)		
34	10 c. purple (to deep)	£15	50 0
	a. Bisected (5 c.)		
35	10 c. brownish purple	£15	65 0
36	10 c. brown (to pale)	£17	65 0
37	10 c. dull violet	£12	50 0
38	10 c. bright red-purple	£10	50 0
	a. Imperf.	£35	
39	12½ c. deep yellow-green ..	£8	35 0
40	12½ c. pale yellow-green ..	£8	30 0
1	12½ c. blue-green	£12	35 0
	a. Imperf.	£35	
	b. Imperf. between (vert. pair) ..		
42	17 c. deep blue	£15	80 0
	a. Imperf.	£50	
43	17 c. slate-blue	£30	£8
43a	17 c. indigo	£20	£5
	b. Imperf.	£60	

* The price of No. 32a is for the very marked re-entry, showing oval frame line doubled above " CANADA ". Slighter re-entries are worth from 20s. upwards in used condition.

As there were numerous P.O. Dept. orders for the 10 c., 12½ c. and 17 c. and some of these were executed by more than one separate printing, with no special care to ensure uniformity of colour, there is a wide range of shade, especially in the 10 c., and some shades recur at intervals after periods during which other shades have predominated. The colour-names given in the above list therefore represent groups only.

The researches of Senator J. A. Calder, F.R.P.S.L., have proved that the perforations may be an aid to the approximate dating of a particular stamp, the gauge used measuring 11¾ × 11¾ from mid-July, 1859, to early in 1863, 12 × 11¾ from early 1863 to early 1865 and 12 × 12 from early 1865 to 1867.

12

(Recess. American Bank Note Co.)

1864 (1 AUG.). *T* **12.** *P* 12.

No.	Description	Unused	Used
44	2 c. rose-red	£9	£6
45	2 c. bright rose	£9	£6
	a. Imperf.	£25	

DOMINION OF CANADA.

13. *Small type.*

14. *Large type.*

On 1 July, 1867, Canada, Nova Scotia, and New Brunswick were united, the combined territory being termed " The Dominion of Canada ". Under the Act of Union provision was made for the admission of Newfoundland, Prince Edward Island, British Columbia, Rupert's Land, and the North-Western Territory.

T **13** *and* **14** (*various frames*). *Engraved and printed by* " The British American Bank Note Co." *at either Montreal or Ottawa.*

Montreal printings.

1868 (MARCH). (A) *Thin rather transparent crisp paper.* *P* 12.

No.	Type	Description	Unused	Used
46	**13**	½ c. black	32 6	17 6
47	**14**	1 c. red-brown	£5	32 6
48	,,	2 c. grass-green	65 0	20 0
49	,,	3 c. red-brown	£6	22 6
50	,,	6 c. blackish brown ..	£6	32 6
51	,,	12½ c. bright blue	95 0	30 0
52	,,	15 c. reddish purple ..	£20	60 0

In these first printings the impression is generally blurred, and the lines of the background are less clearly defined than in later printings.

1868–72. (B) *Medium to stout wove paper.* *P* 12.

No.	Type	Description	Unused	Used
53	13	½ c. black	17 6	17 6
54	,,	½ c. grey-black	12 6	12 6
		a. Imperf. between (pair)		
		b. Watermarked		
55	14	1 c. red-brown	45 0	20 0
		a. Laid paper	£150	£35
		b. Watermarked (1868)	£25	85 0
56	,,	2 c. deep green	60 0	15 0
57	,,	2 c. pale emer.-grn. (1871)	55 0	15 0
		a. Laid paper		
57*b*	,,	2 c. bluish green	75 0	17 6
		c. Watermarked (1868)	£30	£8
58	,,	3 c. brown-red	65 0	8 0
		a. Laid paper	£40	80 0
		b. Watermarked (1868)	£25	47 6
59	,,	6 c. blackish brn. (to choc.)	80 0	17 6
		a. Watermarked (1868)	—	£25
60	,,	6 c. yellow-brown (1870)	90 0	17 6
61	,,	12½ c. bright blue	55 0	25 0
		a. Watermarked (1868)	£25	£8
62		12½ c. pale dull blue (milky)	65 0	30 0
63	,,	15 c. reddish purple	£8	25 0
64	,,	15 c. dull violet-grey	50 0	25 0
		a. Watermarked (1868)	—	£12
		b. Script wmk.*	£95	£40
65	,,	15 c. dull grey-purple	50 0	20 0
66	,,	15 c. clear dp. viol (1880–81)	£20	85 0
67	,,	15 c. deep slate (1881–88)	40 0	15 0
68	,,	15 c. slaty blue	50 0	15 0

The watermark on the stout paper stamps consists of the words "E & G BOTHWELL CLUTHA MILLS," in large double-lined capitals. Portions of one or two letters only may be found on these stamps, which occur in the early printings of 1868.

* The watermark on No. 64*b* is part of the words "Alexr. Pirie & Sons" in script lettering, a very small quantity of paper thus watermarked having been used for printing this stamp.

The papers may, in most cases, be easily divided if the stamps are laid face downwards and carefully compared. The thin hard paper is more or less transparent and shows the design through the stamp; the thicker paper is softer to the feel and more opaque.

The paper of this issue may be still further subdivided in several values into sets on—(a) *Medium to stout wove.* (b) *Thin, soft, very white;* and (c) *Thinner and poorer quality, sometimes greyish or yellowish* (*from* 1878 *to end of issue*).

20

1873–78. (C) *Medium to stout wove paper* *P* 11½×12.

No.	Type	Description	Unused	Used
69	13	½ c. black	35 0	30 0
70	20	5 c. olive-grn. (1 Oct., '75)	£6	40 0
71	14	15 c. dull grey-pur. (Dec., '74)	£20	80 0
72	,,	15 c. lilac-grey (Mar., '77)	£17	55 0
73	,,	15 c. slaty blue	£25	£5

1869 (Jan.). (D) *Colour changed.* *Stout wove paper.* *P* 12.

No.	Type	Description	Unused	Used
74	14	1 c. deep orge. (Jan., '69)	£10	50 0
75	,,	1 c. orge.-yell. (May(?), '69)	90 0	40 0
76	,,	1 c. pale orange-yellow	£8	35 0
		a. Imperf.		

21. *Small type.*

1870–88. *T* 21 (*various frames*). *P* 12 (*or slightly under*).

Montreal printings.

Papers. (*a*) 1870–80. *Medium to stout wove.*
(*b*) 1870–72. *Thin, soft, very white.*
(*c*) 1878–97. *Thinner and poorer quality*

No.	Type	Description	Unused	Used
77	21	1 c. bright orange (*a, b*) (1870–73)	75 0	17 6
78	,,	1 c. orange-yellow (*a*) (1876–79)	25 0	4 6
79	,,	1 c. pale dull yellow (*a*) (1877–79)	10 0	0 8
80	,,	1 c. bright yellow (*a, c*) (1878–97)	8 6	0 2
		a. Imperf. (pair) (*c*)	£8	
		b. Bisected (½ c.) (on "Railway News")	—	£30
		c. Printed both sides	£70	
81	,,	2 c. deep green (*a, b*) (1872–73 and 1876–78)	30 0	1 3
82	,,	2 c. grass-grn. (*c*) (1878–88)	20 0	0 4
		a. Imperf. (pair) (1891–93(?))	£10	
		b. Bisected (1 c.)	—	£15
83	,,	3 c. Indian red (*a*) (Jan., '70)	90 0	17 6
84	,,	3 c. rose-red (*a, b*) (1870–73)	60 0	10 0
85	,,	3 c. dull red (*a*) (1876–88)	27 6	1 6
86	,,	3 c. orange-red (*a, c*) (1876–88)	12 6	1 3
87	,,	5 c. olive-grey (*a, c*) (February, 1876–88)	20 0	2 0
88	,,	6 c. yellowish brown (*a, b, c*) (1872–73 & 1876–90)	27 6	4 6
		a. Bisected (3 c.)	—	£25
89	,,	10 c. pale lilac-magenta (*a*) (1876–?)	80 0	15 0
90	,,	10 c. deep lilac-magenta (*a, c*) (March 1876–88)	75 0	12 6

1873–77. *P* 11½×12. *Medium to stout wove paper.*

No.	Type	Description	Unused	Used
90*a*	21	1 c. bright orange	£6	20 0
91	,,	1 c. orge.-yellow (1873–79)	£5	12 6
92	,,	1 c. pale dull yellow (1877–79)	70 0	12 6
93	,,	2 c. deep green (1873–78)	95 0	15 0
94	,,	3 c. dull red (1875–79)	60 0	10 6
95	,,	3 c. orange-red (1873–79)	55 0	6 6
96	,,	5 c. olive-grey (1876–79)	65 0	10 6
97	,,	6 c. yellowish brn. (1876–79)	60 0	8 0
98	,,	10 c. pale lilac-magenta (1874–79)	£15	55 0
99	,,	10 c. deep lilac-magenta (1876–79)	£12	50 0

27

1882–97. *P* 12. *Thinnish paper often toned.*

No.	Type	Description	Unused	Used
101	27	½ c. black (July, 1882–97)	1 3	1 0
102	,,	½ c. grey-black	1 6	1 6
		a. Imperf. (1891–93 (?))	80 0	
		b. Imperf. between (pair)	£20	

Ottawa printings.

1888–97. *As T* **14** *and* **21** *(various frames).* *P* 12. *Thinnish paper of poor quality, often toned grey or yellowish.*

103 **21** 2 c. dull sea-green (Jan., 1888) 30 0 1 6
104 ,, 2 c. blue-green (July, 1889–91) 42 6 2 0
105 ,, 3 c. rose-carmine (Oct., 1888–April, '89) .. £15 10 0
106 ,, 3 c. bright vermilion (Apr., 1889–97) 6 6 0 2
a. Imperf. (pair) (1891–93(?)) £10
107 ,, 5 c. brownish grey (May, '88) 10 6 0 6
a. Imperf (pair) (1891–93) £15
108 ,, 6 c. deep chestnut (Oct., '90) 27 6 8 6
109 ,, 6 c. pale chestnut .. 27 6 8 6
a. Imperf. (pair) (1891–93(?)) £20
110 ,, 10 c. lilac-pink (Mar., '88) 65 0 15 0
111 ,, 10 c. carm.-pink (1891 (?)) 45 0 10 0
a. Imperf. (pair) (1891–93(?)) £12
112 ,, 10 c. brn'ish red (1894 (?)) 40 0 12 6
a. Imperf. (pair) £10
113 **14** 15 c. slate-pur. (July, '88) 30 0 15 0
114 ,, 15 c. slate-vio. (May, '90) 35 0 15 0
a. Imperf. (brn.-pur.) (pair) £15

NOTE.—The 1 c. showed no change in the Ottawa printings, so is not included. The 2 c. reverted to its previous grass-green shade in 1891. About 1895 remainders of the 15 c. were used concurrently with the 1888 and 1890 shades. They vary from grey and slate to a nearly true blue.

28

29

1893 (17 FEB.). *P* 12.

115 **28** 20 c. vermilion 30 0 10 6
a. Imperf. (pair) £12
116 ,, 50 c. blue 30 0 10 6
a. Imperf. (Prussian blue) (pair) £15

1893 (1 AUG.). *P* 12.

117 **29** 8 c. pale bluish grey .. 35 0 4 6
a. Imperf. (pair) £10
118 ,, 8 c. bluish slate 40 0 5 0
119 ,, 8 c. slate-purple 35 0 3 0
120 ,, 8 c. blackish purple .. 32 6 5 0

30

1897 (19 JUNE). ***Jubilee issue.*** *P* 12.

121 **30** ½ c. black 16 0 16 0
122 ,, 1 c. orange 2 6 1 9
123 ,, 1 c. orange-yellow .. 2 6 1 9
a. Bisected (½ c.) ..
124 ,, 2 c. green 2 9 2 0
125 ,, 2 c. deep green 2 9 2 0
126 ,, 3 c. carmine 2 6 0 8
127 ,, 5 c. slate-blue 17 6 10 0
128 **30** 5 c. deep blue 12 0 8 6
129 ,, 6 c. brown 40 0 42 6
130 ,, 8 c. slate-violet 20 0 22 0
131 ,, 10 c. purple 25 0 30 0
132 ,, 15 c. slate 40 0 40 0
133 ,, 20 c. vermilion 40 0 40 0
134 ,, 50 c. pale ultramarine .. 55 0 40 0
135 ,, 50 c. bright ultramarine .. 60 0 42 6
136 ,, $1 lake £10 £6
137 ,, $2 deep violet £15 £9
138 ,, $3 bistre £20 £12
139 ,, $4 violet £22 £10
140 ,, $5 olive-green £25 £12

31

1897–98. *P* 12.

141 **31** ½ c. grey-blk. (9 Nov., 1897) 1 6 1 3
142 ,, ½ c. black 1 6 1 0
a. Imperf. (pair) .. £15
143 ,, 1 c. blue-green (Dec., 1897 1 6 0 4
a. Imperf. (pair) .. £15
144 ,, 2 c. violet (Dec., 1897) .. 3 0 0 6
a. Imperf. (pair) .. £15
145 ,, 3 c. carmine (Jan., 1898) .. 3 6 0 4
a. Imperf. (pair) £15
146 ,, 5 c. deep blue/*bluish* (Dec., 1897) 7 6 2 0
a. Imperf. (pair) .. £15
147 ,, 6 c. brown (Dec., 1897) .. 12 6 15 0
a. Imperf. (pair) .. £15
148 ,, 8 c. orange (Dec., 1897) .. 12 6 6 6
a. Imperf. (pair) .. £15
149 ,, 10 c. brownish purple (Jan., 1898) 22 6 17 6
a. Imperf. (pair) £15

32

1898–1902. *P* 12.

150 **32** ½ c. black (Sept., 1898) .. 0 4 0 3
a. Imperf. (pair) £15
151 ,, 1 c. blue-green (June, 1898) 1 3 0 1
152 ,, 1 c. deep green/*toned paper* 1 3 0 1
a. Imperf. (pair) .. £15
153 ,, 2 c. purple (Sept., 1898) .. 5 0 0 6
154 ,, 2 c. violet 2 0 0 3
155 ,, 2 c. rose-carm. (20.8.99) .. 1 3 0 1
a. Imperf. (pair) £15
156 ,, 3 c. rose-carm. (June, 1898) 5 0 0 1
157 ,, 5 c. slate-blue/*bluish* .. 15 0 1 0
a. Imperf. (pair) £15
158 ,, 5 c. Prussian blue/*bluish* .. 12 6 1 0
159 ,, 6 c. brown (Sept., 1898) .. 20 0 20 0
a. Imperf. (pair) .. £15
160 ,, 7 c. greenish yell. (23.12.02) 12 6 10 0
161 ,, 8 c. orge.-yell. (Oct., 1898) 30 0 20 0
162 ,, 8 c. brownish orange .. 30 0 20 0
a. Imperf. (pair) .. £15
163 ,, 10 c. pale brownish purple (Nov., 1898) 27 6 8 6
164 ,, 10 c. deep brownish purple 25 0 8 6
a. Imperf. (pair) £15
165 ,, 20 c. olive-green (29.12.00) 50 0 25 0

The 7 c. and 20 c. also exist imperf. but unlike the values listed in this condition, they have no gum. (*Price, either value, £15 pair, un.*)

33

(Designed by Postmaster-General Mulock.)

1898 (7 Dec.). *Imperial Penny Postage. Design in black. British possessions in red. Oceans in colours below. P* 12.

No.	Type		Unused	Used
166	**33**	2 c. lavender	4 0	1 6
167	„	2 c. greenish blue	6 0	2 6
168	„	2 c. blue	7 6	2 6
		a. Imperf. (pair)	£25	

1899 (5 Jan.). *Provisionals used at Port Hood only. No.* 156 *divided vertically and surcharged.*

No.	Type		Unused	Used
169	**32**	" 1," in blue, on ⅓ of 3 c.	—	£100
170	„	" 2," in violet, on ⅔ of 3 c.	—	£60
		a. Surcharge double		

2 CENTS
(34)

1899 (28 July). *No.* 145 *surcharged as T* **34**.

No.	Type		Unused	Used
171	**31**	2 c. on 3 c. carmine	3 0	1 9
		a. Surcharge inverted	£35	

1899 (8 Aug.). *No.* 156 *surcharged as T* **34**.

No.	Type		Unused	Used
172	**32**	2 c. on 3 c. rose-carmine	2 6	1 0
		a. Surcharge inverted	£35	

35

1903–12. *P* 12.

No.	Type		Unused	Used
173	**35**	1 c. pale grn. (1 July, 1903)	3 0	0 1
174	„	1 c. deep green	4 0	0 1
175	„	1 c. green	1 6	0 1
176	„	2 c. rose-car. (1 July, 1903)	1 3	0 1
177	„	2 c. pale rose-carmine	1 0	0 1
		a. Imperf. (pair)	8 0	8 0
178	„	5 c. blue/*bluish* (1.7.03)	8 6	0 8
179	„	5 c. indigo/*bluish*	10 0	0 8
		a. Imperf. (pair) (July, 1907)	£20	£20
180	„	7 c. yell.-olive (1 July, 1903)	15 0	3 0
181	„	7 c. greenish bistre (–.6.12)	20 0	3 0
182	„	10 c. brn.-lilac (1 July, 1903)	25 0	3 6
183	„	10 c. pale dull purple	25 0	4 0
184	„	10 c. dull purple	25 0	3 6
185	„	20 c. pale ol.-grn. (27.9.04)	55 0	10 0
186	„	20 c. deep olive-green	55 0	10 0
187	„	50 c. deep vio. (19 Nov., 1908)	£12	50 0

36. King George V and Queen Mary when Prince and Princess of Wales.

37. Jacques Cartier and Samuel Champlain.

38. King Edward VII and Queen Alexandra.

39. Champlain's House in Quebec.

40. Generals Montcalm and Wolfe.

41. View of Quebec in 1700.

42. Champlain's Departure for the West.

43. Cartier's Arrival before Quebec.

1908 (16 July). *Quebec Tercentenary Issue. Various horizontal designs inscr.* " 1608–1908 IIIe CENTENAIRE DE QUEBEC ". *P* 12.

No.	Type		Unused	Used
188	**36**	½ c. sepia	4 0	4 6
		a. Imperf. (pair)	£18	
189	**37**	1 c. blue-green	4 0	4 6
		a. Imperf. (pair)	£18	
190	**38**	2 c. carmine	3 6	0 8
		a. Imperf. (pair)	£18	
191	**39**	5 c. indigo	20 0	12 6
		a. Imperf. (pair)	£18	
192	**40**	7 c. olive-green	25 0	22 6
		a. Imperf. (pair)	£18	
193	**41**	10 c. violet	40 0	37 6
		a. Imperf. (pair)	£18	
194	**42**	15 c. brown-orange	50 0	50 0
		a. Imperf. (pair)	£18	
195	**43**	20 c. dull brown	50 0	50 0
		a. Imperf. (pair)	£18	

Some of the values are to be found on both *toned* and *white* papers.

44

1912–18. *P* 12.

No.	Type		Unused	Used
196	**44**	1 c. yellow-green	0 6	0 1
		a. With fine horizontal lines across stamp	10 0	6 6
197	„	1 c. bluish green	1 9	0 1
198	„	1 c. deep bluish green	1 3	0 1
199	„	1 c. deep yellow-green	1 0	0 1
200	„	2 c. rose-red	1 6	0 1
201	„	2 c. deep rose-red	1 9	0 1
202	„	2 c. pale rose-red	1 3	0 1
		a. With fine horizontal lines across stamp	8 0	7 6
203	„	2 c. carmine	1 9	0 1
204	„	3 c. brown (1918)	1 0	0 1
205	„	3 c. deep brown	1 0	0 1
205*a*	„	5 c. deep blue	7 6	0 4
206	„	5 c. indigo	8 6	0 6
206*a*	„	5 c. grey-blue	7 6	0 4
207	„	7 c. pale sage-green	15 0	4 0
208	„	7 c. olive-yellow	8 6	0 9
209	„	7 c. yellow-ochre (1916)	3 0	0 6
210	„	10 c. brownish purple	15 0	0 6
211	„	10 c. reddish purple	15 0	0 6
212	„	20 c. olive-green	10 0	0 9
213	„	20 c. olive	10 6	0 9
214	„	50 c. sepia	15 0	3 6
215	„	50 c. grey-black	80 0	6 0

1912 (Nov.)–**1921.** *For use in coil-machines.*

(*a*) *P* 12 × *imperf.*

216	**44**	1 c. yellow-green	1	0	1	0
217	„	1 c. blue-green	4	6	2	0
218	„	2 c. deep rose-red ..	6	6	4	0
218*a*	„	3 c. brown (1921)	1	6	1	9

(*b*) *Imperf.* × *perf.* 8.

219	**44**	1 c. yellow-green	1	6	1	3
220	„	1 c. blue-green	1	9	0	8
221	„	2 c. carmine	3	0	0	6
222	„	2 c. rose-red	3	6	0	8
223	„	2 c. scarlet	4	0	1	3
224	„	3 c. brown (1918)	1	6	1	0

(*c*) *P* 8 × *imperf.*

224*a*	**44**	1 c. blue-green	12	6	6	6
224*b*	„	2 c. carmine	12	6	10	0

The stamps imperf. × perf. 8 were sold in coils over the counter; those perf. 8 × imperf. were on sale in automatic machines. Varieties showing perf. 12 on 2 or 3 adjacent sides and 1 or 2 sides imperf. are from booklets, or the margins of sheets.

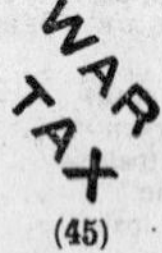

(45)

1915 (12 Feb.). *Optd. with T* **45.**

225	**44**	5 c. blue (Bk.)	37	6	47	6
226	„	20 c. olive-green (Bk.) ..	12	6	15	0
227	„	50 c. sepia (R.)	15	0	20	0

These stamps were intended for tax purposes, but owing to ambiguity in an official circular, dated 16 April, 1915, it was for a time believed that their use for postal purposes was authorised.

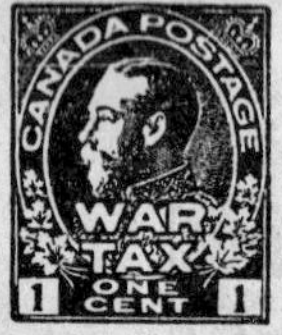

46

47

1915. *P* 12.

228	**46**	1 c. yellow-green	0	8	0	2
229	„	2 c. carmine-red	0	9	0	2
230	„	2 c. rose-carmine	1	3	1	0

Die I.

Die II.

In Die I there is a long horizontal coloured line under the foot of the "T", and a solid bar of colour runs upwards from the "1" to the "T". In Die II this solid bar of colour is absent, and there is a short horizontal line under the left side of the "T", with two short vertical dashes and a number of dots under the right-hand side.

1916 (Jan.). *P* 12.

231	**47**	2 c. + 1 c. rose-red (Die I) ..	3	0	0	3
232	„	2 c. + 1 c. brt. carm. (Die I)	6	6	0	8
233	„	2 c. + 1 c. scarlet (Die I) ..	6	6	0	6

1916 (Sept.). *P* 12.

234	**47**	2 c. + 1 c. carm.-red (Die II)	60	0	6	6

1916. *Imperf.* × *perf.* 8 (*coils*).

235	**47**	2 c. + 1 c. rose-red (Die I) ..	12	6	1	0

1916. *P* 12 × 8.

236	**47**	2 c. + 1 c. carm.-red (Die I)	6	6	5	0
237	„	2 c. + 1 c. brt. rose-red (Die I)	4	6	5	0

1916 (Sept.). *Colour changed.* *P* 12.

238	**47**	2 c. + 1 c. brown (Die I) ..	85	0	10	0
239	„	2 c. + 1 c. yell.-brn. (Die II)	1	0	0	2
240	„	2 c. + 1 c. deep brn. (Die II)	1	3	0	1

Imperf. × *perf.* 8.

241	**47**	2 c. + 1 c. brown (Die I) ..	17	0	3	0
242	„	2 c. + 1 c. yell.-brn. (Die II)	10	0	2	0
243	„	2 c. + 1 c. deep brn. (Die II)	6	6	1	6

48. Quebec Conference, 1864, from painting, "The Fathers of Confederation," by Robert Harris.

1917 (Sept.). *50th Anniversary of the Confederation.* *P* 12.

244	**48**	3 c. bistre-brown	4	0	0	4
		a. Imperf. (pair) (ungummed)	£30			
245	„	3 c. dark brown	4	6	0	4

1922–31. *As T* **44.** (*a*) *P* 12.

246	**44**	1 c. chrome-yellow ..	0	9	0	1
247	„	2 c. deep yellow-green ..	0	8	0	1
248	„	2 c. deep green	1	0	0	1
		a. Thin experimental paper (1924)	2	0	2	6
249	„	3 c. carmine (1923) ..	0	9	0	1
250	„	4 c. olive-yellow	3	0	1	0
251	„	4 c. yellow-ochre	2	0	0	6
252	„	5 c. violet	1	9	0	6
		a. Thin experimental paper (1924)	3	0	3	6
253	„	5 c. reddish violet	3	6	0	4
254	„	7 c. red-brown	3	0	0	9
254*a*	„	8 c. blue (1925)	3	6	0	9
255	„	10 c. blue	4	0	0	6
255*a*	„	10 c. bistre-brown (1925) ..	3	6	0	4
255*b*	„	10 c. yellow-brown ..	4	0	1	0
256	„	$1 brown-orange (1923) ..	20	0	3	6

The $1 differs from T **44** in that the value tablets are oval.

(*b*) *Imperf.* × *perf.* 8.

257	**44**	1 c. chrome-yell. (horiz. pr.)	0	8	0	6
		a. Imperf. between (vert. pair)	2	6		
		b. Thick soft paper (vert. pr.)*	20	0	20	0
258	„	2 c. yellow-green (horiz. pr.)	1	6	0	3
		a. Imperf. between (vert. pr.)	3	0		
		b. Thick soft paper (vert. pr.)*	35	0	35	0
259	„	3 c. carmine (horiz. pair) ..	9	0	1	0
		a. Thick soft paper (vert. pr.)*	75	0	75	0

Used prices are for singles.

Nos. 257, 258, and 259 are the regular coils, which come in horizontal pairs or strips only.

* Nos. 257*b*, 258*b*, and 259*a* are the first printing in sheets (22 sheets in all), on thick soft paper which can be had in vertical pairs, blocks, etc. Nos. 257*a* and 258*a* are a later sheet printing, on the normal paper. The colours differ slightly from those of 257*b* and 258*b* and the lettering of the inscription is sharply embossed as seen from the back of the stamps, whereas in the rare printing there is no embossed effect.

(*c*) *Imperf.* (1924).

260	**44**	1 c. chrome-yellow ..	10	0	12	0
261	„	2 c. deep green	12	6	20	0
262	„	3 c. carmine	6	6	7	6

(d) P 12×imperf.

263	**44**	2 c. deep green	35 0	40 0

(e) P 12×8.

263*a*	**44**	3 c. carmine (24.6.31) ..	1 3	0 8

Nos. 260 to 262 were on sale only at the Philatelic Branch P.O. Dept., Ottawa.

2 CENTS (49) **2 CENTS** (50)

1926. *No.* 249 *surcharged.*

(a) With T **49**, *by the Govt. Printing Bureau.*

264	**44**	2 c. on 3 c. carm. (12.10.26)	15 0	17 6

(b) With T **50**, *by the Canadian Bank Note Co.*

265	**44**	2 c. on 3 c. carm. (10.11.26)	6 6	7 6
		a. Surch. double (partly treble)	£18	

51. Sir J. A. Macdonald.

54. Sir W. Laurier.

52. "The Fathers of Confederation".

53. Parliament Buildings, Ottawa (*horiz.*).

55. Canada, Map 1867–1927 (*horiz.*).

1927 (29 June). 60*th Anniversary of Confederation.*

I. *Commemorative Issue. P* 12.

Inscr. "1867–1927. CANADA CONFEDERATION".

266	**51**	1 c. orange	1 0	0 3
267	**52**	2 c. green	0 9	0 2
268	**53**	3 c. carmine	1 3	1 0
269	**54**	5 c. violet	1 3	0 8
270	**55**	12 c. blue	3 0	1 6

56. Darcy McGee.

57. Sir W. Laurier and Sir J. A. Macdonald.

58. R. Baldwin and L. H. Lafontaine.

II. *Historical Issue. P* 12.

271	**56**	5 c. violet	1 3	0 6
272	**57**	12 c. green	2 6	2 0
273	**58**	20 c. carmine	3 6	2 0

59

1928 (21 Sept.). *Air stamp. P* 12.

274	**59**	5 c. olive-brown	2 0	1 6
		a. Imperf.	£28	
		b. Imperf. between (vert. pair)	£55	
		c. Imperf. between (horiz. pr.)	£55	

60. King George V.

61. Mt. Hurd and Indian Totem poles.

62. Quebec Bridge (*horiz.*).

63. Harvesting with Horses (*horiz.*).

64. Fishing smack *Bluenose* (*horiz.*).

65. Parliament Buildings, Ottawa (*horiz.*).

(Recess-printed by the Canadian Bank Note Co.)

1928–29. *(a) P* 12.

275	**60**	1 c. orange (29.10.28) ..	0 6	0 1
276	,,	2 c. green (17.10.28) ..	0 6	0 1
277	,,	3 c. lake (12.12.28) ..	3 0	2 6
278	,,	4 c. olive-bistre (16.8.28)	1 3	0 10
279	,,	5 c. violet (12.12.28) ..	1 0	0 6
280	,,	8 c. blue (21.12.28) ..	1 6	1 0
281	**61**	10 c. green (5.11.28) ..	1 9	0 6
282	**62**	12 c. grey-black (8.1.29) ..	2 6	2 0
283	**63**	20 c. lake (8.1.29) ..	6 0	2 0
284	**64**	50 c. blue (8.1.29) ..	25 0	8 0
285	**65**	$1 olive-green (8.1.29) ..	65 0	17

(*b*) *Imperf.* × *perf.* 8.

286	**60**	1 c. orange (1929) ..	2 0	2 0
287	„	2 c. green	1 6	0 6

Slight differences in the size of many Canadian stamps, due to paper shrinkage, are to be found.

66

67. Parliamentary Library, Ottawa.

68. The Old Citadel, Quebec.

69. Harvesting with Tractor (*horiz.*).

70. Acadian Memorial Church and statue of "Evangeline" Grand Pre, Nova Scotia (*horiz.*).

71. Mt. Edith Cavell, Canadian Rockies (*horiz.*).

Die I. 1 c. Die II.

Die I. 2 c. Die II.

1 c. Die I. Three thick coloured lines and one thin between "P" and ornament, at right. Curved line in ball-ornament short.

Die II. Four thick lines. Curved line longer.

2 c. Die I. Three thick coloured lines between "P" and ornament, at left. Short line in ball.

Die II. Four thick lines. Curved line longer.

(Recess. The British-American Bank Note Co.)

1930–31. (*a*) *P* 11.

288	**66**	1 c. orange (I) (17.7.30) ..	0 6	0 3
289	„	2 c. green (I) (6.6.30) ..	0 6	0 3
290	„	4 c. yell.-bistre (5.11.30)	1 6	0 10
291	„	5 c. violet (18.6.30) ..	2 0	1 0
292	„	8 c. blue (13.8.30) ..	3 0	2 0
293	**67**	10 c. olive-green (15.9.30) .	2 0	0 6
294	**68**	12 c. grey-black (4.12.30) .	2 6	1 6
295	**69**	20 c. red (4.12.30)	3 6	0 10
296	**70**	50 c. blue (4.12.30) ..	60 0	4 0
297	**71**	$1 olive-green (4.12.30)	50 0	8 6

(*b*) *Imperf.* × *perf.* 8½.

298	**66**	1 c. orange (I)	1 0	0 6
299	„	2 c. green (I)	1 3	0 6

Colours changed and new value.

(*a*) *P* 11.

300	**66**	1 c. green (I) (6.12.30) ..	1 3	0 9
300*a*	„	1 c. green (II)	0 6	0 3
301	„	2 c. scarlet (I) (17.11.30).	0 9	0 4
301*a*	„	2 c. scarlet (II)	0 6	0 4
302	„	2 c. deep brown (I)(4.7.31)	6 6	5 0
302*a*	„	2 c. deep brown (II) ..	0 6	0 1
303	„	3 c. carmine (13.7.31) ..	0 8	0 1
304	„	5 c. blue (13.11.30) ..	1 3	0 6
305	„	8 c. red-orange (5.11.30)	1 9	1 0

(*b*) *Imperf.* × *perf.* 8½.

306	**66**	1 c. green (I)	1 0	0 6
307	„	2 c. scarlet (I)	1 3	0 8
308	„	2 c. deep brown (I)(4.7.31)	1 0	0 6
309	„	3 c. scarlet (13.7.31) ..	1 3	0 4

Some low values in the above and subsequent issues have been printed by both Rotary and "Flat plate" processes. The former can be distinguished by the gum, which has a striped appearance.

For 13 c. bright violet, **T 68**, see No. 325.

72. Mercury and Western Hemisphere.

1930 (4 Dec.). *Air. Recess. P* 11.

310	**72**	5 c. deep brown ..	25 0	22 6

73. Sir Georges Etienne Cartier.

1931 (30 Sept.). *Recess. P* 11.

312	**73**	10 c. olive-green	2 0	0 4

(74)

1932 (22 Feb.). *Air stamp. Surch. with T* **74**. *P* 12.

313	**59**	6 c. on 5 c. olive-brown ..	2 6	1 9
		a. Surch. inverted (vert. pair)	£35	
		b. Triple surcharge	£28	
		c. Double surcharge ..		

Collectors are warned against forged errors of this stamp, bearing unauthorised markings which purport to be the guarantee of Stanley Gibbons Ltd.

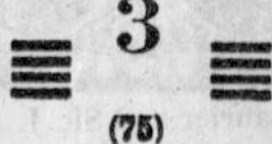

(75)

1932 (21 June). *Surch. with T* **75.** *P* 11.

314 **66** 3 c. on 2 c. scarlet (I) .. 1 9 1 0
314*a* ,, 3 c. on 2 c. scarlet (II) .. 0 6 0 2

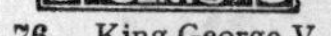

76. King George V. **77.** Duke of Windsor when Prince of Wales.

78. Allegory of the British Empire.

6 6

OTTAWA CONFERENCE
1932

(79)

1932 (12 July). *Ottawa Conference. Recess. P* 11

(*a*) *Postage stamps.*

315 **76** 3 c. scarlet 0 9 0 1
316 **77** 5 c. blue 2 0 0 9
317 **78** 13 c. green 2 9 1 9

(*b*) *Air stamp. Surcharged with T* 79.

318 **72** 6 c. on 5 c. deep brown (B.) 8 0 8 0

Die I.

80. King George V. Die II.

1932 (1 Dec.)–**1933.** *Recess.* (*a*) *P* 11.

319 **80** 1 c. green 0 4 0 1
320 ,, 2 c. sepia 0 6 0 1
321 ,, 3 c. scarlet (Die I) .. 3 0 1 0
321*a* ,, 3 c. scarlet (Die II) .. 0 6 0 1
322 ,, 4 c. yellow-bistre .. 5 0 0 8
323 ,, 5 c. blue 1 3 0 1
324 ,, 8 c. red-orange 3 6 0 9
325 **68** 13 c. bright violet .. 4 0 0 10

(*b*) *Imperf.* × *perf.* $8\frac{1}{2}$ ('33).

326 **80** 1 c. green 0 4 0 4
327 ,, 2 c. sepia 1 9 0 4
328 ,, 3 c. scarlet (Die II) .. 1 3 0 3

Two dies exist of the 3 c. In Die I the pointed end of the right-hand "3" is level with the white horizontal line above CENTS. In Die II the point is higher than the line.

81. Parliament Buildings, Ottawa.

1933 (18 May). *Universal Postal Union Congress* (*Preliminary Meeting*). *Recess. P* 11.

329 **81** 5 c. blue 3 6 1 6

WORLD'S
GRAIN EXHIBITION &
CONFERENCE

REGINA 1933

(82)

1933 (24 July). *World's Grain Exhibition and Conference at Regina. Overprinted with T* **82** *in blue. P* 11.

330 **69** 20 c. red 6 6 3 6

83. S.S. *Royal William*, from painting by S. Skillett.

1933 (17 Aug.). *Centenary of first trans-Atlantic steamboat crossing. Recess. P* 11.

331 **83** 5 c. blue 3 6 1 6

84. Jacques Cartier approaching land.

1934 (1 July). *Fourth Centenary of Discovery of Canada. Recess. P* 11.

332 **84** 3 c. blue 1 9 1 6

85. U.E.L. statue, Hamilton.

1934 (1 July). *150th Anniversary of Arrival of United Empire Loyalists. Recess. P* 11.

333	**85**	10 c. olive-green	6 6	4 0

86. Seal of New Brunswick.

1934. *150th Anniversary of Foundation of Province of New Brunswick. Recess. P* 11.

334	**86**	2 c. red-brown	7 0	3 6

87. Princess Elizabeth. **88.** Duke of York, now King George VI.

89. King George and Queen Mary.

90. Duke of Windsor when Prince of Wales (18×21 *mm.*).

91. Windsor Castle (34×22 *mm.*).

92. *Britannia* (34×22 *mm.*).

(Recess. Canadian Bank Note Co., Ottawa.)

1935 (4 May). *Silver Jubilee. Dated* 1910–1935. *P* 12.

335	**87**	1 c. green	0 4	0 4
336	**88**	2 c. brown	0 6	0 2
337	**89**	3 c. carmine-red	0 8	0 2
338	**90**	5 c. blue	2 6	2 0
339	**91**	10 c. green	2 6	2 6
340	**92**	13 c. blue	6 6	4 6

93. King George V.

94. Royal Canadian Mounted Policeman.

95. Confederation, Charlottetown, 1864.

96. Niagara Falls (*horiz.*).

97. Parliament Buildings, Victoria, B.C. (*horiz.*).

98. Champlain Monument, Quebec (*horiz.*).

99. Daedalus (*horiz.*).

(Recess. Canadian Bank Note Co., Ottawa.)

1935 (1 June–5 Nov.). (*a*) *Postage.* (i.) *P* 12.

341	**93**	1 c. green	0 6	0 1
342	„	2 c. brown	0 8	0 1
343	„	3 c. scarlet	0 10	0 1
344	„	4 c. yellow	1 0	0 6
345	„	5 c. blue	1 6	0 1
		a. Imperf. betwn. (horiz. pr.)	£25	
346	„	8 c. orange	2 0	1 0
347	**94**	10 c. carmine	2 6	0 3
348	**95**	13 c. purple	2 9	0 9
349	**96**	20 c. olive-green	4 0	0 9
350	**97**	50 c. deep violet	9 0	2 0
351	**98**	$1 bright blue	20 0	6 0

(ii.) *Coil stamps. Imperf.×perf.* 8.

352	**93**	1 c. green (5.11.35) ..	0 4	0 2
353	„	2 c. brown (14.10.35) ..	0 8	0 3
354	„	3 c. scarlet (20.7.35) ..	1 0	0 2

(*b*) *Air.* *P* 12.

355	**99**	6 c. red-brown	1 2	0 10

SERVICE STAMPS.

Certain contemporary postage and air stamps have been perforated " O.H.M.S." for official use. We do not list such issues.

REGISTRATION STAMPS.

R 1

(Engraved and printed by the British-American Bank Note Co., Montreal and Ottawa.)

1875 (15 Nov.)–**1888**. *White wove paper. P* 12.

R 1	**R 1**	2 c. orange	3 0	0 8
R 2	„	2 c. orange-red	4 0	1 0
R 3	„	2 c. vermilion	6 6	3 0
		a. Imperf.	75 0	

R 4	R 1	2 c. brick-red (1888) ..	35 0	15 0
R 5	„	5 c. yellow-green ..	3 6	0 8
R 6	„	5 c. dark green	3 6	0 8
		a. Imperf.	60 0	
R 7	„	5 c. blue-green (1888) ..	8 0	0 9
R 8	„	8 c. bright blue	£6	£6
R 9	„	8 c. dull blue	£6	£6

SPECIAL DELIVERY STAMPS.

S 1

I.

II.

Type I. Uniform shading of horizontal lines only in circles containing figures of value. Type I. must show no trace whatever of diagonal shading in the circles.

Type II. Heavy (or sometimes faint) shading crossing the horizontal lines inside circles and behind figures.

1898 (1 July)–**1905.** *P* 12.

S 1	S 1	10 c. yellow-green (I) ..	20 0	8 6
S 2	„	10 c. deep green (II) ..	8 6	2 0
S 3	„	10 c. blue-green (1905) (II)	7 6	4 0

S 2

1922 (Sept.). *P* 12.

S 4	S 2	20 c. carmine-red ..	6 0	3 0

S 3 Mail-carrying, past and present.

1927. 60*th Anniversary of Confederation.* *P* 12.

S 5	S 3	20 c. orange	4 0	5 0

S 4

1930 (2 Sept.). *P* 11.

S 6	S 4	20 c. brown-red	6 0	4 0

1933. *Type as* S 4, *but the inscription* " TWENTY CENTS " *replaced by the single word* " CENTS." *P* 11.

S 7		20 c. brown-red	5 0	6 0

S 5. Allegory of Progress.

1935 (1 June). *P* 12.

S 8	S 5	20 c. scarlet	4 0	4 0

POSTAGE DUE STAMPS.

D 1 D 2

1906 (1 July)–**1928.** *P* 12.

D 1	D 1	1 c. dull violet	0 6	0 3
D 2	„	1 c. red-violet	0 4	0 3
		a. Thin experimental paper (1924)	6 0	6 0
D 3	„	2 c. dull violet	0 8	0 4
D 4	„	2 c. red-violet	0 6	0 3
		a. Thin experimental paper (1924)	4 6	4 6
D 5	„	4 c. violet ('28) ..	6 6	6 6
D 6	„	5 c. dull violet	1 0	0 6
D 7	„	5 c. red-violet	0 9	0 3
		a. Thin experimental paper (1924)	1 0	1 3
D 8	„	10 c. violet ('28) ..	6 0	1 0

(Recess. British-American Bank Note Co.)

1930–32. *P* 11.

D 9	D 2	1 c. bright vio. (14.7.30)	0 9	0 6
D 10	„	2 c. bright vio. (21.8.30)	0 6	0 2
D 11	„	4 c. bright vio. (14.10.30)	1 9	1 0
D 12	„	5 c. bright vio. (12.12.31)	0 9	1 0
D 13	„	10 c. bright vio. (1932) ..	5 0	2 6

D 3

D 4

1933–34. *Recess.* *P* 11.

D 14	D 3	1 c. violet (5.5.34)	..	0	6	0	6
D 15	„	2 c. violet (20.12.33)	..	0	6	0	3
D 16	„	4 c. violet (12.12.33)	..	0	8	0	6
D 18	„	10 c. violet (20.12.33)	..	1	6	0	6

(Recess. Canadian Bank Note Co., Ottawa.)

1935. *P* 12.

D 19	D 4	1 c. violet (14.10.35)	..	0	2	0	2
D 20	„	2 c. violet (9.9.35)	..	0	3	0	1
D 21	„	4 c. violet (2.7.35)	..	0	4	0	2
D 22	„	10 c. violet (16.9.35)	..	0	8	0	2

CAPE OF GOOD HOPE.

SIMPLIFICATION (see p. xii)

Nos. 1 to 22.

3, 4 : 5a, 5b, 6a, 7, 7b, 8, 8a.
13, 14.
18, 18a, 19, 19a, 20, 21.

1. Hope.

2

(Designed by Charles Bell, Surveyor-General; die engraved by W. Humphrys; printed by Perkins Bacon & Co.)

1853 (1 Sept.). *W* 2. *Imperf.*

(a) Paper deeply blued.

1	1	1d. pale brick-red	£40	£10
		a. Deep brick-red	£50	£12
2	„	4d. deep blue	£40	80 0

(b) Paper slightly blued (blueing not so pronounced at back).

3	1	1d. brick-red	£40	£10
		a. Brown-red		
4	„	4d. deep blue	£35	80 0
		a. Pale blue	£40	90 0

Both values are known with the watermark lying sideways.

1855–58. *White paper.* *W* 2. *Imperf.*

5	1	1d. brick-red (1857)	£40	£12
		a. Pale rose (1858)	£12	£5
		b. Deep rose-red	£12	£5
6	„	4d. deep blue (1855)	£10	80 0
		a. Blue	£10	80 0
7	1	6d. slate-lilac (18.2.58) ..	£40	£12
		a. Blued paper	£60	£16
		b. Pale rose-lilac	£30	£8
		c. Deep rose-lilac	£40	£15
8	„	1s. bright yell.-grn. (18.2.58) ..	£50	£15
		a. Deep dark green	£25	£15

The method adopted for producing the plates of the 4d., 6d., and 1s. stamps involved the use of two dies, so that there are two types of each of these values, differing slightly in detail, but existing in equal numbers. For particulars see the *Cape of Good Hope* handbook.

The 1d. and 4d. of this issue are known with watermark lying sideways. The 6d. is known bisected and used with 1d. for 4d. rate.

The 4d. is known in black, and it was, at one time, suggested that a small supply of stamps in this colour was issued on the occasion of the death of the Prince Consort, but there is no official reference to such an issue and the known facts do not support the suggestion.

Varieties. Unofficially rouletted by the Standard Bank of South Africa, Cape Town.

9	1	1d. brick-red		
10	„	4d. blue	—	£30
11	„	6d. rose-lilac	—	£45
12	„	1s. bright yellow-green ..	—	£250

3. Hope.

(Local provisional so-called "wood-block" issue. Engraved on steel by C. J. Roberts. Printed from stereotyped plates by Saul Solomon & Co., Cape Town.)

1861 (Feb.–April). *Laid paper.* *Imperf.*

13	3	1d. vermilion (27 Feb.)	£400	£10 *to* £95
		a. Carmine (7 March)	£400	£12 *to* £100
		b. Brick-red (10 April)	£500	£17 *to* £150
14	„	4d. pale milky blue (23 Feb.) ..	£200	£8 *to* £75
		a. Pale grey-blue (Mar.?)	£225	£10 *to* £80
		b. Pale bright blue (Mar.?)	£225	£10 *to* £75
		c. Deep bright blue (12 April)	—	£20 *to* £175
		d. Blue	£250	£12 *to* £85

Errors of colour.

15	3	1d. pale milky blue	—	£250 *to* £800
		a. Pale bright blue ..		
16	„	4d. vermilion ..	—	£400 *to* £1000
		a. Carmine ..	—	£500 *to* £1250

Variety. Retouch or repair to right-hand lower corner of stereo.

17	3	4d. pale milky blue ..	—	£50 *to* £200
		a. Pale bright blue ..	—	£65 *to* £275

Both values were officially reprinted in March, 1883, on wove paper. The 1d. is in deep red, and the 4d. in a deeper blue than that of the deepest shade of the issued stamp.

Specimens of the reprints have done postal duty, but their use thus was not intended. There are no reprints of the errors or of the retouched 4d.

Early in 1863, Messrs. Perkins Bacon & Co. handed over the four plates used for printing the triangular Cape of Good Hope stamps to Messrs. De La Rue & Co., who made all the subsequent printings of these stamps.

(Printed from the Perkins Bacon plates by De La Rue & Co.)

1863–64. *W* 2. *Imperf.*

18	1	1d. deep carmine-red ..	£10	£9
		a. Deep brown-red	£12	£8
		b. Brownish red	£12	£8

19 **1** 4d. dark blue £9 50 0
a. Pale blue £10 75 0
b. Slate-blue £30 £25
c. Steel-blue .. .. .. — £20
20 ,, 6d. bright mauve £12 £10
21 ,, 1s. bright emerald-green .. £30 £25
a. Pale emerald-green £40

The 1d., 4d., and 1s. of this issue are known with watermark lying sideways.

With the exception of the 4d., these stamps may be easily distinguished from those printed by Perkins Bacon & Co. by their colours, which are quite distinct.

The De La Rue stamps of all values are less clearly printed, the figure of Hope and the lettering of the inscriptions standing out less boldly, while the fine lines of the background appear blurred and broken when examined under a glass. The background as a whole often shows irregularity in the apparent depth of colour, due to wear of the plates.

For note regarding the two dies of the 4d., 6d., and 1s. values, see after No. 8.

Variety. Wmk. Crown CC (sideways).

22 **1** 1d. deep carmine-red .. £400

This was a trial printing, and is only known unused.

All the triangular stamps were demonetised as from 1st October, 1900.

"Hope" seated, with grape-vine branch and ram—attributes of the Colony.

4 (With outer frame-line).

Four Pence.

(5)

(Designed by Charles Bell, Surveyor-General. Die engraved on steel and stamps typo. by De La Rue & Co.)

1864–65. *With outer frame-line surrounding the design. Wmk. Crown CC. P 14.*

23 **4** 1d. carmine-red (May, 1865) 30 0 15 0
a. Rose-red 30 0 15 0
24 ,, 4d. pale blue (Aug., 1865) .. 37 6 5 0
a. Blue 40 0 4 0
b. Ultramarine £7 32 6
c. Deep blue (1871 ?) 55 0 3 0
25 ,, 6d. pale lilac (before 21.3.64) 35 0 17 6
a. Deep lilac 50 0 10 6
b. Violet (to bright) (1877) .. 35 0 2 6
26 ,, 1s. deep green (Jan., 1864) .. £7 20 0
a. Green 27 6 5 0
b. Blue-green 40 0 6 6

The 1d. rose-red, 6d. lilac, and 1s. blue-green are known imperf., probably from proof sheets.

The 1d. and 4d. stamps of this issue may be found with side and/or top outer frame-lines missing, due to wear of the plates.

(Surcharged by Saul Solomon & Co., Cape Town.)

1868 (17 Nov.). *No. 25a surcharged with T 5.*

27 **4** 4d. on 6d. deep lilac (R.) .. 75 0 17 6
a. "Peuce" for "Pence"

Specimens may also be found with bars omitted or at the top of the stamp, due to misplacement of the sheet.

The space between the words and bars varies from $12\frac{1}{2}$ to 16 mm., stamps with spacing $15\frac{1}{2}$ and 16 mm. being rare. There were two printings, one of 120,000 in November, 1868, and another of 1,000,000 in December. Stamps showing widest spacings are probably from the earlier printing.

6 (No outer frame-line).

(Die re-engraved. Typo. by De La Rue.)

1871–77. *Outer frame-line removed.* **Wmk.** *Crown CC. P 14.*

28 **6** ½d. pale grey-blk. (Dec. '75) 5 0 6 0
a. Deep grey-black 5 0 6 0
29 ,, 1d. pale car.-red (Feb. '72) .. 7 6 1 0
a. Deep carmine-red 8 6 1 0
30 ,, 4d. dull blue (Jan. 1877) .. 37 6 2 0
a. Deep blue 37 6 2 6
b. Ultramarine 40 0 2 0
31 ,, 5 s. yellow-orange (25.8.71) £6 12 6

The ½d., 1d., and 5s. are known imperf., probably from proof sheets.

For the 3d. of this issue see Nos. 36 and 39.

THREE PENCE

ONE PENNY

(7) (8)

(Surcharged by Saul Solomon & Co., Cape Town.

1874–76. *Nos. 25a and 26a surch. with T 7.*

32 **4** 1d. on 6d. deep lilac (R.) (1.9.74) £8 50 0
a. "E" of "PENNY" omitted .. — £12
33 ,, 1d. on 1s. green (Nov. '76) .. 27 6 27 6

These provisionals are found with the bar only, either across the centre of the stamp or at the top; with value only; or with the value and bar close together, either at top or foot of the stamp. All such varieties are due to misplacement of sheets during surcharging.

1879 (1 Nov.). *No. 30 surcharged with T 8.*

34 **6** 3d. on 4d. blue (R.) .. 42 6 8 0
a. "PENCB" for "PENCE" .. £65 £12
b. "THB.EE" for "THREE" .. £85 £15
c. Surcharge double .. .. — £65
d. Variety b. double .. ..

The double surcharge must also have existed showing variety a. but only variety b. has been recorded.

There are numerous minor varieties, including letters out of alignment, broken letters, etc., due to defective printing and the use of poor type.

The spacing between the bar and the words varies from $16\frac{1}{2}$ to 18 mm.

THREEPENCE

(9)

(Surcharged by De La Rue & Co.)

1880 (Feb.). *Special printing of the 4d. in new colour, surch. with T 9. Wmk. Crown CC.*

35 **6** 3d. on 4d. pale dull rose .. 27 6 6 0

A minor constant variety exists with foot of "P" in "PENCE" broken off, making the letter appear shorter.

1880 (1 July). *Wmk. Crown CC. P* 14.

36 **6** 3d. pale dull rose £8 22 6

3 3

(10) (11)

(Surcharged by Saul Solomon & Co., Cape Town.)

1880 (Aug.). *No.* 36 *surcharged.*

37 **10** " 3 " on 3d. pale dull rose 25 0 4 6
 a. Surcharge inverted .. £25 35 0

38 **11** " 3 " on 3d. pale dull rose 95 0 12 6
 a. Surcharge inverted .. — £55

The " 3 " (T **10**) is sometimes found broken. Vertical pairs are known showing the two types of surcharge *se-tenant*, and vertical strips of three exist, the top stamp having surcharge T **10**, the middle stamp being without surcharge, and the lower stamp having surcharge T **11**.

1881 (Jan.). *Wmk. Crown CC. P* 14.

39 **6** 3d. pale claret 45 0 7 6
 a. Deep claret 35 0 6 6

This was a definite colour change made at the request of the Postmaster-General owing to the similarity between the colours of the 1d. stamp and the 3d. in pale dull rose. Imperf. copies are probably from proof sheets.

Proofs of this value were printed in brown, on unwatermarked wove paper and imperf., but the colour was rejected as unsuitable.

1882 (July). *Wmk. Crown CA. P* 14.

40 **6** 3d. pale claret 8 6 3 0
 a. Deep claret 9 0 2 6

One
Half-penny.

(12)

(Surcharged by Saul Solomon & Co., Cape Town.)

1882 (July). *Nos.* 39*a and* 40*a surch. with T* **12**.

41 **6** ½d. on 3d. claret (Wmk. CC) £95 £20
42 ,, ½d. on 3d. claret (Wmk. CA) 12 6 10 6
 a. " p " in " penny " omitted .. £50
 b. " y " in " penny " omitted .. £50
 c. Hyphen omitted £20 £15

Varieties also exist with broken and defective letters, and with the obliterating bar omitted or at the top of the stamp.

1882–83. *Wmk. Crown CA. P* 14.

43 **6** ½d. black (1.9.82) 5 0 2 0
 a. Grey-black 4 6 1 6
44 ,, 1d. rose-red (July '82) .. 15 0 0 6
 a. Deep rose-red 12 6 0 6
45 ,, 2d. pale bistre (1.9.82) .. 27 6 1 0
 a. Deep bistre 35 0 0 9
46 **4** 6d. mauve (to b'ght) (Aug. '82) 40 0 5 0
47 **6** 5s. orange (Aug. '83) .. £50 £6

Imperf. pairs of the ½d., 1d., and 2d. are known, probably from proof sheets.

For the 3d. stamp with this watermark see No. 40.

13. " Cabled Anchor."

1884–1890. *W* **13**. *P* 14.

48 **6** ½d. black (Jan. '86) .. 1 6 0 2
 a. Grey-black 1 3 0 2
49 ,, 1d. rose-red (Dec. '85) .. 1 6 0 3
 a. Carmine-red 1 3 0 2
50 ,, 2d. pale bistre (Dec. '84) .. 3 6 0 6
 a. Deep bistre 2 0 0 6
51 ,, 4d. blue (June '90) .. 5 0 1 3
 a. Deep blue 5 0 1 3
52 **4** 6d. reddish pur. (Dec. '84) .. 18 0 5 0
 a. Purple (shades) .. 6 0 1 6
 b. Bright mauve 14 0 1 6
53 ,, 1s. yellow-green (Dec. '85) .. 50 0 6 6
 a. Blue-green (1889) .. 40 0 2 0
54 **6** 5s. orange (July '87) .. 45 0 10 0

All the above stamps are known in imperf. pairs, probably from proof sheets.

For later shades and colour changes, etc., see Nos. 59, *etc.*

2½d

(14)

(Surcharged by De La Rue & Co.)

1891 (Mar.). *Special printing of the* 3d. *in new colour, surcharged with T* **14**.

55 **6** 2½d. on 3d. pale magenta .. 4 0 3 6
 a. Deep magenta .. 2 6 2 6
 b. Fig. " 1 " with horiz. serif 42 6 37 6

Variety b. occurs on two stamps (Nos. 8 and 49) of the pane of 60.

Two types of " d " are found in the surcharge, one with square end to serif at top, and the other with pointed serif.

15

ONE PENNY.

(16)

1892 (June). *W* **13**. *P* 14.

56 **15** 2½d. sage green 4 6 0 10
 a. Olive-green 4 6 0 10

(Surch. by W. A. Richards & Sons, Cape Town.)

1893 (March). *Nos.* 50 *and* 50*a surcharged with T* **16**.

57 **6** 1d. on 2d. pale bistre .. 3 6 0 10
 a. Deep bistre 2 0 0 10
 b. No stop after " PENNY " .. 35 0 22 6
 c. Surcharge double .. .. — £20

Variety b. occurs on stamp No. 42 of the upper left-hand pane, and on No. 6 of the lower right-hand pane.

Minor varieties exist showing broken letters and letters out of alignment or widely spaced. Also with obliterating bar omitted, due to misplacement of the sheet during surcharging.

17. " Hope " standing. View of Table Bay in background.

18. Table Mountain and Bay with Arms of the Colony.

(Des. Mr. Mountford. Typo. De La Rue.)

1893 (Oct.). *W* **13.** *P* 14.

No.	Type		Unused	Used
58	**17**	1d. rose-red	0 10	0 1
		a. Carmine	0 4	0 1

The above stamp is known in imperf. pairs, probably from proof sheets.

1894–98. *New colours, etc.* *W* **13.** *P* 14.

No.	Type		Unused	Used
59	**6**	½d. pale yell.-grn. (Dec. '96)	0 10	0 6
		a. Green	1 9	0 2
60	,,	2d. choc.-brown (Mar. '97)	2 0	1 0
61	**15**	2½d. pale ultram. (May '96)	3 6	0 8
		a. Ultramarine	1 9	0 6
62	**6**	3d. brt. magenta (Sept. '98)	4 0	2 6
63	,,	4d. sage-green (Mar. '97) ..	7 0	1 9
64	,,	1s. blue-green (Jan. '94) ..	16 0	2 6
		a. Yellow-green	27 6	3 0
65	,,	1s. yellow-ochre (May '96)	7 6	1 0
66	,,	5s. brown-orange (June '96)	30 0	9 0

1898–1902. *W* **13.** *P* 14.

No.	Type		Unused	Used
67	**17**	½d. green (Oct. '98) ..	0 6	0 2
68	,,	3d. magenta (Mar. '02) ..	6 0	5 0

(Des. E. Sturman. Typo. De La Rue.)

1900 (Jan.). *W* **13.** *P* 14.

No.	Type		Unused	Used
69	**18**	1d. carmine	0 2	0 1

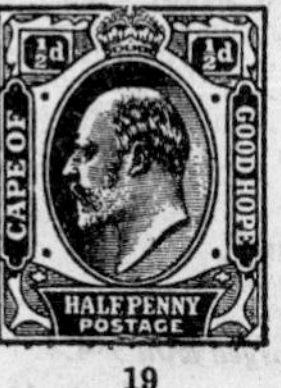

19

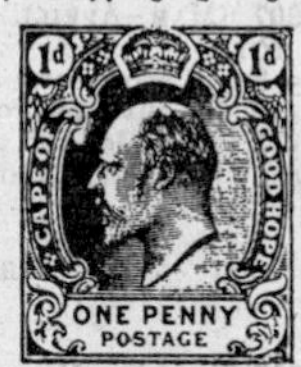

20

(Typo. De La Rue & Co.)

1902–4. *Various frames.* *W* **13.** *P* 14.

No.		Unused	Used
70	½d. green (Dec. '02)	0 6	0 1
71	1d. carmine (Dec. '02) ..	0 4	0 1
72	2d. brown (Oct. '04)	3 0	0 8
73	2½d. ultramarine (Mar. '04) ..	5 0	6 0
74	3d. magenta (Apl. '03) ..	3 6	0 4
75	4d. olive-green (Feb. '03) ..	4 6	0 8
76	6d. bright mauve (Mar. '03) ..	4 6	0 10
77	1s. yellow-ochre (Dec. '02) ..	6 0	1 0
78	5s. brown-orange (Feb. '03)..	27 6	10 0

All values exist in imperf. pairs, from proof sheets.

When the Union of South Africa came into being in 1910 the stamps of the Cape of Good Hope (except the already demonetised triangulars) became available for postal use throughout the Union, until December 31st, 1937, from which date the stamps of the four provinces of the Union were demonetised. For special Union issues see under South Africa.

MAFEKING SIEGE STAMPS.

These stamps should only be purchased from responsible persons, as numerous and well executed forgeries emanated from Kimberley and Cape Town, and many officers and men returning home were swindled in these places by the forgery-monger.

24 March to 17 May, 1900.

I. *Surcharged* " MAFEKING " *and* " BESIEGED *in fancy type,* 1¾ *mm. high, and new value.*

MAFEKING
3d.
BESIEGED.
(1)

MAFEKING
3d.
BESIEGED.
(2)

(A) *Cape of Good Hope stamps. Surcharged as* T 1, *in black.*

No.	Type		Unused	Used
1	**6**	1d. on ½d. green	35 0	25 0
2	**17**	1d. on ½d. green	55 0	35 0
3	,,	3d. on 1d. carmine	35 0	20 0
4	**6**	6d. on 3d. magenta	—	65 0
5	,,	1s. on 4d. sage-green ..	—	50 0

A variety in the setting of each value exists without comma after " MAFEKING."

(B) *Bechuanaland Protectorate stamps of* 1897–1902. *Surcharged as* T 1.

No.		Unused	Used
6	1d. on ½d. vermilion	30 0	20 0
	a. Surch. inverted	—	£50
7	3d. on 1d. mauve	85 0	25 0
	a. Surch. double		
8	6d. on 2d. green and carmine	90 0	25 0
9	6d. on 3d. purple/*yellow* ..	—	85 0
	a. Surch. inverted		
	b. Surch. double		

(C) *British Bechuanaland stamps.*

Surcharged as T 1.

No.		Unused	Used
10	6d. on 3d. lilac & blk. (No. 12)	65 0	27 6
11	1s. on 4d. green & pur.-brown (No. 35)	£20	30 0
	a. Surch. double		
	b. Surch. triple		
	c. Surch. double, one inverted		

II. *Surcharged* " MAFEKING " *and* " BESIEGED " *in thin sans-serif type,* 1½ *mm. high and new value, as* T 2.

(A) *Bechuanaland Protectorate stamps.*

No.		Unused	Used
12	3d. on 1d. mauve (No. 61) ..	50 0	17 6
13	6d. on 2d. grn. & car. (No. 62)	70 0	25 0
14	1s. on 6d. purple/*rose-red* (No. 65)..	£17	40 0

(B) *British Bechuanaland stamps.*

No.		Unused	Used
15	1s. on 6d. purple/*rose-red* (No. 36)..	—	£15
16	2s. on 1s. green (No. 37) ..	£35	£12

In the stamps overprinted " BECHUANALAND PROTECTORATE " and " BRITISH BECHUANALAND " the local surcharge is so adjusted as not to overlap the original overprint.

3

Sergt.-major Goodyear.
(Des. Dr. W. A. Hayes.)

4

General Baden-Powell.
(Des. Capt. Greener.)

III. *Produced by photographic process by Mr. D. Taylor. Horizontally laid paper.* P 12.

(*a*) 18½ mm. *wide.* (*b*) 21 mm. *wide.*

No.	Type		Unused	Used
17	**3**	1d. pale blue/*blue*	35 0	37 6
18	,,	1d. deep blue/*blue*	40 0	42 6
19	**4**	3d. pale blue/*blue* (*a*) ..	40 0	40 0
20	,,	3d. deep blue/*blue* (*a*) ..	40 0	40 0
		a. Imperf. between (horiz. pair)	—	£50
21	**4**	3d. pale blue/*blue* (*b*) ..	£6	60 0
22	,,	3d. deep blue/*blue* (*b*) ..	£6	60 0

Variety. Reversed design.

No.	Type		Unused	Used
23	**4**	3d. blue/*blue* (*a*)		

These stamps vary a great deal in colour from deep blue to pale grey.

Illustrations Types 3 and 4 are actual size, the latter of variety (*a*).

VRYBURG.

TEMPORARY BOER OCCUPATION.

½ PENCE

Z.A.R.

(1)

1899 (Nov.). *Cape stamps surcharged as T* 1, *in black.*

(*a*) *Surcharge* 10 *mm. high.*

1 **6** ½ PENCE, green 40 0 20 0
2 **17** 1 „ rose 30 0 17 6
3 **15** 2½ „ blue £6

Variety with italic " Z."

4 **6** ½ PENCE, green ..
5 **17** 1 „ rose ..
6 **15** 2½ „ blue ..

(*b*) *Surcharge* 12 *mm. high.*

7 **6** ½ PENCE, green .. .. — £7
8 **17** 1 „ rose .. .. — £12
9 **4** 2 „ on 6d. mauve .. .. — £10
9*a* **15** 2½ „ blue .. ..

Variety with italic " Z."

10 **4** 2 PENCE on 6d. mauve ..

BRITISH REOCCUPATION.

V. R.
SPECIAL
POST

(2)

1900 (May). *Provisionals issued by the Military Authorities. Stamps of Transvaal* (*T* **33**) *overprinted with T* **2**, *in black.*

11 ½d. green .. .. .. — 30 0
12 1d. carmine and green .. 85 0 80 0
13 2d. deep brown and green ..
14 2½d. blue and green .. ..

CAYMAN ISLANDS.

1

(T 1 to 13 typo. by De La Rue & Co.)

1901 (19 Feb.). *T* **1**. *Wmk. Crown CA. P* 14.

1 ½d. deep green 2 0 2 6
1a ½d. pale green 1 9 2 6
2 1d. rose-carmine 3 0 2 0
2a 1d. pale carmine 3 6 4 0

2

3

1901 (20 Dec.)–**1902**. *Wmk. Crown CA. P* 14.

3 **2** ½d. green 3 6 4 0
4 „ 1d. carmine 7 6 7 6
5 „ 2½d. bright blue .. 12 6 15 0
6 „ 6d. brown 25 0 27 6
7 **3** 1s. orange 35 0 37 6

1905–6. *Wmk. Mult. Crown CA. P* 14.

8 **2** ½d. green 3 0 4 0
9 „ 1d. carmine (1906) .. 15 0 17 6
10 „ 2½d. bright blue .. 12 6 15 0
11 „ 6d. brown 27 6 30 0
12 **3** 1s. orange 35 0 37 6

1907 (Mar.–April). *Wmk. Mult. Crown CA. P* 14.

13 **3** 4d. brown and blue 40 0 45 0
14 **2** 6d. olive and rose 40 0 45 0
15 **3** 1s. violet and green 45 0 50 0
16 „ 5s. salmon and green .. £12 £15

One
Halfpenny.

(4)

1907 (Sept.). *No.* 9 *surcharged with T* **4**.

17 ½d. on 1d. carmine 45 0 45 0

½D (5) 1D (6) 2½D (7)

1907 (Nov.). *No.* 16 *surcharged with T* **5** *or* **6**, *in black.*

18 ½d. on 5s. salmon and green .. £12 £15
a. Surch. inverted .. ..
b. Surch. double .. ..
c. Surch. double, one inverted ..
d. Surch. omitted (in pair with normal) .. ..
19 1d. on 5s. salmon and green .. £12 £14
a. Surch. double

The ½d. on 5s. may be found with the figures " 1 " or " 2 " omitted, owing to defective printing.

1908 (Feb.). *No.* 13 *surcharged with T* **7**.

24 2½d. on 4d. brown and blue .. £40 £40
a. Surch. double .. ..

The 1d. on 4d. is a revenue stamp and was never authorised for postal use.

8

9

1907–9. *T* **8** *and* **9** (3*d.*, 4*d.*, 1*s. and* 5*s.*) *Wmk. Mult. Crown CA. P* 14.

25 ½d. green, O (1907) .. 1 6 2 0
26 1d. carmine, O (1907) .. 2 6 3 0

27 2½d. ultramarine, O .. 6 0 7 6
28 3d. purple/*yellow*, C 6 6 7 6
29 4d. black and red/*yellow*, C.. 50 0 55 0
30 6d. dull & bright purple, C.. 7 6 8 0
30*a* 6d. dull pur. & vio.-purple, C 7 6 8 0
31 1s. black/*green*, C (1909) .. 10 6 12 6
32 5s. green and red/*yellow*, C.. 60 0 65 0

1908. *Wmk Crown CA.* P 14.

35 **9** 1s. black/*green*, C.. .. .. 25 0 27 6
36 **8** 10s. green and red/*green*, C.. £8 £9

11

1908–9. *T* **11.** *Wmk. Mult. Crown CA.* P 14.

38 ¼d. brown, O 0 8 0 9
39 ¼d. grey-brown, O (1909) .. 0 6 0 6

12 13

1912–20. *T* **12** (*½d., 1d., 2½d., 6d., and 10s.*) *and* **13.** *Wmk. Mult. Crown CA.* P 14.

40 ¼d. brown, O 0 3 0 3
41 ½d. green, O 0 6 0 8
42 1d. red, O (1913) 0 8 0 9
43 2d. pale grey, O 1 6 2 0
44 2½d. bright blue, O (1914) .. 5 0 6 0
44*a* 2½d. deep bright blue, O .. 4 0 5 0
45 3d. purple/*yellow*, C (1920) .. 8 6 9 0
  a. White back (1913) .. 5 0 6 0
  b. On lemon (1915) .. 8 0 9 0
  c. On orange-buff (1920) .. 5 0 6 0
  d. On pale yellow (1920) .. 6 0 6 6
46 4d. blk. & red/*yell.*, C (1913) 4 0 4 6
47 6d. dull & brt. pur., C (1913) 4 0 5 0
48 1s. black/*green*, C (1916) .. 8 0 9 0
  a. White back (1913) .. 8 0 9 0
49 2s. pur. & brt. blue/*blue*, C .. 17 6 20 0
50 3s. green and violet, C .. 20 0 22 6
51 5s. green & red/*yell.*, C (1914) 60 0 65 0
52 10s. deep green and red/*green*, C (1915) 75 0 85 0
  a. White back (1913) .. 75 0 85 0
  b. On blue-green, olive back (1920) 50 0 52 6

WAR STAMP. 1½d (14) WAR STAMP. 1½d (15)

1917 (26 Feb.). *T* **12**, *surcharged with T* **14** *or* **15**, *in black.*

53 **14** 1½d. on 2½d. deep blue .. 5 0 7 6
  a. No fraction bar 50 0 60 0
54 **15** 1½d. on 2½d. deep blue .. 2 6 3 6
  a. No fraction bar 15 0 17 6

In No. 53 the spacing between the word "STAMP" and the top of the figure "1" varies between 1½ mm. and 5 mm.

WAR STAMP 1½d (16) WAR STAMP 1½d (17) WAR STAMP 1½d. (18)

1917 (4 Sept.). *T* **12** *surcharged with T* **16** *or* **17**, *in black.*

55 1½d. on 2½d. deep blue (T **16**) £9
56 1½d. on 2½d. deep blue (T **17**) 0 4 0 6

1919–20. *T* **12** *and* **13** (*2½d. special printing*), *overprinted only, or surcharged in addition.*

57 **16** ½d. green (4.2.19) 0 3 0 5
58 **18** 1½d. on 2d. grey (10.3.20) .. 0 4 0 6
59 **17** 1½d. on 2½d. orge. (4.2.19) .. 0 4 0 6

In T **16** the "R" of "WAR" has a curved foot, and the other letters vary slightly from T **17**. "1½d." is in thin type. In T **17** the "R" has straight foot, and the "1½d." differs.

The ½d. stamps on *buff* paper, and later consignments of the 2d. T **13** on *pinkish*, apparently derived their colour from the paper in which they were packed for despatch to England.

19

(Recess. De La Rue & Co.)

1921–26. *T* **19.** P 14.

(*a*) *Wmk. Mult. Crown CA.*

60 3d. purple/*orange-buff* .. 5 0 6 0
61 3d. purple/*pale yellow* .. 60 0 60 0
62 4d. red/*yellow* 4 0 5 0
63 1s. black/*green* 6 6 6 6
64 5s. yellow-green/*pale yellow* .. 30 0 35 0
65 5s. blue-green/*pale yellow* .. 70 0 80 0
66 5s. deep green/*orange-buff* .. 35 0 40 0
67 10s. carmine/*green* 75 0 85 0

(*b*) *Wmk. Mult. Script CA.*

69 ¼d. yellow-brown 0 2 0 4
70 ½d. pale grey-green 0 4 0 6
71 1d. deep carmine-red .. 0 8 0 9
72 1½d. orange-brown 1 0 1 3
73 2d. slate-grey 1 3 1 6
74 2½d. bright blue 1 6 1 6
75 3d. purple/*yellow* (June, 1923) 1 9 2 0
76 4½d. sage-green (June, 1923) .. 7 6 8 6
77 6d. claret 4 0 4 6
78 6d. deep claret 4 6 5 0
79 1s. black/*green* 7 0 8 0
80 2s. violet/*blue* 15 0 17 6
81 3s. violet 20 0 22 6
82 5s. green/*yellow* 27 6 30 0
83 10s. carmine/*green* (15.9.26) .. 55 0 65 0

20. King William IV and King George V

(Recess. Waterlow & Sons.)

1932 (5 Dec.). *Centenary of the "Assembly of Justices and Vestry."* *T* **20**. *Wmk. Mult. Script CA. P* 12½.

No.	Description	Unused	Used
84	½d. brown	0 8	1 0
85	½d. green	1 3	1 9
86	1d. scarlet	2 6	3 0
87	1½d. red-orange	3 0	3 6
88	2d. grey	6 0	7 0
89	2½d. ultramarine	6 6	7 6
90	3d. olive-green	12 6	15 0
91	6d. purple	22 6	27 6
92	1s. black and brown ..	35 0	40 0
93	2s. black and ultramarine ..	75 0	85 0
94	5s. black and green ..	£8	£10
95	10s. black and scarlet	£25	£30

1935 (6 May). *Silver Jubilee. As T* **13** *of Antigua, inscribed* "CAYMAN ISLANDS". *Recess. D.L.R & Co. Wmk. Mult. Script CA. P* 13½×14.

No.	Description	Unused	Used
96	½d. black and green ..	0 4	0 8
97	2½d. brown and deep blue	4 0	4 6
98	6d. light blue and olive-green	7 6	7 6
99	1s. slate and purple	7 6	12 6

21. Cayman Islands.

22. Cat Boat (*horiz.*).

23. Booby Birds (*horiz.*).

24. Conch Shells and Coconut Palms.

25. Hawksbill Turtles (*horiz.*).

(Recess. Waterlow & Sons.)

1935. *Wmk. Mult. Script CA. P* 12½.

No.	Type	Description	Unused	Used
100	21	½d. black and brown ..	0 3	0 4
101	22	½d. ultram. & yell.-green	0 7	0 10
102	23	1d. ultramarine and scarlet	0 10	1 0
103	24	1½d. black and orange ..	1 3	1 6
104	22	2d. ultramarine & purple	1 9	2 0
105	25	2½d. blue and black ..	2 3	2 6
106	21	3d. black and olive-green	3 0	3 6
107	25	6d bright purple & black	5 0	6 0
108	22	1s. ultramarine & orange	12 6	15 0
109	23	2s. ultramarine & black..	30 0	35 0
110	25	5s. green and black ..	60 0	65 0
111	24	10s. black and scarlet	£7	£8

CEYLON

SIMPLIFICATION (see p. xii)

Nos. 1 to 67.

4. 5, 7, 9, 10, 11, 12, 13, 14, 15, 16, 17, 19. 42, 33, 44, 27, 48a, 50, 51, 53, 67, 54, 55. 65, 58, 59, 61, 62, 63.

Nos. 68 to 117.

71, 72, 75, 78, 96, 98, 100, 83, 102, 103, 105, 106, 108, 109, 110, 111a, 113, 114, 116.

NOTE.—*The prices of the imperf. stamps of Ceylon vary greatly according to condition. The following prices are for fine copies with four margins.*

Poor to medium specimens can be supplied at much lower prices.

1 **2**

(Recess. Perkins Bacon & Co.)

1857 (1 April). *T* **1**. *Blued paper. Wmk. Star, T w* **1**. *Imperf.*

No.	Description	Unused	Used
1	6d. purple-brown	£90	£20

(Typo. De La Rue and Co.)

T **2**. *No wmk. Imperf.*

1857 (Oct.). (*a*) *Blue glazed paper.*

No.	Description	Unused	Used
3	½d. lilac	£80	£20

1858. (*b*) *White glazed paper.*

No.	Description	Unused	Used
4	½d. lilac	£12	£9

3 **4**

(Recess. Perkins Bacon & Co.)

NOTE.—Beware of stamps of Type **3** which are often offered with corners added.

1857–59. *T* **1**, **3** *and* **4**. *White paper. Wmk. Star, T w.* **1**. *Imperf.*

No.	Type	Description	Unused	Used
5	1	1d. blue (24.8.57)	£12	30 0
6	„	1d. deep blue	£15	30 0
		a. Blued paper	—	80 0
7	1	2d. deep green (24.8.57) ..	£7	50 0
8	„	2d. yellow-green	£12	55 0
9	3	4d. dull rose (23.4.59) ..	£750	£175
10	1	5d. chestnut (2.7.57) ..	£25	£12
11	„	6d. purple-brown	£40	£10
12	„	6d. brown	£45	£12
12a	„	6d. deep brown	£60	£12
13	3	8d. brown (23.4.59) ..	£300	£100
14	„	9d. pur.-brn. (23.4.59) ..	£750	£50
15	4	10d. orange-verm. (2.7.57)	£30	£25
16	„	1s. dull violet (2.7.57) ..	£50	£12
17	3	1s. 9d. green (23.4.59) ..	£35	£22
18	„	1s. 9d. yellow-green ..	£60	£35
19	„	2s. blue (23.4.59)	£130	£60

Varieties. Rouletted.

20	½d. lilac (Type 2)		
21	1d. blue		
22	2d. deep green	£75	£55

These rouletted stamps are believed to have been made by some Ceylon firm for their own convenience.

(Printed by Messrs. Perkins Bacon & Co.)

1861. *T* **1, 3,** *and* **4.** *Wmk. Star, T* w. **1.**

(*a*) *Clean-cut perf.* 14 *to* 15½.

23	1d. deep blue	£9	45 0
24	1d. pale blue	£12	70 0
25	2d. green	£18	75 0
27	5d. chestnut	85 0	30 0
29	1s. dull violet	£5	40 0
30	2s. blue	£40	£25

(*b*) *Intermediate perf.* 14 *to* 15½.

31	1d. deep blue	£8	40 0
32	1d. blue	£9	50 0
33	2d. green	£9	60 0
34	4d. dull rose	£55	£20
34*a*	5d. chestnut	£35	£16
35	6d. brown	£50	£10
36	6d. yellowish brown	—	£12
36*a*	6d. olive-brown	—	£10
37	8d. brown	£50	£25
38	9d. dull purple-brown ..	£185	£12
40	1s. bright violet	80 0	55 0
41	1s. dull violet	80 0	40 0

(*c*) *Rough perf.* 14 *to* 15½.

42	1d. blue	95 0	20 0
43	1d. blue (*bleuté paper*) ..	£12	35 0
44	4d. rose-red	£10	£5
45	4d. deep rose-red	£10	£5
47	6d. yellowish brown	£40	£8
48	6d. blackish brown	£25	£8
48*a*	6d. olive-brown	£45	£6
49	8d. brown	£60	£30
50	8d. yellow-brown	£36	£25
51	9d. olive-brown	£35	80 0
52	9d. yellowish brown	£18	80 0
53	9d. deep brown	80 0	80 0
53*a*	10d. orange-vermilion ..	£12	65 0
	b. Imperf. between (pair) ..		
54	1s. dull violet	90 0	35 0
55	2s. blue	£16	£10
56	2s. deep blue	£20	£10

Variety. Prepared for use, but not issued.

57	1s. 9d. green	£35	

(Printed by Messrs. De La Rue & Co.)

1862. *T* **1, 3** *and* **4.** *Smooth paper. No wmk. P* 13.

58	1d. blue	70 0	22 6
59	5d. deep red-brown	£60	£12
60	6d. reddish brown	95 0	60 0
61	6d. deep brown	85 0	60 0
62	9d. brown	£30	£8
63	1s. cold violet	£45	£9

The 1s. is known imperf., but not used. The "no wmk." stamps were printed on paper having the papermaker's name and date, "T H SAUNDERS 1862" across the sheets, and one or more of these letters or figures are often found on the stamps.

T **1.** *No wmk. P* 11½, 12.

64	1d. blue	£18	85 0

1864. *T* **2.** *Glazed paper. No wmk. P* 12½.

65	½d. pale lilac	£8	85 0

(Printed by Messrs. Perkins Bacon & Co., perforated by Messrs. De La Rue & Co.)

1864 (Sept.). *T* **4.** *Wmk. Star, T* w. **1.** *P* 12½.

66	10d. vermilion	£25	40 0
67	10d. orange-red	£20	40 0

5 **6**

(Printed by Messrs. De La Rue & Co.)

T **1** *to* **4.**

1863–66. *Paper medium thin and slightly soft. Printed on paper with the watermarks arranged in four panes, each of* 60, *with the words* "CROWN COLONIES" *between the panes. Portions of these letters often appear on the stamps. Wmk. T* **5.** *The wmk. is* 22½ *mm. high and the Crown and CC are closer together, vertically, than in T* **6**, *and the CC's are oval.*

(*a*) *P* 11½, 12.

68	1d. blue	£18	£5

(*b*) *P* 13.

69	6d. brown	£50	60 0
70	9d. brown	£100	£20

(*c*) *P* 12½.

71	½d. mauve	18 0	17 6
72	½d. lilac	25 0	17 6
73	½d. deep lilac	30 0	17 6
74	1d. dark blue	40 0	10 0
75	1d. blue	40 0	10 0
76	2d. yellow-green	£300	£18
77	2d. deep bottle-green ..	—	£60
78	2d. grey-green	80 0	22 6
79	2d. emerald-green	£15	£8
80	2d. maize	£10	45 0
81	4d. lake-rose	£18	95 0
82	4d. rose	£10	45 0
83	5d. reddish brown	£12	95 0
84	5d. deep sage-green	£45	£10
84*a*	5d. olive-green	£8	70 0
85	6d. brown	60 0	20 0
86	6d. reddish brown	65 0	22 6
87	6d. deep brown	55 0	17 6
88	8d. light carmine-brown ..	75 0	55 0
89	8d. dark carmine-brown ..	75 0	55 0
90	9d. brown	£10	65 0
91	10d. vermilion	£45	60 0
91*a*	10d. orange	£17	75 0
92	2s. pale blue	£12	50 0

The ½d. lilac; 1d. blue; 2d. grey-green; 2d. maize; and 5d. deep sage-green and olive-green, are known imperf., but only unused.

1867. *Paper hand-made. Prepared and used only for these Ceylon stamps. Watermarks arranged in one pane of* 240 *in* 20 *rows of* 12, *with the words* "CROWN COLONIES" *twice in each side margin. Wmk. T* **6.** *The wmk. is* 21 *mm. high and the* "*CC's*" *are nearly round. P* 12½.

93	1d. pale blue	47 6	8 6
94	1d. Prussian blue	37 6	12 6
95	2d. maize	75 0	25 0
96	2d. olive-yellow	60 0	25 0
97	2d. greenish yellow ..	£12	80 0
98	2d. orange-yellow	40 0	22 6
99	4d. pale rose	60 0	35 0
100	4d. rose	35 0	22 6
101	5d. pale sage-green ..	50 0	27 6
102	5d. deep olive-green ..	70 0	27 6
103	5d. deep myrtle-green ..	35 0	32 6
104	6d. deep brown	50 0	22 6
105	6d. blackish brown ..	55 0	27 6
106	6d. red-brown	35 0	25 0
107	8d. pale carmine-brown ..	95 0	70 0
108	8d. deep carmine-brown ..	50 0	27 6
109	9d. bistre-brown	£5	40 0

110	9d. deep brown	30 0	22 6
111	10d. vermilion	£40	£12
111a	10d. orange-red	80 0	25 0
112	10d. orange	80 0	27 6
113	1s. lilac	£8	40 0
114	1s. violet	65 0	20 0
115	2s. pale blue	95 0	40 0
116	2s. blue	75 0	35 0
117	2s. Prussian blue	70 0	30 0

The 1d. pale blue, 6d. deep brown, 9d. deep brown and 10d. orange are known imperf. but only unused

PRINTERS. All stamps from No. 118 to 367 were typo. by De La Rue & Co.

7

8

1866. *T 7. Wmk. Crown CC. P* 12½.

118	3d. rose	95 0	55 0

1867–68. *T 8 and 7. Wmk. Crown CC. P* 14.

119	1d. blue	8 0	6 0
120	3d. pale rose (1867)	40 0	22 6
120a	3d. deep rose	40 0	22 6

9

10

11

12

13

14

15

16

17

18

1872–80. *T 9 to 18. Wmk. Crown CC.*

(*a*) *P* 14.

121	2 c. pale brown	5 0	1 0
122	4 c. grey	8 0	0 6
123	4 c. rosy mauve (1880) ..	17 6	1 0
124	8 c. orange-yellow	15 0	3 6
125	8 c. yellow	12 6	3 6
126	16 c. pale violet	22 6	4 0
127	24 c. green	20 0	4 0
128	32 c. slate (1877)	50 0	7 6
129	36 c. blue	45 0	17 6
130	48 c. rose	40 0	6 0
131	64 c. red-brown (1877) ..	85 0	35 0
132	96 c. drab	55 0	17 6

(*b*) *P* 14 × 12½.

133	2 c. brown	£7	25 0
134	4 c. grey	£6	17 6
135	8 c. orange-yellow	90 0	27 6

(*c*) *P* 12½.

136	2 c. brown	£50	40 0
137	4 c. grey	£30	65 0

19

T 19. *Wmk. Crown CC. P* 12½ × 14.

138	2 r. 50 c. dull rose	£25	£12

Prepared for use and sent out to Ceylon, but not issued unsurcharged.

139	32 c. slate (*perf.* 14 × 12½) ..	£25
140	64 c. red-brown (*perf.* 14 × 12½)	£60
141	2 r. 50 c. dull rose (*perf.* 12½)	£50

SIXTEEN

16

CENTS

(20)

1882. *Nos.* 127 *and* 131 *surcharged as T* 20.

142	16 c. on 24 c. green	37 6	20 0
143	20 c. on 64 c. red-brown ..	12 6	10 0

Variety. Surcharge double.

145	20 c. on 64 c. red-brown ..	—	£50

1883–98. *T 9 to 12. Wmk. Crown CA. P* 14.

146	2 c. pale brown	17 6	1 6
147	2 c. dull green (1884) ..	0 8	0 2
148	4 c. rosy mauve	1 6	0 3
149	4 c. rose (1884)	7 6	7 6
150	8 c. orange	5 0	5 0
150a	8 c. yellow (1898)	6 6	5 0
151	16 c. pale violet	£35	£6

Trial perforation. P 12.

151*a* 2 c. dull green £35
151*b* 4 c. rose .. .. ..
151*c* 24 c. brown-purple £60

Prepared for use and sent out to Ceylon, but not issued unsurcharged. P 14.

152 24 c. brown-purple £40

Postage & FIVE CENTS Revenue (21)

TEN CENTS (22)

Twenty Cents (23)

1885. *T* **10** *to* **19** *surcharged locally, in black.*

I. *Wmk. Crown CC.*

(*a*) *P* 14.

With T **21.**

152*a* 5 c. on 16 c. pale violet .. £60
153 5 c. on 24 c. green £60 65 0
154 5 c. on 32 c. slate 25 0 7 6
a. Surcharge inverted .. — £30
154*b* 5 c. on 32 c. dark grey .. 27 6 8 0
155 5 c. on 36 c. blue 30 0 6 6
a. Surcharge inverted .. — £18
156 5 c. on 48 c. rose £10 25 0
157 5 c. on 64 c. red-brown .. 20 0 6 0
a. Surcharge double .. .. — £13
158 5 c. on 96 c. drab 130 0 35 0

As T **22.**

161 10 c. on 16 c. pale violet .. — £30
162 10 c. on 24 c. green £18 90 0
163 10 c. on 36 c. blue £10 £8
164 10 c. on 64 c. red-brown .. 80 0 50 0
165 20 c. on 24 c. green 40 0 22 6

As T **23.**

166 20 c. on 32 c. slate 30 0 27 6
166*a* 20 c. on 32 c. dark grey .. 22 6 20 0
167 25 c. on 32 c. slate 17 6 12 0
167*a* 25 c. on 32 c. dark grey .. 17 6 12 0
168 28 c. on 48 c. rose 35 0 10 0
a. Surcharge double .. .. — £35

As T **22.**

169 30 c. on 36 c. blue 12 6 8 6
170 56 c. on 96 c. drab 20 0 12 6

Variety. Surcharge inverted.

171 30 c. on 36 c. blue £10 90 0

(*b*) P 14 × 12½.

With T **21.**

172 5 c. on 32 c. slate 60 0 25 0
173 5 c. on 64 c. red-brown .. 85 0 35 0

With T **22.**

174 10 c. on 64 c. red-brown .. 35 0 35 0
a. Imperf. between (vert. pair) £45

One Rupee Twelve Cents

(24)

II. *Wmk. Crown CC.*

With T **24.**

(*a*) *P* 12½. (*b*) *P* 12½ × 14.

175 1 r. 12 c. on 2 r. 50 c. dull rose (*a*) £10 35 0
176 1 r. 12 c. on 2 r. 50 c. dull rose (*b*) 35 0 15 0

III. *Wmk. Crown CA.* P 14.

With T **21.**

177 5 c. on 4 c. rosy mauve
178 5 c. on 4 c. rose .. 3 6 1 0
179 5 c. on 8 c. orange-yellow .. 17 6 4 6
a. Surcharge double .. .. — £12
180 5 c. on 16 c. pale violet .. 22 6 8 6
180*a* 5 c. on 24 c. green .. ..
181 5 c. on 24 c. brown-purple .. £20 £6

Varieties. Surcharge inverted.

182 5 c. on 4 c. rose .. — £20
183 5 c. on 8 c. orange-yellow .. — £28
183*a* 5 c. on 16 c. pale violet .. — 80 0

As T **22.**

184 10 c. on 16 c. pale violet .. — £32
185 10 c. on 24 c. brown-purple 17 6 7 6
186 15 c. on 16 c. pale violet .. 10 0 7 6

REVENUE AND POSTAGE 5 CENTS (25)

10 CENTS (26)

1 R. 12 C. (27)

1885–87. *T* **11** *to* **15, 18** *and* **19** *surch. by Messrs. De La Rue & Co., in black.* P 14.

I. *Wmk. Crown CA.*

With T **25.**

187 5 c. on 8 c. lilac 3 0 0 4

As T **26.**

188 10 c. on 24 c. brown-purple 10 0 6 0
189 15 c. on 16 c. orange-yellow 15 0 10 0
190 28 c. on 32 c. slate 10 0 3 6
191 30 c. on 36 c. olive-green .. 25 0 15 0
192 56 c. on 96 c. drab 18 6 7 6

II. *Wmk. Crown CC (sideways).* P 14.

With T **27.**

193 1 r. 12 c. on 2 r. 50 c. dull rose 45 0 40 0

28

29

1886. *T* **28** (5 *c.*) *and* **29.** *Wmk. Crown CA.* P 14.

Type (*a*) has thicker lines in the background and masses of solid colour under the chin, in front of the throat, at the back of the neck, and at the base. Type (*b*) has thinner lines in the background, and coil and pendent curl clearer.

194 5 c. dull purple (*a*) 6 0 0 4
195 5 c. dull purple (*b*) 0 4 0 1
196 15 c. sage-green 3 6 0 6
197 15 c. olive-green 3 6 0 6
198 25 c. yellow-brown 3 6 2 0
199 28 c. slate 6 0 3 0

Variety with value in yellow.

200 25 c. yellow-brn. and yellow .. 60 0 30 0

30

1887. *T* **30.** *Wmk. Crown CC. P* 14.

201 1 r. 12 c. dull rose 15 0 10 0

This stamp comes on both white and bluish paper with wmk. sideways, and, in a different shade, with upright wmk.

1888–90. *Stamps of* 1883–84 *surcharged in black.*

TWO CENTS (31) — TWO (32)

202 **31** 2 c. on 4 c. rosy mauve .. 0 6 0 8
a. Surcharge inverted 15 0 15 0
b. Double, one inverted .. — 60 0
203 „ 2 c. on 4 c. rose 0 9 0 9
a. Surcharge inverted 15 0 15 0
b. Double .. .. — 40 0
204 **32** 2 (c.) on 4 c. rosy mauve .. 0 6 0 8
a. Surch. inverted 40 0 40 0
b. Surch. double 60 0 60 0
c. Surch. double, one inverted 30 0 20 0
205 „ 2 (c.) on 4 c. rose 1 6 0 8
a. Surch. inverted £6
b. Surch. double 60 0 50 0
c. Surch. double, one inverted 60 0 60 0

2 Cents (33) — Two Cents (34)

206 **33** 2 c. on 4 c. rosy mauve .. 30 0 30 0
a. Surch. inverted .. .. — 50 0
b. Double, one inverted ..
207 „ 2 c. on 4 c. rose 2 6 1 6
a. Surch. inverted 20 0 25 0
b. Surch. double .. ..
c. Surch double, one inverted 15 0 15 0
208 **34** 2 c. on 4 c., rosy mauve .. 30 0 27 6
a. Surch. inverted 80 0 40 0
209 „ 2 c. on 4 c. rose 2 6 1 0
a. Surch. inverted 17 6 17 6
b. Surch. double 50 0 50 0
c. Surch. double, one inverted 15 0 15 0

2 Cents (35)

210 **35** 2 c. on 4 c. rosy mauve .. 25 0 27 6
a. Surch. inverted 80 0 80 0
b. Surch. double, one inverted 80 0 80 0
c. Double .. .. .. — 60 0
d. "s" of "Cents" inverted
e. As d. Whole surch. inverted
211 „ 2 c. on 4 c. rose 4 6 1 6
a. Surch. inverted 10 0 10 0
b. Surch. double 80 0 70 0
c. Surch double, one inverted 25 0 20 0
d. "s" of "Cents" inverted

The 4 c. *rose* and the 4 c. *rosy mauve* are found surcharged "Postal Commission 3 (or 'Three') Cents." They denote the extra commission charged by the Post Office on postal orders which had not been cashed within three months of the date of issue. For a short time the Post Office did not object to the use of these stamps on letters.

POSTAGE

Five Cents

REVENUE
(36)

1890. *No.* 197 *surcharged with T* **36.**

233 5 c. on 15 c. olive-green .. 1 9 2 0
a. Surcharge inverted 25 0 25 0
b. Surcharge double .. .. — £6
c. "Flve" for "Five" .. £6
d. Variety. As c., inverted ..
e. "REVENUE" omitted .. £8 £7
f. Inverted "s" in "Cents" .. 20 0 20 0
g. Variety. As f., and whole surcharge inverted £30
h. "REVENUE" omitted and inverted "s" in "Cents" .. £20
i. "POSTAGE" spaced between "T" and "A" £5

FIFTEEN CENTS (37) — 3 Cents (38)

1891. *Nos.* 198 *and* 199 *surcharged with T* **37.**

239 15 c. on 25 c. yellow-brown .. 8 0 10 0
240 15 c. on 28 c. slate 12 6 8 0

1892. *Stamps of* 1883–84 *and* 1886 *surcharged with T* **38**, *in black.*

241 3 c. on 4 c. rosy mauve .. 1 0 1 0
242 3 c. on 4 c. rose 3 6 5 0
243 3 c. on 28 c. slate 1 6 2 0
a. Surcharge double .. ..

39

1893. *T* **39** (3 *c.*) *and* **29** (30 *c.*). *Wmk. Crown CA. P* 14.

245 3 c. terra-cotta and blue-grn. 0 6 0 4
246 30 c. bright mauve & chestnut 6 0 2 0
247 30 c. bright violet and chestnut 4 0 2 0

1898. *T* **10.** *Wmk. Crown CA. P* 14.

248 4 c. carmine-rose 6 0 6 0

1899. *T* **19.** *Wmk. Crown CA. P* 14.

249 2 r. 50 c. purple/*red* 35 0 35 0

Six Cents (40)

1899. *Provisionals. No.* 196 *surcharged with T* **40**, *in black.*

250 6 c. on 15 c. sage-green .. 0 9 0 10

2 R. 25 C. (41)

T **19.** *Wmk. Crown CC. Surcharged as T* **41**, *in black. P* 14.

254 1 r. 50 c. on 2 r. 50 c. slate .. 20 0 20 0
255 2 r. 25 c. on 2 r. 50 c. yellow 50 0 50 0

43

1899–1900. *Wmk. Crown CA (the two high values wmk. Crown CC).* P 14.

No.	Type	Description				
256	**9**	2 c. pale orange-brown ..	0	6	0	3
257	**39**	3 c. deep green	1	0	0	6
258	**10**	4 c. yellow ..	1	0	1	0
259	**29**	6 c. rose and black ..	0	6	0	2
260	**39**	12 c. sage-green and rose ..	3	0	3	6
261	**29**	15 c. blue	2	6	1	6
262	**39**	75 c. black and red-brown .	5	0	6	0
263	**43**	1 r. 50 c. rose	17	6	15	0
264	,,	2 r. 25 c. dull blue ..	25	0	25	0

44

45

46

47

48

1903–5. *Wmk. Crown CA.* P 14.

No.	Type	Description				
265	**44**	2 c. red-brown	0	10	0	2
266	**45**	3 c. green	1	0	0	4
267	,,	4 c. orange-yellow & blue	3	6	2	6
268	**46**	5 c. dull purple	0	8	0	1
269	**47**	6 c. carmine ..	2	6	0	8
270	**45**	12 c. sage-green & rosine ..	6	0	3	0
271	**48**	15 c. blue	7	0	1	9
272	,,	25 c. bistre..	6	0	7	0
273	,,	30 c. dull violet and green	5	0	2	0
274	**45**	75 c. dull blue & orge. ('05)	10	0	10	6
275	**48**	1 r. 50 c. greyish slate('04)	60	0	55	0
276	,,	2 r. 25 c. brn. & grn. ('04)	57	6	60	0

1904–5. *Wmk. Mult. Crown CA.* P 14.

No.	Type	Description				
277	**44**	2 c. red-brown, O ..	0	2	0	2
278	**45**	3 c. green, O	0	8	0	2
279	,,	4 c. orange & ultram., O	1	6	1	6
280	**46**	5 c. dull purple, OC ..	1	6	0	2
281	**47**	6 c. carmine, O ..	0	8	0	2
282	**45**	12 c. sage-grn. & rosine, O	3	6	1	6
283	**48**	15 c. blue, O	2	6	0	8
284	,,	25 c. bistre, O ('05)	6	0	4	6
285	,,	30 c. violet & grn., O ('05)	5	0	1	0
286	**45**	75 c. dull blue and orange, O ('05) ..	8	6	9	0
287	**48**	1 r. 50 c. grey, O ('05) ..	15	0	15	0
288	,,	2 r. 25 c. brn. & green, O	20	0	17	6

50

51

1908. *T* **50** *and* **51**. *Wmk. Mult. Crown CA.* P 14.

No.	Description				
289	5 c. deep purple, O	0	6	0	1
290	5 c. dull purple, O	1	3	0	2
291	6 c. carmine, O	0	6	0	2

1910–11. *Changes of colour and type and new values. Wmk. Mult. Crown CA.* P 14.

No.	Type	Description				
292	**44**	2 c. brn.-orange, O (1911)	0	3	0	2
293	**48**	3 c. green, O (1911) ..	1	0	0	2
294	,,	10 c. sage-grn. & marone, O	2	6	0	10
295	,,	25 c. grey, O	2	6	2	0
296	,,	50 c. chocolate, O	5	0	5	0
297	,,	1 r. purple/*yellow*, O ..	8	6	10	0
298	,,	2 r. red/*yellow*, O	15	0	17	6
299	,,	5 r. black/*green*, O ..	45	0	55	0
300	,,	10 r. black/*red*, O	£8		£8	

52

53

(A)

(B)

1912–25. *T* **52** *and* **53** (50 *r. to* 1000 *r.*). *Wmk. Mult. Crown CA.* P 14.

Stamps of Type **52** are normally printed in two operations, but the 1 c. and 5 c. together with later issues of the 3 c. and 6 c. were printed from special plates at one operation. These plates are distinguished by a large " C " in the value tablet as illustration B. Except for the 5 c. (which is Die I), the frames also differ slightly from Dies I and II, described in the Introduction, but the 3 c. is similar to Die I and the 1 c. and 6 c. similar to Die II, except that inner top corners of side panels are square and not curved as in Die II.

All stamps with wmk. Mult. Crown CA are Die I unless otherwise stated.

301 1 c. brown, O (B) 0 3 0 1
302 2 c. brown-orange, O .. 0 4 0 1
303 2 c. deep orange-brown, O 0 4 0 1
304 3 c. yellow-green, O (A) .. 2 0 0 2
305 3 c. deep green, O (A) .. 1 9 0 2
306 3 c. blue-green. O (B) .. 0 8 0 1
307 5 c. purple, O (B) 2 0 0 2
308 5 c. bright magenta, O (B) 0 6 0 2
309 6 c. scarlet, O (A) 1 6 0 2
310 6 c. bright scarlet, O (A) .. 1 3 0 2
311 6 c. pale scarlet, O (B) .. 2 0 0 2
312 6 c. carmine, O (B) 2 0 0 1
313 10 c. sage-green, O 2 0 0 9
314 10 c. deep sage-green, O .. 2 0 0 6
315 15 c. ultramarine, O .. 2 6 0 6
316 15 c. deep bright blue, O .. 2 6 0 6
317 25 c. yellow and blue, C .. 4 0 0 6
318 25 c. orange and blue, C .. 4 6 0 6
319 30 c. blue-green & violet, C 5 0 1 0
320 30 c. yellow-grn. & violet, C 6 0 0 6
321 50 c. black and scarlet, C .. 4 6 1 0
322 1 r. purple/*yellow*, C .. 8 0 3 0
 a. *White back* (1914) .. 7 6 6 0
 b. *On lemon* (1916) 15 0 7 0
 c. *On orange-buff* ..
 d. *On pale yellow* 7 0 7 0
323 2 r. black & red/*yellow*, C .. 10 0 10 6
 a. *White back* 12 6 12 6
 b. *On lemon* 40 0 32 6
 c. *On orange-buff* 30 0 20 0
 d. *On pale yellow* 15 0 15 0
324 5 r. black/*green*, C 30 0 25 0
 a. *White back* 30 0 30 0
 b. *On blue-grn., olive back* (1921) 40 0 45 0
 c. *On emerald back* (Die II) .. 50 0 50 0
325 10 r. purple & blk./*red*, C 70 0 35 0
 a. Die II.. .. 65 0 65 0
326 20 r. black and red/*blue*, C £8 £6
327 50 r. dull purple, C .. £20
328 100 r. grey-black, C .. £40
329 500 r. dull green, C .. £80
329*a* 1000 r. purple/*red*, C (1925) £175

The 5 c., 6 c. and 30 c. are known with watermark sideways. (6 c., 3s. 6d. un.; 30 c., 7s. 6d. un.)

WAR
STAMP
(54)

1918 (18 Nov.). *T 52 optd. with T 54.*

330 2 c. brown-orange 0 2 0 2
 a. Overprint inverted 60 0 60 0
 b. Overprint double 60 0 60 0
331 3 c. green (A) 0 3 0 2
 a. Overprint double £7 £7
332 3 c. green (B) 0 4 0 2
333 5 c. purple (B) 0 3 0 2
 a. Overprint double 60 0 60 0
334 5 c. bright magenta (B) .. 0 4 0 2
 a. Overprint inverted 60 0 60 0
 b. Overprint double 40 0 40 0

WAR
STAMP
ONE CENT
(55)

T 52 surcharged with T 55, in black.

335 1 c. on 5 c. purple (B) .. 0 2 0 2
336 1 c. on 5 c. bright magenta (B) 0 2 0 2

As last, without "WAR STAMP."

337 1 c. on 5 c. purple (B) .. 0 2 0 2
338 1 c. on 5 c. bright magenta (B) 0 2 0 2

Collectors are warned against forgeries of the errors in the "WAR STAMP" overprints.

1921–27. *T 52 and 53. Wmk. Mult. Script CA. P 14.*

339 1 c. brown, O (B) (1927) .. 0 1 0 1
340 2 c. brn.-orge., O (Die II).. 0 4 0 1
341 3 c. green, O (B) 1 6 0 1
342 5 c. bright magenta, O (B) 0 4 0 1
343 6 c. carmine-red, O (B) .. 1 9 0 1
344 10 c. sage-green, O (Die I) .. 1 9 0 3
 a. Die II 0 9 0 1
345 15 c. ultramarine, O (Die I) 3 6 1 6
346 25 c. yell. & blue, O (Die I) 3 6 0 6
 a. Die II 2 0 0 3
347 30 c. yell.-grn. & vio., C (Die I) 5 0 0 8
 a. Die II 2 6 0 6
348 50 c. blk. & scarlet, C (Die I) 5 0 1 3
 a. Die II 3 6 0 6
349 1 r. pur./*pale yell.*, C (Die I) 15 0 4 6
 a. Die II 10 0 4 0
350 2 r. black & red/*pale yellow*, C (Die II) .. 15 0 6 6
351 5 r. blk./*emer.*, C (Die II) .. 35 0 25 0
352 20 r. blk & red/*bl.*, C (Die II) £12 £15
353 50 r. dull purple, C .. £15 £18
354 100 r. grey-black, C .. £45 £50

1922–27. *New colours and values. Wmk. Mult. Script CA. P 14.*

355 3 c. slate-grey, O (B) .. 0 6 0 1
356 6 c. bright violet, O (B) .. 0 6 0 2
357 9 c. red/*yellow*, O (Die II) 0 8 0 4
358 12 c. rose-scarlet, O (Die I) 4 0 2 6
 a. Die II 2 0 1 6
359 15 c. grn./*pale yell.*, O (Die I) 2 0 0 6
 a. Die II 1 0 0 4
360 20 c. bright blue, O (Die I) 3 0 0 9
 a. Die II 1 9 0 4
360*b* 100 r. dull purple & blue, C £50

2 Cents.
(56)

(Surcharged at Ceylon Govt. Printing Works.

1926. *Nos. 355 and 356 surcharged as T 56.*

361 2 c. on 3 c. slate-grey .. 0 4 0 4
 a. Surcharge double £5
 b. Bar omitted 80 0
362 5 c. on 6 c. bright violet .. 0 4 0 1

57

1927–29. *T 57. Wmk. Mult. Script CA. P 14.*

363 1 r. dull & bright purple, C 10 0 2 0
364 2 r. green and carmine, C.. 12 6 5 0
365 5 r. green & dull purple, C 27 0 17 6
366 10 r. green & brn.-orange, C 55 0 60 0
367 20 r. dull purple and blue, C £6 £6

1935 (6 May). *Silver Jubilee. As T 13 of Antigua inscribed "CEYLON". Recess. D.L.R. & Co. Wmk. Mult. Script CA. P* 13½ × 14.

368 6 c. ultramarine and grey .. 0 6 0 4
369 9 c. green and indigo .. 2 6 1 9
370 20 c. brown and deep blue .. 4 0 3 6
371 50 c. slate and purple .. 10 0 8 0

58. Tapping rubber.

59. Colombo Harbour.

60. Adam's Peak.

61. Plucking Tea (*vert.*).

62. Coconut Palms (*vert.*).

63. Hill Paddy (rice) (*horiz.*).

64. River scene (*horiz.*).

65. Temple of the Tooth, Kandy (*horiz.*).

66. Ancient Irrigation Tank (*horiz.*).

67. Wild Elephants (*horiz.*).

68. Trincomalee (*horiz.*).

(Recess. De La Rue (2 c., 3 c., 20 c. and 50 c.) and Bradbury, Wilkinson (others).)

1935–36. *Wmk. Mult. Script CA. Various perfs.*

No.	Type	Description	Unused		Used	
372	**58**	2 c. black and carmine (*perf.* 12 × 13)	0	2	0	1
		a. Perf. 14	2	6	1	0
373	**60**	3 c. black and olive-green (*perf.* 13 × 12)	0	3	0	1
		a. Perf. 14	4	6	0	9
374	**59**	6 c. black and blue (*perf.* 11 × 11½)	0	5	0	1
375	**61**	9 c. green and orange (*perf.* 11 × 11½)	0	8	0	10
376	**63**	10 c. black and purple (*perf.* 11½ × 11)	1	0	0	8
377	**64**	15 c. red-brown and green (*perf.* 11½ × 11)	1	9	0	10
378	**62**	20 c. black and ultramarine (*perf.* 12 × 13)	2	9	1	0
379	**65**	25 c. deep blue & chocolate (*perf.* 11½ × 11)	3	6	1	3
380	**66**	30 c. carmine & blue-green (*perf.* 11½ × 11)	4	0	1	6
381	**67**	50 c. black and violet (*perf.* 14)	7	6	2	6
382	**68**	1 r. violet-blue & choc. (*perf.* 11½ × 11)	20	0	10	0

Dates of issue :—1935. May 1, 2 c., 15 c. and 25 c. June 1, 10 c. July 1, 1 r. Aug. 1, 30 c. Oct. 1, 3 c. 1936. Jan. 1, 6 c., 9 c., 20 c. and 50 c.

OFFICIAL STAMPS.

1869. *Issues of* 1863–68 *overprinted* "SERVICE," *in block letters.*

Although these stamps were prepared for use and sent out to the colony, they were never issued.

Prices :

Narrow "SERVICE."

No.				
No. 98.	2d.	..	17	6
,, 104.	6d.	..	20	0
,, 108.	8d.	..	20	0
,, 113.	1s.	..	40	0
,, 116.	2s.	..	40	0
,, 116.	2s. *imperf.*	..	80	0

Wide "SERVICE."

1d. blue	6	0
3d. rose	17	6

On
Service
(O 3)

Contemporary issues overprinted with Type O **3.**

1895–96. *In black.*

No.	Type	Description	Unused		Used	
O 9	**9**	2 c. green	4	6	0	4
O10	**39**	3 c. terra-cotta & bl.-grn.	3	0	3	0
O11	**28**	5 c. dull purple (*b*)	1	0	0	2
O12	**29**	15 c. sage-green	4	0	1	3
O13	,,	25 c. yellow-brown	5	0	2	0
O14	,,	30 c. bright mve. & brn	2	6	1	0
O15	**30**	1 r. 12 c. dull rose	35	0	25	0

The varieties of the 1 r. 12 c. mentioned in note after No. 201 all exist with the "On Service" overprint.

1899. *In red.*

No.	Type	Description	Unused		Used	
O16	**39**	75 c. black & red-brown	5	0	5	0

1900. *In black.*

No.	Type	Description	Unused		Used	
O17	**9**	2 c. pale orange-brown	2	0	0	3
O18	**39**	3 c. deep green	4	0	2	6
O21	**29**	15 c. blue	4	0	1	9

1903. *King Edward VII. In black.*

No.	Type	Description	Unused		Used	
O22	**44**	2 c. orange-brown	6	0	3	0
O23	**45**	3 c. green	3	0	4	0
O24	**46**	5 c. dull purple	5	0	2	0
O25	**48**	15 c. blue	7	6	3	6
O26	,,	25 c. bistre	20	0	20	0
O27	,,	30 c. dull violet & green	10	0	5	0

About half a dozen sheets of the 15 c. were overprinted with a space of 3 mm. instead of 4 mm. between the words "On" and "Service."

BRITISH POSSESSIONS UNDER THE CONTROL OF CEYLON.

MALDIVE ISLANDS.

MALDIVES

(1)

1906. *Stamps of Ceylon optd. with T* **1.** *Wmk. Mult. Crown CA. P* 14.

No.	Type	Description					
1	**44**	2 c. orange-brown, O	..	12	6	15	0
2	**45**	3 c. green, O	..	12	6	15	0
3	,,	4 c. orange & ultram., O	..	22	6	30	0
4	**46**	5 c. dull purple, C	..	7	6	8	0
5	**48**	15 c. blue, O	..	45	0	50	0
6	,,	25 c. bistre, O	..	60	0	65	0

2. Minaret, Juma Mosque, Malé.

3

(Recess. De La Rue & Co.)

1909 (MAY). *T* **2** (18½ × 22½ *mm.*). *Line-engraved. Wmk. Mult. Rosettes, T* **3.** *P* 14.

No.	Description					
8	2 c. orange-brown	..	0	10	0	10
9	3 c. deep myrtle	..	1	3	1	0
10	5 c. purple	..	1	9	1	0
11	10 c. carmine	..	2	0	1	6

4

1933. *T* **2** *redrawn (reduced to* 18 × 21½ *mm.). Photogravure. Wmk. "Harrison & Sons, London", T* **4.** *P* 15 × 14.

No.	Description					
12	2 c. grey	..	0	1	0	1
13	3 c. red-brown	..	0	1	0	3
13*a*	5 c. claret	..	2	6	2	0
14	6 c. scarlet	..	0	3	0	4
15	10 c. green	..	0	3	0	4
16	15 c. black	..	0	5	0	8
17	25 c. brown	..	0	7	0	10
18	50 c. purple	..	1	0	1	6
19	1 r. deep blue	..	2	0	3	0

CHINA.

BRITISH POST OFFICES.

See after **HONG KONG.**

COOK ISLANDS.

(RAROTONGA.)

(These are also known as the Hervey Islands. The islands of Manikiki, Rakahanga, and Pukapuka were annexed to the group in October, 1890, and use the same stamps.)

1

(Printed at the Government Printing Office, Wellington, N.Z.)

1892 (29 FEB.). *No wmk. P* 12½. *Toned paper.*

No.	Type	Description					
1	**1**	1d. black	..	7	6	8	0
		a. Imperf. between (vert. pair)					
2	,,	1½d. mauve	..	7	6	8	6
3	,,	2½d. indigo	..	10	0	12	6
4	,,	10d. dull carmine	..	45	0	45	0
		White paper.					
5	**1**	1d. black	..	6	6	7	6
6	,,	1½d. mauve	..	8	0	8	0
7	,,	2½d. blue	..	15	0	15	0
8	,,	10d. carmine	..	37	6	37	6

Queen Makea Takau.

2

Torea or Wry-bill.

3

1893–99. *Wmk. T* **12***a of New Zealand. (NZ and Star wide apart.)*

(*a*) *P* 12 × 11½. (Aug., 1893.)

No.	Type	Description					
9	**2**	1d. brown	..	5	0	6	0
10	,,	1d. blue (1894)	..	2	0	2	6
11	,,	1½d. mauve	..	2	6	3	0
12	,,	2½d. rose	..	7	6	10	0
12*a*	,,	2½d. rose-carmine	..	10	0	10	6
13	,,	5d. olive-black	..	3	0	4	0
14	,,	10d. green	..	10	0	10	6

(*b*) *P* 11. (1898.)

No.	Type	Description					
14*a*	**3**	½d. blue	..	1	3	1	6
15	**2**	1d. brown	..	4	0	4	6
16	,,	1d. blue	..	1	9	3	0
17	,,	1½d. deep lilac	..	1	3	1	6
17*a*	,,	1½d. deep mauve	..	1	6	2	0
18	**3**	2d. brown	..	1	6	1	9
18*a*	,,	2d. deep brown	..	1	3	1	9
19	**2**	2½d. pale rose	..	6	0	7	6
19*a*	,,	2½d. deep rose	..	3	0	3	6
20	,,	5d. olive-black	..	2	0	2	6
21	**3**	6d. purple	..	5	0	6	0
21*a*	,,	6d. bright purple	..	4	0	4	6
22	**2**	10d. green	..	3	0	4	0
23	**3**	1s. red	..	6	0	6	6
23*a*	,,	1s. deep carmine	..	4	6	5	6

ONE
HALF
PENNY
(5) (6)

1899 (May). *No.* 16 *surcharged with T* **5**.

24 ½d. on 1d. blue 6 0 7 6

Varieties. (i.) *Surcharge inverted.*

25 ½d. on 1d. blue £20 £22

(ii.) *Surcharge double.*

25*a* ½d. on 1d. blue £22 £25

1901. *No.* 15 *overprinted with T* **6**.

26 1d. brown 50 0 60 0

Varieties. (i.) *With Crown inverted.*

27 1d. brown £25 £28

(ii.) *With Crown sideways.*

28 1d. brown £35 £40

(iii.) *With Crown twice.*

28*a* 1d. brown £45 £55

1902. *Cowan paper.* P 11. A. *No wmk.*

29 **3** ½d. blue-green 1 3 1 6
30 „ ½d. yellow-green 1 6 1 9
a. Imperf. between (pair) .. £6
31 **2** 1d. dull rose 3 0 3 6
31*a* „ 1d. rose-red 1 3 1 6
32 „ 1d. rose-lake 1 9 2 6
33 „ 2½d. dull blue 2 6 3 6

B. *Wmk. T* **41** *of New Zealand* (*single-lined N Z and Star, close together; sideways on T* **2**).

34 **3** ½d. yellow-green 1 0 1 0
35 „ ½d. grey-green 4 6 5 0
36 **2** 1d. rose-pink 1 6 1 9
37 „ 1½d. deep mauve 1 6 1 9
38 **3** 2d. deep brown 1 6 1 9
a. No figures of value .. £40
39 **2** 2½d. deep blue 1 6 1 9
40 „ 5d. olive-black 3 0 4 0
41 **3** 6d. purple 3 6 4 0
42 **2** 10d. green 4 0 5 0
43 **3** 1s. carmine 5 0 6 0

1909. *Wmk. T* **41** *of New Zealand.* P 14½ × 14 (½d.) *or* 14 (1d.).

43*a* **3** ½d. green 0 10 1 3
44 **2** 1d. deep red 1 0 1 3

1913–19. *Wmk. T* **41** *of New Zealand. Chalk-surfaced paper.*

45 **3** ½d. dp. grn. (*perf.* 14½ × 14) 0 8 0 10
45*a* „ ½d. deep green (*perf.* 14) .. 1 3 1 6
46 **2** 1d. red (*perf.* 14 × 14½) 0 9 0 10
46*a* „ 1d. red (*perf.* 14) 1 3 1 6
47 „ 1½d. deep mauve (*p.* 14 × 15) 1 9 2 6
47*a* „ 1½d. deep mauve (*perf.* 14) .. 5 0 6 0
47*b* **3** 2d. deep brn. (*perf.* 15 × 14) 4 0 5 0
48 **2** 10d. green (*perf.* 14 × 15) .. 4 0 5 0
49 **3** 1s. carmine (*perf.* 15 × 14) 5 6 6 0

RAROTONGA

APA PENE (8) RAROTONGA (9)

1919. *Current stamps of New Zealand surcharged as T* **8**, *in red* (R.) *or blue* (B.).

T **60*b*** *and* **51** (1d.) *surface-printed.*

P 14 × 15.

50 ½d. green (R.) 0 8 0 10
51 1d. carmine (B.) 0 8 0 10
52 1½d. orange-brown (R.) .. 1 3 1 6
53 2d. yellow (R.) 1 3 1 6
54 3d. chocolate (B.) 1 3 1 9

T **60**, *engraved.* (*a*) P 14 × 14½.

(*b*) P 14 × 13½.

55 2½d. blue (R.) (*a*) 1 9 2 0
56 2½d. blue (R.) (*b*) 1 9 2 0
a. Vert. pair (55/56) 5 0 6 0
57 3d. chocolate (B.) (*a*) 4 6 6 0
58 3d. chocolate (B.) (*b*) 6 0 7 0
a. Vert. pair (57/58) 20 0 22 6
59 4d. violet (B.) (*a*) 2 0 2 6
60 4d. violet (B.) (*b*) 2 0 2 6
a. Vert. pair (59/60) 7 6 8 6
61 4½d. deep green (B.) (*a*) .. 2 0 2 6
62 4½d. deep green (B.) (*b*) .. 2 3 3 0
a. Vert. pair (61/62) 8 6 10 0
63 6d. carmine (B.) (*a*) 3 0 3 6
64 6d. carmine (B.) (*b*) 3 0 3 0
a. Vert. pair (63/64) 10 0 10 6
65 7½d. red-brown (B.) (*b*) .. 5 0 6 0
66 9d. sage-green (R.) (*a*) .. 4 0 4 6
67 9d. sage-green (R.) (*b*) .. 3 0 3 6
a. Vert. pair (66/67) 10 0 12 6
68 1s. vermilion (B.) (*a*) 5 0 5 6
69 1s. vermilion (B.) (*b*) 4 0 5 0
a. Vert. pair (68/69) 12 6 15 0

1921. *T* **154** *of New Zealand overprinted with T* **9**. P 14½ × 14.

70 2s. blue (No. F 166) (R.) .. 10 6 12 0
71 2s. 6d. brown (No. F 167) (B.) 7 6 8 6
72 5s. yell.-grn. (No. F 170) (R.) 15 0 17 6
73 10s. claret (No. F 174) (B.) .. 27 6 35 0
74 £1 rose (No. F 176) (B.) .. 50 0 60 0

10. Capt. Cook landing.

11. Wharf at Avarua.

12. Capt. Cook.

13. Palm Tree.

14. Huts at Arorangi.

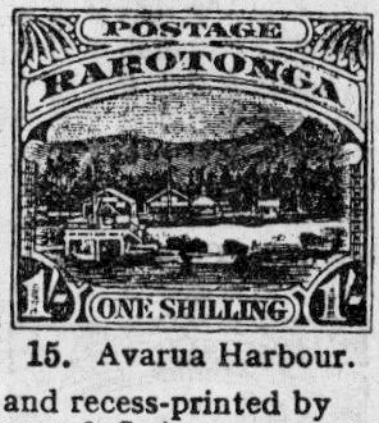

15. Avarua Harbour.

(Designed, engraved and recess-printed by Perkins Bacon & Co.)

1920. *Centres in black, except 6d.* (*brown*). P 14.

75 **10** ½d. green 1 6 1 9
76 **11** 1d. carmine-red 2 0 2 6
a. Centre inverted £130
77 **12** 1½d. dull blue 2 6 3 0
78 **13** 3d. chocolate 3 6 4 0
79 **14** 6d. yellow-orange 4 0 5 0
80 **15** 1s. violet 6 0 7 6

1925. *Wmk. T* **41** *of New Zealand. P* 14.

81 **10** ½d. black and green .. 1 3 1 6
82 **11** 1d. black and deep carmine 1 6 1 9

1926. *As No. 70, but white paper and gum, and overprint in carmine.*

87 2s. blue (C.) 75 0 80 0

T **72** *("Admiral" Type) of New Zealand, overprinted with T* **9**. *(a) "Jones" chalk-surfaced paper.*

88 2s. deep blue (R.) 10 0 12 6

(b) "Cowan" thick chalk-surfaced paper.

89 2s. light blue (R.) 5 0 6 0
90 3s. bright mauve (R.) 7 6 8 6

16. Native Chief.

17. Rarotonga Harbour.

1927. *Wmk. T* **41** *of New Zealand. P* 14.

91 **16** 2½d. red-brown & steel-blue 3 0 3 0
92 **17** 4d. green and violet .. 3 0 4 0

TWO PENCE
(18)

1931. *Surcharged with T* **18**. *P* 14.

(a) No wmk.

93 **12** 2d. on 1½d. blk. & blue (R.) 3 6 4 0

(b) Wmk. T **41** *of New Zealand.*

94 **12** 2d. on 1½d. blk. & blue (R.) 3 0 3 6

1931. *T* **73a** *of New Zealand (various frames) overprinted with T* **9**. *Wmk. T* **41** *of New Zealand. P* 14.

95 2s. 6d. brown (B.) 5 0 6 0
96 5s. green (R.) 12 6 15 0
97 10s. carmine (B.) 22 6 27 6
98 £1 pink (B.) 45 0 55 0

19. Capt. Cook landing.

20. Capt. Cook.

21 Double Maori canoe.

22. Natives working cargo.

23. Port of Avarua.

24. R.M.S. *Monowai.*

25. King George.

(Des. L. C. Mitchell. Recess. Perkins, Bacon.)

1932 (16 Mar.). *No wmk. P* 13.

99 **19** ½d. black and deep green. 0 6 0 9
a. Perf. 14 .. .. 5 0 6 0
100 **20** 1d. black and lake .. 0 9 1 0
a. Centre inverted .. — £100
b. Perf. 14 .. .. 3 6 4 6
101 **21** 2d. black and brown .. 1 0 1 3
a. Centre inverted ..
b. Perf. 14 .. .. 5 0 6 0
102 **22** 2½d. black and deep blue . 4 0 4 6
a. Perf. 14 .. .. 2 0 2 6
103 **23** 4d. black and bright blue. 4 0 4 6
a. Perf. 14 .. .. 3 0 3 6
b. Perf. 14×13 .. .. 5 0 5 0
104 **24** 6d. black and orange .. 4 0 5 0
a. Perf. 14 .. .. 3 0 3 6
105 **25** 1s. black & violet (*perf.* 14) 5 0 6 0

(Recess-printed from Perkins, Bacon's plates at the Government Printing Office, Wellington, N.Z.)

1933–36. *Wmk. T* **41** *of New Zealand. P* 14.

106 **19** ½d. black and deep green 0 1 0 2
107 **20** 1d. black and scarlet ('35) 0 3 0 3
108 **21** 2d. black and brown ('36) 0 6 0 6
109 **22** 2½d. black and deep blue.. 0 6 0 6
110 **23** 4d. black and bright blue. 0 10 1 0
111 **24** 6d. blk. & orge.-yell ('36) 1 6 1 6
112 **25** 1s. black and violet ('36) 5 0 5 0

SILVER JUBILEE
OF
KING GEORGE V.
1910-1935.
(26)

Normal letters.
B K E N
B K E N
Narrow letters.

1935 (7 May). *Silver Jubilee. Optd. with T* **26** *(wider vertical spacing on 6d.). Colours changed. Wmk. T* **41** *of New Zealand. P* 14.

113 **20** 1d. red-brown and lake 0 8 1 6
a. Narrow "K" in "KING" 3 6
b. Narrow "B" in "JUBILEE" 3 6
114 **22** 2½d. dull and deep blue (R.) 3 6 6 6
a. Narrow first "E" in "GEORGE" 10 0
115 **24** 6d. green and orange .. 15 0 20 0
a. Narrow "N" in "KING" 35 0

COOK ISLANDS.
(27)

COOK IS'DS.
(28)

1932–36. *Types of New Zealand optd. with T* **27**. *Wmk. T* **41** *of New Zealand. P* 14.

(a) T **72** *("Admiral" Type).*

116 2s. blue (Bk.) (15.7.36) .. 6 0 6 6
117 3s. mauve (Bk.) (15.7.36) .. 8 0 8 6

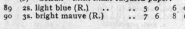

(b) As T 73a ("Arms" Type).

118 2s. 6d. brown (Bk.) (15.7.36) 2 8 4 0
119 5s. green (R.) (15.7.36) .. 10 0 10 0
120 10s. carm.-lake (Bk.) (15.7.36) 10 6 15 0
121 £1 pink (Bk.) (15.7.36) .. 20 0
122 £3 green (R.) ('32) 60 0
123 £5 blue (R.) ('32) £5

CYPRUS.

CYPRUS (1) CYPRUS (2)

(Stamps of Great Britain overprinted by Messrs. De La Rue & Co.)

NOTE.—All Cyprus stamps are perf. 14 unless otherwise stated.

1880.

1 1 ½d. rose 27 6 35 0

Plate No.	Un. s. d.	Used. s. d.	Plate No.	Un. s. d.	Used. s. d.
12.	27 6	35 0	19.	£25	95 0
15.	27 6	35 0			

2 2 1d. red 5 0 6 0
a. Opt. double (Plates 208 and 218) £35
b. Pair, one without opt. (Pl. 208) £45

Plate No.	Un.	Used.	Plate No.	Un.	Used.
174.	£20		208.	25 0	7 6
181.	45 0	40 0	215.	5 0	6 0
184.	—	£20	216.	7 6	7 6
193.	—	—	217.	7 6	8 0
196.	—	—	218.	8 0	8 6
201.	5 0	6 0	220.	£10	45 0
205.	12 6	12 6			

3 2 2½d. rosy mauve 1 3 2 0
a. Large thin "o" (Plate 14) .. 4 6 6 6
b. Large thin "o" (Plate 15) .. 6 6 8 0

Plate No.	Un.	Used.	Plate No.	Un.	Used.
14.	1 3	2 0	15.	2 0	8 0

4 2 4d. (plate 16) sage-green .. 20 0 22 6
5 ,, 6d. (plate 16) grey .. 70 0 70 0
6 ,, 1s. (plate 13) green .. £15 £10

HALF-PENNY (3) HALFPENNY (4)

HALF-PENNY (5) 30 PARAS (6)

1881. *The 1d. of preceding issue surcharged in black.*

7 3 "HALFPENNY" 18 mm. .. 17 6 17 6

"HALFPENN" *for* "HALFPENNY."

7a 3 ½d. on 1d. (*all plates*) *from* £8 £8

Plate No.	Un. s. d.	Used. s. d.	Plate No.	Un. s. d.	Used. s. d.
174.	30 0		215.	70 0	
181.	37 6	35 0	216.	17 6	17 6
201.	17 6	17 6	217.	£10	£10
205.	20 0	22 6	218.	£6	£8
208.	35 0	37 6	220.	75 0	75 0

8 4 "HALFPENNY" 16 or 16½ mm. 50 0 30 0

Plate No.	Un.	Used.	Plate No.	Un.	Used.
201.	50 0	30 0	218.	—	—
216.	55 0				

9 5 "HALFPENNY" 13 mm. .. 17 6 15 0

Plate No.	Un.	Used.	Plate No.	Un.	Used.
201.	—	—	217.	25 0	27 6
205.	30 0		218.	17 6	15 0
215.	17 6	15 0			

10 6 30 paras on 1d. red 42 6 42 6

Plate No.	Un.	Used.	Plate No.	Un.	Used.
201.	42 6	42 6	217.	60 0	50 0
216.	60 0	45 0	220.	80 0	65 0

Errors.

11 5 ½d. on 1d. surch. twice .. 60 0

Plate No.	Un.	Used.	Plate No.	Un.	Used.
205.	65 0		215.	60 0	

12 5 ½d. on 1d. surch. 3 times .. 75 0

Plate No.	Un.	Used.	Plate No.	Un.	Used.
205.	£8		217.	—	—
215.	75 0		218.	—	—

13 5 ½d. on 1d. surch. 4 times ..

"CYPRUS" *double.*

14 5 ½d. on 1d. (pl. 218) £50

Surcharge double, one inverted.

15 6 30 paras on 1d. (pl. 220) .. £25 £15

CYPRUS ONE PIASTRE

7

(Typo. De La Rue & Co.)

1881 (JULY). *T 7. Die I. Wmk. Crown CC.*

16 7 ½ pias. emerald-green .. 15 0 12 6
17 ,, 1 pias. rose 35 0 17 6
18 ,, 2 pias. blue 25 0 12 6
19 ,, 4 pias. pale olive-green .. 80 0 50 0
20 ,, 6 pias. olive-grey £6 75 0

Stamps of Queen Victoria initialled "J. A. B." or overprinted "POSTAL SURCHARGE" with or without the same initials were employed for accounting purposes between the Chief Post Office and sub-offices. The initials are those of the then Postmaster, Mr. J. A. Bulmer.

1/2 (8) 1/2 (9) 1/2 30 PARAS (10)

1882. *T 7, surcharged in black.*

Varieties of T 9; (a) Figures "½" 8½ mm. apart, (b) 6 to 7 mm. apart.

21 8 ½ pias. emerald-green .. 35 0 20 0
22 9 ½ pias. emerald-green (a) £35 80 0
22a ,, ½ pias. emerald-green (b) £70
23 10 30 paras on 1 pias. rose .. £12 32 6

(i.) Small "1" at right.

24 9 ½ pias. emerald-green (a) — £70

(ii.) Large "1" on left.

24a 9 ½ pias. emerald-green (a) .. — £20

Type 8 was made locally, Type 9 in London. Type 9 may be found with the figures "2" of slightly different size.

1882–86. *Wmk. Crown CA. T 7 surcharged in black. Die I.**

25 8 ½ pias. emerald-green .. 15 0 8 0
26 9 ½ pias. emerald-green (a) .. 70 0 8 6
27 ,, ½ pias. emerald-green (b) .. 45 0 22 6

Varieties. (i.) Large "1" on left.

27a 9 ½ pias. emerald-green (a) .. £25 70 0

(ii.) Small "1" on right.

27b 9 ½ pias. emerald-green (a) .. £45 £8

T 7 unsurcharged. Die I.

28 7 ½ pias. emerald-green .. £20 £10
28a ,, ½ pias. dull green .. 5 0 0 8
29 ,, 30 paras pale mauve .. 22 6 12 6
30 ,, 1 pias. carmine 12 6 1 6
31 ,, 2 pias. dull blue 15 0 1 6
32 ,, 4 pias. pale olive-green .. 25 0 12 6
32a ,, 4 pias. deep olive-green .. 70 0 15 0
33 ,, 6 pias. olive-grey 17 6 12 6
34 ,, 12 pias. orange-brown .. 45 0 45 0

Die II.

35 7 ½ pias. dull green 2 0 0 2
36 ,, 30 paras mauve 2 0 4 6
37 ,, 1 pias. carmine 5 0 4 0
38 ,, 2 pias. ultramarine .. 4 6 1 6

* For description and illustration of differences between Die I. and Die II. see Introduction.

No.	Type	Description	s.	d.	s.	d.
38a	7	4 pias. pale olive-green ..	8	6	6	6
39	,,	4 pias. olive-green ..	20	0	10	0
40	,,	6 pias. olive-grey	22	6		
41	,,	12 pias. orange-brown ..	40	0	42	6

1894–96. *T 7. Die II. Wmk. Crown CA.*

No.	Type	Description	s.	d.	s.	d.
42	7	½ pias. green and carmine ..	0	6	0	3
43	,,	30 paras bright mauve & grn.	0	6	0	8
44	,,	1 pias. carmine and blue ..	2	0	0	9
45	,,	2 pias. blue and purple ..	2	6	1	9
46	,,	4 pias. sage-green & purple	8	6	6	6
47	,,	6 pias. sepia and green ..	8	6	8	0
48	,,	9 pias. brown and carmine	7	6	8	0
49	,,	12 pias. orange-brn. & black	17	6	17	6
50	,,	18 pias. greyish slate & brn.	18	6	22	6
51	,,	45 pias. grey-purple & blue ..	40	0	45	0

11

(Typo. De La Rue & Co.)

1903. *Wmk. Crown CA.*

No.	Type	Description	s.	d.	s.	d.
52	11	½ pias. green & carmine ..	1	3	0	4
53	,,	30 paras violet & green ..	1	3	1	6
54	,,	1 pias. carmine and blue ..	10	0	1	6
55	,,	2 pias. blue and purple ..	20	0	6	0
56	,,	4 pias. olive-grn. & pur. ..	20	0	17	6
57	,,	6 pias. sepia and green ..	18	0	20	0
58	,,	9 pias. brown & carmine ..	40	0	42	6
59	,,	12 pias. chestnut & black ..	15	0	15	0
60	,,	18 pias. black and brown ..	30	0	32	6
61	,,	45 pias. dull pur. & ultram.	42	6	45	0

1904–10. *Wmk. Multiple Crown CA.*

No.	Type	Description	s.	d.	s.	d.
61a	11	5 par. bistre & blk. ('07) ..	0	4	0	4
61b	,,	10 par. orange & grn. ('07)	0	10	0	4
61c	,,	10 par. yellow & green ..	1	6	0	6
62	,,	½ pias. green & carmine ..	0	8	0	2
63	,,	30 par. purple & green ..	1	0	0	4
63a	,,	30 par. violet & grn. ('10)	1	6	0	10
64	,,	1 pias. carmine & blue ..	2	6	1	0
65	,,	2 pias. blue and purple ..	3	0	0	10
66	,,	4 pias. olive-green & pur.	8	0	8	6
67	,,	6 pias. sepia and green ..	12	6	12	6
68	,,	9 pias. brown & carmine	10	0	12	0
69	,,	12 pias. chestnut & blk. ('06)	15	0	17	6
70	,,	18 pias. black and brown ..	17	6	18	6
71	,,	45 pias. dull pur. & ultram.	40	0	40	0

12

(Typo. De La Rue & Co.)

1912. *T 12. Wmk. Mult. Crown CA.*

No.	Description	s.	d.	s.	d.
73	10 par. orange and green ..	0	5	0	2
73a	10 par. orge.-yell. & brt. green	0	4	0	2
74	½ pias. green and carmine ..	0	6	0	2
74a	½ pias. yellow-green & carm.	1	0	0	2
75	30 par. violet and green ..	1	0	0	3
76	1 pias. rose-red and blue ..	2	0	0	6
77	1 pias. carmine and blue ..	2	6	0	6
78	2 pias. blue and purple ..	2	9	0	8
79	4 pias. olive-green & purple	3	6	2	0
80	6 pias. sepia and green ..	4	0	2	6
81	9 pias. brown and carmine ..	8	0	6	0
81a	9 pias. pale brown & carmine	8	0	6	0
82	12 pias. chestnut and black ..	10	0	10	0
83	18 pias. black and brown ..	17	6	12	6
84	45 pias. dull purple & ultram.	50	0	30	0

1921–23. *T 12. Wmk. Mult. Script CA.*

No.	Description	s.	d.	s.	d.
85	10 par. orange and green ..	0	7	0	4
86	30 par. violet and green ..	0	9	0	4
87	1 pias. carmine and blue ..	4	6	3	0
88	2 pias. blue and purple ..	5	6	4	0
89	4 pias. olive-green & purple	7	6	5	6
90	6 pias. sepia and green ..	15	0	12	6
91	9 pias. brown and carmine ..	17	6	12	0
92	18 pias. black and brown ..	85	0	75	0
93	45 pias. dull purple & ultram.	£10		£8	

1922–23. *Colours changed and new values.*

(a) Wmk. Mult. Script CA.

No.	Description	s.	d.	s.	d.
94	10 par. grey and yellow ..	1	3	0	6
95	30 par. green	1	6	0	4
96	1 pias. violet and red ..	2	0	1	9
97	1½ pias. yellow and black ..	2	0	1	9
98	2 pias. carmine and blue ..	4	0	5	0
99	2¾ pias. blue and purple ..	5	0	3	6

(b) Wmk. Mult. Crown CA.

No.	Description	s.	d.	s.	d.
100	10s. green & red/*pale yellow*	£15		£20	
101	£1 purple and black/*red* ..	£40		£45	

13

1924–28. *T 13. Chalk-surfaced paper.*

(a) Wmk. Mult. Crown CA.

No.	Description	s.	d.	s.	d.
102	£1 purple & black/*red* ..	£5		£6	

(b) Wmk. Mult. Script CA.

No.	Description	s.	d.	s.	d.
103	¼ pi. grey and chestnut ..	0	4	0	3
104	½ pi. black	0	6	0	4
105	¾ pi. green	0	8	0	3
106	1 pi. purple and chestnut ..	1	0	0	6
107	1½ pi. orange and black ..	2	0	1	3
108	2 pi. carmine and green ..	2	0	2	0
109	2¾ pi. bright blue and purple	4	0	4	0
110	4 pi. sage-green and purple	3	0	2	6
111	4½ pi. black & oran./*emerald*	3	0	2	0
112	6 pi. olive-brown and green	4	0	3	0
113	9 pi. brown and purple ..	6	0	3	0
114	12 pi. chestnut and black ..	12	6	15	0
115	18 pi. black and orange ..	15	0	8	6
116	45 pi. purple and blue ..	30	0	25	0
117	90 pi. green & red/*yellow* ..	40	0	45	0
117a	£5 black/*yellow* ('28)	£45		£50	

1925. *T 13. Wmk. Mult. Script CA.*

No.	Description	s.	d.	s.	d.
118	½ pi. green, C	0	4	0	2
119	¾ pi. black, C	0	6	0	1
120	1½ pi. scarlet, O	1	6	0	4
121	2 pi. yellow and black, C ..	2	0	0	8
122	2½ pi. bright blue, O ..	2	0	0	6

In the above set the fraction bar in the value is horizontal. In Nos. 97, 99, 107 and 109 it is diagonal.

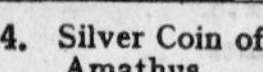

14. Silver Coin of Amathus.

15. Philosopher Zeno

16. Map of Cyprus.

17. Discovery of body of St. Barnabas (*vert.*).

18. Cloister, Abbey of Bella Paise (*vert.*).

19. Badge of Cyprus (*horiz.*).

20. Tekke of Umm Haram (*vert.*).

21. Statue of Richard I, London (*vert.*).

22. St. Nicholas, Famagusta (*vert.*).

23. King George V (*vert.*).

(Recess. Bradbury, Wilkinson & Co.)

1928 (1 Feb.). 50*th anniversary of British rule. Wmk. Mult. Script CA. P* 12.

No.	Type					
123	**14**	¾ pi. deep dull purple ..	1	0	0	5
124	**15**	1 pi. black & greenish blue	1	9	0	9
125	**16**	1½ pi. scarlet	3	0	1	6
126	**17**	2½ pi. light blue	4	0	3	6
127	**18**	4 pi. deep brown.. ..	8	6	10	0
128	**19**	6 pi. blue	12	6	15	0
129	**20**	9 pi. marone	20	0	22	6
130	**21**	18 pi. black and brown ..	30	0	35	0
131	**22**	45 pi. violet and blue ..	60	0	65	0
132	**23**	£1 blue and bistre-brown..	£12		£14	

24. Vouni Palace.

25. Salamis (*horiz.*).

26. Peristerona Church (*horiz.*).

27. Soli Theatre (*horiz.*).

28. Kyrenia Harbour (*horiz.*).

29. Kolossi Castle (*horiz.*).

T 25 to 29 incorporate a miniature portrait of King George V.

. St. Sophia, Nicosia. **31.** Bairakdar Mosque.

32. Queen's Window, St. Hilarion Castle (*vert.*).

33. Buyuk Khan, Nicosia (*vert.*).

34. Forest Scene (*horiz.*).

(Recess. Waterlow & Sons.)

1934 (1 Dec.). *Wmk. Mult. Script CA. P* 12½.

No.	Type					
133	**24**	¼ p. ultram. & orge.-brn.	0	3	0	1
134	**25**	½ p. green.. ..	0	6	0	3
		a. Imperf. betw. (vert. pair)				
135	**26**	¾ p. black and violet ..	0	6	0	2
		a. Imperf. between (pair) ..				
136	**27**	1 p. black and red-brown	0	9	0	9
		a. Imperf. between (horiz pair)				
137	**28**	1½ p. carmine	1	6	1	8
138	**29**	2½ p. ultramarine	2	6	2	6
139	**30**	4½ p. black and crimson ..	3	0	4	0
140	**31**	6 p. black and blue ..	4	0	4	6
141	**32**	9 p. sepia and violet ..	8	0	12	6
142	**33**	18 p. black & olive-green	20	0	22	6
143	**34**	45 p. green and black ..	65	0	70	0

1935 (6 May). *Silver Jubilee. As* T **13** *of Antigua, inscr.* "CYPRUS". *Recess. W'low. & Sons. Wmk. Mult. Script CA. P* 11×12.

No.					
144	¾ p. ultramarine and grey ..	0	6	0	6
145	1½ p. deep blue and scarlet ..	2	0	2	6
146	2½ p. brown and deep blue ..	6	0	6	6
147	9 p. slate and purple ..	15	0	16	0

DOMINICA.

1

(Typo. De La Rue & Co.)

1874 (4 May). *T* **1**. *Wmk. Crown CC. P* 12½.

No.					
1	1d. lilac	25	0	15	0
2	6d. green	95	0	50	0
3	1s. dull magenta	85	0	45	0

1877–79. *T* **1**. *Wmk. Crown CC. P* 14.

No.					
4	½d. olive-yellow (1879) ..	12	6	12	6
5	1d. lilac	8	6	7	6
	a. Bisected vert. or diag. (½d.) ..	—		70	0
6	2½d. red-brown (1879) ..	70	0	45	0
7	4d. blue (1879)	45	0	15	0
	a. Malformed "CE" in "PENCE"	£35		£12	
8	6d. green	70	0	45	0
9	1s. magenta	65	0	50	0

½ (2) 1/2 (3) HALF PENNY (4)

No. 5 *bisected and surcharged.*

1882 (25 Nov.).

No.	Type					
10	**2**	½(d.), in *black*, on half 1d.	85	0	70	0
11	**3**	½(d.), in *red* on half 1d. ..	22	6	20	0
		Varieties. (i.) *Surcharge inverted.*				
12	**2**	½(d.), in *black*, on half 1d. ..	£60		£50	
13	**3**	½(d.), in *red*, on half 1d.	£50		£40	
		(ii.) *Surcharges tête-bêche.*				
13*a*	**2**	½(d.), in *black*, on half 1d. (*pair*)	£85			

1883 (March).

14 **4** ½d. in *black*, on half 1d. .. 50 0 40 0
a. Unsevered pair £10

This surcharge is found reading upwards or downwards.

1883–84. *T* **1.** *Wmk. Crown CA. P* 14.

15 ½d. olive-yellow 8 0 10 0
16 2½d. red-brown (1884) 50 0 20 0

Half Penny (5) — One Penny (6)

1886 (March). *Nos.* 8 *and* 9 *surcharged.*

17 **5** ½d. on 6d. green 20 0 20 0
18 **6** 1d. on 6d. green £800 £500
19 „ 1d. on 1s. magenta 15 0 20 0

Variety. Surcharge double.

19*a* **6** 1d. on 1s. magenta .. — £30

There are numerous varieties of the surcharge on No. 19, due to the different spacing of the letters forming the words "One Penny."

1886. *T* **1.** *Wmk. Crown CA. P* 14.

20 ½d. dull green 1 6 1 9
21 1d. lilac 17 6 15 0
a. Bisected (½d.) .. .. — £10
22 4d. grey 6 0 6 6
a. Malformed "CE" in "PENCE" 70 0 50 0

1887–88. *T* **1.** *Wmk. Crown CA. P* 14.

23 1d. rose 10 0 6 0
23*a* 1d. deep carmine 2 0 2 6
b. Bisected vertically (½d.) .. — £12
24 2½d. ultramarine 5 0 6 0
25 6d. orange 25 0 27 6
26 1s. dull magenta £15 £20

The stamps of Dominica were superseded by the general issue for "Leeward Islands" on 31st October, 1890, but the sets following were in concurrent use with the stamps inscribed "LEEWARD ISLANDS" until 31st December, 1939, when the island came under the administration of the Windward Is.

9. View of Dominica from the sea.

10

(Typo. De La Rue & Co.)

1903. *T* **9** *and* **10** (5*s*.). *Wmk. Crown CC. P* 14.

27 ½d. green and grey-green, OC 2 0 2 6
28 1d. grey and red, OC.. .. 3 0 2 0
29 2d. green and brown, OC .. 8 0 9 6
30 2½d. grey & bright blue, OC .. 10 0 12 6
31 3d. dull pur. & grey-blk., OC 12 6 15 0
32 6d. grey and chestnut, O .. 15 0 17 6
33 1s. magenta & grey-green, OC 20 0 22 6
34 2s. grey-black and purple, O 22 6 25 0
35 2s. 6d. grey-green & maize, O 27 6 30 0
36 5s. black and brown, O .. £6 £7

1907–8. *T* **9** *and* **10** (5*s*.) *Wmk. Multiple Crown CA. P* 14.

37 ½d. green, OC 1 3 1 6
38 1d. grey and red, C 5 0 4 0
39 2d. green and brown, C .. 8 6 10 0
40 2½d. grey and bright blue, C .. 8 6 10 0
41 3d. dull purple & grey-blk., C 10 0 12 0
42 6d. black & chestnut, C ('08) 75 0 75 0
43 1s. magenta & grey-green, C 25 0 27 6
44 2s. grey-blk. & pur., C ('08).. 20 0 22 6
45 2s. 6d. grey-grn. and maize, C ('08) 25 0 27 6
46 5s. black and brown, C ('08) 55 0 60 0

1908–19. *T* **9.** *Wmk. Mult. Crown CA. P* 14.

47 ½d. blue-green, O 0 8 0 8
47*a* ½d. deep green, O (1918) .. 0 6 0 8
48 1d. carmine-red O 1 0 0 6
48*a* 1d. scarlet, O 0 10 0 6
49 2d. grey, O ('09) 3 0 3 6
49*a* 2d. slate, O 2 6 3 0
50 2½d. blue, O 5 0 5 0
50*a* 2½d. bright blue, O 4 0 4 0
51 3d. purple/*yellow*, OC ('09) .. 5 0 6 0
a. On pale yellow 4 0 5 0
52 6d. dull & bright pur., C ('09) 6 6 7 0
52*a* 6d. dull purple, O 6 0 6 0
53 1s. black/*green*, C ('10) .. 7 6 8 0
53*a* 2s. purple and deep blue/*blue*, C (1919) 17 6 20 0

11

(Typo. De La Rue & Co.)

1914. *T* **11.** *Wmk. Mult. Crown CA. P* 14.

54 5s. red and green/*yellow*, C .. 80 0 85 0

WAR TAX

ONE HALFPENNY

(12)

1916. *No.* 47 *surcharged with T* **12**, *in red.*

55 ½d. on ½d. blue-green 0 6 0 9
a. Small "O" in "ONE" .. 6 0 6 6

WAR TAX

(13)

1918 (18 March). *No.* 47 *overprinted locally with T* **13**, *in black.*

56 ½d. blue-green 1 9 2 3

WAR TAX

(14)

1918 (June). *Nos.* 47 *and* 51 *overprinted in London with T* **14**, *in black or red* (*R.*).

57 ½d. blue-green 0 3 0 3
58 3d. purple/*yellow* (R.) 0 9 1 0

WAR TAX
═1½D.═
(15)

1919. *Special printing of T* **9**, *surch. with T* **15.**

No.	Description				
59	1½d. on 2½d. orange (R.) ..	0	6	0	8

1920. *As No.* 59, *but without* " WAR TAX ".

No.	Description				
60	1½d. on 2½d. orange (Bk.) ..	0	10	1	0

1921. *T* **9.** *Colour changed. Wmk. Mult. CA. P* 14.

No.	Description				
61	2s. 6d. black & red/*blue*, C ..	17	6	20	0

1921. *T* **9.** *Wmk. Mult. Script CA. P* 14.

No.	Description				
62	½d. blue-green	1	0	1	6
63	1d. carmine-red	1	6	1	6
64	1½d. orange	4	0	5	0
65	2d. grey	6	0	6	6
66	2½d. bright blue	5	0	6	0
67	6d. purple, C	10	0	12	0
69	2s. purple and blue/*blue* ..	30	0	30	0
70	2s. 6d. black and red/*blue* ..	50	0	52	6

The 1½d. is in a different type with figures of value in the lower corners, and no ornamentation below words of value.

16

(Typo. De La Rue & Co.)

1923 (FEB.)–**1927.** *T* **16.** *Centres in black. Chalk-surfaced paper. P* 14.

(*a*) *Wmk. Mult. Script CA.*

No.	Description				
71	½d. green	0	6	0	8
72	1d. bright violet	1	0	1	0
73	1½d. scarlet	1	6	0	10
74	2d. grey	1	6	1	9
75	2½d. orange-yellow	2	0	3	0
76	3d. ultramarine	3	0	4	0
77	4d. brown	4	0	5	0
78	6d. bright magenta	4	0	4	6
79	1s. black/*emerald*	6	0	6	6
80	2s. blue/*blue*	15	0	17	6
81	2s. 6d. red/*blue*	15	0	18	0
82	3s. purple/*yellow* (1927) ..	20	0	22	6
83	4s. red/*emerald*	25	0	30	0
84	5s. green/*yellow* (1927) ..	25	0	27	6

(*b*) *Wmk. Mult. Crown CA.*

No.	Description				
85	3s. purple/*yellow*	30	0	32	6
86	5s. green/*yellow*	40	0	45	0
87	£1 purple/*red*	£8		£8	

1927–33. *T* **16.** *Colours changed. Centres in black. Chalk-surfaced paper. Wmk. Mult. Script CA. P* 14.

No.	Description				
88	1d. scarlet	0	4	0	6
89	1½d. red-brown	1	0	1	0
90	2½d. ultramarine	1	9	1	9
91	3d. red/*yellow*	2	0	2	6

1935 (6 MAY). *Silver Jubilee. As T* **13** *of Antigua, inscr.* " DOMINICA ". *Recess. D.L.R. & Co. Wmk. Mult. Script CA. P* 13½ × 14.

No.	Description				
92	1d. deep blue and carmine ..	0	6	1	0
93	1½d. ultramarine and grey ..	1	0	1	6
94	2½d. brown and deep blue ..	7	6	8	0
95	1s. slate and purple	15	0	17	6

POSTAL FISCALS.

REVENUE (R 1)   Revenue (R 2)

T **1** *overprinted in black. P* 14.

1879. *With T* R **1.**

(*a*) *Wmk. Crown CC.*

No.	Description				
R 1	1d. lilac	4	0	3	6
	a. Bisected vertically (½d.) ..				
R 2	6d. green	2	0	6	0
R 3	1s. magenta	6	6	20	0

(*b*) *Wmk. Crown CA.*

No.	Description				
R 4	1d. lilac	1	0	2	6

1899 (JUNE). *With T* R **2.** *Wmk. Crown CA.*

No.	Description				
R 6	1d. carmine	22	6	15	0

EAST AFRICA AND UGANDA PROTECTORATES.

See KENYA, UGANDA AND TANGANYIKA.

EAST AFRICA (G.E.A.).

See TANGANYIKA.

EGYPT.

(*The issues of Egypt, an independent sovereign state, are included in this volume at the request of many collectors, and purely as a matter of convenience.*)

SIMPLIFICATION (see p. xii)

Nos. 1 to 71.

1, 2, 4, 5, 7, 8, 9.
11, 12, 22, 14, 25, 17, 20, 21.
26, 28, 45, 30, 47, 32, 49, 59, 51, 53.
62. 64, 66.

Khedive Ismail, 1863–1879.

1 2 3 4 5 6

7

8

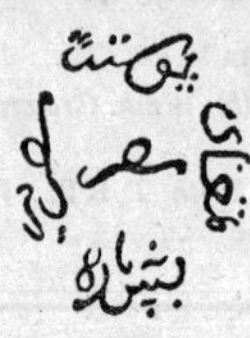

(9)

(Printed by Pellas Bros., Genoa.)

1866 (1 Jan.). *Various designs, T 1 to 7, surcharged, in black, as T 9. The lowest group of characters indicates the value. Wmk. T 8, except the 1 piastre, which has no wmk.*

(*a*) *P* 12½.

No.	Description	Unused	Used
1	5 paras grey	25 0	27 6
	a. Imperf.	55 0	
	b. Imperf. between (pair)	£25	
2	10 paras brown	40 0	30 0
	a. Imperf.	45 0	
	b. Imperf. between (pair)		
	c. Perf. 12½×15		
	d. Perf. 13		
3	20 paras pale blue	45 0	35 0
4	20 paras greenish blue ..	45 0	35 0
	a. Imperf.	50 0	
	b. Imperf. between (pair)	£25	
5	1 pias. mauve	20 0	8 6
	a. Imperf.	42 6	
	b. Imperf. between (pair)	£25	
6	2 pias. yellow	50 0	40 0
	2 pias. orange-yellow ..	47 6	40 0
	a. Imperf.	50 0	
	b. Perf. 12½×15	£8	
	c. Imperf. between (pair) ..	£25	£25
	5 pias. rose	£8	£8
	a. Imperf.	£6	
	b. Error. Opt. 10 pi., perf. 12½ ..		
	c. Error. Opt. 10 pi., perf. 12½×15	£55	£45
	d. Error. Opt. 10 pi., imperf. ..	£25	
	e. Imperf. between (pair) ..		
9	10 pias. slate	£10	£8
	a. Imperf.	£8	
	b. Imperf. between (pair) ..		

(*b*) *P* 12½ × 13 *compound.*

No.	Description	Unused	Used
9c	5 paras grey	55 0	35 0
9d	10 paras brown	55 0	35 0
9e	20 paras blue		
9f	1 pias. mauve	—	30 0
9g	2 pias. yellow	£12	55 0
9h	5 pias. rose	£15	
9j	10 pias. slate		

Proofs of all values exist on smooth paper, without watermark.

1867 (16 July). *Diagonal half of the 2 piastre specially authorized to be used for 1 pias. during a shortage of that value.*

No.	Description	Unused	Used
10	Half of 2 pias. orange-yellow	—	£12

10

11

12

(Des. F. Hoff, Hirschberg, Silesia, litho. V. Penasson, Alexandria.)

1867 (1 Aug.). *T* **10** *and* **11.** *W* **12.** *P* 15 × 12½.

No.	Description	Unused	Used
11	5 par. orange-yellow	12 6	8 0
	a. Imperf. between (pair) ..		
12	10 par. dull lilac	30 0	17 6
	a. Bisected (5 par.)		
13	20 par. deep blue-green ..	20 0	15 0
14	20 par. pale blue-green ..	25 0	12 6
15	1 pias. dull rose-red ..	12 6	6 6
16	1 pias. lake	75 0	30 0
	a. Imperf.	35 0	
17	1 pias. bright rose	6 6	2 0
	a. Imperf. between (pair) ..		
	b. Bisected (20 par.) ..		
18	1 pias. pale rose	7 6	2 0
	a. Imperf.	20 0	
19	2 pias. bright blue	22 6	15 0
20	2 pias. pale blue	27 6	15 0
21	5 pias. brown	95 0	85 0

1869 (July). *T* **10.** *Colours changed.* *W* **12.** *P* 15 × 12½.

No.	Description	Unused	Used
22	10 paras bright mauve ..	17 6	15 0
23	10 paras pale mauve	20 0	17 6
	a. Bisected	—	£8
24	20 paras deep yellow-green ..	20 0	8 6
25	20 paras, pale yellow-green ..	17 6	8 6

There are four minor types of each value. Various values, both imperf. and perf., may be found printed on both sides; these are from the printer's waste sheets, and were not issued, *price* 7s. 6d. *each.*

13

(Printed by V. Penasson, at Alexandria.)

1872 (1 Jan.). *T* **13.** *Thick opaque paper.* *W* **12.** (i.) *P* 12½ × 13½.

No.	Description	Unused	Used
26	5 par. brown	15 0	15 0
27	5 par. pale brown	15 0	15 0
28	10 par. bright mauve	12 6	8 0
29	10 par. dull mauve	15 0	8 6
30	20 par. bright blue	15 0	8 0
31	1 pias. deep rose-red ..	17 6	1 6
32	1 pias. pale rose-red	20 0	1 3
	a. Imperf.	—	25 0
33	2 pias. chrome-yellow ..	95 0	8 6
34	2½ pias. deep violet	25 0	10 0
35	5 pias. yellow-green ..	£6	35 0

(ii.) *P* 13½.

No.	Description	Unused	Used
36	5 par. brown	35 0	30 0
37	5 par. pale brown	37 6	30 0
38	10 par. dull mauve	12 6	8 0
39	20 par. blue	35 0	25 0
40	20 par. pale blue	35 0	25 0
41	1 pias. rose-red	45 0	6 0
42	2 pias. chrome-yellow ..	25 0	8 0
43	2½ pias. violet	£15	£15
43a	5 pias. yellow-green	£6	55 0

1874 (Nov.). *T* **13**, *but printed by the Government at Boulac, on thinner paper.* *W* **12**.

(i.) *P* 12½.

44	10 par. pale lilac	10	0	8	0
45	10 par. grey-lilac	10	0	8	0
	a. Tête-bêche (pair)	£8		£6	
	b. Imperf.	—		22	6
46	20 par. dull pale blue	32	6	10	0
47	20 par. bluish grey	22	6	6	6
	a. Bisected diagonally (10 par.) ..				
48	1 pias. bright red	4	0	1	0
49	1 pias. dull red	2	6	1	3
	a. Tête-bêche (pair)	80	0	85	0
	b. Imperf.	—		22	6
	c. Imperf. between (pair) ..	—		£6	
50	2 pias. yellow	55	0	10	0
	a. Tête-bêche (pair)				
51	2½ pias. deep violet	7	6	6	6
52	2½ pias. pale violet	7	6	6	6
	a. Tête-bêche (pair)	£20		£22	
53	5 pias. green	22	6	17	6
54	5 pias. yellow-green	20	0	22	6
	a. Tête-bêche (pair)				

(ii.) *P* 13½ × 12½.

55	10 par. grey-lilac	7	6	6	6
	a. Tête-bêche (pair)	£8		£8	
56	20 par. dull pale blue	10	0	8	0
57	20 par. bluish grey	6	0	6	0
	a. Imperf. between (pair)				
58	1 pias. bright red	10	0	2	6
	a. Tête-bêche (pair)	£10		£10	
59	2 pias. yellow	6	6	6	6
	a. Tête-bêche (pair)	£22		£22	
	b. Bisected diagonally				

1875. *P* 12½ × 13½.

59*c*	2 pias. yellow	50	0	12	6
	d. Tête-bêche (pair)				
59*e*	2½ pias. violet	25	0	25	0
	f. Tête-bêche (pair)				
59*g*	5 pias. green				

The Alexandria printings have a thick line of colour in the top margin of the sheet and the other margins are all plain, an exception being the 5 paras, which has the line at the right-hand side of the sheet. The Boulac printings have a wide fancy border all round every sheet.

The Alexandria printings are on thick opaque paper, with the impressions sharp and clear. The Boulac printings are on thinner paper, often semi-transparent and oily in appearance, and having the impressions very blurred and badly printed. These are only general distinctions and there are a number of exceptions.

The majority of the Boulac stamps have blind or defective perforations, while the Alexandria stamps have clean-cut perfs.

There seem to be many different compositions of the sheets, containing the *tête-bêche* varieties, settings being known with 1, 3, 9, and 10 inverted stamps in various sheets.

14

(Printed by the Government at Boulac.)

1875 (April). *T* **14**. *Side labels transposed and inverted.* *W* **12**. (i.) *P* 12½.

60	5 par. pale brown	10	0	7	6
61	5 par. brown	12	6	8	6
	a. Tête-bêche (pair)	22	6	27	6
	b. Imperf. between (pair) ..				

(ii.) *P* 13½ × 12½.

62	5 par. pale brown	6	6	6	6
63	5 par. brown	6	6	6	6
	a. Tête-bêche (pair)	15	0	17	6
	b. Imperf.				

(15)

1879 (1 Jan.). *Stamps of* 1872–75 *surcharged as T* **15**, *in black.* (i.) *P* 12½.

64	5 par. on 2½ pias. deep violet	8	6	8	6
65	5 par. on 2½ pias. pale violet	17	6	17	6
	a. Surcharge inverted	45	0	45	0
	b. Tête-bêche (pair)	£40			
66	10 par. on 2½ pias. deep violet	6	6	6	6
67	10 par. on 2½ pias. pale violet	17	6	17	6
	a. Surcharge inverted	55	0	55	0
	b. Tête-bêche (pair)				

(ii.) *P* 12½ × 13½.

68	5 par. on 2½ pias. deep violet	12	6	12	6
69	5 par. on 2½ pias. pale violet	12	6	12	6
	a. Imperf.	80	0		
	b. Surcharge inverted	£15			
70	10 par. on 2½ pias. deep violet	25	0	20	0
71	10 par. on 2½ pias. pale violet	25	0	20	0
	a. Imperf.	£6			
	b. Surcharge inverted	£15			
	c. Tête-bêche (pair)	£35			

16 17

18 19

20 21

(Typo. De La Rue & Co.)

1879 (April). *T* **16** *to* **21**. *W* **12**. *P* 14.

72	5 par. dark brown	0	4	0	1
73	5 par. pale brown	0	6	0	1
74	10 par. mauve	27	6	5	0
75	20 par. pale blue	45	0	2	6

No.	Description	Unused		Used	
76	1 pias. rose	20	0	0	1
77	1 pias. pale rose	20	0	0	1
78	2 pias. orange	17	6	0	8
79	2 pias. orange-yellow	17	6	1	0
80	5 pias. green	27	6	8	6
81	5 pias. blue-green	40	0	7	6

Khedive Tewfik, 1879–92.

1881 (Jan.) *As last, colour changed.*

No.	Description	Unused		Used	
82	10 par. lilac-rose	45	0	12	0

1882 (25 Jan.). *Colour again changed.*

No.	Description	Unused		Used	
83	10 par. bluish grey	12	6	1	6

(22)

1884 (1 Feb.). *Surcharged in black at the Government Printing Office, Cairo with* **T 22.**

No.	Description	Unused		Used	
84	20 paras on 5 pias. green	10	0	3	6
	a. Surcharge inverted	35	0	36	0

1884 (15 Dec.). **T 17, 18, 19,** *and* **21. W 12.** *P* 14.

No.	Description	Unused		Used	
85	10 par. green	0	3	0	2
86	20 par. rose-carmine	4	6	1	0
87	20 par. bright rose	4	0	0	10
88	1 pias. blue	4	6	0	4
89	1 pias. deep ultramarine	4	6	0	3
90	1 pias. pale ultramarine	4	0	0	2
91	5 pias. pale grey	12	0	0	10
92	5 pias. slate	8	6	0	9

23 24

25 26

1888 (1 Jan.). **T 23** *to* **26. W 12.** *P* 14.

No.	Description	Unused		Used	
93	1 mil. pale brown	1	0	0	1
94	1 mil. deep brown	1	3	0	2
95	2 mil. blue-green	1	6	0	1
96	2 mil. green	1	0	0	1
97	5 mil. rose-carmine	2	6	0	4
98	5 mil. bright rose	3	0	0	1
99	5 mil. aniline rose	2	0	0	1
100	10 pias. mauve	17	6	1	3
101	10 pias. aniline mauve	17	6	0	8

Khedive Abbas Hilmi, Jan. 1892–Dec. 1914.

27

1892 (1 Jan.). *T* **27.** *W* **12.** *P* 14.

No.	Description	Unused		Used	
102	3 mil. marone	3	0	1	6

1893 (1 Aug.). *T* **27** *and* **20.** *Colours changed.* *W* **12.** *P* 14.

No.	Description	Unused		Used	
103	3 mil. yellow	4	0	1	0
104	3 mil. orange-yellow	3	6	0	10
105	2 pias. orange-brown	7	6	1	6

1902. *T* **19** *to* **21** *and* **23** *to* **27,** *but printed on chalk-surfaced paper.* *W* **12.** *P* 14.

No.	Description	Unused		Used	
106	1 mil. pale brown	0	8	0	3
107	1 mil. deep brown	0	8	0	1
108	2 mil. green	2	0	0	1
109	3 mil. orange-yellow	2	6	0	1
110	5 mil. pale rose	2	0	0	1
111	5 mil. deep aniline rose	2	0	0	1
112	1 pias. ultramarine	3	6	0	1
113	1 pias. blue	3	0	0	1
114	2 pias. orange-brown	6	0	0	1
115	2 pias. orange	7	6	1	0
116	5 pias. slate-grey	10	0	0	4
117	10 pias. mauve	15	0	2	0

1906. *As T* **25.** *W* **12.** *P* 14. *Chalk-surfaced paper.*

No.	Description	Unused		Used	
118	4 mil. vermilion	3	0	0	4

29. Native boats on the Nile. **30.** Cleopatra with head-dress of Isis.
31. Ras-el-Tin Palace, Alexandria. **32.** Pyramids of Giza.
33. Sphinx. **34.** Colossi of Thebes.

35. Pylon of Karnak Temple, Luxor. **36.** Citadel, Cairo.
37. Rock Temples of Abu Simbel. **38.** Assouan Dam.

(Typo. De La Rue & Co.)

1914 (Jan.). *T* **29** *to* **34** *(small) and* **35** *to* **38** *(large).* *W* **12.** *P* 14.

No.	Type	Description	Unused		Used	
119	**29**	1 mil. sepia	0	4	0	1
120	**30**	2 mils. green	1	0	0	3
121	**31**	3 mils. orange-yellow	1	9	0	3
		a. Double impression				

122 **32** 4 mils. vermilion .. 2 6 1 0
123 **33** 5 mils. lake 3 0 0 1
124 **34** 10 mils. dull blue .. 6 0 0 1
125 **35** 20 mils. olive 8 6 0 1
126 **36** 50 mils. purple 12 6 1 3
127 **37** 100 mils. slate 22 6 1 9
128 **38** 200 mils. marone .. 40 0 3 6

All these have been found imperf., both with and without watermark.

(British Protectorate.)
Sultan Hussein Kamil, Dec., 1914.

(39)

1915 (Oct.). *T* **31**. *Surcharged diagonally with T* **39**, *in black.*

129 2 m. on 3 m. orange-yellow .. 1 0 0 8
a. Surcharge inverted £10 £10

Sultan Ahmed Fuad, 9 Oct., 1919.
(Printed by Harrison & Sons.)

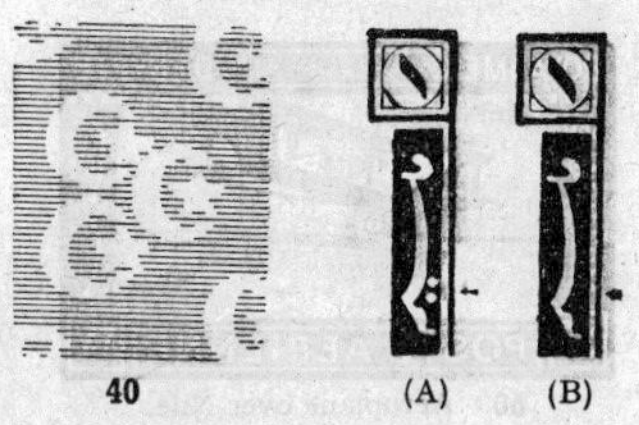

40 (A) (B)

1921–22. *As* 1914, *but W* **40**.

130 **29** 1 mil. sepia (A) .. 0 4 0 2
a. Two dots omitted in upper Arabic character at right as (B) 25 0 25 0
131 **30** 2 mils. green 2 6 2 6
a. Imperf. between (pair) ..
132 **31** 3 mils. orange-yellow .. 2 6 2 6
133 **33** 5 mils. lake 2 6 0 1
a. Imperf. between (pair)
134 **34** 10 mils. dull blue .. 6 6 0 1
135 **35** 20 mils. olive 12 6 0 4
136 **36** 50 mils. purple 22 6 0 4
136*a* **37** 100 mils. slate 35 0 4 0

1921–22. *Colours changed. W* **40**.

137 **30** 2 mils. vermilion (1922) .. 1 6 0 3
138 **32** 4 mils. green (1922) 4 0 4 0
139 **33** 5 mils. pink (Nov. '21) .. 3 0 0 1
140 **34** 10 mils. lake (Sept. '22) .. 3 0 1 3

41. Statue of Rameses II. **42**

1922. *Wmk. T* **40**. *P* 14.

141 **41** 15 mils. indigo 5 0 0 4
142 **42** 15 mils. indigo 5 0 1 3

(Independent Kingdom.)
King Fuad I, 16 March, 1922–28 April, 1936.

(43) " The Kingdom of Egypt, 15 March, 1922."

1922. *T* **29** *to* **38**, **41** *and* **42** *optd. with T* **43**.

(*a*) *W* **40**.

143 1 mil. sepia (A) 1 3 0 8
a. Overprint inverted .. £10
b. Overprint double £12
c. Two dots omitted in Arabic character at right as (B) .. 8 0 8 6
144 2 mils. vermilion 1 6 0 4
a. Overprint double £10
145 3 mils. orange-yellow .. 3 6 2 6
146 4 mils. green 2 6 2 6
a. Overprint inverted ..
147 5 mils. pink 3 6 0 1
148 10 mils. lake 4 0 0 1
149 15 mils. indigo (T 41) .. 8 6 0 6
150 15 mils. indigo (T 42) .. 6 6 1 0
151 20 mils. olive 10 0 0 8
a. Overprint inverted £14
b. Overprint double £14
152 50 mils. purple 12 6 0 8
a. Overprint inverted
153 100 mils. slate 25 0 1 0
a. Overprint inverted ..
b. Overprint double £28

(*b*) *W* **12**.

154 100 mils. slate 75 0 75 0
155 200 mils. marone 30 0 1 6
a. Overprint inverted .. ..

The overprint T **43** exists lithographed (all values), and typographed (1 m. to 50 m.). There were two local and one London printings of the typographed overprint.

44. King Fuad I. **45**

(Photo. Harrison & Sons, Ltd.)

1923–24. *T* **44** (*to* 15 *m.*) *and* **45**. *W* **40**. (*a*) *P* 13½.

156 1 mil. orange (6.10.23) .. 0 4 0 1
157 2 mils. black (6.12.23) .. 0 6 0 1
158 3 mils. brown (21.11.23) .. 2 0 0 4
159 4 mils. green (Dec., '23) .. 1 6 1 0
160 5 mils. chestnut (16.4.23) .. 0 9 0 1
a. Imperf. (pair) £10
161 10 mils. bright rose (6.10.23) 1 9 0 1
162 15 mils. bright blue (Oct., '23) 2 6 0 1

(*b*) *P* 14.

163 20 mils. deep grn. (13.10.23) 5 0 0 4
164 50 mils. bluish grn. (Dec., '23) 15 0 0 3
165 100 mils. purple (Dec., '23) .. 27 6 1 0
166 200 mils. mauve (19.3.24) .. 35 0 8 0
167 £1 indigo-vio. & blue (5.1.24) £10 35 0

No. 167 shows King Fuad in military uniform, the design being otherwise similar to T 45.

46. Thoth writing name of King Fuad.

☞ (This and subsequent issues printed by Survey Dept., Cairo, in photogravure, *unless otherwise stated.*)

1925. *International Geographical Congress.* **T 46.** *Offset-litho.* **W 40.** *P* 11½ × 11.

168	5 m. brown	25	0	30	0
169	10 m. rose-carmine	25	0	30	0
170	15 m. ultramarine	25	0	30	0

There are two printings of the 10 m. and 15 m. differing in shade and in impression.

47

48

1926. 12*th Agricultural Exhibition.* **T 47.** *Offset-litho.* **W 48.** *P* 13½.

171	5 m. brown	6	0	6	0
172	10 m. rosine	6	0	6	0
173	15 m. blue	6	0	6	0
174	50 m. blue-green	20	0	20	0
175	100 m. purple	35	0	35	0
176	200 m. violet	60	0	60	0

49

(Photo. Harrison & Sons, Ltd.)

1926 (2 April). *King's birthday.* **T 49.** **W 40.** *P* 14 × 15.

177	50 pi. purple	£6	35	0

50 Aeroplane over Nile.

1926–29. *Air stamps.* **T 50.** **W 48.** *P* 13½.

178	27 m. deep violet (10.3.26) ..	50	0	50	0
178*a*	27 m. chestnut ('29) ..	17	6	17	6

15

MILLIÈMES

(51)

1926 (Aug.). *Agricultural Exhibition stamps.* **T 47** *surcharged as* **T 51.**

179	5 m. on 50 m. blue-green ..	4	0	4	0
180	10 m. on 100 m. purple ..	4	0	4	0
181	15 m. on 200 m. violet ..	4	0	4	0

52. Ancient Egyptian ship. Temple of Deir-el-Bahari.

1926 (Dec.). *International Navigation Congress.* **T 52.** *Offset-litho.* **W 48.** *P* 13½.

182	5 m. black and brown ..	6	0	6	0
183	10 m. black and red ..	6	0	6	0
184	15 m. black and blue ..	6	0	6	0

PORT
FOUAD

(53)

P O R T F O U A D

(54)

1926 (21 Dec.). *Port Fuad Commemoratives. T* **52** *and* **49** *overprinted respectively as T* **53** *and* **54.**

No.	Description		Unused	Used
185	5 m. black and brown	..	£9	£9
186	10 m. black and red ..	..	£9	£9
187	15 m. black and blue	..	£9	£9
188	50 pi. purple	..	£90	£90

55

1927 (25 Jan.). *International Cotton Congress. T* **55.** *Offset-litho. W* **48.** *P* 13½.

No.	Description		Unused	Used
189	5 m. green and brown	..	5 0	5 0
190	10 m. green and red ..	..	5 0	5 0
191	15 m. green and blue	..	5 0	5 0

56 57

58

1927–37. *T* **56** *to* **58.** *W* **48.**

(i) *Photogravure.* (*a*) *P* 13½.

No.	Type	Description		Unused	Used
192	**56**	1 m. orange	.. ..	0 6	0 1
193	,,	2 m. black ..	.. ..	0 10	0 1
194	,,	3 m. pale brown ..	..	1 6	0 8
194*a*	,,	3 m. deep blue-grn ('31) ..		1 3	0 2
194*b*	,,	3 m. deep brown ('37)	..	1 0	0 2
195	**56**	4 m. bright green ..	..	2 6	0 6
195*a*	,,	4 m. deep brown ('31)	..	3 0	1 0
195*b*	,,	4 m. deep blue-grn. ('33) ..		1 3	0 4
196	,,	5 m. chestnut ..	..	1 9	0 1
196*a*	,,	5 m. deep red-brown ('29)		1 3	0 1
197	,,	10 m. red	..	4 0	0 1
197*a*	,,	10 m. deep lake ('29)	..	4 0	0 1
197*b*	,,	10 m. bright vio. (Oct. '34)		5 0	0 3
197*c*	,,	13 m. carmine ('32)	..	3 0	0 10
198	,,	15 m. bright blue ..	..	5 0	0 1
198*a*	,,	15 m. deep brt. blue ('31) ..		4 0	0 1
198*b*	,,	15 m. purple ('34) ..	..	7 0	0 1
198*c*	,,	20 m. bright blue ('34)	..	8 6	0 6

(*b*) *P* 14.

No.	Type	Description		Unused	Used
199	**57**	20 m. pale sage-green	..	8 6	0 6
199*a*	,,	20 m. deep olive-grn. (1929)		8 6	0 1
199*b*	,,	20 m. ultramarine ('32)	..	7 6	0 3
199*c*	,,	40 m. sepia ('32) ..	..	5 0	0 3
200	,,	50 m. greenish blue	..	15 0	0 4
200*a*	,,	50 m. blue-green ('29)	..	6 6	0 1
201	,,	100 m. claret ..	..	22 6	0 8
201*a*	,,	100 m. purple ('30)	..	15 0	0 4
202	,,	200 m. mauve ..	..	20 0	3 0

(*c*) *P* 13½.

No.	Type	Description	Unused	Used
203	**58**	500 m. greenish blue & brn.	95 0	30 0
204	–	£1 chestnut & greenish slate	£8	35 0

No. 204 is similar in size and design to Type **58**, but vertical.

(ii) *Centre in photogravure, frame offset.* *P* 13½.

No.	Type	Description	Unused	Used
204*a*	**58**	500 m. greenish blue and grey-brown ('32) ..	70 0	12 6
204*b*	–	£1 bright chestnut & dark slate ('37)	80 0	40 0

Nos. 203/4. The inked parts of the frame have a saw-edge due to the photogravure screen.

Nos. 204*a*/4*b*. The ink-edges are smooth.

The shade of the 3 m deep brown, No. 194*b*—the reissue of 1937—is the same as that of the 4 m., No. 195*a*; the original 3 m., No. 194, being considerably paler.

There are considerable differences in the mesh of the screens used at various periods in the preparation of most of the values in T **56** and **57**, with consequent variations in the general appearance of the designs. In T **56** the dots of which the design is composed run either diagonally or vertically.

The above list has been confined to the major shade differences without reference to the screens.

60. Amenhotep.

1927 (29 Dec.). *Statistical Congress.* *T* **60.** *W* **48.** *P* 13½.

No.	Description		Unused	Used
205	5 m. red-brown	.. ..	2 6	2 6
206	10 m. red ..	.. ..	2 6	2 6
207	15 m bright blue	.. ..	3 0	3 6

61. Im Hotep. **62.** Mohamed Ali Pasha.

1928 (15 Dec.). *Medical Congress.* *T* **61** *and* **62.** *W* **48.** *P* 13½.

208	5 m. brown	1	6	1	9
209	10 m. red	1	6	1	6

The 5 m. was printed from two different plates. Stamps printed from the second are in a darker shade.

63. King Farouk when Crown Prince.

1929 (11 Feb.). *Prince's 9th Birthday Anniv.* *T* **63.** *Offset-litho.* *W* **48.** *P* 13½.

210	5 m. slate and brown-purple	3	0	3	0
	a. Centre in black	£15			
211	10 m. slate and carmine-red	3	0	3	0
	a. Centre in brown	£15			
212	15 m. slate and ultramarine ..	3	0	3	0
	a. Centre in brown	£15			
213	20 m. slate and turquoise ..	3	0	3	0
	a. Centre in brown	£15			

The "a" varieties are from a special printing in which the portrait is clearer.

64. Ancient agriculture.

1931 (15 Feb.). *Agricultural and Industrial Exhibition.* *T* **64.** *W* **48.** *P* 13½.

214	5 m. brown	3	0	3	0
215	10 m. red	3	0	3	0
216	15 m. bright blue	3	0	3	0

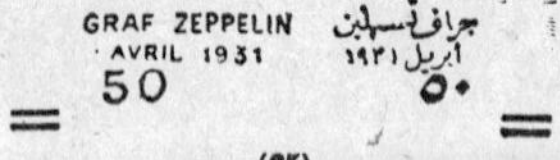

(65)

1931 (6 April). *Air.* *T* **50** *surch. as T* **65.**

217	50 m. on 27 m. chestnut (B.)	70	0	70	0
218	100 m. on 27 m. chestnut (V.)	70	0	70	0

MILLS
50

(66)

1932. *Surcharged as T* **66,** *but with groups of three bars obliterating original value (the* 100 *m. also with vertical bar obliterating inscription at right.*

219	**49**	50 m. on 50 pi. purple	25	0	5	0
220	**45**	100 m. on £1 violet & blue	£20		£20	

67

1933 (19 Jan.). *International Railway Congress Various locomotive types inscribed* "CONGRES INTERNATIONAL DES CHEMINS DE FER. 1935," *as T* **67.** *Offset-litho.* *W* **48.** *P* 13½.

221	5 m. blk. & brn. (*dated* 1852)	8	6	10	0
222	13 m. blk. & red (*dated* 1859) ..	35	0	35	0
223	15 m. blk. & violet (*dated* 1862)	35	0	35	0
224	20 m. blk. & blue (*dated* 1932)	35	0	35	0

68. Aeroplane over Pyramids.

1933 (15 Feb.)–**1938.** *Air.* *Offset-litho.* *W* **48.** *P* 13½.

225	**68**	1 m. black and orange ..	0	4	1	0
226	,,	2 m. black and grey	3	0	3	0
226*a*	,,	2 m. blk. & red-orge. ('38)	5	0	3	0
227	,,	3 m. black and sepia ..	0	6	1	0
228	,,	4 m. black and green ..	2	6	3	0
229	,,	5 m. black and chocolate	0	6	1	0
230	,,	6 m. black and blue-green	2	6	3	0
231	,,	7 m. black and blue ..	2	6	3	0
232	,,	8 m. black and violet ..	1	3	0	8
233	,,	9 m. black and dull red ..	3	0	5	0
234	,,	10 m. sepia and violet ..	2	6	1	3
235	,,	20 m. sepia and blue-green	1	6	0	8
236	,,	30 m. sepia and blue ..	2	6	1	3
237	,,	40 m. sepia and dull red ..	3	6	1	9
238	,,	50 m. sepia and orange ..	6	6	1	9
239	,,	60 m. sepia and grey ..	7	6	5	0
240	,,	70 m. green and blue ..	8	6	6	6
241	,,	80 m. green and sepia ..	10	0	5	0
242	,,	90 m. green and orange ..	12	6	8	6
243	,,	100 m. green and violet ..	12	6	6	0
244	,,	200 m. green and dull red ..	30	0	10	0

For photogravure issue, see Nos. 317/24 in King George VI catalogue.

69. Imperial Airways Aeroplane.

70. Dornier *DO-X* Flying-boat (*horiz.*).

71. "Graf Zeppelin" (*horiz.*).

1933 (20 Dec.). *International Aviation Congress.* W 48. P 13½.

No.	Type	Description					
245	69	5 m. brown	..	.. 17	6	17	6
246	,,	10 m. violet	..	.. 17	6	17	6
247	70	13 m. red	..	.. 22	6	27	6
248	,,	15 m. purple	..	.. 35	0	35	0
249	71	20 m. blue ..	..	.. 35	0	35	0

72. Khedive Ismail Pasha. 73

1934 (1 Feb.). *Tenth Congress of the Universal Postal Union.* W 48.

(*a*) P 13½ × 14.

No.	Type	Description					
250	72	1 m. orange	..	.. 0	6	0	6
251	,,	2 m. black	..	.. 0	6	0	6
252	,,	3 m. sepia	..	.. 0	6	0	6
253	,,	4 m. blue-green ..		.. 1	0	1	0
254	,,	5 m. red-brown ..		.. 1	6	0	6
255	,,	10 m. bright violet		3	0	1	0
256	,,	13 m. red ..	..	.. 5	0	3	0
257	,,	15 m. purple	..	.. 5	0	0	9
258	,,	20 m. blue ..	..	.. 8	0	2	0
259	,,	50 m. greenish blue		.. 12	6	6	0
260	,,	100 m. olive-green ..		.. 35	0	6	0
261	,,	200 m. violet	..	.. 55	0	20	0

(*b*) P 13½.

No.	Type	Description				
262	73	50 p. sepia	..	.. £8	65	0
263	,,	£1 greenish blue ..	..	£16	£8	

74. King Fuad I.

1936–37. W 48. P 13½.

No.	Type	Description					
264	74	1 m. orange (9.10.36)	..	0	6	0	1
265	,,	2 m. black (9.10.36)	..	1	3	0	1
266	,,	4 m. blue-green ('36)	..	1	3	0	4
267	,,	5 m. deep brown (9.10.36)		1	3	0	1
268	,,	10 m. bright violet (8.3.37)		3	0	0	4
269	,,	15 m. deep purple (27.11.36)		4	0	0	1
270	,,	20 m. bright blue ('36)	..	6	6	0	6

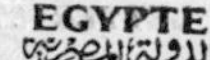

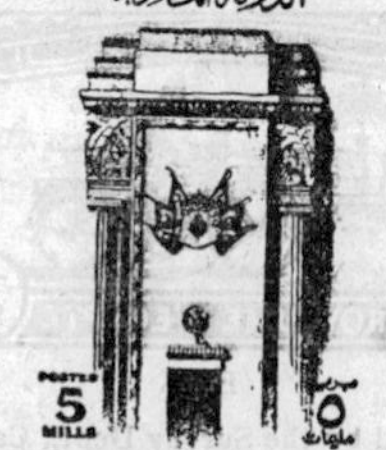

75. Exhibition entrance.

76. Palace of Agriculture.

1936 (15 Feb.). 15*th Agricultural and Industrial Exhibition, Cairo.* T 75, 76 *and similar type inscr.* "15e EXPOSITION AGRICOLE ET INDUSTRIELLE 1936." W 48. P 13½.

271	5 m. brown ..	..	.. 2	6	2	6
272	10 m. bright violet	..	.. 4	0	4	0
273	13 m. scarlet ..	..	.. 6	0	6	0
274	15 m. deep purple	..	.. 7	6	7	6
275	20 m. bright blue	..	.. 10	0	10	0

Horizontal designs:—10 m. and 13 m. as T 76. 15 m. and 20 m. Palace of Industry.

SPECIAL STAMPS FOR THE USE OF BRITISH FORCES IN EGYPT.

From 1 November, 1932, to 29 February, 1936, members of the British Forces in Egypt and their families were allowed to send letters to the British Isles at reduced rates. Special seals, which were on sale at N.A.A.F.I. Institutes and Canteens, were used instead of Egyptian stamps, and were stuck on the back of the envelopes, letters bearing the seals being franked on the front with a handstamp inscribed "EGYPT POSTAGE PREPAID" in a double circle surmounted by a crown. These labels were replaced by special stamps from March, 1936.

A 1. King Fuad I.

(Photo. Survey Dept., Cairo.)

1936. W 48. P 13½ × 14.

No.	Type	Description					
A 1	A 1	3 m. green (9.11.36)	..	0	6	0	4
A 2	,,	10 m. carmine (1.3.36)	..	1	0	0	9

EXPRESS LETTER STAMPS.

E 1

(Printed by the Survey Dept., Cairo.)

1926–29. *Type* **E 1.** *W* **48.** *P* 13½. (*a*) *Photo.*

E 1 20 m. deep green 9 0 6 6

(*b*) *Offset litho.* (*Arabic inscription modified.*)

E 2 20 m. black and red (1929) .. 2 0 2 0

POSTAGE DUE STAMPS.

D 1

(Designed by L. Barkhausen; lithographed by Penasson, Alexandria.)

1884 (1 Feb.). *Type* **D 1.** *W* **12.** • *P* 10½.

D 1 10 paras, red 4 0 4 6
D 2 20 paras, red 6 6 6 6
D 3 1 pias. red 15 0 8 6
D 4 2 pias. red 12 0 3 6
D 5 5 pias. red 8 0 8 6

1886 (1 Aug.). *Type* **D 1.** *No wmk.* *P* 10½.

D 6 10 paras rose-red 7 6 3 6
D 7 20 paras rose-red 10 0 2 6
D 8 1 pias. rose-red 3 6 2 0
a. Imperf. between (pair) .. 70 0 70 0
D 9 2 pias. rose-red 4 0 0 4

D 2 D 3

(Lithographed by Penasson, Alexandria.)

1888 (1 Jan.). *Type* **D 2.** *Two types of* 5 *pias.* (*A*) *with stop after* " piastres." (*B*) *without stop.* *No wmk.* *P* 11½.

D 10 2 mil. green 3 0 2 0
a. Imperf. between (pair) ..
D 11 5 mil. rose-carmine .. 3 0 2 0
D 12 1 pias. blue 10 0 7 6
D 13 2 pias. orange 15 0 7 6
D 14 5 pias. grey (A) £8 £8
D 14*a* 5 pias. grey (B) £6 95 0

Beware of forgeries of the 5 pi. which are often met with.

(Typo. De La Rue & Co.)

1889. *Type* **D 3.** *W* **12** (*as illustration*). *P* 14.

D 15 2 mil. green, OC 0 6 0 1
a. Bisected and used for 1 m. — 10 0
D 16 4 mil. marone, OC .. 0 9 0 1
D 17 1 pias. ultramarine, OC .. 1 6 0 1
D 18 2 pias. orange, OC 2 6 0 8
a. Bisected diagonally (1 pias).

3 Millièmes ٣ اعشار القرش (D 4)

3 Millièmes ٣ أعشار القرش (D 4*a*)

1898. *No.* D 18 *surcharged with Type* D **4.**

D 19 3 m. on 2 pias. orange, O .. 0 6 0 6
a. Surcharge inverted .. 65 0 55 0

A variety exists in which an Arabic figure "٢ (2)" has been inserted in the surcharge in error and a correct figure "٣ (3)" printed immediately above it.

1905. *No.* D 18, *but surcharged with Type* D **4***a*.

D 20 3 m. on 2 pias. orange, OC 1 6 1 6
a. Surcharge inverted .. 95 0 60 0
b. Surcharge double .. £15

In No. D 19 the Arabic figure at right is less than 2 mm. from the next character, which consists of a straight stroke only. In No. D 20 the distance is 3 mm., and the straight character has a comma-like character above it. There are other minor differences.

1918–20(?). *Type* **D 3.** *W* **12** (*sideways*). *P* 14.

D 20*d* 2 mil. bright green .. 2 6 2 6
D 20*e* 4 mil. marone 2 6 0 3
D 20*f* 1 pi. dull ultramarine .. 2 6 1 0

D 5 D 6

(Printed by Harrison & Sons.)

1921–22. *Types* D **5** *and* D **6** (10 *mm.*). *Chalk-surfaced paper.* *W* **40.** *P* 14.

D 21 2 mils. green 0 4 0 4
D 22 2 mils. scarlet 0 4 0 2
D 23 4 mils. scarlet 2 6 2 6
D 24 4 mils. green 0 7 0 2
D 25 10 mils. deep slate-blue .. 3 0 3 6
D 26 10 mils. lake 0 8 0 2

1922. *Types* **D 5, D 6** *and* **D 3** *overprinted with* *T* **43** (*inverted*) *in black.*

D 27 2 mils. scarlet 0 7 0 9
D 28 4 mils. green 0 9 1 0
D 29 10 mils. lake 1 0 0 4
D 30 2 pias. orange 3 0 3 6
a. Overprint normal 15 0 15 0

D 7

(Offset litho by Survey Dept., Cairo.)

1927 (16 Mar.)–**1941.** *W* **48.**

(*a*) 18×22½ *mm.* *P* 13½.

D 31	D 7	2 m. grey-black ..	0	6	0	1
D 31*a*	,,	2 m. red-orange ('38) ..	0	2	0	1
D 32	,,	4 m. yellow-green ..	0	9	0	9
D 32*a*	,,	4 m. blue-green (1929) ..	1	6	1	6
D 32*b*	,,	4 m. sepia ('32)	1	0	0	3
D 33	,,	5 m. red-brown	1	9	0	2
D 33*a*	,,	6 m. grey-green ('41) ..	0	3		
D 34	,,	8 m. purple	0	4	0	4
D 35	,,	10 m. rose-lake	1	3	0	9
D 35*a*	,,	10 m. brown-red (1929) ..	0	4	0	1
D 35*b*	,,	12 m. lake ('41)	0	5		

(*b*) 22×27½ *mm.* *P* 14.

D 36	D 7	30 m. bright violet ..	0	10	0	8

Nos. D 32*a* and D 35*a* are new printings. The floral design is lightly shaded and the white frame-lines are broader than those of Nos. D 32 and D 35.

OFFICIAL STAMPS.

POSTES EGYPTIENNES

SERVICE DE L'ETAT

ميري

O 1

(Typo. De La Rue & Co.)

1892. *Type* O **1.** *W* **12.** *P* 14.

O 1	(No value), chestnut, OC ..	0	2	0	1

This stamp, with overprint 3 P.T. and Arabic equivalent, is a fiscal.

O.H.H.S.
اميري
(O 2)

O.H.H.S.
اميرى
(O 3)

1907. *Contemporary stamps* (*Nos.* 106, *etc.*) *overprinted in London with Type* O **2,** *in black.*

O 2	1 mil. brown	0	2	0	1
O 3	2 mil. green	0	4	0	1
	a. Overprint double				
O 4	3 mil. orange-yellow	0	4	0	1
O 6	5 mil. rose-carmine	0	4	0	1
O 7	1 pias. blue	0	8	0	1
O 8	5 pias. slate-grey	2	6	0	3

1913 (Nov.). *As No.* O 6, *but without Arabic in overprint.*

O 10	5 mil. rose-carmine	0	6	0	1
	a. No stop after "s" ..	—		7	6
	b. Overprint inverted ..	—		27	6
	c. Opt. between inverted commas				

1915. *Nos.* 108 *and* 118 *optd. locally as Type* O **3.**

O 12	2 mil. green	0	6	0	6
	a. No stop after "s" ..	7	6	7	6
	b. Overprint inverted ..	17	6	17	6
	c. Overprint double ..	£30			
O 13	4 mil. vermilion	0	6	0	1
	a. Overprint inverted ..	—		£5	

Stamps of 1914 *similarly overprinted.*

O 14	1 mil. sepia	0	2	0	3
	a. No stop after "s" ..	7	6	7	6
O 16	3 mil. orange-yellow	0	3	0	4
	a. No stop after "s"	12	6	12	6
O 18	5 mil. lake	0	4	0	1
	a. No stop after "s" ..	6	0	6	0

O.H.H.S.
أميرى
(O 4)

O.H.H.S.
أميرى
(O 4*a*)

1915 (Oct.). *Nos.* 108, 118 *and* 123 *with overprint Type* O **4,** *lithographed locally in black.*

O 19	2 mil. green	0	3	0	4
	a. Overprint inverted ..	22	6	22	6
O 20	4 mil. vermilion	0	5	0	2
O 21	5 mil. lake	0	5	0	4
	a. Pair, one stamp without opt.				

1922. *Nos.* 130, *etc., overprinted with Type* O **4*a***

O 22	1 mil. sepia (28.6.22) ..	3	6	4	0
	a. Two dots omitted (No. 130a)	£12			
O 23	2 mil. vermilion (16.6.22) ..	4	0	4	6
O 24	3 mil. orange-yell. (28.6.22)	£5		£5	
O 25	5 mil. pink (13.3.22) ..	3	0	3	6

O.H.E.M.S.
الحكومة
المليكة المصرية
(O 5)

أميرى
(O 6)

1922–23. *Stamps of* 1921 *optd. with Type* O **5.**

O 26	1 mil. sepia	1	0	1	3
	a. Two dots omitted (No. 130a)				
O 27	2 mil. vermilion	1	0	1	3
O 28	3 mil. orange-yellow ..	2	6	3	0
O 29	4 mil. green	3	0	3	6
	a. Two stops after "H". No stop after "s"	£10		£10	
O 30	5 mil. pink	2	0	0	9
	a. Two stops after "H". No stop after "s"	£6		£6	
O 31	10 mil. dull blue	5	0	4	6
O 32	10 mil. lake	6	0	4	0
	a. Two stops after "H". No stop after "s"	£12			
O 33	15 mil. indigo (No. 141) ..	7	6	7	6
	a. Two stops after "H". No stop after "s"				
O 34	15 mil. indigo (No. 142) ..	75	0	80	0
	a. Two stops after "H". No stop after "s"	£45			
O 35	50 mil. purple	20	0	20	0

The 1, 4, 5, 10 (No. O 32), 15 and 50 m. exist with variety "M" widely spaced.

The 4, 5, 10 (No. O 32) and 15 m. exist without the two dots below the lowest line of the overprint.

There were two printings of the 50 m. In one the distance from the top of the "M" to the two dots is 14 mm. and in the other 15 mm.

1924. *T* **44** *and* **45** *optd. with Type* O **6.**

O 36	1 mil. orange	1	0	1	0
O 37	2 mil. black (R.)	2	0	2	0
O 38	3 mil. brown	2	6	2	6
O 39	4 mil. green	3	0	3	0
O 40	5 mil. chestnut	1	6	1	3
O 41	10 mil. bright rose ..	2	6	1	0
O 42	15 mil. bright blue ..	2	6	2	6
O 43	50 mil. bluish green ..	7	6	5	0

All values exist with the left-hand character of the overprint larger.

O 7

(Offset-litho. Survey Dept., Cairo.)

1926. *Type* O **7.** *W* **48.**

(*a*) 18½ × 22½ *mm.* *P* 13½.

No.	Stamp	Unused	Used
O 44	1 m. orange..	0 1	0 2
O 45	2 m. black ..	0 2	0 2
O 46	3 m. brown ..	0 2	0 2
O 47	4 m. yellow-green	0 3	0 2
O 48	5 m. red-brown	0 3	0 2
O 49	10 m. rose-lake	1 6	0 3
O 50	15 m. blue	2 0	0 2

(*b*) 22½ × 27½ *mm.* *P* 13½ × 14.

No.	Stamp	Unused	Used
O 51	20 m. olive-green	2 6	0 6
O 52	50 m. blue-green	2 6	0 6

1934–35. *Type* O 7 (18½ × 22½) *mm.*). *Colours changed.* *W* 48. *P* 13½.

No.	Stamp	Unused	Used
O 53	10 m. bright violet	0 8	0 2
O 54	15 m. purple ..	1 0	0 2
O 55	20 m. blue ('35)	1 3	0 4

SUEZ CANAL COMPANY.

1

(Litho. M. Chézaud, Paris.)

1868 (July). *T* **1.** *Imperf.*

No.	Stamp	Unused	Used
1	1 c. black	50 0	£35
2	5 c. green	22 6	£20
3	20 c. blue	7 6	£12
4	40 c. pink	20 0	£30

These stamps were suppressed in October, 1868. Many forgeries exist, both unused and used.

EIRE.
(IRELAND)

Rialtaṡ Sealadaċ na hÉireann 1922 (1)

Rialtaṡ Sealadaċ na hÉireann 1922. (2)

Rialtaṡ Sealadaċ na hÉireann 1922 (3)

(" Provisional Government of Ireland. 1922.")

1922 (17 Feb.). *T* **104** *to* **108** (*W* **100**) *and* **109** *of Great Britain overprinted in black.*

(*a*) *With T* **1**, *by Messrs. Dollard, Ltd.*

No.	Stamp	Unused	Used
1	½d. green	0 3	0 2
	a. Overprint inverted	£8	£8
2	1d. scarlet	0 4	0 2
	a. Overprint inverted	£6	
3	1d. carmine-red	1 0	0 4
4	2½d. bright ultramarine	1 6	2 0
5	3d. bluish violet	3 6	1 3
6	4d. grey-green	1 9	1 9
7	5d. yellow-brown	2 6	3 0
8	9d. agate	4 6	5 0
	a. Faint grey-black overprint	6 6	6 6
9	10d. turquoise-blue	3 6	4 0

The ½d. with red overprint is an unauthorised printing. (*Price* 60s.)

(*b*) *With T* **2**, *by Messrs. Alex. Thom & Co.*

No.	Stamp	Unused	Used
10	1½d. chestnut	2 6	0 6
	a. Error, " PENCF "	£6	
11	1½d. pale red-brown	1 6	0 6
12	2d. orange (Die I)	0 10	0 1
	a. Overprint inverted	£5	
13	2d. orange (Die II)	0 9	0 1
	a. Overprint inverted	£8	
14	6d. reddish purple, C	3 0	1 3
15	1s. bistre-brown	5 0	1 9

Varieties occur in the relative positions of the lines of the overprint. (i.) " R " (of " Rialtas ") over " Se " (of " Sealadac ") in which the downstroke of the last letter of " Rialtas " is to the left of the apex of the last " a " in " Sealadac." (ii.) " R " over " S "; the left side of the " R " is immediately above the left side of the " S " (or in extreme cases, still further to the left). (iii.) " é " of " héireann " over " 1 " of " 1922." Variations intermediate to the above may also be found.

(*c*) *With T* **3** (*on Bradbury, Wilkinson printings*), *Messrs. Dollard, Ltd.*

No.	Stamp	Unused	Used
17	2s. 6d. chocolate-brown	17 6	25 0
18	2s. 6d. sepia-brown	15 0	25 0
19	5s. rose-red	25 0	45 0
21	10s. dull grey-blue	50 0	85 0

1922 (1 April–July). *Optd. by Messrs. Dollard, Ltd. with T* **1**, *in red or carmine* (C.).

No.	Stamp	Unused	Used
22	2½d. bright ultramarine	1 0	1 3
23	4d. grey-green (R.)	2 3	2 3
24	4d. grey-green (C.) (July)	2 6	3 0
25	9d. agate	6 6	5 0

1922 (June). *Overprinted as T* **2**, *in black, by Messrs. Harrison & Sons.*

No.	Stamp	Unused	Used
26	½d. green	0 4	0 5
27	1d. carmine-red	0 6	0 7
28	1½d. red-brown	0 10	1 0
29	2d. bright orange (Die I)	0 10	0 7
29a	2d. bright orange (Die II)	1 0	1 6

The Harrison overprint measures 15 × 17 mm. (maximum dimensions) against the 14½ × 16 mm. of *T* **2** (Thom printing) and is in much bolder black than the latter, while the individual letters are taller. The " R " of " Rialtas " is always over the " Se " of " Sealadac." This special overprinting was made on stamps for issue in coil or roll form.

1922 (July). *Overprinted as T* **2**, *but bolder, and in shiny blue-black ink by Messrs. Alex. Thom & Co., Ltd.*

No.	Stamp	Unused	Used
30	1½d. bright chestnut	0 9	0 4
31	2d. orange (Die I)	7 6	0 2
32	2d. orange (Die II)	0 9	0 1

33	6d. reddish purple, C	2 6	1 3
34	1s. bistre-brown	10 0	2 0

These Thom printings are distinguishable from the Harrison printings by the size of the overprint, and from the previous Thom printings by the intensity and colour of the overprint, the latter being best seen when the stamp is looked through with a strong light behind it.

The 2d. stamp of this issue with inverted overprint was never issued.

1922 (July-Nov.). *Provisional printings by Messrs. Alex. Thom & Co., Ltd.* (a) *Overprinted as T 2, in blue-black, carmine* (C.), *or red* (R.).

35	½d. green	1 0	0 1
	a. Overprint in dull black	15 0	7 6
36	1d. scarlet	0 4	0 1
	a. Overprint in dull black	12 6	
37	2½d. bright ultramarine (C.)	6 6	4 6
38	3d. bluish violet	1 6	1 0
	a. Overprint in dull black	15 0	7 6
39	4d. grey-green (C.)	1 3	1 6
40	5d. yellow-brown	2 6	3 0
41	9d. agate (R.)	3 6	4 0
42	9d. olive-green (R.)	3 0	4 6
43	10d. turquoise-blue	15 0	22 6
	a. Overprint in dull black	60 0	

The varieties with overprint in black are said to be from proof sheets afterwards put into circulation. (See also No. 45*a*.)

(*b*) *Overprinted with T 3 in blue-black.*

44	2s. 6d. grey-brown	£5	£5
45	5s. pale rose-red	85 0	85 0
	a. Overprint in dull black	£7	
46	10s. dull grey-blue	£6	£6

The overprint on Nos. 44 to 46 differs from that of Nos. 17 to 21 in being in blue-black instead of black, the "h" and "é" of "héireann" are closer together, while the impression is bolder and much more sharply defined, and the ink often glossy.

Rialtaṡ Sealaḋaċ na hÉireann 1922.

(4)

Saorstát Éireann 1922

("Irish Free State 1922.")

(5)

1922 (Dec.). *Overprinted by Thom with T 4* (*wider setting*) *in blue-black.*

47	½d. green	0 4	0 2
	a. Overprint in black	—	40 0
48	1d. scarlet	0 4	0 3
49	1½d. red-brown	0 4	0 5
50	2d. orange (Die II)	1 6	0 3
51	1s. olive-bistre	7 6	5 0

The overprint T 4 measures 15¾ × 16 mm. (maximum dimensions)

1922 (Dec.). *Overprinted by Messrs. Thom with T 5, in shiny blue-black or in red* (R.).

52	½d. green	0 3	0 3
	a. No accent in "Saorstat."	£20	
	b. Accent inserted by hand	50 0	50 0
	c. Overprint in dull black	10 0	4 6
53	1d. scarlet	0 4	0 1
	a. No accent and final "t" missing	£50	
	b. Accent inserted by hand	50 0	50 0
	c. Accent and "t" inserted	75 0	
	d. Overprint in dull black	5 0	2 6
54	1½d. red-brown	0 6	0 8
55	2d. orange (Die II)	0 6	0 4
	a. Overprint in dull black	12 6	7 6
56	2½d. bright blue (R.)	1 6	2 0
	a. No accent	60 0	
57	3d. bluish violet	1 6	1 3
	a. No accent	90 0	£6
	b. Overprint in dull black	4 6	2 6
58	4d. grey-green (R.)	1 0	1 0
	a. No accent	50 0	50 0
59	5d. yellow-brown	2 0	2 0
60	6d. reddish purple, C	1 6	0 8
	a. Accent inserted by hand	85 0	£5
	b. Overprint in dull black	10 0	4 0
61	9d. olive-green (R.)	2 6	3 0
	a. No accent	75 0	75 0
62	10d. turquoise-blue	2 0	4 0
63	1s. bistre-brown	2 6	1 3
	a. No accent	£27	
	b. Accent inserted by hand	£6	
64	2s. 6d. chocolate-brown	10 0	12 6
	a. No accent	£10	£10
	b. Accent reversed	£8	
	c. Overprint in dull black	15 0	
	d. Re-entry	£12	
65	5s. rose-red	22 6	27 6
	a. No accent	£15	
	b. Accent reversed	£10	
	c. Overprint in dull black	30 0	
66	10s. dull grey-blue	60 0	70 0
	a. No accent	£38	
	b. Accent reversed	£20	
	c. Overprint in dull black	80 0	

The accents inserted by hand are in dull black. The reversed accents are grave (thus "à") instead of acute ("á"). A variety with "S" of "Saorstat" directly over "é" of "éireann," instead of to left, may be found in all values except the 2½d. and 4d. In the 2s. 6d., 5s., and 10s. it is very slightly to the left in the "S" over "é" variety, bringing the "á" of "Saorstát" directly above the last "n" of "éireann."

1923. *Overprinted by Messrs. Harrison with T 5, in black.*

67	½d. green	0 2	0 1
	a. Long "1" in "1922" (in pair)	2 0	2 6
68	1d. scarlet	0 4	0 4
	a. Long "1" in "1922" (in pair)	2 6	2 6
69	1½d. red-brown	0 9	0 9
	a. Long "1" in "1922" (in pair)	6 6	6 6
70	2d. orange (Die II)	0 6	0 4
	a. Long "1" in "1922" (in pair)	3 0	3 0

In the Harrison overprint the characters are rather bolder than those of the Thom overprint, and the foot of the "1" of "1922" is usually rounded instead of square. The long "1" in "1922" has a serif at foot. The second "e" of "éireann" appears to be slightly raised.

6. "Sword of Light." 7. Map of Ireland.

8. Arms of Ireland. 9. Celtic Cross.

10

(Designed by J. J. O'Reilly, J. Ingram, Miss M. Girling, and Miss L. Williams. Plates made in London.)

PRINTERS. The following and all subsequent issues, with the exception of Nos. 83 to 88 and 99 to 101, were typographed at the Govt. Printing Works, Dublin.

1922 (6 Dec.)–**1934**. *W* **10**. *P* 15×14.

No.	T	Description				
71	6	½d. bright green	0	2	0	1
		a. Imperf.× perf. 14 (1934)	0	6	0	6
72	7	1d. carmine	0	3	0	1
		a. P 15× imp. (single perf.) ('33)	12	6		
		b. P 15× imperf. (1934)	0	6	0	6
73	7	1½d. claret	0	4	0	4
74	„	2d. grey-green	0	4	0	1
		a. Imperf.× perf. 14 (1934)	0	9	0	3
		b. Perf. 15× imperf.				
75	8	2½d. red-brown	0	8	0	4
76	9	3d. ultramarine	0	6	0	1
77	8	4d. slate-blue	0	9	0	4
78	6	5d. bright violet	1	0	0	3
79	„	6d. claret	1	0	0	1
80	8	9d. bright violet	1	6	0	2
81	9	10d. brown	1	9	0	10
82	6	1s. light blue	2	0	0	2

No. 72*a* is imperf. vertically except for a single perf. at each top corner. It was issued for use in automatic machines.

For similar designs with mult. "e" wmk., see Nos. 111 to 122 in King George VI catalogue.

Saorstát
Éireann
1922
(11)

1925–27. *Stamps of Great Britain. T* **109** (*Bradbury, Wilkinson printing*) *overprinted at the Government Printing Office and elsewhere.*

(*a*) *With T* **11** *in black or grey-black.*

No.	Description				
83	2s. 6d. chocolate-brown	5	0	7	6
	a. Wide and narrow date (pr.) ('27)	30	0		
84	5s. rose-red	10	0	15	0
	a. Wide and narrow date (pr.) ('27)	30	0		
85	10s. dull grey-blue	20	0	30	0
	a. Wide and narrow date (pr.) ('27)	60	0		

The varieties with wide and narrow date *se-tenant* are from what is known as the "composite setting," in which some stamps showed the wide date, as T **5**, while in others the figures were close together, as in T **11**.

Single specimens of this printing with wide date may be distinguished from Nos. 64 to 66 by the colour of the ink, which is black or grey-black in the composite setting and blue-black in the Thom printing.

The type of the "composite" overprint usually shows distinct signs of wear.

(*b*) *As T* **5** (*wide date*) *in black.*

No.	Description				
86	2s. 6d. chocolate	6	6	7	6
87	5s. rose-red	10	0	12	6
88	10s. dull grey-blue	25	0	27	6

This printing can be distinguished from the Thom overprints in dull black, by the clear, heavy impression (in deep black) which often shows in relief on the back of the stamp.

12. Daniel O'Connell.

(Designed by Leo Whelan.)

1929 (22 June). *Catholic Emancipation Centenary. T* **12**. *Wmk. T* **10**. *P* 15×14.

No.	Description				
89	2d. grey-green	0	4	0	1
90	3d. blue	0	6	0	6
91	9d. bright violet	1	6	1	0

13. Shannon Barrage.

1930 (15 Oct.). *Completion of Shannon Hydro-Electric Scheme. T* **13**. *Wmk. T* **10**. *P* 15×14.

No.	Description				
92	2d. agate	0	4	0	1

14 **15.** The Cross of Cong.

(Types **14** and **15** designed by G. Atkinson.)

1931 (12 June). *200th anniversary of the Royal Dublin Society. T* **14**. *Wmk. T* **10**. *P* 15×14.

No.	Description				
93	2d. blue	0	4	0	1

1932 (12 May). *International Eucharistic Congress. T* **15**. *Wmk. T* **10**. *P* 15×14.

No.	Description				
94	2d. grey-green	0	4	0	2
95	3d. blue	0	6	0	6

16. Adoration of the Cross. **17.** Hurley Player.

(Des. R. J. King.)

1933 (18 Sept.). "*Holy Year.*" *T* **16.** *Wmk. T* **10.** *P* 15×14.

96	2d. grey-green ..	0	4	0	1
97	3d. blue ..	0	6	0	5

1934 (27 July). *Golden Jubilee of the Gaelic Athletic Association. W* **10.** *P* 15×14.

98 **17**	2d. green ..	0	4	0	1

1935. *Stamps of Great Britain (Waterlow printings). Optd. as T* **5** *(wide date).*

99 **109**	2s. 6d. chocolate (No. 450)	7	6	8	0
100 ,,	5s. bright rose-red (No. 451)	15	0	17	6
101 ,,	10s. indigo (No. 452)	30	0	35	0

POSTAGE DUE STAMPS.

D 1

1925. *P* 14×15. *W* **10.**

D 1 **D 1**	½d. emerald-green ..	0	2	0	2
D 2 ,,	1d. carmine ..	0	3	0	1
D 3 ,,	2d. deep green ..	0	4	0	1
D 4 ,,	6d. plum ..	0	8	0	7

For same design with mult. "e" wmk., see King George VI catalogue.

CONTROL LETTERS.

Note—*Prices are for mint singles with control.*

I.—Margin imperf. P.—Margin perf.

I. *Dollard printings.* (*a*) *In black.*

No.	Control	Value	I.	P.
C. 1	Q 21,	10d.	*	85 0
C. 2	R 21,	½d.	10 0	2 0
C. 3	,,	4d.	£8	*
C. 4	S 21,	½d.	6 0	12 6
C. 5	,,	1d.	6 6	30 0
C. 6	,,	2½d.	35 0	10 0
C. 7	,,	3d.	45 0	25 0
C. 8	,,	4d.	15 0	£6
C. 9	,,	5d.	27 6	32 6
C. 10	,,	9d.	30 0	60 0
C. 11	,,	10d.	60 0	30 0
C. 12	S 22,	½d.	4 0	4 0
C. 13	,,	1d.	2 0	3 0
C. 14	,,	3d.	15 0	45 0
C. 15	,,	4d.	*	25 0
C. 16	,,	5d.	22 6	*
C. 16*a*	,,	9d.	*	£8
C. 16*b*	,,	10d.	*	35 0
C. 17	T 22,	1d.	90 0	40 0

(*b*) *In red or carmine* (C.).

No.	Control	Value	I.	P.
C. 18	R 21,	4d.	15 0	£8
C. 19	S 21,	2½d.	20 0	£5
C. 20	,,	4d.	50 0	*
C. 21	,,	9d.	£6	32 6
C. 22	S 22,	2½d	12 6	12 6
C. 23	,,	4d.	65 0	90 0
C. 24	,,	4d. (C.)	40 0	85 0
C. 25	,,	9d.	£8	35 0

II. *Thom printings.* *T* **2.**

(*a*) *In black.*

No.	Control	Value	I.	P.
C. 26	Q 20,	1½d.	12 6	10 0
C. 27	Q 21,	1½d.	15 0	10 0
C. 28	R 21,	1s.	40 0	60 0
C. 29	S 21,	2d. (Die I.)	7 6	10 0
C. 30	S 21,	6d.	15 0	*
C. 31	S 21,	1s.	45 0	60 0
C. 32	S 22,	2d. (Die I.)	6 6	3 6
C. 33	,,	2d. (,, II.)	6 0	5 0
C. 33*a*	,,	10d.	*	£10
C. 34	,,	1s.	35 0	30 0
C. 35	T 22,	½d.	£6	£6
C. 35*a*	,,	1d.	£6	*
C. 35*b*	,,	1½d.	*	75 0
C. 36	,,	2d. (Die I.)	40 0	*
C. 37	,,	2d. (,, II.)	32 6	*
C. 37*a*	,,	3d.	£6	£7
C. 38	T 22,	6d.	20 0	*

(*b*) *In red or carmine.*

No.	Control	Value	I.	P.
C. 39	S 22,	4d.	*	£8
C. 40	,,	9d. agate	35 0	£7
C. 41	T 22,	2½d.	50 0	40 0
C. 42	,,	4d.	10 0	20 0
C. 43	,,	9d. olive	32 6	30 0

(*c*) *In blue-black.*

No.	Control	Value	I.	P.
C. 44	S 22,	1d.	27 6	20 0
C. 45	,,	2d. (Die I.)	50 0	50 0
C. 46	,,	2d. (,, II.)	17 6	12 6
C. 48	,,	10d.	80 0	90 0
C. 49	,,	1s.	40 0	50 0
C. 50	T 22,	½d.	10 0	7 6
C. 51	,,	1d.	3 6	2 6
C. 52	,,	1½d.	5 0	6 0
C. 53	,,	2d. (Die I.)	50 0	50 0
C. 54	,,	2d. (,, II.)	8 6	3 6
C. 55	,,	3d.	20 0	10 0
C. 56	,,	5d.	17 6	*
C. 57	T 22,	6d.	12 6	*
C. 58	T 22,	1s.	30 0	35 0
C. 59	U 22,	6d.	12 6	*

The Harrison printings being issued in rolls only, are unobtainable with control attached.

III. *Thom printings.* *T* **4** *(wide setting) in blue-black.*

No.	Control	Value	I.	P.
C. 60	T 22,	1d.	30 0	*
C. 61	,,	1½d.	10 0	17 6
C. 62	,,	2d. (Die II.)	£5	50 0
C. 63	,,	1s.	40 0	60 0
C. 64	U 22,	½d.	3 0	1 6
C. 65	,,	1d.	17 6	10 0

IV. "saorstat" *overprint.*

(*a*) *In blue-black or in red* (R.)

No.	Control	Value	I.	P.
C. 66	T 22,	½d.	2 6	3 0
C. 67	,,	1d.	1 0	1 0
C. 68	,,	1½d.	£7	12 6
C. 69	,,	2d. (Die II.)	35 0	15 0
C. 70	,,	2½d. (R.)	6 6	£8
C. 71	,,	4d. (R.)	*	£8
C. 72	,,	5d.	12 6	8 6
C. 73	,,	9d. (R.)	12 6	15 0
C. 74	,,	10d.	80 0	22 6
C. 75	,,	1s.	25 0	*
C. 76	U 22,	6d.	7 6	*
C. 77	U 22,	½d.	1 6	1 0
C. 78	,,	1d.	2 6	2 0
C. 79	,,	1½d.	10 0	10 0
C. 80	,,	3d.	10 0	8 6
C. 81	,,	4d. (R.)	10 0	*
C. 82		1s.	20 0	20 0
C. 83	U 23,	½d.	3 6	1 0
C. 84	,,	1d.	40 0	22 6
C. 85	,,	2½d. (R.)	12 6	10 0
C. 86	,,	4d. (R.)	12 6	*
C. 87	,,	5d.	10 0	*
C. 88	,,	9d. (R.)	15 0	17 6
C. 89	,,	1s.	20 0	17 6

C. 90 V 23,	6d.	7 6	—	
C. 91 V 23,	4d. (R.)	*	10 0	
C. 92 W 23,	6d.	12 6	*	

Only one specimen of C. 90 with perf. margin is known.

(*b*) *In dull black.*

C. 93	T 22,	½d.	60 0	*
C. 94	„	1d.	50 0	*
C. 95	„	2d. (Die II.)	65 0	*
C. 96	U 22,	6d.	60 0	*
C. 97	U 22,	1½d.	*	45 0
C. 98	„	3d.	70 0	*
C. 99	U 23,	½d.	*	60 0
C. 100	„	1d.	*	80 0
C. 101	V 23,	6d.	60 0	*
C. 102	W 23,	6d.	60 0	*

FALKLAND ISLANDS.

—— SIMPLIFICATION (see p. xli) ——

Nos. 3 to 30.

3, 4, 5, 6. 7, 9a, 11a.
11b, 12. 13, 14.
15, 17, 20, 21, 21a, 22, 24, 25, 26, 28, 29, 30.

FALKLAND
PAID.
ISLANDS

(1)

(2)

Types 1 and 2 are illustrations of "franks."
No. 1, black on *white* or coloured papers, 70s.
No. 2, red on *white*, £8.
Genuine franks used on cover are rare.
No. 1 was used from March 11, 1868, and No. 2 only from early in 1877—both up to June, 1878.
Type 1 is known doubly printed.

3

(Eng. and printed by Bradbury Wilkinson.)

1878 (19 June)–**1879.** *T* **3.** *No wmk.* *P* 14, 14½

3	1d. claret	80 0	80 0
4	4d. grey-black (Sept., 1879)	£20	90 0
5	6d. blue-green	30 0	30 0
6	1s. bistre-brown (1878)	20 0	27 6

1884 (Feb.). *T* **3.** *Wmk. Crown CA.* *P* 14, 14½.

6a	1d. dull claret*	£8	70 0
	ab. Imperf. between (vert. pair)		
7	1d. red-brown	35 0	35 0
8	4d. grey-black	12 6	12 6

The plate used for these stamps did not fit the paper, and therefore the wmk. appears in all sorts of positions, a well-centred Crown CA being scarce.

* No. 6*a* can be distinguished from No. 11 by the fact that the latter nearly always has the watermark reversed. On No. 6*a* the watermark is usually normal (or occasionally inverted).

1886. *T* **3.** *Wmk. Crown CA, sideways, to right or left.* *P* 14, 14½.

9	1d. claret (May)	22 6	25 0
9a	1d. pale claret	50 0	50 0
10	4d. grey-black (Dec.)	40 0	20 0

The issues of 1878 to 1886 exist with one or two sides imperf. from the margin of the sheets.

1890–91. *T* **3.** *Wmk. Crown CA, upright.* *P* 14, 14½.

11	1d. claret (1891)	35 0	40 0
11a	4d. olive-black (1890)	10 6	10 6

1891. *The* 1d. *of last issues bisected and used for* ½d.

11b	Half of 1d. red-brown (No. 7)	†	£8
12	Half of 1d. claret (Nos. 9, 9a, 11)	†	£6

In 1891 the postage to the United Kingdom and Colonies was reduced from 4d. to 2½d. per ½ oz. As there were no ½d. or 2½d. stamps in stock, the 1d. was allowed to be bisected and used for half its value until the provisionals appeared.

½d.

(4)

1890–92. *Stamps of* 1884–1891, *bisected diagonally and each half surcharged with T* **4.**

12a	½d. on half of 1d. red-brown (No. 7)	£8	£7
	b. Unsevered pair		
13	½d. on half of 1d. claret (Nos. 9, 9a, 11, 1890)	£10	£10
	a. Unsevered pair	£20	
	b. Surcharge double	£25	
	c. Surcharge inverted	£40	
	d. Surcharge sideways		
14	½d. on half of 1d. orange-brown (No. 18, 1891)	£12	£12
	a. Unsevered pair	£30	
	b. Surcharge inverted	£40	

Bisected stamps were authorised by decree dated 1 Jan., 1891, and were used until 11 Jan., 1892. As the 1d. orange-brown, was issued in Dec., 1891, some of these were surcharged.

1891–1904. *T* **3.** *Wmk. Crown CA.* *P* 14, 14½.

15	½d. blue-green (Dec., 1891)	40 0	45 0
16	½d. deep yellow-green (1892)	1 6	2 0
17	½d. yellow-green	1 3	1 6
18	1d. orange-brn. (Nov., 1891)	17 6	17 6
19	1d. Venetian red (1895)	7 6	8 0
20	1d. brown	12 0	10 6
	a. Imperf. between (horiz. pair)		
21	1d. pale red (1898)	6 0	6 0
21a	1d. orange-red (1904)	5 0	6 0
22	2d. purple (1 Jan., 1896)	4 0	4 6
23	2½d. ultramarine (1891)	40 0	35 0
24	2½d. blue (1892)	6 0	6 6
25	2½d. Prussian blue (1894)	£6	60 0
26	2½d. deep ultramarine	10 0	10 0
27	6d. orange-yellow (1892)	15 0	15 0

No.	Description	Unused	Used
28	6d. yellow	8 6	10 0
29	9d. oran.-verm. (1 Jan., 1896)	12 6	15 0
30	1s. grey-brown (1 Jan., 1896)	8 0	8 6

In the ½d., 2d., 2½d., and 9d. the figures of value in the lower corners were replaced by small rosettes and the words of value are in colour.

There are numerous shades in this issue in addition to those listed.

5

6

(Recess. Bradbury, Wilkinson & Co.)

1898. *T* **5** *and* **6**. *Wmk. Crown CC. P* 14, 14½.

No.	Description	Unused	Used
31	2s. 6d. deep blue (May) ..	£6	£7
32	5s. red (April)	70 0	80 0

7

8

(Recess. De La Rue & Co.)

1904–12. *T* **7** *(to 1s.) and* **8**. *Wmk. Mult. Crown CA. P* 14.

No.	Description	Unused	Used
33	½d. yellow-green (18.7.04) ..	2 0	3 0
	a. Thick paper	4 6	5 0
33b	½d. bright yellow-green ..	2 0	2 6
34	1d. vermilion (18 July, 1904)	2 0	1 3
	a. Thick paper	1 9	1 0
34b	1d. dull coppery-red ..	30 0	35 0
35	2d. purple (18 Feb., 1905) ..	6 0	6 6
36	2½d. ultram. (18 July, 1904) ..	10 0	10 6
36a	2½d. pale ultramarine ..	40 0	45 0
36b	2½d. deep blue (1912) ..	£10	£12
37	6d. orange (April, 1905) ..	20 0	22 6
38	1s. brown (April, 1905) ..	17 6	20 0
39	3s. deep green	37 6	40 0
40	5s. red (28 Feb., 1905) ..	65 0	75 0

1907 (June). *T* **7**. *Wmk. Mult. Crown CA, sideways P* 14.

No.	Description	Unused	Used
41	1d. vermilion	3 6	4 0

9

10

(Recess. De La Rue & Co.)

1912–20. *T* **9** *(to 1s.) and* **10**. *Wmk. Mult. Crown CA. P* 14.

No.	Description	Unused	Used
42	½d. green	1 6	1 9
42a	½d. yellow-green	1 0	1 0
	b. Thick greyish paper (1920) ..	2 0	2 6
43	1d. vermilion	1 6	1 9
43a	1d. scarlet (1918)	1 6	1 9
	b. Thick greyish paper (1920) ..	2 0	2 0
44	2d. purple	3 6	4 0
45	2½d. dark blue	4 0	4 0
46	6d. orange	6 0	6 6
47	1s. yellow-brown (1912) ..	12 6	15 0
47a	1s. bistre-brown (1919) ..	10 6	12 0
	b. Grey-brown on thick greyish paper (1920) ..	20 0	22 6
48	3s. deep green	30 0	32 6
49	5s. red	55 0	60 0
50	10s. red/*green*	55 0	60 0
51	£1 black/*red*	£9	£8

The 2½d. No. 45, was bisected and used as 1d. stamp in S. Georgia in 1923. This procedure was not authorised from Port Stanley.

1914. *T* **10**, *colour changed. Wmk. Mult. Crown CA. P* 14.

No.	Description	Unused	Used
52	5s. purple	20 0	22 6

WAR STAMP

(11)

1918 (Nov.)–**1920.** *As last, overprinted locally, in black, with T* **11**.

No.	Description	Unused	Used
55	½d. green	0 3	0 8
55a	½d. yellow-green	0 9	1 0
	b. Thick greyish paper ..	0 9	1 0
56	1d. scarlet	0 6	0 9
	a. Overprint double	£25	
	b. Overprint double, one albino ..	60 0	
56c	1d. vermilion	0 6	0 8
	d. Thick greyish paper (1920) ..	12 6	15 0
57	1s. yellow-brown (1918) ..	8 0	20 0
58	1s. pale bistre-brown (1919) ..	3 6	5 0
	a. Grey-brn. on thick greyish paper (1920)	6 6	7 6

The later printings of the ½d. and 1d. have the overprint in shiny ink.

1921–25. *T* **9** *and* **10** (3*s.*). *Wmk. Mult. Script CA. P* 14.

No.	Description	Unused	Used
60	½d. bright green	1 3	1 6
61	1d. vermilion (1924)	1 0	1 6
62	2d. purple	4 0	4 6
63	2½d. indigo	5 0	6 0
64	6d. orange (1925)	5 0	7 6
65	1s. bistre-brown	20 0	22 6
66	3s. deep green	35 0	40 0

1923. *T* **9**. *Colour changed. Script wmk. P* 14.

No.	Description	Unused	Used
67	2½d. purple/*yellow*	4 0	5 0

$2\frac{1}{2}$D

(12)

1928. *No.* 62 *surcharged with T* **12**.

No.	Description	Unused	Used
68	2½d. on 2d. purple	£35	£40

13. Whale and penguins. **14.**

(Recess-printed by Messrs. Perkins Bacon & Co.)

1929 (2 Sept.)–**1937**. *T* **13** *and* **14** (*4d.*). *P* 14.

(*a*) *Wmk. Mult. Script CA.*

69	½d. green	0	8	0	10
70	1d. scarlet	1	0	1	0
71	2d. grey	1	6	1	9
72	2½d. blue	2	0	2	6
72*a*	4d. orange ('32)	4	6	5	0
73	6d. purple	4	0	4	6
	a. Reddish purple ('37)	10	6	10	6
74	1s. black/*emerald*	10	6	12	0
	a. On bright emerald ('37)	17	6	18	0
75	2s. 6d. carmine/*blue*	22	6	25	0
76	5s. green/*yellow*	35	0	40	0
77	10s. carmine/*emerald*	55	0	65	0

(*b*) *Wmk. Mult. Crown CA.*

78	£1 black/*red*	£9	£10

15. Romney Marsh Ram.
16. Iceberg. **17.** Whale-catcher.
18. Port Louis.
19. Map of Falkland Islands.
20. South Georgia. **21.** Whale.
22. Govt. House, Stanley.

23. Battle Memorial. **24. King Penguin.**
25. Coat of Arms. **26. King George V.**

(Des. (except 6d.) by G. Roberts. Eng. and recess. Bradbury, Wilkinson & Co.)

1933. *Centenary of British Occupation. T* **15** *to* **22** (*horiz.*) *and* **23** *to* **26** (*vert.*). *Wmk. Mult. Script CA. P* 12.

79	**15**	½d. black and green	1	6	2	6
80	**16**	1d. black and scarlet	4	0	5	0
81	**17**	1½d. black and blue	5	6	7	6
82	**18**	2d. black and brown	10	0	12	6
83	**19**	3d. black and violet	15	0	17	6
84	**20**	4d. black and orange	27	6	30	0
85	**21**	6d. black and slate	30	0	37	6
86	**22**	1s. black and olive-green	47	6	52	6
87	**23**	2s. 6d. black and violet	95	0	110	0
88	**24**	5s. black and yellow	£12		£15	
89	**25**	10s. black and chestnut	£20		£25	
90	**26**	20s. black and carmine	£40		£45	

1935 (7 May). *Silver Jubilee. As T* **13** *of Antigua, inscribed* "FALKLAND ISLANDS". *Recess. B.W. & Co. Wmk. Mult. Script CA. P* 11×12.

91	1d. deep blue and scarlet	0	6	0	10
92	2½d. brown and deep blue	2	6	3	6
93	4d. green and indigo	4	0	5	0
94	1s. slate and purple	8	6	12	0

The 1s. exists with "double flagstaff" variety.

FIJI.

SIMPLIFICATION (see p. xii)

Nos. 1 to 90.

5, 6, 7, 8, 9.
11, 12, 14. 17, 18, 19.
20, 21, 22: 39, 40, 41.
46, 46a: 55, 55a. 64, 69.
82, 73, 90, 86.

Nos. 91 to 183.

If desired this group can be reduced to about 20 stamps by the omission of shades and perfs.

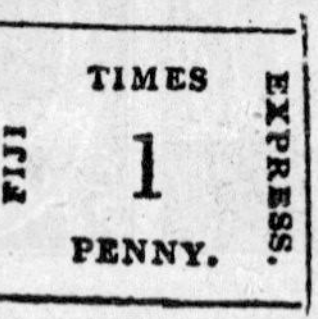

1

(Type-set and printed at the office of *The Fiji Times*, Levuka, Ovalau, Fiji, in sheets of twenty-four stamps arranged in four rows of six stamps of each value in the following order: 6d., 1s., 1d., 3d.)

T 1. *Rouletted in the printing.*

(*a*) **1870** (1 Nov.). *Quadrillé paper.*

1	1d. black/*rose*	£15	£15
2	3d. black/*rose*	£16	£16
3	6d. black/*rose*	£22	£22
4	1s. black/*rose*	£12	£10

(*b*) **1871.** *Laid bâtonné paper.*

5	1d. black/*rose*	85	0	70	0
6	3d. black/*rose*	90	0	90	0
7	6d. black/*rose*	£9		£9	
8	9d. black/*rose*	£9		£9	
9	1s. black/*rose*	£9		£9	

The stamps of the last group were printed from the same plate as the first, but the values of the last three stamps in the bottom row of the sheet were altered to "9d." by inserting figures "9" in place of the figures "3."

There are no reprints of these stamps, but the 1d., 3d., 6d., and 1s. are known in the correct type on *yellow wove* paper; these are probably *proofs*. There are also two different sets of imitations made by the proprietors of *The Fiji Times* to meet the demands of collectors. The first of these were made in 1876 and are on *vertically laid* paper, *imperf.* and *pin-perf.*; these are smaller than the originals. The others were made later and are on thick *wove* paper of a deep *rosy mauve* colour.

King Cakobau, June, 1871, *to* Oct., 1874.

2

3

(Eng. and electrotyped by A. L. Jackson, and printed at the Govt. Printing Office, Sydney.)

1871 (3 Dec.). *T* **2** (*1d. and 3d.*) *and* **3** (*6d.*). *Wove paper. Wmk.* "FIJI POSTAGE" *in small sans-serif capitals across the middle row of stamps in the sheet. P* 12½.

10	1d. pale blue	20	0	20	0
11	1d. deep blue	15	0	15	0
12	3d. yellow-green	25	0	42	6

No.	Description	Unused	Used
13	3d. deep yellow-green	27 6	42 6
14	6d. dull rose	27 6	32 6
15	6d. carmine-rose	30 0	35 0

All three values are known *imperf.*, but were not issued in that condition.

Two

Cents

(4)

1872 (13 Jan.). *T* **2** *and* **3** *surcharged as T* **4**

No.	Description	Unused	Used
16	2 c. on 1d. pale blue	10 0	12 6
17	2 c. on 1d. deep blue	10 0	12 6
18	6 c. on 3d. yellow-green	12 6	15 0
19	12 c. on 6d. carmine-rose	27 6	20 0

Fiji Islands ceded to Great Britain, 10 Oct., 1874.

V.R. (5)   V.R. (6)

1874 (10 Oct.). *Nos.* 16 *to* 19 *overprinted at the "Polynesian Gazette" Office, Levuka, in black*

(*a*) "V.R." *Gothic* (*T* **5**).

No.	Description	Unused	Used
20	1d. (2 c.) blue	£10	70 0
21	3d. (6 c.) green	£16	£10
22	6d. (12 c.) rose	£10	80 0

Varieties.

(i.) *No stop after* "R" (*No.* 13 *on sheet*).

No.	Description	Unused	Used
23	1d. (2 c.) blue		

V.R. (6*a*)

(ii.) *Cross pattée stop after* "R" (*T* **6***a*) (*No.* 26 *on sheet*).

No.	Description	Unused	Used
26	1d. (2 c.) blue		
27	3d. (6 c.) green		
28	6d. (12 c.) rose	—	£20

(iii.) *Round raised stop after* "V" (*No.* 28 *on sheet*).

No.	Description	Unused	Used
29	1d. (2 c.) blue	—	£45
30	3d. (6 c.) green		
31	6d. (12 c.) rose		

(iv.) *Round raised stops after* "V" *and* "R" (*No.* 29 *on sheet*).

No.	Description	Unused	Used
32	1d. (2 c.) blue		
33	3d. (6 c.) green		
34	6d. (12 c.) rose		

V.R. (6*b*)

(v.) *Inverted* "A" *used for* "V" (*T* **6***b*) (*No.* 30 *on sheet*).

No.	Description	Unused	Used
35	1d. (2 c.) blue	—	£45
36	3d. (6 c.) green	£70	
37	6d. (12 c.) rose	—	£45

(vi.) *Overprint inverted.*

No.	Description	Unused	Used
38	6d. (12 c.) rose		

(*b*) "V.R." *Roman* (*T* **6**).

No.	Description	Unused	Used
39	1d. (2 c.) blue	£9	82 6
40	3d. (6 c.) green	£25	£16
41	6d. (12 c.) rose	£7	110 0

Varieties. (i.) *No stop after* "R" (*No.* 43 *on sheet*).

No.	Description	Unused	Used
42	1d. (2 c.) blue	£42	£42
43	3d. (6 c.) green	£65	
44	6d. (12 c.) rose	—	£42

(ii.) *Overprint inverted.*

No.	Description	Unused	Used
45	6d. (12 c.) rose	£65	

Pt I

2d.

(7)

1875 (May ?). *Stamps of* 1874 *surcharged in Levuka with T* **7**, *in red.*

No.	Type	Description	Unused	Used
46	**5**	2d. on 3d. (6 c.) green	£7	65 0
46*a*	**6**	2d. on 3d. (6 c.) green	£9	£5

Varieties.

No.	Type	Description	Unused	Used
47	**5**	No stop after "R"	£35	£15
48	,,	Cross pattée stop after "R"	£45	£18
49	,,	Round raised stop after "V"	£35	£9
50	,,	Round raised stops after "V" and "R"	£50	£18
51	,,	Inverted "A" for "V"	£50	£18
52	**6**	No stop after "R"	£45	£20
53	**5**	No stop after "2d"	£40	£12
54	**6**	Stop between "2" & "d" (2.d)		

1875 (30 Sept.) *Stamps of* 1874, *but surcharged with T* **7** *in black.*

No.	Type	Description	Unused	Used
55	**5**	2d. on 3d. (6 c.) green	£14	£8
55*a*	**6**	2d. on 3d. (6 c.) green	£18	£12

Varieties.

No.	Type	Description	Unused	Used
56	**5**	No stop after "R"	£70	£30
57	,,	Cross pattée stop after "R"	£80	£35
58	,,	Round raised stop after "V"	£65	£28
59	,,	Round raised stops after "V" and "R"	£80	£35
60	,,	Inverted "A" for "V"	£70	£30
61	**6**	No stop after "R"	£75	£35
62	**5**	No stop after "2d"	£70	£30
63	**6**	Stop between "2" and "d" (2.d)		
63*a*	,,	"V.R." double	—	£50

1875 (20 Nov.). *Stamps of* 12 *c. on* 6*d. rose, of* 1872, *surcharged, in Levuka,* "2d." (*T* **7**) *and* "V.R." *Gothic at one operation, in black.*

(*a*) "V.R." *Gothic* (*T* **5**).

No.	Description	Unused	Used
64	2d. on 6d. (12 c.), rose	£18	£8

Varieties.

No.	Description	Unused	Used
65	Surcharge double	—	£50
66	Inverted "A" for "V"	£25	£15
67	Inverted "A" for "V" and round raised stop after "V"	£35	£20
68	Inverted "A" for "V" and round raised stops after "V" and "R"	£35	£20

(*b*) "V.R." *Roman* (*T* **6**).

No.	Description	Unused	Used
69	2d. on 6d. (12 c.) rose	£22	£10

Variety.

No.	Description	Unused	Used
70	Surcharge double	—	£50

(8)   Two Pence (9)

Printed at the Government Printing Office, Sydney, *from the plates of* 1871, *on sheets of paper previously lithographed* "V.R." (*T* **8**), *in black; the* 3*d. surcharged with T* **9**, *in black.*

1876 (31 Jan.). *Wove paper.* *P* 12½.

No.	Description	Unused	Used
71	1d. grey-blue	16 6	15 0
72	1d. dull blue	16 6	15 0
73	2d. on 3d. pale green	15 0	16 6
74	2d. on 3d. deep green	17 0	16 6
75	6d. pale rose	25 0	17 6
76	6d. dull rose	15 0	12 6
77	6d. carmine-rose	15 0	12 6

F

Varieties.

78 1d. doubly printed .. ..
79 1d. void corner .. ..
80 6d. doubly printed .. ..

Most of the above stamps are known *imperf.* and also on laid paper; these are from the printer's trial or waste sheets, and they were never issued. (For list see *Fiji Handbook.*)

The 3d. *green*, is also known without the surcharge "Two Pence"; this variety was not issued.

1877 (5 Jan.). *As last, but laid paper.* P 12½.

81 1d. blue 7 6 10 0
 a. Imperf. between (pair) .. £6
82 1d. deep blue 7 6 10 0
83 2d. on 3d. yellow-green .. 25 0 20 0
84 2d. on 3d. deep yellow-green 25 0 22 6
85 6d. rose 10 0 12 0
86 6d. carmine-rose 10 0 12 0

Varieties.

87 1d. void corner 40 0 30 0
88 2d. on 3d. *perf.* 10 .. ..
89 2d. on 3d. *perf.* 11 .. ..

The 1d., 3d., and 6d. are known without the monogram "V.R.," but these are believed to be only from printer's trial sheets and never issued.

1877 (12 Oct.). *T 2, optd. with T 8 and surch. as T 9. Laid paper.* P 12½.

90 4d. on 3d. mauve 10 0 7 6
 a. Imperf. between (pair) .. £10

10

11

Printed from new plates made from the original dies of 1871, but "C.R." altered to "V.R." Manufactured at the Government Printing Office, Sydney. Paper-maker's name "T. H. SAUNDERS" *or* "SANDERSON" *in double-lined capitals extending over seven stamps in each full sheet.*

1878-1900. T 10 *and* 11 (6d.); *the surcharges on* 1d., 2d., *and* 3d. *as* T 9, *in black. Wove paper.*

(*a*) P 12½ (1878-80).

91 1d. pale ultramarine .. 4 0 4 0
91a 1d. ultramarine 6 0 4 0
92 2d. on 3d. green 4 0 4 6
93 2d. yellow-green 5 0 4 6
94 2d. blue-green 5 0 4 6
95 6d. rose 27 6 3 6

Error of colour.

95a 2d. ultramarine .. ..

(*b*) P 10 (1881-90).

96 1d. dull blue 12 6 3 6
97 1d. ultramarine 6 6 2 0
98 2d. yellow-green 2 6 1 6
99 2d. blue-green 2 0 2 0
100 4d. on 2d. pale mauve .. 10 0 6 0
101 4d. on 2d. dull purple .. 10 0 7 6
102 4d. on 1d. mauve 6 0 6 0
102a 4d. mauve 15 0
103 4d. deep purple 15 0 15 0
104 6d. pale rose 20 0 7 6
105 6d. bright rose 10 0 10 0

(*c*) P 10×12½ (1882).

106 1d. ultramarine 15 0 12 6
107 2d. green 70 0 15 0
108 6d. rose £6 20 0

(*d*) P 12½×10 (1890).

109 1d. ultramarine .. ..

(*e*) P 12×10 *or* 10×12 (1885).

110 1d. ultramarine 15 0 6 0
110a 1d. dull blue .. ..
111 2d. yellow-green 12 6 7 6
111a 6d. rose .. .. ..

(*f*) P 11×10 (1893).

112 1d. ultramarine 1 3 2 0
113 4d. pale mauve 3 6 5 0
114 6d. pale rose 3 0 5 0
115 6d. rose 3 6 5 0

(*g*) P 11 (1897-99).

116 4d. mauve 4 0 4 6
117 6d. dull rose 6 0 6 0
118 6d. bright rose 15 0 10 0

Variety. Printed on both sides (Dec., 1899).

119 6d. dull rose £10 £7

(*h*) P 11×*nearly* 12 (1900).

Under this heading are included all the stamps formerly catalogued as *perfs.* 12×11; 11×12; 11×11½; or 11½×11. They are all compounds of *perf.* 11 with that of the machine gauging *nearly* 12, which has sometimes been measured as 11½ and sometimes as 12.

120 4d. deep purple 8 6
121 4d. bright purple 3 6 4 6
122 6d. rose 12 6
123 6d. bright rose 5 0 3 6

(*i*) *Imperf.* (1883-90)

124 1d. ultramarine .. ..
125 2d yellow-green .. ..
126 4d. on 2d. pale mauve ..
127 6d rose .. .. ..

12

13

1881-1900. T 12. *Electrotyped and printed at the Government Printing Office, Sydney, with watermark of paper-maker's name as in 1878-1900 issue.*

(*a*) P 10 (19 Oct., 1881).

128 1s. pale brown 10 0 6 6
129 1s. deep brown 12 6 7 6

(*b*) P 11×10 (1894).

130 1s. pale brown 7 6 7 6

(*c*) P 11 (1898).

131 1s. pale brown 12 6 10 0

(*d*) P 11×*nearly* 12 (1900).

132 1s. pale brown 8 6 8 6
133 1s. brown 6 6 3 6
134 1s. deep brown 15 0 15 0

1882 (23 MAY). *T* **13**. *Lithographed in Sydney, on toned paper, watermarked with paper-maker's name* "Cowan" *in old English outline type once in each sheet. Centre in first colour. P* 10.

135	5s. dull red and black ..	10	0	12	6

In July, 1900, an electrotyped plate of a 5s. stamp was made and stamps were printed from it with pale orange-red centre and grey-black frame; these are known *perf.* 10, *perf. nearly* 12, and *imperf.* These stamps were sold as remainders with a special obliteration, dated "15 DEC., 00," but were not issued for postal use. The design differs in many particulars from the issued stamp.

2½d. (14) 2½d. (15)

Stamps printed in Sydney and surcharged at the Government Printing Office in Suva.

1891 (1 JAN.). *T* **10** *surcharged in black. P* 10.

(*a*) *Fraction* 1 *mm. from* "2" (*T* 14).

(*b*) *Fraction* 2 *mm. from* "2" (*T* 15).

136	2½d. on 2d. green (*a*) ..	7	6	8	6
137	2½d. on 2d. green (*b*) ..	55	0	55	0

½d. (16) 5d. (17)

1892 (1 MAR.). *T* **10** *surcharged with T* **16**, *in black. P* 10.

138	½d. on 1d. dull blue	20	0	20	0
139	½d. on 1d. ultramarine ..	12	6	5	0

1892 (25 JULY). *T* **10** *surcharged with T* **17**, *in black. P* 10.

140	5d. on 4d. deep purple ..	22	6	22	6
141	5d. on 4d. dull purple ..	20	0	22	6

FIVE PENCE (18) FIVE PENCE (19)

T **11** *surcharged in black. P* 10.

1892 (30 NOV.). *Words* 2 *mm. apart* (*T* 18).

142	5d. on 6d. brownish rose ..	25	0	27	6
143	5d. on 6d. bright rose ..	15	0	20	0

Variety. P 12 × 12½.

144	5d. on 6d. bright rose ..				

1892 (31 DEC.). *Words* 3 *mm. apart* (*T* 19).

145	5d. on 6d. rose	32	6		
146	5d. on 6d. deep rose ..	22	6		
147	5d. on 6d. brownish rose ..	17	6		

20

21. Native Canoe.

22

1891–1902. *T* **20**, **21** (1*d.*, 2*d.*, *and* 5*d.*), *and* **22**.

Printed in Sydney from electrotyped plates on wove paper watermarked in the sheets, either "SANDERSON" *or* "NEW SOUTH WALES GOVERNMENT" *in outline capitals.*

(*a*) *P* 10 (1891–93).

148	½d. slate-grey	1	0	1	0
149	1d. black	1	0	1	0
150	2d. pale green	20	0	3	6
151	2½d. chocolate	5	0	5	0
152	5d. ultramarine	5	0	6	6

(*b*) *P* 11 × 10 (1893–97).

153	½d. slate-grey	5	0	5	0
154	1d. black	1	6	0	9
155	2d. green	1	3	0	9
156	2½d. brown	3	0	3	6
157	2½d. chocolate	6	0	4	0
158	2½d. yellowish brown ..				
159	5d. ultramarine	3	0	3	6

(*c*) *P* 11 (1893–98).

160	½d. slate-grey	1	0	2	0
161	½d. greenish slate	4	0	2	6
162	1d. black	0	6	0	9
163	1d. pale mauve	0	6	0	2
164	1d. rosy mauve	0	6	0	2
165	2d. dull green	1	3	0	10
166	2d. emerald-green	0	9	0	6
167	2½d. brown	1	6	2	0
168	2½d. yellowish brown ..	6	0	6	0
169	5d. ultramarine				

(*d*) *P* 10 × 12 (1894–98).

170	½d. pale grey				
171	1d. black	1	0	1	0
172	2d. dull green	—		£6	

(*e*) *Perf. nearly* 12 (1895–97).

173	½d. grey	10	0		
174	½d. greenish slate	2	6	2	6
175	1d. black	55	0	3	6
176	1d. rosy mauve	1	0	1	6
177	2d. dull green	25	0	10	0

(*f*) *P* 11 *and nearly* 12, *compound* (1897–1902).

178	½d. greenish slate	1	0	1	3
178*a*	1d. black	60	0		
179	1d. pale rosy mauve ..	0	9	1	0
180	1d. rosy mauve	0	6	0	6
181	2d. dull green	3	6	2	6
182	2½d. brown	2	6	3	0
183	2½d. yellow-brown	3	0	3	6

The 2½d. brown is known *doubly printed*, but this only occurs in the remainders and with the special obliteration, and was never issued for postal use.

23

24

(Typo. De La Rue & Co.)

1903 (1 Feb.). *T* **23** *and* **24** (2d., 4d., 6d., *and* 5s.). *Wmk. Crown CA. P* 14.

No.	Stamp	Unused	Used
184	½d. green and pale green ..	1 3	1 9
185	1d. dull purple and black/*red*	2 6	0 8
186	2d. dull purple and orange ..	2 0	2 3
187	2½d. dull purple and blue/*blue*	5 0	6 0
188	3d. dull purple and purple ..	3 0	3 0
189	4d. dull purple and black ..	3 6	4 0
190	5d. dull purple and green ..	4 6	5 0
191	6d. dull purple and carmine	4 0	4 6
192	1s. green and carmine ..	17 6	17 6
193	5s. green and black	40 0	45 0
194	£1 grey-black and ultram...	£9	

1904–9. *T* **23.** *Wmk. Mult. Crown CA. P* 14.

No.	Stamp	Unused	Used
195	½d. green and pale green, O	1 9	1 3
196	1d. purple and black/*red*, O	0 10	0 6
197	1s. green & carm., C (1909)	5 0	6 0

1906–12. *T* **23** *and* **24.** *Wmk. Mult. Crown CA. P* 14.

No.	Stamp	Unused	Used
198	½d. green, O (1908)	1 3	0 4
199	1d. red, O (1906)	0 8	0 3
200	2½d. bright blue, O (1910) ..	1 6	2 0
201	6d. dull purple, C (1910) ..	3 0	3 6
202	1s. black/*green*, C (1911) ..	7 6	8 6
203	5s. green & red/*yell.*, C (1911)	50 0	52 6
204	£1 pur. & blk./*red*, C (1912)	£6	£8

25

26

(Typo. De La Rue & Co.)

1912–23. *T* **25** *and* **26** (*½d., 2d., 4d., 6d., 2s. 6d., and 5s*). *Wmk. Mult. Crown CA. P* 14.

No.	Stamp	Unused	Used
205	½d. brown, O (1916) ..	0 2	0 4
206	½d. deep brown, O (1916) ..	0 3	0 6
207	½d. green, O	0 6	0 6
208	½d. yellow-green, O (1915) ..	0 6	0 6
209	½d. blue-green, O (1917) ..	0 6	0 6
210	1d. carmine, O	1 3	0 6
211	1d. bright scarlet, O (1916) ..	0 6	0 4
212	1d. deep rose, O (1919) ..	0 6	0 3
213	2d. greyish slate O ..	1 6	0 10
214	2½d. bright blue, O ..	2 0	2 6
215	3d. purple/*yellow*, O ..	3 6	4 0
	a. On lemon (1915) ..	5 0	6 0
	b. On pale yellow (Die I) ..	4 0	4 6
	c. On pale yellow (Die II) ..	3 0	3 6
216	4d. black and red/*yellow*, O	8 0	9 0
	a. On lemon	7 6	8 0
	b. On orange-buff ..	35 0	40 0
	c. On pale yellow (Die I) (1921)	5 0	5 0
	d. On pale yellow (Die II) (1923)	4 0	4 6
217	5d. dull pur. & olive-green, C	4 0	5 0
218	6d. dull & bright purple, C	4 0	5 0
219	1s. black/*green*, C ..	15 0	16 0
	a. White back ..	6 6	7 0
	b. On blue-green, olive back (1917)	7 6	8 0
	c. On emerald back (Die I) (1921)	7 6	8 6
	d. On emerald back (Die II) (1922)	8 6	5 0
220	2s. 6d. blk. & red/*blue*, C ('16)	22 6	20 0
221	5s. green and red/*yellow*, C ..	27 6	30 0
222	£1 pur. & blk./*red*, C (Die I)	90 0	95 0
	a. Die II	80 0	85 0

No. 215 exists with wmk. sideways.

WAR STAMP

(27)

1916–19. *T* **25** *overprinted locally with T* **27.**

No.	Stamp	Unused	Used
223	½d. green	0 2	0 4
224	½d. yellow-green (1916) ..	0 3	0 5
	a. Overprint double		
	b. Overprint inverted	£15	
225	1d. carmine	5 0	6 0
226	1d. bright scarlet	0 8	0 8
	a. Overprint omitted (strip of 12, one stamp without opt.) ..	£35	
	b. Overprint inverted	£8	
227	1d. deep rose (1919) ..	0 4	0 6

No. 226*a* occurred on one sheet only, the overprint being so misplaced that all the stamps of the last vertical row of the second pane escaped the overprint entirely. The first impression of the overprint was imprinted on the left-hand margin of the left-hand pane.

1922–27. *T* **25** *and* **26.** (*New values, 1½d. and 2s. T* **26.**) *Wmk. Mult. Script CA. P* 14.

No.	Stamp	Unused	Used
228	½d. deep brown, O	0 9	1 0
229	½d. green, O	0 2	0 2
230	1d. carmine-red, O	3 6	2 6
231	1d. violet, O	0 6	0 8
232	1½d. scarlet, O	0 8	1 0
233	2d. grey, O	1 0	0 6
234	3d. bright blue, O	1 6	1 9
235	4d. black & red/*yellow*, O ..	2 6	3 0
236	5d. dull pur. & sage-green, O	2 0	2 6
237	6d. dull and bright purple, O	2 6	2 9
238	1s. black/*emerald*, C.. ..	6 0	5 0
239	2s. purple & blue/*blue*, C ..	12 6	15 0
240	2s. 6d. black & red/*blue*, C..	15 0	16 0
241	5s. green and red/*yellow*, C..	30 0	32 6

1935 (6 May). *Silver Jubilee. As T* **13** *of Antigua, inscr.* "FIJI." *Recess. D.L.R. & Co. Wmk. Mult. Script CA. P* 13½ × 14.

No.	Stamp	Unused	Used
242	1½d. deep blue and carmine ..	1 0	1 6
243	2d. ultramarine and grey ..	2 0	3 0
244	3d. brown and deep blue ..	6 0	7 0
245	1s. slate and purple ..	10 0	17 6

POSTAGE DUE STAMPS.

D 1

D 2

1917 (Jan.). *Type* D **1.** *Printed locally, on thick, yellowish white laid paper. P* 11.

No.	Stamp	Unused	Used
D 1	½d. black	£20	£12
D 2	1d. black	£5	60 0
D 3	2d. black	60 0	35 0
D 4	3d. black	£5	80 0
D 5	4d. black	£16	£16

1917 (April). *Narrower setting, value in ½d. as Type* D **2.**

No.	Stamp	Unused	Used
D 5*a*	½d. black	£12	£8
D 5*b*	1d. black	£5	40 0

1d. stamps must have wide margins (3½ to 4 mm.) on the vertical sides to be No. D 2. Stamps with narrow margins of approximately the same width on all four sides are No. D 5*b*.

D 3

(Typo. De La Rue & Co.)

1918 (1 June). *Wmk. Mult. Crown CA.* P 14.

D 6 D 3 ½d. black 0 2 0 4
D 7 „ 1d. black 0 4 0 5
D 8 „ 2d. black 0 4 0 6
D 9 „ 3d. black 0 6 0 9
D 10 „ 4d. black 0 9 1 0

GAMBIA.

1

(Typo. and embossed by De La Rue & Co.)

1869 (Jan.). *T* 1. *No wmk. Imperf.*

1 4d. brown £25 £12
2 4d. pale brown £20 £14
3 6d. deep blue £20 £12
3a 6d. blue £22 £12
4 6d. pale blue £60 £28

1874 (Aug.). *T* 1. *Wmk. Crown CC. Imperf.*

5 4d. brown £25 £15
6 4d. pale brown £25 £15
7 6d. deep blue £20 £15
8 6d. blue £20 £15

NOTE.—The prices of Nos. 1 to 8 are for fine copies, with good margins and embossing. Brilliant or poor copies can be supplied at prices consistent with their condition.

1880 (June). *T* 1. *Wmk. Crown CC.* P 14.

10 ½d. deep orange 7 6 8 6
11 ½d. dull orange 6 6 7 6
a. Twice embossed, one inverted ..
12 1d. marone 6 0 6 0
a. Twice embossed £40
13 2d. rose 20 0 15 0
14 3d. pale dull ultramarine .. 22 0 22 0
14a 3d. bright ultramarine .. 25 0 18 0
15 4d. brown £10 27 6
16 4d. pale brown £10 27 6
17 6d. deep blue 60 0 45 0
18 6d. blue 65 0 42 6
19 1s. green £12 £10
20 1s. deep green £12 £10

The wmk. in this issue is found sideways as well as upright.

1886-87. *T* 1. *Wmk. Crown CA, sideways.* P 14.

21 ½d. myrtle-green (1887) .. 1 6 2 0
22 ½d. grey-green (1887) .. 1 6 2 6
23 1d. crimson (1887) .. 3 0 3 6
23a 1d. aniline crimson (1887) .. 17 6 10 0
23b 1d. pale carmine (1887) .. 6 0 6 0
c. Twice embossed .. £30
24 2d. orange (1887) .. 3 6 4 0
25 2d. deep orange (1887) .. 7 6 6 6
25a 2d. yellow-buff (1887) .. £30
25b 2d. yellow £55
26 2½d. ultramarine 7 6 7 6
27 2½d. deep bright blue 5 0 5 0
28 3d. slate-grey 4 0 5 0
29 3d. grey 4 6 5 0
30 4d. brown 6 0 7 6
31 4d. deep brown 6 0 7 6
32 6d. yellowish olive-green .. 75 0 45 6
32a 6d. olive-green .. .. — 45 6
33 6d. bronze-green 12 6 15 0
33a 6d. deep bronze-green .. 17 6 20 0
34 6d. slate-green 12 6 15 0
35 1s. violet 6 6 10 0
a. Twice embossed, one inverted £35
36 1s. deep violet 17 6 17 6
36a 1s. aniline violet £10

The ½d., 1d., 6d. (No. 32) and 1s. with CA watermark are known imperf.

NOTE.—The majority of the stamps of T 1 with so-called "double embossing" are merely specimens in which the printing and embossing do not register accurately, and have no special value.

2

(Typo. De La Rue & Co.)

1898 (Jan.). *T* 2. *Wmk. Crown CA.* P 14.

37 ½d. dull green 2 0 2 0
38 1d. carmine 2 6 2 0
39 2d. orange and mauve .. 6 6 6 6
40 2½d. ultramarine 7 0 7 6
41 3d. purple and blue .. 15 0 12 6
42 4d. brown and blue .. 15 0 15 0
43 6d. olive-green and carmine .. 20 0 22 6
44 1s. violet and green .. 35 0 37 6

3 4

(Typo. De La Rue & Co.)

1902-5. *T* 3 *and* 4 (5*d.*, 7½*d.*, 10*d.*, *and* 1s. 6*d. to* 3s.). *Wmk. Crown CA.* P 14.

45 ½d. green 1 6 1 9
46 1d. carmine 3 6 2 0
47 2d. orange and mauve .. 6 6 7 6
48 2½d. ultramarine 12 6 12 6
49 3d. purple and ultramarine .. 10 0 10 6
50 4d. brown and ultramarine .. 12 0 15 0
51 6d. pale sage-green & carmine 8 0 9 0
52 1s. violet and green .. 42 6 45 0
53 1s. 6d. grn. & carm./*yell.* ('05) 22 6 25 0
54 2s. deep slate and orange .. 22 6 27 6
55 2s. 6d. purple & brn./*yell.* ('05) 27 6 32 6
56 3s. carm. & green/*yellow* ('05) 30 0 35 0

1904-6. *T* 3 *and* 4. *Wmk. Mult. Crown CA.* P 14.

57 ½d. green 1 9 2 0
58 1d. carmine (1904) .. 3 6 1 6
59 2d. orange and mauve (1906) .. 12 6 12 6
60 2½d. bright blue 5 0 6 0
60a 2½d. bright blue & ultramarine 7 6 8 6
61 3d. purple and ultramarine .. 12 0 10 6
62 4d. brown and ultram. ('06) .. 17 6 20 0
63 5d. grey and black 17 6 20 0

64 6d. olive-grn. & carmine ('06) 17 6 20 0
65 7½d. green and carmine .. 22 6 25 0
66 10d. olive and carmine .. 25 0 27 6
67 1s. violet and green .. 45 0 50 0
68 2s. deep slate and orange .. 70 0 75 0

HALF PENNY

(5)

ONE PENNY

(6)

1906 (April). *Nos. 55 and 56 surcharged with T 5 and 6 respectively, in black.*

69 ½d. on 2s. 6d. purple and brn./*yellow* .. 85 0 90 0
70 1d. on 3s., carm. & green/*yell.* 90 0 95 0

Variety. Surcharge double.

71 1d. on 3s. carm. & green/*yellow* £125

The spacing between the words and bars on No. 69 varies from 4 mm. to 5 mm.

A constant variety exists with broken "E" in the surcharge of No. 69 ("HALFPENNY").

1909. *T 3 and 4. Colours changed. Wmk. Mult. Crown CA. P 14.*

72 ½d. blue-green 1 6 1 9
73 1d. red 2 0 0 8
74 2d. greyish slate 6 6 7 6
75 3d. purple/*yellow* 6 6 6 6
75a 3d. purple/*lemon-yellow* .. 6 0 6 0
76 4d. black and red/*yellow* .. 7 6 7 6
77 5d. orange and purple .. 8 6 9 6
78 6d. dull and bright purple .. 10 0 10 0
79 7½d. brown and blue 9 0 9 0
80 10d. pale sage-green & carmine 12 6 15 0
81 1s. black/*green* 15 0 17 6
82 1s. 6d. violet and green .. 22 0 22 6
83 2s. purple & bright blue/*blue* .. 22 6 25 0
84 2s. 6d. black and red/*blue* .. 30 0 32 0
85 3s. yellow and green 35 0 40 6

7

8

(Typo. De La Rue & Co.)

1912–22. *T 7 and 8 (1½d., 5d., 7½d., 10d., and 1s. 6d. to 5s.). Wmk. Mult. Crown CA. P 14.*

86 ½d. pale green, O 0 9 1 0
87 ½d. green, O 0 6 0 8
88 ½d. deep green, O 0 6 0 8
89 1d. red, O 0 9 0 6
89a 1d. rose-red, O 0 9 0 6
90 1d. scarlet, O (1916) .. 1 6 0 6
91 1½d. olive-grn. & blue-grn., O 4 0 4 6
92 2d. greyish slate, O 2 0 2 6
93 2½d. deep bright blue, O .. 6 0 6 6
94 2½d. bright blue, O 5 0 5 0
95 3d. purple/*yellow*, O 5 0 5 0
a. *On lemon* (1917) 30 0 32 6
b. *On orange-buff* (1920) .. 3 0 3 6
c. *On pale yellow* 3 0 3 6
96 4d. black & red/*yellow*, O .. 8 0 8 6
a. *On lemon* 6 6 7 0
b. *On orange-buff* 5 0 5 6
c. *On pale yellow* 5 6 6 0
97 5d. orange & purple, O .. 4 6 5 0
98 6d. dull and bright purple, O 5 0 6 0
99 7½d. brown and blue, O .. 6 0 6 6
100 10d. pale sage-grn. & car., O 7 0 7 6
101 10d. deep sage-grn. & car., O 8 0 8 6
102 1s. black/*green*, O 7 6 7 6
a. *On emerald back* 7 6 8 0
103 1s. 6d. violet & green, O .. 12 6 15 0
104 2s. purple & blue/*blue*, O .. 15 0 22 6
105 2s. 6d. black & red/*blue*, O .. 18 0 20 0
106 3s. yellow and green, O .. 22 6 25 0
107 5s. grn. & red/*pale yell.*, C ('22) 47 6 55 0

1921–22. *T 7 and 8 (New value, 4s., T 8). Wmk. Mult. Script CA. P 14.*

108 ½d. dull green, O 0 8 0 10
109 1d. carmine-red, O 0 10 0 10
110 1½d. olive-grn. & blue-grn., O 12 6 15 0
111 2d. grey, O 4 0 4 6
112 2½d. bright blue, O 4 0 4 6
113 5d. orange and purple, O .. 7 6 8 0
114 6d. dull and bright purple, O 6 6 7 0
115 7½d. brown and blue, O .. 8 0 8 6
116 10d. pale sage-grn. & car., O .. 8 6 9 0
117 4s. black and red, C (1922) 40 0 45 0

9

10

(Recess. De La Rue & Co.)

1922–27. *T 9 (½d. to 10d.) and 10. Portrait and shield in black. P 14.*

(a) *Wmk. Mult. Crown CA.*

118 4d. red/*yellow* 3 0 3 6
119 7½d. purple/*yellow* 8 0 8 6
120 1s. purple/*yellow* 17 6 20 0
121 5s. green/*yellow* 85 0 90 0

(b) *Wmk. Mult. Script CA.*

122 ½d. green 0 4 0 5
123 ½d. deep green 1 0 0 9
124 1d. brown 0 6 0 6
125 1½d. bright rose-scarlet .. 0 9 0 9
126 2d. grey 0 9 1 0
127 2½d. orange-yellow 2 6 2 9
128 3d. bright blue 2 0 2 6
129 4d. red/*yellow* 3 0 3 6
130 5d. sage-green 6 0 6 6
131 6d. claret 6 0 6 6
132 7½d. purple/*yellow* 10 0 12 0
133 10d. blue 8 6 9 0
134 1s. purple/*yellow* 8 0 9 6
135 1s. 6d. blue 12 6 15 0
136 2s. purple/*blue* 15 0 17 6
137 2s. 6d. deep green 17 6 18 6
138 3s. bright aniline violet .. 30 0 32 6
139 3s. slate-purple £40 £45
140 4s. brown 30 0 35 0
141 5s. green/*yellow* 45 0 50 0
142 10s. sage-green 95 0 £6

Beware of faked specimens of No. 139.

1935 (6 May). *Silver Jubilee. As T 13 of Antigua, inscr. "GAMBIA". Recess. B.W. & Co. Wmk. Mult. Script CA. P 11×12.*

143 1½d. deep blue and scarlet .. 0 8 1 0
144 3d. brown and deep blue .. 3 0 4 6
145 6d. light blue and olive-green 5 0 6 0
146 1s. slate and purple .. 8 6 10 6

All values exist with "double flagstaff" variety

GIBRALTAR.

For stamps of Gibraltar overprinted "Morocco Agencies" see under "Morocco."

GIBRALTAR

(1)

1886. (1 Jan.). *Contemporary types of Bermuda overprinted by Messrs. De La Rue & Co. with T* **1**. *Wmk. Crown CA. P* 14.

No.	Stamp	Unused		Used	
1	½d. dull green	5	0	4	0
2	1d. rose-red	10	6	6	6
3	2d. purple-brown	55	0	50	0
4	2½d. ultramarine	60	0	8	6
	a. Optd. in blue-black				
5	4d. orange-red	65	0	550	
6	6d. deep lilac	90	0	750	
7	1s. yellow-brown	£12		£10	

2

3

4

5

(Typo. De La Rue & Co.)

1886 (Dec.). *T* **2, 3, 4** (*2d., 4d., 6d., and 1s.*) *and* **5**. *Wmk. Crown CA. P* 14.

No.	Stamp	Unused		Used	
8	½d. dull green	5	0	4	6
9	1d. rose	7	6	4	6
10	2d. brown-purple	17	6	12	0
11	2½d. blue	20	0	6	0
12	4d. orange-brown	55	0	57	6
13	6d. lilac	55	0	57	6
14	1s. bistre	£6		90	0

5 CENTIMOS

(6)

1889 (July). *Stamps of December*, 1886, *surcharged as T* **6**, *in black*.

No.	Stamp	Unused		Used	
15	5 c. on ½d. green	6	6	6	0
16	10 c. on 1d. rose	6	0	4	0
17	25 c. on 2d. brown-purple	6	0	5	0
18	25 c. on 2½d. bright blue	10	0	5	0
19	40 c. on 4d. orange-brown	17	6	18	6
20	50 c. on 6d. bright lilac	15	0	17	6
	a. Bisected diagonally (25 c.)				
21	75 c. on 1s. bistre	30	0	32	6

Varieties. (i.) *Small* "1" *in surcharge.* (*No.* 32 *on pane.*)

No.	Stamp	Unused		Used	
22	25 c. on 2d. brown-purple	65	0	65	0
23	25 c. on 2½d. bright blue	80	0	80	0

(ii.) *Broken* "N." (*No.* 59 *on pane.*)

No.	Stamp	Unused		Used	
24	25 c. on 2d. brown-purple	65	0	65	0
25	25 c. on 2½d. bright blue	80	0	80	0

Two varieties of the figure "5" of the 5 c., 25 c., 50 c., and 75 c. may also be found.

7

(Typo. De La Rue & Co.)

1889 (Nov.). *T* **7**. *Issue in Spanish currency. Wmk. Crown CA. P* 14.

No.	Stamp	Unused		Used	
26	5 c. green	0	4	0	4
27	10 c. carmine	1	0	0	4
28	25 c. ultramarine	3	6	0	6
29	25 c. deep ultramarine	4	6	0	6
30	40 c. orange-brown	3	0	3	6
31	50 c. bright lilac	3	6	3	6
32	75 c. olive-green	15	0	15	0
33	1 p. bistre	22	6	22	6
34	5 p. slate-grey	22	6	22	6

Error, value omitted.

No.	Stamp	Unused		Used	
35	No value, carmine	£200			

1895. *T* **7**. *Value in second colour. Wmk. Crown CA. P* 14.

No.	Stamp	Unused		Used	
35a	20 c. olive-green	2	0	2	6
36	20 c. olive green & brown	1	9	1	9
37	1 p. bistre and ultramarine	4	0	4	6
38	2 p. black and carmine	6	0	6	6

1898. *Reissue in English currency. T* **2** *to* **5**. *Value in second colour. Wmk. Crown CA. P* 14.

No.	Stamp	Unused		Used	
39	½d. grey-green	1	3	0	4
40	1d. carmine	1	9	0	3
41	2d. brown-pur. & ultramarine	6	6	7	6
42	2½d. bright ultramarine	6	0	1	9
43	4d. orange-brown and green	12	6	12	6
44	6d. violet and red	15	0	15	0
45	1s. bistre and carmine	17	6	17	6

No. 39 is greyer than No. 8, No. 40 brighter and deeper than No. 9, and No. 42 much brighter than No. 11.

8

9

(Typo. De La Rue & Co.)

1903. *T* **8** (*½d. to 1s.*) *and* **9** (*higher values*). *Value in second colour. Wmk. Crown CA. P* 14.

No.	Stamp	Unused		Used	
46	½d. grey-green and green	3	0	2	0
47	1d. dull purple/*red*	3	6	0	4
48	2d. grey-green and carmine	10	0	10	0
49	2½d. dull purple & black/*blue*	6	6	5	0
50	6d. dull purple and violet	15	0	15	0
51	1s. black and carmine	17	6	17	6
52	2s. green and blue	75	0	75	0
53	4s. dull purple and green	75	0	75	0
54	8s. dull purple & black/*blue*	£5		110	0
55	£1 dull purple & black/*red*	£30		£35	

1904–7. *T* **8** *and* **9.** *Wmk. Multiple Crown CA. P* 14.

No.	Description	Unused	Used
56	½d. dull and bright green, OC	2 0	0 6
57	1d. dull purple/*red*, OC ..	1 3	0 4
	a. Bisected (½d.)	—	£8
58	2d. grey-green & carm., OC ..	7 6	4 0
59	2½d. purple & blk./*blue*, C ('07)	10 0	10 6
60	6d. dull pur. & vio., OC, ('06)	8 6	8 6
61	1s. black and carm., OC ('05)	15 0	16 0
62	2s. green & blue, OC (1905) ..	42 6	42 6
63	4s. deep pur. & green, C ..	£5	£6
64	£1 deep pur. & black/red, C	£30	£35

1907–11. *T* **8** *and* **9.** *Wmk. Mult. Crown CA. P* 14.

No.	Description	Unused	Used
66	½d. blue-green, O	1 3	0 2
67	1d. carmine, O	1 6	0 2
68	2d. greyish slate, O (1910) ..	6 6	4 6
69	2½d. ultramarine, O	6 6	4 6
70	6d. dull & bright purple, C ..	45 0	
71	1s. black/*green*, C (1910) ..	20 0	20 0
72	2s. purple & bright blue/*blue*, C (1910)	50 0	45 0
73	4s. black & carm., C (1910) ..	90 0	90 0
74	8s. purple & green, C (1911)	£18	£25

10

11

(Typo. De La Rue & Co.)

1912–24. *T* **10** (*to* 1s.) *and* **11.** *Wmk. Mul Crown CA. P* 14.

No.	Description	Unused	Used
76	½d. blue-green, O	0 3	0 2
76*a*	½d. yellow-green, O (1917) ..	0 4	0 2
77	1d. carmine-red, O	0 6	0 1
77*a*	1d. scarlet, O (1916) ..	0 9	0 1
78	2d. greyish slate, O	3 6	1 6
79	2½d. deep bright blue, O ..	5 0	5 0
79*a*	2½d. pale ultramarine, O ..	4 0	4 0
80	6d. dull purple & mauve, C	5 0	3 0
81	1s. black/*green*, OC	10 0	10 0
	a. On blue-green, olive back (1919)	8 0	8 6
	b. On emerald surface (1923) ..	8 6	9 0
	c. On emerald back (1924) ..	8 0	8 6
82	2s. dull purple & blue/*blue*, C	17 6	15 0
83	4s. black and carmine, C ..	35 0	30 0
84	8s. dull purple and green, C	60 0	50 0
85	£1 dull pur. & black/*red*, C..	£10	£12

WAR TAX

(12)

1918 (15 April). *T* **10** *optd. locally with T* **12.**

No.	Description	Unused	Used
86	½d. green	0 4	0 6

1918 (June). *As last, but overprint darker and in heavy type.*

No.	Description	Unused	Used
87	½d. deep green	0 4	0 6

3 PENCE (I) THREE PENCE (II)

1921–27. *T* **10** *and* **11.** *Wmk. Mult. Script CA. P* 14.

No.	Description	Unused	Used
89	½d. green, O (1927)	0 4	0 2
90	1d. carmine-red, O (1921) ..	1 0	0 2
91	1½d. chestnut, O (1922) ..	3 6	1 0
92	1½d. pale chestnut, O (1924)	3 0	0 4
93	2d. grey, O (1921)	1 9	1 3
94	2½d. bright blue, O (1921) ..	10 0	10 6
95	3d. bright blue, O (I) (1921)	3 0	2 0
96	3d. ultramarine, O (I)	2 6	2 9
97	6d. dull pur. & mve. C ('23)	5 6	5 6
97*a*	6d. bright pur. & magenta, C (1926)	5 0	4 6
98	1s. black/*emerald*, C (1924) ..	6 0	6 0
99	2s. grey-purple and blue/*blue*, C (1924)	15 0	16 0
99*a*	2s. reddish pur. & blue/*blue*, C (1925)	15 0	12 6
100	4s. blk. & carmine, C (1924)	70 0	80 0
101	8s. dull pur. & grn., C (1924)	£20	£22

1925–32. *T* **10** (1s.) *and* **11.** *New values, etc. Wmk. Mult. Script CA. P* 14.

No.	Description	Unused	Used
102	1s. sage-grn. & blk., C (1929)	10 6	10 6
102*a*	1s. olive & black, C (1932) ..	6 6	7 6
103	2s. red-brn. & blk., C (1929)	10 0	10 6
104	2s. 6d. green & black, C ..	12 0	12 0
105	5s. carmine and black, C ..	25 0	27 6
106	10s. deep ultram. & black, C	45 0	55 0
107	£1 orange & blk., C (1927) ..	£5	£6
108	£5 violet & black, C ..	£45	£50

1930. *T* **10** *inscribed* "three pence". *Wmk. Mult. Script CA. P* 14.

No.	Description	Unused	Used
109	3d. ultramarine (II)	4 0	4 0

13. The Rock of Gibraltar.

(Designed by Capt. H. St. C. Garrood. Recess-printed by Messrs. De La Rue & Co.)

1931–33. *T* **13** (*and similar type*). *Wmk. Mult. Script CA. P* 14 *or* 13½ × 14.

No.	Description	Unused	Used
110	1d. scarlet (1.7.31)	1 0	0 9
111	1½d. red-brown (1.7.31) ..	1 6	1 6
112	2d. pale grey ('32)	2 0	1 6
113	3d. blue (1.6.33)	10 0	10 0

Figures of value take the place of both corner ornaments at the base of the 2d. and 3d. denominations.

1935 (6 May). *Silver Jubilee. As T* **13** *of Antigua, inscr.* "gibraltar". *Recess. B.W. & Co. Wmk. Mult. Script CA. P* 11 × 12.

No.	Description	Unused	Used
114	2d. ultramarine & grey-black	1 6	1 9
115	3d. brown and deep blue ..	3 6	5 0
116	6d. green and indigo ..	6 6	8 6
117	1s. slate and purple ..	10 0	12 6

All values exist with the "double flagstaff" variety.

GILBERT AND ELLICE ISLANDS.

GILBERT & ELLICE

PROTECTORATE

(1)

1911. *T 23 and 24 of Fiji overprinted with T 1, in black (on 1s., in red). Wmk. Mult. Crown CA.*

1 ½d. green, O 25 0 27 6
2 1d. red, O 25 0 27 6
3 2d. grey, O 15 0 17 6
4 2½d. ultramarine, O 17 6 20 0
5 5d. purple and olive-green, C 17 6 20 0
6 6d. dull and bright purple, C 17 6 20 0
7 1s. black/*green*, C 25 0 27 6

Nos. 3 and 5 were only issued with the "Gilbert and Ellice Protectorate" overprint.

Pandanus pine.
2

3

(T 2 recess, T 3 typo. De La Rue & Co.)

1911. *T 2. Wmk. Mult. Crown CA.* P 14.

8 ½d. green 4 0 4 0
9 1d. carmine 6 0 6 0
10 2d. grey 5 0 6 0
11 2½d. blue 6 6 6 6

1912–24. *T 3. Wmk. Mult. Crown CA.* P 14.

12 ½d. green, O 0 6 0 8
12a ½d. yellow-green, O (1916) 0 6 0 8
13 1d. carmine, O 1 0 1 3
13a 1d. scarlet, O 1 0 1 3
14 2d. greyish slate, O (1916) 3 6 4 0
15 2½d. bright blue, O (1916) 2 0 2 6
15a 3d. purple/*yellow*, C (1919) 1 6 1 9
16 4d. black & red/*yellow*, C 2 6 2 9
17 5d. dull pur. & sage-grn., C 2 6 3 0
18 6d. dull and bright purple, C 3 6 4 0
19 1s. black/*green*, C 5 0 6 6
20 2s. purple and blue/*blue*, C 10 6 12 0
21 2s. 6d. black & red/*blue*, C 12 6 15 0
22 5s. green & red/*yellow*, C 25 0 27 6
23 £1 purple and black/*red*, C (Die II), ('24) £8 £12

WAR TAX

(5)

1918 (Sept.). *T 3 overprinted with T 5.*

26 1d. red 0 4 0 6

1922–27. *T 3. Wmk. Mult. Script CA.* P 14.

27 ½d. green, O 0 3 0 6
27a 1d. violet, O 0 8 0 10
28 1½d. scarlet, O 1 3 1 6
30 2d. slate-grey, O 1 9 2 0
35 10s. green & red/*emerald*, C 60 0 65 0

1935 (6 May). *Silver Jubilee. As T 13 of Antigua, inscribed "*GILBERT & ELLICE ISLANDS*". Recess. B.W. & Co. Wmk. Mult. Script CA.* P 11×12.

36 1d. ultramarine & grey-black 5 0 8 6
37 1½d. deep blue and scarlet 4 6 6 6
38 3d. brown and deep blue 25 0 32 6
39 1s. slate and purple 55 0 60 0

GOLD COAST.

1

(Typo. De La Rue and Co.)

T 1

1875 (July). *Wmk. Crown CC.* P 12½.

1 1d. blue £6 65 0
2 4d. magenta £8 95 0
3 6d. orange £10 50 0

1876–79. *Wmk. Crown CC.* P 14.

4 ½d. olive-yellow (1879) 17 6 15 0
5 1d. blue 12 6 10 6
a. Bisected diagonally (½d.) — 75 0
6 2d. green (1879) 25 0 17 6
a. Bisected diagonally (1d.) — £8
7 4d. magenta 60 0 15 0
a. Quartered (1d.) — £14
8 6d. orange 45 0 17 6

1883 (May). *No. 7 surcharged locally, in black.*

8a 1d. on 4d. magenta

1883. *Wmk. Crown CA.* P 14.

9 ½d. olive-yellow (Jan. '83) 95 0 35 0
10 1d. blue (May) £28 70 0

1884–89. *Wmk. Crown CA.* P 14.

10a ½d. green (Aug. '84) 1 3 0 9
11 ½d. dull green 0 8 0 4
12 1d. rose-carmine (Aug. '84) 2 0 0 6
12a 1d. carmine 1 3 0 6
b. Bisected diagonally (½d.)
13 2d. grey (Aug. '84) 3 6 1 9
a. Value omitted
13b 2d. slate 2 6 2 0
14 3d. olive-yellow (Sept., '89) 8 6 6 6
14a 3d. olive 7 6 7 6
15 4d. deep mauve (Mar. '85) 4 0 3 0
15a 4d. rosy mauve 4 6 2 6
16 6d. orange (Jan. '89) 8 6 4 6
16a 6d. orange-brown 8 6 4 6
17 1s. violet (1888) 10 6 6 6
17a 1s. bright mauve 6 6 5 0
18 2s. yellow-brown (1888) 40 0 35 0
19 2s. deep brown 10 6 10 0

ONE PENNY.

(2)

1889 (Mar.). *No. 16 surcharged with T 2, in black.*

20 1d. on 6d. orange 90 0 60 0

In some sheets specimens may be found in which the bar and "PENNY" are 8 mm. apart, the normal spacing being 7 mm.

1891 (13 Mar.). *T 1. Value in second colour. Wmk. Crown CA.* P 14.

21 2½d. ultramarine and orange 3 0 1 9

3

4

(Typo. De La Rue & Co.)

1889 (Sept.)–**1894.** *T* **3.** *Wmk. Crown CA.* *P* 14.

22 5s. dull mauve and blue .. 30 0 27 6
23 10s. dull mauve and red .. 70 0 35 0
23*a* 10s. dull mauve and carmine 85 0 40 0
24 20s. green and red .. £120
25 20s. dull mve. & blk/*red* ('94) 85 0 45 0

1898–1902. *T* **3** *and* **4** (*2d., 3d., and 6d.*). *Wmk. Crown CA.* *P* 14.

26 ½d. dull mauve and green .. 0 6 0 4
27 1d. dull mauve and rose .. 0 10 0 4
27*a* 2d. dull mve. & orge.-red ('02) 15 0 17 6
28 2½d. dull mauve and ultram. .. 10 0 12 0
29 3d. dull mauve and orange .. 4 0 4 0
30 6d. dull mauve and violet .. 6 0 4 6
31 1s. green and black 17 6 12 6
32 2s. green and carmine .. 17 6 12 6
33 5s. green and mauve (1900) .. 35 0 30 0
34 10s. green and brown (1900) .. 60 0 30 0

1901 (6 Oct.). *Nos.* 28 *and* 30 *surcharged with T* **2**, *in black.*

35 1d. on 2½d. dull mve. & ultram. 3 0 4 0
36 1d. on 6d. dull mve. & violet .. 3 0 4 0

Variety. "ONE" *omitted.*

37 PENNY on 6d. dull mve. & vio. £15

6

7

(Typo. De La Rue & Co.)

1902. *T* **6** *and* **7** (*2d., 3d., 6d., and 2s. 6d.*). *Wmk. Crown CA.* *P* 14.

38 ½d. dull purple and green .. 0 8 0 4
39 1d. dull purple and carmine .. 0 8 0 3
40 2d. dull purple & orange-red 5 0 5 0
41 2½d. dull purple & ultramarine 6 0 7 6
42 3d. dull purple and orange .. 6 0 4 6
43 6d. dull purple and violet .. 6 0 6 6
44 1s. green and black 6 6 7 0
45 2s. green and carmine .. 25 0 22 6
46 5s. green and mauve 27 6 35 0
47 10s. green and brown 40 0 45 0
48 20s. purple and black/*red* .. £6 £6

1904–7. *T* **6** *and* **7.** *Wmk. Mult. Crown CA.* *P* 14.

49 ½d. dull pur. & grn., O (1907) 3 0 2 6
50 1d. dull pur. & carm., O ('04) 4 0 0 8
a. Chalk-surfaced paper (5.06) .. 3 0 0 6
51 2d. dull pur. and orange-red, O ('04) 4 0 3 0
a. Chalk-surfaced paper (8.06) .. 5 0 5 0
52 2½d. dull pur. & ultram., O (10.06) 20 0 20 0
53 3d. dull pur. orge., O (10.05) 10 6 8 6
a. Chalk-surfaced paper (4.06) .. 8 0 4 0
54 6d. dull pur. & violet, O (5.07) 30 0 10 0
a. Chalk-surfaced paper (9.06) .. 15 0 7 6
57 2s. 6d. green & yellow, C (3.06) 50 0 50 0

1907–13. *T* **6** *and* **7.** *Wmk. Mult. Crown CA.* *P* 14.

59 ½d. dull green, O 0 8 0 2
59*a* ½d. blue-green, O 0 10 0 2
60 1d. red, O 1 3 0 2
61 2d. greyish slate, O (1909) .. 3 0 3 6
62 2½d. blue, O 4 0 3 0
63 3d. purple/*yellow*, C (1909) .. 3 0 1 3
64 6d. dull & deep pur., C (1908) 7 6 2 0
64*a* 6d. dull & brt. pur., C (1911) 6 6 2 6
65 1s. black/*green*, C (1909) .. 7 6 5 0
66 2s. pur. & blue/*blue*, O ('10) .. 22 6 22 6
a. Chalk-surfaced paper 10 6 12 0
67 2s. 6d. blk. & red/*blue*, C ('11) 25 0 27 6
68 5s. green & red/*yell.*, C (1913) 70 0 75 0

8

(Typo. De La Rue & Co.)

1908 (Nov.). *T* **8.** *Wmk. Mult. Crown CA.* *P* 14.

69 1d. red, O 0 4 0 1

9

10

11

(Typo. De La Rue & Co.)

1913–23. *T* **9, 10** (*1d.*), *and* **11** (*2d., 3d., 6d. and 2s. 6d.*). *Wmk. Mult. Crown CA.* *P* 14.

70 ½d. green, O 0 9 0 6
71 ½d. yellow-green, O (1916) .. 0 7 0 6
72 1d. red, O 0 6 0 1
73 1d. scarlet, O 0 6 0 1
74 2d. grey, O 5 0 1 3
75 2d. slate-grey, O 4 0 1 0
76 2½d. bright blue, O 4 0 3 6
77 3d. purple/*yellow*, C ('15) 5 0 1 0
a. White back (1913) 2 6 2 0
b. On orange-buff (1919) .. 12 6 8 6
c. On pale yellow (Die. II) .. 20 0 17 6

78	6d. dull & bright purple, C	5	0	1	6
79	1s. black/*green*, C	6	6	5	0
	a. On blue-green, olive back	8	6	4	0
	b. On emerald back (Die I)	12	0	5	0
	c. On emerald back (Die II)	10	6	4	0
80	2s. pur. & blue/*blue*, C (Die I)	15	0	8	0
	a. Die II	£6		60	0
81	2s. 6d. black and red/*blue*, C (Die I)	12	6	7	6
	a. Die II	35	0	35	0
82	5s. green & red/*yell.*, C (1915)	35	0	35	0
	a. White back	25	0	27	6
	b. On orange-buff	40	0	45	0
	c. On paleyellow (Die I)	60	0	65	0
	d. Die II	60	0	65	0
83	10s. green & red/*grn.*, C (1916)	65	0	65	0
	a. On blue-green, olive back (1919)	50	0	50	0
	b. On emerald back	65	0	65	0
84	20s. pur. & blk./*red*, C (1916)	90	0	60	0

WAR TAX

ONE PENNY

(12)

1918 (JUNE). *T* **10** *surcharged with T* **12.**

85	1d. on 1d. red	0	4	0	6

1921–25. *T* **9** *to* **11.** *Wmk. Mult. Script CA. P* 14.

86	½d. green, O (1922)	0	6	0	4
87	1d. chocolate-brown, O (1922)	0	8	0	2
88	1½d. red, O (1922)	1	6	0	8
89	2d. grey, O (1921)	2	0	1	0
90	2½d. yellow-orange, O (1923)	2	0	2	6
91	3d. bright blue, O (1922)	2	0	1	9
94	6d. dull & brt. pur., C (1922)	4	6	2	0
95	1s. black/*emerald*, C (1925)	8	0	6	0
96	2s. pur. & blue/*blue*, C (1924)	12	6	8	0
97	2s. 6d. blk. & red/*blue*, C('25)	20	0	15	0
98	5s. green & red/*pale yellow*, C (1925)	35	0	37	6
100	15s. dull pur. & grn., C (Die I) (1921)	£10		£10	
	a. Die II (1925)	£7		£7	
102	£2 grn. & orge., C (Die I) ('21)	£20		£20	

In Nos. 88, 100, and 102 (all Type **11**) the words "GOLD COAST" are in distinctly larger letters.

King George V and Christiansborg Castle.

13

(Photo. Harrison & Son, Ltd.)

1928 (1 AUG.). *T* **13.** *Wmk. Mult. Script CA. P* 13½×15.

103	½d. green	0	6	0	1
104	1d. red-brown	0	8	0	1
105	1½d. scarlet	1	9	0	10
106	2d. slate	1	9	0	8
107	2½d. orange-yellow	6	0	6	6
108	3d. blue	3	0	2	0
109	6d. black and purple	5	0	1	9
110	1s. black and vermilion	10	0	4	0
111	2s. black and violet	17	6	8	6
112	5s. carmine and olive-green	35	0	20	0

1935 (6 MAY). *Silver Jubilee. As T* **13** *of Antigua, inscr.* "GOLD COAST". *Recess. B.W. & Co. Wmk. Mult. Script CA. P* 11×12.

113	1d. ultramarine & grey-black	0	6	0	8
114	3d. brown and deep blue	6	0	6	6
115	6d. green and indigo	12	6	15	0
116	1s. slate and purple	15	0	17	6

All values exist with the "double flagstaff" variety.

POSTAGE DUE STAMPS.

D 1

(Typo. De La Rue & Co.)

1923. *Type* D **1.** *Wmk. Mult. Script CA. P* 14.

D 1	½d. black	5	0	6	0
D 2	1d. black	0	2	0	3
D 3	2d. black	0	3	0	5
D 4	3d. black	0	5	0	8

GRENADA.

— **SIMPLIFICATION** (see p. xii) —

Nos. 1 to 29.

2, 3. 5, 6, 7, 8, 13. 14, 19, 15.
21, 22, 23, 16. 24, 26. 27, 29.

1

(Recess. Perkins Bacon & Co.)

1861–62. *No wmk. Rough perf.* 14–16.

1	**1**	1d. bluish green (June, 1861)	£35		50	0
2	„	1d. green (May, 1862)	55	0	27	6
		a. Imperf. between (pair)				
3	„	6d. rose (June, 1861)	£18		50	0

1862 (?). *No wmk. P* 11½.

4	**1**	6d. lake-red	£30			

This stamp has only been found unused.

2

Wmk. s — Wmk. sideways (two points of Star downwards).

1863–71. *W* **2** (*Small Star*). *Rough perf.* 14–16.

5 **1** 1d. green (March (?), 1864) .. 25 0 10 0
6 „ 1d. yell.-grn. (May (?), 1871) 45 0 15 0
7 „ 6d. rose (Feb. (?), 1863) .. £12 15 0
8 „ 6d. orange-red (? 1866) .. £12 15 0
8*a* „ 6d. deep rose (? 1869) (Wmk. s)
9 „ 6d. vermilion (? 1871) .. £12 22 6
a. Double impression ..

1873–80. *W* **2** (*Small Star*). *Clean-cut perf.* 15.

10 **1** 1d. dp. grn. (1873) (Wmk. s) 40 0 25 0
a. Bisected diagonally (½d.)
11 „ 1d. pale green (1878 or '79) (Wmk. s) .. £6 35 0
12 „ 1d. bluish green (1880) .. 65 0 30 0
a. Double impression .. .. — £50
13 „ 6d. dp. verm. (1875) (Wmk. s) £15 22 6

3

1873. *W* **3** (*Large Star*). *Clean-cut perf.* 15.

14 **1** 1d. blue-green (Wmk. s) .. 55 0 27 6
15 „ 6d. orange-vermilion .. £15 22 6

4

1875 (July). *As T* **4**. *W* **3** (*Large Star*). *P* 14

16 1s. deep mauve 90 0 25 0
a. Error. "SHLLIING" .. £175 £75
b. "NE SHILLING" ..
c. Inverted "S" in "POSTAGE" £25 £15

1875 (Dec.). *W* **3** (*Large Star*). *P* 14.

17 **1** 1d. yellow-green 50 0 17 6
18 „ 1d. green 55 0 15 0
a. Bisected .. .. ..

1881 (Apr.). *W* **2** (*Small Star*). *P* 14½, *small holes.*

19 **1** 1d. green (Wmk. s) 30 0 15 0
a. Bisected .. .. ..

1881 (Apr.). *W* **3** (*Large Star*). *P* 14½.

20 **4** ½d. pale mauve (Wmk. s) .. 20 0 20 0
21 „ ½d. deep mauve (Wmk. s) .. 12 6 12 6
a. Imperf. (pair) £15
b. Error. "OSTAGE" (No. 100 on sheet) £8 £6
c. Imperf. Error. "OSTAGE" £75
d. Surcharge double .. £10
e. No hyphen 50 0
22 „ 2½d. rose-lake 40 0 22 6
a. Imperf. (pair) £25
b. Imperf. between (pair) ..
c. No stop after "PENNY" .. £18 45 0
d. Error. "PENCF" (No. 96 on sheet) £20 65 0
23 „ 4d. blue 40 0 25 0

The surcharges of these stamps and of the 1s. of 1875 were made from two founts of type—one about 1½ mm. high, the other 2 mm. high—so we have short and tall letters on the same stamp; also the spacing varies considerably, making some words much shorter than others.

5

1881. *W* **5** (*Broad-pointed Star*). *P* 14½.

24 **4** 2½d. rose-lake .. £12 35 0
a. No stop after "PENNY" .. £38 75 0
b. Error. "PENCF" .. £50 £25
25 „ 2½d. deep claret .. £30 £18
a. No stop after "PENNY" .. £60 £30
b. Error. "PENCF" .. £90 £50
26 „ 4d. blue £12 £25

POSTAGE.

(6)

1883 (Jan.). *Fiscal stamps.* *T* **4**, *printed in orange, and optd. with a Crown and the value in green.* *W* **2** (*Small Star*). *P* 14½.

A. *Overprinted horizontally with T* **6**, *in black.*

27 **4** 1d. orange and green .. £8 75 0
a. "POSTAGE" inverted .. £100 £75
b. "POSTAGE" double .. £70 £60
c. "S" in "POSTAGE" inverted £45 £25

B. *Optd. diagonally with T* **6** *twice on each stamp, the stamps being cut and each half used as ½d.*

28 **4** Half of 1d. orge. & green (½d.) £45 £20
a. Unsevered pair £200 £75

Nos. 27 and 29 come with either normal or sideways wmk.

(7)

C. *Overprinted diagonally with T* **7**, *the stamp being cut and each half used as ½d.*

29 **4** Half of 1d. orange & green .. £15 90 0
a. Unsevered pair £40 £18

A forgery of this pair is frequently offered. The "POSTAGE" is too black and the "O" is thick, instead of thin, as in originals.

Stamps are known with "POSTAGE" written by hand in black or in red. These were apparently used, but were not officially issued.

8

(Typo. De La Rue & Co.)

1883 *Wmk. Crown CA. P 14.*

30 **8** ½d. dull green (Feb.) .. 0 8 0 8
31 „ 1d. carmine (Feb.) .. 27 6 12 6
32 „ 2½d. ultramarine (May) .. 5 0 2 0
33 „ 4d. greyish slate (May) .. 5 0 5 0
34 „ 6d. mauve (May) .. 4 0 5 0
35 „ 8d. grey-brown (Feb.) .. 8 6 8 6
36 „ 1s. pale violet (April) .. 65 0 60 0

All these stamps are printed in rows *tête-bêche* in the sheets, and unused *tête-bêche* pairs of each value can be supplied at the price of two single specimens respectively.

d.
1

POSTAGE.
(9)

1886. *Fiscals, as T 4, surch. with T 9, in black*

A. *Watermark Large Star. P 14.*

37 1d. on 1½d. oran. & grn. (Oct.) 25 0 22 6
a. Inverted £12
b. Double £18
c. Error. "THRFE" £18
d. Error. "PFNCE" £18
e. Error. "HALH" .. ..
f. Bisected diagonally (½d.) ..
38 1d. on 1s. orange & grn. (Dec.) 25 0 27 6
a. No stop after "POSTAGE" ..
b. Error. "SHILLNG" ..
c. Bisected diagonally .. .. — £10
d. Wide space between "ONE" and "SHILLING" ..

B. *Wmk. Small Star. P 14.*

39 1d. on 4d. orge. & grn. (Nov.) 75 0 65 0

10

1887 (Jan.). *Wmk. Crown CA. P 14.*

40 **10** 1d. carmine 1 6 0 8

Note after No. 36 also applies here.

4*d.*
POSTAGE
(11)

HALF
PENNY
POSTAGE
(12)

1888 (31 Mar.). *Fiscal, as T 4, surcharged with T 11, in black. Wmk. Small Star. P 14½.*

A. *4 mm. between value and* "POSTAGE."

41 4d. on 2s. orange and green .. 17 6 17 6
a. Upright "d" (No. 54 on sheet) £18 £18
b. Wide space between "TWO" and "SHILLINGS" .. 95 0 95 0
c. First "S" in "SHILLINGS" inverted £18 £18

B. *5 mm. between value and* "POSTAGE."

42 4d. on 2s. orange and green .. 37 6 37 6
a. Wide space between "TWO" and "SHILLINGS" .. £15 £15
b. First "S" in "SHILLINGS" inverted £30 £30

1889 (Dec.). *Fiscal, as T 4, surcharged with T 12, in black. Wmk. Small Star. P 14½.*

43 ½d. on 2s. orange and green .. 10 0 10 6
a. Surcharge double £20 £20
b. Wide space between "TWO" and "SHILLINGS" .. 40 0 40

POSTAGE
d.
AND 1
REVENUE
(13)

POSTAGE
AND
REVENUE
1d.
(14)

1890 (Dec.). *Fiscal, as T 4, surcharged with T 13, in black. Wmk. Small Star. P 14½.*

44 1d. on 2s. orange and green .. 22 6 25 0
a. Surcharge inverted £20
b. Wide space between "TWO" and "SHILLINGS" £8 £8
c. First "S" in "SHILLINGS" inverted .. .. ..

1891 (Jan.). *Fiscal, as T 4, surcharged with T 14, in black. Wmk. Small Star. P 14½.*

45 1d. on 2s. orange and green .. 22 6 25 0
a. No stop after "1d" £12
b. Wide space between "TWO" and "SHILLINGS" .. £8
c. First "S" in "SHILLINGS" inverted .. .. ..

1891 (Jan.). *Surch. with T 14, in black.*

46 **8** 1d. on 8d. grey-brown .. 15 0 15 0
a. Tete-beche (pair) 35 0
b. Surcharge inverted £18
c. No stop after "1d" £10 £9

2½d.
(15)

1891 (Dec.). *Surch. with T 15, in black.*

47 **8** 2½d. on 8d. grey-brown .. 17 6 17 6
a. Tête-bêche (pair) 35 0
b. Inverted surcharge ..
c. Double surcharge .. .. — £12
d. Double surch., one inverted — £12

There are two types of fraction; in one the "1" has horizontal serif and the "2" commences in a ball; in the other the "1" has sloping serif and the "2" is without ball.

Each type occurs 30 times in the pane of 60.

16

17

(Typo. De La Rue & Co.)

1895–99. *Wmk. Crown CA. P 14.*

48 **17** ½d. mauve & green (1899) 1 3 1 3
49 **16** 1d. mauve & carm. (1896) 1 3 0 6
50 „ 2d. mauve & brn. (1899) .. 27 6 25 0
51 „ 2½d. mauve & ultramarine 5 0 4 0
52 **17** 3d. mauve and orange .. 7 6 8 0
53 **16** 6d. mauve and green .. 8 0 8 6
54 **17** 8d. mauve and black .. 25 0 25 0
55 **17** 1s. green and orange .. 12 6 15 0

21. Flagship of Columbus.

(Recess. De La Rue & Co.)

1898 (15 Aug.). *400th Anniv. of discovery of Grenada by Columbus. Wmk. Crown CC. P 14.*

56	21	2½d. ultramarine	6	6	7	0
		a. Bluish paper	25	0	27	6

22 23

(Typo. De La Rue & Co.)

1902. *Wmk. Crown CA. P 14.*

57	22	½d. dull purple & green	1	6	1	3
58	23	1d. dull purple & carmine	1	6	0	9
59	,,	2d. dull purple & brown	8	6	10	0
60	,,	2½d. dull purple & ultram.	8	6	8	6
61	22	3d. dull purple & orange	6	6	5	0
62	23	6d. dull purple & green	10	0	12	6
63	22	1s. green and orange	17	6	20	0
64	,,	2s. green and ultram.	27	6	30	0
65	23	5s. green and carmine	45	0	50	0
66	22	10s. green and purple	£6		£7	

1904–6. *Wmk. Mult. Crown CA. P 14.*

67	22	½d. pur. & green, O ('05)	8	6	8	6
68	23	1d. pur. & carm., O ('04)	8	6	6	0
69	,,	2d. pur. & brown, O ('05)	27	6	27	6
70	,,	2½d. pur. & ultram, O ('05)	32	6	35	0
71	22	3d. pur. & orge., OC, ('05)	7	0	7	6
72	23	6d. pur. & grn., OC ('06)	10	0	10	6
73	22	1s. green & orge., O ('05)	12	0	15	0
74	,,	2s. grn. & ultram., OC ('06)	35	0	35	0
75	23	5s. grn. & carm., O ('06)	60	0	62	6
76	22	10s. grn. & purple, O ('06)	£15		£15	

24. Badge of the Colony. **25**

(Recess. De La Rue & Co.)

1906. *Wmk. Mult. Crown CA. P 14.*

77	24	½d. green	1	6	1	3
78	,,	1d. carmine	1	9	0	8
79	,,	2d. orange	7	6	7	6
80	,,	2½d. blue	15	0	8	0
81	,,	2½d. ultramarine	20	0	12	6

(Typo. De La Rue & Co.)

1908. *Wmk. Crown CA. P 14.*

82	25	1s. black/*green*, C	25	0	27	6
83	,,	10s. green and red/*green*, C	£5		£6	

1908–11. *Wmk. Mult. Crown CA. P 14.*

84	25	3d. dull purple/*yellow*, C	5	0	6	0
85	,,	6d. dull purple & purple, C	25	0	27	6
86	,,	1s. black/*green*, C (1911)	12	6	12	6
87	,,	2s. blue & purple/*blue*, C	27	6	27	6
88	,,	5s. green & red/*yellow*, C	50	0	55	0

26

WAR TAX
(27)

WAR TAX
(28)

(Typo. De La Rue & Co.)

1913 (Jan.)–**1921.** *Wmk. Mult. Crown CA. P 14.*

89	26	½d. yellow-green, O	0	6	0	2
90	,,	½d. green, O	0	4	0	2
91	,,	1d. red, O	0	6	0	2
92	,,	1d. scarlet, O (1916)	0	6	0	2
93	,,	2d. orange, O	1	6	1	9
94	,,	2½d. bright blue, O	2	6	2	0
95	,,	2½d. dull blue, O	2	6	2	6
96	,,	3d. purple/*yellow*, C	3	0	2	6
		a. White back	4	0	4	6
		b. On lemon	3	6	4	0
		c. On pale yellow	3	0	3	6
97	,,	6d. dull & bright pur., C	4	6	5	0
98	,,	1s. black/*green*, C	7	6	8	6
		a. White back	6	0	7	6
		b. On blue-green, olive back	90	0	£5	
		c. On emerald surface	10	6	10	6
		d. On emerald back	6	0	7	6
99	,,	2s. purple & blue/*blue*, C	15	0	20	0
100	,,	5s. grn. & red/*yellow*, C	25	0	27	6
		a. On pale yellow	30	0	32	6
101	,,	10s. green & red/*green*, C	70	0	75	0
		a. On emerald back	60	0	62	6

1916 (1 June)–**1918.** *Optd. locally with* **T 27**, *in black.*

109	26	1d. carmine	7	6	8	6
		a. Small "A" in "WAR"	15	0	17	6
		b. Very small "A" in "TAX"	15	0	17	6
110	,,	1d. red	15	0	17	6
		a. Small "A" in "WAR"	25	0	30	0
		b. Very small "A" in "TAX"	25	0	30	0
		c. "T△X"	65	0	70	0

Variety a. occurs three times on the pane—on Nos. 29, 38 and 48. Variety b. occurs only once—on No. 11. Variety c. occurs on second stamp from left on bottom row of the left-hand pane. The normal "A" is 2¼ mm. high, that of Variety a. 2 mm., and of Variety b. 1½ mm.

Overprinted with **T 28** *in London.*

(*a*) *On white paper.*

111	26	1d. scarlet (Sept., '16)	0	4	0	4

(*b*) *On bluish paper.*

112	26	1d. carmine-red (May, '18)	0	4	0	6

1921–31. *Wmk. Mult. Script CA. P 14.*

113	26	½d. green, O	0	6	0	2
114	,,	1d. carmine-red, O	0	10	0	4
115	,,	2d. orange, O	1	6	1	6
116	,,	2½d. deep dull blue, O	10	0	10	0
116*a*	,,	2½d. bright blue, O (1926)	2	6	2	0
116*b*	,,	2½d. bright ultram., O ('31)	2	9	2	9
117	,,	6d. dull & bright pur., C	6	0	6	6
118	,,	1s. black/*emerald*, C	8	0	9	0
119	,,	2s. pur. & blue/*blue*, C	15	0	17	6
120	,,	5s. grn. & red/*pale yell.* C	25	0	27	6
121	,,	10s. grn. & red/*emer.*, C	35	0	40	0

1921–23. *Colours changed and new values. Wmk. Mult. Script CA. P 14.*

122 **26** 1d. brown, O 0 6 0 2
123 ,, 1½d. rose-red, O 1 0 1 0
124 ,, 2½d. grey, O 2 6 3 0
125 ,, 3d. bright blue, O 3 0 4 0
126 ,, 5d. dull pur. & sage-grn. C 4 0 4 6
127 ,, 9d. dull purple & black, C 6 0 6 6
128 ,, 3s. green and violet, C .. 20 0 22 6

1926–29. *New values and colours. Wmk. Mult. Script CA. P 14.*

129 **26** 2d. grey, O 1 6 1 6
130 ,, 3d. purple/*yellow*, C .. 2 0 2 0
131 ,, 4d. black and red/*yellow*, C 3 0 3 0
132 ,, 6d. black and carmine, C 4 6 4 6
133 ,, 1s. chestnut, C .. 6 6 6 6
134 ,, 2s. 6d. black and carmine/*blue*, C ('29) 17 6 20 0

29. Grand Anse Beach.

30. Badge of the Colony.

31. Grand Etang.

32. St. George's.

(Recess. Waterlow & Sons.)

1934 (23 Oct.)–**1936.** *Wmk. Mult. Script CA. P 12½.*

135 **29** ½d. green 0 2 0 3
a. Perf. 12½×13½ ('36) .. 0 8 1 0
136 **30** 1d. black and sepia .. 0 6 0 6
a. Perf. 13½×12½ ('36) .. 1 6 1 9
137 **31** 1½d. black and scarlet .. 0 8 0 10
a. Perf. 12½×13½ ('36) .. 2 6 3 0
138 **30** 2d. black and orange .. 1 0 1 3
139 **32** 2½d. blue 1 3 1 6
140 **30** 3d. black & olive-green .. 2 0 2 6
141 ,, 6d. black and purple .. 4 0 4 6
142 ,, 1s. black and brown .. 10 0 10 6
143 ,, 2s. 6d. black & ultram... 20 0 22 6
144 ,, 5s. black and violet .. 40 0 42 6

1935 (6 May). *Silver Jubilee. As* **T 13** *of Antigua, inscr. "*GRENADA*". Recess. W'low. & Sons. Wmk. Mult. Script CA. P 11×12.*

145 ½d. black and green 0 4 0 8
146 1d. ultramarine and grey .. 0 9 1 0
147 1½d. deep blue and scarlet .. 3 0 3 6
148 1s. slate and purple .. 15 0 17 6

POSTAGE DUE STAMPS.

D 1

1d.
SURCHARGE
POSTAGE
(D 2)

(Typo. De La Rue & Co.)

1892. *Wmk. Crown CA. P 14.*

201 D 1 1d. blue-black 4 6 1 9
202 ,, 2d. blue-black 7 0 2 0
203 ,, 3d. blue-black 10 0 4 0

Nos. 35 and 34 surch. locally as Type **D 2**, *in black.*

204 **8** 1d. on 8d. grey-brown .. 85 0 5 6
205 ,, 2d. on 8d. grey-brown .. £18 20 0
206 ,, 1d. on 6d. mauve 30 0 4 0
a. Surcharge double .. .. — 70 0
207 ,, 2d. on 6d. mauve 30 0 7 0

1906. *Wmk. Mult. Crown CA. P 14.*

208*a* D 1 1d. blue-black 1 0 1 0
209 ,, 2d. blue-black 1 3 1 3
210 ,, 3d. blue-black 2 6 2 6

1921–22. *As Type* **D 1**, *but inscribed "*POSTAGE DUE*". Wmk. Mult. Script CA. P 14.*

211 1d. black 0 2 0 2
212 1½d. black 0 3 0 3
213 2d. black 0 3 0 3
214 3d. black 0 5 0 8

GRIQUALAND WEST.

Stamps of the Cape of Good Hope. **T 4** *(4d., 6d., and 1s.) and* **6** *(½d., 1d., 4d., and 5s.), wmk. Crown CC, perf. 14, with various opts.*

1874. *With manuscript surcharge.*

1 1d. in red on 4d. blue (T 4) .. £9 £8

1877 (MAR.). *Overprinted " G.W.", in black.*

2		1d. red	£5	40 0
		a. Overprint double	—	£16

Overprinted " G.W.", in red.

3		4d. blue (T 6)	55 0	22 6

(1) (2) (3) (4) (5) (6)

A. *Overprinted with large capital letter.*

1877. I. *First printings, in black on the 1d. and in red on the other values. Six principal varieties of type.*

4	1	½d. slate	6 6	7 6
5	2	½d. slate	20 0	22 6
6	3	½d. slate	10 0	12 6
7	4	½d. slate	20 0	22 6
8	5	½d. slate	25 0	30 0
9	6	½d. slate	8 6	7 6
10	1	1d. carmine	6 0	4 0
11	2	1d. carmine	45 0	40 0
12	3	1d. carmine	12 6	10 0
13	4	1d. carmine	20 0	10 0
14	5	1d. carmine	37 6	20 0
15	6	1d. carmine	10 0	5 0
16	1	4d. blue (T 4)	85 0	20 0
17	2	4d. blue (T 4)	£12	60 0
18	3	4d. blue (T 4)	£7	35 0
19	4	4d. blue (T 4)	—	£6
20	5	4d. blue (T 4)	—	£7
21	6	4d. blue (T 4)	£6	30 0
22	1	4d. blue (T 6)	65 0	12 6
23	2	4d. blue (T 6)	—	60 0
24	3	4d. blue (T 6)	£5	22 6
25	4	4d. blue (T 6)	£5	22 6
26	5	4d. blue (T 6)	—	60 0
27	6	4d. blue (T 6)	80 0	20 0
28	1	6d. dull violet	35 0	17 6
29	2	6d. dull violet	90 0	30 0
30	3	6d. dull violet	50 0	20 0
31	4	6d. dull violet	£6	60 0
32	5	6d. dull violet	85 0	60 0
33	6	6d. dull violet	30 0	15 0
34	1	1s. green	30 0	10 0
		a. Inverted	—	£10
35	2	1s. green	£5	40 0
36	3	1s. green	35 0	15 0
37	4	1s. green	90 0	20 0
38	5	1s. green	£5	30 0
39	6	1s. green	40 0	12 6
40	1	5s. orange	£10	10 0
41	2	5s. orange	—	40 0
42	3	5s. orange	£12	10 0
43	4	5s. orange	—	40 0
44	5	5s. orange	£20	45 0
45	6	5s. orange	£10	10 0

The setting of the above was in two panes of 60. Sub-types of Types **1**, **2**, and **5** are found. (See also Nos. 71*a*, etc.)

(7) (8) (9) (10) (11)

(12) (13) (14)

1878. II. *Second printing in black for all values. Nine principal varieties of type, one of which is the same as T 6 in the first printing.*

46	7	1d. carmine	5 0	4 0
47	8	1d. carmine	7 6	7 6
48	9	1d. carmine	20 0	20 0
49	10	1d. carmine	90 0	
50	11	1d. carmine	20 0	20 0
51	12	1d. carmine	22 6	20 0
52	13	1d. carmine	85 0	60 0
53	14	1d. carmine	£6	£5
54	6	4d. blue (T 6)	£8	50 0
55	7	4d. blue (T 6)	50 0	15 0
56	8	4d. blue (T 6)	£8	50 0
57	9	4d. blue (T 6)	80 0	25 0
58	10	4d. blue (T 6)	£15	£5
59	11	4d. blue (T 6)	£8	50 0
60	12	4d. blue (T 6)	£8	50 0
61	13	4d. blue (T 6)	£15	£5
62	14	4d. blue (T 6)		
63	6	6d. dull violet	£15	80 0
64	7	6d. dull violet	£6	30 0
65	8	6d. dull violet	£15	80 0
66	9	6d. dull violet	£7	50 0
		a. Overprint double		
67	10	6d. dull violet		
68	11	6d. dull violet	£15	80 0
69	12	6d. dull violet	£15	80 0
70	13	6d. dull violet	—	£6
71	14	6d. dull violet		

The 1d. T **6**, of this printing can only be distinguished from the same variety of the first printing when it is *se-tenant* with another type.

The type without horizontal or vertical serifs, previously illustrated as T **10**, is a broken " G " of the type now shown under that number.

Minor varieties may be found of T **7** and **12**.

Overprinted in red.

71*a*	7	4d. blue (T 6)		
71*b*	,,	1s. green		
71*c*	8	1s. green		
71*d*	7	5s. orange		
71*e*	8	5s. orange		

The other types which should apparently exist are not known. It is probable that these stamps are from a new setting of the first printing in which these types were introduced, and not from impressions in red from the second printing, as a block of 5s. stamps overprinted with T **3** is known, the arrangement of which proves that it does not come from the first setting.

(15) (16)

B. *Overprinted with small capital letter.*

1878 (JULY). I. *First printing, in black, or in red. Two varieties of small " antique " capital, T* **15** *and* **16**, *one upright and the other italic.*

Red overprint.

72	15	½d. slate	7 6	
73	16	½d. slate	6 0	
74	15	4d. blue (T 6)	£9	80 0
75	16	4d. blue (T 6)	—	75 0

Red overprint inverted.

76	15	½d. slate	7 6	7 6
77	16	½d. slate	6 0	7 6
78	15	4d. blue (T 6)	£8	50 0
79	16	4d. blue (T 6)	£12	80 0

*Red overprint double.**

80	15	½d. slate	40 0	
81	16	½d. slate	60 0	

Red overprint double, both inverted.

81*a*	15	½d. slate	60 0	

Black overprint.

81*b*	15	½d. slate	£8	£5
81*c*	16	½d. slate		
82	15	1d. carmine	7 6	1 6

83	16	1d. carmine	4 0	1 6
84	15	4d. blue (T 4)	—	£5
85	16	4d. blue (T 4)	—	£6
86	15	4d. blue (T 6)	60 0	10 0
87	16	4d. blue (T 6)	£5	7 6
88	15	6d. dull violet	50 0	20 0
89	16	6d. dull violet	—	20 0

Black overprint inverted.

90	15	½d. slate	60 0	
91	16	½d. slate	40 0	
92	15	1d. carmine	10 0	7 6
93	16	1d. carmine	60 0	25 0
94	15	4d. blue (T 6)	£6	75 0
95	16	4d. blue (T 6)	£10	30 0

Black overprint double.

96	15	1d. carmine	£6	60 0
97	16	1d. carmine	—	70 0
97*a*	15	4d. blue (T 6)	—	£6
97*b*	16	4d. blue (T 6)		

Black overprint double, both inverted.

98	15	1d. carmine	£6	80 0
99	16	1d. carmine	—	£5
99*a*	15	4d. blue (T 6)		
99*b*	16	4d. blue (T 6)		

Black opt. normal, with red opt. inverted.

100	15 . 15	½d. slate	£9	
101	15 . 16	½d. slate	95 0	
102	16 . 15	½d. slate	£6	

Black opt. inverted, with red opt. inverted.

103	15 . 15	1d. carmine	50 0	50 0
104	16 . 16	1d. carmine	55 0	55 0

G

(17)

II. *Second printing, in black only.*

Small ordinary capital, T 17, *always upright.*

105	½d. slate	7 6	5 0
106	1d. carmine	6 0	1 3
107	4d. blue (T 6)	10 0	2 0
108	6d. mauve	50 0	5 0
109	1s. green	50 0	4 6
110	5s. orange	150 0	5 0

Varieties. (i.) *Overprint inverted.*

111	1d. carmine	—	70 0
111*a*	4d. blue (T 6)	—	40 0
112	6d. mauve	—	50 0

(ii.) *Overprint double.*

112*a*	½d. slate	£8	£6
112*b*	1d. carmine	—	£5
113	4d. blue (T 6)	—	£5
113*a*	6d. mauve	—	£5
114	1s. green	£8	£6
115	5s. orange	£12	65 0

(iii.) *Overprint treble.*

116	1d. carmine		
117	5s. orange	—	£6

Besides the type shown above, which is the commonest, there are in this printing three or four minor varieties differing in the shape and size of the body of the letter. In this setting are also found at least two varieties very like the upright "antique" of the first printing in small capitals.

The stamps of Griqualand West became obsolete in October, 1880, when the stock on hand of Cape stamps overprinted with small "G" was returned from Kimberley to Cape Town and redistributed among various post offices in Cape Colony, where they were used as ordinary Cape stamps.

HELIGOLAND.

Collectors should be on their guard against reprints of Heligoland stamps, which are very numerous and of little value.

1 2

(Engraved by Herr Schilling and printed at the Government Printing Works, Berlin.)

1867. T **1.** *Head embossed in colourless relief. Rouletted.*

1	½ sch. green and rose (Die I.)	70 0	95 0
2	½ sch. green and rose (Die II.)	£8	£12
3	1 sch. rose and blue-green	55 0	70 0
4	2 sch. rose and grass-green	7 6	17 6
5	6 sch. rose and green	6 6	55 0

In Nos. 1 to 9, the second colour is that of the spandrels in the ½ and 1 sch., and of the central background also in the 2 and 6 sch. In Die I the small curl below the chignon is solid and projects downwards, while in Die II it is in the shape of a hook opening to the left.

1869–72. T **1.** P. 13½ × 14½.

6	½ sch. yellow-green and rose	15 0	20 0
7	½ sch. blue-green and rose	15 0	20 0
8	1 sch. rose & pale blue-green	30 0	40 0
9	1 sch. rose and yellow-green	40 0	40 0

1873. T **1.** P 13½ × 14½.

10	¼ sch. rose and green	7 6	£12
11	¾ sch. deep rose & pale green	17 6	£15
12	¼ sch. green and rose	10 0	£12
13	1½ sch. rose and green	12 6	45 0

Error, colours reversed.

14	¼ sch. green and deep rose	17 6	£12

In Nos. 10, 11, 13 and 14 the second colour is that of the central background.

In No. 12 the second colour is also that of the side labels and side marginal lines.

1875. T **2.** *Head embossed in colourless relief.* P 13½ × 14½.

15	1 pf. (½d.) deep green & rose	5 0	50 0
16	2 pf. (½d.) deep rose & green	6 0	90 0
17	5 pf. (½d.) deep yell.-grn & rose	6 0	10 6
18	5 pf. (½d.) deep green & rose	12 6	17 6
19	10 pf. (1½d.) deep rose and deep green	12 6	10 0
20	10 pf. (1½d.) scarlet and pale blue-green	10 0	10 6
21	10 pf. (1½d.) rose aniline and pale yellow-green	20 0	25 0
22	25 pf. (3d.) deep green & rose	10 6	12 6
23	50 pf. (6d.) deep rose & green	12 6	15 0

The first colour given above is that of the central background, the second that of the frame.

3

(Engraved by Herr A. Schiffner and printed at the Imperial Printing Works, Berlin.)

1876. *T* 3. *P* 13½ × 14½.

24 3 pf. (⅜d.) green, red, & yellow-orange .. 17 6 £6
24*a* 3 pf. (⅜d.) pale grn, red, & yell. 40 0
25 20 pf. (2½d.) rose, grn. & yellow 17 6 7 6
26 20 pf. (2½d.) rose-carmine, deep green and orange 75 0 25 0
27 20 pf. (2½d.) dull red, pale green and lemon .. 10 0 10 6
28 20 pf. (2½d.) vermilion aniline, bright green and lemon .. 12 6 15 0

Colours. 3 pf. (1) Frame and top band of shield. (2) Centre band of shield. (3) Border of shield.

20 pf. (1) Frame and centre band. (2) Upper band. (3) Border of shield.

4

5

(Engraved by Herr A. Schiffner and printed at the Imperial Printing Works, Berlin.)

1879. *T* 4 *and* 5. (*a*) *P* 13½ × 14½.

29 1 m. (1s.) deep grn., scar., & blk. 20 0 45 0
30 1 m. (1s.) deep grn., rose aniline, and black .. 50 0 50 0
31 5 m. (5s.) deep green, rose aniline, and black .. 30 0 £10

(*b*) *P* 11½.

32 1 m. (1s.) deep green, scarlet, and black .. £8
33 5 m. (5s.) deep green, scarlet, and black .. £10
a. Imperf. between (pair) £50

The stamps perf. 11½ are given above on the ground that specimens exist on the original envelopes, and are known to have been genuinely postally used.

Numerous reprints of the ¼ sch. (including the *error*), ½ sch. (Die. II), ¾ sch., 1 sch., 1½ sch., 2 sch., 6 sch., 1 pf., 2 pf., and 3 pf. were made between 1875 and 1895. It is quite impossible to describe all the reprints in a note; but collectors should be cautious not to purchase stamps of which reprints exist, unless they have been passed by an expert.

Heligoland was ceded to Germany, 9 Aug., 1890.

HONG KONG.

PRINTERS. The dies of all the postage and postage due stamps of Hong Kong were engraved and the stamps surface-printed by De La Rue & Co. unless otherwise stated.

1

2

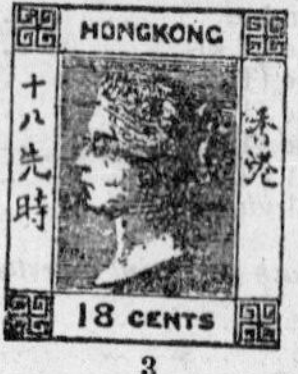

3

1862 (8 Dec.). *No wmk.* *P* 14.

1 1 2 c. brown 40 0 20 0
a. Deep brown 50 0 30 0
2 ,, 8 c. yellow-buff 60 0 22 6
3 ,, 12 c. pale greenish blue .. 55 0 25 0
4 3 18 c. lilac 60 0 25 0
5 ,, 24 c. green £6 35 0
6 ,, 48 c. rose £15 60 0
7 ,, 96 c. brownish grey £14 55 0

NOTE.—*Mint or fine used specimens of the earlier Hong Kong stamps are rarely met with and are worth considerably more than our prices, which are for stamps in average condition. Inferior specimens can be supplied at much lower prices.*

1863–74. *Wmk. Crown CC.* *P* 14.

8 1 2 c. deep brown (1865) .. 25 0 7 6
a. Brown 15 0 2 6
b. Pale yellowish brown .. 17 6 2 6
9 2 4 c. grey (1863) 6 6 5 0
a. Slate 10 6 3 0
b. Deep slate 17 6 4 6
c. Greenish grey 35 0 10 0
d. Bluish slate 35 0 10 6
e. Variety. Perf. 12½. (1874) £20 £8
10 ,, 6 c. lilac (1863) 35 0 10 6
a. Mauve 37 6 17 6
11 1 8 c. pale dull orange (1865) 37 6 5 0
a. Brownish orange .. 55 0 6 0
b. Bright orange 40 0 5 0
12 ,, 12 c. pale gr'nish blue ('64 ?) 70 0 10 6
a. Pale blue 6 6 6 0
b. Deep blue 30 0 8 0
13 3 18 c. lilac (1866) £25 75 0
14 ,, 24 c. green (1865) 35 0 7 6
a. Pale green 50 0 8 0
b. Deep green 75 0 12 0
15 2 30 c. vermilion (1863) .. 90 0 17 6
a. Orange-vermilion .. 80 0 20 0
16 ,, 30 c. mauve (1871) 25 0 7 6
17 3 48 c. pale rose (1865) .. 60 0 20 0
a. Rose-carmine 40 0 12 6
b. Bright claret .. ..
18 ,, 96 c. olive-bistre (1865) £50 £10
19 ,, 96 c. brownish grey (1866) 45 0 17 6
a. Brownish black 55 0 17 6

There is a wide range of shades in this issue, of which we only indicate the main groups.

No. 12 is the same shade as No. 3 without wmk., the impression having a waxy appearance.

16 cents. (4) 28 cents. (5)

1876–77. *Nos.* 13 *and* 16 *surch. with T* 4 *or* 5.

20 3 16 c. on 18 c. lilac (1877) .. £9 55 0
21 2 28 c. on 30 c. mauve (1876) 65 0 25 0

1877 (Aug.). *Wmk. Crown CC.* *P* 14.

22 3 16 c. yellow 90 0 27 6

5 cents. (6) 10 cents. (7)

1880 (MAR.). *Surcharged with T 6 or 7.*

23 1 5 c. on 8 c. bright orange (No. 11*b*) 60 0 20 0
a. Surcharge inverted
24 3 5 c. on 18 c. lilac (No. 13) 40 0 20 0
25 1 10 c. on 12 c. pale blue (No. 12*a*) 60 0 20 0
a. Blue 50 0 17 6
26 3 10 c. on 16 c. yellow (No. 22) £6 35 0
a. Surcharge inverted
27 „ 10 c. on 24 c. green (No. 14) 45 0 20 0

1880. *Wmk. Crown CC. P 14.*

28 1 2 c. dull rose 15 0 6 6
a. Rose 12 6 6 6
29 2 5 c. blue 25 0 10 0
30 „ 10 c. mauve 37 6 10 0
31 3 48 c. brown 85 0 35 0

1882-83. *Wmk. Crown CA. P 14.*

32 1 2 c. rose-lake 25 0 17 6
a. Rose-pink 45 0 35 0
b. Variety. Perf. 12 .. ..
33 „ 2 c. carmine 2 0 0 4
a. Aniline carmine 3 6 0 4
34 2 5 c. pale blue 4 0 0 4
a. Blue 2 6 0 4
35 „ 10 c. dull mauve 35 0 10 0
36 „ 10 c. green (1883) 22 6 2 0
a. Deep blue-green £16 15 0

20 CENTS	50 CENTS	1 DOLLAR
(8)	(9)	(10)

1885 (JUNE). *Surcharged with T 8 to 10.* (*Wmk Crown CA. P 14.*)

37 2 20 c. on 30 c. orange-red .. 15 0 4 0
a. Double surcharge .. ..
38 3 50 c. on 48 c. yellowish brn. 25 0 15 0
39 „ $1 on 96 c. grey-olive .. 37 6 22 6

1891 (1 JAN.). *Wmk. Crown CA. P 14.*

40 2 10 c. purple/*red* 2 0 0 4
41 „ 30 c. yellowish green .. 22 6 15 0
a. Grey-green 15 0 10 0

NOTE.—No. 41, and the provisionals formed by surcharging this stamp, should not be confused with faded or washed copies of the grey-green, which turns to a very yellow-green shade when damped.

Surch. with T 8 to 10. (*Wmk. Crown CA. P 14.*

42 2 20 c. on 30 c. yellowish green (No. 41) 22 6 30 0
a. Grey-green (No. 41*a*) .. 10 6 15 0
43 3 50 c. on 48 c. dull purple .. 20 0 22 6
44 „ $1 on 96 c. purple/*red* .. 40 0 35 0

弍	五十	五十	壹員
(11) (20 c.)	(12) (50 c.)	(12*a*)	(13) ($1)

1891. *Surch. with T 8 to 10. As Nos. 42 to 44, but handstamped Chinese character added at top of label at left.* (*T 11 to 13.*)

45 2 20 c. on 30 c. yellowish grn. 10 0 4 6
a. Grey-green 5 0 3 0
b. Type 11 double £18
c. Type 11 double, one inverted
d. Type 11 at each side .. £16
e. Type 11 omitted (pair with normal) .. £12
f. Type 11 at each side and Type 12 (50 c.) twice at left .. ..
g. Type 11 large £5 40 0
h. "20 CENTS" double

45 3 50 c. on 48 c. dull purple .. 8 6 4 0
a. Type 12 double £15
b. Type 12 inverted ..
c. Type 12 double, one inverte £16
d. Type 12 at each side .. £10
e. Type 12 inverted at left, normal at right
f. Type 12 omitted (pair with normal) 95 0
g. Chinese characters larger (T 12*a*) 17 6 10 0
47 3 $1 on 96 c. purple/*red* .. 30 0 10 0
a. Type 13 at each side .. — £16

1841 Hong Kong JUBILEE 1891	7 cents.	14 cents.
(14)	(15)	(16)

1891 (22 JAN.). *50th Anniversary of establishment of Colony. Overprinted with T 14.*

48 1 2 c. carmine (No. 33) .. 10 6 15 0
a. Short "J" in "JUBILEE" 35 0 35 0
b. Short "U" in "JUBILEE" 30 0 30 0
c. Broken "1" in "1891" .. 37 6 37 6
d. Tall narrow "K" in "KONG" £8 £8
e. Overprint double .. .. — £40
f. Space between "O" and "N" of "HONG" .. 70 0 70 0

This overprint was applied in a setting of 12, and other less marked varieties therefore exist.

1891. *Surcharged with T 15 or 16.*

49 2 7 c. on 10 c. green (No. 36) (Jan.) 6 6 5 0
a. Antique "t" in "cents." .. £10 40 0
b. Surcharge double £35 £8
50 „ 14 c. on 30 c. mauve (No. 16) (Apr.) 25 0 22 6
a. Antique "t" in "cents." ..

The true antique "t" must not be confounded with a small "t" with short foot, which is sometimes mistaken for it. In the antique "t" the cross-bar is accurately bisected by the vertical stroke, the latter being thick at the top. The lower curve bends towards the right and does not turn upwards so far as in the normal.

Dangerous forgeries of these two surcharges exist.

1896 (?). *Wmk. Crown CA. P 14.*

51 2 4 c. slate-grey 2 0 0 6

1898. *Surcharged with T 10, and hand-stamped Chinese characters as T 13. Wmk. Crown CA. P 14.*

52 3 $1 on 96 c. black 17 6 8 0
a. Grey-black 25 0 12 6
b. Type 13 double .. £5
c. Type 13 inverted ..
d. Type 13 double, one inverted .. ..
e. Type 13 at each side £16
f. Type 13 inverted at left, normal at right ..
g. Type 13 normal at left, inverted at right .. £6
h. Type 13 twice at left, once at right ..

Surcharged with T 10 only.

53 3 $1 on 96 c. black 70 0 70 0
a. Grey-black 95 0

10 CENTS	拾	拾
(17)	(18)	(19)

1898 (April). *Surcharged with* **T 17.**

No.	Type	Description	Unused		Used	
54	2	10 c. on 30 c. grey-green (No. 41*a*)	17	6	17	6
		a. Figures "10" widely spaced (1½ mm.) ..				

As No. 54, *but with Chinese character,* **T 18,** *in addition.*

No.	Type	Description	Unused		Used	
55	2	10 c. on 30 c. grey-green (No. 41*a*)	12	6	12	6
		a. Yellowish green				
		b. Figures "10" widely spaced (1½ mm.)	30	0	30	0
		c. Chinese character large (Type 19)	45	0		
		d. Stamps with and without Chinese surch. *se-tenant* (pair)				

1900–02. *Wmk. Crown CA.* *P* 14.

No.	Type	Description	Unused		Used	
56	1	2 c. dull green	0	8	0	4
57	2	4 c. carmine	1	3	0	4
58	,,	5 c. yellow	4	0	4	0
59	,,	10 c. ultramarine	2	0	0	6
60	1	12 c. blue (1902)	7	6	8	6
61	2	30 c. brown (1901)	6	6	7	6

20

21

22

23

1903. *Wmk. Crown CA.* *P* 14.

No.	Type	Description	Unused		Used	
62	20	1 c. dull purple and brown	0	6	0	2
63	,,	2 c. dull green	1	0	0	6
64	21	4 c. purple/*red*	1	3	0	4
65	,,	5 c. dull grn. & brn.-orange	3	0	1	9
66	,,	8 c. slate and violet ..	3	0	1	0
67	20	10 c. purple and blue/*blue* ..	5	0	0	10
68	23	12 c. green & purple/*yellow*	3	6	1	9
69	,,	20 c. slate and chestnut ..	5	0	3	6
70	22	30 c. dull green and black ..	8	6	5	0
71	23	50 c. dull green & magenta	17	6	12	6
72	20	$1 purple and sage-green	15	0	10	6
73	23	$2 slate and scarlet ..	50	0	52	6
74	22	$3 slate and dull blue ..	60	0	62	6
75	23	$5 purple and blue-green	65	0	60	0
76	22	$10 slate and orange/*blue* ..	£7		95	0

1904–7. *Wmk. Mult. Crown CA.* *P* 14.

No.	Type	Description	Unused		Used	
77	20	2 c. dull green, C	0	10	0	6
		a. Ordinary paper	1	3	0	6
78	21	4 c. purple/*red*, C	1	0	0	6
		a. Ordinary paper	1	9	0	6
79	,,	5 c. dull grn. & brn.-orge., C	2	0	1	0
		a. Ordinary paper	4	0	3	6
80	22	6 c. orange-verm. & pur., C (1907)	2	6	1	3
81	21	8 c. slate & violet, C (07)	3	6	1	0
82	20	10 c. pur. & blue/*blue*, O	6	0	1	6
83	23	12 c. grn. & pur./*yell.*, C ('07)	7	0	2	6
84	,,	20 c. slate and chestnut, C..	5	0	1	6
		a. Ordinary paper	7	6	2	0
85	22	30 c. dull green & black, C..	7	0	3	0
		a. Ordinary paper	8	0	4	0
86	23	50 c. green & magenta, C ..	7	6	3	[illegible]
		a. Ordinary paper	10	0	4	0
87	20	$1 pur. & sage-green, C..	17	6	5	0
		a. Ordinary paper	20	0	7	6
88	23	$2 slate and scarlet, C ..	50	0	25	0
		a. Ordinary paper	45	0	30	0
89	22	$3 slate & dull blue, C ..	45	0	27	6
90	23	$5 pur. & blue-green, C..	70	0	50	0
91	22	$10 slate & orge./*blue*, C ..	£8		£5	
		a. Ordinary paper	£9		£[illegible]	

1907–11. *Wmk. Mult. Crown CA.* *P* 14.

No.	Type	Description	Unused		Used	
92	20	1 c. brown, O (1910) ..	0	4	0	3
93	,,	2 c. deep green, O ..	1	9	0	[illegible]
		a. Green	1	0	0	[illegible]
94	21	4 c. carmine-red, O ..	1	0	0	[illegible]
95	20	10 c. bright ultramarine, O	2	6	0	6
96	23	20 c. pur. & sage-grn., C ('11)	8	0	5	0
97	22	30 c. purple and orange-yellow, C ('11)	7	6	5	0
98	23	50 c. black/*green*, C (1911)	8	0	7	6
99	,,	$2 car.-red & blk., C ('10)	42	6	45	0

24

25

26

27

28

(A)

(B)

1912–21. *Wmk. Mult. Crown CA.* *P* 14.

No.	Type	Description	Unused		Used	
100	24	1 c. brown, O	0	4	0	2
		a. Black-brown	0	6	0	4
		b. Crown broken at right ..	52	6		
101	,,	2 c. deep green, O ..	0	6	0	2
		a. Green	0	8	0	2
102	25	4 c. carmine-red, O ..	0	8	0	2
		a. Scarlet	1	3	0	2
103	26	6 c. yellow-orange, O ..	2	6	0	8
		a. Brown-orange	1	0	0	8
104	25	8 c. grey, O	5	0	0	8
		a. Slate	5	0	0	9
105	24	10 c. ultramarine, O ..	4	0	0	8
		a. Deep bright ultramarine ..	3	6	0	6
106	27	12 c. purple/*yellow*, C ..	5	0	3	0
		a. White back	2	6	2	6
107	,,	20 c. purple & sage-grn., C	5	0	1	0
108	28	25 c. purple and magenta, C (1914) .. (A)*	10	0	5	0
109	,,	25 c. purple and magenta, C (1920) .. (B)*	17	6	12	6
110	26	30 c. pur. & orge.-yell., C..	10	0	1	6
		a. Purple and orange ..	7	6	2	0

No.	Type	Description	Unused	Used
111	27	50 c. black/*blue green*, C	10 0	2 0
		a. White back	5 0	2 0
		b. On blue-green, olive back	35 0	5 0
		c. On emerald surface	12 6	7 6
		d. On emerald back	7 6	4 6
112	24	$1 pur. & blue/*blue*, C	15 0	4 0
113	27	$2 car.-red & grey-blk., C	30 0	15 0
114	26	$3 green and purple, C	35 0	25 0
115	27	$5 green & red/*green*, C	65 0	35 0
		a. White back	45 0	30 0
		b. On blue-green, olive back	65 0	25 0
116	26	$10 purple & black/red, C	60 0	17 6

* In Type A of the 25 c. the upper Chinese character in the left-hand label has a short vertical stroke crossing it at the foot. In Type B this stroke is absent.

1921–37. *Wmk. Mult. Script CA.* P 14.

No.	Type	Description	Unused	Used
117	24	1 c. brown, O	0 2	0 3
118	,,	2 c. blue-green, O	0 6	0 2
		a. Yellow-green	0 4	0 2
118b	,,	2 c. grey, O (Apr. '37)	0 8	0 3
119	25	3 c. grey, O ('31)	0 6	0 3
120	,,	4 c. carmine-rose, O	0 8	0 2
		a. Carmine-red	0 6	0 2
		b. Top of lower Chinese character at right broken off	12 6	12 6
121	25	5 c. violet, O ('31)	0 8	0 3
122	,,	8 c. grey, O	3 6	3 6
123	,,	8 c. orange, O	1 0	1 3
124	24	10 c. bright ultram., O	0 8	0 2
124a	27	12 c. purple/*yellow*, C ('33)	1 0	1 0
125	,,	20 c. pur. & sage-grn., C	2 0	1 0
126	28	25 c. pur. & mag., C (B)	2 0	1 3
127	26	30 c. pur. & chrome-yell. C	5 0	2 0
		a. Purple and orange-yellow	3 0	1 0
128	27	50 c. black/*emerald*, C ('24)	4 0	1 3
129	24	$1 pur. & blue/*blue*, C	7 6	2 6
130	27	$2 carmine-red & grey-black, C	12 6	5 0
131	26	$3 green and dull purple, C ('26)	25 0	12 6
132	27	$5 green and red/*emerald*, C ('25)	40 0	17 6

1935 (6 MAY). *Silver Jubilee. As* T **13** *Antigua, inscr.* "HONG KONG". *Recess. B.W. & Co. Wmk. Mult. Script CA.* P 11 × 12.

No.	Description	Unused	Used
133	3 c. ultramarine & grey-black	0 4	0 5
134	5 c. green and indigo	1 3	0 9
135	10 c. brown and deep blue	4 0	4 6
136	20 c. slate and purple	6 0	7 6

The 5 c. exists with "double flagstaff" variety.

POSTAGE DUE STAMPS.

D 1

1924. *Wmk. Mult. Script CA (upright or sideways).* P 14.

No.	Type	Description	Unused	Used
D1	D 1	1 c. brown	0 3	0 3
D2	,,	2 c. green	0 3	0 3
D3	,,	4 c. scarlet	0 6	0 8
D4	,,	6 c. yellow	0 8	0 6
D5	,,	10 c. bright ultramarine	0 9	0 8

All values exist with upright and with sideways watermark.

For same design, in other colours, see King George VI catalogue.

FISCALS, ETC., USED FOR POSTAGE.

I. Stamps inscribed "STAMP DUTY."

NOTE.—The dated circular "HONG KONG" cancellation with "PAID ALL" in lower segment normally indicates fiscal, not postal, use, but a few instances are known where it was applied *in red*, for postal purposes.

F 1

F 2

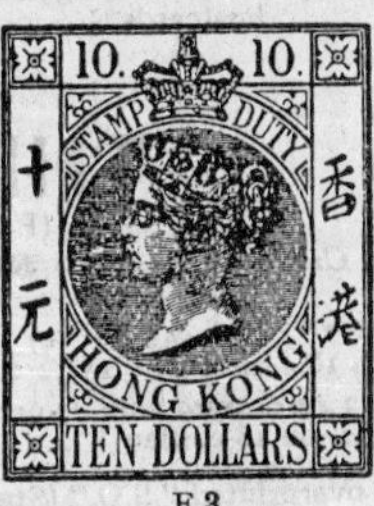

F 3

(Typo. De La Rue & Co.)

1874–1902. *Wmk. Crown CC.*

(*a*) P 15½ × 15.

No.	Type	Description	Unused	Used
F1	F 1	$2 olive-green	40 0	6 6
		a. Thin paper	60 0	10 0
F2	F 2	$3 dull violet	12 6	6 0
		a. Thin paper	17 6	10 0
		b. Bluish paper		
F3	F 3	$10 rose-carmine	£8	£5

(*b*) P 14.

No.	Type	Description	Unused	Used
F4	F 1	$2 dull bluish grn. (1890)	17 6	12 6
F5	F 2	$3 dull mauve (1902)	15 0	10 0
		a. Bluish paper		
F6	F 3	$10 grey-green (? 1884)	£5	

12 CENTS. (F 4)

5 DOLLARS (F 5)

1882. *No.* F3 *surcharged with Type* F **4.**

No.	Type	Description	Unused	Used
F7	F 3	12 c. on $10 rose-carmine	20 0	40 0

1891 (JAN.). *Surcharged with Type* F **5.** *Wmk. Crown CA.* P 14.

No.	Type	Description	Unused	Used
F8	F 3	$5 on $10 purple/*red*	30 0	30 0

F 6

(F 7)

(Typo. De La Rue.)

1890. *Wmk. Crown CA.* P 14.

F9 F 6 2 c. dull purple 1 6 2 6

1897 (Sept.). *Surcharged with Type* F 7.

F10 F 1 $1 on $2 olive-green (No. F1) 12 6 12 6

a. Chinese surcharge wholly omitted £18 £10

F11 „ $1 on $2 dull bluish green (No. F4) 20 0 20 0

a. Chinese surcharge wholly omitted 50 0 40 0

b. Diag. portion of Chinese surcharge omitted

II. Stamps specially surcharged for use on Postcards.

3 CENTS (P 1) THREE (P 2)

1879. *Wmk. Crown CC.* P 14. *Surcharged as Type* P 1.

P1 3 3 c. on 16 c. yellow (No. 22) 32 6 27 6

P2 „ 5 c. on 18 c. lilac (No. 13) .. 22 6 27 6

No. P 2 *surcharged with Type* P 2.

P3 3 3 on 5 c. on 18 c. lilac .. £22

III. Stamps overprinted "S.O." (Stamp Office) or "S.D." (Stamp Duty).

S. O. S. D.

印 厘 (S 1) 印 厘 (S 2)

1891. *Overprinted with Types* S 1 *or* S 2.

S1 S 1 2 c. carmine (No. 33) .. 20 0 20 0

S2 S 2 2 c. carmine (No. 33) .. 15 0 7 6

S3 S 1 10 c. purple/*red* (No. 40) .. 22 6 22 6

Other fiscal stamps are found apparently postally used, but there is no evidence that this use was authorised.

CHINA.

BRITISH POST OFFICES.

CHINA (1)

1917–21. *Stamps of Hong Kong, 1912–21 (wmk Mult. Crown CA), overprinted with* T 1, *in black.*

1 1 c. brown, O 0 4 0 4

a. Crown broken at side .. £6

2 2 c. green, O 0 8 0 3

3 4 c. carmine-red, O 0 8 0 2

4 6 c. orange, O 1 3 0 8

5 8 c. slate, O 1 9 0 8

6 10 c. ultramarine, O 2 6 0 6

7 12 c. purple/*yellow*, C .. 3 6 1 3

8 20 c. pur. & sage-green, C 4 6 1 0

9 25 c. purple & magenta, C (A) 6 0 2 6

11 30 c. pur. & orange-yellow, C 7 0 1 3

12 50 c. blk./*bl.-grn.*, C (*olive back*) 15 0 4 0

a. On emerald surface .. 12 6 7 6

b. On emerald back .. 10 6 6 0

13 $1 reddish purple and bright blue/*blue*, C 17 6 3 6

13*a* $1 grey-pur. & blue/*blue*, C 22 6 4 6

14 $2 car.-red & grey-black, C 40 0 25 0

15 $3 green and purple, C .. 50 0 50 0

16 $5 green and red/*blue-green*, C (*olive back*) .. 40 0 40 0

17 $10 pur. & black/*red*., C .. 80 0 85 0

1922–27. *As last, but wmk. Mult. Script CA.*

18 1 c. brown, O 0 4 0 4

19 2 c. green, O 0 4 0 4

20 4 c. carmine-rose, O .. 0 6 0 6

a. Lower Chinese character at right broken at top .. 30 0 30 0

21 6 c. orange-yellow, O .. 0 10 1 0

22 8 c. grey, O 1 0 1 3

23 10 c. bright ultramarine, O .. 1 3 1 3

24 20 c. purple and sage-green, C 1 6 1 9

25 25 c. purple & magenta, C (B) 2 6 2 9

26 50 c. black/*emerald*, C (1927) 4 6 5 0

27 $1 purple & blue/*blue*, C .. 15 0 15 0

28 $2 car.-red & grey-black, C 25 0 27 6

The use of these stamps was discontinued as from 1st Oct., 1930, on the closing of the British P.O.'s concerned.

INDIA.

SIMPLIFICATION (see p. xii)

Nos. 1 to 34.

2, 3, 14, 23, 32.

(1)

1852 (1 July). T 1. *Embossed*

S.1 ½ a. white £30 £12

S.2 ½ a. blue £40 £16

S.3 ½ a. scarlet .. .. .. — £125

These stamps were issued under the authority of Sir Bartle Frere, Commissioner in Scinde. They were suppressed in October, 1854.

GENERAL ISSUES.

Under the Honourable East India Company

2

3

(Actual size of ½ a. and 1 a. stamps. Enlargements of 4 a. stamps are proportionate.)

(Lithographed in Calcutta at the office of the Surveyor-General on paper watermarked as T 2 with the Arms of the East India Co. in the sheet).

1854 (April). *T* **3.**

1	½ a. vermilion	£25	
	a. Retouched on the printing stone, several varieties		

This stamp, with 9½ arches in the side border, was prepared for use and a supply was sent to Bombay, but was not officially issued.

4

1854 (1 Oct.). *Die I.* *T* **4.**

2	½ a. blue	50	0	20	0
	a. Printed on both sides				
3	½ a. pale blue	85	0	20	0
4	½ a. deep blue	60	0	20	0
5	½ a. indigo	85	0	35	0

We give the official date of issue, but copies are known which were put on sale as much as a fortnight earlier.

For these stamps a small intermediate or matrix stone of 24 impressions was first made, from which at least 7 primary transfers of 96 impressions were made, four being dated May, 1854, and three probably dated June, 1854. From the first May transfer a large number of secondary transfers were made, while from the last June transfer three secondary transfers are known, dated July, 1854.

These stamps were printed between 5 May and 29 July, 1854. (Printing 30 millions.)

Varieties.

(*a*) *On the intermediate transfer, once in each setting of 24, repeated 4 times in the sheet.*

5*a*	Touch up of chignon, hair on neck, arches .. *From*	£12	75	0
5*b*	Touch up of eye, hair on forehead .. .. *From*	£8	45	0

(*b*) *On the primary transfers, once in each sheet.*

5*c*	Many varieties .. *From*	£8	50	0

(*c*) *On the secondary transfers, occurring rarely in later printings.*

5*d* Several varieties .. ..

4*a*

Die II. *T* **4*a***

6	½ a. blue	80	0	75	0
7	½ a. indigo	80	0	75	0

One primary transfer was made direct from this Die, and dated August, 1854, and two secondary transfers are known.

The bulk were printed between 1 and 12 August, 1854, with some extra sheets on or before 2 Nov. (Printing about 2 millions.)

Varieties.

(*a*) *On the primary transfer.*

7*a*	Several varieties .. *From*	£12	£15

(*b*) *On the secondary transfers.*

7*b* Several varieties .. ..

5

Die III. *T* **5.**

8	½ a. pale blue	£28	55	0
8*a*	½ a. blue	£25	50	0
9	½ a. greenish blue	£30	75	0
10	½ a. deep blue	£32	70	0

It is believed that only one primary transfer was made direct from this Die, and at least six secondary transfers were made from it. One of these secondary transfers was dated August, 1855. The secondary transfers often show considerable retouching.

These stamps were printed between 3 July and 25 August, 1855. (Printing about 4½ millions.)

Varieties.

(*a*) *On the primary transfer.*

10*a* Eye and chignon (Nos. 46, 66) — £10

(*b*) *On the secondary transfers.*

10*b* Many varieties .. ..

THE THREE DIES OF THE ½ ANNA.

DIE I. *Chignon shading* mostly solid blobs of colour. *Corner ornaments*, solid blue stars with long points, always conspicuous. *Band below diadem* always heavily shaded. *Crown and jewels.* The middle and right-hand jewels usually show a clearly defined cross. *Outer frame lines.* Stamps with white or faintly shaded chignons and weak frame-lines are usually Die I (worn state).

DIE II. *Chignon* normally shows much less shading. A strong line of colour separates hair and chignon. *Corner ornaments.* The right corner ornament is characteristic (see illustration) but tends to disappear. It never obliterates the white cross. *Band below diadem.* As Die I but heavier, sometimes solid. *Crown and jewels.* As Die I but usually fainter. *Outer frame lines.* Always strong and conspicuous.

DIE III. *Chignon shading* shows numerous fine lines, often blurred. *Corner ornaments* have a small hollow blue star with short points, which tends to disappear as in Die II. *Band below diadem,* shows light shading or hardly any shading. *Crown and jewels.* Jewels usually marked with a solid squat star. Between the stars there appears a characteristic white ω. *Frame lines* variable.

The above notes give the general characteristics of the three Dies, but there are a few exceptions due to retouching, etc.

6

(*See note below No.* 14.)

Die I. *T* **6.**

11	1 a. deep red	£15	60	0
12	1 a. red	£15	50	0

a. Retouches on the printing stones, many varieties. Used from 60s. *to* £8 *each*

Printing of these stamps commenced on 26 July, 1854, and continued into August. (Printing, see note below No. 14.)

7

Die II. T **7.** *With more lines in the chignon than in Die I, and with white curved line where chignon joins head.**

13	1 a. red..	50	0	40	0
14	1 a. dull red	45	0	40	0

a. Retouches on the printing stones, several varieties. Used, 40s. *to* £8 *each.*

* Very worn printings of Die II may be found with chignon nearly as white as in Die I.

In stamps of Die I, however, the small blob of red projecting from the hair into the chignon is always visible.

These stamps were printed in August and September, 1854. (Total printing, Dies I and II together, about 7½ millions.)

8

Die III. T **8.** *With pointed bust.*

15	1 a. red	£25	£8
16	1 a. dull red	£25	£8

a. Retouches on the printing stones. From £8

These stamps were printed between 7 July and 25 August, 1855. (Printing, about 1½ million.)

9

NOTE.—*Our catalogue prices for four annas stamps are for cut-square specimens in good condition. Stamps cut to shape are worth very little.*

1854 (15 Oct.). *Die I. T* **9**. *Imperf. Blue wavy line separating the stamps on each side, and blue rosettes where the lines cross. Head in first colour.*

		Un-used.	Used.	Used. pairs.
17	4 a. indigo and red ..	£70	£20	£90
18	4 a. blue and pale red	—	£17	£90
	a. Head inverted (cut to shape)	—	£300	
	b. Retouches			

These stamps were printed between 14 and 28 October, 1854. (Printing, 206,000.)

9a

Die I. T **9a**. *With hardly any lines in the upper part of the chignon and the lines on the lower band of the diadem very deficient.*

19	4 a. blue and red ..	£50	£16	£50
20	4 a. indigo and red ..	£50	£15	£50
	a. Head inverted ..			
	b. Retouches on the printing stones, several varieties.	*Used (singles), from £18 to £35 each.*		

These stamps were printed between 1 and 13 December, 1854. (Printing about 400,000.)

9b

Die II. T **9b**. *With the lines of the chignon retouched but not the lines on the lower band of the diadem, which are much shorter and more defective than on Die I in its early state.*

		Un-used.	Used.	Used. pairs.
21	4 a. blue and red ..	£70	£25	£80

These stamps were printed between 6 March and 1 April, 1855. (Printing about 140,000.)

Die II. T **9b**, *but the stamps are spaced 2 to 2½ mm. apart horizontally and vertically, and there are no blue dividing lines or corner rosettes.*

22	4 a. indigo and red	£35	£12	£35
23	4 a. blue and red ..	£26	£10	£26
24	4 a. blue and pale red	£35	£12	£28
	a. Retouches on the printing stones, many varieties.	*Used singles, £12 to £30 each.*		

These stamps were printed between 2 April and 9 May, 1855. (Printing about 540,000.)

Die II. T **9b**, *but the stamps are spaced 5½ to 6 mm. apart horizontally, and 4 mm. vertically, and there are no blue dividing lines or rosettes.*

25	4 a. blue and red	£55	£18	£7
26	4 a. indigo and red	—	£18	£7
	a. Retouches on the printing stones of which there are many varieties.	*Used singles, from £18 to £30*		

These stamps were printed between 4 October and 3 November, 1855. (Printing 380,000.)

For identification of the stamps of Die II when the margins are insufficient, see *The Four Annas Lithographed Stamps of India*, 1854–55, by D. R. Martin, R.E., and E. A. Smythies, F.R.P.S.L. (*Stanley Gibbons, Ltd.* 15s. net, post. extra.)

Serrated perf. about 18, or pin-perf.

27 ½ a. blue (Die I) ..
28 1 a. red (Die I) ..
29 1 a. red (Die II) ..
30 4 a. blue & red (Die II)

This is believed to be an unofficial perforation. Most of the known specimens bear Madras circle postmarks (C122 to C126), but some are known with Bombay postmarks. Beware of fakes.

10

11

(Plate made at the Mint, in Calcutta. Printed at the Stamp Office.)

1854 (6 Oct.). *T* **10.** *Same wmk. Imperf.*

31	2 a. pale green	55 0	35 0
32	2 a. deep green	40 0	22 6
33	2 a. dull green	60 0	30 0
34	2 a. emerald-green	—	£5

There is a wide range of shade in the 2 a., the main groups being blue-green, yellow-green, and green, varying in brightness and depth.

Many stamps show traces of lines external to the design shown in our illustration. Stamps with this frame on all four sides are scarce.

Many reprints of the ½, 1, 2, and 4 a. exist.

PRINTERS. All Indian stamps from No. 35 to 200 were typographed by De La Rue & Co.

1855 (Oct.) *T* **11.** *Blue glazed paper. No wmk. P* 14.

35	4 a. black	62 6	15 0
	a. Imperf.		
	b. Bisected	—	£22
36	8 a. carmine (Die I)	55 0	18 0
	a. Imperf.		
	b. Bisected	—	£22

In the 8 a. the paper varies from deep blue to almost white.

For difference between Die I and Die II in the 8 a., see illustrations above No. 73.

1856-64. *T* **11.** *No wmk. Paper yellowish to white. P* 14.

37	½ a. blue (Die I)	10 0	1 0
	a. Imperf.	£7	£14
38	½ a. pale blue (Die I)	8 6	1 0
39	1 a. brown	15 0	2 0
	a. Imperf. between (vert. pair)		
	b. Imperf.	£18	
	c. Bisected		
40	1 a. deep brown	10 0	2 0
41	2 a. dull pink	85 0	25 0
	a. Imperf.		
42	2 a. yellow-buff	40 0	8 0
	a. Imperf.	£12	
43	2 a. yellow	42 6	9 0
44	2 a. orange	65 0	10 0
	a. Imperf.		
45	4 a. black	32 6	3 6
	a. Bisected diagonally (2 a.)	—	£20
	b. Imperf.	£16	£18
46	4 a. grey-black	32 6	2 6
47	4 a. green (1864)	90 0	25 0
48	8 a. carmine (Die I)	35 0	10 0
49	8 a. pale carmine (Die I)	35 0	12 6
	a. Bisected	—	£25

Prepared for use, but not officially issued.

50	2 a. yellow-green	£8	£15
	a. Imperf.	£7	

This stamp is known with trial obliterations, and a few are known postally used. It also exists *imperf.*, but is not known used

For difference between Die I and Die II in the ½ a., see illustrations above No. 75.

On the 1 November, 1858, Her Majesty Queen Victoria assumed the government of the territories in India "heretofore administered in trust by the Honourable East India Company," and subsequent issues of postage stamps are therefore—

UNDER THE CROWN

12

13

1860 (9 May). *T* **12.** *No wmk. P* 14.

51	8 p. purple/*bluish*	£5	50 0
52	8 p. purple/*white*	10 0	5 0
	a. Bisected diagonally (4 p.)	—	£30
	b. Imperf.	£24	
53	8 p. mauve	15 0	6 0

The bisected stamps of the issues of 1855-60 listed above were used exclusively in the Straits Settlements during shortage of stocks of certain values. Prices are for Singapore cancellations on original. Penang marks are considerably rarer.

1865. *T* **11** *and* **12.** *Paper yellowish to white. Wmk. Elephant's Head, T* **13.** *P* 14.

54	½ a. blue (Die I)	6 0	0 4
	a. Imperf.	—	£17
55	½ a. pale blue (Die I)	2 6	0 4
56	8 p. purple	8 6	7 6
57	8 p. mauve	15 0	9 0
58	1 a. pale brown	6 0	0 6
59	1 a. deep brown	2 6	0 2
60	1 a. chocolate	5 0	0 2
61	2 a. yellow	17 6	4 0
62	2 a. orange	22 6	2 0
	a. Imperf.	—	£40
63	2 a. brown-orange	12 6	1 6
64	4 a. green	55 0	20 0
65	8 a. carmine (Die I)	£7	40 0

14

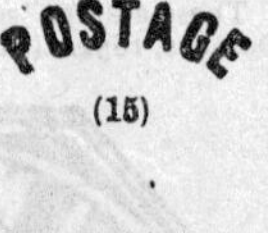

(15)

POSTACE

(16)

1866 (28 June). *T* **14** *overprinted in green. P* 14 *(at sides only).*

(*a*) *As T* **15.**

66	6 a. purple	£6	60 0

Variety. Overprint inverted.

67	6 a. purple		

There are 20 different types of this overprint, varying considerably in arrangement of the letters.

(*b*) *With T* **16.**

68	6 a. purple	£15	70 0

17

18

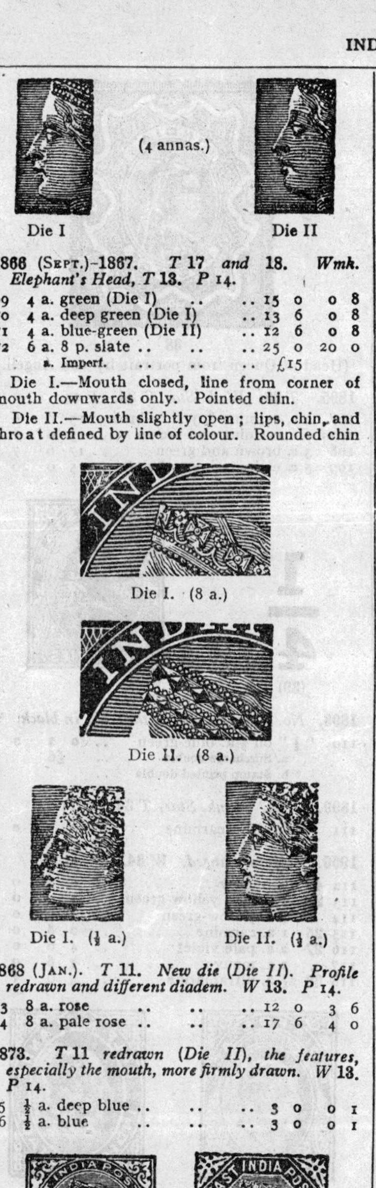

(4 annas.)

Die I Die II

1866 (Sept.)–**1867.** *T* **17** *and* **18.** *Wmk. Elephant's Head, T* **13.** *P* 14.

69	4 a. green (Die I)	15 0	0 8
70	4 a. deep green (Die I) ..	13 6	0 8
71	4 a. blue-green (Die II) ..	12 6	0 8
72	6 a. 8 p. slate	25 0	20 0
	a. Impert.	£15	

Die I.—Mouth closed, line from corner of mouth downwards only. Pointed chin.

Die II.—Mouth slightly open; lips, chin, and throat defined by line of colour. Rounded chin

Die I. (8 a.)

Die II. (8 a.)

Die I. (½ a.) Die II. (½ a.)

1868 (Jan.). *T* **11.** *New die (Die II). Profile redrawn and different diadem.* *W* **13.** *P* 14.

73	8 a. rose	12 0	3 6
74	8 a. pale rose	17 6	4 0

1873. *T* **11** *redrawn (Die II), the features, especially the mouth, more firmly drawn.* *W* **13.** *P* 14.

75	½ a. deep blue	3 0	0 1
76	½ a. blue	3 0	0 1

19 20

1874. *T* **19** *and* **20.** *W* **13.** *P* 14.

77	9 p. bright mauve	7 0	9 0
78	9 p. pale mauve	8 0	10 0
79	1 r. slate	15 0	3 0

21 22

1876 (Oct.). *T* **21** *and* **22.** *W* **13.** *P* 14.

80	6 a. olive-bistre	6 6	4 0
81	6 a. pale brown	3 6	1 6
82	12 a. Venetian red	7 6	8 0

The 8 pies, mauve, is found variously surcharged "NINE" or "NINE PIE" by local postmasters, who thus indicated that the 8 pies stamp was being sold for 9 pies, as was the case at one period. Such surcharges were made without Government sanction.

The stamps of India, wmk. Elephant's Head, surcharged with a Crown and value in "cents," were used in the Straits Settlements; q.v.

EMPIRE OF INDIA.

Queen Victoria assumed the title of Empress of India, 1877. The change is marked by the inscription on the stamps being altered from "EAST INDIA" to "INDIA."

23 24 25 26 27 28 29 30

31

32

33

34

1882-88. *T* **23** *to* **33.** *Wmk. Star, T* **34.** *P* 14.

No.	Description				
84	½ a. deep blue-green	0	4	0	1
85	½ a. blue-green	0	4	0	1
	a. Double impression	£8			
86	9 p. rose	1	6	1	9
87	9 p. aniline carmine	1	0	1	3
88	1 a. brown-purple	0	9	0	1
89	1 a. plum	0	6	0	1
90	1 a. 6 p. sepia	1	0	0	10
91	2 a. pale blue	1	0	0	1
92	2 a. blue	1	9	0	1
	a. Double impression	£17		£17	
93	3 a. orange	10	0	2	0
94	3 a. brown-orange	2	0	0	4
95	4 a. olive-green	3	0	0	6
96	4 a. slate-green	1	9	0	6
97	4 a. 6 p. yellow-green ..	6	6	2	6
98	8 a. dull mauve	8	0	2	0
99	8 a. magenta	5	0	1	0
100	12 a. purple/*red*	6	6	3	0
101	1 r. slate	7	6	2	6

A sheet of 2 a. stamps with a very marked double impression was issued in Karachi in 1896–97. Most of the stamps were used on telegrams, but a few were bought locally and saved.

2½ As.

(35)

1891 (1 Jan.). *No.* 97 *surcharged with T* **35.**

No.	Description				
102	2½ a. on 4½ a. yellow-green	2	0	1	6

There are several varieties in this surcharge due to variations in the relative positions of the letters and figures.

36

37

1892 (Jan.)–**1897.** *T* **36** *and* **37.** *Centre in first colour. W* **34.** *P* 14.

No.	Description				
103	2½ a. yellow-green	1	3	0	6
104	2½ a. pale blue-green (1897)	2	6	0	6
105	1 r. green and rose ..	10	0	2	0
106	1 r. green & aniline carmine	7	6	1	0

38

(Head of Queen from portrait by von Angeli.)

1895. *T* **38.** *Wmk. Star, T* **34.** *P* 14.

No.	Description				
107	2 r. carmine & yellow-brown	15	0	6	0
107*a*	2 r. carmine and brown ..	15	0	6	0
108	3 r. brown and green ..	17	6	7	6
109	5 r. ultramarine and violet ..	25	0	20	0

1/4

(39)

40

1898. *No.* 85 *surcharged with T* **39,** *in black.*

No.	Description				
110	"¼" on ½ a. blue-green ..	0	2	0	2
	a. Surcharge double ..	£6			
	b. Stamp printed double ..				

1899. *T* **40.** *Wmk. Star, T* **34.** *P* 14.

No.	Description				
111	3 p. aniline carmine ..	0	1	0	1

1900. *Colours changed. W* **34.** *P* 14.

No.	Type	Description				
112	**40**	3 p. grey	0	3	0	3
113	**23**	½ a. pale yellow-green ..	1	0	0	1
114	,,	½ a. yellow-green ..	0	8	0	1
115	**25**	1 a. carmine	0	8	0	1
116	**27**	2 a. pale violet	4	6	0	8
117	,,	2 a. mauve	3	6	0	3
118	**36**	2½ a. ultramarine ..	5	0	3	0

41

42

43

44

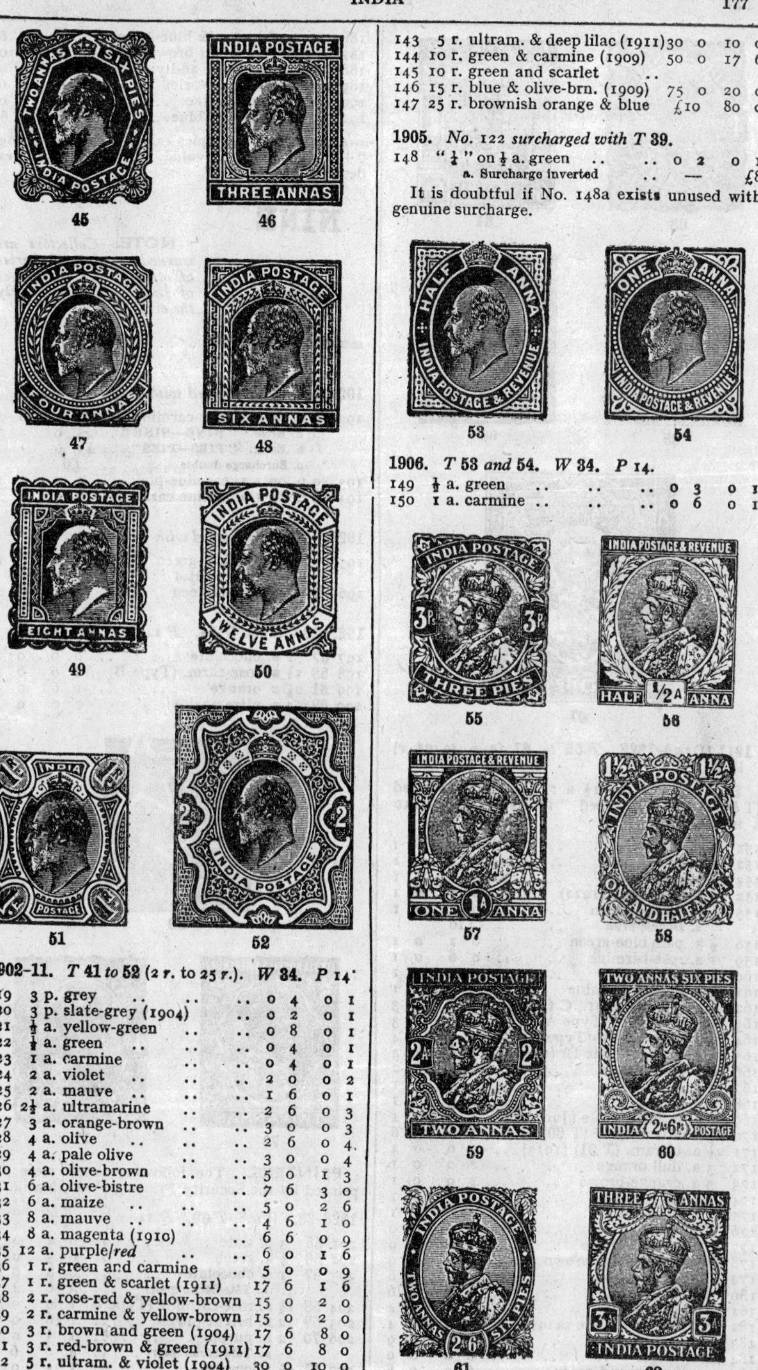

45 46 47 48 49 50 51 52 53 54 55 56 57 58 59 60 61 62

1902–11. *T* **41** *to* **52** (*2 r.* to *25 r.*). *W* **34.** *P* 14.

No.	Description				
119	3 p. grey	0	4	0	1
120	3 p. slate-grey (1904) ..	0	2	0	1
121	½ a. yellow-green	0	8	0	1
122	½ a. green	0	4	0	1
123	1 a. carmine	0	4	0	1
124	2 a. violet	2	0	0	2
125	2 a. mauve	1	6	0	1
126	2½ a. ultramarine	2	6	0	3
127	3 a. orange-brown	3	0	0	3
128	4 a. olive	2	6	0	4
129	4 a. pale olive	3	0	0	4
130	4 a. olive-brown	5	0	1	3
131	6 a. olive-bistre	7	6	3	0
132	6 a. maize	5	0	2	6
133	8 a. mauve	4	6	1	0
134	8 a. magenta (1910) ..	6	6	0	9
135	12 a. purple/*red*	6	0	1	6
136	1 r. green and carmine ..	5	0	0	9
137	1 r. green & scarlet (1911)	17	6	1	6
138	2 r. rose-red & yellow-brown	15	0	2	0
139	2 r. carmine & yellow-brown	15	0	2	0
140	3 r. brown and green (1904)	17	6	8	0
141	3 r. red-brown & green (1911)	17	6	8	0
142	5 r. ultram. & violet (1904)	30	0	10	0
143	5 r. ultram. & deep lilac (1911)	30	0	10	0
144	10 r. green & carmine (1909)	50	0	17	6
145	10 r. green and scarlet ..				
146	15 r. blue & olive-brn. (1909)	75	0	20	0
147	25 r. brownish orange & blue	£10		80	0

1905. *No.* 122 *surcharged with T* **39.**

No.	Description				
148	"¼" on ½ a. green	0	2	0	1
	a. Surcharge inverted ..	—		£8	

It is doubtful if No. 148a exists unused with genuine surcharge.

1906. *T* **53** *and* **54.** *W* **34.** *P* 14.

No.	Description				
149	½ a. green	0	3	0	1
150	1 a. carmine	0	6	0	1

63 64 65 66

67

1911 (Dec.)–1922. *T* **55** *to* **67** (1 *r. to* 25 *r*) *W* **34.** *P* 14.

Two types of the 1½ a.: (A) As illustrated (T 58); (B) Inscribed "1½ As." "ONE AND A HALF ANNAS."

No.	Value	Description	s.	d.	s.	d.
151	3 p.	pale grey	0	7	0	1
152	3 p.	grey	0	3	0	1
153	3 p.	slate-grey	0	6	0	1
154	3 p.	blue-slate (1922)	0	3	0	1
155	½ a.	yellow-green	0	2	0	1
		a. Double print	£10			
156	½ a.	pale blue-green	0	2	0	1
159	1 a.	rose-carmine	0	6	0	1
160	1 a.	carmine	0	4	0	1
161	1 a.	aniline carmine	0	6	0	1
162	1 a.	pale-rose-car., C (1918)	0	8	0	3
163	1½ a.	chocolate (Type A)(1919)	1	6	0	3
164	1½ a.	grey-brown (Type A)	3	0	0	4
165	1½ a.	choco. (Type B) (1921)	1	9	1	3
166	2 a.	dull purple	0	9	0	2
167	2 a.	mauve	1	3	0	1
168	2 a.	violet	1	9	0	1
169	2 a.	bright purple (Jan. '19)	1	6	0	1
170	2½ a.	ultramarine (T 60)	3	6	3	6
171	2½ a.	ultram. (T 61) (1913)	2	0	0	4
172	3 a.	dull orange	2	0	0	1
173	3 a.	orange-brown	1	9	0	1
174	4 a.	deep olive	3	0	0	1
175	4 a.	olive-green	2	0	0	1
176	6 a.	bistre	3	0	0	9
177	6 a.	yellow-bistre	3	0	0	9
178	6 a.	deep bistre-brown	3	6	0	9
179	8 a.	purple	4	0	0	6
180	8 a.	mauve	6	0	0	6
181	8 a.	deep lilac	3	6	0	4
182	8 a.	bright aniline mauve	5	0	0	4
183	12 a.	dull claret	8	0	0	9
184	12 a.	claret	6	0	0	9
185	1 r.	brown and green	6	0	0	6
186	1 r.	red-brown & blue-green	6	0	0	6
187	2 r.	carmine and brown	10	0	0	10
188	5 r.	ultramarine and violet	20	0	3	0
189	10 r.	green and scarlet	35	0	6	6
190	15 r.	blue and olive	50	0	15	0
191	25 r.	orange and blue	85	0	17	6

A variety of the 3 pies exists with line joining "P" and "S" of value at right, sometimes described as "3 Rs."

NINE

PIES

(68)

NOTE.—*Collectors are warned against forgeries of all the later surcharges of India, and particularly the errors.*

1921. *T* **57** *surcharged with T* **68**, *in black.*

No.	Description	s.	d.	s.	d.
192	9 p. on 1 a. rose-carmine	0	4	0	2
	a. Error. "NINE—NINE"	45	0		
	b. Error. "PIES—PIES"	45	0		
	c. Surcharge double	£6			
193	9 p. on 1 a. carmine-pink	0	4	0	2
194	9 p. on 1 a. aniline carmine	0	6	0	2

1922. *T* **56** *surcharged with T* **39.**

No.	Description	s.	d.	s.	d.
195	¼ on ½ a. yellow-green	0	2	0	1
	a. Surcharge inverted	25	0		
196	¼ on ½ a. blue-green	0	2	0	2

1922–26. *Wmk. T* **34.** *P* 14.

No.	Type	Description	s.	d.	s.	d.
197	57	1 a. chocolate	0	6	0	1
198	58	1½ a. rose-carm. (Type B)	1	6	0	4
199	61	2½ a. orange	1	6	0	4
200	62	3 a. ultramarine	2	0	0	4

69

70

71

PRINTERS. The following issues were all printed by the Security Printing Press, Nasik.

1926–33. *Wmk. T* **69.** *P* 14.

No.	Type	Description	s.	d.	s.	d.
201	55	3 p. slate	0	2	0	1
202	56	½ a. green	0	3	0	1
203	57	1 a. chocolate	0	8	0	1
		a. Tête-bêche (pair)	3	6	4	0
204	58	1½ a. rose-carmine (Type B)	1	0	0	4
205	59	2 a. bright purple	1	6	0	8
206	70	2 a. purple	1	3	0	1
		a. Tête-bêche (pair)	4	6	6	0
207	61	2½ a. orange	1	3	0	1

No.	Type	Description				
208	62	3 a. ultramarine	1	6	0	3
209	,,	3 a. blue ('31) ..	1	3	0	3
210	63	4 a. pale sage-green	1	3	0	1
211	71	4 a. sage-green	1	6	0	1
212	65	8 a. reddish purple	2	6	0	1
213	66	12 a. claret	3	6	0	2
214	67	1 r. chocolate and green	5	0	0	1
215	,,	2 r. carmine and orange	8	6	0	8
216	,,	5 r. ultram. & purple	20	0	2	0
217	,,	10 r. green and scarlet	35	0	5	0
218	,,	15 r. blue and olive	50	0	30	0
219	,,	25 r. orange and blue	75	0	32	6

72

(Designed by Mr. Grant.)

1929 (22 Oct.). *Air stamps.* T **72.** W **69.** P 14.

No.	Description				
220	2 a. deep blue-green	2	0	1	0
221	3 a. blue	2	6	1	6
222	4 a. olive-green	4	0	1	3
223	6 a. bistre	5	0	2	0
224	8 a. purple	7	0	4	0
225	12 a. rose-red	12	6	10	0

73. Purana Qila.
74. War Memorial Arch.
75. Council House.
76. The Viceroy's House.
77. Government of India Secretariat.
78. Dominion Columns and the Secretariat.

(Designed by H. W. Barr.)

1931 (9 Feb.). *Inauguration of New Delhi. Various designs as* T **73.** W **69.** P 14.

No.	Type	Description				
226	73	¼ a. olive-grn. & orge.-brn.	0	8	0	4
227	74	½ a. violet and green	1	0	0	4
228	75	1 a. mauve and chocolate	1	0	0	3
229	76	2 a. green and blue	2	0	1	0
230	77	3 a. chocolate and carmine	4	0	1	6
231	78	1 r. violet and green	15	0	12	6

In T 78 the portrait is central.

79

80

81

82

83

1932-36. *Wmk.* T **69.** P 14.

No.	Type	Description				
232	79	½ a. green ('34)	0	3	0	1
233	80	9 p. deep grn. (22.4.32)	0	4	0	2
234	81	1 a. chocolate ('34)	0	6	0	1
235	82	1¼ a. mauve (22.4.32)	0	10	0	1
236	70	2 a. vermilion	3	0	0	10
236*a*	59	2 a. vermilion ('34)	1	6	0	3
236*b*	,,	2 a. ver. ('36) (*small die*)	1	6	0	4
237	62	3 a. carmine	2	0	0	3
238	83	3½ a. ultramarine (22.4.32)	2	6	0	4
239	64	6 a. bistre ('35)	4	0	1	0

The 9 p. exists printed both by offset-lithography and typography.

No. 236*a* measures 19 × 22.6 mm. and No. 236*b* 18.4 × 21.8 mm.

84. Gateway of India, Bombay.
85. Victoria Memorial, Calcutta.
86. Rameswaram Temple, Madras.
87. Jain Temple, Calcutta.
88. Taj Mahal, Agra.
89. Golden Temple, Amritsar.
90. Pagoda in Mandalay.

1935. *Silver Jubilee. Various designs as* T **84.** W **69.** P 14.

No.	Type	Description				
240	84	½ a. black & yellow-green	0	3	0	4
241	85	9 p. black and grey-green	0	6	0	4
242	86	1 a. black and brown	0	6	0	2
243	87	1¼ a. black & bright violet	0	8	0	2
244	88	2½ a. black and orange	1	9	1	0
245	89	3½ a. black and dull ultram.	2	6	2	6
246	90	8 a. black and purple	8	6	6	6

OFFICIAL STAMPS.

Service.

(O 1)

1866 (1 Aug.). T **11,** *overprinted locally with Type* O **1,** *in black.* P 14.

A. *No wmk.*

No.	Description				
501	½ a. blue	—		35	0
502	½ a. pale blue	—		35	0
	a. Inverted				
503	1 a. brown	—		55	0
504	1 a. deep brown	—		55	0
505	8 a. carmine	6	0	12	6

B. *Wmk. Elephant's Head, T* **13.**

506 ½ a. blue £6 15 0
507 ½ a. pale blue £6 17 6
a. Inverted .. .. ..
b. No dot on "i" (No. 50 on pane)
c. No stop. (No. 77 on pane) ..
508 1 a. brown 70 0 20 0
509 1 a. deep brown 70 0 20 0
a. No dot on "i" .. ..
b. No stop .. .. ..
510 2 a. orange 47 6 32 6
511 2 a. yellow 37 6 27 6
a. Inverted .. .. ..
b. Imperf. .. .. ..
512 4 a. green 35 0 27 6
a. Inverted .. .. .. — £20

T **17** *overprinted with Type* O **1** *in black.*

513 4 a. green (Die I) £12 60 0

A variety may be found on all values with wide and more open capital "S". This is Nos. 57, 86, 91, 109, 110, 222, and 290 on sheet. Price four times the normal price.

Reprints exist of Nos. 506, 508, and 513; the latter is Die II instead of Die I.

1872 (Jan.). *T* **12** *optd. with Type* O **1** *in black. Wmk. Elephant's Head, T* **13.**

514 8 p. purple 27 6 45 0
a. No dot on "i" £15
b. No stop £15

Reprints of the overprint have been made, in a different setting, on the 8 pies, purple, no watermark.

O 2

1866. *Type* O 2. *Thick blue glazed paper. Surcharged* "SERVICE—TWO ANNAS," *in two lines, in black. P* 14 (*at sides only*).

515 2 a. purple £10 £8

O 3

O 4

Types O **3**, O **4** *and similar type. Overprinted* "SERVICE POSTAGE," *in two lines, in green. P* 14 *at sides only*).

516 2 a. purple £17 £12
517 4 a. purple £33 £22
518 8 a. purple £90 £45

So-called reprints of Nos. 515 to 518 are known, but in these the surcharge differs entirely in the spacing, etc., of the words; they are more properly described as Government imitations. There are two varieties of these imitations of No. 515 with surcharges in *black* and in *green* respectively.

O 6

1867. *Type* O **6.** *Ordinary paper lilac-coloured. Wmk. Large Crown. Optd.* "SERVICE POSTAGE", *in a semi-circle, in green. P* 15½ × 15.

519 ½ a. mauve £7 60 0
a. Overprint double £28

Reprints have been made of the overprint of this stamp.

Service.

(O 7)

1867–73. *Wmk. Elephant's Head, T* **13.** *P* 14. *Overprinted by Messrs. De La Rue & Co. with Type* O **7** *in black.*

520 **11** ½ a. blue (Die I) .. 15 0 1 0
521 „ ½ a. pale blue (Die I) .. 10 0 1 3
522 „ ½ a. blue (Die II) .. 95 0 22 6
523 „ 1 a. brown 15 0 1 0
524 „ 1 a. deep brown .. 12 6 0 8
525 „ 1 a. chocolate 15 0 2 6
526 „ 2 a. yellow 7 6 1 9
527 „ 2 a. orange 6 0 0 6
528 **17** 4 a. pale green (Die I) .. 4 6 1 0
529 „ 4 a. green (Die I) .. 2 0 0 5
530 **11** 8 a. rose (Die II) .. 4 0 1 0
530*a* „ 8 a. pale rose (Die II) .. 6 0 1 6

Prepared for use, but not issued.

530*b* **18** 6 a. 8 p. slate £10

On H. M. S.

(O 8)

On H. M. S.

(O 9)

1874–82. *Overprinted with Type* O **8**, *in black.*

531 **11** ½ a. blue (Die II) .. 3 0 0 2
532 „ 1 a. brown 3 0 0 3
533 „ 2 a. yellow 10 0 4 6
533*a* „ 2 a. orange 10 0 4 6
534 **17** 4 a. green (Die I) .. 3 6 1 3
535 **11** 8 a. rose (Die II) .. 4 0 4 0

Overprinted in blue-black.

536 **11** ½ a. blue (Die II) .. — 7 6
537 „ 1 a. brown £6 25 0

1883–99. *Wmk. Star, T* **34.** *P* 14. *Overprinted with Type* O **9**, *in black.*

No.	Type	Description	Unused	Used
537*a*	**40**	3 p. aniline carmine	0 6	0 6
538	**23**	½ a. deep blue-green	0 8	0 1
		a. Overprint double	—	£8
539	**23**	½ a. blue-green	0 6	0 1
540	**25**	1 a. brown-purple	0 4	0 1
		a. Overprint inverted	£8	£10
		b. Overprint double		
541	**25**	1 a. plum	0 4	0 1
542	**27**	2 a. pale blue	2 6	0 1
543	,,	2 a. blue	0 9	0 1
544	**29**	4 a. olive-green	1 9	0 3
544*a*	,,	4 a. slate-green	1 6	0 3
545	**31**	8 a. dull mauve	5 0	1 0
546	,,	8 a. magenta	1 6	0 4
547	**37**	1 r. green and rose	4 0	1 3
548	,,	1 r. green and carmine	2 6	0 6

1900. *Overprinted with Type* O **9** *in black.*

No.	Type	Description	Unused	Used
549	**23**	½ a. pale yellow-green	1 3	0 2
549*a*	,,	½ a. yellow-green	1 3	0 1
550	**25**	1 a. carmine	0 9	0 1
		a. Overprint inverted	—	£12
		b. Overprint double	—	£13
551	**27**	2 a. pale violet	6 0	0 3
552	,,	2 a. mauve	6 0	0 3

1902–5. *Stamps of King Edward VII overprinted with Type* O **9**, *in black.*

No.	Description	Unused	Used
554	3 p. grey	1 0	0 2
555	3 p. slate-grey (1905)	0 5	0 2
556	½ a. green	0 7	0 1
557	1 a. carmine	0 4	0 1
558	2 a. violet	1 6	0 3
559	2 a. mauve	0 6	0 1
560	4 a. olive	1 3	0 1
561	4 a. pale olive	1 0	0 1
562	6 a. olive-bistre	1 3	0 1
563	8 a. mauve	2 6	0 4
564	8 a. magenta	2 6	0 4
565	1 r. green and carmine (1905)	3 0	0 3

1906. *Optd. with Type* O **9**, *in black.*

No.	Description	Unused	Used
566	½ a. green (No. 149)	0 2	0 1
567	1 a. carmine (No. 150)	0 4	0 1

On

H. S.

M.

(O 9*a*)

1909. *T* **52** *optd. with Type* O **9*a***, *in black.*

No.	Description	Unused	Used
568	2 r. carmine and yell-brown	8 6	1 0
568*a*	2 r. rose-red & yellow-brn.	6 6	1 0
569	5 r. ultramarine and violet	17 6	3 0
570	10 r. green and carmine	30 0	9 0
570*a*	10 r. green and scarlet	40 0	9 0
571	15 r. blue and olive-brown	40 0	18 0
572	25 r. brownish orange & blue	65 0	35 0

SERVICE (O 10) SERVICE (O 11)

1912. *Stamps of King George V. (wmk. Single Star, T* **34**) *overprinted with Type* O **10** (14 *mm.*) *or* O **11** (*rupee values* 21½ *mm.*), *in black.*

No.	Description	Unused	Used
573	3 p. grey	0 4	0 2
574	3 p. slate-grey	0 4	0 2
575	3 p. blue-slate	0 4	0 2
576	½ a. yellow-green	0 2	0 1
577	½ a. pale blue-green	0 2	0 1
580	1 a. rose-carmine	0 3	0 1
581	1 a. carmine	0 3	0 1
582	1 a. aniline carmine	0 3	0 1
	a. Overprint double	—	£12
583	2 a. mauve	0 6	0 1
584	2 a. purple	0 6	0 1
585	4 a. deep olive	1 0	0 1
586	4 a. olive-green	0 9	0 1
587	6 a. yellow-bistre	2 0	0 9
588	6 a. deep bistre-brown	2 0	0 9
589	8 a. purple	2 0	0 3
589*a*	8 a. mauve	1 6	0 3
590	8 a. bright aniline mauve	3 0	0 6
591	1 r. red-brown and blue-grn.	2 6	0 4
592	2 r. rose-carmine & brown	6 0	1 9
593	5 r. ultramarine and violet	12 6	5 0
594	10 r. green and scarlet	30 0	15 0
595	15 r. blue and olive	40 0	22 6
596	25 r. orange and blue	65 0	45 0

NINE

PIES

(O 12)

1921. *No.* 580 *surch. with Type* O **12**, *in black.*

No.	Description	Unused	Used
597	9 p. on 1 a. rose-carmine	0 6	0 4

1922. *No.* 197 *optd. with Type* O **10**, *in black.*

No.	Description	Unused	Used
598	1 a. chocolate	0 4	0 1

ONE RUPEE

ONE RUPEE (O 13) (O 14)

1925. *Service stamps surcharged.*

(*a*) *Issue of* 1909, *as Type* O **13.**

No.	Description	Unused	Used
599	1 r. on 15 r. blue and olive	5 0	2 6
600	1 r. on 25 r. chestnut & blue	20 0	10 0
601	2 r. on 10 r. green & scarlet	6 0	3 6
601*a*	2 r. on 10 r. green & carmine		

(*b*) *Issue of* 1912, *with Type* O **14.**

No.	Description	Unused	Used
602	1 r. on 15 r. blue and olive	12 6	10 0
603	1 r. on 25 r. orange & blue	6 0	2 0
	a. Surcharge inverted	£15	

Error. Issue of 1912, *as Type* O **13.**

No.	Description	Unused	Used
604	2 r. on 10 r. green & scarlet	£30	

ONE ANNA (O 15)

SERVICE ONE ANNA (O 16)

1926. No. 562 *surcharged with Type* O **15.**

No.	Description	Unused	Used
605	1 a. on 6 a. olive-bistre	1 0	0 6

1926. *Postage stamps of* 1911–22 (*wmk. Single Star*), *surcharged as Type* O **16.**

No.	Description	Unused	Used
606	1 a. on 1½ a. (No. 163)	0 8	0 4
607	1 a. on 1½ as. (No. 165)	1 0	0 8
	a. Error. 1 a. on 1 a. (No. 187)	£5	
608	1 a. on 2½ a. (No. 171)	1 3	0 8

The surcharge on No. 608 has no bars at top.

SERVICE (O 17) — **SERVICE** (O 18)

1926–31. *Stamps of King George V (wmk. Multiple Star, T* **69***) overprinted with Types* O **17** *(13½ mm.) or* O **18** *(19¾ mm. rupee values), at the Nasik Press, in black.*

No.	Type	Stamp				
609	55	3 p. slate (1.10.29)	0	1	0	1
610	56	½ a. green ('31)	0	2	0	2
611	57	1 a. chocolate	0	3	0	1
612	70	2 a. purple	0	5	0	2
613	71	4 a. sage-green	0	9	0	2
615	65	8 a. reddish purple	2	0	0	2
616	66	12 a. claret	1	8	0	4
617	67	1 r. chocolate & grn. ('30)	4	0	0	3
618	,,	2 r. carmine & orge. ('30)	8	6	1	6
620	,,	10 r. green & scarlet ('31)	35	0	11	6

1930. *As No. 611, but optd. as Type* O **10** *(14 mm.)*

No.	Type	Stamp				
625	57	1 a. chocolate	1	6	0	9

1932–36. *Stamps of King George V (wmk. Mult. Star, T* **69***) optd. with Type* O **17** *(13½ mm.), at Nasik.*

No.	Type	Stamp				
626	79	½ a. green ('35)	0	2	0	2
627	80	9 p. deep green	0	3	0	2
627*a*	81	1 a. chocolate ('36)	0	4	0	2
628	82	1¼ a. mauve	0	4	0	1
629	70	2 a. vermilion	1	0	0	3
630	59	2 a. vermilion ('35)	0	9	0	6
630*a*	,,	2 a. verm. ('36) (*small die*)	1	0	0	2
631	61	2½ a. orange (22.4.32)	0	9	0	3
632	63	4 a. sage-green ('35)	1	0	0	3
633	64	6 a. bistre ('36)	1	3	1	0

Stamps overprinted "POSTAL SERVICE" or "I. P. N." are not used as postage stamps, and are therefore omitted.

FOR USE WITH THE CHINA EXPEDITIONARY FORCE.

C. E. F.

(C)

Contemporary stamps of India overprinted with Type C, *in black.*

1900. *Stamps of Queen Victoria.*

C 1	3 pies, carmine	0	4	0	5
C 2	½ a. green	0	4	0	5
C 3	1 a. brown-purple	0	9	0	10
C 4	2 a. ultramarine	2	6	3	0
C 5	2½ a. green	2	6	3	0
C 6	3 a. orange	2	6	3	0
C 7	4 a. olive-green	2	6	2	6
C 8	8 a. magenta	2	0	3	0
C 9	12 a. purple/*red*	3	6	5	0
C10	1 r. green and carmine	5	0	6	0

Prepared, but not issued.

C10*a*	1½ a. sepia	£5			

1904 (27 Feb.). *T* **25**.

C11	1 a. carmine	10	0	10	0

1904. *Stamps of King Edward VII.*

C12	3 pies, pale grey	1	3	1	3
C12*a*	3 pies, slate-grey	1	6	1	6
C13	1 a. carmine	5	0	4	6
C14	2 a. pale violet	2	6	0	9
C15	2½ a. ultramarine	3	0	4	0
C16	3 a. orange-brown	3	0	3	6
C17	4 a. olive-green	3	6	4	0
C18	8 a. magenta	4	0	4	6
C19	12 a. purple/*red*	7	0	7	0
C20	1 r. green and carmine	5	0	5	6

1909. *Nos.* 149 *and* 150.

C21	½ a. green	1	3	1	3
C22	1 a. carmine	1	3	1	0

1913–21. *Stamps of King George V. Wmk. Star.*

C23	3 p. slate-grey (1913)	0	4	0	6
C24	½ a. green	0	6	0	8
C25	1 a. aniline carmine	0	9	1	0
C26	1½ a. chocolate (Type A)	1	6	2	0
C27	2 a. mauve	2	0	3	0
C28	2½ a. bright blue (T 61)	2	6	3	0
C29	3 a. orange-brown	3	6	4	0
C30	4 a. olive-green	6	0	7	0
C32	8 a. mauve	7	6	8	6
C33	12 a. claret	7	0	9	0
C34	1 r. red-brown and blue-grn.	40	0	55	0

FOR USE WITH INDIAN EXPEDITIONARY FORCES, 1914–22.

I. E. F.

(E)

1914. *Stamps of India (King George V) overprinted with Type* E *in black.*

E1	3 pies, slate-grey	0	2	0	2
	a. No stop after "F"	7	6	4	0
	b. No stop after "E"	10	0	10	0
	c. Overprint double	10	0	10	0
E2	½ a. yellow-green	0	2	0	2
	a. No stop after "F"	10	0	10	0
E3	1 a. aniline carmine	0	3	0	4
	a. No stop after "F"	12	6	6	6
E4	1 a. carmine	0	3	0	4
E5	2 a. mauve	0	8	0	10
	a. No stop after "F"	30	0	30	0
	b. No stop after "E"	40	0	40	0
E6	2½ a. ultramarine (T 61)	0	9	1	6
	a. No stop after "F"	35	0	40	0
E7	3 a. orange-brown	1	3	1	6
	a. No stop after "F"	40	0	45	0
E8	4 a. olive-green	1	3	1	6
	a. No stop after "F"	45	0	50	0
E9	8 a. purple	2	6	3	6
	a. No stop after "F"	50	0	60	6
E10	8 a. mauve	10	6	14	0
E11	12 a. dull claret	10	0	10	6
	a. No stop after "F"	55	0	65	0
E12	12 a. claret	4	0	5	0
E13	1 r. red-brown & blue-green	5	0	5	6

STAMPS OF INDIA OVERPRINTED FOR USE IN INDIAN STATES.

The following are the types of Indian stamps overprinted for use in the six States of CHAMBA, FARIDKOT, GWALIOR, JIND, NABHA, and PUTTIALLA (or PATIALA) (except where otherwise stated):—

Head of Queen Victoria: ½ a. (**23**), 1 a. (**25**), 1½ a. (**26**), 2 a. (**27**), 2½ a. (**36**), 3 a. (**28**), 4 a. (**29**), 6 a. (**21**), 8 a. (**31**), 12 a. (**32**), 1 r. (**33** and **37**), 2, 3, and 5 r. (**38**), 3 pies (**40**).

Head of King Edward VII.: 3 pies (**41**), ½ a. (**42**), 1 a. (**43**), 2 a. (**44**), 2½ a. (**45**), 3 a. (**46**), 4 a. (**47**), 6 a. (**48**), 8 a. (**49**), 12 a. (**50**), 1 r. (**51**), 2, 3, and 5 r. (**52**).

Head of King George V.: 3 pies (**55**), ½ a. (**56** and **79**), 9 pies (**80**), 1 a. (**57** and **81**), 1¼ a. (**82**), 1½ a. (**58** A and B), 2 a. (**59** and **70**), 2½ a. (**61**), 3 a. (**62**), 3½ a. (**83**), 4 a. (**63** and **71**), 6 a. (**64**), 8 a. (**65**), 12 a. (**66**), rupee values (**67**).

The minor varieties, such as smaller letters, etc., formerly given, being mostly due to broken letters and unequal inking when printing, are now omitted. Variations in the length of words due to unequal spacing when setting are also omitted.

CHAMBA.

CHAMBA
STATE
(1)

1886–95. *Head of Queen Victoria. Overprinted with T* **1**, *in black.*

No.	Description	Unused	Used
1	½ a. deep green	0 4	0 5
2	1 a. brown-purple	1 0	1 6
3	1 a. plum	0 9	1 0
4	1½ a. sepia (1895)	3 6	4 6
5	2 a. dull blue	1 3	1 3
6	2 a. ultramarine	1 6	2 0
7	2½ a. green (1895)	15 0	20 0
8	3 a. orange (1887)	7 6	8 6
9	3 a. brown-orange	2 0	2 3
10	4 a. olive-green	2 0	2 6
11	4 a. slate-green	1 6	2 0
12	6 a. olive-bistre (1890)	5 0	6 0
13	6 a. bistre-brown	6 0	7 0
14	8 a. dull mauve (1887)	7 6	8 6
15	8 a. magenta	2 6	3 0
16	12 a. purple/*red* (1890)	3 6	5 0
17	1 r. slate (1887)	32 6	37 6
18	1 r. green and carmine (1895)	3 6	4 6
19	2 r. carm. & yell.-brn. (1895)	40 0	
20	3 r. brown & green (1895)	40 0	
21	5 r. ultram. & violet (1895)	45 0	

Variety. " CHAMBA " *twice.*

No.	Description	Unused	Used
23	2 a. blue		

Varieties. (i.) " CHMABA " *for* " CHAMBA."

No.	Description	Unused	Used
24	½ a. green	£6	
25	1 a. brown-purple	£15	
26	2 a. blue	£30	
27	3 a. orange	£60	
28	4 a. olive-green	£30	
29	8 a. dull mauve	£50	
30	12 a. purple/*red*	£75	
31	1 r. slate		

(ii.) " S⊥ATE " *for* " STATE."

No.	Description	Unused	Used
32	12 a. purple/*red*	£80	

(iii.) " 8TATE " *for* " STATE."

No.	Description	Unused	Used
32a	½ a. green	£15	
32b	1 a. brown-purple		
32c	2 a. blue		
32d	4 a. olive-green		

1900–4. *Overprinted with T* **1**.

No.	Description	Unused	Used
33	3 pies, carmine	0 4	0 6
34	3 pies, grey (1904)	0 6	0 8
35	½ a. pale green (1902)	0 8	0 10
35a	½ a. green	0 3	0 7
36	1 a. carmine (1902)	0 4	0 6
37	2 a. pale violet (1903)	10 0	15 0

Variety. Overprint inverted.

No.	Description	Unused	Used
38	3 pies, grey	£5	

1903–5. *Head of King Edward VII. Overprinted with T* **1**.

No.	Description	Unused	Used
39	3 pies, pale grey	0 3	0 4
40	3 pies, slate-grey (1905)	0 3	0 4
41	½ a. green	0 4	0 5
42	1 a. carmine	0 6	0 8
43	2 a. pale violet (1904)	1 6	2 0
43a	2 a. mauve	1 3	1 6
44	3 a. orange-brown (1905)	1 6	1 6
45	4 a. olive-green (1904)	1 9	2 0
46	6 a. olive-bistre (1905)	2 0	2 0
47	8 a. dull mauve (1904)	2 6	2 6
47a	8 a. magenta	4 0	5 0
48	12 a. purple/*red* (1905)	4 0	4 0
49	1 r. green & carmine (1904)	4 6	5 0

1907. *Nos.* 149 *and* 150 *of India overprinted with T* **1**.

No.	Description	Unused	Used
50	½ a. green	0 3	0 3
51	1 a. carmine	1 0	1 3

1913. *Head of King George V. Overprinted with T* **1**.

No.	Description	Unused	Used
52	3 p. slate-grey	0 1	0 2
53	½ a. green	0 3	0 5
54	1 a. rose-carmine	0 6	0 8
54a	1 a. aniline carmine	0 6	0 8
55	2 a. mauve	1 0	1 3
57	3 a. orange-brown	1 3	1 6
58	4 a. olive	1 0	1 6
59	6 a. olive-bistre	1 0	2 0
60	8 a. purple	1 9	2 6
61	12 a. dull claret	2 6	3 6
62	1 r. brown and green	5 0	6 0

CHAMBA
(2)

1921. *No.* 192 *of India overprinted with T* **2** *in black.*

No.	Description	Unused	Used
63	9 p. on 1 a. rose-carmine	4 0	5 0

1922–27. *Overprint T* **1**. *New values, etc.*

No.	Description	Unused	Used
64	1 a. chocolate	0 5	0 7
65	1½ a. chocolate (Type A)	20 0	30 0
66	1½ as. chocolate (Type B)	0 8	0 10
67	1½ as. rose-carmine (Type B)	1 9	3 0
68	2½ a. ultramarine (Type **61**)	1 9	3 0
69	2½ a. orange	1 9	3 0
70	3 a. ultramarine	3 6	5 0

CHAMBA STATE (3) — CHAMBA STATE (4)

1927–37. *Head of King George V (Nasik printing, wmk. Mult. Star) overprinted at Nasik with T* **3** *or* **4** *(1 r.).*

No.	Type	Description	Unused	Used
71	**55**	3 p. slate	0 1	0 2
72	**56**	½ a. green	0 3	0 4
73	**80**	9 p. deep green	0 3	0 4
74	**57**	1 a. chocolate	0 5	0 5
74a	**82**	1¼ a. mauve	0 9	1 0
75	**58**	1½ a. rose-carmine (Type B)	0 5	0 6
76	**70**	2 a. purple	0 9	0 9
77	**61**	2½ a. orange	0 7	0 9
78	**62**	3 a. bright blue	1 6	2 0
79	**71**	4 a. sage-green	0 10	1 0
79a	**64**	6 a. bistre ('37)	20 0	
80	**65**	8 a. reddish purple	1 9	2 0
81	**66**	12 a. claret	2 9	4 0
82	**67**	1 r. chocolate & green	3 6	4 0

1935–36. *New types and colours. Optd. as T* **3**.

No.	Type	Description	Unused	Used
83	**79**	½ a. green	0 4	0 3
84	**81**	1 a. chocolate	0 4	0 5
85	**59**	2 a. vermilion	0 8	0 9
86	**62**	3 a. carmine	1 0	1 3
87	**63**	4 a. sage-green ('36)	1 0	1 3

OFFICIAL STAMPS.

SERVICE

CHAMBA
STATE
(O 1)

1886–98. *Head of Queen Victoria. Overprinted with T* O **1** *in black.*

No.	Description	Unused	Used
O 1	½ a. deep green	0 6	0 2
O 2	1 a. brown-purple	1 3	0 9
O 3	1 a. plum	0 8	0 4
O 4	2 a. dull blue	1 3	1 6
O 5	2 a. ultramarine (1887)	1 0	1 3
O 6	3 a. orange (1890)	8 6	10 0
O 7	3 a. brown-orange	5 0	5 6
O 8	4 a. olive-green	1 9	1 0
O 9	4 a. slate-green	3 0	3 6

O10	6 a. olive-bistre (1890)	4 6	5 0
O11	6 a. bistre-brown	12 6	15 0
O12	8 a. dull mauve (1887)	4 0	4 6
O13	8 a. magenta	4 6	5 0
O14	12 a. purple/*red* (1890)	17 6	22 6
O15	1 r. slate (1890)	20 0	25 0
O16	1 r. green & carm. (1898)	12 6	17 6

Varieties. (i.) "CHMABA" *for* "CHAMBA."

O17	½ a. deep green	90 0	
O18	1 a. brown-purple	£10	
O19	2 a. blue	£25	
O20	3 a. orange	£35	
O21	4 a. olive-green	£25	
O22	8 a. dull mauve	£60	
O23	12 a. purple/*red*	£60	
O24	1 r. slate	£70	

(ii.) "SERV CE."

O25	½ a. deep green	—	£8
O26	1 a. brown-purple	£15	
O27	4 a. olive-green	£45	

(iii.) "SERVICE" *double.*

O28	1 a. plum	—	60 0

(iv.) "8TATE" *for* "STATE."

O28a	½ a. green		
O28b	1 a. purple-brown		
O28c	4 a. olive-green		

1902–4. *Colours changed.*

O29	3 pies, grey (1904)	0 6	0 6
O30	½ a. pale green	0 7	0 7
O30a	½ a. green	0 6	0 6
O31	1 a. carmine	0 9	1 0
O32	2 a. pale violet (1903)	6 6	8 6

1903–5. *Head of King Edward VII. Overprinted as Type* O 1.

O33	3 pies, pale grey	2 0	0 8
O33a	3 pies, slate-grey (1905)	0 2	0 2
O34	½ a. yellow-green	0 4	0 5
O35	1 a. carmine	0 7	0 8
O36	2 a. pale violet (1904)	1 9	1 9
O37	2 a. mauve	1 0	0 6
O38	4 a. olive-green (1905)	1 6	1 9
O39	8 a. dull mauve (1905)	3 0	3 6
O40	8 a. magenta	3 6	4 0
O42	1 r. grn. and carmine (1905)	3 6	4 0

1907. *Nos.* 149/50 *of India, optd. with Type* O 1.

O43	½ a. green	1 6	1 0
	a. Inverted overprint		
O44	1 a. carmine	3 6	2 6

The error, No. O43*a*, is due to the existence of an inverted cliché which was corrected after a few sheets had been printed.

1913–14. *Head of King George V. Service stamps of India, overprinted with T* 1, *in black.*

O45	3 pies, slate-grey	0 2	0 1
O45a	3 pies, grey	0 3	0 2
O46	½ a. yellow-green	0 3	0 2
O46a	½ a. pale blue-green	0 4	0 2
O47	1 a. aniline carmine	0 4	0 3
O47a	1 a. rose-carmine	0 5	0 2
O48	2 a. mauve (1914)	0 8	0 10
O50	4 a. olive	1 3	1 6
O52	8 a. purple	1 9	2 3
O54	1 r. brown and green (1914)	3 6	5 0

1914. *Head of King George V. Stamps of India, overprinted with Type* O 1, *in black.*

O55	2 a. mauve	15 0	20 0
O56	4 a. olive	30 0	40 0

The 2 a. mauve, King Edward VII, overprinted "On H.M.S.", was discovered in Calcutta, but was not sent to Chamba, and is an unissued variety. (Price 40s.)

1921. *No.* 597 *of India overprinted with T* 2 *a top, in black.*

O57	9 p. on 1 a. rose-carmine	1 6	2 6

1925. *As* 1913–14. *New colour.*

O58	1 a. chocolate	0 5	0 3

CHAMBA STATE
SERVICE
(O 2)

CHAMBA STATE
SERVICE
(O 3)

1927–39. *Head of King George V (Nasik printing, wmk. Mult. Star), overprinted at Nasik with Type* O 2 *or Type* O 3 *(rupee values).*

O59	**55**	3 p. slate	0 2	0 2
O60	**56**	½ a. green	0 3	0 3
O60a	**80**	9 p. deep green	0 3	0 4
O61	**57**	1 a. chocolate	0 6	0 3
O61a	**82**	1¼ a. mauve	0 4	0 5
O62	**70**	2 a. purple	0 8	0 10
O64	**71**	4 a. sage-green	0 9	1 0
O65	**65**	8 a. reddish purple	1 6	2 0
O66	**66**	12 a. claret	2 6	3 0
O67	**67**	1 r. chocolate & green	3 0	3 6
O67a	,,	2 r. carmine & orge. ('39)		
O67b	,,	5 r. ultram. & pur. ('39)		
O67c	,,	10 r. grn. and scar. ('39)		

1935–39. *New types and colours. Optd. with Type* O 2.

O68	**79**	½ a. green	0 2	0 2
O69	**81**	1 a. chocolate	0 3	0 3
O70	**59**	2 a. vermilion	0 6	0 8
O71	,,	2 a. verm. ('39) (*small die*)	0 5	0 6
O72	**63**	4 a. sage-green ('36)	0 8	0 10

FARIDKOT.

For earlier issues, see under **Indian Feudatory States.**

FARIDKOT
8TATE
(1)

1887 (1 Jan.)**–1900.** *Head of Queen Victoria. Overprinted with T* 1, *in black.*

101	½ a. deep green	0 8	0 10
102	1 a. brown-purple	1 3	1 6
103	1 a. plum	3 0	3 0
104	2 a. blue	3 6	3 6
105	2 a. deep blue	3 6	4 0
106	3 a. orange	3 6	4 6
107	3 a. brown-orange	3 6	4 6
108	4 a. olive-green	4 6	5 6
109	4 a. slate-green	4 6	5 0
110	6 a. olive-bistre	8 6	10 0
111	6 a. bistre-brown	5 0	6 6
112	8 a. dull mauve	8 6	10 0
113	8 a. magenta	10 0	12 6
114	12 a. purple/*red* (1900)	25 0	35 0
115	1 r. slate	27 6	35 0
116	1 r. green and carmine (1893)	20 0	25 0

Varieties. (i.) "ARIDKOT."

117	4 a. olive-green	£10	
118	6 a. olive-bistre	£15	
119	8 a. dull mauve	£18	
120	1 r. slate		

(ii.) "FARIDKCT." (Broken "O").

121	½ a. deep green	50 0	
122	1 a. plum	65 0	
123	2 a. blue	90 0	
124	3 a. orange	£8	
125	4 a. olive-green	£8	
126	8 a. dull mauve	£10	
127	1 r. green and carmine		

1900. *Overprinted with T* 1.

128	3 pies, carmine	2 0	3 0

OFFICIAL STAMPS.

SERVICE

FARIDKOT
STATE
(O 1)

1886-96. *Head of Queen Victoria. Overprinted with Type* O 1, *in black.*

151	½ a. deep green	0 10	0 10
152	1 a. brown-purple	1 0	1 3
153	1 a. plum	2 6	2 0
154	2 a. dull blue	5 0	3 6
155	2 a. deep blue	3 0	4 0
156	3 a. orange	4 0	4 6
157	3 a. brown-orange	4 0	4 6
158	4 a. olive-green	5 0	5 6
159	4 a. slate-green	4 6	5 6
160	6 a. olive-bistre	35 0	37 6
161	6 a. bistre-brown	12 6	15 0
162	8 a. dull mauve	5 0	6 0
163	8 a. magenta	10 0	12 6
164	1 r. slate	22 6	27 6
165	1 r. green & carmine (1896)	40 0	50 0

Varieties. (i.) "ARIDKOT."

166	6 a. olive-bistre	£15	

(ii.) "FARIDKCT." (Broken "O").

167	½ a. deep green	90 0	
168	1 a. plum	60 0	
169	2 a. blue	£5	
169*a*	3 a. orange		
170	4 a. olive-green	£6	
171	8 a. dull mauve	£7	

(iii.) "SERVIC."

172	6 a. olive-bistre	£12	

(iv.) "SERV CE."

173	½ a. deep green	£5	
174	1 a. plum		
175	2 a. blue		
176	4 a. olive-green		
177	8 a. dull mauve		

This State ceased to use overprinted stamps after March 31, 1901.

GWALIOR.

गवालियर

GWALIOR
(1)

1885 (May). *Head of Queen Victoria. Overprinted with T* 1, *in black. The* 4 *a. is India T* 17.

(A) *Space between two lines of overprint* 13 *mm. Hindi inscription* 13 *to* 14 *mm. long.*

1	½ a. deep green	22 6	15 0
2	1 a. brown-purple	25 0	20 0
3	2 a. dull blue	20 0	10 0

A variety exists of the ½ a. in which the space between the two lines of overprint is only 9½ mm. but this is probably from a proof sheet.

(B) June. *Space between two lines of overprint* 15 *mm. on* 6 *a. and* 16 *to* 17 *mm. on other values.*

(*a*) *Hindi inscription* 13 *to* 14 *mm. long.*

4	½ a. deep green	22 6	
5	1 a. brown-purple	25 0	
6	1½ a. sepia	30 0	
7	2 a. dull blue	25 0	
8	4 a. green	42 6	
9	6 a. olive-bistre	50 0	
10	8 a. dull mauve	65 0	
11	1 r. slate	60 0	

(*b*) *Hindi inscription* 15 *to* 15½ *mm. long.*

12	½ a. deep green	25 0	
13	1 a. brown-purple	35 0	
14	1½ a. sepia	50 0	
15	2 a. dull blue	45 0	
16	4 a. green	60 0	
17	6 a. olive-bistre	65 0	
18	8 a. dull mauve	65 0	
19	1 r. slate	65 0	

These two overprints are both found on the same sheet in the proportion of three of the former to one of the latter.

GWALIOR
गवालियर
(2)

Overprinted with T 2.

A. Sept., **1885.** *In red.*

(*a*) *Hindi inscription* 13 *to* 14 *mm. long.*

20	½ a. deep green	1 0	1 6
21	2 a. dull blue	8 6	10 0
22	4 a. green	16 6	20 0
23	1 r. slate	15 0	20 0

(*b*) *Hindi inscription* 15 *to* 15½ *mm. long.*

24	½ a. deep green	1 9	1 9
25	2 a. dull blue	22 6	22 6
26	4 a. green	55 0	55 0
27	1 r. slate	35 0	40 0

Reprints have been made of Nos. 20 to 23, but the majority of the specimens have the word "reprint" overprinted upon them.

(*The* 4 *a. below is T* 29.)

B. **1885-96.** *In black.*

(*a*) *Hindi inscription* 13 *to* 14 *mm. long.*

28	½ a. deep green (1889)	1 3	1 3
29	9 pies, carmine (1891)	35 0	35 0
30	1 a. brown-purple	1 6	0 9
31	1½ a. sepia	0 10	1 0
32	2 a. dull blue	4 6	4 6
33	3 a. orange	5 6	5 6
33*a*	3 a. brown-orange	5 0	5 0
34	4 a. olive-green (1889)	7 6	6 0
35	4 a. slate-green	7 6	6 0
36	6 a. olive-bistre	6 6	7 6
37	6 a. bistre-brown	2 0	2 0
38	8 a. dull mauve	6 6	7 6
39	12 a. purple/*red* (1891)	17 6	18 6
40	1 r. slate (1889)	50 0	

(*b*) *Hindi inscription* 15 *to* 15½ *mm. long.*

41	½ a. deep green	0 4	0 3
	a. Overprint double	—	£8
42	9 pies, carmine	45 0	45 0
43	1 a. brown-purple	1 3	0 10
44	1 a. plum	1 0	0 6
45	1½ a. sepia	0 9	1 0
46	2 a. dull blue	2 0	1 0
47	2 a. deep blue	3 0	1 6
48	2½ a. green (1896)	6 0	8 0
49	3 a. orange	7 6	6 6
50	3 a. brown-orange	2 0	1 6
51	4 a. olive-green	3 0	3 0
52	4 a. slate-green	3 0	2 6
53	6 a. olive-bistre	5 0	6 0
54	6 a. bistre-brown	3 0	4 0

55 8 a. dull mauve 4 6 3 6
56 8 a. magenta 12 0 14 0
57 12 a. purple/*red* 4 6 2 0
58 1 r. slate 4 0 4 6
59 1 r. green & carmine (1896) .. 7 6 9 0
60 2 r. carm. & yell.-brn. ('96) .. 10 0 15 0
61 3 r. brown & green (1896) .. 15 0 17 6
62 5 r. ultram. & violet (1896) .. 20 0 22 6

Varieties.

(*a*) "GWALICR" *for* "GWALIOR."

63 ½ a. deep green 100 0
64 2½ a. green £25
65 1 r. green and carmine .. £30

(*b*) "GWALIOR" *spaced* "GWALI OR."

65*a* ½ a. deep green .. ..
65*b* 1 a. plum .. .. ..
65*c* 2 a. blue .. .. ..
65*d* 3 a. orange .. .. ..

1899–1908. *Overprinted with* **T 2** (*b*).

66 3 pies, carmine 0 2 0 2
67 3 pies, grey (1904) 12 6
68 ½ a. pale green (1901) 0 6 0 6
69 1 a. carmine (1901) 0 8 0 6
70 2 a. pale violet (1901) .. 0 10 0 10
71 2½ a. ultramarine (1903) .. 1 9 1 9

Variety. Overprint inverted.

72 3 p. carmine £12 £10

"GWALIOR" 13 *mm. long. Overprint spaced* 2¾ *mm.* (1908).

72*a* 3 r. brown and green .. 30 0
72*b* 5 r. ultramarine and violet .. 50 0

1903–8. *Head of King Edward VII. Overprinted as* **T 2**. "GWALIOR" 14 *mm. long. Overprint spaced* 1¾ *mm.*

73 3 pies, pale grey 0 4 0 2
74 3 pies, slate-grey (1905) .. 0 2 0 2
75 ½ a. green 0 5 0 4
76 1 a. carmine 0 5 0 3
77 2 a. pale violet (1904) .. 1 6 1 6
77*a* 2 a. mauve 1 6 0 10
78 2½ a. ultramarine (1905) .. 22 6
79 3 a. orange-brown (1904) .. 1 6 1 6
80 4 a. olive-green (1905) .. 2 3 2 0
80*a* 4 a. slate-green 4 0 4 0
81 6 a. olive-bistre (1906) .. 3 0 3 6
82 8 a. dull mauve (1905) .. 4 6 5 6
82*a* 8 a. magenta 2 0 2 6
83 12 a. purple/*red* (1905) .. 3 6 4 0
84 1 r. green & carmine (1905) .. 4 6 5 6
84*a* 2 r. carmine and yellow-brown 70 0 80 0

"GWALIOR" 13 *mm. long. Overprint spaced* 2¾ *mm.* (1908).

85 3 pies, pale grey 1 0 0 2
85*a* 3 pies, slate-grey 0 3 0 2
86 1 a. carmine 1 6 1 0
87 2 a. mauve 0 10 0 6
88 2½ a. ultramarine 2 6 3 0
89 3 a. orange-brown 1 3 1 3
90 4 a. olive-green 1 0 1 0
91 6 a. olive-bistre 2 3 2 9
92 8 a. dull mauve 3 6 4 0
92*a* 8 a. magenta 3 6 4 0
93 12 a. purple/*red* 3 6 4 0
94 1 r. green and carmine .. 7 6 3 6
95 2 r. carmine & yellow-brown .. 12 6 15 0
96 3 r. brown and green 30 0 32 6
97 5 r. ultramarine & violet .. 25 0 27 6

1907. *Nos.* 149 *and* 150 *of India overprinted as* **T 2**. "GWALIOR" 14 *mm. long. Overprint spaced* 1¾ *mm.*

98 ½ a. green 0 3 0 2

"GWALIOR" 13 *mm. long. Overprint spaced* 2¾ *mm.*

99 ½ a. green 0 3 0 1
100 1 a. carmine 0 4 0 2

1912–14. *Head of King George V. Optd. as* **T 2**.

101 3 pies, slate-grey 0 1 0 1
102 ½ a. green 0 2 0 1
a. Overprint inverted .. ..
103 1 a. aniline carmine 0 4 0 2
a. Overprint double 35 0
104 2 a. mauve 0 7 0 2
105 3 a. orange-brown 1 0 0 3
106 4 a. olive (1913) 1 0 0 3
107 6 a. olive-bistre 1 6 0 8
108 8 a. purple (1913) 2 0 1 0
109 12 a. dull claret (1914) .. 3 0 1 6
110 1 r. brown and green .. 3 6 3 0
111 2 r. carmine-rose & brn. .. 6 0 3 6
112 5 r. ultramarine & violet .. 17 6 10 0

GWALIOR
(3)

1922. *No.* 192 *of India overprinted with* **T 3**.

113 9 p. on 1 a. rose-carmine .. 0 6 0 6

1923–27. *Opt.* **T 2**. *New colours and values.*

114 1 a. chocolate ('23) .. 0 4 0 1
115 1½ as. chocolate (Type B) ('25) 1 0 1 6
116 1½ as. rose-carm. (Type B) ('27) 0 6 0 4
117 2½ a. ultramarine (T 61) ('25) 1 6 1 9
118 2½ a. orange ('27) .. 1 0 0 8
119 3 a. ultramarine ('24) .. 1 6 0 4

GWALIOR
गवालियर
(4)

GWALIOR
गवालियर
(5)

1928–36. *Head of King George V* (*Nasik printing, wmk. Mult. Star*), *optd. at Nasik with* **T 4** *or* **5** (*rupee values*).

120 **55** 3 p. slate ('32) 0 1 0 1
121 **56** ½ a. green ('30) 0 2 0 2
121*a* **80** 9 p. deep green ('33) .. 0 2 0 1
122 **57** 1 a. chocolate 0 6 0 1
122*a* **82** 1½ a. mauve ('36) .. 0 4 0 2
123 **70** 2 a. purple 0 6 0 2
124 **62** 3 a. bright blue 0 8 0 6
125 **71** 4 a. sage-green 0 10 0 5
126 **65** 8 a. reddish purple .. 1 2 0 8
127 **66** 12 a. claret 1 8 1 2
128 **67** 1 r. chocolate & green .. 3 0 2 0
129 " 2 r. carmine & orange .. 5 6 2 6
130 " 5 r. ultram. & purp. ('29) 12 6 12 6
131 " 10 r. green & scarlet ('30) 25 0 27 6
132 " 15 r. blue & olive ('30) .. 37 6 40 0
133 " 25 r. orange and blue ('30) 60 0 66 0

1936. *New types and colours. Optd. with* **T 4**.

134 **79** ½ a. green 0 2 0 3
135 **81** 1 a. chocolate 0 3 0 4
137 **59** 2 a. vermilion 0 6 0 4

OFFICIAL STAMPS.

गवालियर

सरविस
(O 1)

1895–96. *Head of Queen Victoria. Overprinted with Type* O **1**, *in black.*

O 1 ½ a. deep green 0 3 0 1
O 2 1 a. brown-purple 1 6 0 3
O 3 1 a. plum 1 0 0 2
O 4 2 a. dull blue 2 6 0 8
O 5 2 a. deep blue 1 3 0 5
O 6 4 a. olive-green 5 0 5 0
O 7 4 a. slate-green 1 6 1 0
O 8 8 a. dull mauve 7 6 6 0
O 9 8 a. magenta 4 0 3 6
O10 1 r. green & carmine (1896) 5 0 5 6

Varieties. (i.) *The last two characters of the lower word transposed, so that it reads "Sersiv".*

No.	Description	Unused	Used
O11	½ a. deep green	15 0	15 0
O12	1 a. plum	25 0	20 0
O13	2 a. deep blue	60 0	
O14	4 a. olive-green	£10	
O15	8 a. magenta	£45	
O16	1 r. green and carmine	£55	

(ii.) *Fourth character in lower word omitted.*

No.	Description	Unused	Used
O17	½ a. deep green	—	15 0
O18	1 a. plum	—	20 0
O19	2 a. deep blue	80 0	50 0
O20	4 a. olive-green	—	100 0
O21	8 a. magenta		

(iii.) *Overprint double.*

No.	Description	Unused	Used
O21a	½ a. deep green	—	£8

1901–4. *Overprinted with Type* O 1.

No.	Description	Unused	Used
O22	3 pies, carmine (1902)	1 0	1 0
O23	3 pies, grey (1904)	0 9	0 6
O24	½ a. pale green	0 6	0 1
O24a	½ a. green	0 4	0 1
O25	1 a. carmine	2 0	0 3
O26	2 a. pale violet (1903)	1 0	1 6

1903–5. *Head of King Edward VII. Overprinted as Type* O 1. *Overprint spaced* 10 *mm.*

No.	Description	Unused	Used
O27	3 pies, pale grey	0 4	0 1
O27a	3 pies, slate-grey (1905)	0 2	0 1
O28	½ a. green	0 6	0 3
O29	1 a. carmine	0 4	0 2
O30	2 a. pale violet (1905)	1 9	0 7
O30a	2 a. mauve	1 6	0 7
O31	4 a. olive-green (1905)	5 0	5 0
O35	8 a. dull mauve (1905)	3 6	2 0
O35a	8 a. magenta	3 6	
O37	1 r. green & carmine (1905)	4 6	3 6

Overprint spaced 8 *mm.*

No.	Description	Unused	Used
O38	3 pies, pale grey	1 9	0 7
O39	3 pies, slate-grey	1 9	0 6
O40	½ a. green	1 9	0 3
O41	1 a. carmine	0 6	0 2
O42	2 a. mauve	2 0	0 8
O43	4 a. olive-green	6 0	2 0
O44	8 a. dull mauve	10 0	2 6
O45	1 r. green and carmine	10 0	10 0

1907. *Nos.* 149 *and* 150 *of India overprinted as Type* O 1. *Overprint spaced* 10 *mm.*

No.	Description	Unused	Used
O46	½ a. green	0 6	0 1
O47	1 a. carmine	1 3	0 1

Overprint spaced 8 *mm.*

No.	Description	Unused	Used
O48	½ a. green	0 6	0 1
O49	1 a. carmine	17 6	6 6

1913. *Head of King George V. Overprinted with Type* O 1. *Overprint spaced* 10 *mm.*

No.	Description	Unused	Used
O50	3 pies, slate-grey	0 1	0 1
O51	½ a. green	0 1	0 1
O52	1 a. aniline carmine	0 4	0 2
	a. Overprint double	40 0	
O53	2 a. mauve	0 7	0 1
O55	4 a. olive	1 0	0 3
O57	8 a. purple	1 6	0 9
O58	1 r. brown and green	4 0	1 6

1922. *No.* 597 *of India optd. with T* 3.

No.	Description	Unused	Used
O59	9 p. on 1 a. rose-carmine	0 6	0 4

1923. *Overprint Type* O 1. *New colour.*

No.	Description	Unused	Used
O60	1 a. chocolate	0 4	0 1

गवालियर

सरविस

(O 2)

1927–35. *Head of King George V (Nasik printing, wmk. Mult. Star), optd. at Nasik as Type* O 1 *(but top line of overprint measures* 13 *mm. instead of* 14 *mm.) or with Type* O 2 *(rupee values).*

No.	Type	Description	Unused	Used
O61	55	3 pies slate	0 1	0 1
O62	56	½ a. green	0 2	0 3
O62a	80	9 p. deep green ('35)	0 2	0 3
O63	57	1 a. chocolate	0 4	0 1
O63a	82	1¼ a. mauve ('33)	0 4	0 4
O64	70	2 a. purple	0 6	0 2
O65	71	4 a. sage-green	1 0	0 6
O66	65	8 a. reddish purple ('28)	1 3	0 6
O67	67	1 r. chocolate & green	2 6	1 3
O67a	,,	2 r. car. & orange ('35)	4 6	5 0
O68	,,	5 r. ultram. & pur. ('32)	11 6	15 0
O69	,,	10 r. green & scar. ('32)	22 0	27 6

1936–37. *New types. Optd. as Type* O 1 *(*13 *mm.).*

No.	Type	Description	Unused	Used
O73	79	½ a. green	0 3	0 4
O74	81	1 a. chocolate	0 4	0 5
O75	59	2 a. vermilion	0 5	0 6
O76	,,	2 a. vermilion (*small die*)	0 4	0 3
O77	63	4 a. sage-green ('37)	0 8	0 5

JIND.

For earlier issues, see under INDIAN FEUDATORY STATES.

JHIND STATE

(1)

1885. *Head of Queen Victoria. Overprinted with T* 1, *in black. The* 4 *a. is India T* 17.

No.	Description	Unused	Used
101	½ a. deep green	3 6	3 6
102	1 a. brown-purple	17 6	17 6
103	2 a. dull blue	12 6	12 6
104	4 a. green	30 0	30 0
105	8 a. dull mauve	£7	
106	1 r. slate	£7	

Varieties. Overprint inverted.

No.	Description	Unused	Used
107	½ a. deep green	£5	£5
108	1 a. brown-purple		
109	2 a. dull blue		
110	8 a. dull mauve	£50	
111	1 r. slate		

All six values exist with reprinted overprint. In these the words "JHIND" and "STATE" are 8 and 9 mm. in length respectively, whereas in the originals the words are 9 and 9½ mm.

JEEND STATE (2)

JHIND STATE (3)

1885. *Overprinted with T* 2, *in red on* ½, 2, *and* 4 *a., and* 1 *r.; in black on* 1 *and* 8 *a.*

No.	Description	Unused	Used
112	½ a. deep green	35 0	
113	1 a. brown-purple	35 0	
114	2 a. dull blue	35 0	
115	4 a. green	40 0	
116	8 a. dull mauve	37 6	
117	1 r. slate	50 0	

1886. *Overprinted with T* 3, *in red.*

No.	Description	Unused	Used
118	½ a. green	22 6	
119	2 a. dull blue	32 6	
120	4 a. green	45 0	
121	1 r. slate	55 0	

Varieties. "JEIND" *for* "JHIND.

No.	Description	Unused	Used
122	½ a. green	£12	
123	2 a. dull blue	£15	
124	1 r. slate	£65	

1886–98. *Overprinted with T 3, in black. The 4 a. is India T 29.*

125	½ a. deep green (1888)	0	3	0	3
126	1 a. brown-purple	1	3	1	3
127	1 a. plum	1	0	1	0
128	1½ a. sepia (1897)	3	6	3	0
129	2 a. dull blue (1891)	2	0	0	9
130	2 a. ultramarine	2	6	1	0
132	3 a. brown-orange	1	9	1	9
133	4 a. olive-green (1891) ..	3	0	2	0
134	4 a. slate-green	3	0	2	0
135	6 a. olive-bistre (1891) ..	6	0	6	0
136	6 a. bistre-brown	5	0	5	0
137	8 a. dull mauve	5	0	5	0
138	8 a. magenta	4	6	4	6
139	12 a. purple/*red* (1897) ..	5	0	5	6
140	1 r. slate (1891)	8	6	9	6
141	1 r. green & carmine (1898)	10	0	15	0
142	2 r. carmine & yell-brn. ('97)	£5			
143	3 r. brown and green (1897)	£10			
144	5 r. ultram. & violet (1897)	£10			

Varieties. (i.) "JEIND" *for* "JHIND."

145	1 a. brown-purple	£12			
146	8 a. dull mauve	£45			

(ii.) *Overprint inverted.*

147	½ a. deep green	£10			

Varieties exist in which the word "JHIND" measures 10½ mm. and 9¾ mm. instead of 10 mm. Such varieties are to be found on Nos. 125, 126, 129, 131, 133, 137, and 140.

1900–4. *Overprinted with T 3.*

148	3 pies, carmine	0	4	0	6
149	3 pies, grey (1904)	0	2	0	3
150	½ a. pale green (1902) ..	1	6	2	0
150a	½ a. green	5	0	5	0
151	1 a. carmine (1902)	1	6	2	0

1903–9. *Head of King Edward VII. Overprinted with T 3.*

152	3 pies, pale grey	0	6	0	4
152a	3 pies, slate-grey (1905) ..	0	4	0	4
153	½ a. green	0	8	0	5
154	1 a. carmine	0	4	0	4
155	2 a. pale violet	1	6	1	6
155a	2 a. mauve (1906)	1	0	1	0
155b	2½ a. ultramarine (1909) ..	1	6	2	0
156	3 a. orange-brown	1	0	1	0
157	4 a. olive-green	1	9	2	0
157a	4 a. slate-green	1	9	2	0
158	6 a. bistre (1905)	2	6	3	0
159	8 a. dull mauve	2	0	2	6
159a	8 a. magenta	2	0	2	6
160	12 a. purple/*red* (1905) ..	3	0	4	0
161	1 r. green and carmine(1905)	4	0	5	0

Variety. Overprint double.

162	3 a. orange-brown	£5			

1907–9. *Nos. 149 and 150 of India overprinted with T 3.*

163	½ a. green	0	3	0	3
164	1 a. carmine (1909)	0	4	0	3

1913. *Head of King George V. Optd. with T 3.*

165	3 pies, slate-grey	0	6	0	7
166	½ a. green	0	6	0	6
167	1 a. aniline carmine	0	9	0	9
168	2 a. mauve	2	0	2	6
170	3 a. orange-brown	7	6	8	6
172	6 a. olive-bistre	12	6	15	0

JIND
STATE

(4)

1914–27. *Head of King George V. Optd. with T 4.*

173	3 pies, slate-grey	0	2	0	2
174	½ a. green	0	4	0	4
175	1 a. aniline carmine ..	0	4	0	4
175a	1½ a. choc. (Type A) (1922)	2	0	2	6
175b	1½ as. choc. (Type B) (1924)	2	6	3	0
176	2 a. mauve	0	7	0	3
176a	2½ a. ultram. (Type 61) (1922)	2	6	3	0
177	3 a. orange-brown	1	0	1	3
178	4 a. olive	1	3	1	6
179	6 a. olive-bistre	1	6	1	9
180	8 a. purple	1	6	2	0
181	12 a. dull claret	2	6	2	6
182	1 r. brown and green ..	4	0	5	0
183	2 r. carmine & yell.-brown	10	0	12	6
184	5 r. ultramarine and violet	45	0	55	0

1922. *No. 192 of India overprinted* "JIND" *in block capitals, in black.*

185	9 p. on 1 a. rose-carmine ..	5	0	6	6

1924–27. *Overprint T 4. New colours.*

186	1 a. chocolate	0	8	0	8
187	1½ as. rose-carmine (Type B)	1	3	1	6
188	2½ a. orange	1	3	1	6
189	3 a. bright blue	1	6	2	0

JIND STATE (5)

JIND STATE (6)

1927–37. *Head of King George V (Nasik printing, wmk. Mult. Star), overprinted at Nasik with T 5 or 6 (rupee values).*

190	55	3 pies, slate	0	2	0	2
191	56	½ a. green	0	3	0	3
191a	80	9 p. deep green ..	0	3	0	3
192	57	1 a. chocolate	0	5	0	2
192a	82	1¼ a. mauve	0	4	0	2
193	58	1½ a. rose-carm. (Type B)	0	5	0	4
194	70	2 a. purple	0	8	0	6
195	61	2½ a. orange	0	8	0	10
196	62	3 a. bright blue ..	1	0	1	3
196a	83	3½ a. ultramarine ('37) ..	0	10	1	0
197	71	4 a. sage-green ..	1	0	1	0
197a	64	6 a. bistre ('37) ..	1	3	1	6
198	65	8 a. reddish purple ..	2	0	2	6
199	66	12 a. claret	3	0	3	6
200	67	1 r. chocolate & green ..	4	0	4	6
201	„	2 r. carmine & orange ..	7	6	8	6
202	„	5 r. ultramarine & pur.	17	6	20	0
203	„	10 r. green & carmine ..	27	6	30	0
204	„	15 r. blue and olive ..	45	0	50	0
205	„	25 r. orange and blue ..	75	0	85	0

1934. *New types and colours. Optd. with T 5.*

206	79	½ a. green	0	2	0	1
207	81	1 a. chocolate	0	5	0	2
208	59	2 a. vermilion	0	6	0	5
209	62	3 a. carmine	0	8	0	6
210	63	4 a. sage-green	0	9	1	0

OFFICIAL STAMPS.

JHIND STATE SERVICE

(15)

SERVICE

JHIND
STATE

(16)

1885. *Head of Queen Victoria. Overprinted with T 15, in black.*

O1	½ a. deep green	0	9	0	9
O2	1 a. brown-purple	0	6	0	4
O3	2 a. dull blue	15	0	15	0

Overprinted as T **15**, *but* "JHIND STATE" *inverted.*

O4	½ a. deep green	50 0	30 0
O5	1 a. brown-purple	10 0	10 0
O6	2 a. dull blue	£30	

The three values have had the overprint reprinted in the same way as the ordinary stamps of 1885. See note after No. 111.

1855. *Overprinted with T* **2** *and* "SERVICE", *in colour given in brackets.*

O7	½ a. deep green (R)	30 0	
O8	1 a. brown-purple (Bk) ..	30 0	
O9	2 a. dull blue (R)	32 6	

1886. *Overprinted with T* **16**, *in red.*

O10	½ a. deep green	30 0	
O11	2 a. dull blue	40 0	

Varieties. (i.) "ERVICE" *for* "SERVICE".

O12	½ a. deep green		
O13	2 a. dull blue		

(ii.) "JEIND" *for* "JHIND".

O14	½ a. deep green	£12	
O15	2 a. dull blue	£22	

1886–97. *Overprinted with T* **16**, *in black.*

O16	½ a. deep green (1888) ..	0 6	0 2
O17	1 a. brown-purple	25 0	
O18	1 a. plum	1 6	0 9
O19	2 a. dull blue (1893) ..	2 0	1 0
O20	2 a. ultramarine	1 6	1 0
O21	4 a. olive-green (1892) ..	3 0	1 6
O22	4 a. slate-green	3 6	3 6
O23	8 a. dull mauve (1892) ..	6 0	6 0
O24	8 a. magenta	8 6	10 0
O25	1 r. grn. & carmine (1897) ..	15 0	17 6

Varieties. (i.) "ERVICE" *for* "SERVICE".

O26	1 a. brown-purple		

(ii.) "JEIND" *for* "JHIND".

O27	1 a. brown-purple	£12	

Varieties mentioned in note after No. 147 exist on Nos. O16, O19, O21, and O24.

Varities with "SERVICE" measuring 11½ mm. are to be found in the case of Nos. O16, O20, O22, O24, and O25.

1902. *Overprinted with T* **16**, *in black.*

O28	½ a. yellow-green	1 0	0 6

1903–6. *Head of King Edward VII. Overprinted with T* **16**.

O29a	3 pies, pale grey	1 0	0 3
O29b	3 pies, slate-grey (1906) ..	0 7	0 1
O30	½ a. green	1 6	0 3
O31	1 a. carmine	3 6	0 2
O32	2 a. pale violet	2 6	1 0
O32a	2 a. mauve	1 3	0 3
O33	4 a. olive-green	3 0	2 0
O34	8 a. dull mauve	6 6	6 6
O34a	8 a. magenta	5 0	5 0
O36	1 r. green & carmine (1906)	7 6	7 6

Variety. "HIND".

O36a	½ a. green	—	£7
O36b	1 a. carmine	—	£15

1907. *Nos.* 149 *and* 150 *of India optd. with T* **16**.

O37	½ a. green	0 8	0 1
O38	1 a. carmine	1 3	0 2

1914–27. *Head of King George V. Service stamps of India overprinted with T* **4**, *in black.*

O39	3 pies, slate-grey	0 3	0 1
O40	½ a. green	0 3	0 1
O41	1 a. aniline carmine ..	0 4	0 2
O41a	1 a. pale rose-carmine ..	0 6	0 3
O42	2 a. mauve	0 5	0 2
O44	4 a. olive	0 8	0 4
O45	6 a. yellow-bistre	1 6	2 0
O46	8 a. purple	1 3	1 6
O48	1 r. brown and green ..	3 0	2 0
O49	2 r. carmine & yellow-brn.	8 6	10 0
O50	5 r. ultramarine & violet ..	30 0	35 0

1924. *As* 1914–27. *New colour.*

O51	1 a. chocolate	0 4	0 2

JIND STATE SERVICE (17)

JIND STATE SERVICE (18)

1927–37. *Head of King George V (Nasik printing, wmk. Mult. Star), optd. with T* **17** *or* **18** *(rupee values).*

O52	**55**	3 pies, slate	0 1	0 2
O53	**56**	½ a. green	0 3	0 3
O53a	**80**	9 p. deep green	0 3	0 3
O54	**57**	1 a. chocolate	0 3	0 1
O54a	**82**	1¼ a. mauve	0 4	0 2
O55	**70**	2 a. purple	0 9	0 2
O56	**61**	2½ a. orange ('37) ..	0 7	0 6
O57	**71**	4 a. sage-green	0 9	0 4
O57a	**64**	6 a. bistre ('37) ..	1 3	1 6
O58	**65**	8 a. reddish purple ..	1 9	2 0
O59	**66**	12 a. claret	2 3	3 0
O60	**67**	1 r. chocolate & green	3 0	3 6
O61	,,	2 r. carmine & orange ..	6 0	7 0
O62	,,	5 r. ultram. & purple ..	15 0	17 6
O63	,,	10 r. green & carm. ..	30 0	35 0

1934. *New types overprinted with T* **17**.

O64	**79**	½ a. green	0 2	0 2
O65	**81**	1 a. chocolate	0 4	0 2
O66	**59**	2 a. vermilion	0 5	0 4
O67	**63**	4 a. sage-green	0 10	0 6

NABHA.

NABHA STATE (1)

NABHA STATE (2)

1885 (MAY). *Head of Queen Victoria. Overprinted with T* **1**, *in black. The* 4 *a. is India T* **17**.

1	½ a. deep green	1 9	2 0
2	1 a. brown-purple	15 0	17 6
3	2 a. dull blue	12 6	15 0
4	4 a. green	25 0	
5	8 a. dull mauve	£5	
6	1 r. slate	£5	

All six values have had the overprint reprinted. On the reprints the words "NABHA" and "STATE" both measure 9½ mm. in length, whereas on the originals these words measure 11 and 10 mm. respectively. The varieties with overprint double formerly catalogued are now known to be reprints.

1885 (Nov.). *Overprinted with T* **2**, *in red.*

10	½ a. deep green	1 6	1 6
11	2 a. dull blue	2 0	2 6
12	4 a. green	13 6	16 6
13	1 r. slate	40 0	45 0

1887–97. *Optd. with T* **2**, *in black. The* 4 *a. is India T* **29**.

14	½ a. deep green	0 9	0 4
15	9 p. carmine (1892)	2 0	2 6
16	1 a. brown-purple	2 0	1 0
17	1 a. plum	0 8	0 6
18	1½ a. sepia (1891)	1 6	1 9
19	2 a. dull blue	2 6	1 3
20	2 a. ultramarine	2 6	1 3
21	3 a. orange (1889)	6 0	6 0
22	3 a. brown-orange	2 6	2 0
23	4 a. olive-green	2 6	1 6
24	4 a. slate-green	2 6	2 0
25	6 a. olive-bistre (1889) ..	5 6	6 0
26	6 a. bistre-brown	6 0	6 6
27	8 a. dull mauve	4 0	4 6
28	12 a. purple/*red* (1889) ..	4 6	4 6

No.	Description				
29	1 r. slate	10	0	12	6
30	1 r. green & carmine (1893) ..	5	0	5	0
31	2 r. carmine & yell.-brn, ('97)	55	0	60	0
32	3 r. brown & green (1897) ..	55	0	70	0
33	5 r. ultramarine & vio. (1897)	55	0	70	0

Varieties. (i.) "ABHA" *for* "NABHA."

34	1½ a. sepia	£10			

(ii.) "N BHA" *for* "NABHA."

35	1 r. green and carmine ..				

Nos. 10, 11, 12, 13, and 27 have had the overprint reprinted, but in nearly every case the reprints have had the word "SPECIMEN" overprinted upon them.

1900 (Nov.). *Overprinted with T* **2**.

36	3 pies, carmine	0	2	0	3

1903–10. *Head of King Edward VII. Overprinted with T* **2**.

37	3 pies, pale grey	0	6	0	6
37*a*	3 pies, slate-grey (1906) ..	0	4	0	3
38	½ a. green	0	8	0	6
	a. Error, "NABH"	£5			
39	1 a. carmine	1	0	1	0
40	2 a. pale violet	3	0	3	0
40*a*	2 a. mauve	0	10	0	10
40*b*	2½ a. ultramarine (1910) ..	40	0		
41	3 a. orange-brown	1	3	1	3
42	4 a. olive-green	1	6	1	6
43	6 a. olive-bistre	2	0	2	6
44	8 a. dull mauve	3	0	3	0
44*a*	8 a. magenta	3	3	3	3
45	12 a. purple/*red*	4	0	4	6
46	1 r. green and carmine ..	4	6	5	0

1907. *Nos.* 149 *and* 150 *of India optd. with T* **2**.

47	½ a. green	0	6	0	6
48	1 a. carmine	1	0	1	0

1913. *Head of King George V. Overprinted with T* **2**.

49	3 pies, slate	0	1	0	2
50	½ a. green	0	3	0	2
51	1 a. aniline carmine	0	4	0	4
52	2 a. mauve	0	5	0	5
53	3 a. orange-brown	0	7	0	8
54	4 a. olive	0	9	0	8
55	6 a. olive-bistre	1	0	1	3
56	8 a. purple	1	6	1	9
57	12 a. dull claret	2	0	2	3
58	1 r. brown and green ..	2	6	3	0

1924. *As* 1913. *New colour.*

59	1 a. chocolate	0	4	0	4

NABHA STATE (**3**)   **NABHA STATE** (**4**)

1928–37. *Head of King George V (Nasik printing, wmk. Mult. Star), optd. as T* **3** *or* **4** *(rupee values).*

No.	Type	Description				
60	**55**	3 p. slate ('32)	0	1	0	2
61	**56**	½ a. green	0	3	0	3
61*a*	**80**	9 p. deep green ('37) ..	0	3	0	3
62	**57**	1 a. chocolate	0	3	0	3
63	**82**	1¼ a. mauve ('37) ..	0	4	0	4
64	**70**	2 a. purple ('32) ..	0	6	0	7
65	**61**	2½ a. orange ('32) ..	0	7	0	9
66	**62**	3 a. bright blue ('30) ..	0	8	0	10
67	**71**	4 a. sage-green ('32) ..	0	10	1	0
71	**67**	2 r. carm. & orange ('32)	7	6	8	6
72	,,	5 r. ultram. & purple ('32)	17	6	20	0

1936–37. *New types and colours. Optd. as T* **3**.

No.	Type	Description				
73	**79**	½ a. green	0	2	0	3
74	**81**	1 a. chocolate	0	4	0	4
75	**62**	3 a. carmine ('37) ..	0	9	1	0
76	**63**	4 a. sage-green ('37) ..	1	0	1	3

OFFICIAL STAMPS.

NABHA STATE SERVICE (O 8)   SERVICE NABHA STATE (O 9)

1885 (May). *Head of Queen Victoria. Optd. with Type* O **8**, *in black.*

O1	½ a. deep green	3	6	3	0
O2	1 a. brown-purple	1	0	1	3
O3	2 a. dull blue	45	0	45	0

The three values have had the overprint reprinted in the same way as the ordinary stamps of 1885.

1885 (Nov.). *Optd. with Type* O **9**, *in red.*

O4	½ a. deep green	5	0	4	0
O5	2 a. deep blue	2	6	2	6

1888–97. *Optd. with Type* O **9**, *in black. The* 4 *a. is India T* **29**.

O 6	½ a. deep green	0	6	0	2
O 7	1 a. brown-purple (1892) ..	1	6	1	0
O 8	1 a. plum	1	9	1	0
O 9	2 a. dull blue	2	0	2	6
O10	2 a. ultramarine	2	9	3	3
O11	3 a. orange (1891) ..	7	6	7	6
O12	3 a. brown-orange	7	6	7	6
O13	4 a. olive-green	2	0	2	0
O14	4 a. slate-green	2	6	2	6
O15	6 a. olive-bistre (1889) ..	6	6	7	6
O16	6 a. bistre-brown	95	0		
O17	8 a. dull mauve (1889) ..	5	0	6	6
O18	12 a. purple/*red* (1889) ..	15	0	16	0
O19	1 r. slate (1889)	32	6	42	6
O20	1 r. green & carmine (1897)	15	0	20	0

Varieties. (i.) "SERVICE." *with stop.*

O21	½ a. deep green	17	6	3	0
O22	1 a. plum	4	6	1	6

(ii) "NABHA STATE" *double.*

O23	1 a. plum	£6			

(iii.) "S ATE" *for* "STATE."

O23*a*	½ a. deep green				

Nos. O4, O5 and O7 exist with reprinted overprint, but in nearly every case the stamps bear the word "SPECIMEN."

1903–06. *Head of King Edward VII. Optd. with Type* O **9**.

O24	3 pies, pale grey (1906) ..	3	0	3	0
O25	3 pies, slate-grey (1906) ..	1	3	1	3
O26	½ a. green	0	8	0	9
O27	1 a. carmine	0	9	0	9
O28	2 a. pale violet	3	0	3	0
O29	2 a. mauve	2	3	2	3
O30	4 a. olive-green	1	9	1	3
O32	8 a. dull mauve	3	0	3	6
O34	1 r. green and carmine ..	5	0	6	0

1907. *Nos.* 149 *and* 150 *of India optd. with Type* O **9**.

O35	½ a. green	0	5	0	6
O36	1 a. carmine	0	7	0	7

1913. *Head of King George V. Optd. with Type* O **9**.

O37	4 a. olive	40	0		
O38	1 r. brown and green ..	£6			

1913 *Official stamps of India overprinted with T* **2**, *in black.*

O39	3 pies, slate-grey	0	4	0	5
O39*a*	3 pies, bluish slate	0	3	0	4

No.		Description	Unused	Used
O40		½ a. green	0 3	0 2
O41		1 a. aniline carmine	0 4	0 3
O42		2 a. mauve	0 6	0 6
O43		4 a. olive	0 10	1 0
O44		8 a. dull mauve	1 6	1 9
O46		1 r. brown and green	3 0	3 6

NABHA STATE
SERVICE
(O 10)

1932–45. *Head of King George V (Nasik printing, wmk. Mult. Star), optd. at Nasik as Type* **O 10.**

No.	Type	Description	Unused	Used
O47	**55**	3 p. slate	0 1	0 2
O50	**81**	1 a. chocolate ('35)	0 3	0 4
O50*a*	**63**	4 a. sage-green ('45)		
O51	**65**	8 a. reddish purple ('37)	4 6	5 0

PATIALA.

PUTTIALLA STATE (1)

PUTTIALLA
STATE (2)

1884. *Head of Queen Victoria. Overprinted with T* **1**, *in red. The 4 a. is India T* **17.**

No.	Description	Unused	Used
1	½ a. deep green	3 0	3 0
2	1 a. brown-purple	20 0	17 6
3	2 a. dull blue	7 6	10 0
4	4 a. green	12 6	15 0
5	8 a. dull mauve	£6	£7
6	1 r. slate	50 0	65 0

Varieties. (i.) *Overprint double.*

No.	Description	Unused	Used
7	½ a. deep green	—	£12
8	1 a. brown-purple		

(ii.) *Overprint inverted.*

No.	Description	Unused	Used
9	8 a. dull mauve		

(iii.) *Overprinted in red and also in black.*

No.	Description	Unused	Used
10	1 a. brown-purple	£10	
11	8 a. dull mauve	40 0	

1885. *Overprinted with T* **2.** (*a*) *In red.*

No.	Description	Unused	Used
12	½ a. deep green	1 0	1 0
13	2 a. dull blue	3 0	2 6
14	4 a. green	5 0	5 0
15	1 r. slate	12 6	15 0

(*b*) *In black.*

No.	Description	Unused	Used
16	1 a. brown-purple	0 6	0 6
17	8 a. dull mauve	4 0	5 0

The ½, 2, and 4 a. (T 29), and 1 r. (all overprinted in black), formerly catalogued, are only proofs.

Varieties. (i.) *Optd. in red and also in black.*

No.	Description	Unused	Used
18	1 a. brown-purple	10 0	
19	4 a. green	£10	

(ii.) "AUTTIALLA" *for* "PUTTIALLA"

(*a*) *In red.*

No.	Description	Unused	Used
20	½ a. deep green	6 0	
21	2 a. dull blue	15 0	
22	1 r. slate	£15	

(*b*) *In black.*

No.	Description	Unused	Used
23	1 a. brown-purple	35 0	
24	8 a. dull mauve	£15	

(*c*) *Overprinted in red and also in black.*

No.	Description	Unused	Used
25	1 a. brown-purple	£15	£10

(iii.) "STATE" *only, in red.*

No.	Description	Unused	Used
32	½ a. deep green		

All six values exist with reprinted overprints, and the error "AUTTIALLA STATE" has been reprinted in complete sheets on all values, and in addition in black on the ½, 2, 4 a., and 1 r. Nearly all these impressions, however, are found with the word "REPRINT" overprinted upon them.

The error "PUTTILLA" formerly catalogued is considered as doubtful by various authorities.

PATIALA
STATE
(3)

1891–96. *Overprinted with T* **3** *in black. The 4 a. is India T* **29.**

No.	Description	Unused	Used
33	½ a. deep green	0 4	0 3
34	9 p. carmine	1 0	1 3
35	1 a. brown-purple	0 9	0 4
36	1 a. plum	—	0 8
37	1½ a. sepia	1 4	2 0
38	2 a. dull blue (1896)	2 0	0 8
39	2 a. ultramarine	2 6	0 8
41	3 a. brown-orange	1 9	2 0
42	4 a. olive-green (1896)	2 0	1 6
43	4 a. slate-green	1 0	1 0
44	6 a. bistre-brown	2 0	1 6
44*a*	6 a. olive-bistre	5 0	
45	8 a. dull mauve		
45*a*	8 a. magenta (1896)	2 6	2 6
46	12 a. purple/*red*	2 6	3 0
47	1 r. green and carmine (1896)	7 6	10 0
48	2 r. carm. & yellow-brn. ('95)	75 0	
49	3 r. brown & green (1895)	90 0	
50	5 r. ultramarine & violet (1895)	£6	

Varieties. "PATIALA" *omitted.*

No.	Description	Unused	Used
51	1 a. plum	£10	£10
52	4 a. olive-green	£15	£15

1899–1902. *Overprinted with T* **3**, *in black.*

No.	Description	Unused	Used
56	3 pies, carmine (1899)	0 2	0 2
57	½ a. pale green	0 8	0 9
58	1 a. carmine	0 10	0 10

1903–06. *Head of King Edward VII. Overprinted with T* **3**, *in black.*

No.	Description	Unused	Used
59	3 pies, pale grey	0 5	0 3
60	3 pies, slate-grey (1906)	0 3	0 2
61	½ a. green	0 3	0 2
62	1 a. carmine	0 5	0 3
63	2 a. pale violet	0 6	0 4
64	3 a. orange-brown	0 10	0 6
65	4 a. olive-green (1905)	1 3	0 8
66	6 a. olive-bistre (1905)	2 0	1 6
67	8 a. dull mauve (1906)	3 0	2 0
68	12 a. purple/*red* (1906)	3 6	4 6
69	1 r. green & carmine (1905)	4 6	5 6

1912. *Nos.* 149 *and* 150 *of India optd. with T* **3.**

No.	Description	Unused	Used
70	½ a. green	0 3	0 4
71	1 a. carmine	0 4	0 5

1912–26. *Head of King George V. Stamps overprinted with T* **3.**

No.	Description	Unused	Used
72	3 pies, slate-grey	0 1	0 1
73	½ a. green	0 3	0 1
74	1 a. aniline carmine	0 5	0 3
74*a*	1½ a. chocolate (Type A)	1 6	2 0
75	2 a. mauve	0 5	0 5
76	3 a. orange-brown	1 0	0 10
77	4 a. olive	0 9	0 6
78	6 a. olive-bistre	1 0	1 0
79	8 a. purple	1 6	1 6
80	12 a. dull claret	1 9	1 6
81	1 r. brown and green	3 0	2 6
82	2 r. carmine & yellow-brown	6 0	7 6
83	5 r. ultramarine and violet	17 6	20 0

1923–26. *As* 1912–26. *New colours.*

84	1 a. chocolate ..	0	6	0	4
87	3 a. bright blue ..	1	0	1	3

PATIALA STATE (4)

PATIALA STATE (5)

1928–34. *Head of King George V (Nasik printing, wmk. Mult. Star) optd. at Nasik with T* **4** *or* **5** *(rupee values).*

88	**55**	3 p. slate ..	0	1	0	2
89	**56**	½ a. green ..	0	2	0	1
89*a*	**80**	9 p. deep green ..	0	2	0	2
90	**57**	1 a. chocolate ..	0	3	0	2
90*a*	**82**	1¼ a. mauve ..	0	4	0	2
91	**70**	2 a. purple ..	0	6	0	3
91*a*	**61**	2½ a. orange ..	0	6	0	6
92	**62**	3 a. bright blue ..	0	8	0	5
93	**71**	4 a. sage-green ..	1	0	0	6
94	**65**	8 a. reddish purple ..	2	0	1	6
96	**67**	1 r. chocolate and green	4	0	2	6
97	,,	2 r. carmine and orange	7	6	8	6

The 9 p. exists printed both by offset-lithography and typography.

1935–37. *New types. Optd. with T* **4**.

102	**79**	½ a. blue-green ('37) ..	0	2	0	2
103	**81**	1 a. chocolate ('36) ..	0	4	0	2
104	**59**	2 a. vermilion ('36) ..	0	5	0	5
105	**62**	3 a. carmine ('37) ..	0	9	1	0
106	**63**	4 a. sage-green ..	0	8	0	10

OFFICIAL STAMPS.

PUTTIALLA SERVICE STATE

(O 1)

1884. *Head of Queen Victoria. Optd. with Type* O **1**, " SERVICE " *in black, the rest in red.*

O1	½ a. deep green ..	2	0	1	0
O2	1 a. brown-purple ..	0	5	0	2
O3	2 a. dull blue ..	£7		20	0

Varieties. (i.) *Red overprint inverted.*

O4 1 a. brown-purple £8 £5

(ii) *Red overprint double.*

O5 1 a. brown-purple .. .. — £4

(iii.) " SERVICE " *double.*

O6 1 a. brown-purple .. .. — £5

(iv.) " SERVICE " *inverted.*

O7 1 a. brown-purple .. ..

SERVICE PUTTIALLA STATE (O 2)

SERVICE PUTTIALLA STATE (O 3)

1885–90. *Optd. with Type* O **2**, " SERVICE." *in black, the rest in red.*

O8 ½ a. deep green 1 3 0 6

Varieties. (i) " SERVICE " *double.*

O9 ½ a. deep green .. .. — 75 0

(ii.) " AUTTIALLA " for " PUTTIALLA."

O10 ½ a. deep green 40 0 12 6

Overprinted with Type O **3**, *all in red.*

O12 2 a. dull blue 1 0 0 9

Errors. (i.) " PUTTILLA."

O13 2 a. blue .. ..

The error No. O13 is probably from an essay sheet.

(ii.) *Overprint double, one inverted.*

O14 2 a. blue .. ..

The 2 a. with Type O **3**, in black, is a proof.

Overprinted with Type O **3**, *all in black.*

O16 ½ a. deep green (1890) .. 0 6 0 4

Overprinted with Type O **2**, *all in black.*

O17 1 a. brown-purple 0 6 0 3

Varieties. (i.) " SERVICE " *double.*

O18 1 a. brown-purple £10 £10

(ii) *Overprint double, one inverted.*

O18*a* 1 a. brown-purple .. ..

(iii.) " AUTTIALLA " *for* " PUTTIALLA."

O19 1 a. brown-purple .. £5

There are reprints of Nos. O8, O12, and O17. The first has the word " SERVICE " in the large type in *red* instead of the small type in *black*, and the last has the word in the large type in *black* in place of the small type. The 2 a. with Type O **3**, in *black*, is a proof. The ½ a. " AUTTIALLA " has also been reprinted, but nearly all the above have been overprinted " REPRINT ".

SERVICE PATIALA STATE (O 4)

1891–1903. *Optd. with Type* O **4**, *in black.*

O20	½ a. deep green (1895) ..	0	4	0	1
O21	1 a. plum (1900) ..	0	9	0	4
O22	2 a. dull blue (1898) ..	2	6	1	3
O23	2 a. deep blue ..	3	0	3	0
O25	3 a. brown-orange ..	1	3	1	0
O26	4 a. olive-green ..	1	0	1	0
O27	4 a. slate-green ..	0	10	1	0
O28	6 a. bistre-brown ..	2	0	2	0
O29	8 a. dull mauve ..	2	0	2	0
O30	8 a. magenta (1898) ..	1	9	2	0
O31	12 a. purple/*red* ..	2	0	2	0
O32	1 r. slate ..	2	6	1	9
O33	1 r. green & carmine (1903)	15	0		

Errors. " SERVICE " *inverted.*

O34	½ a. deep green	40	0		
O35	1 a. plum	40	0		
O36	2 a. dull blue	40	0		

These errors are genuine, but it is believed they were never issued.

Varieties. " SERV CE."

O37 ½ a. deep green £6
O38 3 a. brown-orange .. ..
O39 4 a. olive-green .. ..
O40 8 a. dull mauve .. ..
O41 12 a. purple/*red* .. ..
O42 1 r, slate .. ..

Varieties are known in which the letters of the word " SERVICE " are irregularly spaced, making the length about 11½ mm. instead of the usual 10½ mm.

1902. *Colour changed.*

O43		1 a. carmine	.. ..	0 9	0 3

1903–10. *Head of King Edward VII. Optd. with Type* O **4**, *in black.*

O44	3 pies, pale grey	.. ..	0 6	0 6
O45	3 pies, slate-grey (1909)	..	0 4	0 4
O46	½ a. green	.. ..	0 2	0 1
O47	1 a. carmine	.. ..	0 4	0 1
O48	2 a. pale violet (1905)	..	0 5	0 4
O48*a*	2 a. mauve	.. ..	0 5	0 4
O49	3 a. orange-brown	..	2 6	3 0
O50	4 a. olive-green (1905)	..	0 9	0 4
O51	8 a. dull mauve	.. ..	1 6	1 0
O52	8 a. magenta (1910)	..	1 9	2 0
O54	1 r. green & carmine (1906)		3 0	2 6

1907. *Nos.* 149/50 *of India optd. with Type* O **4**.

O55	½ a. green	.. .. ..	0 2	0 1
O56	1 a. carmine	.. .. ..	0 5	0 1

1913–26. *Head of King George V. Service stamps of India optd. with T* **3**, *in black.*

O57	3 pies, slate-grey	.. ..	0 2	0 1
O57*a*	3 pies, bluish slate	.. ..	0 1	0 1
O58	½ a. green	.. .. ..	0 2	0 2
O59	1 a. carmine	.. .. ..	0 4	0 2
O60	2 a. mauve	.. .. ..	0 6	0 1
O62	4 a. olive	.. .. ..	0 10	0 3
O63	6 a. yellow-bistre	.. ..	1 0	0 8
O64	8 a. purple	.. .. ..	1 3	0 6
O66	1 r. brown and green	..	3 6	4 0
O67	2 r. carmine & yellow-brn.		10 0	12 6
O68	5 r. ultramarine & violet	..	20 0	25 0

1925. *As* 1913–26. *New colour.*

O69	1 a. brown	.. .. ..	0 6	0 4

PATIALA STATE
SERVICE
(O 5)

PATIALA STATE
SERVICE
(O 6)

1927–36. *Head of King George V (Nasik printing, wmk. Mult. Star), optd. at Nasik with Type* O **5** *or Type* O **6** *(rupee values).*

O70	**55**	3 p. slate	.. ..	0 1	0 1
		a. Blue overprint	..	0 2	
O71	**56**	½ a. green	.. ..	0 2	0 2
O73	**57**	1 a. chocolate	.. ..	0 3	0 1
O74	**82**	1¼ a. mauve	.. ..	0 3	0 2
O76	**70**	2 a. purple	.. ..	0 7	0 4
O76*a*	,,	2 a. vermilion	.. ..	0 5	0 5
O76*b*	**61**	2½ a. orange	.. ..	0 5	0 3
O77	**71**	4 a. sage-green	.. ..	0 9	0 2
O78	**65**	8 a. reddish purple	..	1 3	0 4
O80	**67**	1 r. chocolate & green		3 3	1 3
O81	,,	2 r. carm. & orge. ('36)		6 0	6 6

1935–39. *New types. Optd. with Type* O **5**.

O86	**79**	½ a. green ('36)	.. ..	0 2	0 1
O87	**81**	1 a. chocolate ('36)	.. ..	0 3	0 1
O88	**59**	2 a. vermilion	.. ..	0 4	0 1
O89	,,	2 a. verm. ('39) *(small die)*		0 4	0 1
O91	**63**	4 a. sage-green ('36)	..	0 7	0 4

INDIAN STATES.

ALWAR.

1 (1 a.)

1877. *T* **1**. *Lithographed. Rouletted.*

1	¼ a. grey-blue	.. .. ..	1 6	1 6
2	¼ a. ultramarine	.. .. ..	1 0	1 3
	a. Imperf. between (pair)	..	—	20 0
4	1 a. brown	.. .. ..	1 9	2 6
	a. Imperf. between (pair)	..	6 6	
5	1 a. red-brown	.. .. ..	1 6	2 6

1899–1901. *Type redrawn. P* 12.

7	¼ a. emerald-green	.. ..	1 9	2 0
	a. Imperf. between (pair)	..	12 0	12 0
	b. Imperf.	.. ..	5 0	
8	¼ a. pale green	.. ..	1 9	2 6

1899. *T* **1**. *Stamps printed further apart. P* 12.

9	¼ a. slate-blue	.. ..	1 9	2 6
	a. Imperf. between (pair)	..	20 0	
10	¼ a. emerald-green	.. ..	2 0	
11	¼ a. deep green	.. ..	7 0	

The stamps of Alwar became obsolete in the latter part of 1902.

BAMRA.

1 (¼ a.) **2** (½ a.) **3** (1 a.)

4 (2 a.) **5** (4 a.) **6** (8 a.)

(Printed by the Jagannata Ballabh Press, Deogarh.)

1888. *T* **1** *to* **6**. *Imperf.*

1	¼ a. black/*yellow*	.. ..	57 6
2	½ a. black/*rose*	.. ..	32 6
3	1 a. black/*blue*	.. ..	37 6
4	2 a. black/*green*	.. ..	32 6
5	4 a. black/*yellow*	.. ..	30 0
6	8 a. black/*rose*	.. ..	32 6

Varieties. (i.) *Lettered* " postaɘe."

6*a*	¼ a. black/*yellow*	.. ..	
6*b*	½ a. black/*rose*	.. ..	
7	1 a. black/*blue*	.. ..	£15

(ii.) *Lettered* " postge."

8	2 a. black/*green*	.. ..	£15
9	4 a. black/*yellow*	.. ..	£15
10	8 a. black/*rose*	.. ..	£10

(iii.) *Last native character inverted.*

10*a*	¼ a. black/*yellow*	.. ..	

(7)

T **7**. *With last native character as in illustration.*

10*b*	¼ a. black/*yellow*	.. ..	

These stamps were all printed from the same plate of 96 stamps, 12 × 8.

In printing the ¼ a., 4 a., and 8 a., the whole plate was used, and there are therefore 96 varieties of type. For the 1 a. the first 9 vertical rows were used (=72 varieties). For the 2 a. the first 10 vertical rows were used (=80 varieties).

The number of rows used for the ½ a. is not known, but was at least 11.

One stamp in each sheet has the scroll ornament inverted.

There are two forms of the third native character. In the first five horizontal rows it is as in T 1 and in the last three rows as in T 4.

These stamps have been reprinted, the ¼ a. and ½ a. in blocks of 8 varieties, and all the values in blocks of 20 varieties. T 1 has the fourth character, in the native inscription, in the form which distinguishes the reprints.

8

1890 (July)–1893. *T 8. Black on coloured paper. Various settings, the first showing 20 varieties of the ¼ a., ½ a., 1 a., 2 a., and 4 a., and 10 varieties of the 8 a. and 1 rupee, the remaining settings showing 16 varieties of each value.*

A. "Postage" *with capital* "P."

1. *The native characters in the fourth line are in one group.*

11	¼ a. on *mauve*	2	0	2	6
12	¼ a. on *mauve* (Quatrer)	12	6		
13	¼ a. on *mauve* (Postage)	12	6		
14	¼ a. on *bright rose* (1891)	1	9	2	3
15	¼ a. on *magenta* (1893)	1	6	2	3
16	¼ a. on *magenta* (enna)	32	6		
17	¼ a. on *magenta* (BVMRV)	32	6		
18	¼ a. on *magenta* (BAMRV)	32	6		
19	½ a. on *blue-green*	2	0	2	6
20	½ a. on *green* (1891)	3	0	3	6
21	1 a. on *yellow* ..	6	6	5	0
22	2 a. on *mauve* ..	3	6		
23	4 a. on *mauve* ..	35	0		
24	4 a. on *rose-red* ..	5	0		
25	8 a. on *mauve* ..	6	6		
26	1 r. on *mauve* ..	10	0		

Errors. (i.) *Lettered* "Eeudatory."

27	¼ a. on *mauve* ..	12	6	15	0
28	½ a. on *blue-green*	17	6		
29	1 a. on *yellow* ..	30	0		
30	2 a. on *mauve* ..	22	6		
31	4 a. on *mauve* ..	55	0		
32	4 a. on *rose-red* ..	37	6		
33	1 r. on *mauve* ..	70	0		

(ii.) *Lettered* "BAMBA" (1891).

34	4 a. on *rose-red* ..	47	6
35	8 a. on *mauve* ..	80	0
36	1 r. on *mauve* ..	90	0

(iii.) "Foudatory" *and* "Postagc" (1891).

37	8 a. on *mauve* ..	80	0

(iv.) "Postagc" (1891).

38	1 r. on *mauve* ..	80	0

2. *Characters in fourth line divided into two groups* (1891–93).

39	¼ a. on *magenta* (1893)	8	6	5	0
39a	½ a. on *blue-green*	15	0		
40	1 a. on *yellow* ..	2	6	2	6
40a	1 a. on *orange* ..	6	0	6	0
41	2 a. on *rose-red*	2	6	2	6
42	2 a. on *bright rose*	2	0		
43	4 a. on *rose-red*	3	0	4	0
44	4 a. on *bright rose*	3	0		
45	8 a. on *rose-red*	7	6		
46	8 a. on *bright rose*	7	6		
47	1 r. on *bright rose*	10	0	10	0

Errors. (i.) *Lettered* "annas." (1893.)

48 1 a. on *orange* £5

(ii.) "rupee" *with small* "r." (1893.)

49 1 r. on *bright rose* £6

B. "postage" *with small* "p." (1891–93.)

1. *Characters in one group.*

50	¼ a. on *bright rose* (1891)	1	9	1	9
51	¼ a. on *magenta* (1893)	1	9	1	9
52	½ a. on *blue-green*	3	6	4	0
53	½ a. on *green* (1893)	3	6		
54	4 a. on *rose-red* (1891) ..	10	0		
55	8 a. on *mauve* (1891)	7	6		
56	1 r. on *mauve* (1891)	12	6		

Errors. *Lettered* "enna."

57	½ a. on *blue-green*	17	6
58	½ a. on *green*	22	6

2. *Characters in two groups.*

59	¼ a. on *magenta* (1893)	6	0	6	0
60	1 a. on *yellow* ..	3	0	3	0
60a	1 a. on *orange* ..	10	0		
61	2 a. on *rose-red*	3	6	4	0
62	2 a. on *bright rose*	3	6	4	0
63	4 a. on *rose-red*	5	0	5	0
64	4 a. on *bright rose*	5	0	5	0
65	8 a. on *rose-red*	5	0	5	0
66	8 a. on *bright rose*	10	0		
67	1 r. on *bright rose*	10	0	10	0

Errors. (a) "rupee" *with small* "r."

68 1 r. on *bright rose* £5

(b) *As No. 68, but second and third native characters in first group, and first, fourth and fifth characters in second group.*

69 1 r. on *bright rose* .. ..

There are 10 settings of Type 8. The first setting (of 20 varieties) has capital "P" throughout. The remaining settings (of 16 varieties) have capital "P" and small "p" mixed.

There are 4 sizes of the central ornament, which represents an elephant's trunk holding a stick:—

(*a*) 4 mm. long.
(*b*) 5 mm. long.
(*c*) 6½ mm. long.
(*d*) 11 mm. long.

These ornaments are also found inverted. Ornaments (*a*) are found in all settings; (*b*) in all settings from the 3rd to the 10th; (*c*) in the first and second settings; and (*d*) only in the first setting.

Varieties Nos. 12, 13 and 27 to 33 belong to the first setting; varieties 34 to 38 to the second setting; No. 39*a* is an error in the third setting; varieties 17, 18 and 39 are from the fifth setting; No. 16 from the seventh and ninth; No. 48 from the ninth setting; and Nos. 49 and 68 from one of the last four settings.

The characters are in two groups in the values from 1 anna upwards, in all settings from the third to the tenth.

The stamps of Bamra have been obsolete since 1894.

BARWANI.

1. Rana Ranjitsingh.

1921. *T* **1.** *Perf.* (*a*) *Thick paper.*

1 ¼ a. blue-grey 8 6
2 ½ a. blue 7 0

(*b*) *Thin wove paper.*

3 ¼ a. green 2 0 2 6
4 ½ a. deep blue 2 0 2 6

T **1.** *Colours changed.* *Perf.*

5 ¼ a. deep blue (wove) 1 0
6 ½ a. deep green (laid) 1 6
a. Imperf. 2 6

All issues that we have seen have been in sheets 1, 4, variously perforated to give stamps perf. on of 2, 3 or 4 sides.

2. Rana Ranjitsingh. 3

1922–31. *T* **2.** P 11. (*a*) *Thick glazed paper.*

7 1 a. scarlet 1 0
a. Imperf. between (pair)
7*b* 1 a. carmine-pink ('31) .. 1 0 1 3
8 2 a. magenta 1 3 2 0

(*b*) *Unglazed paper.*

9 2 a. purple/*toned* 12 6

1923–24. *T* **1.** *Colour changed.* *Pin-perf.*

10 ½ a. black (*wove paper*) .. 12 6 15 0
11 ½ a. pink (*laid paper*) 0 8 0 9
a. Imperf. between (pair) .. 6 0
12 ½ a. deep blue-green (*laid p.*) ..
a. Imperf. between (pair) .. 6 0

1927–31. *T* **3.** (*a*) *Wove paper.* *Pin-perf.*

13 4 a. cinnamon 1 9

(*b*) *Thick glazed paper.* P 11.

13*a* 4 a. red-brown ('31) 1 9 2 6

1927. *T* **1.** *Perf.*

14 ¼ a. blue (*laid*) 0 6
15 ½ a. green (*wove*) 0 6

1928. *T* **1.** P 11. (*a*) *Wove paper.*

16 ¼ a. bright blue 1 3
a. Tête-bêche (horiz. pair) .. 6 0
17 ½ a. emerald 2 0
a. Tête-bêche (vert. pair) .. 4 6

(*b*) *Thick glazed paper.*

18 ¼ a. deep blue 0 8 0 10
a. Imperf. between (pair) ..
19 ½ a. myrtle 0 8 0 8
a. Imperf. between (pair) ..

4. Rana Devi Singh.

1932. *T* **4.** *Typo.* P 11 *or* 12.

20 ¼ a. slate 0 3 0 4
21 ½ a. green 0 3 0 4
22 1 a. chocolate 0 6 0 8
23 2 a. purple 0 6 0 7
24 4 a. olive 1 6 1 6

1935. *Typo.* P 11.

25 **1** ¼ a. grey-black 0 1 0 2
26 **2** 1 a. chocolate 0 5 0 6
27 **3** 4 a. sage-green 0 9 1 0

(22) a. Perf. 8½ .. ..
*23*a* **4** 2 a. magenta .. ..

BHOPAL.

The correct English inscription on these stamps is "H.H. NAWAB SHAH JAHAN BEGAM." The words given in brackets, in the lists, are errors of spelling found on certain varieties in the sheets. Almost all may be found with the embossed centre inverted or sideways.

Nawab Shah Jahan Begam, 1868–1901.

1 (¼ a.)

1876–77. *T* **1.** *Double frame, 20 varieties of each value.* *Lithographed.*

1 ¼ a. black 80 0
1*a* ¼ a. black (BFGAM) £6
2 ¼ a. black (BEGAN) £6
3 ¼ a. black (EGAM) £6
4 ½ a. red 6 6 10 0
4*a* ½ a. red (BFGAM) 25 0
5 ½ a. red (BEGAN) 25 0
6 ½ a. red (EGAM) 25 0

2 (½ a.)

T **2.** *Single frame, 20 varieties of the* ¼ *a.*

7 ¼ a. black .. .. .. — £30
8 ½ a. red 7 6 10 0
9 ½ a. red (NWAB) 25 0

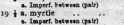

3 (½ a.)

T 3. 40 varieties (2 plates), all lettered "BEGAM" for "BEGAM."

10	½ a. black	1 0	2 0

It should be noted that in Nos. 1 to 10 the value is expressed in two different forms at the bottom.

4 (½ a.)

5 (½ a.)

1878–79. *T 4. Value in parenthesis; 32 varieties.*

11	½ a. green (*imperf.*)	2 6	4 0
12	½ a. green (*perf.*)	2 0	3 0

T 5. Value not in parenthesis; 32 varieties. Imperf.

13	½ a. red	2 6	3 0
14	½ a. red (JAHN)	12 6	
15	½ a. red (NWAB)	12 6	
16	½ a. red (EEGAM)	12 6	
17	½ a. brown	6 6	12 6
18	½ a. brown (JAHN)	27 6	
19	½ a. brown (NWAB)	27 6	
20	½ a. brown (EEGAM)	27 6	

1880. *T 5 redrawn; value not in parenthesis; 32 varieties of each value. No errors on sheet of ½ a.*

(*a*) *Imperf.*

21	½ a. blue-green	3 0	
22	½ a. blue-green (NAWA)* ..	12 6	
22*a*	½ a. blue-green (CHAH) ..	12 6	
23	½ a. brown-red	4 6	6 0

(*b*) *Perf.*

24	½ a. blue-green	1 6	
25	½ a. blue-green (NAWA)* ..	7 6	
25*a*	½ a. blue-green (CHAH) ..	15 0	
26	½ a. brown-red	2 0	

* For "NAWAB"—"B" omitted.

1884. *T 5 again redrawn; 32 varieties, some with value in parenthesis, others not. Perf.*

27	½ a. greenish blue	2 0	
28	½ a. greenish blue (ANAWAB)	5 0	

In this plate there is a slanting dash under and to left of the letters "JA" of "JAHAN," instead of a character like a large comma, which exists on all the previous varieties of this design.

1895. *T 5 again redrawn; 8 varieties. Laid paper.*

29	½ a. red (*imperf.*)	3 0	3 6
29*a*	½ a. red (*perf.*)	—	£8

In these cases where the same design has been redrawn several times, and each time in a number of varieties of type, it is very difficult for the general collector, who collects only single specimens, to distinguish the various issues. Nos. 11 and 12 may be distinguished from Nos. 21 and 24 by the presence or absence of the parenthesis marks (); 13, 17, and 23 differ principally in colour, and 13 and 29 are very much alike, but differ in the value as well as in paper.

6 (1 a.)

1881. *T 6. 24 varieties of each value. Imperf.*

31	½ a. black	1 0	
32	½ a. red	1 9	
33	1 a. brown	1 9	2 6
34	2 a. blue	1 9	
35	4 a. buff	3 6	

Errors. "NWAB" for "NAWAB."

36	½ a. black	8 6	
37	½ a. red	8 6	
38	1 a. brown	8 6	
39	2 a. blue	10 0	
40	4 a. buff	20 0	

In this issue all the values were produced from the same drawing, and therefore show exactly the same varieties of type. The value in this and all the following is given in only one form.

Many values in this and the following issues may be found with inverted centres. These can be supplied at double the price of the normal stamps.

7 (½ a.)

1886. *T 7, similar to T 6; larger lettering; 32 varieties.* (*a*) *Imperf.*

49	½ a. pale red (BEGAN) ..	1 3	5 0
50	½ a. pale red (BEGAM) ..	12 6	
51	½ a. pale red (NWAB) ..	12 6	

(*b*) *Perf.*

52*a*	½ a. pale red (BEGAN) ..	80 0	
52*b*	½ a. pale red (BEGAM)		
52*c*	½ a. pale red (NWAB)		

Almost all the varieties on this sheet are lettered "BEGAN."

8 (4 a.)

1886. *T 8. T 6 redrawn; 24 varieties. The "M" of "BEGAM" is an inverted "W." All the varieties are rather larger in width than in height.*

Wove paper. Imperf.

53	4 a. yellow	7 6	
54	4 a. yellow (EEGAM) ..	15 0	

Laid paper. Imperf.

55	4 a. yellow	3 6	
56	4 a. yellow (EEGAM) ..	10 0	

Laid paper. Perf.

57	4 a. yellow	1 6	3 0
58	4 a. yellow (BEGAM) ..	3 6	

1889. *T 6 again redrawn; 32 varieties, lettered "BEGAN."*

59	¼ a. black (*perf.*)	1 9	3 0
60	¼ a. black (*perf.*) (EEGAN)	7 6	
	a. Imperf. between (pair) ..		
61	¼ a. black (*imperf.*)	2 6	3 0
62	¼ a. black (*imperf.*) (EEGAN) ..	10 0	

9 (½ a.)

1889–90. *T 9. T 6 again redrawn; 24 varieties of each value, all with "M" like an inverted "W." Wove paper. Imperf.*

63	½ a. black	1 0	1 9
64	1 a. brown	1 9	2 6
65	1 a. brown (EEGAM) ..	12 6	12 6
65*a*	1 a. brown (BBGAM) ..	12 6	
66	2 a. blue	1 0	1 6
67	2 a. blue (BBEGAM) ..	20 0	
68	2 a. blue (NAWAH) ..	20 0	
69	4 a. orange-yellow	1 6	5 0

Perf.

70	½ a. black	1 6	2 6
71	1 a. brown	2 0	3 0
72	1 a. brown (EEGAM) ..	12 6	
72*a*	1 a. brown (BBGAM) ..	12 6	
73	2 a. blue	1 9	2 6
74	2 a. blue (BBEGAM) ..	20 0	35 0
75	2 a. blue (NAWAH) ..	20 0	25 0
76	4 a. orange-yellow	3 0	4 0

Nos. 69 and 76 are nearly square, in many cases rather larger in height than in width. The 2 a. and 4 a. exist on thin and also on a rather thicker paper.

1891. *As last, but 32 varieties.*

77	½ a. red (*imperf.*)	1 6	2 0
78	½ a. red (*perf.*)	1 0	1 6

1894–98. *T 6 again redrawn; 24 varieties, almost all showing a character inside the octagon below, as in T 9. Wove paper.*

79	1 a. deep brown (*imperf.*) ..	1 9	2 6
79*a*	1 a. red-brown (*imperf.*) ..	30 0	
	b. Printed on both sides ..	—	£15
80	1 a. deep brown (*perf.*) ..	5 0	5 0

10 (1 a.)

T 10. As Nos. 79 to 80, but printed from a fresh transfer (?), showing the lines blurred and shaky. Wove paper. Imperf. (1898.)

81	1 a. purple brown	6 0	7 6
81*a*	1 a. purple-brown (NAWAH) ..	50 0	
82	1 a. purple-brown/*buff* ..	2 6	4 6
82*a*	1 a. pur.-brn./*buff* (NAWAH) ..	20 0	

Variety, without embossing.

83	1 a. purple-brown	2 6	
83*a*	1 a. purple-brown (NAWAH) ..	20 0	
83*b*	1 a. purple-brown/*buff* ..	7 6	
83*c*	1 a. pur.-brn./*buff* (NAWAH) ..	30 0	

11 (½ a.)

1895. *T 11; 8 varieties, lettered* "EEGAM. *White laid paper.*

84	½ a. black (*imperf.*)	2 6	3 0
85	½ a. black (*imperf.*) (NAW B) ..	25 0	25 0
86	½ a. black (*perf.*)	4 0	4 0
87	½ a. black (*perf.*) (NAW B) ..	20 0	

12 (½ a.)

T 12. Narrow label at bottom; 8 varieties, lettered "W W" for "H. H."

88	½ a. black (*imperf.*)	1 6	2 0

12a

T 12a ; 8 *varieties.*

90	½ a. red (*imperf.*)	2 6	3 0

No. 90 is a combination of Types 1 and 6, having the double outer frame to the octagon and the value in one form only. The note upon the stamps of Types 4 and 5 applies here also. Nos. 53 to 83 are varieties of type of Nos. 31 to 35, though distinguishable by certain details or by the paper. Nos. 53 and 69 differ, as a rule, in colour.

13 (¼ a.)

1884. *T* 13 ; 32 *varieties. Perf.*

92	¼ a. blue-green	20 0	
93	¼ a. blue-green (JAN)	25 0	
94	¼ a. blue-green (BEGM)	50 0	
95	¼ a. blue-green (NWAB)	50 0	
96	¼ a. blue-green (SHAHAN)	50 0	
97	¼ a. blue-green (JAHA)	50 0	
98	¼ a. blue-green (JN)	50 0	

14 (¼ a.)

1895. *T* 14, *double-lined frame round each stamp ; 6 varieties lettered* " JAN." *Laid paper.*

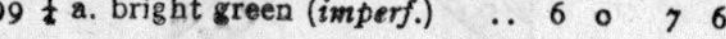

99	¼ a. bright green (*imperf.*)	6 0	7 6

15 (¼ a.)

1884. *T* 15 ; 32 *varieties of each value. Laid paper. Imperf.*

101	¼ a. blue-green	50 0	50 0
102	¼ a. blue-green (NWAB)	75 0	
103	¼ a. blue-green (SAH)	75 0	
104	¼ a. blue-green (NAWA)*	75 0	
105	½ a. black	1 3	1 6
106	½ a. black (NWAB)	7 6	
107	½ a. black (SAH)	7 6	
108	½ a. black (NAWA)*	7 6	

Perf.

109	¼ a. blue-green	0 6	
110	¼ a. blue-green (NWAB)	4 0	
111	¼ a. blue-green (SAH)	4 0	
112	¼ a. blue-green (NAWA)*	4 6	
113	½ a. black	0 6	1 0
114	½ a. black (NWAB)	6 6	
115	½ a. black (SAH)	6 6	
116	½ a. black (NAWA)*	6 6	

The ¼ a. of this issue is in *blue-green*, or *greenish blue.* Both values were printed from the same stone, the value alone being altered. There are therefore exactly the same varieties of type of each. These are the only stamps of this design upon laid paper. Nos. 104, 108, 112, and 116 have also " JANAN " for " JAHAN."

1886. *T* 15 *redrawn ;* 32 *varieties of each value. Wove paper. Imperf.*

117	¼ a. green	0 6	0 9
118	¼ a. green (NAWA)*	2 0	
119	¼ a. green (NWAB)	3 0	4 6
120	¼ a. green (NWABA)	5 0	
121	¼ a. green (NAWAA)	5 0	
122	¼ a. green (BEGAAM)	7 6	
123	½ a. red	1 0	1 6
124	½ a. red (SAH)	5 0	
125	½ a. red (NAWABA)	5 0	6 0

The ¼ a. varies from *yellow-green* to *deep green.*

Perf.

126	¼ a. green	1 0	1 6
127	¼ a. green (NAWA)*	7 6	
128	¼ a. green (NWAB)	10 0	
129	¼ a. green (NWABA)	10 0	
130	¼ a. green (NAWAA)	7 6	
131	¼ a. green (BEGAAM)	10 0	

Nos. 122 and 131 are lettered " NWABA " (like Nos. 120 and 129) as well as " BEGAAM."

1888. *T* 15 *again redrawn ;* 32 *varieties, letters in upper angles smaller. Wove paper. Imperf.*

132	¼ a. deep green	1 0	1 6
133	¼ a. deep green (SAH)	7 6	7 6
134	¼ a. deep green (NAWA)*	7 6	7 6

Perf.

135	¼ a. deep green	2 0	2 0
136	¼ a. deep green (SAH)	12 6	
137	¼ a. deep green (NAWA)*	12 6	
	a. Imperf. between (pair)	30 0	

Nos. 101 to 137 have the dash under the letters " JA," as in Nos. 27, 28.

* For " NAWAB "—" B " omitted.

The ¼ anna stamps of 1886 and 1888 are not easy to distinguish without reference to entire sheets, and are practically varieties of the same stamp for the general collector.

1891. *T* 15 *again redrawn ;* 32 *varieties, lettered* " NWAB." *Wove paper.* (*a*) *Imperf.*

138	½ a. red	0 9	1 6
139	½ a. red (SAH)	15 0	

(*b*) *P* 3 *to* 4½, *or about* 7.

140	½ a. red	1 6	2 6
141	½ a. red (SAH)	10 0	

Nos. 138 to 141 have the comma under " JA."

1894. *T 15 again redrawn; letters in corners larger than in 1888, value in very small characters; 32 varieties, all with "G" in left-hand lower corner. Wove paper.* (a) *Imperf.*

142 ½ a. green .. .. .. 1 0 | 1 0
142*a* ½ a. green (value in brackets) 20 0
143 ½ a. green (NAWAH) .. 20 0

(*b*) *Perf.*

144 ½ a. green .. .. .. 1 3 | 1 3
144*a* ½ a. green (value in brackets) 20 0
145 ½ a. green (NAWAH) .. 20 0

Nos. 142 to 145 have neither the dash nor the comma under "JA." The variety with value in ackets is the first stamp on the sheet.

16 (½ a.)

1896. *T 16; oval narrower, stops after "H.H.", space after "NAWAB." The line down the centre is under the first "H" of "SHAH" or between "HA" instead of being under the second "H" or between "AH." Wove paper. Imperf.*

146 ½ a. bright green .. .. 0 4 | 0 6
146*a* ½ a. bright green (SHAN) .. 3 6 | 3 6
146*b* ½ a. pale green .. .. 0 9 | 1 0
146*c* ½ a. pale green (SHAN) .. 6 6 | 6 6
147 ½ a. black .. .. .. 0 9 | 0 9
147*a* ½ a. black (SHAN) 15 0

1899. *T 15. Printed apparently from a transfer from the stone of 1891; the first "A" of "NAWAB" always absent. Numerous defective and malformed letters. Wove paper. Imperf.*

148 ½ a. black (NWAB) .. .. 0 9 | 3 0
149 ½ a. black (NWASBAHJAHNI) 7 6
151 ½ a. black (SBAH) 7 6
152 ½ a. black (SBAN) 7 6
153 ½ a. black (NWIB) 7 6
154 ½ a. black (BEIAM) 10 0
155 ½ a. black (SHH) 7 6

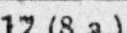

17 (8 a.)

18 (½ a.)

1890–91. *T 17; 10 varieties. Single-line frame to each stamp. Wove paper.*

156 8 a. slate-grn. (*imperf.*) 10 0
157 8 a. slate-grn. (*imperf.*) (HAH) 30 0
158 8 a. slate-grn. (*imperf.*) (JABAN) 30 0
159 8 a. slate-grn. (*perf.*) .. 12 6
160 8 a. slate-grn. (*perf.*) (HAH) 25 0
161 8 a. slate-grn. (*perf.*) (JABAN) 25 0

Thin laid paper. (a) *Imperf.*

162 8 a. green-black 7 6
163 8 a. green-black (HAH) .. 20 0
164 8 a. green-black (JABAN) .. 20 0

(*b*) *Perf.*

165 8 a. green-black .. .. 10 0 | 10 0
166 8 a. green-black (HAH) .. 20 0 | 20 0
167 8 a. green-black (JABAN) .. 20 0 | 20 0

1893. *T 17 redrawn. No frame to each stamp, but a frame to the sheet.* 10 *varieties. Wove paper.* (a) *Imperf.*

168 8 a. green-black .. .. 6 0 | 7 6

(*b*) *Perf.*

169 8 a. green-black .. .. 6 6 | 7 6

Thin laid paper. Imperf.

170 8 a. green-black 12 6

1898. *Defective transfer from the stone of* 1893. *Lettering irregular. Wove paper. Imperf.*

171 8 a. green-black .. .. 6 0 | 12 6
172 8 a. green-black (BEGAM) .. 25 0
173 8 a. black 7 6
174 8 a. black (BEGAM) 25 0

1896–1901. *T 18.* 32 *varieties. Imperf.*

175 ½ a. black .. .. .. 1 6 | 2 6

Printed from a fresh transfer (?)*, lines shaky. Imperf.* (1899).

176 ½ a. black .. .. .. 5 0 | 5 0

Variety, without embossing.

177 ½ a. black 2 6

The same, on thick wove paper (1901).

178 ½ a. black 20 0

Nawab Sultan Jahan Begam, 1901–1926.

19 (½ a.)

1902. *T 19.* 16 *varieties of* ½ *a.,* 8 *varieties of each of the other values. Thin, yellowish wove paper. Imperf.*

179 ½ a. red .. .. .. 2 0 | 2 6
180 ½ a. rose-red .. .. .. 3 0 | 3 6
181 ½ a. black .. .. .. 2 6 | 3 0
182 1 a. brown .. .. .. 2 6 | 3 0
183 2 a. blue .. .. .. 3 0 | 3 6
184 4 a. orange 4 6
185 4 a. yellow 4 6
186 8 a. lilac 5 6
187 1 r. rose .. .. .. 7 6 | 10 0

These have the same octagonal embossed device as the previous issues. The ½ a., 1 a., 4 a., 8 a., and 1 rupee have been found with the embossing inverted.

1903. *With a circular embossed device. 32 varieties (two plates) of ¼ a., 8 fresh varieties of ½ a. and 2 a., 4 a., 8 a., and 1 r., as before.*

187*a*	¼ a. rose-red	1 0	1 0
188	¼ a. red	1 6	2 0
188*a*	¼ a. red/*laid*	1 0	
188*b*	¼ a. rose/*laid*	3 0	
189	½ a. black	1 0	1 6
190	1 a. brown	1 3	
191	1 a. red-brown	1 3	
192	2 a. blue	1 9	
192*a*	2 a. blue/*laid*		
192*b*	4 a. orange	4 0	
193	4 a. yellow	2 6	4 6
194	8 a. lilac	3 0	5 0
195	1 r. rose	4 0	

No. 168 overprinted with initial of the new Begum in red.

196	8 a. green-black	25 0	25 0

Some of the previous stamps remained on sale (and probably in use) after the issue of the series of 1902, and some of these were afterwards put on sale with the new form of embossing; fresh plates were made of some of the old designs, in imitation of the earlier issues, and impressions from these were also sold with the new embossed device. The ordinary postal issues of Bhopal having become obsolete since July 1, 1908, we think it well to give a list of all these varieties, so far as they are known to us. It is said that all were available for postal use, but there is no doubt that they were made primarily for sale to collectors, and we should recommend the general collector either to ignore them altogether, or only to accept specimens that have passed through the post.

1903-4. *Stamps of earlier issues, embossed with the new circular device.*

197	¼ a. black (No. 63)	3 0	5 0
198	2 a. blue (No. 66)	3 0	
199	2 a. blue (No. 67)		
200	2 a. blue (No. 68)	12 6	
201	4 a. orange-yellow (No. 76) ..	8 6	
202	½ a. red (No. 77)	0 9	
203	½ a. red (No. 78)	0 9	1 0
203*a*	1 a. deep brown (No. 79) ..	1 0	
204	1 a. red-brown (No. 79*a*) ..	0 9	1 6
205	1 a. deep brown (No. 80) ..	1 6	
205*a*	½ a. black (No. 105) ..	2 0	
205*b*	½ a. black (No. 106) ..	20 0	
205*c*	½ a. black (No. 107) ..	20 0	
205*d*	½ a. black (No. 108) ..	20 0	
206	½ a. black (No. 113) ..	0	
207	½ a. black (No. 114) ..	12 6	
208	½ a. black (No. 115) ..	12 6	
209	½ a. black (No. 116) ..	12 6	
210	¼ a. green (No. 142) ..	2 0	
210*a*	¼ a. green (No. 142*a*) ..		
210*b*	¼ a. green (No. 143) ..		
211	¼ a. olive-green (as No. 142)	20 0	
211*a*	¼ a. olive-green (as No. 142*a*)	8 6	
211*b*	¼ a. olive-green (as No. 143)	15 0	
212	¼ a. black/*wove* (as No. 142)	1 3	
213	¼ a. black/*wove* (as No. 142*a*)	6 0	
213*a*	¼ a. black/*wove* (as No. 143)		
214	¼ a. black/*laid* (as No. 142) ..	6 0	
214*a*	¼ a. black/*laid* (as No. 142*a*)		
214*b*	¼ a. black/*laid* (as No. 143) ..		
216	8 a. green-black (No. 168) ..	17 6	
217	8 a. green-black (No. 170) ..	17 6	

Nos. 211 to 214*b* are from the stone of Nos. 142 and 143, but were not previously known in *olive-green* or in *black*.

Old designs redrawn, also with the new embossing. Imperf.

1\. *T* 7, *24 fresh varieties, all lettered* "BEGAN."

222	½ a. yellow	5 0	
223	½ a. orange	1 3	
223*a*	½ a. orange/*laid*	1 9	

2\. *T* 9. *Two plates, each of 24 varieties.*

(*a*) *With inverted* "W" for "M" *in* "BEGAM."

224	¼ a. black	1 0	

(*b*) *With inverted* "M" *for* "W" *in* "NAWAB" *and inverted* "W" *for* "M" *in* "BEGAM."

225	¼ a. black	3 0	

Variety. "BEGAN" *instead of* "BEGAM."

226	¼ a. black	20 0	

3\. *Type similar to that of No. 90, with double outer frame to octagon and value in one form at foot.*

227	½ a. carmine/*laid*	1 3	
227*a*	½ a. carmine/*wove*		
228	½ a. black/*wove*		

4\. *T* 13, *32 fresh varieties.*

229	¼ a. black/*wove*	0 6	
229*a*	¼ a. black/*wove* ((*pin-perf.*) ..	2 0	
230	¼ a. green/*wove*	1 0	
231	¼ a. red/*wove*	1 3	
232	¼ a. red/*laid*	2 0	
233	¼ a. lilac/*thick laid*	7 6	
	a. Printed on both sides ..		

No. 233 is from another stone, containing an unknown number of varieties.

5\. *T* 16, *probably 32 fresh varieties.*

234	¼ a. red/*laid*	5 0	
	a. Printed on both sides		
234*b*	¼ a. bright red/*wove* (*without embossing*)	2 6	

The following new varieties are found with the old embossing. Wove paper.

235	1 a. red-brown (No. 204) ..		
236	½ a. orange (No. 223) ..	5 0	
237	¼ a. black (as No. 234) ..	6 0	
237*a*	½ a. red (T 7)	12 6	
238	¼ a. black (No. 212) ..	5 0	
238*a*	¼ a. black (No. 225) ..		
240	¼ a. black (No. 229) ..	8 6	
240*a*	¼ a. green (No. 230) ..	5 0	

New embossing on wove.

240*b*	½ a. brownish red (T 15) ..	5 0	

Another redrawing of T 17 (embossing ?).

241	8 a. blue	12 6	

51

(Recess. Perkins Bacon & Co.)

1908. *T* 51. *P* 13½.

242	1 a. green	0 8	0 10
	a. Printed both sides	75 0	

OFFICIAL STAMPS.

SERVICE
(52)

SERVICE
(53)

SERVICE
(53*a*)

PRINTERS. 1908 issue recess-ptd. and optd. by Perkins, Bacon & Co. T **54** and subsequent types and opts., ptd. at Indian Govt. Ptg. Wks., Nasik.

1908 (1 JULY). *As T* **51**, *but inscribed* "H. H. BEGUM'S SERVICE" *at left. No wmk.* P 13 *to* 15. *Overprinted* (*a*) *with T* **52**.

No.	Description	Unused	Used
301	½ a. yellow-green	0 6	0 2
	a. Pair, one without overprint	30 0	
302	1 a. carmine-red	0 6	0 1
303	2 a. ultramarine	1 3	0 3
304	4 a. brown	3 0	0 6

(*b*) *With T* **53**.

No.	Description	Unused	Used
305	½ a. yellow-green	0 6	0 4
306	1 a. carmine-red	2 6	2 6
307	2 a. ultramarine	2 0	0 6
308	4 a. brown	—	0 6
	a. Overprint inverted	15 0	

The difference between the two overprints lies in the form of the letters, especially noticeable in the letter "R."

54

1930–31. *T* **54**, *overprinted with T* **53a**. *Litho.* P 14.

No.	Description	Unused	Used
309	½ a. sage-green (1931)	0 4	0 3
310	1 a. carmine-red (1.7.30)	0 6	0 3
311	2 a. ultramarine (1.7.30)	0 10	0 4
312	4 a. chocolate (1.7.30)	1 3	0 8

The ½ a., 2 a., and 4 a. are inscribed "POSTAGE" at left.

1932–33. *T* **51** *re-drawn. Inscribed* "POSTAGE" *at left. Overprinted with T* **52**. *Litho.*

(*a*) "BHOPAL STATE" *at right.* P 13.

No.	Description	Unused	Used
313	½ a. orange	0 3	0 1
	a. Perf. 11½	0 6	0 1
	b. Perf. 14	—	0 3

(*b*) "BHOPAL GOVT." *at right.* P 13½.

No.	Description	Unused	Used
314	½ a. yellow-green	0 2	0 1
315	1 a. carmine-red	0 4	0 2
316	2 a. ultramarine	0 5	0 4
317	4 a. chocolate	0 8	0 6

¼A (55) THREE PIES (56) ONE ANNA (57)

1935–36. *Nos.* 314, 316 *and* 317 *surch. as T* **55** *to* **57**.

No.	Type	Description	Unused	Used
318	**55**	¼ a. on ½ a. yellow-grn. (R)	1 3	1 0
319	**56**	3 p. on ½ a. yellow-grn. (R.)	0 4	0 3
		a. "THEEE PIES"	10 0	
320	**55**	¼ a. on 2 a. ultram. (R.)	1 3	1 0
321	**56**	3 p. on 2 a. ultram. (R.)	0 5	0 3
		a. "THEEE PIES"	12 6	
322	**55**	¼ a. on 4 a. chocolate (R.)	10 0	6 6
323	,,	¼ a. on 4 a. chocolate (Bk.) (25.5.36)	7 6	5 0
324	**56**	3 p. on 4 a. chocolate (R.)	3 0	1 6
		a. "THEEE PIES"	25 0	
325	,,	3 p. on 4 a. chocolate (Bk.) (25.5.36)	1 0	0 9
326	**57**	1 a. on ½ a. yellow-grn. (V.)	0 9	0 4
		a. First "N" in "ANNA" inverted	10 0	
327	,,	1 a. on 2 a. ultram. (R.)	0 8	0 6
		a. First "N" in "ANNA" inverted	7 6	
328	,,	1 a. on 2 a. ultramarine (Bk.) (25.5.36)	1 6	0 9
329	,,	1 a. on 4 a. chocolate (B.)	0 9	0 6
		a. First "N" in "ANNA" inverted	10 0	

Nos. 318 to 325 are arranged in composite sheets of 100 (10 × 10). The two upper horizontal rows of each value are surcharged as T **55** and the next five rows as T **56**. The remaining three rows are also surcharged as T **56** but in a slightly narrower setting.

The surcharge on No. 323 differs from T **55** in the shape of the figures and letter.

BHOR.

1 (½ a.)

2 (1 a.)

1879. *T* **1** *and* **2**. *Very thick to thin native paper. Imperf.*

No.	Description	Unused	Used
1	½ a. lake	2 6	4 0
2	½ a. pink	2 6	4 0
3	1 a. lake	4 6	5 6
4	1 a. pink	4 0	6 0

3. Pant Sachiv Shankarro Chimnaji.

1901. *T* **3**. *Typographed on white wove paper. Imperf.*

No.	Description	Unused	Used
5	½ a. red	2 0	3 6

BIJAWAR.

1. Maharaja Sir Sarwant Singh Bahadur.

1935. *Typo.* I. *P* 11. II. *Roul.* 7.

			I		II	
1	1	3 p. brown ..	0	4	0	2
		a. Printed on gummed side		†	10	0
2	„	6 p. carmine	0	6	0	3
3	„	9 p. violet ..	0	4	0	4
4	„	1 a. blue	0	4	0	4
5	„	2 a. deep green	0	6	0	6

BUNDI.

The characters denoting the value are below the dagger, except in Nos. 3, 12, and 19.

All the stamps of Bundi *until* 1915–18, are *imperf*.

1

1894 (May). *T* 1. *Each stamp with a distinct frame and the stamps not connected by the framing lines. Numerous varieties on the sheet.*

Laid paper.

1	½ a. slate-grey	—	£25

2 (Block of four stamps).

1894 (Dec.). *T* 2. *The stamps are all joined together, with no space at all between them.* 294 *varieties. Thin wove paper.*

2	½ a. slate-grey	10	0	10	6

Errors. (*a*) *Value at top and name below.*

3	½ a. slate-grey	60	0

(*b*) *Right upper ornament omitted.*

3*b*	½ a. slate-grey	£6

(*c*) *Last two letters of value below the rest.*

3*c*	½ a. slate-grey	£6

3

1896 (Nov.). *T* 3. *Dagger shorter, lines thicker. Stamps separate, and only joined by the framing lines at the top and sides of the sheet.* 168 *varieties. Laid paper.*

4	½ a. slate-grey	1	3	1	9

Error. Last two letters of value below the rest.

4*a*	½ a. slate-grey	65	0

4. (1 *anna*).

5. (2 *annas*).

6. (2 *annas*).

1897–1900. *T* 4, 5, *and* 6. *No shading in centre of blade of dagger. The stamps have spaces between them, but are connected by the framing lines, both vertically and horizontally. Laid paper.*

I. *Blade of dagger comparatively narrow, and either triangular, as in T* 4 *and* 6, *or with the left-hand corner not touching the bar behind it, as in T* 5 (1897–98).

5	4	1 a. brick-red	3	6		
6	5	1 a. brick-red	4	6		
7	„	2 a. yellowish green ..	3	0	6	0
8	6	2 a. emerald-green	2	6		
9	5	4 a. yellow-green ..	5	0	7	0
10	„	8 a. brick-red	10	0	12	6
11	„	1 r. yellow/*blue*	15	0		

7

2. *Blade varying in shape, but as a rule not touching the bar; value above and name below the dagger, instead of the reverse* (Jan., 1898).

12	7	4 a. emerald-green	6	0		

8. (½ *anna*).

9. (8 *annas*).

Blade wider and (except on the ½ a.) almost diamond-shaped; it almost always touches the bar (1898–1900).

13	8	½ a. slate-grey (5.2.98) ..	1	3	1	9
14	9	1 a. brick-red (–.7.98) ..	1	9	1	3
15	,,	2 a. pale green (9.11.98) ..	2	6	1	9
		a. First two characters of value (= two) omitted ..	12	6		
16	9	8 a. brick-red (–.7.98) ..	3	6	4	6
17	,,	1 r. yellow/*blue* (–.7.98) ..	7	0		

Variety on wove paper.

18	9	1 r. yellow/*blue*	10	0	15	0

10

1898 (9 Nov.).

4. *Inscriptions as on No. 12; point of dagger to left.*

19	10	4 a. pale green	8	6		

All the above stamps are lithographed in large sheets, containing as many varieties of type as there are stamps on the sheets. Of No. 10 there are 104 varieties, and of each of the others 120. Nos. 17 and 18 were printed from the same stone. The shape of the dagger is, of course, not identically the same all over the sheet, but Nos. 5, 6, 7, 8 represent different sheets. No. 14 is rather smaller than any of the rest of that issue.

The above stamps became obsolete in the latter part of 1902.

11. Maharao Raja Sir Raghubir Singh.

1915-18. *T* 11. *Rouletted in colour.*

20	½ a. indigo-blue	0	3		
20a	½ a. blue	0	4		
21	½ a. ultramarine	0	4	0	4
22	½ a. black	0	4		
22a	½ a. grey-black	0	4		
23	1 a. vermilion	0	8		
23a	1 a. carmine	0	6		
24	2 a. emerald	0	8		
24a	2 a. dark green	1	3		
25	2½ a. olive-yellow	0	10		
26	3 a. brown	1	0		
27	4 a. yellow-green	1	6		
27a	4 a. pale grass-green	1	9		
28	6 a. ultramarine	3	0		
28a	6 a. indigo-blue	2	0		
29	8 a. orange	2	6		
30	10 a. olive	3	0		
31	12 a. blue-green	3	6		
32	1 r. lilac	4	0		
33	2 r. black and brown ..	8	6		
34	3 r. brown and blue	15	0		
35	4 r. red and green	17	6		
36	5 r. green and red	21	0		

Nos. 35 and 36 have an ornamental border around the design in red and green respectively.

SERVICE STAMPS.

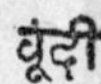

सरविस

(O 2)

1918. *T* 11 *overprinted with Type* O 2.

101	½ a. deep blue (R.)	0	8
	a. Inverted		
	b. Sideways	3	6
102	½ a. deep blue	0	8
	a. Inverted	3	6
	b. Double	8	6
103	½ a. black (R.)	0	8
	a. Double	6	6
	b. Sideways	3	6
104	1 a. red	0	8
	a. Double	6	6
	b. Inverted		
	c. Sideways	2	6
	d. Sideways, double	6	0
	e. Sideways, omitted (pair) ..	6	0
	f. Sideways on back ..	6	0
105	2 a. emerald	0	10
106	2½ a. olive-yellow	1	0
107	3 a. brown	1	3
108	4 a. yellow-green	1	6
109	6 a. blue	1	9
110	8 a. orange	2	0
111	10 a. olive	2	6
112	12 a. blue-green	3	6

113	1 r. lilac	4	0
114	2 r. black and brown ..	8	6
115	3 r. brown and blue ..	15	0
116	4 r. red and green	12	6
117	5 r. green and red	15	0

BUNDI

SERVICE

(O 3)

919. *T* **11** *optd. horizontally with Type* O **3.**

118	½ a. deep blue	0	3
	a. Inverted	2	6
119	½ a. black	0	4
120	1 a. carmine	0	6
121	2 a. green	0	6
122	2½ a. yellow	0	7
123	3 a. brownish carmine ..	0	8
124	4 a. yellow-green	0	10
125	6 a. blue	1	3
126	8 a. orange	1	6
127	10 a. olive	1	9
128	12 a. blackish green	2	0
129	1 r. violet	2	6
130	2 r. brownish carmine & blk.	4	0
131	3 r. blue and brown ..	6	0

All sorts of fancy varieties of Bundi "SERVICE" overprints have been seen, in various colours, double, inverted, sideways, etc. They appear to be entirely speculative.

BUSSAHIR (BASHAHR).

1

2

3

4

5

6

7

8

(9)

1895 (20 JUNE). *T* **1** *to* **8.** *Laid paper. Overprinted* " R. S." *in a monogram, T* **9.**

(B.) *In pale greenish blue* (R.) *In rose.*
(M.) *In mauve.* (L.) *In lake.*

The initials are those of the Tika Raghunath Singh, son of the then Raja, who was the organiser and former director of the State Post Office.

(*a*) *Imperf.*

1	½ a. pink (M.) (1.9.95) ..	30	0		
2	½ a. grey (R.)	20	0	20	0
3	½ a. grey (M.)				
4	1 a. vermilion (M.)	10	0		
5	2 a. orange-yellow (M.) ..	12	6		
6	2 a. orange-yellow (L.) ..	10	0		
7	2 a. orange-yellow (R.) ..	25	0		
8	2 a. orange (L.)	7	6		
9	4 a. slate-violet (R.) ..	25	0		
10	4 a. slate-violet (M.) ..	25	0		
11	4 a. slate-violet (L.) ..	20	0		
	a. Without overprint				
12	8 a. red-brown (M.)	7	6		
13	8 a. red-brown (B.)	25	0		
	a. Without overprint	10	0		
13*b*	12 a. green (L.)	15	0		
13*c*	1 r. ultramarine (R.) ..	15	0		
13*d*	1 r. ultramarine (L.) ..	25	0		
13*e*	1 r. ultramarine (M.) ..				

(*b*) *Perf. with a sewing machine ; gauge and size of holes varying between* 7 *and* 11½.

14	½ a. pink (B.)	7	6	15	0
15	½ a. pink (M.)	—		15	0
16	½ a. grey (R.)	8	6	15	0
17	1 a. vermilion (M.)	8	6	8	6
18	2 a. orange-yellow (B.) ..	7	0	7	6
19	2 a. orange-yellow (M.) ..	15	0	8	6
20	4 a. slate-violet (B.) ..	5	0	10	0
21	4 a. slate-violet (R.) ..	7	6	10	0
22	4 a. slate-violet (M.) ..	10	0	12	6
	a. Without overprint	5	0		
23	8 a. red-brown (B.)	8	6		
23*a*	8 a. red-brown (R.)	8	6		
24	8 a. red-brown (M.)	4	0	6	0
	a. Without overprint				
25	12 a. green (R.)	6	0	6	6
25*a*	12 a. green (M.)	8	6		
26	12 a. green (L.)	8	6		
	a. Without overprint	17	6		
27	1 r. ultramarine (R.) ..	6	0	8	6
28	1 r. ultramarine (M.) ..	25	0		
	a. Without overprint				

1899. *As* 1895, *but pin-perf. or rouletted.*

31	1 a. vermilion (M.)	25	0	17	6
32	2 a. orange-yellow (L.) ..	10	0	15	0
33	2 a. orange-yellow (M.) ..	7	6		
34	4 a. slate-violet (R.) ..	12	6		
34*a*	4 a. slate-violet (L.) ..	10	0		
34*b*	4 a. slate-violet (M.) ..	15	0		
34*c*	4 a. slate-violet (B.) ..				
35	12 a. green (R.)	17	6		
36	1 r. ultramarine (R.) ..	22	6	15	0

All the above were in sheets of 24, and were no doubt printed at a comparatively early date.

being uniformly on *laid* paper. They seem to have been *overprinted* and perforated as required. Those first *issued* for use were *perforated*, but they were subsequently supplied *imperf.*, both to collectors and for use, and some of the last supplies of certain values were *pin-perf.*, or rouletted like the later types. No rule seems to have been observed as to the colour of the *overprinted* monogram; *pale blue*, *rose*, and *mauve* were used from the first. The *pale blue* varies to *greenish blue* or *blue-green*, and appears quite *green* on the *yellow* stamps. The *lake* is possibly a mixture of the *mauve* and the *rose*—it is a quite distinct colour and apparently later than the others. Specimens without overprint are either remainders left in the Treasury or copies that have escaped accidentally; they have been found sticking to the backs of others that bore the overprint.

Varieties may also be found doubly overprinted, in two different colours.

11 12 13 14 15 16

(Printed at the Bussahir Press by Maulvi Karam Bakhsh.)

1896–98. *T* **11** *to* **16.** *Wove paper. Monogram* "R.S.". *T* **9.**

I. *Printed (singly?) from plates or dies line-engraved. Pin perf. or rouletted.*

42	**11**	¼ a. deep violet (R.) ..	—		£8	
43	**12**	½ a. bluish grey (R.) ..	—		£8	

1900–01. *Lithographed in sheets of various sizes.*

(*a*) *Imperf.*

44	**11**	¼ a. slate-violet (R.) ..	2	6		
44*a*	,,	¼ a. slate-violet (M.) ..	6	6	8	6
44*b*	,,	¼ a. slate-violet (L.) ..	3	6		
45*c*	,,	¼ a. slate-violet (B.) ..	3	6		
46	**12**	½ a. blue (R.)	2	0	2	0
46	,,	½ a. blue (M.)	3	6		
46*a*	,,	½ a. pale blue (M.)	2	0	3	6
44*b*	,,	½ a. pale blue (R.)	20	0		
47	**13**	1 a. deep olive (R.) ..	7	6	8	6
48	,,	1 a. dull olive (R.)	12	6		
49	,,	1 a. dull olive (L.)	7	0		

Variety. Without overprint.

50	**12**	½ a. blue				

(*b*) *Pin-perf. or rouletted.*

51	**11**	¼ a. slate-violet (R.) ..	3	6	4	6
52	,,	¼ a. slate-violet (L.) ..	3	6	4	6
52*a*	,,	¼ a. slate-violet (M.) ..				
53	**12**	½ a. pale blue (R.)	1	6	3	0
54	,,	½ a. pale blue (L.)	3	0		
55	,,	½ a. pale blue (M.)	2	6		
55*a*	,,	½ a. grey-blue (M.)				
56	**13**	1 a. greenish grey (M.) ..	10	0		
57	,,	1 a. dull olive (R.)	5	0		
57*a*	,,	1 a. dull olive (L.)				
58	,,	1 a. grey-buff (R.)	6	0		
59	,,	1 a. dull olive (L.)	8	0	8	0
60	**14**	2 a. orange yellow (B.) ..	30	0	45	0

The ¼ a. and ½ a. are in sheets of 24, the 1 a. and 2 a. in square blocks of 4.

Colours of ¼ a. and 1 a. changed; 2 a. with dash before "STATE" *and characters added in left lower label. Overprinted with monogram, T* **9.**

(*a*) *Imperf.*

69	**11**	¼ a. vermilion (M.) ..	1	6	2	0
69*a*	,,	¼ a. vermilion (B.)	1	9		
		b. Without overprint ..	—		20	0
70	**13**	1 a. vermilion (M.) ..	1	6	2	6
70*a*	,,	1 a. vermilion (B.)	4	0		
71	**15**	2 a. ochre (M.) (Sept., 1900)	4	6		
72	,,	2 a. yellow (M.) (Nov., 1900)	6	6		
72*a*	,,	2 a. orange (M.) (1901) ..	8	6	8	6
73	,,	2 a. orange (B.)	25	0		
74	**16**	4 a. claret (R.)	8	6	12	0
74*a*	,,	4 a. claret (B.)	12	6		
74*b*	,,	4 a. claret (M.)	10	0		

(*b*) *Pin-perf. or rouletted.*

75	**11**	¼ a. vermilion (M.) ..	2	6	3	6
76	,,	¼ a. vermilion (B.) ..	3	0		
77	**13**	1 a. vermilion (M.) ..	2	6		
77*a*	,,	1 a. vermilion (B.) ..	6	0		
77*b*	,,	1 a. brown-red (Mar. 1901)				
78	**15**	2 a. ochre (M.) (Sept. '00)	8	6		
78*a*	,,	2 a. ochre (B.)				
79	,,	2 a. yellow (M) (Nov. '00)	5	0		
80	,,	2 a. yellow (R)	6	0		
80*a*	,,	2 a. yellow (B.)				
81	,,	2 a. orange (M.) (1901) ..	6	0		
81*a*	,,	2 a. orange (B.)	15	0		
82	**16**	4 a. claret (R.)	10	0		
82*a*	,,	4 a. claret (B.)	12	6		
83	,,	4 a. claret (M.)	12	6		

The ¼ a. and 1 a. are in sheets of 24; the 2 a. in sheets of 50 differing throughout in the dash and the characters added at lower left; the 4 a. is in sheets of 28.

(17)

The stamps of Bussahir have been obsolete since March 31, 1901. Numerous remainders were sold after this date, and all values have since been reprinted in the colours of the originals, or in fancy colours from the original stones, or from new ones. Printings were also made from new types, similar to those of the second issue of the 8 a., 12 a., and 1 r. values in sheets of 8.

The stamps formerly catalogued with large overprint "R.N.S." (*T* **17**) are now believed never to have been issued for use.

Remainders are also found with overprint "P.S.", the initials of Padam Singh who succeeded Raghunath Singh in the direction of the Post Office, and with the original monogram

"R.S." in a damaged state, giving it the appearance of a double-lined "R."

Reprints are frequently found on laid paper.

Collectors are warned against obliterated copies bearing the Rampur postmark with date "19 MA 1900." Many thousand remainders and reprints were thus obliterated for export after the closing of the State Post Office.

CASHMERE.

See JAMMU-KASHMIR.

CHARKHARI.

1

1894. *T* 1. *Imperf. Value in the plural.*

1	1 annas, dull green	£12	
2	2 annas, dull green	£12	
3	4 annas, dull green	£12	

1894–97. *T* 1, *with value in the singular. Imperf.*

6	¼ a. rose	£8		80	0
7	¼ a. magenta	3	0	3	6
8	¼ a. purple	1	0	1	9
9	¼ a. violet	2	0	2	6
11	½ a. purple	2	0	3	0
12	½ a. violet	3	6	4	6
13	1 a. emerald	3	6	4	6
14	1 a. green	3	0	4	6
15	1 a. deep green	4	0	6	0
16	2 a. emerald	3	6	6	0
17	2 a. green	4	0		
17a	2 a. deep green	3	6	4	0
18	4 a. emerald	4	0	6	0
19	4 a. green	4	6	6	0
20	4 a. deep green	4	6	7	6

Minor varieties may be found with the first "A" in "ANNA" not printed.

All the values are known upon various coloured papers, but these are proofs, or trial impressions of some kind.

1905–7. *Numerals changed: in the ¼ a. and ½ a. the figures "4" and "2" are smaller than before; in the* 1 *a.,* 2 *a., and* 4 *a. the figures are of quite different shape.*

32	¼ a. violet	7	6
33	½ a. violet	10	0
34	1 a. green	12	6
35	2 a. green	15	0
36	4 a. green	20	0

2

3

1909–11. *T* 2. *Litho. Wove paper.* *P* 11.

38	1 pice, chestnut (Die I)	20	0		
39	1 pice, turquoise-blue (Die I)	0	6	1	3
39a	1 pice, gr'nish blue ('11) (Die I)	0	8	1	3
40	½ anna, scarlet	1	0		
41	1 anna, pale green	1	3		
42	2 annas, blue	1	6		
43	4 annas, deep green	1	9		
44	8 annas, brick-red	1	9		
45	1 rupee, chestnut	4	0		

1912–19. Die II.

46	1 pice, turquoise-blue	0	6	0	8
46a	½ a. red	0	8		
46b	1 a. olive-green (1919)	0	8		

Die III.

Redrawn values under the crossed swords.

46c	1 pice, turquoise-blue	1	9	1	9
46d	1 pice, light brown	3	0		

The native characters denoting the value vary in shape and size throughout the sheets, particularly in the 1 pice. In Die II of this value these characters are notably larger and heavier, the first extending right over the "I" of "INDIA," which word is also larger than in Die I.

1919–24. *T* 3. *Imperf.*

49	1 pice, violet	10	0	10	0
50	1 pice, purple	12	6	12	6

4 (actual size 63 × 25 mm.)

1925. *T* 4. *Handstamped. Imperf.*

51	1 a. violet	3	0	3	0

1930–40. *T* 2. *Typographed. Imperf.*

52	1 pice, deep blue	0	4		
53	¼ anna, deep olive	0	6		
53a	½ anna, red-brown ('40)	0	2		
54	1 anna, green	0	8		
54a	1 anna, chocolate ('40)	0	3		
55	2 annas, light blue	0	10		
	a. Tête-bêche (pair)	6	6		
56	4 annas, carmine	2	0		
	a. Tête-bêche (pair)	8	6		

5. Imlia Palace.

(Typographed.)

1931 (23 JUNE). *T* 5 *and similar designs.* *P* 11 *or* 12.

57	½ a. blue-green	0	1	0	1
58	1 a. blackish brown	0	1	0	1
	a. Imperf. between (horiz. pair)	7	6		
59	2 a. violet	0	2	0	1
60	4 a. olive-green	0	2	0	1
61	8 a. magenta	0	3	0	1
62	1 r. green and rose	0	6	0	1
63	2 r. red and brown	1	0	0	1
64	3 r. chocolate and blue-green	2	0	0	1
	a. Imperf. between (horiz. pair)	—		15	0
65	5 r. turquoise and purple	2	6	0	1

Designs:—½ a. The Lake. 2 a. Industrial School. 4 a. Bird's-eye view of City. 8 a. The Fort. 1 r. Guest House. 2 r. Palace Gate. 3 r. Temples at Rainpur. 5 r. Goverdhan Temple.

This issue has been the subject of speculative manipulation, large stocks being thrown on the market cancelled to order at very low prices and unused at less than face value. Numerous errors, probably produced clandestinely, are offered. The issue was an authorised one but has now been withdrawn by the State authorities.

COCHIN.

1

2

(Dies made by P. Orr & Sons, of Madras, and stamps printed by the Cochin Government at Ernakulam.)

1892 (1 April). *T* 1 (*½ and 1 p.*) *and* 2. *No watermark, or wmk. a large Umbrella in the sheet. P 12.*

1 ½ puttan, buff 2 0 1 3
1a ½ puttan, orange-buff .. 2 6 1 6
1b ½ puttan, yellow 3 0 1 9
c. Imperf. 52 6 52 6
2 1 puttan, purple 3 0 2 0
3 2 puttans, deep violet .. 3 0 2 0

Error. 1 puttan in colour of 2 puttans.

4 1 puttan, deep violet .. £12

1896 (End of). *Similar to T* 1, *but much larger. P 12.* (*a*) *Wmk. Arms and inscription in sheet.*

5 1 puttan, violet 3 0 8 6

(*b*) *Wmk. Conch Shell to each stamp.*

6 1 puttan, deep violet .. 3 6

This stamp was originally printed for provisional use as a fiscal; afterwards it was authorised for postal use.

On laid paper.

7 ½ puttan, orange-buff 65 0 27 6
7a ½ puttan, orange .. .. — 27 6
7b ½ puttan, yellow .. .. — 27 6

1897. *T* 1 *and* 2. *Wmk. a small Umbrella in each stamp. P 12.*

7c ½ p. buff 2 6 1 0
8 ½ p. orange 2 0 1 3
8a ½ p. yellow 2 0 2 0
9 1 p. purple 2 0 2 0
9a 1 p. deep violet 3 0
10 2 p. deep violet 4 0 3 0

Imperf.

10a 2 p. deep violet 60 0 55 0

The paper watermarked with a small umbrella is more transparent than that of the previous issue. The wmk. is not easy to distinguish.

3

4

5

6

1898. *T* 3 *to* 6. *Thin yellowish paper. Wmk. small Umbrella on each stamp. P 12.*

11 3 pies, blue 0 6 0 9
12 ½ p. green 0 6 0 5
13 1 p. pink 0 10 0 8
a. Tête-bêche (pair) £15
13b 1 p. red 1 6 0 6
13c 1 p. carmine-red 1 0 0 6
14 2 p. deep violet 1 3 1 6
a. Imperf. between (pair) ..

Variety. Laid paper.

15 1 p. pink .. .. .. — 50 0
a. Tête-bêche (pair) .. ..

1903. *T* 3 *to* 6. *Wmk. small Umbrella on each stamp. P 12 but on thick white paper.*

16 3 pies, blue 0 3 0 3
17 ½ p. green 0 6 0 3
18 1 p. pink 0 8 0 6
a. Tête-bêche (pair) £15
19 2 p. deep violet 1 3 0 8
a. Double impression ..

Variety. Stamp sideways (pair).

20 ½ p. green 22 6 22 6

There are several minor varieties caused by defective clichés, such as "THREF" for "THREE," figure of value broken or damaged, small "I" in "PIES" in the 3 p., and broken "L" in "ANCHAL" in the ½ p.

2 (7) 2 (7a)

1909. *T* **3** (*paper and perf. of* 1903) *surcharged with T* **7**, *in black.*

22	2 on 3 pies, rosy mauve ..	0 6	0 6

Varieties.

(i.) *Surcharged as T 7a.*

22a	2 on 3 pies, rosy mauve ..	37 6

(ii.) *Surcharge T 7 inverted.*

23	2 on 3 pies, rosy mauve ..	45 0

(iii.) *Tête-bêche (pair).*

24	2 on 3 pies, rosy mauve ..	45 0

Varieties ii. and iii. were caused by the inversion of one stamp (No. 7) in the plate and the subsequent inversion of the corresponding surcharge to correct the error.

8. Raja Sir Rama Varma I. 8a

(Recess. Perkins, Bacon & Co.)

1911–23. *T* **8**. *W* **8a**. *P* 14.

No.	Description	Unused	Used
26	2 pies, brown	0 3	0 3
	a. Imperf.	—	30 0
27	3 pies, blue	0 3	0 3
	a. Perf. 14×12½	—	3 0
28	4 pies, green	0 6	0 3
28a	4 pies, apple-green	0 6	0 3
29	9 pies, carmine	0 9	0 6
30	1 a. brown-orange	0 9	0 4
31	1½ a. purple	1 0	0 8
32	2 a. grey	2 0	0 10
33	3 a. vermilion	4 6	4 6

9. Maharaja Sir Rama Varma II. 10.

(Recess. Perkins, Bacon & Co.)

1918–23. *T* **9** (1 *a.*) *and* **10**. *W* **8a**. *P* 14.

No.	Description	Unused	Used
35	2 p. brown	0 3	0 1
36	4 p. green	0 3	0 1
37	6 p. red-brown (1922) ..	0 4	0 1
38	8 p. sepia	0 4	0 3
39	9 p. carmine	0 8	0 6
40	10 p. blue	0 6	0 6
41	1 a. orange	0 6	0 3
42	1½ a. purple (1921)	0 8	0 4
43	2 a. grey	1 0	0 4
44	2½ a. yellow-green (1922) ..	1 6	0 9
45	3 a. vermilion	1 6	0 8

2 2 2

Two pies (11) Two pies (12) Two pies (13)

2 2

Two Pies (14) Two Pies (15)

1922–29. *T* **8** (*P* 14), *surcharged, in black.*

No.	Type	Description	Unused	Used
46	11	2 p. on 3 p. blue	0 6	0 2
		a. Surcharge double ..		
47	12	2 p. on 3 p. blue	0 10	0 10
		a. Capital "P" in "Pies" ..	7 0	7 0
		b. Surcharge double		
		c. As a. Surcharge double ..		
48	13	2 p. on 3 p. blue (6.24) ..	0 6	0 4
		a. Capital "P" in "Pies" ..	2 6	2 6
		b. Perf. 14×12½	1 9	1 9
		c. As a. Perf. 14×12½ ..	7 0	7 0
49	14	2 p. on 3 p. blue ('29) ..	0 3	0 4
		a. Surcharge with Type 15 ..	6 0	

There are four settings of these overprints. The first (July, 1922) consisted of 39 stamps with Type **11**, and 9 with Type **12**, and in Type **11** the centre of the "2" is above the "o" of "Two." In the second setting (May, 1924) there were 36 of Type **11** and 12 of Type **12**, and the centre of the figure is above the space between "Two" and "Pies." The third setting (June, 1924) consists of stamps with Type **13** only.

The fourth setting (1929) was also in sheets of 48, No. 49a being the first stamp in the fourth row.

ONE ANNA
ഒരു അണ

Three Pies
൩ 3

ANCHAL & REVENUE (16)

മൂന്ന പൈ (17)

1928. *T* **10** *surcharged with T* **16**.

No.	Description	Unused	Used
50	1 a. on 2½ a. yellow-green ..	0 8	0 10
	a. "REVENUF" for "REVENUE"	12 6	16 6

1932-38. *T* 10 *surcharged as T* 17. *Wmk. T* 8a. *P* 14.

No.	Description	Unused	Used
51	3 p. on 4 p. green	0 8	0 4
52	3 p. on 8 p. sepia	0 6	0 5
53	9 p. on 10 p. blue	0 6	0 5

18. Maharaja Sir Rama Varma III.

(Recess. Perkins, Bacon & Co.)

1933-38. *T* 18 (*but frame and inscription of* 1 *a. as T* 9). *Wmk. T* 8a. *P* 13 × 13½.

No.	Description	Unused	Used
54	2 p. brown ('36)	0 3	0 1
55	4 p. green	0 2	0 1
56	6 p. red-brown	0 4	0 2
57	1 a. brown-orange	0 4	0 2
58	1 a. 8 p. carmine	0 4	0 2
59	2 a. grey ('38)	0 6	0 3
60	2¼ a. yellow-green	0 9	0 3
61	3 a. vermilion ('38)	1 3	0 4
62	3 a. 4 p. violet	0 8	0 6
63	6 a. 8 p. sepia	1 0	0 9
64	10 a. blue	1 4	0 10

1934. *Surcharged as T* 14. *W* 8a. *P* 14.

No.	Description	Unused	Used
65	10 6 p. on 8 p. sepia (R.)	0 3	0 3
66	,, 6 p. on 10 p. blue (R.)	0 4	0 3

For lithographed and surcharged issues see King George VI catalogue.

OFFICIAL STAMPS.

ON

C G

S

(O 1)

1913. *T* 8 *overprinted with Type* O 1.

No.	Description	Unused	Used
O 2	3 p. blue (R.)	8 6	0 4
O 3	4 p. green	3 0	0 3
	a. Overprint inverted	—	42 6
O 4	9 p. carmine	3 0	0 4
O 5	1½ a. purple	12 6	0 6
	a. Overprint double		
O 6	2 a. grey	4 6	0 6
O 7	3 a. vermilion	6 0	0 8
O 8	6 a. violet	7 0	1 9
O 9	12 a. ultramarine	22 6	2 6
O10	1½ r. deep green	12 0	12 0

On No. O2 the overprint is larger, with serifs.

1919-33. *T* 10 *overprinted as Type* O 1.

No.	Description	Unused	Used
O11	4 p. green	0 4	0 1
	a. Overprint double		
O12	6 p. red-brown (1922)	0 8	0 1
O12a	8 p. sepia	0 8	0 1
O13	9 p. carmine	3 0	0 4
O14	10 p. blue	6 0	0 1
O15	1½ a. purple (1921)	0 8	0 3
O15a	2 a. grey	1 3	0 4
O16	2¼ a. yellow-green	1 9	0 4
O17	3 a. vermilion	4 6	1 0
	a. Overprint inverted	—	12 0
O19	6 a. violet (1924)	3 0	1 6
O19a	12 a. ultramarine (1929)	3 0	1 0
O19b	1½ r. deep green ('33)	8 6	

8

Eight pies

(O 2)

1923. *T* 8 *and* 10 *surch. with Type* O 2.

No.	Description	Unused	Used
O20	8 pies on 9 p. carm. (No. O 4)	12 6	0 2
	a. Capital "P" in "Pies"	—	2 6
O21	8 pies on 9 p. carm. (No. O13)	12 6	0 2
	a. Capital "P" in "Pies"	—	1 6
	b. "F" for "E" in "Eight"	—	2 0

Varieties with smaller "i" or "t" in "Eight" and small "i" in "Pies" are also known.

1925 (April). *T* 10 *surch. as Type* O 2.

No.	Description	Unused	Used
O22	10 pies on 9 p. carm. (No. O 13)	17 6	0 3

1929. *T* 8 *surcharged as Type* O 2.

No.	Description	Unused	Used
O23	10 pies on 9 p. carm. (No. O 4)	20 0	2 0

ON

C G

S

(O 3)

ON

C G

S

(O 4)

1931. *T* 10 *overprinted with Type* O 3.

No.	Description	Unused	Used
O24	4 p. green	0 4	0 1
O25	6 p. red-brown	1 3	0 1
O26	8 p. sepia	0 6	0 1
O27	10 p. blue	0 6	0 2
O28	2 a. grey	1 0	0 1
O29	3 a. vermilion	1 3	0 4
O30	6 a. violet	3 6	0 4

1933. *T* 10 *surcharged in red as T* 14.

No.	Description	Unused	Used
O32	6 pies on 8 p. sepia (No. O26)	0 4	0 3
O33	6 pies on 10 p. blue (No. O27)	0 4	0 3

1933-44. (*a*) *Recess ptg., optd. in typo. with Type* O 3. *W* 8a. *P* 13 × 13½.

No.	Description	Unused	Used
O35	18 4 p. green	0 2	0 2
O35a	,, 6 p. red-brown ('34)	0 3	0 1
O36	,, 1 a. brown-orange	0 6	0 1
O37	,, 1 a. 8 p. carmine	0 5	0 2
O38	,, 2 a. grey	1 0	0 1
O39	,, 2¼ a. yellow-green	0 8	0 3
O40	,, 3 a. vermilion	1 3	0 2
O41	,, 3 a. 4 p. violet	1 0	0 2
O42	,, 6 a. 8 p. sepia	3 0	0 4
O43	,, 10 a. blue	3 0	0 6

DATIA.

See DUTTIA.

DECCAN.

See HYDERABAD.

DHAR.

1 2

1897. *T* 1. *Type-set. Imperf.*

1	½ pice, black/*red*	1 6	2 0
2	½ anna, black/*magenta* ..	2 6	3 0
3	1 anna, black/*green*	4 0	5 0

These stamps were impressed with an oval handstamp, in *black*, before being issued.

Variety, without control.

3*a*	½ pice, black/*red*	12 6	

Errors. The three characters forming the second word in the lower line transposed thus:—(a) 2nd, 3rd, 1st; (b) 3rd, 2nd, 1st.

4	½ pice, black/*red* (*a*)	4 0	
5	½ pice, black/*red* (*b*)	8 6	

1898–1900. *T* 2. *P* 11 *to* 12.

6	½ a. carmine	2 6	3 6
	a. Imperf.		
7	½ a. deep rose	2 0	
8	1 a. reddish purple	1 6	
9	1 a. violet	7 6	
	a. Imperf. between (pair) ..	35 0	
10	2 a. deep green	8 6	

1900. *T* 1. *With oval handstamp.*

11	¼ a. black/*orange*	2 6	3 0
12	2 a. black/*yellow*	7 6	10 0

Variety. Handstamp omitted.

12*a*	¼ a. black/*orange*	7 0	

Error. With the ornament of the right upper corner transposed with one of those in the top of the frame.

12*b*	2 a. black/*yellow*	12 6	

T 1 *with five characters below at left, instead of four*

13	½ pice, black/*red*	1 6	

Varieties of T 1.

(i.) *No line at top.*

14	½ pice, black/*red*	5 0	
15	¼ a. black/*orange*	7 6	
16	½ a. black/*magenta*	10 0	

(ii.) *No line above lower inscription.*

17	½ pice, black/*red*	15 0	
18	½ a. black/*magenta*	15 0	
18*a*	1 a. black/*green*		

(iii.) *No line at bottom.*

19	½ pice, black/*red*	7 6	
20	¼ a. black/*orange*	10 0	
21	½ a. black/*magenta*	15 0	
21*a*	1 a. black/*green*	25 0	
21*b*	2 a. black/*yellow*	10 0	

(iv.) *No line at left.*

22	½ pice, black/*red*	7 0	7 0
22*a*	¼ a. black/*orange*	8 6	
22*b*	½ a. black/*magenta*	8 6	
23	1 a. black/*green*		

(v.) *No line at top or bottom.*

24	½ pice, black/*red*	12 6	

(vi.) *Line below upper inscription.*

25	½ pice, black/*red*	4 6	
26	½ a. black/*magenta*	3 6	
26*a*	1 a. black/*green*		

(vii.) *No line above lower inscription or at left.*

27	½ a. black/*magenta* ..		

(viii.) *No stop after lower inscription.*

28	½ pice, black/*red* (No. 13) ..	6 0	

There are other cases in which the stop sometimes fails to print, but this seems to be the only one in which it is really absent.

There are believed to be six settings of the type-set stamps, distinguishable by the arrangements of the corner ornaments.

The stamps of Dhar have been obsolete since March 31, 1901.

DUTTIA (DATIA).

1 (4 a.) (Ganesh.)

2 (½ a.)

1893. *T* 1. *Imperf.*

1	½ a. black/*orange*	£10	
2	½ a. black/*blue-green*	£12	
3	2 a. black/*yellow*	£10	
4	4 a. black/*rose*	£8	

T 2. *Imperf.*

5	1 a. red	£15	

1897(?). *T* 2. *Imperf.* (*a*) *Wove paper.*

6	½ a. black/*green*	7 0	
	a. Value in one group ..	16 0	
7	1 a. black/*white*	12 6	
8	2 a. black/*yellow*	8 6	
9	2 a. black/*lemon*	12 0	
10	4 a. black/*rose*	8 6	

(*b*) *Laid paper.*

11	1 a. black/*white*	7 6	

3 (½ a.)

4 (½ a.)

T 3. *Name spelt* " DATIA."

12 ½ a. black/*green* 37 6
13 1 a. black/*white* 50 0
14 2 a. black/*yellow* 75 0
15 4 a. black/*rose* 75 0

1899-1906. *T* 4. *Rouletted in colour or in black horizontally and at end of rows.*

16 ½ a. vermilion 1 6
16a ½ a. rose-red 2 6
17 ½ a. pale rose 3 0
18 ½ a. lake 3 6
19 ½ a. carmine 4 6
19a ½ a. brownish red 4 6
20 ½ a. black/*blue-green* 2 6
21 ½ a. black/*deep green* 2 6
22 ½ a. black/*yellow-green* 2 0
22a ½ a. black/*dull green* (1906) .. 3 0
23 1 a. black/*white* 1 9
24 2 a. black/*lemon-yellow* 3 0
25 2 a. black/*orange-yellow* 3 6
26 2 a. black/*buff-yellow* 3 0
26a 2 a. black/*pale yellow* (1906) .. 2 6
27 4 a. black/*deep rose* 1 9

Varieties. (*a*) *Tête-bêche* (*pairs*).

27a ½ a. brownish red £6
27b 4 a. black/*deep rose* .. ..

(*b*) *Rouletted in black between horizontal rows, but imperf. at top and bottom and at ends of rows.*

27c 1 a. black/*white* .. ..

1904-5. *T* 4. *Without rouletting.*

28 ½ a. red.. .. .. .. 1 6
29 ½ a. black/*green* 6 0
30 1 a. black (1905) 1 9

1911. *T* 4. *P* 13½. *Very wide apart.*

31 ½ a. carmine 1 3
a. Closer together 1 9

1912(?). *Printed close together. Coloured roulette × imperf.*

31b ½ a. black/*green* 3 6

Printed wide apart. P 13½ × *coloured roulette.*

31c ½ a. carmine 3 0

P 13½ × *imperf.*

31d ½ a. black/*dull green* 2 6

1916. *T* 4. *Colours changed. Imperf.*

32 ½ a. deep blue 0 9
33 ½ a. green 1 9
34 1 a. purple 2 6
a. Tête-bêche (pair) 12 0
35 2 a. brown 2 6
35a 2 a. lilac 4 6

The figure on the stamps is intended to represent the Hindu divinity " Ganesh " or " Ganesa."

All the stamps of Duttia are impressed with a circular handstamp (as a rule in *blue*) before issue.

This handstamp is an impression of the seal of Maharaja Sir Bhawani Singh, and has a figure of " Ganesa " in centre, surrounded by an inscription in Devanagari.

1918. *Colours changed. Imperf.*

36 ½ a. blue 0 6
37 1 a. pink 0 7

P 11½.

38 ½ a. black .. .. ..

1920. *T* 4. *Rouletted.*

39 ½ a. blue 0 4 0 8
40 ½ a. pink 0 6 0 10

1920(?). *T* 4. *Rough perf. about* 7.

41 ½ a. dull red 1 9

FARIDKOT.

1 (1 folus)

2 (1 paisa)

1879-86. *T* 1 *and* 2. *Rough, handstamped impressions. Imperf.*

(*a*) *Native thick laid paper.*

N1 1 folus, ultramarine 8 6 5 0
N2 1 paisa, ultramarine 27 6 20 0

(*b*) *Ordinary laid paper.*

N3 1 folus, ultramarine 1 3
N3a 1 paisa, ultramarine .. .. — 6 0

(*c*) *Wove paper, thick to thinnish.*

N4 1 folus, ultramarine 1 9 1 9
N5 1 paisa, ultramarine 3 0 3 0

Variety, tête-bêche (*pair*).

N6 1 folus, ultramarine 17 6

(*d*) *Thin wove, whity brown paper.*

N7 1 paisa, ultramarine 25 0 15 0

3

T 3. *Wove paper. Imperf.*

N8 1 paisa, ultramarine 3 0 6 0
a. Tête-bêche (pair) 25 0

It is doubtful whether stamps of Type 3 were ever used for postage.

These stamps became obsolete upon the introduction of the surcharged Indian stamps on 1st January, 1887, and it is now known that the impressions of these types in various colours, the ½ anna labels, and the later printings from re-engraved dies (which were formerly believed to have been employed for local postage), were never in circulation at all.

HOLKAR.

See **INDORE.**

HYDERABAD.

(DECCAN.)

1

2

(Type 1 engraved by Mr. Rapkin. Plates by Messrs. Nissen & Parker, London.)

1869. *T* **1.** *P* 11½.

No.	Description				
1	1 a. olive-green	15	0	8	6
	a. Imperf. between (pair)	40	0	40	0

Reprints in the colour of the issue, and also in fancy colours, were made in 1880 on white wove paper, perforated 12½.

1871 (Jan.). *T* **2.** *Locally engraved; 240 varieties of each value; wove paper.* *P* 11½.

No.	Description				
2	½ a. brown	4	0	6	0
3	2 a. sage-green ..	30	0	22	6

The stamps formerly catalogued as on laid paper are now omitted, as, although stamps exist showing traces of lines in the paper, they do not appear to be printed on true laid paper.

Reprints of both values were made in 1880 on white wove paper, perforated 12½; the ½ a. is in orange-brown, and the 2 a. in bright green and in blue-green.

3

(Recess. Bradbury, Wilkinson & Co.)

A

Ordinary type.

B

Variety.

In A the coloured lines surrounding each of the four labels join a coloured circle round their inner edge, in B this circle is missing.

c *d*

c is the normal.
d has the character ʌ omitted.

1871–1909. *T* **3.** (*a*) *Rough perf.* 11½.

No.	Description				
6	½ a. red-brown	22	6		
7	1 a. purple-brown	62	6		
8	2 a. green (A)				
9	3 a. ochre-brown	27	6		
10	4 a. slate	62	6		
11	8 a. deep brown				
12	12 a. dull blue	82	6		

(*b*) *P* 12½.

No.	Description				
13	½ a. red-brown	0	10	0	2
13*a*	½ a. orange	3	0		
14	½ a. orange-brown	0	4	0	3
15	½ a. brick-red	0	6	0	1
	a. Imperf. between (pair) ..	10	0	10	0
16	½ a. rose-red	0	6	0	1
17	1 a. purple-brown	3	0	3	6
18	1 a. drab	0	10	0	4
	a. Imperf. (pair)	—		22	6
19	1 a. grey-black	1	3	0	3
20	1 a. black (1909)	0	8	0	3
21	2 a. green (A)	1	3	0	3
22	2 a. deep green (A)	1	3	0	3
23	2 a. blue-green (A)	1	9	0	6
24	2 a. pale green (A)	1	9	0	4
25	2 a. sage-green (A) (1909) ..	1	9	0	6
26	3 a. ochre-brown	1	9	1	6
27	3 a. chestnut	1	6	1	6
28	4 a. slate	3	0	1	9
	a. Imperf. between (pair) ..	22	6		
29	4 a. greenish grey	2	6	1	9
30	4 a. olive-green	2	6	3	0
31	8 a. deep brown	3	0	3	6
32	12 a. pale ultramarine ..	4	6	4	6
33	12 a. grey-green	4	0	4	0

Error of colour.

No.	Description				
34	½ a. magenta	30	0	6	0

Varieties. (i.) *Coloured circle missing as in* B.

No.	Description				
35	2 a. pale green	80	0		
36	2 a. sage-green				
36*a*	2 a. blue-green				

(ii.) *Character omitted as* (*d*).

No.	Description				
36*b*	3 a. chestnut				

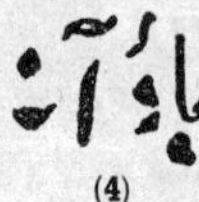
(4)

1900. *T* 3 *surcharged with T* 4, *in black.* *P* 12½

No.	Description				
37	¼ a. on ½ a. orange-brown ..	0	4	0	

Variety. Surcharge inverted.

No.	Description				
37*a*	¼ a. on ½ a. orange-brown ..	—		22	4

5

(Engraved by Khusrat Ullah, Hyderabad.)

1902. *T* **5.** *P* 12½.

No.	Description				
38	¼ a. deep blue	5	0	3	6
39	¼ a. pale blue	5	0	3	6

6

6a

(Recess. Allan G. Wyon, London.)

1905. *T 6. Wmk. T 6a. P 12½.*

40	¼ a. blue	1 6	0 3
	a. Imperf.	27 6	
41	½ a. orange	2 6	0 6
42	½ a. vermilion	2 6	0 4
	a. Imperf.	27 6	

1908-11. *T 6. New values and changes of colour. Wmk. T 6a. (a) P 12½.*

43	¼ a. grey	0 10	0 2
	a. Imperf. between (pair)		
44	½ a. green	1 6	0 2
45	½ a. pale green	1 9	0 2
46	1 a. carmine	0 4	0 1
47	2 a. lilac	0 10	0 1
48	3 a. brown-orange (1909)	1 0	0 2
49	4 a. olive-green (1909)	1 6	0 8
50	8 a. purple (1911)	4 0	
51	12 a. blue-green (1911)		

(b) P 11½, 12.

52	¼ a. grey	2 6	0 6
53	½ a. green	2 6	0 9
54	½ a. pale green	—	0 6
55	1 a. carmine	1 9	0 6
56	2 a. lilac	0 8	0 6
57	3 a. brown-orange	3 0	
58	4 a. olive-green	4 0	
59	8 a. purple		
60	12 a. blue-green	6 0	

(c) P 11.

60a	¼ a. grey	—	4 0
61	1 a. carmine	2 6	
62	2 a. lilac	0 8	0 4
63	3 a. brown-orange	0 8	0 6
64	4 a. olive-green		
	a. Imperf. between (pair)		
65	8 a. purple	1 6	
66	12 a. blue-green		

(d) P 13½.

66a	½ a. green		
66b	2 a. pale claret	—	0 2
66c	3 a. brown-orange	—	0 3
66d	4 a. olive-green	1 9	1 6
66e	8 a. purple	2 6	2 0
66f	12 a. blue-green	4 0	3 0

1912. *T 6. New plates engraved by Messrs. Bradbury, Wilkinson & Co., copying Wyon's plates.*

(a) P 12½.

67	¼ a. grey-black	0 1	0 1
	a. Imperf. between (pair)		
68	½ a. deep green	0 6	0 1

(b) P 11½, 12.

69	¼ a grey-black	0 6	0 2
70	½ a. deep green	0 6	0 3

(c) P 11.

71	¼ a. grey-black	0 8	0 1
72	½ a. deep green	0 6	0 1

(d) P 13½.

73	¼ a. grey-black	0 3	0 1
73a	¼ a. purple	0 3	0 1
73b	½ a. deep green		
	a. Imperf. between (pair)		

Many values may be found with compound perforations.

The following are the differences in the ¼ a. and ½ a. between the original plates by Wyon and the copies made by Messrs. Bradbury, Wilkinson & Co.

In Wyon's ½ a. stamp the fraction of value is closer to the end of the label than in the Bradbury copy; in both, the value in English and the label below are further apart than in the copies.

Wyon's ¼ a. measures 19¾ × 20 mm., and the ½ a. 19½ × 20½ mm.; both stamps from the Bradbury plates measure 19¾ × 21½ mm.

7

1915. *T 7. Inscribed* "Post & Receipt."

(a) P 11.

74	½ a. green	0 3	0 1
	a. Imperf.		
75	1 a. carmine	0 6	0 1
	a. Imperf.		

(b) P 12½.

82	½ a. green	0 3	0 1
83	1 a. carmine		

(c) P 13½.

84	½ a. green	0 6	0 1
85	1 a. carmine	0 4	0 1
86	1 a. scarlet		

8

1927 (1 Feb.). *T 8. Wmk. of native characters, as T 6a. P 13½.*

87	1 r. yellow	5 0	5 0

9. (4 pies)

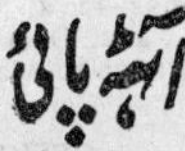

10. (8 pies)

1930 (6 May). *T 6 and 7 surcharged as T 9 and 10 respectively. Wmk. T 6a. P 13½.*

88	4 p. on ¼ a. grey-black (R.)	—	8 6
89	4 p. on ¼ a. purple (R.)	0 3	0 1
90	8 p. on ½ a. green (R.)	0 4	0 1

11. Symbols.

12. The Char Minar.

13. Bidar College.

14. Victory Tower, Daulatabad.

(Recess-printed at the Mint, Hyderabad.)

1931 (12 Nov.). *T* **11** *to* **14** (*and similar types*). *Wmk. T* **6***a*. *P* 13½.

No.	Type	Description	Unused	Used
91	**11**	4 p. black	0 1	0 1
92	,,	8 p. green	0 3	0 2
93	**12**	1 a. brown	0 4	0 2
94	–	2 a. violet	0 6	0 3
95	–	4 a. ultramarine	0 8	0 2
96	–	8 a. orange	1 3	0 8
97	**13**	12 a. scarlet	2 0	1 9
98	**14**	1 r. yellow	2 6	2 3

Designs:—2 a. The High Court of Justice (horiz.). 4 a. Osman Sagar Reservoir (horiz.). 8 a. Entrance to Ajanta Caves (vert.).

OFFICIAL STAMPS.

سرکاری

(O 1)

1873–1909. *T* **1** *and* **2** *overprinted as Type* O **1.**

In red.

No.	Description	Unused	Used
201	1 a. olive-green	—	22 6
202	½ a. brown	—	52 6
203	2 a. sage-green	—	75 0

In black.

No.	Description	Unused	Used
204	1 a. olive-green		
205	½ a. brown	—	22 6
206	2 a. sage-green	—	32 6

Imitations of these overprints on genuine stamps and on reprints are found horizontally or vertically in various shades of red, in magenta and in black.

T **3** *overprinted as Type* O **1.**

In red.

(*a*) *Rough perf.* 11½.

No.	Description	Unused	Used
207	½ a. red-brown		
209	2 a. green		
211	4 a. slate		

Probably all values exist.

(*b*) *Perf.* 12½.

No.	Description	Unused	Used
214	½ a. red-brown	15 0	15 0
215	1 a. purple-brown	20 0	15 0
216	1 a. drab	15 0	
217	2 a. green	20 0	
218	2 a. deep green	20 0	
219	3 a. ochre-brown		
220	4 a. slate	20 0	17 6
221	8 a. deep brown	20 0	
	a. Imperf. between (pair) ..	75 0	
222	12 a. blue	25 0	

In black.

(*a*) *Rough perf.* 11½.

No.	Description	Unused	Used
223	½ a. red-brown		
225	2 a. green		
228	8 a. deep brown ..		

Probably all values exist

(*b*) *Perf.* 12½.

No.	Description	Unused	Used
230	½ a. red-brown	7 6	5 0
231	½ a. orange-brown (1909) ..	—	5 0
232	1 a. purple-brown	—	6 0
233	1 a. drab	5 0	5 0
	a. Overprint inverted		
234	1 a. black (1909)	1 6	0 2
235	2 a. green	5 0	
	a. Overprint inverted		
236	2 a. sage-green (1909) ..	—	1 6
237	3 a. ochre-brown	5 0	3 0
238	4 a. slate	6 0	6 0
239	4 a. greenish grey	10 0	
240	8 a. deep brown	15 0	15 0
241	12 a. blue	15 0	

Variety. Coloured circle missing as in B.

No.	Description	Unused	Used
242	2 a. sage-green (1909) ..	—	10 0

The use of *Official Stamps* (Serkari) was discontinued in 1878, but was resumed in 1909, when the current stamps were overprinted with the old dies.

1909–11. *T* **6** *overprinted as Type* O **1**, *in black.*

The Wyon and Bradbury stamps are here distinguished by the use of the letters (W.) and (B.W.) respectively.

(*a*) *Perf.* 12½.

No.	Description	Unused	Used
243	½ a. orange	—	2 6
244	½ a. vermilion	2 6	0 4
	a. Inverted		
245	½ a. green (W.)	—	0 1
246	½ a. pale green (W.)	—	0 1
248	1 a. carmine	2 6	0 2
	a. Double		
249	2 a. lilac	—	0 6
250	3 a. brown-orange	0 6	0 3
	a. Inverted		

251 4 a. olive-green (1911) .. 1 6 0 8
252 8 a. purple (1911) .. 2 6 1 0
253 12 a. blue-green (1911) .. 2 6 1 6

(*b*) *Perf.* 11½, 12.

254 ½ a. green (W.) .. 4 0 2 0
255 ½ a. pale green (W.) .. — 1 6
a. Inverted
257 1 a. carmine .. — 1 6
258 2 a. lilac .. 8 0 5 0
259 3 a. brown-orange
260 4 a. olive-green
261 8 a. purple
262 12 a. blue-green

(*c*) *Perf.* 11.

262*a* 1 a. carmine .. — 15 0

سرکاری

(O 2)

1911-12. T 6 *overprinted with Type* O 2, *in black.*

(*a*) *Perf.* 12½.

263 ¼ a. grey (W.) .. — 1 6
264 ¼ a. grey-black (B.W.) .. 0 1 0 1
a. Inverted
265 ½ a. pale green (W.) .. — 0 2
266 ½ a. deep green (B.W.) .. 0 4 0 1
a. Inverted
267 1 a. carmine .. 0 6 0 1
a. Inverted
268 2 a. lilac .. 0 6 0 1
269 3 a. brown-orange .. 0 9
a. Inverted
270 4 a. olive-green .. 3 0 0 8
a. Inverted
271 8 a. purple
272 12 a. blue-green

(*b*) *Perf.* 11½, 12.

273 ¼ a. grey (W.) .. — 0 1
274 ¼ a. grey-black (B.W.) .. 0 1 0 2
275 ½ a. pale green (W.) .. — 0 2
276 ½ a. deep green (B.W.) .. — 0 1
277 1 a. carmine .. 0 1
278 2 a. lilac .. 2 0 0 3
279 3 a. brown-orange
280 4 a. olive-green .. 1 0 0 4
281 8 a. purple
282 12 a. blue-green

(*c*) P 11.

283 ¼ a. grey-black (B.W.) .. 0 2 0 1
284 ½ a. deep green (B.W.) .. 0 3 0 2
285 1 a. carmine .. 0 4 0 2
286 2 a. lilac .. 0 5 0 3
287 3 a. orange-brown
288 4 a. olive-green .. 1 0 0 4
289 8 a. purple .. — 1 0
290 12 a. blue-green

(*d*) P 13½.

291 ¼ a grey-black (B.W.) .. 0 1
291*a* ¼ a. lilac (B.W.) .. 0 1 0 1
292 ½ a. deep green (B.W.) .. 0 1 0 1
293 1 a. carmine .. — 0 1
293*a* 2 a. pale claret .. 0 9 0 4
295 3 a. brown-orange .. — 0 6
295*a* 4 a. olive-green .. 1 6 0 4
297 8 a. purple .. 1 6 1 0
298 12 a. blue-green .. 2 6 1 3

1919. T 7 *overprinted with Type* O 2.

(*a*) P 11.

299 ½ a. green .. 2 0 0 3
300 1 a. carmine .. — 0 1
a. Inverted

(*b*) P 12½.

300*c* 1 a. carmine

(*c*) P 13½.

301 ½ a. green .. 0 2 0 1
a. Inverted
302 1 a. carmine .. 0 4 0 1
303 1 a. scarlet .. 0 5 0 1

1930-34. T 6 *and* 7 *surch. at top of stamp, in red, as* T 9 *or* 10.

304 4 p. on ¼ a. grey-black (291) ('34) .. — 15 0
304*a* 4 p. on ¼ a. lilac (291*a*) .. 0 3 0 1
b. Red opt. superimposed on T O 2
305 8 p. on ½ a. green (301) .. 0 3 0 1
a. Red opt. superimposed on T O 2
b. Red opt. on No. 292 .. — 10 0
c. Red opt. on No. 293

In Nos. 304*b* and 305*a*, T 9 and 10 were applied in the middle of the stamp and cover Type O 2 instead of being above it.

1934-35. *Nos.* 91/8 *optd. with Type* O 2.

306 4 p. black .. 0 1 0 1
307 8 p. green .. 0 2 0 1
a. Opt. inverted
308 1 a. brown .. 0 3 0 1
309 2 a. violet .. 0 5 0 1
310 4 a. ultramarine .. 0 8 0 4
311 8 a. orange ('35) .. 1 3 1 0
312 12 a. scarlet ('35) .. 1 10 1 6
313 1 r. yellow ('35) .. 2 6 2 0

INDORE.

(HOLKAR.)

1. Maharaja Tukoji Rao Holkar II.

(Lithographed by Messrs. Waterlow & Sons, Ltd.)

1886. T 1. P 15.

(*a*) *Thick white paper.*

1 ½ a. bright mauve .. 4 0 4 6

(*b*) *Thin white or yellowish paper.*

2 ½ a. pale mauve .. 1 9 2 0
3 ½ a. dull mauve .. 2 9 3 6

2

1889. T 2. *Imperf.*

4 ½ a. black/*pink* .. 3 0 3 0

3. Maharaja Shivaji Rao Holkar I.

(Recess. Waterlow & Sons, Ltd.)

1889–92. *T* **3.** *Medium wove paper.* *P* 14 *to* 15.

No.	Stamp	Unused	Used
5	¼ a. orange	0 3	0 4
	a. Imperf. between (pair)	10 0	
	b. Very thick wove paper	2 6	1 0
5c	½ a. dull violet	0 10	0 10
6	½ a. brown-purple	0 4	0 3
7	1 a. green	2 0	1 9
	a. Imperf. between (pair)	12 6	
8	2 a. vermilion	2 0	1 6
	a. Very thick wove paper	12 6	12 6

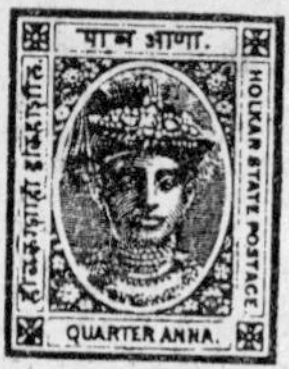

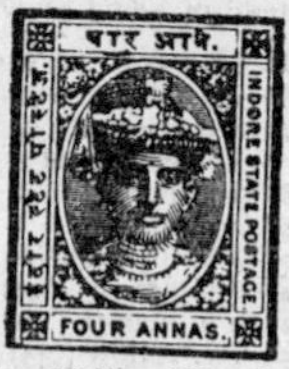

4. Maharaja Tukoji Rao Holkar III. **5**

1904–9. *T* **4** (¼ *a.*) *and* **5.** *P* 13½, 14.

No.	Stamp	Unused	Used
9	¼ a. orange	0 3	0 2
9a	½ a. lake (1909)	6 0	0 3
	b. Imperf.	16 0	
10	1 a. green (1907)	6 0	0 2
11	2 a. brown (1905)	6 0	0 4
12	3 a. violet	7 6	0 10
13	4 a. ultramarine	8 6	0 8

पाव आना.

(6)

1905. *No.* 6 *surcharged* "QUARTER ANNA" *in Devanagari, as T* **6**, *in black.*

No.	Stamp	Unused	Used
14	¼ a. on ½ a. brown-purple	7 6	7 6

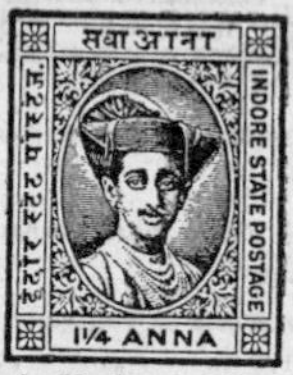

7. Maharaja Yeshwant Rao Holkar II.

1928–38. *T* **7.** *Recess.* *P* 13 *to* 14.

No.	Stamp	Unused	Used
15	¼ a. orange	0 1	0 2
16	½ a. claret	0 2	0 2
17	1 a. green	0 3	0 2
18	1¼ a. green ('33)	0 3	0 3
19	2 a. sepia	0 8	0 10
19a	2 a. bluish green ('36)	0 6	0 6
20	3 a. deep violet	0 8	0 10
21	3½ a. violet ('34)	0 9	0 10
22	4 a. ultramarine	1 6	1 9
22a	4 a. yellow-brown ('38)	0 9	0 10
23	8 a. slate-grey	3 0	3 6
23a	8 a. red-orange ('38)	1 3	1 9
24	12 a. carmine ('34)	2 0	2 6

As T **7**, *but larger* (23 × 28 *mm.*).

No.	Stamp	Unused	Used
25	1 r. black and light blue	2 6	2 9
26	2 r. black and carmine	5 0	6 0
27	5 r. black and brown-orange	12 6	13 6

OFFICIAL STAMPS.

SERVICE (21) **SERVICE** (22)

1904–6. *T* **4** *and* **5** *overprinted with T* **21** *in black.* *P* 13½, 14.

No.	Stamp	Unused	Used
100	¼ a. orange (1906)	0 2	0 4
101	½ a. lake	0 2	0 1
101a	½ a. brown-lake	0 2	0 1
102	1 a. green	0 2	0 3
103	2 a. brown (1905)	0 4	0 6
104	3 a. violet (1906)	0 6	0 8
105	4 a. ultramarine (1905)	0 8	0 10

Varieties. (i.) *Overprint inverted.*

No.	Stamp	Unused	Used
106	½ a. lake	10 0	
106a	½ a. brown-orange	16 0	

(ii.) *Overprint double.*

No.	Stamp	Unused	Used
106b	½ a. lake	4 6	

(iii.) *Imperf.*

No.	Stamp	Unused	Used
107	½ a. lake	6 0	
108	3 a. violet	6 0	

T 5 *overprinted with T* **22**, *in black.* *P* 13½, 14.

No.	Stamp	Unused	Used
109	½ a. lake	0 2	0 6

These two overprints differ chiefly in the shape of the letter "R."

JAIPUR.

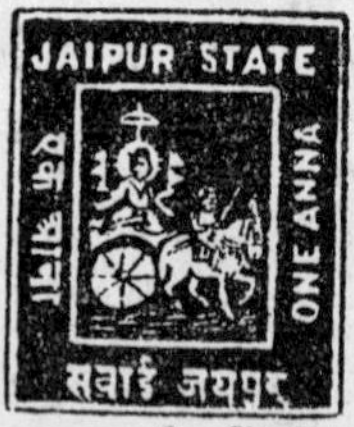

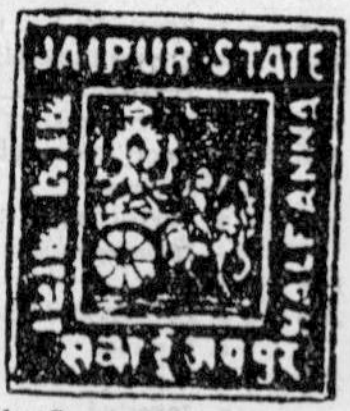

1. Chariot of the Sun. **2**

1904. *T* **1.** *Value at sides in small letters and characters.* 36 *varieties* (2 *plates*) *of the* ½ *a. In Plate I the stamps are* 2½ *mm. apart horizontally; while in Plate II they are* 4½ *mm. apart.* 12 *varieties each of the* 1 *a. and* 2 *a. Roughly perf.* 14.

No.	Stamp	Unused	Used
1	½ a. pale blue (Plate I)	10 0	12 6
2	½ a. ultramarine (Plate I)	10 0	12 6
2a	½ a. ultramarine (Plate II)	£10	80 0
2b	½ a. grey-blue (Plate II)	£10	
3	1 a. dull red	5 0	6 6
4	1 a. scarlet	6 0	
5	2 a. pale green	7 0	8 0
6	2 a. emerald-green	8 0	

Variety. *Imperf.* (Plate II)

No.	Stamp	Unused	Used
6a	½ a. pale blue	80 0	80 0

T **2**, *value in larger letters and characters.* 24 *varieties on one plate.* *Roughly perf.* 14.

No.	Stamp	Unused	Used
7	½ a. pale blue	6 0	7 0
8	½ a. deep blue	5 0	7 6
9	½ a. ultramarine	4 6	7 0
	a. Imperf.		

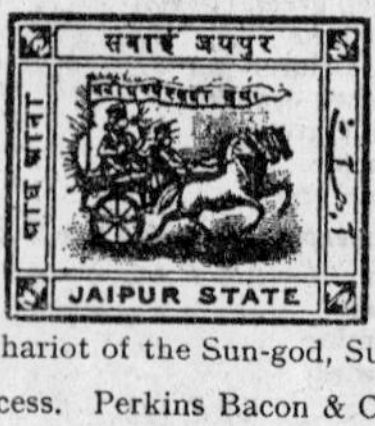

3. Chariot of the Sun-god, Surya.

(Recess. Perkins Bacon & Co.)

1904. *T* **3.** *P* 12 *and* 12½.

No.	Stamp	Unused	Used
10	½ a. blue	6 0	4 6
10a	1 a. brown-red		
11	1 a. carmine	4 0	1 6
12	2 a. deep green	6 0	6 0

1905–8. *T* **3.** *P* 13½.

No.	Description				
13	¼ a. olive-yellow (1906)	0	3	0	3
14	½ a. blue	0	6	0	6
14a	½ a. indigo	0	10	0	10
15	1 a. brown-red (1906)	4	0	4	0
15a	1 a. bright red (1908)	0	8	0	8
16	2 a. deep green	1	3	1	0
17	4 a. chestnut	3	0	3	6
18	8 a. bright violet	3	6	4	6
19	1 r. yellow	5	6	7	0
20	1 r. orange-yellow	7	6		

4. Chariot of the Sun-god, Surya.

(Typographed at the Jail Press, Jaipur.)

1911. *T* 4. *Thin wove paper. Imperf. Six varieties of each value.*

No.	Description				
21	¼ a. green	0	6	0	8
	a. Doubly printed				
21b	¼ a. greenish yellow	0	6	0	8
22	½ a. ultramarine	0	8	0	10
	a. Doubly printed	8	6		
22b	½ a. grey-blue	0	8	0	10
23	1 a. rose-red	0	9	1	6
24	2 a. greyish green	3	0	4	0
25	2 a. deep green	2	6	3	6

One sheet of the ¼ a. is known in blue.

Varieties. (i.) "¼" *inverted in right upper corner.*

No.	Description		
26	¼ a. green	2	6
26a	¼ a. greenish yellow	2	6

(ii.) *No stop after* "STATE".

No.	Description		
27	¼ a. green	1	9
27a	¼ a. greenish yellow	1	9
28	½ a. ultramarine	1	3
28a	½ a. grey-blue	2	6

(iii.) *Large* "J" *in* "JAIPUR."

No.	Description		
29	½ a. ultramarine	3	6
29a	½ a. grey-blue	5	6

(iv.) *Error.* "⅛" *for* "½" *in lower left corner.*

No.	Description		
29b	½ a. ultramarine	12	6
29c	½ a. grey-blue	12	6

(Typographed as last.)

1913–18. *T* **3.** *Paper-maker's wmk.* "DORLING & CO., LONDON," *in sheet.* *P* 11.

No.	Description				
30	¼ a. olive-yellow	0	3	0	3
31	¼ a. olive	0	3	0	3
	a. Imperf. between (horiz. pair)	5	0		
32	½ a. ultramarine	0	3	0	4
	a. Imperf. between (pair)				
33	1 a. carmine (1918)	0	6	0	8
34	2 a. green (1918)	0	7	0	9
35	4 a. chocolate	1	6		
36	4 a. pale brown	1	6		

1922. *As No.* 33, *but colour changed. Thin paper.*

No.	Description				
36a	1 a. rose-red				
37	1 a. scarlet	0	5		

(5)

1926. *T* **3** *surcharged with T* **5**, *in red.*

No.	Description				
38	3 a. on 8 a. bright violet	1	0	1	6
39	3 a. on 1 r. yellow	1	0	2	0

6. Sun-god Chariot.

7. Maharaja Sir Man Singh Bahadur. **8.** Sowar in Armour.

9. Maharajas Sawai Jai Singh and Sir Man Singh.

(Printed by the Security Printing Press, Nasik.)

1931 (14 MAR.). *Investiture of H.H. the Maharaja of Jaipur as Ruler. T* **6** *to* **9** (*various central designs*). *No wmk.* *P* 14.

No.	Type	Description				
40	**6**	¼ a. black & deep lake	0	3	0	3
41	**7**	½ a. black and violet	0	1	0	1
42	**8**	1 a. black and blue	0	6	0	6
43	,,	2 a. black and buff	0	8	0	9
44	,,	2½ a. black and carmine	5	0	6	0
45	**6**	3 a. black and myrtle	1	6	1	9
46	,,	4 a. black & olive-green	2	6	3	0
47	,,	6 a. black and deep blue	4	6	6	0
48	**8**	8 a. black and chocolate	4	0	4	6
49	**6**	1 r. black and pale olive	5	0	5	6
50	,,	2 r. black and yellow-green	8	6	9	6
51	**9**	5 r. black and purple	15	0	16	6

Designs:—1 a. Elephant with State Banner. 2½ a. Dancing Peacock. (Inscribed "POSTAGE".) 3 a. Bullock Carriage. 4 a. Elephant Carriage. ("POSTAGE & REVENUE".) 6 a. Albert Museum. 8 a. Sireh-Deorhi Gate. 1 r. Chandra Mahal. ("POSTAGE & REVENUE".) 2 r. Amber Palace. ("POSTAGE & REVENUE".)

Eighteen of these sets were issued for presentation purposes with a special surcharge "INVESTITURE—MARCH 14, 1931" in red. Some are known postally used.

10. Maharaja Sir Man Singh Bahadur.

One Rupee

(11)

(Printed by the Security Printing Press, Nasik.)

1932. *No wmk. P* 14. *Inscr.* "POSTAGE & REVENUE".

No.	Type	Description	Unused	Used
52	10	1 a. black and blue ..	0 4	0 5
53	,,	2 a. black and buff ..	0 6	0 8
54	,,	4 a. black and grey-green ..	0 10	1 0
55	,,	8 a. black and chocolate ..	1 6	1 9
56	,,	1 r. black and yellow-bistre	3 6	4 6
57	,,	2 r. black and yellow-green	6 0	7 6

For stamps of similar design, but inscribed "POSTAGE", see King George VI Catalogue.

1936. *Nos.* 57 *and* 51 *surch. with T* **11**.

No.	Type	Description	Unused	Used
68	10	1 r. on 2 r. black and yellow-green (R.) ..	3 0	3 6
69	9	1 r. on 5 r. blk. & pur. (Bk.)	3 0	3 6

OFFICIAL STAMPS.

SERVICE (O 1)   SERVICE (O 2)

1929–30. *T* **3** *typographed. P* 11, 12, *or compound.* (*a*) *Overprinted with Type* O **1**.

No.	Description	Unused	Used
O1	½ a. olive	0 3	0 2
O2	½ a. ultramarine (Bk.) ..	0 4	0 1
	a. Imperf. between (horiz. pair)		
O3	½ a. ultramarine (R.) ('30) ..	0 4	0 2
O3*a*	1 a. rose-red		
O4	1 a. scarlet	0 8	0 2
O5	2 a. green	0 6	0 4
O6	4 a. pale brown	0 9	1 0
O7	8 a. bright violet (R.) ..	3 0	3 6
O8	1 r. orange-vermilion ..	5 0	6 0

(*b*) *Overprinted with Type* O **2**.

No.	Description	Unused	Used
O 9	½ a. ultramarine (Bk.) ..	—	0 3
O10	½ a. ultramarine (R.) ..	—	0 3
O11	8 a. bright violet		
O12	1 r. orange-vermilion ..	15 0	

आध आना (O 3)   SERVICE (O 4)

1932. *No.* O **5** *surcharged with Type* O **3**.

No.	Description	Unused	Used
O13	½ a. on 2 a. green	—	0 9

1931–37. *Nos.* 41/3 *and* 46 *optd. at Nasik with Type* O **4**, *in red.*

No.	Type	Description	Unused	Used
O14	7	½ a. black and violet ..	0 2	0 1
O15	8	1 a. black and blue ..	—	0 3
O16	8	2 a. black and buff ('36) ..	0 6	0 4
O17	6	4 a. blk. & olive-grn. ('37)	0 10	0 6

1932–37. *Nos.* 52/6 *optd. at Nasik with Type* O **4**, *in red.*

No.	Type	Description	Unused	Used
O18	10	1 a. black and blue ..	0 3	0 2
O19	,,	2 a. black and buff ..	0 6	0 3
O20	,,	4 a. blk. & grey-grn. ('37)	1 2	0 8
O21	,,	8 a. blk. & chocolate ..	1 6	1 9
O22	,,	1 r. black & yell.-bistre ..	2 3	2 6

JAMMU AND KASHMIR.

1 (½ anna)

2 (1 anna)

3 (4 annas)

Characters denoting the value (on the circular stamps only) are approximately as shown in the central circle of the stamps illustrated above.

THE CIRCULAR STAMPS. (Types **1** to **3**).

(A)* *Handstamped in water colours.*

1866 (APRIL (?)). *On native-made paper, usually having the appearance of laid paper, varying from thick to thin, and tinted grey or brown.*

No.	Description	*Cut* □ Unused	*Cut* □ Used	*Cut* O Unused	*Cut* O Used
1	½ a. grey-black	95 0	25 0	45 0	12 6
2	1 a. grey-black	—	—	65 0	
3	4 a. grey-black	—	—	65 0	85 0
4	1 a. ultramarine	—	—	£6	£6
5	4 a. ultramarine	£10	45 0	£7	25 0
6	1 a. blue-black	£11	—	—	£6
7	4 a. blue-black				

These stamps were used in Jammu and Srinagar (Kashmir).

1869–77. *Reissued for use in Jammu only.*

No.	Description			
8	½ a. red ..	35 0	—	22 6
9	1 a. red ..	22 6	—	10 0
10	4 a. red ..	47 6	—	22 6
11	½ a. orange-red	90 0	—	50 0
12	1 a. orange-red	27 6	—	8 6
13	4 a. orange-red	40 0	—	12 6

1874–76. *Special printings.*

No.	Description			
14	½ a. deep black	6 0	—	3 6
15	1 a. deep black	40 0	—	27 6
16	4 a. deep black	£8	—	27 6
17	½ a. bght. blue	27 6	—	15 0
18	1 a. bght. blue	22 6	—	10 6

19 4 a. bght. blue	22 6	—	8 6	
20 ½ a. emld.-grn.	20 0	—	8 6	
21 1 a. emld.-grn.	27 6	—	17 6	
22 4 a. emld.-grn.	27 6	—	12 6	
23 ½ a. yellow ..	£6	—	45 0	
24 1 a. yellow ..	£6	—	45 0	
25 4 a. yellow ..	£6	—	45 0	

(B) *Handstamped in oil colours.*

1877–78. (*a*) *Native paper, as in first issue.*

26 ½ a red ..	16 6	20 0	8 6	8 6
27 1 a. red ..	£5	£5	60 0	60 0
28 4 a. red ..	15 0	25 0	7 6	12 6
29 ½ a. black ..	8 6	20 0	6 0	12 6
30 1 a. black ..	50 0	60 0	27 6	27 6
31 4 a. black ..	£6	£5	55 0	55 0
32 ½ a. slate-blue	80 0	80 0	55 0	55 0
33 1 a. slate-blue	£8	£8	75 0	75 0
34 4 a. slate-blue	6 0	—	2 6	
35 ½ a. sage-green	£5	—	50 0	45 0
36 1 a. sage-green	£6	—	65 0	
37 4 a. sage-green	75 0	—	35 0	

(*b*) *European laid paper.*

38 ½ a. dull red ..	—	75 0	—	42 6
39 1 a. dull red ..	75 0	—	32 6	
40 4 a. dull red ..	60 0	—	32 6	
41 ½ a. black ..	5 0	30 0	3 6	12 6
42 1 a. black ..				
43 4 a. black ..				
44 ½ a. slate-blue	3 0	—	3 6	
45 1 a. slate-blue	£6	£6	70 0	
46 4 a. slate-blue	12 6	—	8 6	
47 1 a. sage-green	£25	—	£15	
48 ½ a. yellow ..	80 0	—	52 6	

(*c*) *Very thick European laid paper.*

49 ½ a. black ..	25 0	37 6	17 6	17 6
50 1 a. red ..	75 0	75 0	37 6	37 6
51 4 a. slate-blue	22 6	32 6	16 0	22 6

(*d*) *Thick yellow wove paper.*

51*a* ½ a. red ..

Forgeries exist of the ½ a. and 1 a. in types which were at one time supposed to be authentic.

Reprints also exist in great abundance and in numerous fancy colours, both on *native* paper, usually thinner and smoother than that of the originals, and on thin wove European papers, on which the originals were never printed. There are also imitations, which were found among the official stock, on native and on European laid and wove papers which can be recognized by their not agreeing in type with the illustrations given above. All these reprints, etc., are in *oil* colours.

THE RECTANGULAR STAMPS.

I. FOR **JAMMU.**

½ a. ½ a.

1 a. 4 ½ a.

T 4 to 11 have a star at the top of the oval band; the characters denoting the value are in the upper part of the inner oval. All are dated 1923, corresponding with A.D. 1866.

T 4. *Printed in blocks of four, three varieties of ½ anna and one of 1 anna.*

1867. *In water colour on native paper.*

52 ½ a. black	75 0	60 0
53 1 a. black	£25	£25
54 ½ a. indigo	75 0	75 0
55 1 a. indigo	£8	£8
56 ½ a. deep ultramarine	75 0	75 0
57 1 a. deep ultramarine	£8	£8
58 ½ a. deep violet-blue	80 0	80 0
59 1 a. deep violet-blue	£10	£9

1868–77. *In water colour on native paper.*

60 ½ a. red	6 0	6 0
61 1 a. red	12 6	12 6
62 ½ a. orange-red	12 6	12 6
63 1 a. orange-red	32 6	
64 ½ a. orange	£5	
65 1 a. orange		

1874–76. *Special printings; in water colour on native paper.*

66 ½ a. bright blue	£8	75 0
67 1 a. bright blue	£5	£7
68 ½ a. emerald-green	£35	
69 1 a. emerald-green	£25	

1877. *In oil colour.* (*a*) *On native paper.*

70 ½ a. red	20 0	17 6
71 1 a. red	37 6	37 6
72 ½ a. brown-red	—	75 0
73 1 a. brown-red		
74 ½ a. black	£25	£20
75 1 a. black		
76 ½ a. deep blue		
77 1 a. deep blue		
78 ½ a. deep green		
79 1 a. deep green		

(*b*) *On European laid paper.*

80 ½ a. red	—	£20
81 1 a. red		
82 ½ a. brown-red		
83 1 a. brown-red		

(*c*) *On thin laid, bâtonné paper.*

84 ½ a. red		
85 1 a. red		

The circular and rectangular stamps listed under the heading "Special Printings" did not supersede those in *red*, which was the normal colour for Jammu down to 1878. It is not known for what reason other colours were used during that period, but these stamps were printed in 1874 or 1875 and were certainly put in use. The rectangular stamps were again printed in *black* at that time, but impressions of the two periods can only be distinguished by the obliterations, which until 1868 were in *magenta* and after that in *black*.

There are reprints of these, in *oil* colour, *brown-red* and *bright blue*, on native paper; they are very clearly printed, which is not the case with the originals in *oil* colour.

II. FOR **KASHMIR.**

5

1866 (Sept.(?)) *T* **5.** *Printed from a single die. Native laid paper.*

86	½ a. black	£40	£20

Forgeries of this stamp are commonly met with, copied from an illustration in *Le Timbre-Poste.*

6 (½ a.)

7 (1 a.)

1866. *T* **6** *and* **7.** *Native laid paper.*

87	½ a. black	£27	£15
88	1 a. black	£25	£20

The ½ a. was printed in a block of twenty varieties, and the 1 a. in a strip of five varieties.

8 (¼ a.)

9 (2 a.)

10 (4 a.)

11 (8 a.)

1867. *T* **6** *to* **11.** *Native laid paper.*

90	¼ a. black	1 9	1 9
91	½ a. ultramarine	2 6	1 3
92	½ a. violet-blue	3 6	2 6
92*a*	1 a. ultramarine	£40	£25
94	1 a. orange	12 6	8 6
95	1 a. brown-orange	8 6	6 0
96	1 a. orange-vermilion ..	8 6	6 6
97	2 a. yellow	12 0	12 0
98	2 a. buff	15 0	15 0
99	4 a. green	18 6	15 0
100	4 a. sage-green	32 6	27 6
101	8 a. red	15 0	15 0

Of the above, the ¼ a., 1 a., and 2 a. were printed in strips of five varieties, the ½ a. in a block of twenty varieties, and the 4 a. and 8 a. from single dies. Recent research seems to show that the varieties hitherto catalogued upon European papers were never put in circulation, though some of them were printed while these stamps were still in use.

Nos. 86 to 101 are in *water* colour.

III. For JAMMU AND KASHMIR.

In the following issues there are 15 varieties on the sheets of the ⅛ a., ¼ a., and ½ a.; 20 varieties of the 1 a. and 2 a. and 8 varieties of the 4 a. and 8 a. The value is in the lower part of the central oval.

12 (¼ a.)

13 (½ a.)

14 (1 a.)

15 (2 a.)

16 (4 a.)

17 (8 a.)

1878–79. *T* **12** *to* **17.** *Various papers.*

1. *Ordinary white laid.*

(*a*) *Rough perf.* 10 *to* 13.

102	½ a. slate-violet	65 0	£5
103	½ a. red	4 6	5 0
104	1 a. red	£15	£10

(*b*) *Imperf.*

105	½ a. slate-violet	4 0	4 0
106	1 a. slate-purple	12 6	12 6
107	1 a. mauve	12 6	10 0
108	2 a. violet	12 6	12 6
109	2 a. bright mauve	12 6	12 6
110	2 a. violet-blue	15 0	15 0
111	2 a. dull blue	20 0	20 0
112	¼ a. red	6 6	8 6
113	½ a. red	4 0	4 0
114	1 a. red	2 6	3 0
115	2 a. red	55 0	35 0
116	4 a. red	45 0	35 0

Variety on thick laid paper.

117	1 a. red	70 0	

2. *Ordinary wove paper. Imperf.*

118	½ a. red	10 0	10 0
119	1 a. red	9 6	9 6
120	2 a. red	70 0	12 6

Varieties on very thick wove paper.

121	½ a. red	35 0	
122	1 a. red	8 6	8 6
123	2 a. red	10 0	10 0

3. *Thin wove paper.*

(*a*) *Rough perf.* 10 *to* 13.

124	½ a. deep red	80 0	55 0

(*b*) *Imperf.*

125	⅛ a. red	1 6	1 6
126	½ a. red	0 9	0 6
127	1 a. red	1 6	2 6
128	2 a. red	1 6	1 6
129	4 a. red	4 6	4 6
130	8 a. red	5 6	5 6
131	⅛ a. orange	10 0	7 6
132	½ a. orange	15 0	15 0
133	1 a. orange	8 6	8 6
134	2 a. orange	8 6	8 6
135	4 a. orange	15 0	
136	8 a. orange	22 6	

These three papers seem to have been used at first indiscriminately, the ½ a. and 1 a. on thin wove having been found on letters of 1878. A little later the use of the thicker papers was given up (almost if not quite entirely), and all the varieties that follow are on thin paper, of various qualities. All the following are *imperforate.*

4. *Thin bâtonné paper. Printed in water colour.*

137	⅛ a. ultramarine	—	£12

It is quite uncertain when this stamp was issued, but it was certainly as early as the middle of 1880. Almost all the copies known are *used.*

18 (⅛ a.)

1883–94. *T* 12 *to* 18. *Thin wove paper, yellowish to white. Imperf.*

138	⅛ a. yellow-brown	0 8	1 0
139	⅛ a. yellow	0 8	1 0
140	¼ a. sepia	1 6	0 8
141	¼ a. brown	0 8	0 6
	a. Double impression		
142	¼ a. pale brown	0 8	0 6
142*a*	¼ a. green (*error of colour*) ..	75 0	
143	½ a. dull blue	7 6	
144	½ a. bright blue	9 0	
145	½ a. vermilion	4 0	1 6
146	½ a. rose	4 6	1 0
147	½ a. orange-red	3 6	1 0
148	1 a. greenish grey	0 9	0 9
149	1 a. bright green	2 6	3 0
150	1 a. dull green	0 8	0 8
151	1 a. blue-green	3 6	
152	2 a. red/*yellow*	1 3	1 6
153	2 a. red/*yellow-green* ..	1 3	2 0
154	2 a. red/*deep green*	4 6	4 6
155	4 a. deep green	3 6	4 0
156	4 a. green	3 6	3 6
157	4 a. pale green	5 6	5 6
158	4 a. sage-green	4 6	
159	8 a. pale blue	6 0	6 0
159*a*	8 a. deep blue	6 0	6 0
160	8 a. bright blue	6 6	6 6
161	8 a. indigo-blue	9 0	9 0
161*a*	8 a. slate-lilac	9 0	9 0

Printed in water-colour.

161*b*	8 a. dull grey-blue ..		

Well-executed forgeries of the ⅛ a. to 8 a. have come from India in great quantities, mostly postmarked; they may be detected by the type which does not agree with any variety on the genuine sheets, and also in the low values by the margins being filled in with colour all but a thin white frame round the stamp. The forgeries of the 8 a. are in sheets of eight, like the originals. Fresh forgeries of nearly all values have recently been seen, showing all varieties of type. All values are on thin, coarse wove paper.

1889–94. *T* 12 *to* 18. *Thin laid paper. Imperf.*

162	⅛ a. yellow	30 0	27 6
163	¼ a. brown	8 6	12 6
165	½ a. orange-red	17 6	10 0
166	1 a. grey-green	£10	£6
168	8 a. blue	£7	£5

19

T 19 represents a ½ a. stamp, which exists in sheets of twelve varieties, in *red* and in *black*, on thin wove and laid papers, also in *red* on native paper, but which does not appear ever to have been issued for use. It was first seen in 1886. The ¼ a. *brown* and the 4 a. *green*, exist on ordinary white laid paper; the ½ a. *red* on native paper; the ¼ a. in *bright green*, on thin white wove (this may be an error in the colour of the 4 a.); and the 8 a. in *lilac* on thin white wove. None of these are known to have been in use.

OFFICIAL STAMPS.

1878. *T* 12 *to* 17. *On ordinary white laid paper.*

169	½ a. black	5 0	5 0
170	1 a. black	10 0	10 0
171	2 a. black	22 6	

The 4 a. and 8 a. exist on this paper, but it is uncertain whether a supply of those values was printed for use.

1880. *On thin wove paper.*

174	¼ a. black	0 8	0 8
	a. Double print	£6	
175	½ a. black	0 8	0 2
176	1 a. black	0 8	0 6
177	2 a. black	1 0	0 8
178	4 a. black	1 6	1 6
179	8 a. black	1 6	

1889–94. *Thin laid paper.*

180	¼ a. black	6 0	10 0
181	½ a. black	4 0	6 0
182	1 a. black	10 0	
183	2 a. black	£8	
184	4 a. black	75 0	50 0
185	8 a. black	75 0	50 0

The stamps of Kashmir have been obsolete since Nov. 1, 1894.

JHALAWAR.

(Figure of an Apsara, "RHEMBA" a dancing nymph of the Hindu Paradise.)

1 (1 paisa) 2 (¼ anna)

1887-90. *T* **1** *and* **2.** (*a*) *Laid paper.*

1	1 paisa, yellow-green	4 6	8 6
1a	1 paisa, blue-green	10 0	12 6
2	¼ anna, deep green	1 3	2 6
3	¼ anna, pale green	1 0	2 6

(*b*) *Wove paper.*

3a	1 paisa, deep yellow-green	35 0	
4	¼ anna, green	50 0	

The stamps of Jhalawar have been obsolete since Nov. 1, 1900.

JIND.

1 (½ a.)

2 (1 a.)

3 (2 a.)

4 (4 a.)

5 (8 a.)

T **1** *to* **5.** *Imperf.*

The letter "R" on stamp is the initial of Raghbir Singh, at one time Rajah.

1874. *Thin yellowish paper.*

1	½ a. blue	10 0	3 6
2	1 a. rosy mauve	8 6	8 6
3	2 a. yellow	1 9	3 6
3a	2 a. brown-buff	17 6	12 6
4	4 a. green	27 6	7 6
5	8 a. indigo-purple	£6	60 0
5a	8 a. slate-blue	£5	50 0

Variety, without frame to value.

5b	½ a. blue	£12	75 0

1876. *Stout blue laid paper.*

6	½ a. blue	1 0	1 3
7	1 a. purple	3 6	
8	2 a. brown	2 6	4 6
9	4 a. green	1 9	
10	8 a. slate-blue	8 6	9 6
11	8 a. purple	17 6	

1885. *T* **1.** *Stout blue laid paper.* *P* 12.

12	½ a. blue	6 0	8 6

6 (½ a.) 7 (½ a.)

8 (1 a.) 9 (2 a.)

10 (4 a.) 11 (8 a.)

1882-84. *T* **6** *to* **11.** *25 varieties of each value. Imperf.*

(*a*) *Thin yellowish wove paper.*

13	½ a. pale buff	0 8	0 10
13a	½ a. buff	0 8	0 10
14	½ a. red-brown	0 8	1 3
	a. Double printed	5 0	
15	½ a. lemon	1 9	2 6
16	½ a. buff	3 6	3 6
17	½ a. brown-buff	3 6	3 6
18	1 a. brown	2 6	2 6
19	1 a. chocolate	3 6	3 6
20	2 a. blue	2 6	3 0
20a	2 a. deep blue	3 6	4 0
21	4 a. sage-green	3 0	3 6
22	4 a. blue-green	5 6	6 6
23	8 a. red	10 0	7 6

(*b*) *Laid paper.*

24	½ a. brown-buff	3 6	
25	½ a. lemon	4 0	
26	1 a. brown	3 0	
26b	2 a. blue		
27	8 a. red	12 6	12 6

(*c*) *Thick white wove paper.*

27b	½ a. brown-buff	40 0	
28	1 a. brown	15 0	
29	8 a. red	15 0	15 0

1885. *T* **6** *to* **11.** *P* 12.

(*a*) *Thin yellowish wove paper.*

29a	½ a. buff	0 9	1 0
30	½ a. brown-buff	2 6	2 6
30a	½ a. chestnut	4 6	
30b	½ a. lemon	1 3	1 6
31	½ a. pale buff	1 3	1 6
32	½ a. brown-buff	3 0	2 6

33	1 a. brown	3	6	4	6
34	2 a. blue	4	6		
34a	2 a. deep blue	6	0	6	0
35	4 a. sage-green	8	6	8	6
36	4 a. bluish green	8	6		
	a. Imperf. between (pair) ..	22	6		
37	8 a. red	22	6		

(*b*) *Laid paper.*

38	¼ a. brown-buff	35	0		
39	½ a. lemon	50	0	25	0
40	1 a brown	10	0		
41	8 a. red	15	0	12	6

(*c*) *Thick white wove paper.*

42	8 a. red	37	6		

These stamps have not been used for postal purposes since July, 1885, but are said to have been used later as fiscals. Other varieties exist, but they must be either fiscals or reprints, and it is not quite certain that all of those listed above were issued as early as 1885.

All the above stamps of Jind were lithographed by the Jind State Rajah's Press, Sungroor.

For later issues, see under INDIAN CONVENTION STATES.

KASHMIR.

See JAMMU AND KASHMIR.

KISHANGARH.

1

1899. *T* 1. (*a*) *Toned wove paper.*

1	1 a. green (*imperf.*)	4	6	6	0
2	1 a. green (*pin-perf.*)	15	0		

(*b*) *White wove paper.*

2a	1 a. blue-green (*imperf.*) ..	6	0	6	6

1900. *T* 1. *Thin white wove paper. Imperf.*

3	1 a. blue	37	6		

2 (¼ a.)

3 (½ a.)

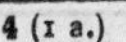
4 (1 a.)

Maharaja Sardul Singh.
5 (2 a.)

6 (4 a.)

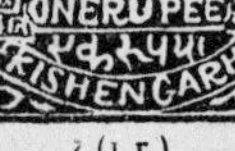

7 (1 r.)

8 (2 r.)

9 (5 r.)

1899–1901. *T* 2 *to* 9. *Thin white wove paper.*

(*a*) *Imperf.*

4	¼ a. pale green	35	0		
5	¼ a. carmine	4	6		
6	¼ a. pink	1	6		
7	½ a. dull green	30	0	30	0
7a	½ a. yellow-green	32	6	27	6
8	½ a red	35	0	20	0
9	½ a. deep blue	6	0	6	6
10	½ a. pale blue	3	6	5	0
11	½ a. lilac	12	6	15	0
12	½ a. slate-blue	6	6	7	6
13	1 a. lilac	6	0	5	0
15	1 a. slate	8	6	6	6
15a	1 a. brown-lilac	8	6	6	0
16	1 a. pink	20	0		
17	2 a. dull orange	16	0	20	0
18	4 a. chocolate	8	6		
	a. Thick laid paper	40	0		
19	1 r. dull green	15	0		
20	2 r. red-brown	45	0		
21	5 r. mauve	75	0		

(*b*) *Pin-perf.*

24	¼ a. sage-green	10	0		
	a. Imperf. between (pair) ..	20	0		
25	¼ a. carmine	1	3	3	0
	a. Double printed	20	0		
26	¼ a. bright pink	1	6		
27	½ a. green	6	6	6	6
	a. Imperf. between (pair) ..	15	0		
28	½ a. yellow-green	8	0	8	0
30	½ a. deep blue	4	0	3	6
31	½ a. blue	1	6	1	9
32	1 a. lilac	3	6	2	6
32a	1 a. red-lilac on laid paper ..	—		80	0
34	1 a. slate	4	0	6	0
35	1 a. pink	10	0		
36	2 a. dull orange	6	0	4	6
37	4 a. chocolate	6	0	6	0
38	1 r. dull green	10	0	12	6
38a	1 r. yellow-green	15	0		
39	2 r. red-brown	20	0		
41	5 r. magenta	30	0		

All varieties of this issue (Nos. 4 to 41) exist in *tête-bêche* vertical pairs from the centre of the sheet. They can be supplied when in stock.

10 (¼ a.)

1901. *T* **10** (¼ *a.*) *and* **4** (1 *a.*). *Toned wove paper. Pin-perf.*

45 ¼ a. dull pink 6 0 7 6
46 1 a. violet 22 6

These are printed from plates, in sheets of 24. All the others, except Nos. 1, 2, and 3, are printed singly on paper with spaces ruled in pencil.

The 1 a. (No. 46) differs from T 4 in having an inscription in native characters below the words "ONE ANNA".

11 (½ a.)

12. Maharaja Sardul Singh.

1903. *T* **11** *and* **12.** *Thick white wove glazed paper.*

8 varieties of ½ *a.,* 10 *of* 2 *a. Imperf.*

47 ½ a. pink 7 6 5 0
47*a* 2 a. dull yellow 7 6 8 0

12*a* (8 a.)

1904. *T* **12***a*. *Thin paper. Pin-perf.*

48 8 a. grey 10 0

Variety, tête-bêche (pair).

49 8 a. grey 32 6

13. Maharaja Madan Singh. **14.**

(*T* **13.** Recess. Perkins Bacon & Co.)

1904–5. *T* **13.** *P* 12½, 13.

50 ¼ a. carmine 0 8 0 5
51 ½ a. chestnut 0 6 0 6
52 1 a. blue 0 9 0 10
53 2 a. orange-yellow 3 0 3 6
54 4 a. brown 2 6 3 0
54*a* 8 a. violet (1905) 4 0 4 6
55 1 r. green 6 6 8 6
56 2 r. olive-yellow 12 0 15 0
57 5 r. purple-brown 22 6 27 6

1913. *T* **14.** *Printed from half-tone blocks on thick white chalk-surfaced paper. Rouletted in colour* (¼ *a.*) *or plain* (2 *a.*).

57*a* ¼ a. ultramarine 2 6 3 0
57*b* 2 a. purple 10 6

T **14.** *Value spelt* "TWO ANNA". *Thin wove paper. Rouletted.*

58 2 a. deep violet 10 6
a. Tête-bêche (pair) 22 6

No. 58 is printed in four rows, each inverted in respect to that above and below it.

15

(Printed at the Diamond Soap Works, Kishangarh.)

1914. *T* **15.** *Thick surfaced paper. Rouletted. Inscribed* "KISHANGARH."

59 ¼ a. pale blue 0 4 0 4
a. "OUARTER" 6 0
b. Imperf. 3 0
60 2 a. purple 2 6

Errors. "KISHANGAHR" *for* "KISHANGARH."

61 ¼ a. pale blue 5 0
a. Imperf. .. .. ..
62 2 a. purple 8 6

1913–16. *T* **14** *on thick surfaced paper. Value spelt* "TWO ANNAS." *Rouletted.*

63 ¼ a. blue (1913) 0 3 0 4
64 ½ a. green (1915) 0 3 0 4
a. Printed both sides 20 0
b. Emerald-green. 0 8
65 1 a. red 0 4 0 6
66 2 a. purple (1915) 0 8 0 10
67 4 a. bright blue 1 3 1 9
68 8 a. brown 1 9 3 0
69 1 r. mauve 4 0 6 0
70 2 r. deep green 8 6 9 6
71 5 r. brown 20 0 22 6

16. Maharaja Yagyanarain Singhji. **17.**

1928–36. *T* **16** *and* **17.** *Thick surfaced paper. Pin-perf.*

72	**16**	¼ a. light blue	.. .. 0 1	0 2
73	,,	½ a. yellow-green ..	.. 0 2	0 3
74	**17**	1 a. carmine	.. .. 0 3	0 5
75	,,	2 a. purple	.. .. 0 8	0 10
75*a*	,,	2 a. magenta ('36)	0 4	0 6
76	**16**	4 a. chestnut	.. .. 0 7	0 10
77	,,	8 a. violet ..	.. .. 1 3	1 9
78	,,	1 r. light green	.. .. 2 6	3 0
79	,,	2 r. lemon-yellow ('29)	.. 5 0	6 6
80	,,	5 r. claret ('29)	.. .. 17 6	18 0
		a. Imperf. ..	.. .. 25 0	

The 4 a. to 5 r. are slightly larger than, but otherwise similar to, the ¼ a. and ½ a. The 8 a. has a dotted background covering the whole design.

OFFICIAL STAMPS

ON
K S
D
(31)

1918. *Overprint T* **31**, *in black, on* (i.) *Stamps of* 1899–1901. (*a*) *Imperf.*

101	1 a. slate	—	3 0
	a. Inverted	6 0	
102	4 a. chocolate	—	50 0
	a. Inverted		

(*b*) *Pin-perf.*

103	½ a. pink	0 8	0 8
104	½ a. blue		
105	1 a. lilac	3 6	
	a. Inverted		
106	1 a. slate		
107	1 a. violet	7 0	
108	2 a. dull orange		
109	4 a. chocolate	25 0	20 0
110	1 r. dark green	£6	£5
111	2 r. red-brown	£12	£12
112	5 r. magenta ..	£15	£15

(ii.) *Stamp of* 1903.

113	2 a. yellow	30 0	30 0

(iii.) *Stamps of* 1904–5.

114	½ a. carmine ..	30 0	20 0
115	½ a. chestnut ..	0 6	0 8
116	1 a. blue	15 0	6 0
117	2 a. orange-yellow		
118	4 a. brown	30 0	30 0
119	8 a. violet	£6	£5
120	1 r. green	£20	£15
121	5 r. purple-brown		

(iv.) *Stamps of* 1913–16.

122	½ a. blue	0 8	0 8
123	½ a. green	1 0	1 0
124	1 a. carmine	0 10	0 10
125	2 a. purple ..	1 6	1 6
126	4 a. bright blue	52 6	52 6
127	8 a. brown	75 0	62 6
128	1 r. lilac	£5	£5
129	2 r. deep green		
130	5 r. brown		

All the above have been reported with overprint inverted, and many with overprint in red and in all sorts of fancy positions. Some irregularities took place at the sale of these latter, and it is doubtful if the varieties should be chronicled.

LAS BELA.

1

2

(Printed by Messrs. Thacker & Co., Bombay.) *Black impression. Pin-perf.*

1897–98. *T* **1.** *Thick paper.*

1	½ a. on *white*	8 6	6 0

1898–1900. *T* **1.**

2	½ a. on *greyish blue* (1898)	4 0	4 0
3	½ a. on *greenish grey* (1899)	4 0	4 0
4	½ a. on *thin white surfaced paper* (1899)	12 0	
5	½ a. on *slate* (1900)		
	a. Imperf. between (pair)	27 6	

1901–2. *T* **1** *and* **2.**

6	½ a. on *pale grey*	4 0	4 0
7	½ a. on *pale green* (1902)	8 6	12 6
8	1 a. on *orange*	7 6	8 6

Errors. Lettered "BFLA" *for* "BELA."
(11 July, 1901.)

9	½ a. on *greenish grey*	20 0	
10	½ a. on *pale grey*	20 0	

There are at least 14 settings of the above ½ a. stamps, the sheets varying in size from 16 to 30 varieties.

1904. *T* **1.** *Stamps printed wider apart.*

11	½ a. on *pale blue*	8 6	
	a. Imperf. between (pair)	27 6	
12	½ a. on *pale green*	8 0	12 0

There are three plates of the above two stamps, each consisting of 18 varieties.

All the coloured papers of the ½ a. show coloured fibres, to a greater or less extent, like what are termed "*granite*" papers.

The stamps of Las Bela have been obsolete since March, 1907.

MORVI.

1. Maharaja Sir Lakhdirji Waghji. **2.**

1931 (1 April). *T* **1.** *Typo. P* 12.

1	3 p. scarlet	0 4	0 5
2	½ a. blue ..	0 6	0 8
3	1 a. brown-red	0 6	0 8
4	2 a. yellow-brown	1 0	1 3

1932–33. *T 2. Typo. P* 11.

5 3 p. carmine-rose 0 3 0 4
6 6 p. green 0 5 0 8
7 6 p. emerald-green 0 5 0 8
8 1 a. ultramarine 0 6 0 8
9 2 a. bright violet ('33) 1 0 1 3

3. Maharaja Sir Lakhdirji Waghji.

1934. *Typo. London ptg. P* 14.

10 3 3 p. carmine 0 4 0 5
11 „ 6 p. emerald-green 0 4 0 5
12 „ 1 a. purple-brown 0 5 0 8
13 „ 2 a. bright violet 0 8 0 10

1935. *Typo. Morvi Press ptg. Rough perf.* 11.

14 3 3 p. scarlet 0 2 0 3
15 „ 6 p. grey-green 0 3 0 4
16 „ 1 a. chocolate 0 4 0 5
17 „ 2 a. dull violet 0 5 0 6

NANDGAON

1

(2)

1892 (Feb.). *T 1 optd. with T 2 in purple.*

1 ½ a. blue 12 0
2 2 a. rose 45 0

Without overprint.

3 ½ a. blue 2 0 4 6
3*a* ½ a. dull blue 4 6
4 2 a. rose 10 0 12 0

3 (2 a.)

1893–94. *T 3 overprinted with T 2 in purple or grey.*

1. *Printed wide apart on the sheet, no wavy lines between the stamps.*

6 2 a. red 5 0

Without the overprint.

7 ½ a. green 1 9
8 2 a. red 3 0

2. *Printed closer together, wavy lines between the stamps, the characters for " half " and " two " smaller than before.*

9 ½ a. green 1 9 2 9
10 1 a. rose, on *laid* 2 9 6 6
11 1 a. rose, on *wove* 3 0 6 6
12 2 a. dull carmine 2 6 6 6

Without the overprint.

13 ½ a. green 3 6 8 6
13*a* 1 a. rose, on *laid* 12 0
14 1 a. rose, on *wove* 5 0 8 6

It is stated that the stamps of T 1 were never put in circulation, and that no stamps were regularly issued for postal use without the control mark, but it is very doubtful whether these statements are correct. The 1 a. exists in *ultramarine* and in *brown*, but these appear to be reprints in fancy colours.

The stamps of Nandgaon have been obsolete since July, 1895.

NAWANAGAR.

1 (1 docra)

1877. *T 1. Laid paper. Imperf.*

1 1 docra, slate-blue 0 8 3 0
2 1 docra, deep blue 1 3
3 1 docra, indigo 1 3
4 1 docra, ultramarine 1 3 2 6
5 1 docra, slate-blue (*perf.*) .. 8 6 22 6

Varieties, tête-bêche (pair).

5*a* 1 docra, slate-blue 20 0 25 0
5*b* 1 docra, deep blue 30 0
5*c* 1 docra, indigo 30 0
5*d* 1 docra, ultramarine 30 0
5*e* 1 docra, slate-blue (*perf.*) .. £7

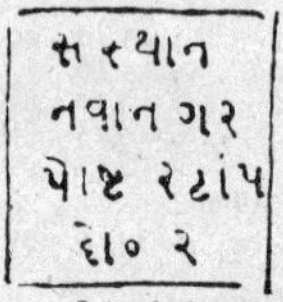

2 (2 do.) 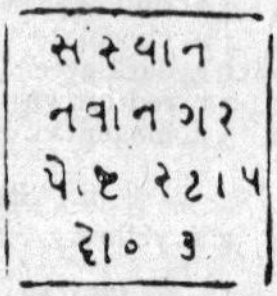 3 (3 do.)

1880. *T 2 and 3. Black impression. Wove paper. Stamp* 15 *to* 18 *mm. wide.*

6 1 docra, *deep mauve* 1 9 8 6
6*a* 1 docra, *rose* 2 9
7 2 docra, *yellow-green* 2 9 17 6
8 2 docra, *blue-green* 3 0
9 3 docra, *orange-yellow* 4 0
10 3 docra, *yellow* 4 6 21 0

Error on sheet of one setting of the 3 docra.

10*a* 2 docra, *yellow* 75 0

T 3, on laid paper.

10*b* 3 docra, *yellow* 45 0

T 2 and 3, 14 *mm. wide only.*

11 1 docra, *magenta* 1 3
11*a* 1 docra, *rose* 2 6 6 0
12 2 docra, *yellow-green* 2 6 4 6
13 2 docra, *blue-green* 6 0
14 3 docra, *yellow* 2 6 4 6

As No. 14, *but on laid paper.*

15 3 docra, *yellow* 20 0

There are several different settings of each value of this series.

4 (1 docra)

1893. *T* **4.** *Thick wove paper.* (*a*) *P* 12.

16	1 docra, black	4 0	
17	3 docra, orange	7 6	

(*b*) *Imperf.*

18	1 docra, black	27 6	

Thick laid paper. *P* 12.

18*a*	1 docra, black		

T 4, *thin wove paper.* (*a*) *P* 12.

19	1 docra, black	0 10	2 0
	a. Imperf. between (pair) ..	6 6	
19*b*	1 docra, grey	1 6	
20	2 docra, green	1 6	3 0
21	3 docra, orange-yellow ..	2 6	
	a. Imperf between (pair) ..		
21*b*	3 docra, orange	2 9	5 0

(*b*) *Imperf.*

21*c*	1 docra, black	25 0	
21*d*	2 docra, green	27 6	
21*e*	3 docra, orange	25 0	

Thin, soft wove paper. *P* 12.

22	1 docra, black		
23	2 docra, deep green	8 6	
24	3 docra, brown-orange ..	10 0	

The stamps of this State are obsolete. We believe that they went out of use at the end of 1895.

NEPAL.

Strictly speaking, this country should not be included among the Native Feudatory States, as it is independent, but should be transferred to Part II like Afghanistan. It has, however, been decided to leave it in this group of Native stamps, for the convenience of collectors.

1 (1 a.)

2 (½ a.)

1881. *T* **1.** *White paper.* (*a*) *Pin-perf.*

1	1 a. milky blue	6 6	7 6
1*a*	1 a. bright blue	6 6	
2	2 a. purple	10 6	
3	4 a. green	16 0	

Variety, tête-bêche (*pair*).

3a	2 a. purple	£5	

(*b*) *Imperf.*

4	1 a. milky blue	5 6	5 6
4*a*	1 a. bright blue	5 6	5 6
5	2 a. purple	8 6	8 6
	a. Tête-bêche (pair)	£5	
6	4 a. green	8 6	

1886. *T* **1.** *Native paper.* *Imperf.*

6*a*	1 a. grey-blue	1 9	0 5
6*b*	1 a. blue	1 9	
7	1 a. deep blue	2 0	0 8
8	2 a. purple	3 6	1 3
8*a*	2 a. violet	3 6	1 3
9	4 a. green	2 6	1 9

Varieties, tête-bêche (*pair*).

9*a*	1 a. blue	12 6	6 6
10	1 a. deep blue	15 0	8 6
11	2 a. purple	30 0	8 6
11*a*	2 a. violet	25 0	8 6
12	4 a. green	30 0	15 0

Nos. 7, 8, 9 are found on thick rough paper, and also on thin soft native paper.

1899–1906. *T* **2** (½ a.) *and* **1.** *Native paper.*

(*a*) *Imperf.*

13	½ a. black-brown	2 6	2 6
13*a*	1 a. slate-blue		
13*b*	1 a. pale blue		
14	2 a. lavender (1904)	3 6	1 9
14*a*	2 a. red-lilac	3 0	
15	4 a. deep green (1906) ..	4 0	2 9

Varieties, tête-bêche (*pair*).

16	½ a. black-brown (1904) ..	17 6	
16*a*	1 a. slate-blue		
16*b*	1 a. pale blue		
17	2 a. lavender (1904)	20 0	15 0
17*a*	2 a. red-lilac	20 0	
18	4 a. deep green (1906) ..	27 6	

(*b*) *Pin-perf.*

19	½ a. black-brown (1900) ..	0 10	
20	1 a. slate-blue	4 0	2 9
21	1 a. pale blue	3 0	2 6
21*a*	2 a. lavender	6 6	
22	2 a. violet	4 0	3 0
22*a*	2 a. red-lilac	6 6	
23	4 a. green	5 6	3 6
23*a*	4 a. deep green (1906) ..	10 6	

Varieties, tête-bêche (*pair*).

24	½ a. black-brown (1904) ..	17 6	
25	1 a. slate-blue	17 6	
26	1 a. pale blue	17 6	
27	2 a. violet	17 6	
27*a*	2 a. red-lilac	30 0	
28	4 a. green	20 0	
28*a*	4 a. deep green (1906) ..	27 6	

1903–6. *T* 1 *redrawn, fewer lines in frame.*

(*a*) *Native paper.*

29	1 a. grey-blue (*imperf.*) ..	3 6	3 0
29*a*	1 a. grey-blue (*pin-perf.*) ..	6 0	
30	1 a. ultramarine (*imperf.*) ..	3 0	2 6
31	1 a. ultramarine (*pin-perf.*) ..	10 6	

Varieties, tête-bêche (*pair*).

32	1 a. grey-blue (*imperf.*) ..	10 0	7 6
33	1 a. grey-blue (*pin-perf.*) ..	25 0	
34	1 a. ultramarine (*imperf.*) ..	15 0	
34*a*	1 a. ultramarine (*pin-perf.*) ..	30 0	

(*b*) *White wove paper.*

35	1 a. grey-blue (*imperf.*) ..	35 0	
36	1 a. grey-blue (*pin-perf.*) ..	25 0	

Varieties, tête-bêche (*pair*).

37	1 a. grey-blue (*imperf.*) ..	80 0	
38	1 a. grey-blue (*pin-perf.*) ..	80 0	

Siva Mahadeva.

3 (2 pice)

(Recess. Messrs. Perkins Bacon & Co.)

1907. *T* **3.** *White wove paper. Date* (= 1907) *in lower corners. P* 13½, 14.

39	2 pice, brown	0 5	0 4
40	4 pice, green	0 9	0 7
41	8 pice, carmine	1 0	0 10
42	16 pice, purple	1 6	1 3

4

1929. *T* **4.** *Date* (= 1929) *in lower corners. P* 13½–14.

43	2 pice, brown	0 4	0 3
44	4 pice, green	0 6	0 4
45	8 pice, scarlet	0 9	0 5
46	16 pice, purple	1 0	0 8
47	24 pice, orange	1 6	1 0
48	32 pice, blue	2 0	1 3
	Size 26 × 19½ *mm.*		
49	1 r. vermilion	2 6	3 6
	Size 27⅞ × 21¼ *mm.*		
50	5 r. black and red-brown .	12 0	15 0

5

1935. *As T* **4,** *but re-engraved. Date in lower corner tablets altered, as in T* **5** (= 1935). *Recess. P* 13½.

51	2 p. brown	0 2	0 1
52	4 p. green	0 3	0 2
53	8 p. scarlet	5 0	6 0
54	16 p. purple	0 8	0 4
55	24 p. orange	1 0	0 6
56	32 p. blue	1 4	0 9

NOWANUGGUR.

See NAWANAGAR.

ORCHHA.

1 2

1913. *T* **1.** *Thin wove paper. Imperf.*

1	½ a. green	1 3	3 0
2	1 a. red	1 9	4 0

1914–16. *T* **2.** *Thin wove paper. Imperf.*

3	½ a. ultramarine (1915) ..	0 3	0 8
4	½ a. green	0 5	0 7
5	1 a. red	0 6	0 10
5*a*	1 a. brick-red	0 4	0 8
6	2 a. brown (1916) ..	0 8	0 10
7	4 a. ochre	0 10	1 4

We do not catalogue the two stamps (½ a. and 1 a.) in a similar type which were made in 1900, as these were a speculation on the part of a native jeweller.

POONCH.

The stamps of Poonch are all *imperf.* and printed in water-colours.

1

2

1876. *T* **1** (22 × 21 mm.). *Yellowish white, wove paper.*

1	6 pies red	—	£5

1877. *As T* **1** (19 × 17 *mm.*). *Same paper.*

1*a*	½ anna, red		

1879. *T* **2** (21 × 19 *mm.*). *Same paper.*

2	½ anna, red	—	£20

3 (½ a.)

4 (1 a.)

5 (2 a.)

6 (4 a.)

1880. *T* **3** *to* **6.** *Yellowish white, wove paper.*

3	½ a. red	45 0	22 6
4	1 a. red	55 0	32 6
5	2 a. red	65 0	65 0
6	4 a. red	65 0	

1884. *T* **3** *to* **6.** *Toned wove bâtonné paper.*

7	½ a. red	6 0	6 0
8	1 a. red	10 0	
9	2 a. red	12 0	12 0
10	4 a. red	21 0	

These are sometimes found gummed.

7. (1 pice)

1884–87. *T* **3** *to* **7.** *Various papers.*

(*a*) *White laid bâtonné or ribbed bâtonné.*

11	1 pice, red	12 6	15 0
12	½ anna, red	1 3	1 6
13	1 anna, red	1 9	
14	2 annas, red	3 0	4 0
15	4 annas, red	6 0	

(d) Thick white laid paper.

No.	Description	Unused	Used
22a	1 pice, red	45 0	
23	½ anna, red	10 0	
24	1 anna, red	17 6	
25	2 annas, red	35 0	
26	4 annas, red	37 6	

(e) Yellow wove bâtonné.

No.	Description	Unused	Used
27	1 pice, red	10 0	12 6
28	½ anna, red	12 6	10 0
29	1 anna, red	20 0	
30	2 annas, red	10 0	15 0
31	4 annas, red	4 0	5 0

(f) Orange-buff wove bâtonné.

No.	Description	Unused	Used
32	1 pice, red	1 3	1 3
33	½ anna, red	17 6	
34	2 annas, red	32 6	
35	4 annas, red	12 6	

(g) Yellow laid paper.

No.	Description	Unused	Used
36	1 pice, red	2 6	3 0
37	½ anna, red	6 6	
38	1 anna, red	20 0	
39	2 annas, red	17 6	17 6
40	4 annas, red	30 0	

(h) Yellow laid bâtonné.

No.	Description	Unused	Used
41	1 pice, red	27 6	10 0

(i) Buff laid or ribbed bâtonné paper thicker than (f).

No.	Description	Unused	Used
42	1 anna, red	45 0	
43	4 annas, red	65 0	

(j) Blue-green laid paper (1887).

No.	Description	Unused	Used
44	½ anna, red	22 6	
45	1 anna, red	18 6	18 6
46	2 annas, red	20 0	
47	4 annas, red	22 6	

(k) Yellow-green laid paper.

No.	Description	Unused	Used
48	½ anna, red		

(l) Blue-green wove bâtonné.

No.	Description	Unused	Used
49	1 pice, red	45 0	55 0
50	1 anna, red	1 3	3 6

(m) Lavender wove bâtonné.

No.	Description	Unused	Used
51	1 anna, red	55 0	
52	2 annas, red	1 9	4 0

(n) Various coloured papers.

No.	Description	Unused	Used
53	1 p. red/*grey-blue laid*	15 0	17 6
54	1 p. red/*lilac laid*	£5	£5
55	1 p. red/*blue wove bâtonné*	1 6	2 9

1888. *T 3 to 7 in aniline rose on various papers.*

No.	Description	Unused	Used
56	1 p. on *blue wove bâtonné*	6 0	
56a	1 p. on *buff laid*	12 6	
57	½ a. on *white laid*	25 0	
58	1 a. on *green laid*	30 0	
59	1 a. on *green wove bâtonne*	6 6	
60	2 a. on *lavender wove bâtonné*	7 6	4 6
61	4 a. on *yellow laid*	27 6	22 6

OFFICIAL STAMPS.

1888. *T 3 to 7. White laid bâtonné paper.*

No.	Description	Unused	Used
101	1 pice, black	1 6	2 9
102	½ anna, black	2 0	4 0
103	1 anna, black	2 6	
104	2 annas, black	2 6	3 6
105	4 annas, black	3 6	

White toned wove bâtonné paper.

No.	Description	Unused	Used
106	1 pice, black	2 0	
107	½ anna, black	6 6	7 0
108	1 anna, black	21 0	21 0
109	2 annas, black	12 0	
110	4 annas, black	18 6	

The stamps of Poonch have been obsolete since 1894.

RAJNANDGAON.

The stamps formerly listed, incorrectly, under the above heading will now be found under the heading of NANDGAON.

RAJPIPLA.

1 (1 pice)

2 (2 a.)

3 (4 a)

1880. *T 1 to 3.* (*a*) *P* 11.

No.	Description	Unused	Used
1	1 p. blue	1 6	6 0

(*b*) *P* 12½.

No.	Description	Unused	Used
2	2 a. green	7 0	12 0
	a. Imperf. between (pair)	25 0	
3	4 a. red	8 6	17 6

The stamps of this state have been obsolete since 1886.

SIRMOOR.

1 (1 pice)

2

1879-80. *T 1.* *P* 11½.

No.	Description	Unused	Used
1	1 pice, pale green	6 0	
2	1 pice, blue on *laid*	4 0	
	a. Imperf. between (pair)		
	b. Imperf.		

(Printed at Calcutta.)

1892. *T 2.* *Thick wove paper.* *P* 11½.

No.	Description	Unused	Used
4	1 pice, yellow-green	1 0	1 3
	a. Imperf. between (pair)		
5	1 pice, deep green	0 8	0 10
	a. Imperf. between (pair)	—	12 6
6	1 pice, blue	0 10	1 0
	a. Imperf. between (pair)	6 0	

Variety. Imperf. (pair).

No.	Description	Unused	Used
6b	1 pice blue		

These were originally made as *reprints*, about 1891, to supply collectors after the first issue was exhausted, but there being very little demand for them they were subsequently put into use. The original stone having been cleaned off, the design was copied (perforations and all!) from an illustration cut from a dealer's catalogue.

3. Raja Sir Shamsher Parkash.

(Litho. Waterlow & Sons.)

1885–88. *T* **3.** *P* 14 *to* 15.

There were seven printings of the 3 and 6 pies, six of the 1 anna, and four of the 2 annas, all in sheets of seventy, made up of groups of transfers showing two or more minor varieties. There are two distinct varieties of the 3 p. and 6 p., as shown in Types A and B, C and D. Of these B and D are the types of the sixth printing of those values, and A and C those of all the other printings.

A B

C D

A and C have large white dots evenly placed between the ends of the upper and lower inscriptions; B has small white dots, and less space between the ends of the inscriptions; D has large spaces, and large white dots *not* in the centres of the spaces, especially at the left side.

The last printing of each value is only known with the Waterlow overprint, T **18.**

7	3 pies, chocolate (A)	1	3	1	0
8	3 pies, brown (B)	0	6	0	6
9	3 pies, orange (A)	1	3	0	10
10	3 pies, orange (B)	0	8		
	a. Imperf.	£10			
11	6 pies, blue-green (C)	3	6	3	6
12	6 pies, green (C)	3	0	3	0
13	6 pies, deep green (C)	1	0	1	0
14	6 pies, yellowish green (D) ..	0	8	0	10
15	1 anna, bright blue	3	0	3	0
16	1 anna, dull blue	2	6	1	9
17	1 anna, grey-blue	0	10	1	3
18	2 annas, pink	2	6	1	6
19	2 annas, rose-red	1	3	1	3

4

(Recess. Waterlow & Sons.)

1895–99. *T* **4.** *P* 13 *to* 15.

20	3 pies, orange-brown	0	8	0	8
21	6 pies, green	0	8	0	6
22	1 anna, blue	0	10	0	8
23	2 annas, rose	1	0	1	3
24	3 annas, yellow-green ..	2	6	4	0
25	4 annas, deep green	3	0	6	0
26	8 annas, deep blue	3	6	6	0
27	1 rupee, vermilion	6	0	9	0

5. Raja Sir Surendar Bikram Parkash.

(Recess. Waterlow & Sons.)

1899. *T* **5.** *P* 13 *to* 15.

28	3 annas, yellow-green	2	6	3	6
29	4 annas, deep green	2	6	3	6
30	8 annas, deep blue	4	0	7	0
31	1 rupee, vermilion	7	0	12	0

OFFICIAL STAMPS.

NOTE.—*The varieties occurring in the machine printed* "On S.S.S." *overprints may, of course, also be found in the inverted and double overprints, and many of them are known thus. We do not however think that any useful purpose will be served by listing them separately.*

I. Machine-printed.

On

S. S.

S.

(11)

1890. *T* **3** *overprinted with T* **11.**

(*a*) *In black.*

50	6 p. green	£8			
	a. Stop before first "S" ..				
51	2 a. rose-red	25	0	35	0
	a. Stop before first "S" ..	£6			

(*b*) *In red.*

52	6 p. green	6	6	4	0
	a. Stop before first "S" ..	50	0		
53	1 a. blue	25	0	15	0
	a. Stop before first "S" ..	85	0		

(*c*) *Doubly overprinted, in red and in black.*

53*b*	6 p. green				
	c. Stop before first "S" ..				

On On

S. S. S. S.

S. S.

(12) (13)

1891. *T* **3** *overprinted with T* **12.**

(*a*) *In black.*

54	3 p. orange	4	0		
	a. Overprint inverted				
55	6 p. green	4	0	4	0
	a. Overprint double				
	b. No stop after lower "S" ..				
	c. Raised stop before lower "S"				
56	1 a. blue				
57	2 a. rose-red	25	0		

(b) In red.

58 6 p. green 36 6 16 0
- a. Overprint inverted .. ..
- b. Overprint double .. ..

59 1 a. blue 25 0 36 6
- a. Overprint inverted .. ..
- b. Overprint double .. ..
- c. No stop after lower "S" .. ..

1892–97. *T 3 overprinted with T 13.*

(a) In black.

60 3 p. orange 1 0 1 3
- a. Overprint inverted .. ..
- b. First "S" inverted and stop raised .. .. ..
- c. No stop after lower "S" .. ..
- d. Raised stop after second "S"

61 6 p. green 1 9 2 3
- a. First "S" inverted and stop raised .. ..
- b. Raised stop after second "S"

62 1 a. blue 16 0 8 6
- a. Overprint double .. ..
- b. First "S" inverted and stop raised .. .. ..
- c. No stop after lower "S" .. ..
- d. Raised stop after second "S"

63 2 a. rose-red 8 6 8 6
- a. Overprint inverted .. ..
- b. First "S" inverted and stop raised .. .. ..
- c. No stop after lower "S" .. ..
- d. Raised stop after second "S"

(b) In red.

64 6 p. green 3 6 3 0
- a. Overprint inverted .. ..
- b. First "S" inverted and stop raised .. .. ..

65 1 a. blue 16 0 3 6
- a. Overprint inverted .. ..
- b. Overprint double .. ..
- c. First "S" inverted and stop raised .. .. ..
- d. No stop after lower "S" .. ..

(c) Doubly overprinted in black and red.

65e 6 p. green .. .. ..

There are six settings of this overprint. The inverted "S" variety occurs in the second and fifth settings, and the missing stop in the second setting of all values except the 6 pies. In the fifth setting occurs the raised stop after second "S."

On S. S. S. (14)

On S. S. S. (15)

1896. *T 3 overprinted as T 14, in black.*

66 3 p. orange 12 6 6 6
- a. Comma after first "S" 30 0
- b. Overprint inverted .. ..

67 6 p. green 8 6 3 0
- a. Comma after first "S" .. .. — 20
- b. Comma after lower "S" .. .. — 35 0
- c. "S" at right inverted .. ..

68 1 a. blue 12 6 5 0
- a. Comma after first "S" .. .. — 35 0
- b. Comma after lower "S" .. ..

69 2 a. carmine 20 0
- a. Comma after first "S" .. ..

There are four settings of this overprint: (1) 23 mm. high, includes the comma after lower "S"; (2) 25 mm. high, with variety, comma after first "S"; (3) and (4) 25 mm. high, with no important varieties.

1898 (Nov.). *T 3 overprinted with T 15, in black.*

70 6 p. green .. .. .. — 6 6
- a. Small "S" at right .. ..
- b. Comma after lower "S" .. ..
- c. Lower "S" inverted and stop raised .. .. ..

71 1 a. blue .. .. .. — 10 0
- a. Small "S" at right .. ..
- b. Small "S" without stop .. ..

There are two settings of this overprint. Nos. 70a and 71a occur in the first setting, No. 71b in the first setting, and Nos. 70b and 70c in the second setting.

On S S S (16)

On S. S. S. (17)

1899. *T 3 overprinted as T 16 (but with stop after each "S"), in black.*

72 3 p. orange .. .. .. — 8 6
73 6 p. green .. .. .. — 6 0

1900. *T 3 overprinted as T 17, in black.*

74 3 p. orange .. .. .. — 16 0
- a. Raised stop after lower "S" .. — 60 0

75 6 p. green .. .. .. — 15 0
- a. Raised stop after lower "S" .. — 65 0
- b. Comma after first "S" ..

76 1 a. blue .. .. .. — 20 0
- a. Raised stop after lower "S" .. — 75 0

77 2 a. carmine .. ..
- a. Raised stop after lower "S" ..

There are two settings of this overprint: (1) 22 mm. high, with raised stop variety; (2) 23 mm. high, with "comma" variety in the 6 pies.

On S. S. S. (18)

On S S S (19)

(Overprinted by Messrs. Waterlow & Sons.)

1900. *T 3 overprinted with T 18, in black.*

78 3 p. orange 3 6 3 0
79 6 p. green 1 3 1 6
80 1 a. blue 0 10 0 10
81 2 a. carmine 5 0 6 6

II. Handstamped. The word "On" and each letter "S" struck separately.

1894. *T 3 handstamped with T 19.*

(a) In black.

94 3 p. orange 4 0 4 0
- a. "On" sideways .. ..

95 6 p. green 10 6 7 6
- a. "On" only .. ..

96 1 a. blue 10 6 10 6

97 2 a. rose-red 10 6 10 6
- a. "On" only .. ..
- b. "On" sideways .. ..

(b) In red.

98 6 p. green 40 0

1896. *T* **3** *handstamped with letters similar to those of T* **13**, *with stops, but irregular, in black.*

98*a* 3 p. orange .. .. ..
98*b* 6 p. green .. .. ..
c. "On" omitted .. ..
98*d* 2 a. rose-red .. .. ..

1896. *T* **3** *handstamped with letters similar to those of T* **14**, *with stops, but irregular, in black.*

99 3 p. orange 10 0
a. "On" double .. ..
100 6 p. green .. .. .. — 20 0
101 1 a. blue .. .. .. — 25 0
102 2 a. rose-red .. .. .. — 30 0

In No. 99*a* the second "On" is over the lower "S."

ON on

S S S S

S S

(20) (21)

1896. *T* **3**, *handstamped with T* **20**, *in black.*

103 3 p. orange 30 0 30 0
104 2 a. rose-red 30 0

T **3**, *handstamped with T* **21**, *in black.*

104*a* 3 p. orange .. .. ..
104*b* 6 p. green .. .. ..
105 1 a. blue 60 0

On On

S. S. S S

S. S

(21*a*) (22)

T **3**, *handstamped with T* **21***a*, *in black.*

106 3 p. orange .. .. ..
106*a* 6 p. green .. .. ..
106*b* 1 a. blue .. .. ..

T **3**, *handstamped with T* **22**, *in black.*

107 3 p. orange 20 0 20 0
108 6 p. green 20 0 20 0
a. "On" only .. ..
109 1 a. blue 25 0 25 0
a. "On" only .. ..
110 2 a. rose-red 27 6 25 0

Mixed overprints.

(*a*) *Handstamped "On" as in T* **19**, *and press-printed overprint T* **13** *complete.*

111 6 p. green .. .. ..

(*b*) *Handstamped overprint as T* **14**, *and press-printed overprint T* **13**, *complete.*

112 6 p. green .. .. ..

Various other types of these handstamps are known to exist, but in the absence of evidence of their authenticity we do not list them. It is stated that stamps of T **4** were never officially overprinted.

The stamps of this State have been obsolete since March 31, 1902.

SORUTH (JUNAGADH).

The name "Soruth" (or "Sorath") was used some centuries ago for all the territory now known as Kathiawar (but still referred to by many Indians as "Saurashtra"). Strictly speaking the name should be applied only to a portion of Kathiawar including the states of Junagadh, Porbandar and Jafarabad, of which only Junagadh issues stamps. As collectors have known these issues under the heading of "Soruth" for so long, we are retaining the name.

1

1864(?). *T* **1**. *Imperf.*

1 1 a. black/*blue laid* £20 20 0
2 1 a. black/*white* .. .. — £6

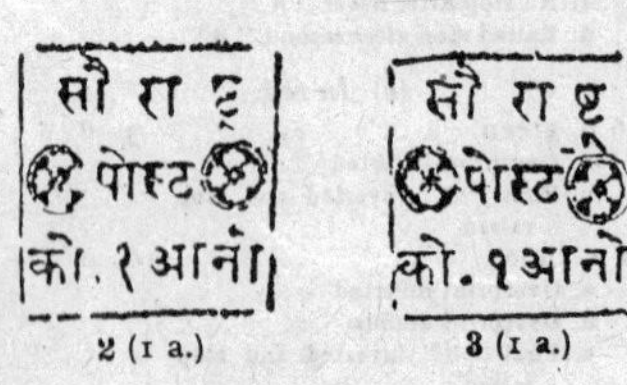

2 (1 a.) **3** (1 a.)

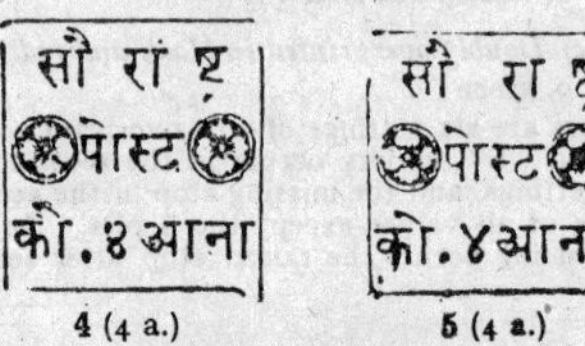

4 (4 a.) **5** (4 a.)

1868. *T* **2** *to* **5** (*two types of the characters for "1" and "4" as shown in the illustrations*). *Imperf.*

(*a*) *Wove paper.*

3 **2** 1 a. black/*pink* £5 20 0
4 ,, 1 a. black/*yellow* .. ..
5 **2** 1 a. black/*azure* £20 £6
6 **3** 1 a. black/*azure* .. ..

(*b*) *Laid paper.*

7 **2** 1 a. black/*azure* 25 0 15 0
7*a* **3** 1 a. black/*azure* 50 0 20 0
8 ,, 1 a. red/*white* 20 0 16 6
9 **4** 4 a. black/*white* 50 0 50 0
10 **5** 4 a. black/*white* £5 £5

Official imitations, consisting of 1 a. carmine-red on white wove and white laid, 1 a. black on blue wove, 4 a. black on white wove, 4 a. black on blue wove, 4 a. red on white laid—all imperforate; 1 a. carmine-red on white laid, 1 a. black on blue wove, 4 a. black on white laid and blue wove—all perforated 12, were made in 1890. Entire sheets of originals have 20 stamps, the imitations only 4 or 16.

6

7

T 6 and 7.

1877. *Imperf.*

(a) Medium laid paper, lines wide apart.
(b) Thick laid paper, lines wide apart.
(c) Thick laid paper, lines close together.

11 1 a. dull yellow-green (*a*) 0 9 1 0
12 1 a. grey-green (*a*) 1 0 1 3
13 1 a. dull yellow-green (*b*) .. 0 9 1 0
13*a* 1 a. deep blue-green (*b*) .. 3 0
14 1 a. bright green (*c*) 0 9 1 3
15 4 a. pale red (*a*) 2 6 3 6
16 4 a. brown-red (*a*) 2 6
16*a* 4 a. vermilion (*a*) 3 0
17 4 a. vermilion/*toned* (*b*) .. 2 6 3 0
17*a* 4 a. scarlet/*bluish* (*b*) 2 6 3 0
17*b* 4 a. scarlet (*b*) .. .. .. — 3 0

1886. *P* 12. *(a) Wove paper.*

18 1 a. pale green 2 0 2 0
19 1 a. deep green 4 6 1 3
19*a* 1 a. blue-green 3 6 1 9
20 4 a. red 1 9
21 4 a. brown-red 1 9

Error of colour.

21*a* 1 a. blue .. .. .. — 80 0

Varieties. Imperf.

22 1 a. green 10 0 5 0
23 4 a. red .. ..
23*a* 4 a. brown-red 50 0

(b) Toned laid paper.

24 1 a. pale green 0 10 0 4
25 1 a. deep green 0 8 0 4
26 1 a. blue-green 1 6 1 3
27 1 a. bright green 1 0 0 6
27*a* 1 a. dull emerald-green .. 1 9
28 4 a. brick-red 1 6 1 3
29 4 a. red 1 6 1 3
30 4 a. carmine 1 6 1 6

Error of colour.

30*a* 1 a. blue .. .. ..

(c) Bluish white laid paper.

31 1 a. pale green 0 10 0 10
 a. Imperf. between (pair) .. 6 0
32 1 a. deep green 1 3 0 8
32*a* 1 a. yellow-green 3 0
33 4 a. scarlet 3 6

There is a very wide range of colours in both values. The laid paper is found both vertical and horizontal.

The 1 a. was issued first in sheets of 15 varieties, and afterwards in sheets of 20; the 4 a. is in horizontal strips of 5 varieties.

Three pies. ત્રણ પાઇ. (8)   One anna. એક આનો. (8*a*)

1913. *T* 6 *and* 7. *P* 12. *Surcharged with T* 8 *or* 8*a, in black.*

(a) On yellowish wove paper.

34 3 p. on 1 a. emerald 0 8 0 8
 a. Imperf. .. .. ..

(b) On white wove paper.

35 3 p. on 1 a. emerald 0 6 0 6
 a. Imperf. between (pair) .. 6 0
35*b* 1 a. on 4 a. carmine 2 0 2 0
 a. Capital "A" in "Anna" .. 6 0

Variety. Surcharge inverted.

36 3 p. on 1 a. emerald 16 6 11 6

(c) On white laid paper.

37 3 p. on 1 a. emerald .. ..
 a. Imperf. .. .. .. — 50 0
38 1 a. on 4 a. red 4 0 4 0
 a. Capital "A" in "Anna" ..
 b. Inverted .. .. ..
 c. Double .. .. ..
 d. Double, one inverted .. ..

(d) On toned wove paper.

39 1 a. on 4 a. red 1 9 2 6
 a. Imperf. .. .. ..
 b. Capital "A" in "Anna" .. 10 0

1915. *T* 7 *and* 6. *P* 12.

40 3 p. bright green 1 3 0 10
 a. Imperf. 0 8 0 10
41 1 a. red 1 3 1 3
 a. Imperf. 1 6 1 6
 b. Imperf. between (pair) ..

Nawab Sir Mahabat Khanji Rasulkhan.
9 10
(Printed at Junagadh State Press.)

1923. *T* 9 *and* 10. *Blurred impression. Pin-perf.*

42 3 p. mauve 0 4 0 3
43 1 a. red (*shades*) 1 0 1 0

No. 42 exists on wove and on laid papers.

ત્રણ પાઇ (11)   ત્રણ પાઈ (12)

T 10, *surcharged with T* 11 *or* 12.

44 **11** 3 p. on 1 a. red 0 10 0 10
45 **12** 3 p. on 1 a. red 1 9 1 9

T **11** has right vertical stroke straight, and T **12** stroke curved to right, at top. Four stamps in the setting of 16 have surch. T **12**.

1924. *T* **10**. *Clear impression. Pin-perf.*

46 1 a. carmine .. .. ..

This printing is in sheets of 4 × 4, No. 43 being in two rows of 8.

1928. *T* **10**. *Imperf.*

47 1 a. carmine 0 10 0 10

1929 (Aug.). *T* **9**. *Laid paper. Wmk. State Arms (part on each sheet). Imperf.*

48 3 p. mauve 0 10 0 10
 a. Perf. 11 × imperf. (pair) .. 1 9 1 9

13. Junagadh City.
14. Gir Lion. (*horiz.*).

15. Nawab Sir Mahabat Khanji Rasulkhan.

16. Kathi Horse (*horiz.*).

(Printed at Nasik.)

1929 (1 Oct.)–**1937.** *P* 14. *Inscr.* " POSTAGE."

No.	Type	Description	Unused	Used
49	13	3 p. black and blackish green	0 1	0 1
50	14	½ a. black and deep blue ..	0 1	0 1
51	15	1 a. black and carmine ..	0 8	0 4
52	16	2 a. black and orange ..	0 5	0 4
53	13	3 a. black and carmine ..	0 7	0 7
54	14	4 a. black and purple ..	0 8	0 8
55	16	8 a. black and yellow-green	1 3	1 3
56	15	1 r. black and pale blue ..	2 6	2 6

For T **15** inscribed " POSTAGE AND REVENUE ", see King George VI Catalogue.

OFFICIAL STAMPS.

SARKARI	SARKARI
(O 1)	(O 2)

1929. *Centres in black. Overprinted with Type* O **1** *in red.*

No.	Type	Description	Unused	Used
O1	13	3 p. blackish green ..	0 1	0 1
O2	14	½ a. deep blue ..	0 2	0 1
O3	15	1 a. carmine (No. 51)	0 3	0 1
O4	16	2 a. orange ..	0 4	0 2
O5	13	3 a. carmine ..	0 8	0 3
O6	14	4 a. purple ..	1 0	0 4
O7	16	8 a. yellow-green ..	1 9	1 0
O8	15	1 r. pale blue ..	4 0	4 6

1932–33. *Centres in black. Overprinted with Type* O **2** *in red.*

No.	Type	Description	Unused	Used
O 9	13	3 a. carmine ..	0 6	0 4
O10	14	4 a. purple ..	0 7	0 5
O11	16	8 a. yellow-green ..	1 2	1 0
O12	15	1 r. pale blue ..	2 3	2 0

TRAVANCORE.

1. Conch or Chank Shell. **2**

1888. *T* **1** (*and similar types*). *Laid paper. P* 12.

No.		Description	Unused	Used
1		1 ch. ultramarine ..	4 0	2 6
2		2 ch. red ..	4 0	4 6
3		4 ch. green ..	15 0	15 0

1889–94. *T* **1** (*and similar types*). *Wove paper. Wmk. T* **2**. *P* 12.

No.	Description	Unused	Used
4	½ ch. purple ..	0 8	0 1
4a	½ ch. lilac ..	0 6	0 1
5	1 ch. ultramarine ..	0 7	0 1
5a	1 ch. dull blue ..	1 0	0 1
6	2 ch. orange-red ..	2 6	0 8
6a	2 ch. carmine ..	1 6	0 6
7	2 ch. rose ..	1 0	0 3
	a. Imperf. between (pair) ..	30 0	
8	4 ch. green ..	3 0	0 8

Impressions of the 1, 2, and 4 chuckrams in various abnormal colours on *laid* paper have been met with. These are proofs.

3. Conch Shell.

1899–1901. *Types as* **1** *and* **3** (¾ chuckram). *W* **2**. *P* 12.

No.	Description	Unused	Used
9	½ ch. bright purple ..	1 0	0 3
9a	½ ch. dull purple ..	0 8	0 3
10	¾ ch. black ..	0 3	0 1
11	1 ch. violet-blue ..	4 6	1 0
12	2 ch. pale pink ..	2 0	0 8
13	4 ch. yellow-green ..	2 0	0 9

1903–39. *Types as* **1** *and* **3**, *new shades. W* **2**. *P* 12.

No.	Description	Unused	Used
14	½ ch deep violet ..	0 1	0 1
14a	½ ch. violet ..	0 3	0 1
14b	¾ ch. mauve ('32) ..	0 4	0 1
14c	¾ ch. violet ('39) ..	0 3	0 1
15	1 ch. indigo ..	0 6	0 1
16	1 ch. pale blue ..	1 0	0 1
16a	1 ch. deep blue ..	0 8	0 1
17	2 ch. scarlet ..	0 8	0 1
18	4 ch. blue-green ..	3 6	0 8
18a	4 ch. dull green ..	4 0	0 4
18b	4 ch. deep green (1911) ..	3 0	0 3

The above may also be found without wmk., but these are from watermarked sheets, the watermarks being more widely spaced on the sheet than the stamps.

¼	⅜
(4)	(5)

1906. *Stamps as T* **1** *surch. with T* **4** *or* **5**.

No.	Description	Unused	Used
19	"¼" on ½ ch. dull purple ..	1 3	0 4
20	"¼" on ½ ch. bright purple ..	0 6	0 4
20a	"¼" on ½ ch. violet ..	0 3	0 3
21	"⅜" on ½ ch. dull purple ..	1 0	0 4
22	"⅜" on ½ ch. bright purple ..	0 10	0 4
22a	"⅜" on ½ ch. violet ..	0 7	0 3

Varieties. Surcharge inverted.

No.	Description	Unused	Used
23	"¼" on ½ ch. bright purple ..	70 0	25 0
23a	"⅜" on ½ ch. dull purple ..		
24	"⅜" on ½ ch. violet		

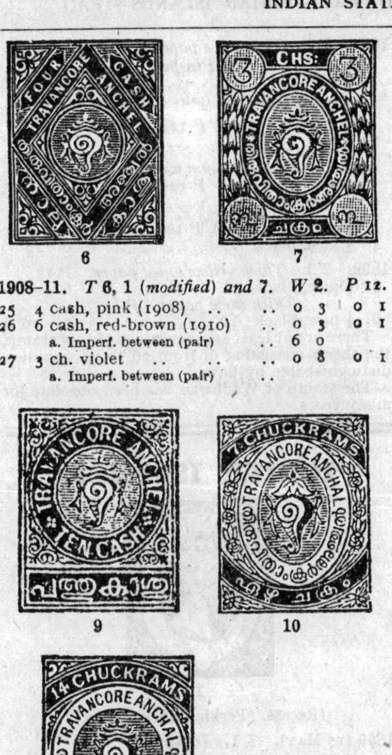

6 7

1908–11. *T* **6, 1** *(modified) and* **7.** *W* **2.** *P* 12.

25 4 cash, pink (1908) 0 3 0 1
26 6 cash, red-brown (1910) 0 3 0 1
a. Imperf. between (pair) .. 6 0
27 3 ch. violet 0 8 0 1
a. Imperf. between (pair) ..

9 10

11

1 C
(12)

1916–33. *T* **9, 1** *(modified),* **10** *and* **11.** *W* **2.** *P* 12.

28 **9** 10 cash, pink (1921) 0 4 0 1
a. Imperf. between (pair) ..
29 **1** 1½ ch. claret (1920) 0 8 0 1
29*a* ,, 1½ ch. rose ('33) 0 4 0 1
30 **10** 7 ch. purple 2 0 0 6
31 **11** 14 ch. orange 3 6 0 8
31*a* ,, 14 ch. yellow .. ..

1921–22. *Nos.* 25 *and* 15 *surcharged as T* **12.**

32 1 c. on 4 cash, pink 0 1 0 1
a. Inverted .. .. — 6 0
33 5 c. on 1 ch. indigo (R.) .. 0 2 0 1
a. Inverted .. .. .. — 2 6

1922–32. *T* **9.** *W* **2.** *P* 12.

34 5 cash, olive-bistre 0 4 0 1
a. Imperf. between (pair) .. 12 0
35 5 cash, chocolate ('32) .. 0 3 0 1
a. Imperf. between (pair) .. 6 0

13. Sri Padmanabha Shrine.

14. State Chariot.

15. Maharaja Sir Bala Rama Varma.

(Typographed by Calcutta Chromotype Co.)

1931 (6 Nov.). *Coronation issue. T* **13** *to* **15.** *Wmk. as T* **2.** *P* 12.

36 6 cash, black and green .. 0 6 0 4
37 10 cash, black & ultramarine .. 0 6 0 4
38 3 chuckrams, black & purple 0 6 0 6

1932. *Wmk. as T* **2.** *P* 12.

(*a*) *No.* 29 *surcharged as T* **12** *(slightly smaller).*

39 1 c. on 1½ ch. claret 0 3 0 2
a. Surcharge inverted 3 0
b. Imperf. between (pair) ..
40 2 c. on 1½ ch. claret 0 4 0 2
a. Surcharge inverted 4 0
b. Imperf. between (pair) ..

(*b*) *T* **9** *surcharged as T* **12** *(wider spaced).*

41 1 c. on 5 cash, chocolate .. 0 4 0 2
a. Surcharge inverted 3 0
b. Pair, with and without surcharge
42 1 c. on 5 cash, slate-purple .. 0 2 0 2
43 2 c. on 10 cash, pink 0 3 0 2
a. Surcharge inverted 4 0
b. Imperf. between (pair) ..

OFFICIAL STAMPS.

On

S S

(S 1)

1911 (16 Aug.)–**1930.** *Contemporary stamps overprinted as Type* S **1.**

S 1 4 cash, pink 0 2 0 1
a. Inverted .. .. .. — 4 0
S 2 5 cash, olive-bistre 0 4 0 1
a. Inverted .. .. .. — 3 0
S 2*b* 5 cash, chocolate 0 1 0 1
c. Inverted 2 6
S 3 6 cash, red-brown 0 3 0 1
a. One "S" omitted ..
b. Inverted .. .. .. — 3 0
S 4 10 cash, pink 0 4 0 1
a. Inverted .. .. .. — 3 0
b. Double .. .. ..
c. First "S" inverted ..
d. Imperf. between (pair) ..
e. "S" at left omitted ..
f. "Ou" for "On" ..
S 4*g* 10 cash, scarlet .. ..
S 5 ½ ch. violet (R.) 0 4 0 1
a. Inverted .. .. .. — 2 6
b. Imperf. between (pair) ..
S 6 1 ch. indigo (R.) 0 6 0 1
a. Inverted .. .. .. — 4 0
b. Double .. .. .. — 6 0
c. "nO" for "On" ..
S 7 1½ ch. claret 0 6 0 1
a. Inverted .. .. .. — 4 0
b. Stamp doubly printed ..
c. Imperf. between (pair) ..
d. "S" at right omitted ..
e. "S" at right inverted
S 8 2 ch. scarlet 0 6 0 1
a. Inverted 4 0
S 9 3 ch. violet 0 8 0 1
a. One "S" omitted ..
b. Inverted .. .. .. — 10 0
c. Double .. ..

S10	4 ch. deep green (No. 18*b*)	1 3	0 1
	a. Inverted	12 6	
	b. Imperf. between (pair) ..		
S10*c*	7 ch. brown-purple.. ..	1 9	0 3
S10*d*	14 ch. orange	2 6	0 4
	e. Imperf. between (pair) ..		
S10*f*	14 ch. yellow	—	0 4
	In deep blue.		
S11	4 cash, pink..	—	0 4
S12	6 cash, red-brown	3 6	0 6
S13	10 cash, pink..	—	0 6
S14	1½ ch. claret	—	0 8
S15	4 ch. deep green	—	1 3

On 1 ch

S S 8 c

(S 2) (S 3)

1930-35. *Stamps overprinted as Type* S 2 *or smaller.*

S16	**6**	4 cash, pink	0 3	0 2
S17	**9**	5 cash, chocolate ..	0 4	0 3
		a. Inverted	25 0	
S18	**1**	6 cash, red-brown ..	0 3	0 1
		a. "nO" for "On" ..	6 0	
S19	**9**	10 cash, pink	0 4	0 2
		a. Imperf. between (pair)	6 0	
S20	**1**	½ ch. violet (Bk.) ..	0 1	0 2
S21	,,	½ ch. violet (R.)	0 1	0 2
S22	**3**	¾ ch. black (R.) (*s*) ..	0 4	0 1
S23	,,	¾ ch. black (R.)	0 3	0 2
S24	,,	¾ ch. mauve	0 3	0 1
S25	**1**	1 ch. indigo (R.) ..	0 4	0 4
S26	,,	1½ ch. carmine-rose ..	0 8	0 5
S27	,,	1½ ch. carmine-rose (*s*) ..	0 6	0 3
S28	,,	1½ ch. rose	0 6	0 1
S29	**7**	3 ch. violet (Bk.) ..	0 6	0 1
S30	,,	3 ch. violet (R.)	0 6	0 1
		a. Inverted		
S31	**1**	4 ch. green (R.)	0 8	0 6
S32	,,	4 ch. green (Bk.) ..	0 9	0 6
S33	**10**	7 ch. brown-purple ..	1 3	0 6
		a. Imperf. between (pair)		
S34	**11**	14 ch. orange	2 6	1 3
		a. Imperf. between (pair)		

1932. *Official stamps surch. as T* 12 *or* S 3.

(*a*) *Overprint Type* S 1.

S34*b*	6 c. on 5 cash, olive-bistre ..	1 9	0 6
S35	6 c. on 5 cash, chocolate ..	0 3	0 1
	a. Surcharge inverted	4 0	
S36	12 c. on 10 cash, pink ..	0 3	0 2
	a. Surcharge inverted	4 0	
	b. "c" of "12 c." omitted ..	4 0	
	c. "Ou" for "On"		
S37	1 ch. 8 c. on 1¼ ch. claret ..	0 6	0 4

(*b*) *Overprint Type* S 2.

S38	6 c. on 5 cash, chocolate ..	0 4	0 1
	a. "8" at right inverted ..		
S39	12 c. on 10 cash, pink ..	0 3	0 1
	a. Surcharge inverted.. ..	4 0	
	b. "c" of "12 c." omitted ..	4 0	
S40	1 ch. 8 c. on 1¼ ch. claret ..	0 6	0 1

WADHWAN.

1

1888. *T* **1.** *Thin wove paper.*

(*a*) *Pin-perf.*

1	½ pice, black	5 0	8 6
	a. Imperf. between (pair) ..	42 6	

(*b*) *P* 12½.

2	½ pice, black		

T **1.** *Medium wove paper.*

(*a*) *P* 12½.

3	½ pice, black		

(*b*) *P* 12.

4	½ pice, black	6 0	12 6

1892. *T* **1.** *Thick yellow toned paper.* *P* 12.

5	½ pice, black	2 6	8 6

Thick wove paper. *P* 12.

6	½ pice, black	3 0	3 6

There are at least seven settings of this stamp, the sheets consisting of from 20 to 42 varieties, distinguishable by flaws.

The stamp of Wadhwan has been obsolete for many years.

IONIAN ISLANDS.

1

(Recess. Perkins Bacon & Co.)

1859 (15 May). *T* **1.** *Imperf.*

1	(½d.) orange (no wmk.) ..	35 0	£20
2	(1d.) blue (wmk. "2") ..	30 0	£17
3	(2d.) carmine (wmk. "1") ..	25 0	£12

On the 30th May, 1864, the islands were ceded to Greece, and these stamps became obsolete.

Collectors are warned to exercise special care in purchasing used specimens as dangerous forgeries have been made with genuine stamps purporting to have been used on original covers.

IRAQ.

(*The issues of Iraq, an independent sovereign state, are included in this volume at the request of many collectors, and purely as a matter of convenience.*)

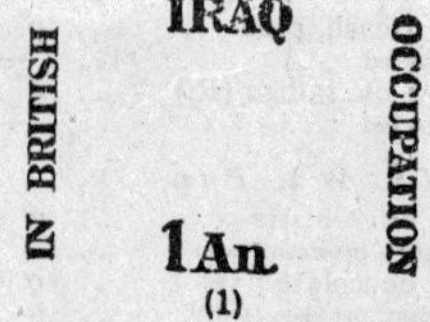

(1)

1918 (1 Sept.)–**1920.** *Turkish pictorial issue of 1913 surcharged, in black, as T* **1.** *No wmk. P* 12.

1	½ a. on 5 par., dull purple ..	0 6	0 6
2	½ a. on 10 par., green ..	0 4	0 2
3	1 a. on 20 par. red ..	0 5	0 1
3*a*	1½ a. on 5 par. dull purple ('20)	0 6	0 6
4	2½ a. on 1 pias. bright blue	1 3	0 10
5	3 a. on 1½ pias. grey & rose..	1 6	1 0
	a. Overprinted in red and in black	£75	
6	4 a. on 1¾ pias. red-brn. & grey	1 9	1 0
	a. Centre inverted		

7	6 a. on 2 pias. black & green	3 0	1 9
8	8 a. on 2½ pias. grn. & orge..	3 0	1 6
9	12 a. on 5 pias. deep lilac ..	3 6	3 6
10	1 r. on 10 pias. red-brown ..	4 0	2 6
11	2 r. on 25 pias. yellow-green	10 0	8 6
12	5 r. on 50 pias. rose	22 0	15 0
13	10 r. on 100 pias. indigo ..	35 0	25 0

1922. *As No.* 10, *but* " toughra " *in circle at top of stamp consists of a single device instead of two.*

13*a*	1 r. on 10 pi. red-brown ..	£12	40 0

1921. *As* 1918–20, *but wmk. Mult. Script CA.*

14	½ a. on 10 par. green ..	0 4	0 5
15	1½ a. on 5 par. dull purple ..	0 9	1 0
16	2 r. on 25 pias. yellow-green	15 0	15 0

King Faisal, 1921–33.

2. Sunni Mosque, Muadhdham.

3. Guffahs on the Tigris (*horizontal*).

4. Winged Cherub.

5. Bull from Babylonian wall-sculpture (*horiz.*).

6. Arch of Ctesiphon (*horizontal*).

7. Tribal Standard, Dulaim Camel Corps (*vert.*).

8. Shiah Mosque, Kadhimain (*horizontal*).

9. Allegory of Date Palm.

(Des. Miss Edith Cheesman (T **2, 3, 7** and **8**) and Mrs. C. C. Garbett (Miss M. J. Maynard) (remainder). Recess. Bradbury, Wilkinson & Co.)

1923–5. *T* **2** *to* **9.** *Wmk. Mult. Script CA. P* 12.

17	**2**	½ a. olive-green	0 3	0 2
18	**3**	1 a. brown	0 3	0 1
19	**4**	1½ a. lake	0 6	0 6
20	**5**	2 a. orange-buff	0 6	0 2
21	**6**	3 a. grey-blue	1 0	0 6
22	**7**	4 a. violet	1 3	0 8
23	**8**	6 a. greenish blue	1 6	0 8

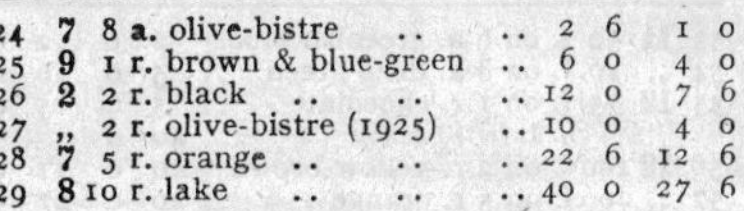

24	**7**	8 a. olive-bistre	2 6	1 0
25	**9**	1 r. brown & blue-green ..	6 0	4 0
26	**2**	2 r. black	12 0	7 6
27	,,	2 r. olive-bistre (1925) ..	10 0	4 0
28	**7**	5 r. orange	22 6	12 6
29	**8**	10 r. lake	40 0	27 6

With the exception of Nos. 25 and 26, later printings of these stamps and of No. 30 are on a thinner paper.

10. King Faisal.

(Recess. Bradbury, Wilkinson & Co., Ltd.)

1927. *T* **10.** *Wmk. Mult. Script CA. P* 12.

30	1 r. red-brown	10 0	4 0

11. King Faisal. **12**

(Recess. Bradbury, Wilkinson & Co., Ltd.)

1931. *Wmk. Mult. Script CA. P* 12.

31	**11**	½ a. green	0 5	0 2
32	,,	1 a. red-brown	0 7	0 3
33	,,	1½ a. scarlet	0 10	0 8
34	,,	2 a. orange..	1 0	0 4
35	,,	3 a. blue	1 3	0 6
36	,,	4 a. slate-purple	2 0	1 0
37	,,	6 a. greenish blue ..	2 0	0 9
38	,,	8 a. deep green	3 0	1 9
39	**12**	1 r. chocolate	4 6	2 6
40	,,	2 r. yellow-brown ..	8 6	7 0
41	,,	5 r. orange	18 6	18 6
42	,,	10 r. scarlet	40 0	45 0
43	**10**	25 r. violet	£30	£30

(New Currency 1000 fils. = 1 dinar.)

(13) **(14)**

(Surcharged at Govt. Printing Works, Baghdad.)

1932 (1 April). *Ordinary issues of* 1923–5 *and* 1931 *surcharged with new values in* " Fils " *or* " Dinar " *as T* **13** *or* **14**.

44	**11**	2 f. on ½ a. green (R.) ..	0 3	0 2
45	,,	3 f. on ½ a. green ..	0 3	0 2
46	,,	4 f. on 1 a. red-brown (G.)	0 4	0 4
47	,,	5 f. on 1 a. red-brown ..	0 4	0 4
		a. Inverted Arabic " 5 " ..	55 0	55 0
48	**11**	8 f. on 1½ a. scarlet ..	1 6	1 0
49	,,	10 f. on 2 a. orange ..	0 9	0 4
		a. Inverted Arabic " 1 " ..	60 0	
50	**11**	15 f. on 3 a. blue ..	1 6	1 6
51	,,	20 f. on 4 a. slate-purple ..	1 6	1 9
52	**7**	25 f. on 4 a. violet ..	2 0	2 6
		a. " Flis " for " Fils " ..	£35	£35
		b. Inverted Arabic " 5 " ..		

No.	Type	Description	Unused		Used	
53	11	30 f. on 6 a. greenish blue	2	6	2	0
54	„	40 f. on 8 a. deep green ..	5	0	6	0
55	12	75 f. on 1 r. chocolate ..	5	0	5	0
		a. Inverted Arabic "5" ..	40	0		
56	12	100 f. on 2 r. yellow-brown	10	0	11	0
57	„	200 f. on 5 r. orange ..	20	0	22	6
58	„	½ d. on 10 r. scarlet ..	45	0	50	0
		a. No bar in English "½" ..	£45			
59	10	1 d. on 25 r. violet	£8		£8	

15

1932 (9 May). *T* **10** *to* **12**, *but with values altered to "*FILS*" or "*DINAR*" as in T* **15**. *Wmk. Mult. Script CA. P* 12.

No.	Type	Description	Unused		Used	
60	11	2 f. ultramarine	0	4	0	2
61	„	3 f. green	0	5	0	2
62	„	4 f. brown-purple ..	0	6	0	2
63	„	5 f. grey-green	0	7	0	2
64	„	8 f. scarlet	0	8	0	3
65	„	10 f. yellow	0	9	0	3
66	„	15 f. blue	0	10	0	2
67	„	20 f. orange	1	3	0	4
68	„	25 f. mauve	1	6	0	8
69	„	30 f. bronze-green	1	9	0	6
70	..	40 f. violet	2	3	1	0
71	12	50 f. brown	3	6	1	6
72	„	75 f. dull ultramarine ..	5	6	2	0
73	„	100 f. deep green	6	0	2	0
74	„	200 f. scarlet	13	6	4	6
75	10	½ d. deep blue	27	6	20	0
76	„	1 d. claret	60	0	60	0

King Ghazi, September 7, 1933–April 4, 1939.

16 17

18. King Ghazi.

(Recess. Bradbury, Wilkinson & Co., Ltd.)

1934 (11 June)–**1938**. *No wmk. P* 12.

No.	Type	Description	Unused		Used	
76a	16	1 f. violet (7.8.38) ..	0	2	0	1
77	„	2 f. ultramarine	0	2	0	1
78	„	3 f. green	0	3	0	1
79	„	4 f. brown-purple ..	0	3	0	1
80	„	5 f. grey-green	0	5	0	2
81	„	8 f. scarlet	0	10	0	2
82	„	10 f. yellow	1	6	0	3
83	„	15 f. blue	1	3	0	4
84	„	20 f. orange	1	9	0	4
85	„	25 f. mauve	2	0	0	8
86	„	30 f. bronze-green	2	3	0	8
87	„	40 f violet..	3	0	1	3
88	17	50 f. brown	3	6	1	3
89	„	75 f. blue	5	0	3	0
90	„	100 f. deep green	8	0	3	6
91	„	200 f. scarlet	17	6	7	6
92	18	½ d. deep blue	35	0	17	6
93	„	1 d. claret..	60	0	50	0

OFFICIAL STAMPS.

ON STATE SERVICE

(O 1)

1920–22. *Postage stamps of 1918–21 with additional wording, Type* O 1, *in the surcharge in black.*

(*a*) *No wmk.*

No.	Description	Unused		Used	
O 1	½ a. on 10 par. blue-green ..	0	9	0	2
O 2	1 a. on 20 par. red	1	0	0	2
O 3	1½ a. on 5 par. purple-brown	2	0	0	10
O 4	2½ a. on 1 pias. blue	2	6	2	6
O 5	3 a. on 1½ pias. black and rose	2	0	1	6
O 6	4 a. on 1¾ pias. red-brown and grey-blue	3	6	3	0
O 7	6 a. on 2 pias. black & green	3	0	2	9
O 8	8 a. on 2½ pias. yellow-green and orange-brown ..	4	0	3	0
O 9	12 a. on 5 pias. purple ..	6	0	7	0
O10	1 r. on 10 pias. red-brown ..	7	6	7	0
O11	2 r. on 25 pias. olive-green..	22	6	17	6
O12	5 r. on 50 pias. rose-carmine	27	6	20	0
O13	10 r. on 100 pias. slate-blue..	60	0	40	0

No. 13*a*, *similarly surcharged.*

No.	Description	Unused		Used	
O14	1 r. on 10 pi. red-brown (1922)	60	0	30	0

(*b*) *Wmk. Mult. Script CA.*

No.	Description	Unused		Used	
O15	½ a. on 10 par. green ..	0	4	0	4
O16	1 a. on 20 par. red	0	8	0	4
O17	1½ a. on 5 par. purple-brown	1	0	1	6
O18	4 a. on 1¾ pias. red-brown and grey-blue	1	9	1	9
O19	6 a. on 2 pias. black & green	4	6	5	6
O20	8 a. on 2½ pias. yellow-green and orange-brown ..	3	0	3	6
O21	12 a. on 5 pias. purple ..	6	0	6	
O22	2 r. on 25 pias. olive-green	17	6	17	

ON STATE SERVICE (O 2)

ON STATE SERVICE (O 3)

1923. *T* **2** *to* **9** *overprinted with Types* O **2** *or* O **3**.

No.	Description	Unused		Used	
O23	½ a. olive-green	0	3	0	3
O24	1 a. brown	0	4	0	4
O25	1½ a. lake	0	6	0	8
O26	2 a. orange-buff	0	8	0	4
O27	3 a. grey-blue	0	10	0	10
O28	4 a. violet	1	0	1	3
O29	6 a. greenish blue	1	6	1	6
O30	8 a. olive-bistre	2	0	1	9
O31	1 r. brown and blue-green ..	5	0	4	0
O32	2 r. black (R.)	15	0	7	6
O33	5 r. orange	27	6	17	6
O34	10 r. lake	47	6	40	0

ON STATE SERVICE (O 4)

ON STATE SERVICE (O 5)

1924–25. *T* **2** *to* **9** *optd. with Types* O **4** *or* O **5**.

No.	Description	Unused		Used	
O35	½ a. olive-green	0	4	0	2
O36	1 a. brown	0	5	0	1
O37	1½ a. lake	0	8	0	4
O38	2 a. orange-buff	0	10	0	3
O39	3 a. grey-blue	1	3	0	6
O40	4 a. violet	1	9	0	4
O41	6 a. greenish blue	2	6	0	6
O42	8 a. olive-bistre	3	6	0	8
O43	1 r. brown and blue-green ..	7	0	4	0
O44	2 r. olive-bistre (1925) ..	8	6	4	6
O45	5 r. orange	20	0	17	6
O46	10 r. lake	35	0	25	0

See Note below No. 29.

1927. *T 10 overprinted with Type* O **5.**

O47		1 r. red-brown	9	

ON STATE SERVICE

ON STATE SERVICE رسمي

(O 6)

رسمي

(O 7)

1931. *Overprinted.* (*a*) *As Type* O **6.**

O48	**11**	½ a. green	0 6	0 4
O49	„	1 a. red-brown	0 6	0 3
O50	„	1½ a. scarlet	1 3	1 0
O51	„	2 a. orange	1 6	0 4
O52	„	3 a. blue	1 9	0 6
O53	„	4 a. slate-purple	2 0	0 4
O54	„	6 a. greenish blue ..	2 3	2 3
O55	„	8 a. deep green	3 3	2 9

(*b*) *As Type* O **7**, *horizontally*.

O56	**12**	1 r. chocolate	7 0	5 0
O57	„	2 r. yellow-brown ..	13 6	13 6
O58	„	5 r. orange	30 0	30 0
O59	„	10 r. scarlet	45 0	45 0

(*c*) *As Type* O **7**, *vertically upwards.*

O60	**10**	25 r. violet	£30	£30

1932 (1 April). *Official issues of* 1924–25 *and* 1931 *surcharged with new values in* "fils" *or* "dinar," *as T* **13** *or* **14.**

O61	**11**	3 f. on ½ a. green ..	0 10	0 9
O62	„	4 f. on 1 a. red-brown (G.)	0 10	0 3
O63	„	5 f. on 1 a. red-brown ..	0 10	0 6
		a. Inverted Arabic "5" ..		
O64	**4**	8 f. on 1½ a. lake ..	2 3	0 8
O65	**11**	10 f. on 2 a. orange ..	1 3	0 4
		a. Inverted Arabic "1" ..	45 0	45 0
O66	„	15 f. on 3 a. blue ..	2 3	0 9
O67	„	20 f. on 4 a. slate-purple	3 0	1 0
O68	„	25 f. on 4 a. slate-purple	3 0	2 0
O69	**8**	30 f. on 6 a. greenish blue	3 3	2 0
O70	**11**	40 f. on 8 a. deep green ..	4 0	2 6
		a. "Flis" for "Fils" ..	£35	
O71	**12**	50 f. on 1 r. chocolate ..	5 0	4 0
		a. Inverted Arabic "5" ..	£15	
O72	**12**	75 f. on 1 r. chocolate ..	13 6	10 0
		a. Inverted Arabic "5" ..		
O73	**2**	100 f. on 2 r. olive-bistre..	10 0	6 0
O74	**7**	200 f. on 5 r. orange ..	17 6	17 6
O75	**8**	½ d. on 10 r. lake ..	40 0	40 0
O76	**10**	1 d. on 25 r. violet ..	85 0	85 0

1932 (9 May). *Overprinted.* (*a*) *As Type* O **6.**

O77	**11**	2 f. ultramarine	0 2	0 2
O78	„	3 f. green	0 3	0 2
O79	„	4 f. brown-purple ..	0 4	0 2
O80	„	5 f. grey-green	0 6	0 3
O81	„	8 f. scarlet	0 7	0 1
O82	„	10 f. yellow	0 8	0 3
O83	„	15 f. blue	1 0	0 4
O84	„	20 f. orange	1 3	0 4
O85	„	25 f. mauve	1 6	0 8
O86	„	30 f. bronze-green ..	1 9	0 6
O87	„	40 f. violet	2 0	0 6

(*b*) *As Type* O **7**, *horizontally.*

O88	**12**	50 f. brown	2 6	1 3
O89	„	75 f. dull ultramarine ..	3 6	1 6
O90	„	100 f. deep green	6 0	2 6
O91	„	200 f. scarlet	12 6	7 6

(*c*) *As Type* O **7**, *vertically upwards.*

O92	**10**	½ d. deep blue	35 0	35 0
O93	„	1 d. claret	60 0	65 0

1934 (June)–**1938.** *Overprinted.*

(*a*) *As Type* O **6.**

O 93*a*	**16**	1 f. violet (7.8.38) ..	0 1	0 2
O 94	„	2 f. ultramarine	0 1	0 1
O 95	„	3 f. green	0 2	0 1
O 96	„	4 f. brown-purple ..	0 2	0 1
O 97	„	5 f. grey-green	0 3	0 2
O 98	**16**	8 f. scarlet	0 6	0 2
O 99	„	10 f. yellow	0 10	0 3
O100	„	15 f. blue..	0 9	0 8
O101	„	20 f. orange	1 3	0 3
O102	„	25 f. mauve	1 6	1 0
O103	„	30 f. bronze-green ..	1 9	1 6
O104	„	40 f. violet	2 0	1 0

(*b*) *As Type* O **7**, *horizontally.*

O105	**17**	50 f. brown	2 6	1 6
O106	„	75 f. blue..	4 0	3 0
O107	„	100 f. deep green	4 6	3 6
O108	„	200 f. scarlet	8 6	7 0

(*c*) *As Type* O **7**, *vertically upwards.*

O109	**18**	½ d. deep blue	22 6	15 0
O110	„	1 d. claret	40 0	32 6

BAGHDAD.

(BRITISH OCCUPATION.)

IN BRITISH BAGHDAD OCCUPATION

2 Ans

(1)

1917 (Sept.). *Stamps of Turkey surcharged as T* **1**, *in black.*

(*a*) *Pictorial designs of* 1913. *T* **32**, *etc., and* **31.**

1	¼ a. on 2 par. claret	£5	£5
2	¼ a. on 5 par. dull pur. ..	50 0	50 0
	a. Value omitted		
3	½ a. on 10 par. green	£12	
4	½ a. on 10 par. grn. (T **31**) ..	£50	
5	1 a. on 20 par. red	£15	£15
6	2 a. on 1 pias. bright blue ..	£6	£6

(*b*) *As* (*a*), *but overprinted with small Star, in blue* (B.) *or red* (R.).

7	1 a. on 20 par. red (B.) ..	£12	£12
	a. "OCCUPATION" omitted ..		
8	2 a. on 1 pias. bright blue (R.)	£90	

(*c*) *Postal Jubilee stamps, T* **56.**

9	½ a. on 10 par. carmine ..	£15	
10	1 a. on 20 par. blue	£35	
	a. Value omitted		
11	2 a. on 1 pias. blk. & violet ..	55 0	55 0
	a. "BAGHDAD" omitted ..		

(*d*) *T* **30** *with opt. T* **26.**

12	2 a. on 1 pias. bright blue ..	£10	£10

(*e*) *Stamps overprinted with Star and Arabic date* "1331" *within Crescent, T* **53** (*except No.* 16, *T* **60**), *in red* (R.), *black, or blue* (B.).

13	½ a. on 10 par. green (T **30**) (R.)	75 0	75 0
14	1 a. on 20 par. rose (T **30**) ..	£17	
	a. Value omitted	£160	£100
	b. Overprinted with Type 26 in addition	£125	£150
15	1 a. on 20 par. rose (No. 257)	£17	
	a. Value omitted		
16	1 a. on 20 par. carm. (No. N44)	£90	
17	2 a. on 1 pias. ultram. (T **30**) (R.)	£5	£5
18	2 a. on 1 pias. dull blue (No. 218) (R.)	£7	£7

(*f*) *Stamps with similar opt., but date between Star and Crescent* (*Nos.* 19 *and* 22, *T* **54**; *others T* **57**).

19	½ a. on 10 par. grey-green (No. 248) (R.)	80 0	80 0
	a. "OCCUPATION" omitted ..	£100	
20	½ a. on 10 par. carm. (T **56**) (B.)	£8	£8
21	1 a. on 20 par. rose (T **30**)	80 0	80 0
22	1 a. on 20 par. rose (No. 320)	£12	£12
23	1 a. on 10 par. on 20 par. claret (T **16**)	£10	£10
	a. "OCCUPATION" omitted ..		

No.	Description	Unused	Used
24	2 a. on 1 pias. ultram. (T **30**) (R.)	£7	£7
	a. "OCCUPATION" omitted ..		
	b. "BAGHDAD" omitted ..		
25	2 a. on 1 pias. ultram. (No. 323)	£40	

The last group (*f*) have the Crescent obliterated in violet-black ink, as this included the inscription, "Tax for the relief of children of martyrs."

MOSUL. (MESOPOTAMIA.)

POSTAGE

I.E.F. 'D'

1 Anna (1) **4** I (*normal*). **4** II (*small* "4").

1919 (Feb.). *Turkish Fiscal stamps surcharged as T* **1**, *in black. P* 12½ (*except* ½ *a., P* 11½ *and* 1 *a., P* 12).

(*a*) Central design shows large "toughra" or sign-manual of El Ghazi 7 mm. high.

(*b*) Smaller "toughra" of Sultan Rechad 5½ mm. high.

No.	Description	Unused	Used
1	½ a. on 1 pi. green and red ..	0 6	0 8
2	1 a. on 20 paras, blk./*red* (*a*) ..	0 8	0 8
2*a*	1 a. on 20 paras, blk./*red* (*b*) ..	6 0	4 6
	b. Imperf. between (pair) ..	£6	
3	2½ a. on 1 pi. mauve & yell. (*b*)	1 0	1 0
	a. No bar to fraction	35 0	35 0
4	3 a. on 20 par. green (*a*) ..	1 6	1 9
5	3 a. on 20 par. grn. & orge. (*b*)	35 0	40 0
6	4 a. on 1 pi. dark violet (*a*) (I)	3 0	3 0
	a. "4" omitted		
	b. Small "4" (II)	3 0	3 0
7	8 a. on 10 par. lake (*a*) ..	4 0	4 6
	a. Surcharge inverted		
	b. Surcharge double	£10	£10
	c. No comma after "D" ..	30 0	
	d. Inverted. No comma after "D"		
	e. Error. 8 a. on 1 pi. dark violet	£16	

IRELAND (IRISH FREE STATE).

See EIRE.

JAMAICA.

(*For British stamps used in Jamaica see under* Great Britain.)

PRINTERS.—*All the stamps of Jamaica were typographed by De La Rue & Co. unless otherwise stated.*

The official dates of issue are given, where known, but where definite information is not available the dates are those of earliest known use, etc.

1

2

3 4 5 6

7

A

PRICES.—The prices for the issue of 1860–63 are for good average copies. Fine well-centred copies are worth considerably more in most cases.

1860 (23 Nov.)–**1863**. *W* **7**. *P* 14.

No.	Type	Description	Unused	Used
1	**1**	1d. pale blue	45 0	10 0
		a. Pale greenish blue ..	55 0	17 6
		b. Blue	35 0	6 6
		c. Deep blue	60 0	20 0
		d. Bisected (½d.) Nov., (61)	—	£15
2	**2**	2d. rose	60 0	20 0
		a. Deep rose	67 6	25 0
3	**3**	3d. green (10.9.63)	50 0	12 6
4	**4**	4d. brown-orange	£10	25 0
		a. Red-orange	£10	22 6
5	**5**	6d. dull lilac	£10	20 0
		a. Grey-purple	£10	20 0
		b. Deep purple	£25	40 0
6	**6**	1s. yellow-brown	£15	25 0
		a. Purple-brown	£10	22 6
		b. Dull brown	£8	20 0
	A	c. "$" for "S" in "SHILLING" ..	£50	£25

The diagonal bisection of the 1d. was authorised by a P.O. notice dated 20 Nov., 1861. Specimens are only of value when on original envelope or wrapper. The authority was withdrawn as from 1 Dec., 1872. Fakes are frequently met with. Other bisections were unauthorised.

The so-called "dollar variety" of the 1s. occurs once in each sheet of stamps in all shades and in later colours, etc., on the second stamp in the second row of the left upper pane. The prices quoted above are for the dull brown shade, the prices for the other shades being proportionate to their normal value.

All values except the 3d. are known imperf., mint only.

There are two types of watermark in the 3d. and 1s., one being short and squat and the other elongated.

8

9

10

1870–83. *Wmk. Crown CC.* (*a*) *P* 14.

No.	Type	Description	Unused	Used
7	8	½d. claret (29.10.72)	7 6	2 0
		a. Deep claret (1883)	10 0	3 0
8	1	1d. blue (20.8.73)	27 6	1 9
		a. Deep blue	35 0	2 0
9	2	2d. rose (April, '70)	35 0	0 10
		a. Deep rose	40 0	1 0
10	3	3d. green (1.3.70)	90 0	10 0
11	4	4d. brown-orange (1872) ..	90 0	12 6
		a. Red-orange	£10	10 0
12	5	6d. mauve (10.3.71) ..	30 0	7 6
13	6	1s. dull brn. (to deep)(23.2.73)	20 0	8 0
	A	a. "$" for "S" in "SHILLING"	£25	£12
		(*b*) *P* 12½.		
14	9	2s. Venetian red (27.8.75)	10 0	10 0
15	10	5s. lilac (27.8.75)	55 0	55 0

The ½d., 1d., 4d., 2s. and 5s. are known imperforate.

1883–97. *Wmk. Crown CA.* *P* 14.

No.	Type	Description	Unused	Used
16	8	½d. yellow-green (1885) ..	0 8	0 6
		a. Green	0 6	0 3
17	1	1d. blue (1884)	60 0	2 6
18	1	1d. rose (to deep) (3.3.85) ..	20 0	1 6
		a. Carmine	10 0	1 0
19	2	2d. rose (to deep) (17.3.84)	55 0	4 0
20	,,	2d. grey (1885)	35 0	1 6
		a. Slate	20 0	1 3
21	3	3d. sage-green (1886) ..	3 6	1 3
		a. Pale olive-green	3 0	1 0
22	4	4d. red-orange* (9.3.83) ..	£18	10 0
		a. Red-brown (shades) ..	5 0	1 3
23	5	6d. deep yellow (4.10.90) ..	15 0	7 6
		a. Orange-yellow	12 0	7 6
24	6	1s. brn. (to deep) (Mar. '97)	10 0	7 6
		a. Chocolate	20 0	10 6
	A	b. "$" for "S" in "SHILLING"	£20	£15
25	9	2s. Venetian red (1897) ..	25 0	20 0
26	10	5s. lilac (1897)	40 0	40 0

* No. 22 is the same colour as No. 11*a*.

The 1d. carmine, 2d. slate, and 2s. are known imperf. All values to the 6d. inclusive are known perf. 12. These are proofs.

11

TWO PENCE
HALF-PENNY
(12)

1889–91. *Value tablet in second colour. Wmk. Crown CA. P* 14.

No.	Type	Description	Unused	Used
27	11	1d. purple & mve. (8.3.89)	0 8	0 1
28	,,	2d. green (8.3.89)	3 6	2 6
		a. Deep green (brown gum) ..	3 0	3 6
29	,,	2½d. dull pur. & blue (25.2.91)	4 6	1 0

A very wide range of shades may be found in the 1d. The head-plate was printed in many shades of purple, and the duty-plate in various shades of mauve and purple and also in carmine, etc. The variations in the other values are not so numerous nor so pronounced.

(Surcharged by C. Vendryes, Kingston.)

1890 (4 (?) JUNE). *No.* 22*a surch. with T* **12.**

No.	Type	Description	Unused	Used
30	4	2½d. on 4d. red-brown ..	10 6	9 0
		a. Spacing between lines of surcharge 1½ mm. ..	25 0	20 0
		b. Surcharge double	£8	95 0
		c. "PFNNY" for "PENNY"	45 0	45 0
		d. "PFNNF" ("F" for "E" and broken "K" for "Y"	95 0	80 0

This provisional was issued pending receipt of No. 29 which is listed above for convenience of reference.

Three settings exist. (1) Ten varieties arranged in a single vertical row and repeated six times in the pane. (2) Twelve varieties, in two horizontal rows of six, repeated five times, alternate rows show 1 m. and 1½ mm. spacing between lines of surcharge. (3) Three varieties, arranged horizontally and repeated twenty times. All these settings can be reconstructed by examination of the spacing and relative position of the words of the surcharge and of the broken letters, etc., which are numerous.

A variety reading "PFNNK", with the "K" unbroken, is a forgery.

Varieties c. and d. may be found in the double surcharge.

Surcharges misplaced either horizontally or vertically are met with, the normal position being central at the foot of the stamp with "HALF-PENNY" covering the old value.

13. Llandovery Falls, Jamaica, from a photograph by Dr. James Johnston.

(Engraved and recess-printed by De La Rue & Co.)

1900–1. *Wmk. Crown CC* (*sideways*). *P* 14.

No.	Type	Description	Unused	Used
31	13	1d. red (1.5.00)	2 6	0 6
32	,,	1d. slate-blk. & red (25.9.01)	2 0	0 4
		a. Blued paper	15 0	15 0
		b. Imperf. between (pair) ..		

Many shades exist of both centre and frame of the bi-coloured 1d. which was, of course, printed from two plates, and the design shows minor differences from that of the 1d. red which was printed from a single plate.

14. Arms of Jamaica.

1903–4. *Wmk. Crown CA. P* 14.

33 **14** ½d. grey & dull grn. (16.11.03) 1 6 0 4
a. "SER.ET" for "SERVIET" 25 0 25 0

34 ,, 1d. grey & carm. (24.2.04) .. 1 0 0 3
a. "SER.ET" for "SERVIET" 22 6 22 6

35 ,, 2½d. grey & ultram. (16.11.03) 4 0 1 9
a. "SER.ET" for "SERVIET" 40 0 45 0

36 ,, 5d. grey & yellow (1.3.04) .. 17 6 20 0
a. "SER.ET" for "SERVIET" £40

The "SER.ET" variety occurs once in each sheet of stamps on the second stamp in the fourth row of the left upper pane.

The centres of the above and later bi-coloured stamps in the Arms type vary in colour from grey to grey-black.

1905–11. *Wmk. Mult. Crown CA. P* 14.

37 **14** ½d. grey and dull green, C (24.11.05) 1 9 0 4
a. "SER.ET" for "SERVIET" 22 6 22 6

38 ,, 1d. grey & carm., C (20.11.05) 4 0 0 4

39 ,, 2½d. grey & ultramarine, C (12.11.07) 5 0 2 6

40 ,, 2½d. pale ultram., O (21.9.10) 4 0 3 0
a. *Deep ultramarine*, O .. 4 0 2 6

41 ,, 5d. grey & orange-yellow, C (24.4.07) 35 0 35 0
a. "SER.ET" for "SERVIET" £50 £60

42 ,, 6d. dull & bright purple, C (18.8.11) 6 0 7 6

43 ,, 5s. grey & vio., C (Nov. '05) 30 0 25 0

See note above *re* grey centres.

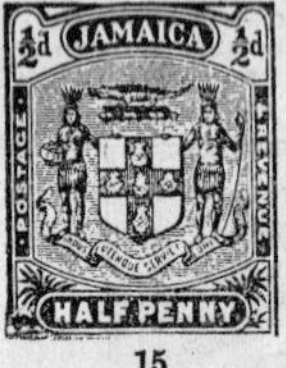

15

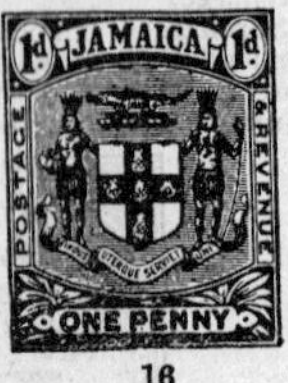

16

Arms type redrawn.

1906. *Wmk. Mult. Crown CA. P* 41.

44 **15** ½d. yellow-grn., O (8.11.06) 0 6 0 1
a. *Dull green* 0 6 0 1
b. *Deep green* 0 4 0 1

45 **16** 1d. carmine, O (1.10.06) .. 0 6 0 1

Queen Victoria types.

1905–11. *Wmk. Mult. Crown, CA. P* 14.

46 **3** 3d. olive-green, O (15.5.05).. 5 0 1 3
a. *Sage-green*, O (1907) .. 5 0 1 3

47 ,, 3d. purple/*yell.*, O (10.3.10) 8 6 6 0
a. *Pale pur./yell.*, C (11.7.10) .. 3 6 3 0

48 **4** 4d. red-brown, O (6.6.08) .. 50 0 42 6

49 ,, 4d. black/*yellow*, C (21.9.10) 27 6 30 0

50 ,, 4d. red/*yellow*, O (3.10.11) .. 2 6 3 0

51 **5** 6d. dull orange, O (27.6.06).. 25 0 15 0
a. *Golden yellow*, O (Sept., '09) 22 6 17 6

52 ,, 6d. lilac, O (19.11.09) .. 10 0 10 6
a. *Purple*, C (July, '10) .. 7 6 7 6

53 **6** 1s. brown, O (Nov. '06) .. 12 0 10 0
a. *Deep brown*, O 15 0 10 0
A b. "$" for "S" in "SHILLING" £30 £25

54 **6** 1s. black/*green*, C (21.9.10).. 15 0 16 0
A a. "$" for "S" in "SHILLING" £20 £20

55 **9** 2s. Venetian red, O (Nov. '08) 70 0 75 0

56 ,, 2s. purple/*blue*, C (21.9.10).. 15 0 12 6

17

18

King Edward VII.

1911 (3 Feb.). *Wmk. Mult. Crown CA. P* 14.

57 **17** 2d. grey, O 3 6 4 0

King George V.

1912–20. *Wmk. Mult. Crown CA. P* 14.

58 **18** 1d. carmine-red, O (5.12.12) 0 8 0 1
a. *Scarlet*, O (1916) 0 6 0 1

59 ,, 1½d. brn.-orge., O (13.7.16).. 3 0 0 3
a. *Yellow-orange*, O 4 0 0 3

60 ,, 2d. grey, O (2.8.12) .. 3 0 1 9
a. *Slate-grey*, O 3 0 2 0

61 ,, 2½d. blue, O (13.2.13) .. 3 0 1 3
a. *Deep bright blue*, O .. 2 6 1 3

62 ,, 3d. purple/*yellow*, C (6.3.12) 5 0 0 9
a. *White back*, C (2.4.13) .. 3 0 1 6
b. *On lemon*, C (25.9.16) .. 10 0 1 3

63 ,, 4d. blk. & red/*yell.*, C (4.4.13) 4 6 2 0
a. *White back*, C (7.5.14) .. 4 6 5 0
b. *On lemon*, C (1916) .. 40 0 40 0
c. *On pale yellow*, C (1919) .. 10 0 6 6

64 ,, 6d. dull and bright purple, C (14.11.12) 8 6 3 0
a. *Dull purple and bright mauve*, C (1915) 8 6 2 0
b. *Dull purple and bright magenta*, C (1920) .. 6 0 2 0

65 ,, 1s. black/*green*, C (2.8.12).. 10 0 4 6
a. *White back*, C (4.1.15) .. 10 0 10 0
b. *On blue-grn., olive back*, C ('20) 10 0 10 0

66 ,, 2s. pur. & bright blue/*blue*, C (10.1.19) 22 6 25 0

67 ,, 5s. grn. & red/*yellow*, C (5.9.19) 60 0 60 0
a. *On pale yellow*, C 50 0 55 0
b. *On orange-buff*, C 52 6 55 0

For the ½d. in this design and the 6d. with Script wmk. see Nos. 107 and 90.

The paper of No. 67 is a bright yellow and the gum rough and dull. No. 67*a* is on practically the normal creamy "pale yellow" paper, and the gum is smooth and shiny. The paper of No. 67*b* approaches the "coffee" colour of the true "orange-buff," and the colours of both head and frame are paler, the latter being of a carmine tone.

WAR STAMP.	WAR STAMP.	WAR STAMP.
(19)	(20)	(21)

(Overprinted locally.)

1916 (1 April–Sept.). *Overprinted with T* **19.**

68 **15** ½ d. yellow-green 0 4 0 3
a. No stop after "STAMP" .. 10 0 10 0
b. Overprint double 90 0 90 0
c. Overprint inverted .. . 70 0 70 0
d *Blue-green* 0 6 0 4
da. No stop after "STAMP" .. 10 0 10 0

69 **18** 3d. purple/*yell.* (white back) 5 0 6 0
a. *On lemon* (June, '16) .. 2 6 3 6
aa. No stop after "STAMP" .. 20 0 22 6
b. *On pale yellow* (Sept., '16) .. 2 6 3 6

Minor varieties: ½d. (i) Small "P"; (ii) Space between "W" and "A"; (iii) "WARISTAMP" (raised quad between words); (iv) Two stops after "STAMP." 3d. "WARISTAMP."

Note.—The above and succeeding stamps with

"WAR STAMP" overprint were issued for payment of a special war tax on letters and postcards or on parcels. Ordinary unoverprinted stamps could also be used for this purpose.

1916 (Sept.–Dec.). *Overprinted with T* **20**.

No.	Type	Description	Unused	Used
70	15	½d. blue-green (*shades*) (2.10.16)	0 3	0 3
		a. No stop after "STAMP" ..	10 0	10 0
		b. Overprint omitted (in pair)	£12	£12
		c. "R" inserted by hand ..	£10	£10
71	18	1½d. orange (1.9.16) ..	0 5	0 2
		a. No stop after "STAMP"	10 0	10 0
		b. "S" in "STAMP" omitd.	£5	£5
		c. "S" inserted by hand ..	80 0	
		d. "R" in "WAR" omitted	£12	£12
		e. "R" inserted by hand ..	£10	£10
		f. Inverted "d" for "P" ..	£6	£6
72	"	3d. purple/*lemon* (2.10.16)	2 0	1 9
		aa. Overprint inverted ..	£15	
		a. No stop after "STAMP"	20 0	20 0
		b. "S" in "STAMP" omitd.	£12	£12
		c. "S" inserted by hand ..	£8	£8
		d. "S" inserted inverted ..	£12	£12
		e. *On yellow* (Dec., '16) ..	12 6	12 6
		ea. "S" in "STAMP" omitd.	£12	£12
		eb. "S" inserted by hand ..	£12	£12
		ec. "S" inserted inverted ..	£15	£15

Minor varieties such as raised quads, small stop, double stop, spaced letters and letters of different sizes also exist in this overprint.

1917 (March). *Overprinted with T* **21**.

No.	Type	Description	Unused	Used
73	15	½d. blue-green (*shades*) (25.3.17)	0 2	0 1
		a. No stop after "STAMP"	7 6	7 6
		b. Stop inserted and "P" impressed a second time ..	£12	
		c. Overprinted on back only..	60 0	
		d. Overprint inverted ..	15 0	15 0
74	18	1½d. orange (3.3.17) ..	0 3	0 1
		a. No stop after "STAMP"	10 0	10 0
		b. Stop inserted and "P" impressed a second time ..	£12	
		c. Overprint double ..	£7	£8
		d. Overprint inverted ..	£8	£10
75	"	3d. purple/*yellow* (3.3.17)	1 0	1 3
		a. No stop after "STAMP"	15 0	17 6
		b. Stop inserted and "P" impressed a second time ..	£15	
		c. Overprint inverted ..	£10	
		d. Overprint sideways (reading up)	£25	

There are numerous minor varieties in this overprint.

WAR STAMP

(22)

(Overprinted by De La Rue & Co.)

1919 (4 Oct.). *Overprinted with T* **22**.

No.	Type	Description	Unused	Used
76	15	½d. green (R.)	0 2	0 2
77	18	3d. purple/*yellow* (R.) ..	1 6	1 3
		a. Pale purple/buff (R.) ..	1 0	1 0
		b. Deep purple/buff (R.) ..	5 0	4 0

We list the most distinct variations in the 3d. The buff tone of the paper varies considerably in depth.

23. Jamaica Exhibition, 1891.

24. Arawak woman preparing cassava.

26. King's House, Spanish Town.

25. War contingent embarking.

27. Return of war contingent.

INVERTED NORMAL

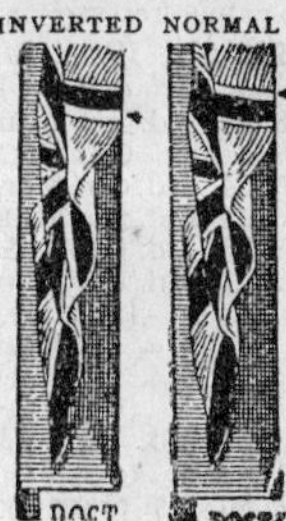

A B

28. Landing of Columbus.

29. Cathedral, Spanish Town.

30. Statue of Queen Victoria.

31. Admiral Rodney memorial.

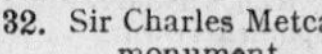

32. Sir Charles Metcalfe monument.

33. Jamaican scenery.

34

(The ½d. and 1d. typographed and the other values recess-printed by De La Rue & Co.)

1919–21. *Wmk. Mult. Crown CA (sideways on 1d., 1½d. and 10s.). P 14.*

No.	Type	Description	s.	d.	s.	d.
78	**23**	½d. green and olive-green, C (12.11.20)	0	3	0	3
79	**24**	1d. car. & orge., C (3.10.21)	0	10	0	1
80	**25**	1½d. grn. (shades) (4.7.19) ..	1	0	0	1
81	**26**	2d. indigo & grn. (18.2.21)	2	6	2	6
82	**27**	2½d. deep blue and blue (A) (18.2.21)	5	0	4	0
		a. Blue-black and deep blue (A)	3	0	1	3
83	**28**	3d. myrtle-grn. & blue (8.4.21)	2	6	0	4
84	**29**	4d. brn. & deep green (21.1.21)	6	6	6	6
85	**30**	1s. orange-yellow and red-orange (10.12.20) ..	15	0	15	0
		a. Frame inverted	£375		£275	
86	**31**	2s. light blue and brown (10.12.20)	22	6	20	0
87	**32**	3s. violet-blue and orange (10.12.20)	55	0	60	0
88	**33**	5s. blue and yellow-orange (15.4.21)	40	0	42	6
		a. Blue and pale dull orange ..	42	6	47	6
89	**34**	10s. myrtle-grn. (6.5.20) ..	65	0	70	0

The 2½d. of the above series showed the Union Jack at left incorrectly as indicated in Illustration A. In the issue on paper with Script wmk. the design was corrected (Illustration B).

A 6d. stamp illustrating the abolition of slavery was prepared and sent out in April, 1921, but for political reasons was not issued and the stock was destroyed. "SPECIMEN" copies are known on both the Mult. CA and Script CA papers, and are worth about £25 each.

1921 (21 Oct.). *Wmk. Mult. Script CA. P 14.*

No.	Type	Description	s.	d.	s.	d.
90	**18**	6d. dull pur. & bt. mag., C	4	6	2	3

35. "POSTAGE & REVENUE" added.

36. Port Royal in 1853.

(Printing as before; the 6d. recess-printed.)

1921–29. *Wmk. Mult. Script CA (sideways on 1d. and 1½d.). P 14.*

No.	Type	Description	s.	d.	s.	d.
91	**23**	½d. grn. & olive-green, C (5.2.22)	0	4	0	1
		a. Green and deep olive-grn., C	0	6	0	1
92	**35**	1d. carmine and orange, C (5.12.22)	0	6	0	1
93	**25**	1½d. grn. (*shades*) (2.2.21)	1	0	0	1
94	**26**	2d. indigo & grn. (4.11.21)	2	0	0	3
		a. Indigo and grey-green ('25)	1	6	0	3
95	**27**	2½d. deep blue and blue (4.11.21) (B)	2	6	0	6
		a. Dull blue and blue (B) ..	1	9	0	4
96	**28**	3d. myrtle-green and blue (6.3.22)	1	9	0	2
		a. Green and pale blue ..	1	6	0	1
97	**29**	4d. brn. & dp. grn. (5.12.21)	2	6	0	8
		a. Chocolate and dull green ..	1	9	0	4
98	**36**	6d. black & blue (5.12.22)	12	6	1	0
		a. Grey and dull blue ..	10	6	1	0
99	**30**	1s. orange and red-orange (4.11.21)	6	6	1	3
		a. Orange-yell. and brn.-orange	6	6	1	0
100	**31**	2s. light blue and brown (5.2.22)	8	6	3	
101	**32**	3s. violet-blue and orange (23.8.21)	35	0	15	0
102	**33**	5s. blue and yellow-brown (8.11.23)	50	0	30	0
		a. Blue and pale dull orange ..	75	0	60	0
		b. Blue and yellow-orange ('27)	30	0	30	0
		c. Blue and pale bistre-brown (1929)	25	0	27	6
103	**34**	10s. myrtle-green (Mar. (?) '22)	45	0	50	0

The frame of No. 102*a* is the same colour as that of No. 88*a*.

The designs of all values of the pictorial series, with the exception of the 5s. and 10s. (which originated with the Governor, Sir Leslie Probyn), were selected by Mr. F. C. Cundall, F.S.A. The 1d. and 5s. were drawn by Miss Cundall, the 3d. by Mrs. Cundall, and the 10s. by De La Rue & Co. The 6d. is from a lithograph. The other designs are from photographs, the frames of all being the work of Miss Cundall and Miss Wood.

37

Designs from photos by Miss Violet F. Taylor. Frames designed by Mr. F. C. Cundall, F.S.A., and drawn by Miss Cundall. Engraved and recess-printed by Bradbury, Wilkinson & Co.)

1923 (1 Nov.). *Child Welfare. Wmk. Mult. Script CA. P* 12.

104	**37**	½d.+½d. black and green	7	6	15	0
105	–	1d.+½d. black and scarlet	7	6	15	0
106	–	2½d.+½d. black and blue	35	0	45	0

The designs of the two higher values are as Type **37** but with pictures of other children.

These stamps were sold at a premium of ½d. for the benefit of the Child Welfare League. They were on sale annually from 1 November to 31 January, until 31 January, 1927, when their sale ceased and the remainders were destroyed on 21 February, 1927.

Labels bearing a red cross and an aeroplane, with or without the inscription "JAMAICA" or "JAMAICA Half penny" were sold by the Jamaica Patriotic Stamp League in aid of various war-time funds. Their use on correspondence was not forbidden and they are frequently found postmarked, but they performed no postal function.

1927 (Nov.). *Wmk. Mult. Script CA. P* 14.

107	**18**	½d. green, O	0	1	0	1

40

41

42

Die I

Die II

(Recess-printed by Messrs. De La Rue & Co.)

1929–32. *Wmk. Mult. Script CA. P* 14.

108	**40**	1d. scarlet (Die I)	0	6	0	1
		a. Die II (1932)	0	4	0	1
109	**41**	1½d. chocolate	1	0	0	2
110	**42**	9d. marone	3	6	1	9

In Die I the shading below JAMAICA is formed of thickened parallel lines, and in Die II of diagonal cross-hatching.

43. Coco Palms at Columbus Cove.

44. Wag Water River, St. Andrew.

45. Priestman's River, Portland.

(Dies engraved and recess-printed by Messrs. Waterlow & Sons, Ltd.)

1932. *Wmk. Mult. Script CA. P* 12½.

111	**43**	2d. black and green ..	0	10	0	10
112	**44**	2½d. greenish blue & ultram.	1	3	1	0
113	**45**	6d. grey-black & purple	3	6	2	6

1935 (6 May). *Silver Jubilee. As T* **13** *of Antigua, inscr.* "JAMAICA". *Recess. B.W. & Co. Wmk. Mult. Script CA. P* 11×12.

114	1d. deep blue and scarlet ..	0	6	0	3
115	1½d. ultramarine & grey-black	1	0	0	10
116	6d. green and indigo ..	7	6	8	6
117	1s. slate and purple ..	12	6	12	6

The 1½d., 6d. and 1s. exist with the "double flagstaff" variety.

POSTAL FISCALS.

Revenue stamps were authorised for postal use by Post Office notice of 12 *October,* 1887.

F 1

(Typographed by De La Rue & Co.)

1860–73 (Issued). *P* 14.

(*a*) *Wmk. Pineapple* (*T* 7).

F1	**F 1**	1d. rose (1860 ?)	65	0	65	0
		a. Imperf.				

(*b*) *Wmk. Crown CC.*

F2	**F 1**	1d. rose (1868 or earlier) ..	10	0	12	6

(*c*) *Wmk. CA over Crown* (*T w.* 7 *sideways, covering two stamps*).

F3	**F 1**	1d. rose (1873 or earlier) ..	5	0	2	6
		a. Imperf.				

F 2

F 3

(Typographed by De La Rue & Co.)

1855–74 (Issued). *Glazed paper.* P 14.

(*a*) *No wmk.*

No.	Type	Description	Unused	Used
F4	F 2	1½d. blue/*blue* (1857)	20 0	22 6
		a. Imperf. (1855)		
		b. *Blue on white*	32 6	32 6
F5	,,	3d. purple/*blue* (1857)	32 6	35 0
		a. Imperf. (1855)		
		b. *Purple on lilac* (1857)	16 0	16 0
		ba. Imperf. (1855)		
		c. *Purple on white* (1857)	20 0	20 0

(*b*) *Wmk. Crown CC.*

No.	Type	Description	Unused	Used
F6	F 2	3d. purple/*lilac* (1874)	2 6	4 6

All the above stamps *imperf.* are exceedingly rare postally used.

1858 (1 Jan.) (Issued). *No wmk.* P 15½ × 15.

No.	Type	Description	Unused	Used
F7	F 3	1s. rose/*bluish*	27 6	37 6
F8	,,	5s. lilac/*bluish*	65 0	£6
F9	,,	10s. green/*bluish*	65 0	£6

Telegraph stamps were also used postally, but no authority was given for such use.

OFFICIAL STAMPS.

OFFICIAL

(O 1)

(Overprinted by C. Vendryes, Kingston.)

1890 (1 April). *No.* 16 *overprinted with Type* O1.

(*a*) "OFFICIAL" 17 *to* 17½ *mm. long.*

No.	Type	Description	Unused	Used
O1	8	½d. green	1 6	1 0
		a. "O" omitted		
		b. One "I" omitted		
		c. Both "I"s omitted	£6	130 0
		d. "L" omitted	—	£25
		e. Overprint inverted	40 0	40 0
		f. Overprint double	40 0	30 0
		g. Overprint double, one inverted		
		h. Overprint double, one vert.	£30	
		j. Pair, overprints tête-bêche		

(*b*) "OFFICIAL" 15 *to* 16 *mm. long.*

No.	Type	Description	Unused	Used
O2	8	½d. green	10 0	10 0
		a. Overprint double	£30	

There were four (or possibly five) settings of this overprint, all but one being of the longer type. There are numerous minor varieties, due to broken type, etc. (*e.g.* a broken "E" used for "F"), and with sufficient material the settings can be reconstructed.

Stamps with the long local overprint were reissued in 1894 during a temporary shortage of No. O3.

OFFICIAL

(O 2)

(Overprinted by De La Rue & Co.)

1890–91. *Overprinted with* T O 2. *Wmk. Crown CA.* P 14.

No.	Type	Description	Unused	Used
O3	8	½d. green (1891)	1 0	0 3
O4	11	1d. rose (1.4.90)	1 0	0 3
O5	,,	2d. grey (1.4.90)	1 0	0 6

KENYA, UGANDA AND TANGANYIKA.

For earlier issues see "British East Africa" and "Uganda."

For the issues of the Mandated Territory of Tanganyika and the war-time issues that preceded them see "Tanganyika."

PRINTERS. All the stamps listed below were printed by Messrs. De La Rue & Co., and were typographed unless otherwise stated.

1

2

1903–4. T 1. *Wmk. Crown CA.* P 14.

No.	Description	Unused	Used
1	½ a. green	3 0	3 0
2	1 a. grey and red	2 0	1 6
3	2 a. dull & bright purple	8 0	10 0
4	2½ a. blue	10 0	10 6
5	3 a. brown-purple & green	15 0	17 6
6	4 a. grey-green and black	8 6	10 0
7	5 a. grey & orange-brown	25 0	25 0
8	8 a. grey and pale blue	22 6	22 6

T 2. *Wmk. Crown CC.* P 14.

No.	Description	Unused	Used
9	1 r. green, OC	10 0	10 0
10	2 r. dull & bright purple, O	30 0	25 0
11	3 r. grey-green & black, O	40 0	40 0
12	4 r. grey & emer.-green, O	50 0	50 0
13	5 r. grey and red, O	55 0	60 0
14	10 r. grey and ultramarine, OC	£8	£9
15	20 r. grey and stone, O	£25	£25
16	50 r. grey and red-brown, O	£40	£35

1904. T 1. *Wmk. Mult. Crown CA.* P 14.

No.	Description	Unused	Used
17	½ a. grey-green, OC	1 0	0 8
18	1 a. grey and red, OC	0 9	0 4
19	2 a. dull & bright purple, OC	3 6	3 0
20	2½ a. blue, O	10 6	10 0
20*a*	2½ a. ultramarine & blue, O	6 6	7 6
21	3 a. brown-pur. & green, OC	6 0	6 6
22	4 a. grey-green & black, OC	5 0	5 0
23	5 a. grey & orge.-brown, OC	6 0	7 6
24	8 a. grey and pale blue, OC	8 0	9 0

1906–07. *T* 2. *P* 14.

No.	Description	Unused		Used	
25	1 r. green, C (*fisc. canc.* 1/–)	10	6	8	6
26	2 r. dull & brt. pur., C (1906)	20	0	15	0
27	3 r. grey-green & black, C ..	35	0	35	0
28	4 r. grey & emer-.grn, C ..	40	0	45	0
29	5 r. grey and red, C	45	0	50	0
30	10 r. grey and ultramarine, C	£10		£12	
31	20 r. grey and stone, C ..	£25		£30	
32	50 r. grey and red-brown, C ..	£45		£50	

1907–08. *T* 1, *but value expressed in "cents" instead of "annas." Wmk. Mult. Crown CA. P* 14.

No.	Description	Unused		Used	
33	1 c. brown, O (1908) ..	0	4	0	1
34	3 c. grey-green, O	0	8	0	3
34*a*	3 c. blue-green, O	0	8	0	6
35	6 c. red, O	2	0	0	3
36	10 c. lilac & pale olive, C ..	3	6	3	0
37	12 c. dull & bright purple, C	4	0	3	0
38	15 c. bright blue, O	6	0	3	6
39	25 c. grey-green & black, C ..	6	0	3	6
40	50 c. grey-grn. & orge.-brn., C	10	0	10	6
41	75 c. grey & pale blue, C ('08)	10	6	10	6

Original

Redrawn

1910. *T* 1 *redrawn. Printed from a single plate. Wmk. Mult. Crown CA. P* 14.

No.	Description	Unused		Used	
42	6 c. red, O	0	8	0	3

In the redrawn type a fine white line has been cut around the value tablets and above the name tablet separating the latter from the leaves above. East Africa and Uganda is in shorter and thicker letters and Protectorates in taller letters than in No. 35.

3

4

1912–22. *T* 3 *and* 4 (*rupee values*). *Wmk. Mult. Crown CA. P* 14.

No.	Description	Unused		Used	
43	1 c. black, O	0	2	0	1
44	3 c. green, O	0	6	0	1
44*a*	3 c. deep blue-grn., O (1917)	0	6	0	3
45	6 c. red, O	0	6	0	1
45*a*	6 c. scarlet, O (1917) ..	0	6	0	1
45*b*	10 c. yellow-orange, O ..	2	0	0	2
46	10 c. orange, O (1921) ..	1	6	0	2
47	12 c. slate-grey, O	1	6	1	0
48	15 c. bright blue, O	2	0	1	0
49	25 c. black & red/*yellow*, C ..	3	6	1	6
	a. White back	1	9	2	0
	b. On lemon (1916)	15	0	3	0
	c. On orange-buff (1921) ..	32	6	6	6
	d. On pale yellow (1921) ..	4	0	3	0
50	50 c. black and lilac, C ..	4	0	2	0
51	75 c. black/*green*, C	6	6	4	6
	a. White back	5	0	5	0
	b. On blue-green, olive back ..	22	6	7	6
	c. On emerald surface	£10		£10	
	d. On emerald back	6	0	6	6
52	1 r. black/*green*, C	7	6	4	0
	a. On emerald back	15	0	12	0
53	2 r. red and black/*blue*, C ..	12	6	10	0
54	3 r. violet and green, C ..	20	0	17	6
55	4 r. red & green/*yellow*, C ..	30	0	22	0
	a. On pale yellow	35	0		
56	5 r. blue and dull purple, C	32	6	27	6
57	10 r. red and green/*green*, C ..	50	0	32	6
58	20 r. black & purple/*red*, C ..	£10		£6	
58*a*	20 r. purple & blue/*blue*, C ('18)	£8		£6	
59	50 r. carmine and green, C ..	£20		£20	
60	100 r. purple & black/*red*, C ..	£65		£65	
61	500 r. green & red/*green*, C ..	£275		£275	

4

cents

(5)

1919. *T* 3 *surcharged with T* 5, *in black.*

No.	Description	Unused		Used	
62	4 c. on 6 c. scarlet	0	3	0	3
	a. Bars omitted	30	0		
	b. Surcharge double	£6			
	c. Surcharge inverted	£6			
	d. Surcharge omitted (in pair) ..	£15			

1921–22. *T* 3 *and* 4. *Wmk. Mult. Script CA. P* 14.

No.	Description	Unused		Used	
63	1 c. black, O	0	4	0	4
64	3 c. green, O	0	4	0	4
65	3 c. blue-green, O	1	0	0	4
66	6 c. carmine-red, O	0	6	0	2
67	10 c. orange, O	0	9	0	2
68	12 c. slate-grey, O	2	6	3	0
69	15 c. bright blue, O	2	0	2	6
71	50 c. black & dull purple, C ..	8	6	8	6
73	2 r. red and black/*blue*, C ..	17	6	20	0
74	3 r. violet and green, C ..	27	6	30	0
76	5 r. blue and dull purple, C	45	0	47	6
77	50 r. carmine and green, C ..	£80		£80	

6

7

1922. *T* 6 (*cent values*) *and* 7. *Wmk. Mult. Script CA* (*sideways on T* 7). *P* 14.

No.	Description	Unused		Used	
78	1 c. pale brown	0	2	0	2
79	1 c. deep brown	0	3	0	3
80	5 c. dull violet	0	4	0	1
81	5 c. bright violet	0	6	0	1

82	10 c. green	0 7	0 2
83	12 c. jet-black	7 6	8 0
84	12 c. grey-black	4 0	4 6
85	15 c. rose-carmine	0 9	0 2
86	20 c. dull orange-yellow	1 0	0 2
87	20 c. bright orange	1 0	0 2
88	30 c. ultramarine	1 3	0 4
89	50 c. grey	2 0	0 4
90	75 c. olive	4 0	3 6
91	1s. green, C	4 6	1 6
92	2s. dull purple, C	6 0	4 6
93	3s. brownish grey, C	10 0	5 6
93*a*	3s. jet-black, C	20 0	20 0
94	5s. carmine-red, C	18 6	10 0
95	10s. bright blue, C	37 6	30 0
96	£1 black and orange, C	75 0	77 6
97	£5 black and blue, C	£12	£15
98	£10 black and green, C	£20	£25
99	£25 black and red, C	£50	£60
100	£50 black and brown, C	£100	£110

1925–27. *T* **6** *and* **7**. *New colours and values. Wmk. Mult. Script CA. P* 14.

100*a*	5 c. green	0 4	0 1
100*b*	10 c. black	0 8	0 1
101	2s. 50 c. brown, C	10 0	10 0
102	4s. grey, C	17 6	20 0
103	7s. 50 c. orange-yellow, C	35 0	37 6
104	£2 green and purple, C	£12	£14
105	£3 purple and yellow, C	£14	£15
106	£4 black and magenta, C	£15	£18
107	£20 red and green, C	£45	£50
108	£75 purple and grey, C	£150	£160
109	£100 red and black, C	£200	£225

8. Kavirondo Cranes.

9. Dhow on Lake Victoria.

10. East African Lion. **12.** Jinja Bridge by Ripon Falls.

11. Kilimanjaro (*horizontal*).

13. Mt. Kenya.

14. Lake Naivasha (*horizontal*).

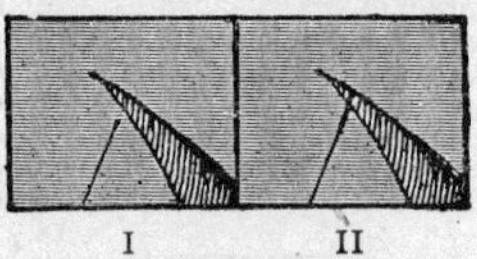

I II

(Des. 1 c., 20 c. and 10s., R. C. Luck. 10 c. and £1, A. Ross. 15 c. and 2s. G. Gill Holmes. 30 c. and 5s. R.N. Ambasana. 65 c. L. R. Cutts. T **10** typo., remainder recess. De La Rue & Co.)

1935 (1 May)–**1936.** *T* **9** *to* **14** (*various views with miniature portrait of King George V inset*). *Wmk. Mult. Script CA. P* 11½×13 (**10**), 13×11½ (*Nos.* 111*a*, 111*c and* 118*a*), 14 (**9** *and* **14**) *and* 13 (*remainder*).

110	**8**	1 c. black and red-brown	0 1	0 1
111	**9**	5 c. black and green (I)	0 3	0 2
		a. Perf. 13×11½ (I)		
		b. Rope joined to sail (II) (perf. 14)	2 6	0 6
		c. Rope joined to sail (II) (perf. 13×11½)	—	90 0
112	**10**	10 c. black and yellow, C	0 7	0 2
113	**11**	15 c. black and scarlet	0 6	0 3
114	**8**	20 c. black and orange	0 10	0 2
115	**12**	30 c. black and blue	1 4	1 0
116	**9**	50 c. bright purple & blk. (I	2 0	0 8
117	**13**	65 c. black and brown	6 0	3 0
118	**14**	1s. black and green	5 0	3 0
		a. Perf. 13×11½ (1936)	—	£8
119	**11**	2s. lake and purple	15 0	10 0
120	**14**	3s. blue and black	17 6	17 6
121	**12**	5s. black and carmine	27 6	27 6
122	**8**	10s. purple and blue	50 0	52 6
123	**10**	£1 black and red, C	£8	£8

1935 (7 May). *Silver Jubilee. As T* **13** *of Antigua, inscribed* " KENYA UGANDA TANGANYIKA ". *Recess. D.L.R. & Co. Wmk. Mult. Script CA. P* 13½×14.

124	20 c. light blue & olive-green	0 10	0 4
125	30 c. brown and deep blue	4 6	4 6
126	65 c. green and indigo	7 6	7 6
127	1s. slate and purple	10 6	12 0

POSTAGE DUE STAMPS.

D 1 D 2

(Typo. De La Rue & Co.)

1928-33. *Type* D 1. *Wmk. Mult. Script CA. P* 15 × 14.

No.	Type	Description	Unused	Used
D1		5 c. violet	0 3	0 4
D2		10 c. vermilion	0 4	0 6
D3		20 c. yellow-green	0 6	0 9
D4		30 c. brown (1931)	1 0	1 3
D5		40 c. dull blue	1 3	1 6
D6		1s. grey-green ('33)	2 6	3 6

1935 (1 May). *Wmk. Mult. Script CA. P* 14.

No.	Type	Description	Unused	Used
D 7	D 2	5 c. violet	0 2	0 3
D 8	,,	10 c. scarlet	0 3	0 4
D 9	,,	20 c. green	0 4	0 5
D10	,,	30 c. brown	0 6	0 8
D11	,,	40 c. ultramarine	0 7	0 9
D12	,,	1s. grey	1 4	1 6

KUWAIT.

KUWAIT (1) KUWAIT (2)

1923 (1 Apr.)–**1924.** *Stamps of India* (*King George V*), *overprinted with T* 1 *or* 2 (*rupee values*, 15½ *mm.*). *Star wmk.. P* 14.

No.	Type	Description	Unused	Used
1	56	½ a. green	0 9	0 4
2	57	1 a. chocolate	0 9	0 4
3	58	1½ a. chocolate (A)	0 6	0 9
4	59	2 a. mauve	1 0	1 0
5	61	2 a. 6 p. ultramarine	1 6	2 0
6	62	3 a. orange-brown	4 0	4 6
		a. Overprint Inverted	70 0	
7	62	3 a. ultramarine (1924)	2 6	2 0
8	63	4 a. olive-green	3 0	2 6
9	64	6 a. yellow-bistre	6 0	2 6
10	65	8 a. purple	4 0	5 0
11	66	12 a. claret	6 0	7 6
12	67	1 r. brown and green	12 6	6 6
13	,,	2 r. carm. & yellow-brn.	25 0	22 6
14	,,	5 r. ultramarine & violet	27 6	30 0
15	,,	10 r. green and scarlet	55 0	60 0

Ordinary and Service stamps with overprint "KOWEIT" were prepared for use but were not issued. These sets are rare.

1929-37. *Stamps of India* (*Nasik printing*), *overprinted as T* 1 *or* 2 (*rupee values*, 19 *mm.*). *Mult. Star wmk. P* 14.

No.	Type	Description	Unused	Used
16	56	½ a. green	0 6	0 4
16a	79	½ a. green ('34)	0 6	0 6
17	57	1 a. chocolate	1 0	0 4
17a	81	1 a. chocolate ('34)	0 8	0 9
18	70	2 a. purple	1 0	0 10
19	,,	2 a. vermilion	6 0	6 0
19a	59	2 a. vermilion ('34)	0 10	1 0
19b	..	2 a. verm. (*small die*) ('37)	0 10	1 0
20	62	3 a. bright blue	2 6	1 6
21	,,	3 a. carmine	1 9	2 0
22	71	4 a. sage-green	3 6	4 6
22a	63	4 a. sage-green ('34)	1 6	2 0
22b	64	6 a. bistre ('37)	2 0	3 0
23	65	8 a. reddish purple	3 0	4 0
24	66	12 a. claret	4 6	5 0
25	67	1 r. chocolate and green	7 6	8 6
26	,,	2 r. carmine and orange	12 6	15 0
27	,,	5 r. ultram. & pur. ('37)	35 0	40 0
28	,,	10 r. green & scarlet ('34)	60 0	70 0
29	,,	15 r. blue and olive ('37)	£5	£6

1933-34. *Air stamps of India overprinted as T* 2 (16½ *mm.*). *Mult. Star wmk. P* 14.

No.	Type	Description	Unused	Used
31	72	2 a. deep blue-green	17 6	20 0
32	,,	3 a. blue	6 6	7 6
33	,,	4 a. drab	£8	£8
34	,,	6 a. bistre ('34)	12 6	15 0

OFFICIAL STAMPS.

KUWAIT SERVICE (O 1) KUWAIT SERVICE (O 2)

1923-24. *Stamps of India* (*King George V*), *overprinted with Types* O 1 *or* O 2 (*rupee values*, 15½–16 *mm.*). *Star wmk. P* 14.

No.	Type	Description	Unused	Used
O 1	56	½ a. green	0 6	0 9
O 2	57	1 a. chocolate	0 9	1 0
O 3	58	1½ a. chocolate (A)	1 0	1 3
O 4	59	2 a. mauve	1 6	2 0
O 5	61	2 a. 6 p. ultramarine	1 6	2 0
O 6	62	3 a. orange-brown	5 6	6 6
O 7	,,	3 a. ultramarine (1924)	2 0	2 6
O 8	63	4 a. olive-green	2 6	3 0
O 9	65	8 a. purple	3 6	4 6
O10	67	1 r. brown and green	6 0	7 6
O11	,,	2 r. carmine & yell.-brn.	15 0	17 6
O12	,,	5 r. ultramarine & violet	32 6	37 6
O13	,,	10 r. green and scarlet	60 0	65 0
O14	,,	15 r. blue and olive	75 0	85 0

1929-33. *Stamps of India* (*Nasik printing*), *overprinted as Types* O 1 (*spaced* 10 *mm.*) *or* O 2 (14½ *mm. between* × 19–20 *mm. wide*). *Mult. Star wmk. P* 14.

No.	Type	Description	Unused	Used
O16	57	1 a. chocolate	0 6	0 9
O17	70	2 a. purple	1 0	1 3
O19	62	3 a. blue	1 0	1 3
O20	71	4 a. sage-green	1 6	2 0
O21	65	8 a. reddish purple	2 6	3 0
O22	66	12 a. claret	3 6	4 0
O23	67	1 r. chocolate & green	4 6	6 0
O24	,,	2 r. carmine & orange	10 0	12 6
O25	,,	5 r. ultram. & purple	25 0	30 0
O26	,,	10 r. green and scarlet	40 0	45 0
O27	,,	15 r. blue and olive	60 0	70 0

LABUAN.

1

(Recess. De La Rue & Co.)

1879 (May). *T* 1. *Wmk. CA over Crown, sideways. P* 14.

No.	Description	Unused	Used
1	2 c. blue-green	£18	£16
2	6 c. orange-brown	£6	95 0
3	12 c. carmine	£22	£16
4	16 c. blue	30 0	37 6

This watermark is always found sideways, and extends over two stamps, a single specimen showing only a portion of the Crown or the letters CA, which latter are tall and far apart. This paper was chiefly used for long fiscal stamps.

1880 (Jan.)–**1881.** *T* 1. *Wmk. Crown CC. P* 14.

No.	Description	Unused	Used
5	2 c. yellow-green	12 0	12 0
6	6 c. orange-brown	37 6	37 6
7	10 c. brown	37 6	37 6
8	12 c. carmine	95 0	95 0
9	16 c. blue (1881)	42 6	42 6

8 8 EIGHT CENTS Eight Cents

(2) (3) (4) (5)

1880 (Aug.). *No.* 8 *surcharged with numeral in centre, in black, and the original value obliterated, as T* 2, *in red or black.*

11 8 c. on 12 c. carmine £15 £12
a. "8" inverted £15 £12
b. "12" not obliterated .. £18 £12
c. As b. with "8" inverted ..

No. 4 *surcharged with two upright figures and No.* 8 *surcharged with numeral in centre, and another across the original value as T* 3.

12 6, in *red*, on 16 c. blue .. £25 £17
a. With one "6" only ..
13 8, in *black*, on 12 c. carmine £15 £10
a. Both "8's" upright ..

1881 (Mar.) *No.* 8 *surcharged as T* 4.

14 8 c. on 12 c. carmine 85 0 85 0

1881 (June). *No.* 8 *surcharged as T* 5.

15 8 c. on 12 c. carmine .. 27 6 27 6
a. Double £7
b. Inverted £27
c. Error "Eighr" £110

The error was No. 6 in the first printing, but this was soon corrected, and the error is very scarce.

1882 (April). *T* 1. *Wmk. Crown CC. P* 14.

16 8 c. carmine 37 6 37 6

1883–86. *T* 1. *Wmk. Crown CA. P* 14.

17 2 c. green 6 0 11 6
18 8 c. carmine 95 0 75 0
19 10 c. yellow-brown 22 6 22 6
20 16 c. blue 45 0 45 0
21 40 c. amber 15 0 15 0

One Dollar A.S.H. 2 CENTS 2 Cents

(6) (7) (8)

1883 (May). *No.* 9 *surcharged "One Dollar, A. S. H.," by hand, in red.*

[The initials are those of the postmaster, Mr. A. S. Hamilton.]

22 $1 on 16 c. blue £50 £40

1885 (June). *Nos.* 18 *and* 9 *surcharged as T* 7.

23 2 c. on 8 c. carmine 40 0
a. Double ..
24 2 c. on 16 c. blue £22 £22

1885 (July). *No.* 20 *surcharged as T* 8.

25 2 c. on 16 c. blue 75 0 75 0
a. Double .. ..

2 Cents 6 Cents

(9) (10)

1885 (Sept.) *No.* 18 *surch. diagonally, as T* 9.

26 2 c. on 8 c. carmine 37 6 37 6

1885–6. *T* 1. *Wmk. Crown CA. P* 14.

27 2 c. rose-red (Sept. 1885) .. 3 6 4 0
28 2 c. pale rose-red 2 0 2 6
29 8 c. deep violet (Sept., 1885) .. 15 0 13 6
30 8 c. mauve (1886) 8 6 8 6
32 10 c. sepia (May, 1886) .. 7 0 6 6
33 16 c. grey (May, 1886) .. 35 0 35 0

This is the last set of stamps issued by the Government.

From Jan. 1st, 1890, the administration of Labuan was transferred to the British North Borneo Co., and the following stamps were issued by that Company.

1891 (Aug.). *T* 1, *surcharged as T* **10**, *in black* (B.) *or red* (R.). *Wmk. Crown CA. P* 14.

34 6 c. on 8 c. deep violet (B.) .. 27 6 27 6
a. Inverted 37 6 37 6
b. Double £7
c. Double, one inverted .. £14
d. "Cents" omitted £14
e. Imperf. between (pair) ..
35 6 c. on 8 c. mauve (B.) .. 6 0 6 0
a. Inverted 27 6 22 6
b. Double, one inverted ..
c. Double, both inverted ..
d. "6" omitted £8
e. Pair, one without surcharge .. — £16
f. Inverted. "Cents" omitted .. £12
g. Pair, one without surch., one surch. inverted .. £16
36 6 c. on 8 c. mauve (R.) .. £12 82 6
a. Inverted £14 97 6
37 6 c. on 16 c. blue (B.) .. £50 £40
a. Inverted £65
38 6 c. on 40 c. amber (B.) .. £60 £45
a. Inverted £70 £70

(Recess. De La Rue & Co.)

1892. *T* 1. *No wmk. P* 14.

39 2 c. rose-lake 1 0 1 0
40 6 c. bright green 2 0 2 6
41 8 c. violet 3 0 3 0
42 8 c. pale violet 3 6 4 0
43 10 c. brown 4 6 4 6
44 10 c. sepia-brown 3 0 4 0
45 12 c. bright blue 3 6 4 0
46 16 c. grey 5 0 6 0
47 40 c. amber 15 0 17 6
48 40 c. brown-buff 18 6 20 0

The 6 c., 12 c., 16 c., and 40 c. are in sheets of 10, as are all the earlier issues. The other values are in sheets of 30.

Two CENTS Six CENTS

(11) (11a)

1892 (Dec.). *Nos.* 47 *and* 46 *surch. as T* **11** *or* **11a**

49 2 c. on 40 c. amber ('92) .. 75 0 75 0
a. Inverted £8
50 6 c. on 16 c. grey (29 Dec., '92) 95 0 75 0
a. Inverted £5 80 0
b. Sideways £5 £5
c. "Six" omitted .. ..
d. "Cents" omitted .. ..

There are 10 types of each of these surcharges.

(Litho. De La Rue & Co.)

1894. (April). *T* 1. *No wmk. P* 14.

51 2 c. carmine-pink 2 0 0 9
52 6 c. bright green 6 6 2 6
53 8 c. bright mauve 6 6 2 6
54 10 c. brown 7 6 2 6
55 12 c. pale blue 10 0 5 0
56 16 c. grey 10 0 3 6
57 40 c. orange-buff 15 0 5 0

The prices in the "used" column (Nos. 51 *to* 57) *are for stamps "cancelled to order."*

Collectors are warned against forgeries of this issue placed on the market in 1922.

12

1894. *T* **24** *to* **32** *of North Borneo (colours changed), with* "LABUAN" *engraved on vignette plate as in T* **12.**

(*a*) *Name and central part of design in black.*

62	1 c. grey-mauve	1 6	2 0
63	2 c. blue	1 6	2 0
	a. Imperf. (pair)	£12	
64	3 c. ochre	1 0	3 6
65	5 c. green	1 6	3 6
67	6 c. brown-lake	1 6	3 6
	a. Imperf. (pair)	£12	
68	8 c. rose-red	1 6	3 6
69	8 c. pink	6 0	6 0
70	12 c. orange-verm. (*canc.* 6d.)	2 6	4 0
71	18 c. olive-brown (*canc.* 6d.)	4 0	7 0
72	18 c. olive-bistre	6 0	7 0

(*b*) *Name and central part in blue.*

73	24 c. pale mauve (*canc.* 1s. 3d.)	3 6	6 6
74	24 c. dull lilac	7 6	7 6

Nos. 62 to 74 can be supplied "cancelled to order" at prices considerably lower than those which are given above for postally used specimens.

LABUAN

40

CENTS

(22)

1895 (June). *The 1 dollar stamp of the State of North Borneo* (No. 83) *surcharged as T* **22.**

75	4 c. on $1 scarlet	1 3	1 9
76	10 c. on $1 scarlet	2 6	2 9
77	20 c. on $1 scarlet	3 0	3 0
78	30 c. on $1 scarlet	3 6	3 6
79	40 c. on $1 scarlet	4 6	5 6

Nos. 75 to 79 can be supplied "cancelled to order" at half the prices quoted above for postally used stamps.

LABUAN (23)

1846 JUBILEE 1896 (24)

T **32a** *to* **32c** *of North Borneo (as Nos.* 81 *to* 83) *overprinted with T* **23,** *in black.*

80	25 c. green (*canc.* 2s. 6d.)	6 0	6 6
81	50 c. marone (*canc.* 3s. 6d.)	7 6	8 0
82	$1 blue (*canc.* 4s. 6d.)	9 6	10 6

Errors. Overprint omitted.

82a	25 c. green (*canc.* 8s.)	16 0	
	aa. Imperf.	27 6	
82b	50 c. marone (*canc.* 8s.)	16 0	
	bb. Imperf.	27 6	
82c	$1 blue (*canc.* 8s.)	16 0	
	cc. Imperf.	27 6	

1896. *Jubilee issue. Commemorative of the cession of Labuan to Great Britain. Nos.* 62 *to* 68, *overprinted with T* **24,** *in black.*

83	1 c. black & grey-mauve	5 0	6 0
84	2 c. black & blue	5 0	6 0
	a. Imperf. between (pair)	50 0	
85	3 c. black and ochre	3 6	4 0
86	5 c. black and green	3 6	4 0
87	6 c. black and brown-lake	3 0	3 6
88	8 c. black and pink	4 0	4 6

Error. "JEBILEE" *for* "JUBILEE."

88a	1 c. black and grey-mauve	—	£8
88b	2 c. black and blue		
88c	3 c. black and ochre		

Varieties. Overprint double.

88d	1 c. black and grey-mauve	85 0	85 0
88e	3 c. black and ochre	30 0	
88f	5 c. black and green		
88g	6 c. black and brown-lake		

Overprint in orange.

88h	1 c. black and mauve	65 0	65 0

1897 (April). *Stamps of North Borneo,* 1897 (*T* **34** *to* **45**), *inscribed* "LABUAN" *as in T* **12.**

(*a*) *Name and central part in black.*

89	1 c. greyish purple	2 0	2 0
89a	1 c. brown	1 6	1 6
90	2 c. blue (*canc.* 2d.)	1 9	1 9
91	3 c. ochre	1 9	1 9
	a. Imperf. between (pair)		
92	5 c. green (*canc.* 4d.)	4 0	2 6
93	6 c. brown-lake	4 0	4 0
	a. Imperf. between (pair)		
94	8 c. rose-red	5 0	5 0
94a	8 c. vermilion	10 0	8 0
95	12 c. vermilion	6 0	7 0
96	18 c. olive-bistre	5 0	6 0
	a. Imperf. between (pair)		

(*b*) *Name and central part in blue.*

97	24 c. grey-lilac	4 6	5 0

The 12, 18, and 24 c. above were errors; in the 12 c., "LABUAN" is *over* the value at the top; the 18 c. has "POSTAL" REVENUE instead of "POSTAGE AND" REVENUE, and the 24 c. has "POSTAGE AND REVENUE" *omitted.*

1897 (Oct.)–**1898.** *Stamps of North Borneo (T* **42, 46** *and* **47**), *inscribed* "LABUAN" *as in T* **12.**

98	12 c. black and vermilion	6 0	7 6
99	18 c. black and olive-bistre	7 6	8 6
100	24 c. blue and greyish mauve	6 0	6 0

In the 12 c. "LABUAN" is now correctly placed at foot of stamp. The 18 c. and 24 c. have the inscriptions on the stamps corrected, but the 18 c. still has "LABUAN" *over* the value at foot, and was further corrected as follows.

As No. 99, but "LABUAN" *at top.*

101	18 c. black and olive-bistre	7 6	8 6

Nos. 83 to 101 (excluding the errors etc.) can be supplied "cancelled to order" at about one-third of the prices quoted above for postally used specimens.

4

CENTS

(38)

1899. *Contemporary stamps surch. with T* **38.**

102	4 c. on 5 c. black & green	3 0	3 6
103	4 c. on 6 c. black & brn.-lake	3 0	3 6
104	4 c. on 8 c. black & rose-red	3 0	3 6
105	4 c. on 12 c. black & verm.	4 0	4 6
106	4 c. on 18 c. blk. & olive-bistre	4 0	4 6
107	4 c. on 24 c. blue & grey-mve.	4 0	4 6
108	4 c. on 25 c. green (No. 80)	4 0	4 6
109	4 c. on 50 c. marone (No. 81)	3 0	3 6
110	4 c. on $1, blue (No. 82)	3 0	3 6

Variety. Surcharge double.

110*a*	4 c. on 18 c. blk. & olive-bist.		

1900. *T* **35, 37** *and* **38** *of North Borneo inscribed* "LABUAN" *as in T* 12.

No.	Description	Unused	Used
111	2 c. black & grn. (*canc.* 6d.)	2 0	3 6
112	4 c. black & yell.-brown ..	1 0	2 6
	a. Imperf. between (pair) ..	45 0	
113	4 c. black & carm. (*canc.* 3d.)	1 0	3 6
114	5 c. blk. & pl. blue (*canc.* 6d.)	2 6	4 0

1902. *T* **41** *and* **43** *of North Borneo inscribed* "LABUAN" *as in T* **12.**

No.	Description	Unused	Used
115	10 c. brown and slate-lilac ..	4 0	5 6
116	16 c. green and chestnut ..	4 0	5 6

42

(Recess. Waterlow & Sons.)

1902-03. *T* **42.** *Centre in first colour. P* 13½ *to* 15 *etc.*

No.	Description	Unused	Used
116*a*	1 c. black and purple ..	0 6	1 9
117	2 c. black and green.. ..	0 6	1 3
117*a*	3 c. black and sepia ..	0 6	1 9
118	4 c. black and carmine ..	0 6	1 3
119	8 c. black and vermilion ..	0 8	1 3
120	10 c. brown and slate-blue ..	0 8	1 6
	a. Imperf. between (pair) ..	80 0	
121	12 c. black and yellow ..	0 10	1 6
122	16 c. green and brown ..	1 0	2 0
123	18 c. black and pale brown ..	1 0	2 0
124	25 c. green and greenish blue ..	1 3	3 0
125	50 c. dull purple and lilac ..	1 6	5 0
126	$1 claret and orange ..	3 0	12 0

Set of 12 un. (Set 1660), 10s.

No.	*Error of colour.*		*Canc.*
126*a*	25 c. black & greenish blue	—	75 0

Nos. 116*a to* 126 *can be supplied "cancelled to order" at about one quarter of the prices quoted above for postally used stamps.*

4
cents
(43)

1904. *Issues of* 1895 *and* 1897-8 *surcharged with T* **43,** *in black.*

No.	Description	Used
127	4 c. on 5 c. (No. 92) ..	2 6
128	4 c. on 6 c. (No. 93) ..	2 6
129	4 c. on 8 c. (No. 94) ..	2 6
130	4 c. on 12 c. (No. 98) ..	2 6
131	4 c. on 18 c. (No. 101) ..	2 6
132	4 c. on 24 c. (No. 100) ..	2 6
133	4 c. on 25 c. (No. 80) ..	3 6
134	4 c. on 50 c. (No. 81) ..	3 6
135	4 c. on $1 (No. 82) ..	3 6

Varieties. (i.) *Surcharge double.*

136	4 c. on 50 c. (No. 81)	£5

(ii.) *Surcharge triple.*

137	4 c. on 50 c. (No. 81) ..	

LABUAN **(44)**   **LABUAN** **(45)**

1905. *Nos.* 81, 83 (*in Labuan colour*), *and* 84 *to* 86 *of North Borneo overprinted locally with T* **44** (25 *c. and* $2) *or* **45,** *in black.*

No.	Description	Unused	Used
139	25 c. indigo	£55	£25
139*a*	$1 blue	—	£16
140	$2 dull green	£70	£27
141	$5 bright purple	£65	£27
142	$10 brown	—	£110

The overprint on No. 140 is 12 mm. long.

POSTAGE DUE STAMPS.

POSTAGE DUE
(101)

1901. *Contemporary stamps overprinted with T* **101,** *vertically, in black.*

No.	Description	Unused	Used
201	2 c. black & grn. (No. 111)	3 6	3 6
202	3 c. black & ochre (No. 91) ..	2 6	2 6
203	4 c. black & carm. (No. 113)	3 0	3 0
204	5 c. black & pl. bl. (No. 114)	2 6	2 6
205	6 c. blk. & brn.-lake (No. 93)	3 0	3 0
206	8 c. blk. & verm. (No. 94*a*) ..	3 6	3 6
207	12 c. black & verm. (No. 98)	6 0	6 0
208	18 c. black & olive-bis. (No. 101)	3 6	3 6
209	24 c. blue & grey-mve. (No. 100)	3 6	3 6

Nos. 201 *to* 209 *can be supplied "cancelled to order" at prices considerably lower than those which are given above for postally used specimens.*

Varieties. (i.) *Overprint double.*

No.	Description	Unused	Used
210	2 c. black and green.. ..	35 0	
211	4 c. black and carmine ..		

(ii.) *Frame inverted.*

No.	Description	Unused	Used
212	8 c. black and vermilion ..	—	£70

By Letters Patent passed under the Great Seal of the United Kingdom dated 30 October, 1906, Labuan was incorporated with "Straits Settlements."

LAGOS.

PRINTERS. All the stamps of Lagos were typographed by De La Rue & Co.

1

Type 1.

1874 (10 JUNE)-**1875** (MAR.). *Wmk. Crown CC. P* 12½.

The colour of the words of value (the second colour given below) frequently differs from that of the body of the stamp.

No.	Description	Unused	Used
1	1d. lilac-mauve	25 0	25 0
2	2d. blue	25 0	25 0
3	3d. red-brown (1875) ..	85 0	40 0
4	3d. red-brn. & chestnut ('75) ..	65 0	35 0
5	4d. carmine	50 0	40 0
6	6d. blue-green	70 0	40 0
8	1s. orange ('75) (value 15½ mm.)	£17	£8
9	1s. orange ('75) (value 16½ mm.)	£12	50 0

1876. *Wmk. Crown CC. P* 14.

No.	Description	Unused	Used
10	1d. lilac-mauve	25 0	22 6
11	2d. blue	27 6	22 6
12	3d. red-brown	70 0	32 6
13	3d. chestnut	80 0	35 0
14	4d. carmine	£6	20 0
15	6d. green	40 0	22 6
16	1s. orange (value 16½ mm. long)	£20	75 0

No. 14 exists with wmk. sideways.

1882 (June)–**1885** (Mar.). *Wmk. Crown CA. P* 14.

17 1d. lilac-mauve 22 6 15 0
18 2d. blue 75 0 25 0
19 3d. chestnut 22 6 20 0
20 4d. carmine 85 0 27 6
21 1s. orange (1885) 8 6 10 0

1884 (Dec.)–**1886** (Oct.). *Wmk. Crown CA. P* 14.

22 ½d. dull green (1886) 0 8 0 10
23 1d. rose-carmine 1 3 0 8
24 2d. grey 17 6 15 0
25 4d. pale violet 37 6 25 0
26 6d. olive-green 7 6 7 6
27 2s. 6d. olive-black (1886) .. £25 £20
28 5s. blue (1886) £30 £25
29 10s. purple-brown (1886) .. £75 £45

We would warn collectors against clever forgeries of Nos. 27 to 29 on genuinely watermarked paper.

1887–1902. *Wmk. Crown CA. P* 14.

30 2d. dull mauve and blue .. 4 0 3 0
31 2½d. ultramarine (1891) .. 2 6 2 0
31*a* 2½d. blue 75 0 40 0
b. Larger letters of value ..
32 3d. dull mauve & chestnut .. 6 0 6 0
33 4d. dull mauve and black .. 5 0 5 0
34 5d. dull mauve and grn. ('94) 6 0 6 6
35 6d. dull mauve and mauve .. 6 6 7 6
35*a* 6d. dull mve. & car. (Oct. '02) 15 0 12 6
36 7½d. dull mauve & car. ('94) .. 7 6 8 6
37 10d. dull mauve & yell. ('94) 8 6 10 0
38 1s. yellow-green and black .. 15 0 15 0
38*a* 1s. blue-green and black .. 17 6 15 0
39 2s. 6d. green and carmine .. 25 0 25 0
40 5s. green and blue 35 0 35 0
41 10s. green and brown .. 55 0 55 0

HALF PENNY

(2)

(3)

1893 (Aug.). *No.* 33 *surcharged with T* **2.**

42 ½d. on 4d. dull mauve & black 6 0 7 0
a. Surcharge double 85 0 90 0
b. Surcharge treble .. ..
c. Error. ½d. on 2d. (No. 30) ..

There were four settings of this surcharge, a scarce setting in which "HALF PENNY" is 16½ mm. and three others in which the length is 16 mm.

1904 (22 Jan.-Nov.). *T* **3.** *Wmk. Crown CA. P* 14

44 ½d. dull green and green .. 5 0 4 6
45 1d. purple and black/*red* .. 4 0 1 0
46 2d. dull purple and blue .. 15 0 10 0
47 2½d. dull purple and blue/*blue* 5 0 6 0
a. Larger letters of value ..
48 3d. dull purple and brown .. 10 0 7 6
49 6d. dull purple and mauve .. 47 6 17 6
50 1s. green and black 47 6 30 0
51 2s. 6d. green and carmine .. £8
52 5s. green and blue 95 0 £5
53 10s. green and brown (Nov.) .. £30

1904 (22 Oct.)–**1905.** *T* **3.** *Wmk. Mult. Crown CA. P* 14.

54 ½d. dull green & green, OC .. 1 3 1 0
55 1d. purple & black/*red*, OC .. 0 10 0 6
56 2d. dull purp. & blue, OC ('05) 3 0 2 0
57 2½d. dull pur. & bl./*blue*, C ('05) 5 0 5 0
58 3d. dull pur. & brn, OC ('05) 4 6 4 6
59 6d. dull pur. and mauve, OC 7 6 5 0
60 1s. green and black, OC .. 15 0 12 6
61 2s. 6d. green and carm., OC 20 0 22 6
62 5s. green and blue, OC (1905) 25 0 30 0
63 10s. green and brown, OC .. 45 0 47 6

By an Order in Council dated 16 February, 1906, the administration of the Southern Nigerian Protectorate was amalgamated with that of the colony of Lagos, and the combination was styled the Colony and Protectorate of Southern Nigeria.

LEEWARD ISLANDS.

Issues superseding the earlier issues, or in concurrent use with the later issues (from 1903), *of* Antigua, Dominica (*to* 31 Dec., 1939), Montserrat, Nevis, St. Christopher, St. Kitts-Nevis, and Virgin Islands.

PRINTERS. All the stamps of Leeward Islands were typographed by De La Rue & Co. except where otherwise stated.

1

2

1890. *T* **1** *and* **2** (1*s. and* 5*s.*). *Name and value in second colour. Wmk. Crown CA. P* 14.

1 ½d. dull mauve and green .. 0 9 0 6
2 1d. dull mauve and rose .. 0 8 0 3
3 2½d. dull mauve and blue .. 4 0 3 0
4 4d. dull mauve and orange .. 10 6 10 0
5 6d. dull mauve and brown .. 9 0 9 0
6 7d. dull mauve and slate .. 12 6 12 6
7 1s. green and carmine 30 0 20 0
8 5s. green and blue 70 0 70 0

(3)

One
Penny

(4)

One Penny

(5)

1897. *Jubilee issue, commemorative of Queen Victoria's sixty years reign. T* **1** *and* **2** *overprinted with T* **3** *in black.*

9 ½d. dull mauve and green .. 7 6 7 6
10 1d. dull mauve and rose .. 8 6 8 6
11 2½d. dull mauve and blue .. 8 0 8 0
12 4d. dull mauve and orange .. 25 0 22 6
13 6d. dull mauve and brown .. 35 0 37 6
14 7d. dull mauve and slate .. 35 0 37 6
15 1s. green and carmine .. 85 0 85 0
16 5s. green and blue £18 £22

Varieties. (i.) *Overprint inverted.*

16*a* ½d. dull mauve and green ..

(ii.) *Overprint double.*

16*b* ½d. dull mauve and green .. 70 0
16*c* 1d. dull mauve and rose .. £6
16*d* 2½d. dull mauve and blue .. 75 0
16*e* 4d. dull mauve and orange ..
16*f* 6d. dull mauve and brown ..

1902. *Stamps of* 1890 *surcharged; the* 4*d. and* 6*d. with T* **4,** *and the* 7*d. with T* **5.**

17 1d. on 4d. dull mauve & orange 5 0 6 0
18 1d. on 6d. dull mauve & brown 5 0 6 0
19 1d. on 7d. dull mauve and slate 5 0 6 0

Varieties. (i.) *Tall narrow "O" in "One."*
(In pair with normal.)

20	1d. on 4d. dull mauve & orange	20	0	22	6
21	1d. on 6d. dull mauve & brown	20	0	22	6

(ii.) *Surcharge double.*

21a 1d. on 4d. dull mauve & orange

6

7

8

1902. *T* **6** (½*d.*, 1*d.*, 2½*d.*, *and* 6*d.*), **7** (½*d.*, 2*d.*, 3*d. and* 2*s.* 6*d.*) *and* **8** (1*s. and* 5*s.*). *Wmk. Crown CA. P* 14.

22	½d. dull purple and green	1	3	1	3
23	1d. dull purple & carmine	1	3	0	10
24	2d. dull purple and ochre	6	6	6	6
25	2½d. dull purple & ultramarine	6	0	6	0
26	3d. dull purple and black	10	0	10	6
27	6d. dull purple and brown	7	6	8	6
28	1s. green and carmine	12	0	12	6
29	2s. 6d. green and black	25	0	22	6
30	5s. green and blue	35	0	37	6

1905–8. *T* **6** *to* **8.** *Wmk. Mult. Crown CA. P* 14.

31	½d. dull pur. & grn., OC ('06)	1	6	1	6
32	1d. dull purple & carm., C	4	0	2	0
33	2d. dull pur. & ochre, C (1908)	10	0	10	6
34	2½d. dull pur. & ultram., C	30	0	35	0
35	3d. dull purple & black, OC	12	6	12	6
36	6d. dull pur. & brn., C (1908)	20	0	22	6
37	1s. green & carmine, C (1908)	25	0	27	6

1907–11. *T* **6** *to* **8.** *Wmk. Mult. Crown CA. P* 14.

39	¼d. brown, O (1909)	0	4	0	6
40	½d. dull green, O	1	3	1	0
41	1d. bright red, O	5	0	0	10
41a	1d. rose-carmine, O	6	0	1	0
41b	2d. grey, O (1911)	6	0	6	6
42	2½d. bright blue, O	5	0	5	0
43	3d. purple/*yellow*, C (1910)	5	0	6	0
44	6d. dull & bright pur., C ('11)	10	0	10	6
45	1s. black/*green*, C (1911)	10	6	10	6
46	2s. 6d. black & red/*blue*, C ('11)	22	6	22	6
47	5s. green & red/*yellow*, C ('11)	45	0	45	0

10

11

12

1912–22. *T* **10, 11** (½*d.*, 1*d.*, 2½*d.*, *and* 6*d.*) *and* **12** (1*s. and* 5*s.*). *Wmk. Mult. Crown CA. P* 14.

48	¼d. brown, O	0	4	0	4
49	¼d. pale brown, O	0	4	0	4
50	½d. yellow-green, O (1913)	0	4	0	4
51	½d. deep green, O	0	4	0	4
52	1d. carmine-red, O	1	0	0	4
53	1d. bright scarlet, O (1915)	0	10	0	3
54	2d. slate-grey, O	2	0	2	0
55	2½d. bright blue, O	2	6	2	6
55a	2½d. deep bright blue, O	2	0	2	0
56	3d. purple/*yellow*, C	3	0	2	6
	a. White back	50	0	40	0
	b. On lemon	2	6	3	6
	c. On orange-buff	2	6	4	0
	d. On pale yellow				
57	4d. black & red/*pale yellow*, C (Die II) (1922)	1	9	2	6
58	6d. dull & bright purple, C	4	0	4	6
59	1s. black/*green*, C	5	0	4	6
	a. White back	40	0	37	6
	b. On blue-green, olive back	4	6	5	0
60	2s. pur. & blue/*blue*, C (Die II) (1922)	10	0	10	6
61	2s. 6d. black & red/*blue*, C	12	6	10	0
62	5s. green and red/*yellow*, C	15	0	17	6
	a. White back	27	6	35	0
	b. On lemon (1916)	20	0	25	0

1921–32. *Wmk. Mult. Script CA. P* 14.

63	10	¼d. brown, O (Die II)	0	1	0	2
		a. Die I ('32)	0	3	0	4
64	11	½d. blue-green, O (Die II)	0	4	0	4
		a. Die I ('31)	0	8	0	8
65	,,	1d. carmine-red, O (Die II)	1	3	1	6
66	10	2d. slate-grey, O	1	0	1	0
67	,,	4d. blk. & red/*pale yellow*, C	2	6	3	0
68	,,	5d. dull pur. & olive-grn., C	2	6	2	6
69	11	6d. dull and bright purple, C (Die II)	3	0	4	0
		a. Die I ('32)	4	0	4	6
70	12	1s. black/*emer.*, C (Die II)	5	0	6	0
		a. Die I ('32)	12	6	15	0
71	10	2s. purple & blue/*blue*, C	12	6	15	0
71a	,,	2s. red-pur. & blue/*blue*, C ('26)	15	0	17	6
72	,,	2s. 6d. black & red/*blue*, C	17	6	20	0
73	,,	3s. bright grn. & vio., C	25	0	25	0
74	,,	4s. black and red, C	30	0	30	0
75	12	5s. grn. & red/*pale yellow*, C	25	0	25	0

1922–32. *Colours changed, etc. Wmk. Mult. Script CA. P* 14.

76	11	1d. bright violet, O	0	6	0	4
77	,,	1d. bright scar., O (Die II) ('29)	0	6	0	4
		a. Die I ('32)	1	6	2	0
78	10	1½d. carmine-red, O	1	0	1	3
79	,,	1½d. red-brn., O (Die II) ('29)	0	8	0	8
		a. Die I (32)	2	0	2	6
80	11	2½d. orange-yellow, O	15	0	20	0
81	,,	2½d. bright blue, O (Die II)	2	0	2	0
		a. Die I (32)	3	0	3	6
82	10	3d. ultramarine, O	12	0	12	0
83	,,	3d. purple/*yellow*, C	2	0	2	0

13

1928. *T* **13.** *P* 14. *Wmk. Mult. Script CA.*

84 10s. green and red/*green*, C .. 65 0 70 0

Wmk. Mult. Crown CA.

85 £1 purple and black/*red*, C .. £8 £9

1935 (6 May). *Silver Jubilee. As T* **13** *of Antigua, inscribed* "LEEWARD ISLANDS". *Recess. W'low. & Sons. Wmk. Mult. Script CA.* P 11×12.

86 1d. deep blue and scarlet .. 0 8 0 10
87 1½d. ultramarine and grey .. 1 3 2 0
88 2½d. brown and deep blue .. 7 6 8 6
89 1s. slate and purple 15 0 17 6

LONG ISLAND.
(AEGEAN SEA.)

1916 (7th to 26th May). *Turkish fiscal stamps optd* "G.R.I., Postage", *and new value. No wmk.* P 12.

1 ½d. in carmine, on 20 paras, green and buff £55
2 1d. in black, on 10 paras, carmine and buff £55
3 2½d. in magenta, on 1 pias., violet and buff £70

G.R.I.
LONG ISLAND
Postage &
Revenue
ONE PENNY

1

1916 (7th to 26th May). *T* **1.** *Imperf.*

(i) *Type-written in various colours or carbons, on pale green paper, ruled with horizontal grey lines. In sheets of sixteen, initialled by the Civil Administrator in red ink. No watermark.*

4 ½d. black £8
a. Error. "7" for "&" .. ..
5 ½d. blue £10
6 ½d. mauve £22
a. "G. R. I." twice .. ..

Of the above three stamps there were 140 in all.

(ii) *Type-written in various colours or carbons on thin horizontally laid paper, watermarked in the sheets in double-lined capitals* "SILVER LINEN." *In sheets of twenty, each stamp initialled in red ink.*

7 ½d. mauve 80 0
a. Error. "7" for "&" .. £20
8 ½d. black £6
a. Error. "postage" for "Postage" £25
9 ½d. blue £8

Of the above three stamps there were 280 in all.

10 1d. mauve 65 0 £10
a. Error. "ONR" for "ONE" £25
b. Error. "Postegg" for "Postage" £22
11 1d. black 90 0
a. Error. "7" for "&" and "RVEVUE" £25
12 1d. blue 90 0
a. Error. "ONR" for "ONE" £15
13 1d. red £7 £11
a. Error. "7" for "&" .. £25
b. Error. "ONR" for "ONE" £18

Of the above four stamps there were 1178 in all.

14 2½d. black £14
15 2½d. blue £16 £25
15*a* 2½d. mauve .. .. ..

Of the above three stamps there were 80 in all.

16 6d. mauve £8 £12
16*a* 6d. black £20
17 1s. mauve 75 0
a. Error. "ISLANA" for "ISLAND" £25
18 1s. blue £6
19 1s. black 75 0
a. Error. "ISLANA" for "ISLAND" £25
b. Error. "Postge" for "Postage" £35
c. Error. "Rebeuue" ..

Of the above three stamps there were 532 in all.

(iii) *Type-written in various colours or carbons on thin wove paper. In sheets of twenty-four, each stamp initialled in pencil. No watermark.*

20 ½d. black £6
20*a* ½d. mauve £11
21 1d. black £6 £12
21*a* 1d. red £27 £27
22 2d. mauve 75 0
23 2d. black £6
a. "ISLAD" £100
b. Error. 1d. in the sheet of 2d.

Of the above two stamps there were 288 in all.

24 2½d. black £6
24*a* 2½d. mauve £30 £15
25 6d. blue £6
26 6d. black £6
a. Error. "Rvenne" for "Revenue" £30
b. Error. 2d. in sheet of 6d. .. £35

Of the above two stamps there were 244 in all.

MADAGASCAR.
BRITISH CONSULAR MAIL.

1

(*Illustration reduced. Actual size* 38 × 65 *mm.*)

1884 (MAR.). *T* **1**. *Rouletted vertically on coloured lines. With circular handstamp,* "BRITISH VICE-CONSULATE ANTANANARIVO" in black.

(*a*) *Inscribed* "LETTER".

1 6d. magenta 35 0 35 0
2 1s. magenta 35 0 35 0
3 1s. 6d. magenta 40 0 40 0
4 2s. magenta 45 0 45 0

Variety. Handstamp in violet.

5 6d. magenta .. .. ..

(*b*) *Inscribed* "POSTAL PACKET".

6 1d. magenta (1 oz.) 30 0 20 0
7 2d. magenta (2 oz.) 30 0 30 0
8 3d. magenta (3 oz.) 30 0 30 0
9 4d. magenta (1 oz.) .. ..

Varieties. (i) *Handstamp in violet.*

10 4d. magenta £9

(ii) *The* "1" of "1 oz." *altered by pen to* "4" *in black ink.*

11 4d. magenta (4 oz.) 110 0 110 0

(iii) *Without handstamp.*

12 1d. magenta £16
13 4d. magenta £16

Several of the values are known with the handstamp inverted and also double printed.

1886. *Provisionals. No.* 2 *with* "SHILLING" *erased and* "PENNY" *written above in red ink, and the same stamp with* "1 oz." *altered in red to* "4½d.", *and the Vice-Consul's initials,* "W.C.P.", *added.*

14 1d. on 1s. magenta .. ..
15 4½d. on 1s. magenta .. .. —

1886. *Colour changed.*

16 6d. rose-red 60 0 60 0

As T **1**, *but handstamp reading,* "British Consular Mail—ANTANANARIVO."

(*a*) *In black.*

16*a* 4d. magenta 130 0

(*b*) *In violet.*

16*b* 4d. magenta £11

Nos. 1 to 16*b* exist in three types; in the first the period after "B" is solid; in the second it appears as a small circle; and in the third the period after "M" appears as a small circle.

2

(*Illustration reduced. Actual size* 45 × 68 mm.)

1886. *T* **2**. *Rouletted vertically on coloured lines.*

(*a*) *With period after* "POSTAGE" *and value.*

(1) *Handstamp in black.*

17 1d. rose 25 0 25 0
18 1½d. rose 30 0 30 0
19 2d. rose 25 0 25 0
20 3d. rose 25 0 25 0
21 4½d. rose 40 0 40 0
22 8d. rose 80 0
23 9d. rose .. .. ..

(2) *Handstamp in violet.*

24 1d. rose 60 0 60 0
25 1½d. rose 80 0 80 0
26 2d. rose 60 0
27 3d. rose 30 0 30 0
28 4½d. rose 50 0 40 0
28*a* 8d. rose 80 0
29 9d. rose 170 0

(*b*) *Without period after* "POSTAGE" *and value. Handstamp in violet.*

30 1d. rose £8
30*a* 1½d. rose £8
31 3d. rose £10
31*a* 4½d. rose £5
32 6d. rose £5

Variety. "POSTAGE" *measures* 24½ *mm. in place of* 29½ *mm.*

33 4d. rose 100 0
34 8d. rose £6
34*a* 1s. 6d. rose .. ..
34*b* 2s. rose £10

1886. *As T* **2**, *but handstamp reading* "BRITISH CONSULAR MAIL, ANTANANARIVO". (*a*) *With period after* "POSTAGE" *and the value. Rouletted or serpentine perf. on coloured lines.*

(1) *Handstamp in black.*

35 1d. rose 12 6 12 6
36 1½d. rose 12 6 12 6
37 2d. rose 25 0 25 0
38 3d. rose 17 6 17 6
39 4½d. rose 17 6 17 6
40 8d. rose 25 0 25 0
41 9d. rose 20 0 20 0
a. Without handstamp £15

The stamps of this set are printed in horizontal strips of 4. These are separated by alternate lines of serpentine perf. and roulettes, both on coloured lines.

(2) *Handstamp in violet.*

41*b* 8d. rose .. .. ..
42 9d. rose 40 0 40 0

(3) *Handstamp in red.*

43 3d. rose .. .. .. — £8
44 4½d. rose .. .. .. — 60 0

(*b*) *Without period after* "POSTAGE" *and the value. Rouletted on coloured lines.*

(1) *Handstamp in black.*

45 1d. rose 12 6 12 6
a. Without handstamp 100 0
46 1½d. rose 25 0 25 0
47 2d. rose 15 0 15 0
48 3d. rose 15 0 15 0
a. Without handstamp .. ..
49 4½d. rose 20 0 20 0
a. Without handstamp £13
50 6d. rose 17 6 17 6
. Without handstamp £13

(2) *Handstamp in violet.*

51 1d. rose 25 0 25 0
52 1½d. rose 35 0 35 0
53 2d. rose 30 0 30 0
54 3d. rose 25 0 25 0
55 4½d. rose 40 0 40 0
56 6d. rose 40 0 40 0

(*c*) "POSTAGE" *24½ mm. long in place of 29½ mm.*

(1) *Handstamp in black.*

57 4d. rose 20 0 20 0
a. Without handstamp £11
58 8d. rose 100 0
a. Without handstamp .. ..
59 1s. rose 40 0 40 0
60 1s. 6d. rose 50 0 50 0
61 2s. rose 70 0 70 0

(2) *Handstamp in violet.*

62 4d. rose 50 0
63 8d. rose 60 0
64 1s. rose 100 0
65 1s. 6d. rose £6
66 2s. rose £7

Variety. "CONSULAR" *omitted.*

66*a* 1d. rose

These stamps were suppressed in 1887.

BRITISH INLAND MAIL.

4

1895 (JAN.). *T* **4.** *Typographed. Rouletted on black lines.*

(*a*) *Thick laid paper.*

69 4d. black 20 0 3 0

Error. The word "FOUR" *spelt* "FUOR".

69*a* 4d. black .. .. .. — £12

(*b*) *Wove paper.*

70 1d. blue-grey 15 0 1 6
71 6d. pale yellow 15 0 4 0
72 8d. salmon 15 0 3 0
73 1s. fawn 20 0 3 0
74 2s. bright rose 20 0 5 0
75 4s. grey 25 0 4 0

There are six types of each value, printed in groups repeated four times on each sheet; the upper and lower groups are *tête-bêche.*

5. Malagasy Runners.

1895 (MAR.). *T* **5.** *The inscription in the lower label varies for each value. Lithographed. P 12.*

78 2d. blue 1 3
a. Imperf. between (pair) ..
79 4d. rose 1 3
a. Imperf. between (pair) .. 30 0
80 6d. green 2 6
a. Imperf. between (pair) ..
81 1s. slate-blue 3 6
a. Imperf. between (pair) ..
82 2s. chocolate 4 6
a. Imperf. between (pair) ..
83 4s. bright purple 6 6
a. Imperf. between (pair) ..

This post was suppressed when the French entered Antananarivo at the end of September, 1895.

MALTA.

1

(Typo. De La Rue & Co.)

Type 1.

A. **1860** (DEC.)–**1863.** *No wmk. P 14.*

(i) *Blued paper.* (*1 Dec.,* 1860.)

1 ½d. buff £20 £20
a. Imperf. .. .. ..

(ii) *White paper.* (*Nov.,* 1861–63.)

2 ½d. pale buff £10 £8
3 ½d. brown-orange £8 £8
4 ½d. buff 80 0 70 0

The impression of Nos. 2 and 4 is clear, No. 3 being the blurred and muddy printing. In Nos. 3 and 4, and also No. 5, specks of carmine can be detected with a magnifying glass, and the inks are always muddy. Specimens also exist in which parts of the design are pure rose, due to defective mixing of the ink.

B. **1863–68.** *Wmk. Crown CC. P 14.*

5 ½d. buff (June, 1863) 75 0 50 0
6 ½d. bright orange (1864) .. 60 0 40 0
7 ½d. brown-red (1867) 75 0 45 0

Specimens of No. 5 exist on thin, surfaced paper, and others, reissued in 1865 and 1866, are on unsurfaced paper. The ink of No. 6 is mineral and, unlike No. 12, does not stain the paper. Most specimens are on thin, surfaced paper. Some shades of No. 7 may be described as chestnut. The ink of No. 7 is never muddy but clear, although sometimes in excess, and this distinguishes it from No. 5, with the deep shades of which it might otherwise be confused.

1868–71. *P 12½, rough* (*No.* 8), *or clean-cut* (*No.* 9).

8 ½d. buff-brown (1868) .. 35 0 35 0
a. Imperf. between (vert. pair) ..
9 ½d. yellow-orange (May, 1871) 50 0 50 0

1870–78. *P 14.*

10 ½d. dull orange (April, 1870) 60 0 45 0
11 ½d. orange-buff (1873) .. 60 0 50 0
12 ½d. golden yell. (*aniline*) (10.74) 75 0 70 0
13 ½d. yellow-buff 40 0 37 6
14 ½d. pale buff 37 6 37 6

1878 (JULY). *P 14×12½.*

15 ½d. yellow-buff 45 0 40 0
a. Perf. 12½×14 .. ..

1880–81. *P 14.*

16 ½d. bright orange-yellow (4.80) 30 0 25
17 ½d. yellow (Apl., 1881) .. 25 0 22

C. **1882** (April). *Wmk. Crown CA. P* 14.

18	½d. orange-yellow	30 0	30 0
19	½d. red-orange	15 0	15 0

2

3

4

(Typo. De La Rue & Co.)

1885 (1 Jan.). *T* **1, 2, 3** (*2d., 4d., and 1s.*), *and* **4.** *Wmk. Crown CA. P* 14.

20	½d. green	0 8	0 4
21	1d. rose	12 6	7 6
22	1d. carmine	1 6	0 4
23	2d. grey	2 6	2 0
24	2½d. dull blue	7 6	1 6
24*a*	2½d. bright blue	7 6	0 10
25	2½d. ultramarine	3 6	0 10
26	4d. brown	6 6	3 6
27	1s. violet	15 0	8 6
28	1s. pale violet	22 6	8 6

Variety. Imperf. (1893).

29	4d. brown (*pair*)	£150	£120

5

(Typo. De La Rue & Co.)

1886. *T* **5.** *Wmk. Crown CC. P* 14.

30	5s. rose	50 0	45 0

6. Gozo fishing boat. **7.** Ancient Maltese galley with Maltese flag.

8. Emblematic figure of Malta.

9. Shipwreck of St. Paul on the island and the attack by the asp.

(Recess. De La Rue & Co.)

1899 (4 Feb.). *P* 14.

T **6** *and* **7.** *Wmk. Crown CA.*

31	4½d. sepia	15 0	12 6
32	5d. vermilion	17 6	15 0

T **8** *and* **9.** *Wmk. Crown CC.*

33	2s. 6d. olive-grey	30 0	25 0
34	10s. blue-black	70 0	70 0

10. Harbour of Valletta.

One Penny

(**11**)

(Recess. De La Rue & Co.)

1901 (1 Jan.). *T* **10.** *Wmk. Crown CA. P* 14.

35	¼d. brown	0 6	0 4
36	¼d. red-brown	0 3	0 3

1902 (4 July). *Nos.* 24 *and* 24*a surcharged locally at the Government Printing Office with T* **11**, *in black.*

37	1d. on 2½d. dull blue	0 10	0 8
	a. Surcharge double		
38	1d. on 2½d. bright blue ..	0 8	0 8

Errors. " One Pnney ".

39	1d. on 2½d. dull blue	20 0	20 0
	a. Surcharge double, with error " One Pnney ".		
40	1d. on 2½d. bright blue ..	20 0	20 0

12

(Typo. De La Rue & Co.)

1903–4. *T* **12.** *Centre in first colour. Wmk. Crown CA. P* 14.

No.	Type	Description				
41		½d. green	2	0	0	3
42		1d. black and red	1	6	0	6
43		2d. purple and grey	15	0	10	6
44		2½d. marone and blue	15	0	6	0
45		3d. grey and purple	3	6	3	0
46		4d. black and brown (1904)	17	6	12	6
47		1s. grey and violet	15	0	8	0

1904–06. *Wmk. Mult. Crown CA. P* 14.

No.	Type	Description				
48	10	¼d. red-brown, O (1905)	0	6	0	3
49	12	½d. green, O	1	0	0	1
50	,,	1d. black & red, O ('05)	2	6	0	4
51	,,	2d. purple & grey, O ('05)	8	0	5	0
52	,,	2½d. marone & blue, O	6	6	5	0
54	,,	4d. black & brown, O ('06)	12	6	12	6
55	6	4½d. brown ('05)	15	0	12	6
56	7	5d. vermilion	15	0	10	6
57	12	1s. grey and violet, O	12	6	6	0

1907–11. *Wmk. Mult. Crown CA. P* 14.

No.	Type	Description				
58	10	¼d. deep brown, O ('10)	0	6	0	3
59	12	½d. deep green, O (1909)	0	6	0	1
60	,,	1d. red, O	1	0	0	4
61	,,	2d. grey, O (1911)	3	6	3	0
62	,,	2½d. bright blue, O (1911)	3	6	2	6
62a	,,	4d. blk. & red/*yell.*, O (1911)	5	0	6	0
63	6	4½d. orange (1911)	7	6	7	6
64	7	5d. pale sage-green (1910)	10	6	10	6
67	12	1s. black/*green*, O (1911)	12	6	10	0
68	,,	5s. green & red/*yell.*, C ('11)	50	0	35	0

13

14

15

(Typo. De La Rue & Co.)

1914–22. *Wmk. Mult. Crown CA. P* 14.

No.	Type	Description				
69	13	¼d. brown, O	0	4	0	2
70	,,	¼d. deep brown, O (1919)	0	4	0	2
71	,,	½d. green, O	0	8	0	1
72	,,	½d. deep green, O (1919)	0	8	0	1
73	,,	1d. carmine-red, O	0	8	0	3
74	,,	1d. scarlet, O (1915)	0	8	0	3
75	,,	2d. grey, O	8	0	5	0
76	,,	2d. deep slate, O (1919)	10	0	6	6
77	,,	2½d. bright blue, O	3	0	1	0
78	14	3d. purple/*yellow*, C (1920)	4	6	5	0
		a. On orange-buff	7	6	6	6
79	13	6d. dull and bright pur., C	7	6	6	6
80	,,	6d. dull pur. & mag., C ('19)	8	6	5	0
81	14	1s. black/*green*, C (1915)	15	0	6	0
		a. White back	12	6	8	6
		b. On blue-green, olive back	12	6	5	0
		c. On emerald surface	10	0	12	6
		d. On emerald back	20	0	10	6
86	15	2s. pur. & brt. blue/*blue*, C	32	6	20	0
86a	,,	2s. dull pur. & bl./*bl.*, C ('21)	50	0	30	0
87	,,	5s. green & red/*yellow*, C	£8		£7	

1914–15. *T* **10** *and* **7.** *Wmk. Mult. Crown CA. P* 14.

No.	Description				
89	4d. black	12	6	10	0
90	4d. grey-black	12	6	10	0
91	5d. deep sage-green	10	6	10	6

The design of the 4d. differs in various details from that of Type **10**.

WAR TAX

(16)

1918. *T* **13** *and* **12** *optd. with T* **16**, *in black.*

No.	Description				
92	½d. deep green (Jan.)	0	2	0	1
93	3d. grey and purple (March)	0	8	0	9

17

(Recess. De La Rue & Co.)

1919–20. *T* **8** *and* **17.** *Wmk. Mult. Crown CA. P* 14.

No.	Description				
94	2s. 6d. grey-green	80	0	55	0
95	2s. 6d. olive-grey (1920)	85	0	60	0
96	10s. black	£65			

18

(Type **18.** Typo. De La Rue & Co.)

1921–22. *Wmk. Mult. Script CA. P* 14.

No.	Type	Description				
97	13	¼d. brown, O	0	4	0	4
98	,,	½d. green, O	0	6	0	6
99	,,	1d. scarlet, O	0	4	0	3
100	18	2d. grey, O (1921)	2	6	2	6
101	13	2½d. bright blue, O	4	0	4	6
102	,,	6d. dull & bright pur., C	10	0	10	6
103	15	2s. pur. & blue/*blue*, C	40	0	45	0
104	17	10s. black, O	£22			

SELF-GOVERNMENT

(19)

SELF-GOVERNMENT

(20)

1922 (12 Jan.–Apr.). *Optd. with* T **19** *or* **20** (*large stamps*), *in black or red* (R.).

(*a*) *Wmk. Crown CC.*

105	**9**	10s. blue-black, O (R.).) ..	£11	£12

(*b*) *Wmk. Mult. Crown CA.*

106	**13**	½d. green, O	0 4	0 4
107	,,	2½d. bright blue, O ..	6 6	6 6
108	**14**	3d. purple/*orange-buff*, C	5 0	6 0
109	**13**	6d. dull & bright pur., C	6 6	6 6
110	**14**	1s. black/*emerald*, C ..	8 0	5 0
111	**15**	2s. dull purple and blue/ *blue*, C (R.)	£6	£7
112	**8**	2s. 6d. olive-grey, O ..	30 0	32 6
113	**15**	5s. green & red/*yellow*, C	50 0	55 0

(*c*) *Wmk. Mult. Script CA.*

114	**13**	¼d. brown, O	0 4	0 4
115	,,	½d. green, O	0 8	0 10
116	,,	1d. scarlet, O	0 6	0 6
117	**18**	2d. grey, O	1 9	1 9
118	**13**	2½d. bright blue, O ..	1 6	1 9
119	,,	6d. dull & bright purple, C	8 0	8 6
120	**15**	2s. dull purple and blue/ *blue*, C (R.)	35 0	35 0
121	**17**	10s. black, O (R.) ..	£6	£6

One Farthing

(21)

1922 (15 April). *No.* 100 *surcharged with* T **21** *in black.*

122	¼d. on 2d. grey	0 2	0 3

22 23

(Designed by C. Dingli (T **22**) and G. Vella (**23**). Printed by De La Rue & Co.).

1922 (Aug.)–**1925**. T **22** *and* **23**. *Wmk. Mult. Script CA. P* 14.

(*a*) *Typographed on chalk-surfaced paper.*

123	**22**	¼d. brown	0 4	0 3
123*a*	,,	¼d. chocolate-brown ..	0 4	0 2
124	,,	½d. green	0 4	0 3
125	,,	1d. orange and purple ..	1 9	0 8
126	,,	2d. bistre-brn. & turquoise	1 9	1 0
127	,,	3d. bright ultramarine ..	3 0	3 0
127*a*	,,	3d. cobalt	4 0	4 0
128	,,	4d. yellow and bright blue	4 6	6 0
129	,,	6d. olive-green and violet ..	4 0	4 6
130	**23**	1s. indigo and sepia ..	6 6	4 6
131	,,	2s. brown and blue ..	18 6	16 0
132	,,	2s. 6d. bright mag. & black	18 6	16 0
133	,,	5s. orange-yellow & bright ultramarine ..	27 6	27 6
134	,,	10s. slate-grey and brown ..	40 0	42 6

Stamps of T **22** have the watermark sideways. In T **23** it is upright.

(*b*) *Recess-printed.*

135	**22**	£1 black & carm.-red (1922)	£8	£9
136	,,	£1 black & brt. carm. (1925)	£6	£6

No. 135 is the first printing, with watermark sideways. No. 136 has the watermark upright.

1923–24. T **22**. *New colour and value. Wmk. Mult. Script CA. P* 14.

137	1d. bright violet (25.4.24) ..	0 8	0 8
138	1½d. brown-red (1.10.23) ..	1 0	0 6

Two pence halfpenny

(24)

POSTAGE

(25)

1925. T **22** *surcharged with* T **24**.

139	2½d. on 3d. cobalt (3 Dec.) ..	1 6	1 9
140	2½d. on 3d. brt. ultra. (24 Dec.)	2 0	2 6

1926 (Feb.). T **22**. *Wmk. Mult. Script CA. P* 14.

141	2½d. ultramarine	1 3	2 0
142	3d. black/*yellow*	1 9	2 6

1926 (1 April). T **22** *and* **23** *optd. with* T **25**.

143	¼d. brown	0 3	0 3
144	½d. green	0 2	0 3
145	1d. bright violet	0 6	0 4
146	1½d. brown-red	0 6	0 3
147	2d. bistre-brown & turquoise	1 0	0 6
148	2½d. ultramarine	1 3	0 10
149	3d. black/*yellow*	1 3	1 3
	a. Overprint inverted	£12	
150	4d. yellow and bright blue ..	9 0	12 0
151	6d. olive-green and violet ..	3 0	3 0
152	1s. indigo and sepia ..	8 6	7 6
153	2s. brown and blue	55 0	65 0
154	2s. 6d. bright magenta & blk.	15 0	20 0
155	5s. orge.-yell. & bright ultra.	18 6	22 6
156	10s. slate-grey and brown ..	25 0	32 6

26

27. Valletta Harbour.

28. St. Publius.

29. Mdina (Notabile).

30

31. Neptune.

32. Ruins at "Mnaidra."

33. St. Paul.

(T **26** typo., others recess by Waterlow & Sons, Ltd.)

1926–27. *T* **26** (*P* 15×14) *and* **27** *to* **33** (*P* 12½). *Inscr.* "POSTAGE." *Wmk. Mult. Script CA.*

No.	Type	Description				
157	**26**	¼d. brown ..	0	3	0	3
158	,,	½d. yellow-green ..	0	3	0	2
159	,,	1d. rose-red ..	0	4	0	5
160	,,	1½d. chestnut ..	0	8	0	6
161	,,	2d. greenish grey ..	1	0	1	3
162	,,	2½d. blue ..	1	9	2	0
162*a*	,,	3d. violet ..	2	0	2	6
163	,,	4d. black and red ..	2	6	2	6
164	,,	4½d. lavender and ochre ..	3	0	3	6
165	,,	6d. violet and scarlet ..	3	0	3	6
166	**27**	1s. black ..	6	6	5	0
167	**28**	1s. 6d. black and green ..	10	0	10	6
168	**29**	2s. black and purple ..	10	6	12	6
169	**30**	2s. 6d. black and vermilion	12	6	12	6
170	**31**	3s. black and blue ..	17	6	17	6
171	**32**	5s. black and green ..	25	0	25	0
172	**33**	10s. black and carmine ..	50	0	55	0

AIR

MAIL

(34)

1928 (1 Apr.). *T* **26** *overprinted with T* **34.**

No.	Description				
173	6d. violet and scarlet ..	3	6	4	6

POSTAGE AND REVENUE (35)

POSTAGE AND REVENUE. (36)

1928 (1 Oct.–Dec.). *T* **26** *to* **33** *optd.*

No.	Type	Description				
174	**35**	¼d. brown ..	0	2	0	2
175	,,	½d. yellow-green ..	0	2	0	2
176	,,	1d. rose-red ..	0	4	0	6
177	,,	1d. chestnut (Dec. '28) ..	0	6	0	4
178	,,	1½d. chestnut ..	0	9	0	6
179	,,	1½d. rose-red (Dec. '28) ..	0	10	0	4
180	,,	2d. greenish grey ..	1	6	1	9
181	,,	2½d. blue ..	2	0	1	9
182	,,	3d. violet ..	2	6	1	9
183	,,	4d. black and red ..	2	6	2	0
184	,,	4½d. lavender and ochre ..	2	6	2	6
185	,,	6d. violet and scarlet ..	4	6	3	6
186	**36**	1s. black (R.) ..	6	6	4	6
187	,,	1s. 6d. black and green (R.)	8	6	8	0
188	,,	2s. black and purple (R.)	10	6	10	0
189	,,	2s. 6d. black & verm. (R.)	15	0	12	6
190	**36**	3s. black and blue (R.) ..	20	0	17	6
191	,,	5s. black and green (R.) ..	27	6	32	6
192	,,	10s. black and carmine (R.)	55	0	57	6

1930 (20 Oct.). *Printer, processes, wmk. and perfs. as for* 1926–27 *issue. Designs as T* **26** *to* **33**, *but inscribed* "POSTAGE (&) REVENUE."

No.	Description				
193	¼d. brown ..	0	3	0	3
194	½d. yellow-green ..	0	2	0	1
195	1d. chestnut ..	0	4	0	4
196	1½d. rose-red ..	0	6	0	4
197	2d. greenish grey ..	0	10	0	10
198	2½d. blue ..	1	0	0	8
199	3d. violet ..	1	0	0	10
200	4d. black and red ..	1	3	2	0
201	4½d. lavender and ochre ..	2	6	2	0
202	6d. violet and scarlet ..	3	0	2	0
203	1s. black ..	6	0	5	0
204	1s. 6d. black and green ..	10	0	10	6
205	2s. black and purple ..	10	6	10	6
206	2s. 6d. black and vermilion	15	0	15	0
207	3s. black and blue ..	17	6	18	6
208	5s. black and green ..	27	6	30	0
209	10s. black and carmine ..	60	0	60	0

1935 (6 May). *Silver Jubilee. As T* **13** *of Antigua, inscribed* "MALTA". *Recess. B.W. & Co. Wmk. Mult. Script CA. P* 11×12.

No.	Description				
210	½d. black and green ..	0	3	0	6
211	2½d. brown and deep blue ..	3	6	5	0
212	6d. light blue and olive-green	6	6	6	6
213	1s. slate and purple ..	10	0	12	6

All values exist with the "double flagstaff" variety.

POSTAGE DUE STAMPS.

POSTAGE DUE

½d.

MALTA.

D 1

D 2

1925. *Type* D 1, *type-set locally. Imperf.*

No.	Description				
D 1	½d. black ..	0	2	0	4
D 2	1d. black ..	0	3	0	4
D 3	1½d. black ..	0	4	0	6
D 4	2d. black ..	0	5	0	6
D 5	2½d. black ..	0	6	0	9
	a. "2" of "½" omitted ..	£16			
D 6	3d. black/*grey* ..	0	8	1	0
D 7	4d. black/*buff* ..	1	3	1	6
D 8	6d. black/*buff* ..	1	6	1	9
D 9	1s. black/*buff* ..	2	6	3	0
D10	1s. 6d. black/*buff* ..	3	6	4	0

All the above may be had in *tête-bêche* pairs from the junction of the panes, price about four times that of a single stamp. Dangerous forgeries of No. D 5*a* are now in circulation.

(Typo. Bradbury, Wilkinson & Co., Ltd.)

1925. *Type* D 2. *Wmk. Mult. Script CA* (*sideways*). *P* 12.

No.	Description				
D11	½d. green ..	0	1	0	1
D12	1d. violet ..	0	2	0	2
D13	1½d. brown ..	0	3	0	3
D14	2d. grey ..	0	4	0	4
D15	2½d. orange ..	0	5	0	6
D16	3d. blue ..	0	6	0	6
D17	4d. olive-green ..	0	7	0	8
D18	6d. purple ..	0	9	0	10
D19	1s. black ..	1	6	1	9
D20	1s. 6d. carmine ..	2	3	2	6

MAURITIUS.

— SIMPLIFICATION (see p. xli) —

Nos. 1 to 34.

(1, 2). 22a, 24a. 29. 30. 32, 34.

1

2

(Engraved on copper by Mr. J. Barnard.)

1847 (21 SEPT.). *T* **1.** *Head of Queen on groundwork of diagonal and perpendicular lines. Imperf.*

1	1d. orange-red	£5000	£3500
2	2d. deep blue	£5000	£3500

NOTE.—*As the value of early Mauritius stamps depends so much on condition, we now indicate the approximate range of prices for each variety in used condition.*

1848 (MAY). *T* **2.** *Lettered "POST PAID." 12 varieties on the sheet. Imperf.*

Earliest impressions, thick yellowish paper.

		Un.	Used.
2a	1d. orange	£1300	£100 to £500
2b	2d. indigo-blue	£1300	£200 to £750
	Error, lettered "PENOE."		
2c	2d. indigo-blue	—	£400 to £1000
	Early impressions. Thin white or yellowish paper.		
3	1d. vermilion	£500	£70 to £200
4	2d. deep blue	—	£70 to £300
5	2d. blue	£750	£50 to £250
	Error, lettered "PENOE" (No. 7).		
6	2d. blue	—	£100 to £300
	Early impressions. Blue paper.		
7	1d. vermilion	£450	£50 to £200
8	2d. blue	—	£40 to £150
9	2d. blue (PENOE)	—	£70 to £250
	Intermediate impressions, showing the diagonal lines clearly, but few or none of the perpendicular lines. White or yellowish paper.		
10	1d. red	£400	£25 to £95
11	2d. deep blue	£300	£25 to £100
12	2d. blue	£200	£20 to £85
13	2d. blue (PENOE)	£350	£50 to £150
	Blue paper.		
14	1d. red	£275	£15 to £75
15	2d. deep blue	—	£20 to £85
16	2d. blue	£175	£15 to £75
17	2d. blue (PENOE)	—	£40 to £150
	Worn impressions, diagonal lines only. White or yellowish paper.		
18	1d. red	£90	£10 to £40
19	1d. red-brown	£90	£10 to £40
20	2d. blue	£125	£15 to £60
21	2d. blue (PENOE)	—	£20 to £75
	Blue paper.		
22	1d. red	£40	£8 to £30
	b. Doubly printed		
23	1d. red-brown	£50	£8 to £30
24	2d. blue	£95	£10 to £45
	b. Doubly printed		
25	2d. blue (PENOE)	—	£15 to £50
	Latest impressions, background nearly worn away and very few lines showing.		
22a	1d. red	£30	£3 to £15
23a	1d. red-brown	—	£3 to £15
24a	2d. blue	—	£5 to £25
25a	2d. blue (PENOE)	£100	£8 to £40

3

(Engraved on copper by Mr. Lapirot.)

1859 (MARCH). *T* **3.** *12 varieties on the sheet. Imperf. Early impressions.*

26	2d. deep blue	£250	£20 to £85
27	2d. blue	£150	£12 to £60

1859 (AUG.). *Intermediate prints. Lines of background, etc., partly worn away.*

28	2d. blue	£75	£10 to £35

1859 (OCT.). *Impressions from worn plate; bluish paper.*

29	2d. blue	£30	£4 to £16

4

5

1859 (OCT.). *T* **4.** *Bluish paper. Imperf.*

(The plate of 1848 re-engraved by Mr. Sherwin.)

30	2d. deep blue	£700	£30 to £175

Autotype illustrations in deep blue, on stout white wove paper faced with blue, were taken in 1877 from a sheet reprinted in black from the original plate.

(Lithographed in the colony by Mr. Dardenne.)

1859 (DEC.). *T* **5.** *White laid paper. Imperf.*

31	1d. deep red	£175	£20 to £75
31a	1d. red	£125	£15 to £60
32	1d. dull vermilion	£75	£10 to £50
33	2d. slate-blue	£200	£15 to £55
33a	2d. blue	£75	£6 to £30
34	2d. pale blue	£55	£5 to £25
	Retouched varieties.		
34a	2d. blue, heavy retouch on neck	—	£25 to £70
34b	2d. blue, slight retouches (several varieties)	—	£18 to £45

6

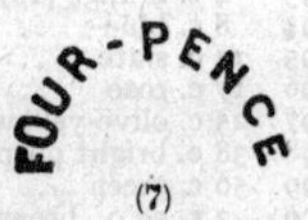

(7)

(Recess. Perkins Bacon & Co.)

1854 (8 April). *T* **6** *surcharged with T* **7**, *in black. Imperf.*

35	4d. green	£35	£22

1858–59. *T* **6.** *No value expressed. Imperf.*

36	(4d.) green	£15	£8
37	(6d.) vermilion	12 6	75 0
38	(9d.) dull magenta	£10	£5

Prepared for use, but not issued.

39	(No value), red-brown (1849) ..	3 0	
40	(No value), blue (1858) ..	1 6	

Remainders of these were overprinted "L.P.E. 1890" in *red*, perforated at the London Philatelic Exhibition and sold as souvenirs, but these of course have no philatelic interest.

No. 38 *was reissued in Nov.,* 1862, *as* 1d.; *stamps obliterated* "B 53" *were so used.*

41	(1d.) dull magenta	—	£10

8

(Recess. Perkins Bacon & Co.)

1859. *T* 8. *Imperf.*

42	6d. blue	£15	40 0
43	1s. vermilion	£25	70 0

1861. *T* 8. *Colours corrected. Imperf.*

44	6d. dull purple-slate	25 0	40 0
45	1s. yellow-green	£15	£7

1862. *T* 8. *Intermediate perf.* 14 *to* 16.

46	6d. slate	22 6	25 0
	a. Imperf. between (pair) ..	£50	
47	1s. deep green	£80	£8

9

10

(Typo. De La Rue & Co.)

1860–63. *T* **9.** *No wmk. P* 14.

48	1d. purple-brown	47 6	12 6
49	2d. blue	70 0	15 0
50	4d. rose	70 0	7 6
51	6d. green (1862)	£12	75 0
52	6d. slate (1863)	70 0	40 0
53	9d. dull purple	40 0	22 6
54	1s. buff (1862)	85 0	40 0
55	1s. green (1863)	£10	95 0

1863–72. *T* **9** (10d. *T* **10**). *Wmk. Crown CC. P* 14.

56	1d. purple-brown (1870) ..	15 0	6 6
57	1d. brown	17 6	7 6
58	1d. bistre	20 0	7 6
59	2d. pale blue	20 0	7 6
60	2d. bright blue	17 6	4 6
61	3d. deep red	30 0	17 6
61*a*	3d. dull red	20 0	12 6
62	4d. rose	12 6	2 0
63	6d. dull violet (1864) ..	35 0	15 0
64	6d. yellow-green (1865) ..	30 0	6 6
65	6d. blue-green	25 0	5 0
66	9d. yellow-green (1872) ..	50 0	55 0
67	10d. marone (1872)	40 0	12 6
68	1s. yellow	45 0	8 6
69	1s. orange	45 0	8 6
70	1s. blue (1870)	40 0	10 0
71	5s. rosy mauve	55 0	35 0
72	5s. bright mauve (1865) ..	80 0	25 0

Variety. Imperf.

73	2d. blue	£35	£25

½ d

HALF PENNY

(11)

Prepared for use, but not issued.

No. 53 *surcharged with T* **11**, *in red* (R). *or black* (B.).

74	½d. on 9d. dull purple (R.) ..	£20	
	a. Error. "PRNNY"		
75	½d. on 9d. dull purple (B.) ..	£35	

HALF PENNY

(12)

1876. *Nos.* 53 *and* 67 *surcharged with T* **12.**

76	½d. on 9d. dull purple	8 6	10 0
77	½d. on 10d. marone	6 6	8 0

Varieties. (i.) *Surcharge inverted*

78	½d. on 9d. dull purple	£15	

(ii.) *Surcharge double.*

78*a*	½d. on 9d. dull purple ..		

HALF PENNY

(13)

One Penny

(14)

One Shilling

(15)

1877. *T* **9** *and* **10**, *wmk. Crown CC, surcharged in black. P* 14.

April. *With T* **13.**

79	½d. on 10d. rose	3 0	7 6

6 Dec. *With T* **14** *or* **15.**

80	1d. on 4d. rose-carmine ..	7 6	8 6
81	1s. on 5s. rosy mauve	£5	80 0
82	1s. on 5s. bright mauve ..	£8	£6

2 CENTS

(16)

2 Rs. 50 C.

(17)

1878 (3 Jan.). *T* **10** *(with lower label blank) surch. with T* **16**, *in black. Wmk. Crown CC. P* 14.

83	2 c. dull rose	7	6	7	6

1878. *T* **9** *surcharged as T* **16** *or* **17**, *in black. Wmk. Crown CC. P* 14.

84	4 c. on 1d. bistre	6	6	7	0
85	8 c. on 2d. blue	7	6	3	0
86	13 c. on 3d. orange-red ..	10	0	12	0
87	17 c. on 4d. rose	32	6	10	0
88	25 c. on 6d. slate-blue	22	6	15	0
89	38 c. on 9d. pale violet ..	12	6	12	6
90	50 c. on 1s. green	15	0	12	6
91	2 r. 50 c. on 5s. bright mauve	22	6	22	6

18  19

20  21

22  23

24  25

26

(Typo. De La Rue & Co.)

1879–80. *T* **18** *to* **26**. *Wmk. Crown CC. P* 14.

92	2 c. Venetian red	12	6	6	6
93	4 c. orange (1879)	7	6	3	0
94	8 c. blue	7	6	2	0
95	13 c. slate	50	0	50	0
96	17 c. rose	15	0	8	6
97	25 c. olive-yellow (1879) ..	32	6	15	0
98	38 c. bright purple	50	0	50	0
99	50 c. green	6	6	6	6
100	2 r. 50 c., brown-purple ..	25	0	22	6

1882–83. *T* **18, 19** *and* **23**. *Wmk. Crown CA. P* 14.

101	2 c. Venetian red	5	0	2	6
102	4 c. orange	6	0	1	0
103	25 c. olive-yellow (1883) ..	10	0	6	0

16 CENTS
(26*a*)

SIXTEEN CENTS
(28)

1883 (26 Feb.). *No.* 96 *surcharged as T* **26a**.

(*a*) *Surcharge* 14 *mm. long and* 3½ *high.*
(*b*) *Surcharge* 15 *mm. long and* 3½ *high.*
(*c*) *Surcharge* 15 *mm. long and* 2½ *high.*

104	16 c. on 17 c. rose (*a*) ..	20	0	20	0
	a. Surcharge double				
105	16 c. on 17 c. rose (*b*) ..	18	0	17	6
106	16 c. on 17 c. rose (*c*) ..	40	0	35	0

1883 (14 July). *T* **22**. *Wmk. Crown CA. Surcharged with T* **28**. *P* 14.

107	16 c. on 17 c. rose	15	0	4	6

2 CENTS
(29)

1885 (11 May). *No.* 98 *surcharged with T* **29**.

108	2 c. on 38 c. bright purple ..	17	6	17	6

Varieties. (i.) *Without bar.*

108*a*	2 c. on 38 c. bright purple ..	—		60	0

(ii.) *Surcharge inverted.*

109	2 c. on 38 c. bright purple ..	£15		£15	

(iii.) *Surcharge double.*

109*a*	2 c. on 38 c. bright purple ..	£20			

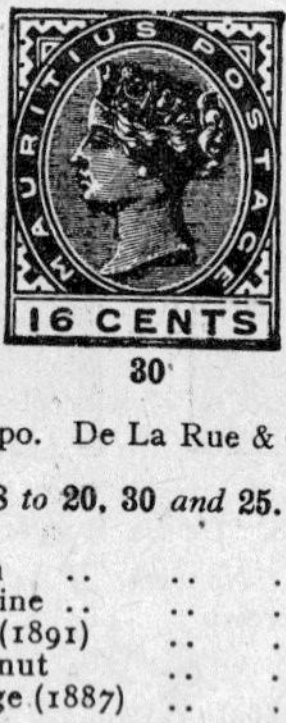

30

(Typo. De La Rue & Co.)

1885–91. *T* **18** *to* **20**, **30** *and* **25**. *Wmk. Crown CA. P* 14.

110	2 c. green	1	0	0	3
111	4 c. carmine	1	3	0	2
112	8 c. blue (1891)	3	6	2	6
113	16 c. chestnut	4	0	1	0
114	50 c. orange (1887)	20	0	8	6

2 CENTS
(31)

1887 (6 July). *No.* 95 *surcharged with T* **31.**

115	2 c. on 13 c. slate (R.) ..	17	6	17	6

Varieties. (i.) *Surcharge inverted.*

116	2 c. on 13 c. slate	70	0	70	0

(ii.) *Surcharge double, one on the back of the stamp.*

116*a*	2 c. on 13 c. slate	£18			

(iii.) *Surcharge double.*

116*b*	2 c. on 13 c. slate	—		£12	

TWO CENTS (32) TWO CENTS (33)

1891 (Sept.). *Surcharged with T* **32** *on* 4 *c.*, 17 *c.*, *and* 38 *c.* (*No.* 98), *and as T* **33** *on* 38 *c.* (*No.* 89), *in black.*

117	2 c. on 4 c. (No. 111) ..	1	6	0	6
118	2 c. on 17 c. (No. 96) ..	25	0	27	6
119	2 c. on 38 c. (No. 89) ..	3	6	3	6
120	2 c. on 38 c. (No. 98) ..	3	6	3	6

Varieties. (i.) *Surcharge inverted.*

120*a*	2 c. on 4 c.	85	0		
120*b*	2 c. on 17 c...	£10			
121	2 c. on 38 c. (No. 89) ..	£5			
121*a*	2 c. on 38 c. (No. 98) ..	£16			

(ii.) *Surcharge double.*

121*b*	2 c. on 4 c.	£8		90	0
121*c*	2 c. on 17 c...	£22			
122	2 c. on 38 c. (No. 98) ..	75	0		
122*a*	2 c. on 38 c. (No. 89) ..	£18			

(iii.) *Surcharge double, one inverted.*

122*b*	2 c. on 4 c.	85	0	85	0
122*c*	2 c. on 38 c. (No. 89) ..	60	0		
122*d*	2 c. on 38 c. (No. 98) ..	75	0		

Minor varieties are also known with portions of the surcharge missing, due to defective printing.

ONE CENT (34) ONE CENT (35)

1893 (1 Jan.). *T* **18** *and* **30** *surcharged with T* **34** *and* **35** *respectively, in black. Wmk. Crown CA. P* 14.

123	1 c. on 2 c. pale violet ..	0	3	0	4
124	1 c. on 16 c. chestnut ..	1	0	1	3

1893-94. *T* **18** (1 *c.*) *and* **30** (15 *c.*). *Wmk. Crown CA. P* 14.

125	1 c. pale violet	0	6	0	4
126	15 c. chestnut	1	0	0	6
127	15 c. blue	5	0	1	3

MAURITIUS 1 CENT

36

(Typo. De La Rue & Co.)

1895-99. *T* **36.** *Wmk. Crown CA. P* 14.

128	1 c. dull purple & ultram. ..	0	4	0	2
129	2 c. dull purple and orange..	0	4	0	1
130	3 c. dull purple & deep pur.	0	8	0	6
131	4 c. dull purple & emerald ..	0	8	0	4
131*a*	6 c. green and rose-red ..	2	0	1	0
132	18 c. green & ultramarine ..	4	0	2	6

MAURITIUS POSTAGE 1837 1897 DIAMOND JUBILEE STELLA CLAVISQUE MARIS INDICI V R THIRTY SIX CENTS

37

(Typo. De La Rue & Co.)

1898 (23 May). *Jubilee issue. T* **37.** *Wmk. CA. over Crown, sideways. P* 14.

133	36 c. orange & ultramarine	7	6	8	0

6 CENTS (38) 15 CENTS (39)

1899. *Nos.* 132 *and* 133 *surcharged with T* **38** *and* **39** *respectively.*

134	6 c. in *red*, on 18 c. grn. & ult.	1	6	1	6
	a. Surcharge inverted	£7		£6	
135	15 c. in *blue*, on 36 c. or. & ult.	3	0	3	0
	a. Bar of surcharge omitted ..				

The space between "6" and "cents" varies from $2\frac{1}{2}$ to 4 mm.

MAURITIUS MAHÉ DE LA BOURDONNAIS 15 CENTS 1699 1899

40. Admiral Mahé de La Bourdonnais, Governor of Mauritius, 1734-46.

(Recess. De La Rue & Co.)

1899 (Dec.). *Bicentenary of birth of La Bourdonnais. T* **40.** *Wmk. Crown CC. P* 14.

136	15 c. ultramarine	4	6	4	6

4 Cents (41) 12 CENTS (42)

1900. *No. 113 surcharged with T* **41.**

137	4 c. on 16 c. chestnut ..	1 6	1 9

T **36.** *Wmk. Crown CA.* *P* 14.

138	1 c. grey and black ..	0 3	0 3
139	2 c. dull and bright purple ..	0 6	0 4
140	4 c. purple & carmine/*yellow*	0 10	0 4
141	15 c. green and orange ..	10 6	10 6

1902. *No. 132 surcharged with T* **42.**

142	12 c. on 18 c. green & ultram.	5 0	6 0

The bar cancelling the original value seems in some cases to be one thick bar and in others two thin ones.

Postage & Revenue.

(43)

1902. *Various stamps overprinted with T* **43.**

143	4 c. pur. & car./*yell.* (No. 140)	0 8	0 8
144	6 c. green & red (No. 131*a*)	1 9	1 9
145	15 c. green & orange (No. 141)	2 6	2 6
146	25 c. olive-yellow (No. 103)	5 0	4 6
147	50 c. green (No. 99) ..	7 6	6 0
148	2 r. 50 c. brn.-pur. (No. 100)	52 6	55 0

No. 133 *surcharged as T* **42,** *but with longer bar, in black.*

149	12 c. on 36 c. orange & ultram.	2 6	2 6
	a. Surcharge inverted ..	£15	£8

The note below No. 142 also applies to No. 149.

44

(Typo. De La Rue & Co.)

1902–5. *T* **36** (*wmk. Crown CA*) *and* **44** (1 *r. wmk. Crown CC,* 2½ *and* 5 *r. wmk. Crown CA*). *P* 14.

150	3 c. green & carmine/*yellow*	2 0	1 9
151	4 c. grey-green and violet ..	1 3	0 4
152	4 c. black and carmine/*blue*	1 9	0 6
153	5 c. dull & bright purple/*buff*	3 0	4 0
154	5 c. dull pur. & black/*buff* ..	2 0	1 3
155	6 c. purple & carmine/*red* ..	1 6	0 10
156	8 c. green and black/*buff* ..	1 9	2 0
157	12 c. grey-black and carmine	1 9	1 9
158	15 c. black & blue/*blue* ('05)	7 6	1 6
159	25 c. green & carmine/*grn.*, OC	7 6	7 6
160	50 c. dull grn. & deep grn./*yell.*	10 6	12 6
161	1 r. grey-black and carmine	20 0	15 0
162	2½ r. green & black/*blue* ..	22 6	25 0
163	5 r. purple & carmine/*red* ..	50 0	55 0

1904–07. *T* **36** *and* **44** *Wmk. Mult. Crown CA. P* 14.

164	1 c. grey & black, C (1907) ..	0 6	0 3
165	2 c. dull & brt. pur., OC ('05)	1 0	0 2
166	3 c. grn. & carm./*yell.*, C ..	7 6	7 6
167	4 c. black & carm./*blue*, OC	1 3	0 4
168	6 c. purple & carm./*red*, OC	1 9	0 6
171	15 c. black & blue/*blue*, C ('07)	6 0	3 0
174	50 c. grn. & dp. grn./*yellow*, C	5 0	5 0
175	1 r. grey-blk. & car., C ('07)	10 6	7 6

46

47

(Typo. De La Rue & Co.)

1910. *Wmk. Mult. Crown CA. P* 14.

181	**46**	1 c. black, O	0 3	0 [illegible]
182	,,	2 c. brown, O	0 3	0 1
183	,,	3 c. green, O	0 6	0 3
184	,,	4 c. pale yellow-green and carmine, O	0 6	0 2
185	**47**	5 c. grey and carmine, O	2 0	1 6
186	**46**	6 c. carmine-red, O ..	0 8	0 3
186*a*	,,	6 c. pale red, O	1 0	0 3
187	,,	8 c. orange, O	2 0	1 3
188	**47**	12 c. greyish slate, O ..	1 9	1 6
189	**46**	15 c. blue, O	2 6	0 6
190	**47**	25 c. black & red/*yell.*, C ..	7 6	6 0
191	,,	50 c. dull pur. & black, C	7 6	7 6
192	,,	1 r. black/*green*, C ..	10 6	8 6
193	,,	2½ r. black & red/*blue*, C ..	25 0	27 6
194	,,	5 r. green & red/*yell.*, C ..	35 0	35 0
195	,,	10 r. green & red/*green*, C	£5	70 0

In Nos. 188, 190 and 195, the value labels are as in T **49.**

48

49

(Typo. De La Rue & Co.)

1913–23. *T* **48** *and* **49** (12 *c.,* 25 *c., and* 10 *r.*). *Wmk. Mult. Crown CA. P* 14.

196	5 c. grey & carm., O (1915)	1 3	0 8
197	5 c. slate-grey & carmine, O	1 6	0 8
198	12 c. greyish slate, O (1915) ..	1 9	1 6
199	25 c. black & red/*yell.*, C ('13)	2 6	2 0
	a. *White back* (1916)	3 6	4 6
	b. *On orange-buff*	27 6	27 6
	c. *On pale yellow* (Die I) ..	20 0	17 6
	d. *On pale yellow* (Die II) ..	2 6	3 0
200	50 c. dull purple and blk., C	22 6	22 6
201	1 r. black/*blue-green*, C (*olive back*) (1917)	7 6	6 6
	a. *On emerald surface*	25 0	25 0
	b. *On emerald back* (Die II) ..	6 0	6 0
202	2 r. 50 c. blk. & red/*blue*, C	12 6	12 6
203	5 r. grn. & red/*orge.-buff*, C ..	70 0	75 0
	a. *On pale yellow* (Die I) ..	95 0	95 0
	b. *On pale yellow* (Die II) ..	£9	£10
204	10 r. green & red/*green*, C ..	70 0	75 0
	a. *On blue-green, olive back* ..	£40	
	b. *On emerald surface*	90 0	95 0
	c. *On emerald back* (Die I) ..	70 0	70 0
	d. *On emerald back* (Die II) ..	50 0	55 0

1921–34. *Wmk. Mult. Script CA. P* 14.

(*a*) *T* **46.** (*Arms.*)

205	1 c. black, O	0 3	0 3
206	2 c. brown, O	0 4	0 2
207	4 c. pale olive-grn. & car., O	1 3	0 3
208	4 c. green, O	0 8	0 3
209	6 c. carmine, O	1 3	0 8
210	6 c. bright mauve, O ..	0 8	0 4

210*a* 8 c. orange, O 1 9 3 0
211 10 c. grey, O 2 0 2 6
212 12 c. carmine-red, O 2 0 1 6
213 15 c. blue, O 4 0 2 6
214 20 c. blue, O 2 6 2 0

MAURITIUS 12c (A) MAURITIUS 12c (B)

Two types of duty plate in the 12 c. In Type B, the letters of "MAURITIUS" are larger; the extremities of the downstroke and the tail of the "2" are pointed, instead of square, and the "c" is larger.

(*b*) *T* **48** **49.** (*King.*)

215 5 c. grey & car. O (Die II) 0 3 0 2
215*a* 5 c. grey & car. O (Die I) ('32) 0 6 0 6
216 12 c. grey, O (1921) (A) .. 4 0 4 6
216*a* 12 c. pale grey, O ('28) (A 1 9 0 10
216*b* 12 c. grey, O ('34) (B) .. 0 10 0 6
217 12 c. carmine-red, O ('22) 2 0 2 6
218 25 c. black and red/*paley low*, C (Die II) 1 3 0 10
218*a* 25 c. black and red/*pale yellow*, C (Die I) ('32) 3 6 4 0
219 50 c. dull pur. & black, C 6 0 2 6
220 1 r. blk./*emer.*, C (Die II) 6 0 1 3
220*a* 1 r. blk./*emer.*, C (Die I)('32 20 0 15 0
221 2 r. 50 c. blk. & red/*blue*, C 12 6 7 6
222 5 r. green & red/*yellow*, C .. 25 0 17 6
223 10 r. grn. & red/*emer.*, C ('28) 50 0 55 0

1924. *T* **44**, *but Arms similar to T* **46** *Wmk. Mult. Script CA. P* 14.

224 50 r. dull purple & green, C £18 £20

3
Cents

(50)

1925. *T* **46** *surcharged as T* **50.**

225 3 c. on 4 c. green 5 0 4 0
226 10 c. on 12 c. carmine-red .. 1 0 1 0
227 15 c. on 20 c. blue 1 9 2 0

1926. *T* **46** (*Arms*). *Wmk. Mult. Script CA. P* 14.

228 2 c. purple/*yellow*, O 0 3 0 3
229 3 c. green, O 0 4 0 4
230 4 c. brown, O 0 6 0 8
231 10 c. carmine-red, O 1 6 2 0
232 12 c. grey, O 1 3 1 6
233 15 c. cobalt, O 1 3 0 6
234 20 c. purple, O 2 0 1 9

1926–34. *As T* **49** (*King*). *Wmk. Mult. Script CA. P* 14.

235 1 c. black, O 0 3 0 3
236 2 c. brown, O 0 2 0 1
237 3 c. green, O 0 4 0 3
238 4 c. sage-green and carmine, O (Die II) ('27) .. 0 8 0 4
238*a* 4 c. sage-green and carmine, O (Die I) ('32) 1 3 1 0
238*b* 4 c. green, O (Die I) ('33) .. 0 8 0 6
239 6 c. sepia, O ('28) 1 0 0 8
240 8 c. orange, O 4 0 4 6
241 10 c. carmine-red, O (Die II) 0 8 0 8
241*a* 10 c. car.-red, O (Die I) ('32) 1 3 1 0
242 15 c. Prussian blue, O ('28) 1 9 0 8
243 20 c. purple, O ('27) 2 6 1 3
244 20 c. Prussian blue, O (Die I) ('33) 2 6 2 0
244*a* 20 c. Prussian blue, O (Die II) ('34) 1 6 1 6

1935 (6 MAY). *Silver Jubilee. As T* **13** *of Antigua, inscr.* "MAURITIUS". *Recess D.L.R. & Co. Wmk. Mult. Script CA. P* 13½ × 14.

245 5 c. ultramarine and grey .. 0 8 1 3
246 12 c. green and indigo .. 4 0 4 6
247 20 c. brown and deep blue .. 7 6 10 0
248 1 r. slate and purple .. £6 £6

EXPRESS DELIVERY STAMPS.

EXPRESS DELIVERY 15c. (91)

EXPRESS DELIVERY (INLAND) 15c. (92)

EXPRESS DELIVERY (INLAND) 15 c. (93)

(FOREIGN) EXPRESS DELIVERY 18 CENTS (94)

1903. *No.* 136 *surcharged in red.*

E1 15 c. on 15 c. ultramarine .. 3 6 3 6
E2 **92** 15 c. on 15 c. ultramarine . 7 6 7 6
E3 **93** 15 c. on 15 c. ultramarine .. 3 0 3 0
a. Surcharge double ..
b. Surcharge inverted .. — 80 0
c. "INLAND" inverted ..
d. "A" of "INLAND" inverted .. ..
e. Imperf. between (pair) ..
f. Surcharge double, both inverted .. ..

In T **92** the word "INLAND" was inserted at a second printing on stamps already surcharged with T **91** (No. E. 1); T **93** is a new setting of the surcharge made at one printing.

1904. *T* **44** (*without value in label*), *wmk. Crown CC, surcharged with T* **94**, *in black. P* 14.

E4 18 c. green 6 6 7 6

Error "FORE!GN" (*note of exclamation* "!" *instead of* "I").

E5 18 c. green £22

1904. *T* **44** *surcharged with T* **93**, *in red.*

E6 15 c. grey-green 2 6 1 6
a. Surcharge double 95 0 85 6
b. Surcharge inverted .. £8 £0
c. "LNIAND" £9 £8

Variety c. inverted is a forgery.

POSTAGE DUE STAMPS.

D1

(Typo. De La Rue & Co.)

1933. *T* **D 1.** *Wmk. Mult. Script CA. P* 15 × 14.

D1	2 c. black	0	1	0	2
D2	4 c. violet	0	2	0	3
D3	6 c. scarlet	0	3	0	5
D4	10 c. green	0	3	0	5
D5	20 c. bright blue	0	6	0	9

FISCALS USED FOR POSTAGE.

INLAND
REVENUE
(101)

INLAND REVENUE
(102)

1889. *T* **19**, *wmk. Crown CA, overprinted in black. P* 14.

R1	**101** 4 c. carmine	4	0	3	0
R2	**102** 4 c. lilac	6	0	6	0

103

(Typo. De La Rue & Co.)

1896–98. *T* **103.** *Wmk. Crown CA. P* 14.

R2a	4 c. dull purple	12	6
R3	4 c. green (1898)	10	0

MESOPOTAMIA.

See under **IRAQ.**

MONTSERRAT

1

MONTSERRAT
(2)

(T 1. Recess. De La Rue & Co.)

1876 (SEPT.). *T* **1.** *Wmk. Crown CC. P* 14. *Stamps of Antigua overprinted with T* **2**, *in black.*

1	1d. red	12	6	12	6
	a. Bisected (½d.)	—		£15	
	b. Inverted "S"	£30		£25	
2	6d. green	40	0	30	0
	a. Bisected (used as 2½d.) ..				
	b. Inverted "S"	£40		£30	
3	6d. blue-green	£20			

The 1d. stamp of this issue was bisected and used as a ½d. in 1883. This bisected stamp is often seen surcharged with a small "½" in *black;* such surcharge is bogus. The 6d. in **blue-green is only known unused.**

3 (Die I.)

(Typo. De La Rue & Co.)

1880 (JAN.). *T* **3.** *Wmk. Crown CC. P* 14.

4	2½d. red-brown	£8		95	0
5	4d. blue	60	0	45	0

1884–85. *T* **1** (1d.) *and* **3.** *Wmk. Crown CA P* 14.

6	½d. dull green	4	0	4	6
7	1d. red	10	0	10	0
	a. Inverted "S"				
8	1d. rose-red	15	0	15	0
	a. Bisected vertically (½d.) ..	—		£6	
9	2½d. red-brown	80	0	65	0
10	2½d. ultramarine	10	6	12	6
11	4d. blue	£35		£10	
12	4d. mauve	10	6	10	6

1884 (MAY). *T* **1.** *Wmk. Crown CA. P* 12.

13	1d. red	55	0	45	0
	a. Inverted "S"				
	b. Bisected (½d.)	—		£18	

The stamps for Montserrat were superseded by the general issue for Leeward Islands in 1890, but the following issues were or are in concurrent use with the stamps inscribed "LEEWARD ISLANDS".

4. Device of the Colony.

5

(Typo. De La Rue & Co.)

1903. *T* **4.** *Wmk. Crown CA. P* 14.

14	½d. grey-green and green ..	3	0	4	0
15	1d. grey-black and red ..	2	6	2	0
16	2d. grey and brown	10	6	10	6
17	2½d. grey and blue	8	6	10	0
18	3d. dull orange & deep purple	12	6	15	0
19	6d. dull purple and olive ..	20	0	20	0
20	1s. green and bright purple ..	25	0	25	0
21	2s. green and brown-orange ..	35	0	35	0
22	2s. 6d. green and black ..	35	0	35	0

T **5.** *Wmk. Crown CC. P* 14.

23	5s. black and scarlet ..	£10		£10	

1903–08. *T* **4** *and* **5.** *Wmk. Multiple Crown CA. P* 14.

24	½d. grey-green and green, OC	1	9	2	0
25	1d. grey-black & red, C ('08)	30	0	30	0
26	2d. grey and brown, OC ..	4	0	5	0
27	2½d. grey and blue, C ('06) ..	10	0	10	6
28	3d. dull orge. & deep pur., OC	5	0	6	0
29	6d. dull purple & olive, OC ..	10	6	12	6
30	1s. grn. & brt. pur., C ('08) ..	17	6	17	6
31	2s. green & orange, C ('08) ..	50	0	50	0
32	2s. 6d. green & black, C ('08)	50	0	50	0
33	5s. black and red, C ('07) ..	£8		£9	

1908–13. *T* 4 *and* 5. *Wmk. Mult. Crown CA. P* 14.

No.			
35	½d. deep green, O	0 10	1 0
36	1d. rose-red, O	2 6	1 6
38	2d. greyish slate, O	5 0	6 0
39	2½d. blue, O	5 0	5 0
40	3d. purple/*yellow*, C	5 0	6 0
	a. White back (1913)	17 0	20 0
43	6d. dull and deep purple, C ..	10 6	10 6
43*a*	6d. dull & bright purple, C ..	10 0	10 6
44	1s. black/*green*, C	12 6	12 6
45	2s. pur. & brt. blue/*blue*, C ..	25 0	25 0
46	2s. 6d. black & red/*blue*, C ..	25 0	27 6
47	5s. red and green/*yellow*, C ..	75 0	80 0

7

(Typo. De La Rue & Co.)

1914. *T* 7. *Wmk. Mult. Crown CA. P* 14.

48	5s. red and green/*yellow*, C ..	£8	£10

8

1916–23. *T* 8. *Wmk. Mult. Crown CA. P* 14.

No.			
50	½d. green, O	0 6	0 6
51	1d. scarlet, O	1 0	0 10
52	1d. carmine-red, O	0 10	0 9
53	2d. grey, O	3 0	3 0
54	2½d. bright blue, O	2 0	2 6
55	3d. purple/*yellow*, C	3 6	4 0
	a. On pale yellow	3 0	4 0
56	4d. grey-black and red/*pale yellow*, C (1923)	12 6	15 0
57	6d. dull and deep purple, C ..	6 0	6 6
58	1s. blk./*blue-grn.*, C (*olive back*)	10 6	12 0
59	2s. purple and blue/*blue*, C ..	17 0	20 0
60	2s. 6d. black & red/*blue*, C ..	20 0	22 6
61	5s. green and red/*yellow*, C ..	47 6	50 0

WAR STAMP

(9)

1917 (Oct.). *T* 8 *optd. with T* 9.

62	½d. green (R.)	0 2	0 4

1918. *As No.* 62, *but overprinted in black.*

No.			
63	½d. green	0 2	0 4
64	½d. deep green	0 3	0 5

1919. *T* 8. *Special printing in orange. Value and* "WAR STAMP" *as T* 9 *inserted in black at one printing.*

No.			
65	1½d. black and orange ..	0 3	0 4

1922–29. *T* 8. *Wmk. Mult. Script CA. P* 14.

No.			
66	½d. brown, O	0 6	0 8
67	½d. green, O	0 4	0 4
68	1d. bright violet, O	0 8	0 8
68*a*	1d. carmine, O (1929) ..	0 6	0 6
69	1½d. orange-yellow, O ..	4 0	5 0
70	1½d. carmine, O	1 0	1 3
70*a*	1½d. red-brown, O (1929) ..	0 9	1 0
71	2d. grey, O	1 3	1 6
72	2½d. deep bright blue, O ..	2 6	2 9
72*a*	2½d. pale bright blue, O ('26)	1 3	1 6
73	2½d. orange-yellow, O (1923)	3 0	4 0
74	3d. dull blue, O (1923) ..	1 9	2 0
74*a*	3d. purple/*yellow*, C (1927) ..	2 0	2 6
75	4d. black & red/*pale yell.*, C	2 6	2 9
76	5d. dull purple and olive, C	20 0	25 0
77	6d. pale & bright purple, C	3 0	3 6
78	1s. black/*emerald*, C.. ..	8 0	8 6
79	2s. purple and blue/*blue*, C..	12 0	12 6
80	2s. 6d. black and red/*blue*, C	15 0	17 6
81	3s. green and violet, C ..	18 0	20 0
82	4s. black and scarlet, C ..	25 0	22 6
83	5s. grn. & red/*pale yellow*, C	35 0	40 0

10. Plymouth.

(Recess. De La Rue & Co., Ltd.)

1932 (18 April). *Tercentenary issue. T* 10. *Wmk. Mult. Script CA. P* 14.

84	½d. green	2 0	2 6
85	1d. scarlet	2 6	4 0
86	1½d. red-brown	8 0	10 0
87	2d. grey	10 6	12 6
88	2½d. ultramarine	10 6	15 0
89	3d. orange	17 6	20 0
90	6d. violet	27 6	37 6
91	1s. olive-brown	55 0	65 0
92	2s. 6d. purple	£6	£7
93	5s. chocolate	£9	£12

1935 (6 May). *Silver Jubilee. As T* 13 *of Antigua, inscr.* "MONTSERRAT". *Recess. W'low & Sons. Wmk. Mult. Script CA. P* 11×12.

94	1d. deep blue and scarlet ..	1 0	1 3
95	1½d. ultramarine and grey ..	1 3	1 9
96	2½d. brown and deep blue ..	17 6	20 0
97	1s. slate and purple	30 0	35 0

MOROCCO.
(BRITISH POST OFFICES).

I. FOR GENERAL USE AT THE BRITISH POST OFFICES THROUGHOUT MOROCCO.

Morocco

Agencies

(1)

1898. *Contemporary stamps of Gibraltar (T 7) overprinted.*

I. *Local overprint at the office of the* "Gibraltar Chronicle." *Wide* "M" *and ear of* "g" *projecting upwards, T* 1.

(*a*) *In black.*

No.	Description		
1	5 c. green	0 8	0 10
2	10 c. carmine	1 0	0 8
	a. Overprint double		
3	20 c. olive-green	3 0	3 6
	a. Overprint double		
3*b*	20 c. olive-green and brown	4 0	3 0
4	25 c. ultramarine	2 6	2 6
5	40 c. orange-brown	5 0	6 0
6	50 c. bright lilac	17 6	20 0
7	1 p. bistre and ultramarine	4 0	5 0
8	2 p. black and carmine	5 0	6 0

Error of overprint "Λ" for "A."

(*No.* 36 *on right-hand pane.*)

No.	Description		
9	5 c. green	25 0	25 0
10	10 c. carmine	£15	£15
11	20 c. olive-green and brown	25 0	27 6
12	25 c. ultramarine	£8	£5
13	40 c. orange-brown	£12	£12
14	50 c. bright lilac	£15	£15
15	1 p. bistre and ultramarine	£12	£12
16	2 p. black and carmine	£17	£17

This error occurs once in a sheet of 120 (two panes).

(*b*) *In blue.*

No.	Description		
17	40 c. orange-brown	20 0	22 6
18	50 c. bright lilac	3 6	4 0
19	1 p. bistre and ultramarine	60 0	65 0

The *blue* overprint can be easily distinguished by looking through the stamp in front of a strong light.

Morocco
Agencies
(2)

Morocco
(3)

II. *London overprint, in black. Narrow* "M" *and ear of* "g" *level with top of letter, T* 2.

No.	Description		
22	5 c. green	1 0	0 6
23	10 c. carmine	1 6	0 4
24	20 c. olive-green	3 6	3 0
25	25 c. ultramarine	4 0	3 0
26	40 c. orange-brown	8 0	8 0
27	50 c. bright lilac	7 6	6 6
28	1 p. bistre and ultramarine	12 6	10 6
29	2 p. black and carmine	15 0	15 0

Varieties. (A) *With broad top to* "M," *as T* 3 (*No.* 39 *on left-hand pane.*)

(B) *Hyphen between letters* "n-c" *of* "Agencies." (*No.* 17 *on right-hand pane.*)

No.	Description	A		B	
30	5 c. green	5 0	5 0	7 6	7 6
31	10 c. carmine	5 0	5 0	7 6	7 6
32	20 c. ol.-grn.	12 6	12 6	12 6	12 6
33	25 c. ultram.	12 6	12 6	15 0	15 0
34	40 c. orge.-brn	42 6	42 6	60 0	60 0
35	50 c. bt. lilac	65 0	65 0	65 0	65 0
36	1 p. bis. & ul.	90 0	90 0	90 0	90 0
37	2 p. blk. & car.	£9	£9	£12	£12

1903–5. *T* 8 *of Gibraltar, but with value in Spanish currency, overprinted with T* 2 *in black. Wmk. Crown CA. P* 14.

No.	Description		
46	5 c. grey-green & green	3 0	3 0
47	10 c. dull purple/*red*	5 0	3 0
48	20 c. grey-green & car. (1904)	7 6	8 6
49	25 c. purple & black/*blue*	4 0	2 0
50	50 c. purple and violet (1905)	27 6	32 6
51	1 p. black and carmine (1905)	15 0	16 0
52	2 p. black and blue (1905)	32 6	32 6

Varieties. (A) *As T* 3. (B) *Hyphen between letters* "n-c."

No.	Description	A		B	
53	5 c.	12 6	12 6	17 6	17 6
54	10 c.	17 6	17 6	16 6	16 6
55	20 c.	20 0	20 0	25 0	25 0
56	25 c.	25 0	25 0	17 6	17 6
57	50 c.	£14	£14	£12	£12
58	1 p.	£10	£10	£9	£9
59	2 p.	£15	£15	£12	£12

1905–06. *As No.* 46, *etc., but wmk. Mult. Crown CA.*

No.	Description		
67	5 c. grey-green & green, OC	3 0	2 6
68	10 c. dull purple/*red*, OC	2 6	1 6
69	20 c. grey-grn. & car., O ('06)	5 0	5 0
70	25 c. pur. & blk./*blue*, C ('06)	10 0	10 0
71	50 c. purple and violet, C	15 0	12 6
72	1 p. black and carmine, C	22 6	22 6
73	2 p. black and blue, C	20 0	20 0

Varieties. (A) *As T* 3. (B) *Hyphen between letters* "n-c."

No.	Description	A		B	
74	5 c.	17 6	17 6	£15	—
75	10 c.	7 6	7 6	†	
76	20 c.	50 0	50 0	†	
77	25 c.	£5	£5	†	
78	50 c.	£8	£8	†	
79	1 p.	£9	£9	†	
80	2 p.	£10	£10	†	

MOROCCO
AGENCIES

MOROCCO
AGENCIES

5 CENTIMOS
(4)

6 PESETAS
(5)

1907–12. *Contemporary stamps of Great Britain (King Edward VII) surcharged as T* 4 (5 *c. to* 1 *p.*) *and* 5 (3 *p. to* 12 *p.*), *in black.*

No.	Description		
82	5 c. on ½d. pale green, O	1 3	0 8
83	10 c. on 1d. scarlet, O	1 9	0 6
84	15 c. on 1½d. purple & grn., C	3 6	2 0
	a. "1" of "15" omitted	£70	
85	20 c. on 2d. green & carm., C	3 0	2 0
86	25 c. on 2½d. bright blue, O	3 6	2 6
87	40 c. on 4d. grn. & pur.-brn., C	4 0	6 0
88	40 c. on 4d. orange, O (1910)	2 0	2 6
89	50 c. on 5d. pur. & blue, C	5 0	5 0
90	1 p. on 10d. pur. & carm., C	9 0	10 0
91	3 p. on 2s. 6d. lilac, C	20 0	20 0
92	6 p. on 5s. carmine, O	35 0	35 0
93	12 p. on 10s. ultramarine, O	55 0	55 0

On No. 93 and on Nos. 101–2 in the next set the words "MOROCCO" and "AGENCIES" are the same length.

Contemporary stamps of G.B. optd. "MOROCCO AGENCIES," *as in T* 4 *and* 5, *but without values in Spanish currency, in black.*

No.	Description		
94	½d. pale green, O	0 6	0 6
95	1d. scarlet, O	1 3	0 6
96	2d. green and carmine, C	3 6	3 0
97	4d. green and pur.-brn., C	8 0	8 0
98	4d. pale orange, O (1912)	2 0	2 6
99	6d. dull purple, C	3 6	2 6
100	1s. green and carmine, C	7 0	7 0
101	2s. 6d. lilac, C	45 0	45 0
102	2s. 6d. purple, C	45 0	40 0

1912. *Nos.* 339, 342, *and* 283 *of Great Britain surch. as T* 4, *in black.*

No.	Description		
103	**5 c. on ½d. green**	0 6	0 6
104	**10 c. on 1d. scarlet**	0 6	0 6
	a. No cross on crown	30 0	22 6
105	**25 c. on 2½d. bright blue**	3 0	3 6

1913. *Nos.* 286 *and* 315 *of Great Britain opt.* "MOROCCO AGENCIES" *as in T* **4** *and* **5.**

105a 4d. bright orange 2 6 3 0
106 2s. 6d. dull purple 45 0 47 6

No. 319 *of Great Britain surch. as T* 5.

107 12 p. on 10s. bright ultram. .. 55 0 60 0

Nos. 82 to 102 are the De La Rue printings, Nos. 105 to 107 being Harrison (p. 15×14) or Somerset House printings.

MOROCCO AGENCIES

15 CENTIMOS

(6)

1914–15. *Nos.* 351 *and* 362 *of Great Britain surch. with T* **4** *or* **6.**

108 5 c. on ½d. green (1914) .. 0 4 0 4
108a 15 c. on 1½d. brown (1915) 0 10 0 8

II. FOR USE IN THE SPANISH ZONE OF NORTHERN MOROCCO.

MOROCCO AGENCIES 10 CENTIMOS

(S 1)

Contemporary stamps of Great Britain surcharged in Spanish currency (value in "centimos" *or* "pesetas")

1914–15. *Surch. as Type* S **1.** *W* **100.**

109 10 c. on 1d. scarlet 0 3 0 3
110 20 c. on 2d. orange 1 0 1 0
111 25 c. on 2½d. ultramarine .. 2 6 2 6
114 1 p. on 10d. turquoise .. 2 6 3 0

Nos. 109 to 114 were, until 1917, also used in all zones.

MOROCCO AGENCIES 3 CENTIMOS

(S 2)

MOROCCO AGENCIES 6 PESETAS

(S 3)

1917–26. *Surch. as Types* S **2** *or* S **3**, *in black or red* (R.). *W* **100.**

115 3 c. on ½d. green 0 2 0 3
116 40 c. on 4d. grey-green .. 1 0 1 0

On Nos. 116 and 129, the words "MOROCCO AGENCIES" are as in T **6**.

Waterlow printings.

117 6 p. on 5s. rose-carmine .. 8 0 9
118 6 p. on 5s. pale rose-carmine £7
119 12 p. on 10s. deep blue (R.) 42 6 47 6

De La Rue printings.

120 3 p. on 2s. 6d. grey-brn. (1918) 22 6 27 6
121 3 p. on 2s. 6d. chestnut .. 22 6 27 6
122 12 p. on 10s. blue (R.) .. 35 0 40 0

Bradbury-Wilkinson printing.

123 3 p. on 2s. 6d. choc.-brn. (1926) 6 0 6 6

1925–31. *Surch. as T* **4**, **6**, S **1** *or* S **2.** *W* **111.**

124 5 c. on ½d. green ('31) .. 0 4 0 6
125 10 c. on 1d. scarlet ('29) .. 0 8 0 10
126 15 c. on 1½d. red-brown .. 1 3 1 6
127 20 c. on 2d. orange ('31) .. 1 0 1 3
128 25 c. on 2½d. blue 1 3 1 6
129 40 c. on 4d. grey-green ('30) .. 1 6 1 9

MOROCCO AGENCIES 10 CENTIMOS

(S 4)

1935 (8 May). *Silver Jubilee stamps of Great Britain surch. as Type* S **4.**

130 **123** 5 c. on ½d. green (B.) .. 1 3 2 0
131 " 10 c. on 1d. scarlet (B.) .. 12 6 17 6
a. "CENTIMES" for "CENTIMOS" (must be in pair with normal) £75
132 **123** 15 c. on 1½d. red-brn. (B.) 2 6 3 6
133 " 25 c. on 2½d. blue (R.) .. 7 6 15 0

Beware of forgeries of the error, No. 131a.

1935–37. *Harrison photo. ptgs. Surch. as T* **4**, **6**, S **1**, *or* S **2**.

134 **118** 5 c. on ½d. green (17.6.36) 0 6 0 8
135 **119** 10 c. on 1d. scarlet .. 1 0 1 3
136 **118** 15 c. on 1½d. red-brown .. 6 0 7 6
137 **120** 20 c. on 2d. orange ('36) .. 0 6 0 6
138 **119** 25 c. on 2½d. ultram. ('36) 10 0 15 0
139 **120** 40 c. on 4d. deep grey-green (18.5.37) .. 0 9 0 9
140 **122** 1 p. on 10d. turquoise-blue (21.4.37) .. 1 0 1 3

MOROCCO 10 AGENCIES CENTIMOS

(S 5)

1936. *Stamps of Great Britain (King Edward VIII). Surch. as Type* S **5.** (A) *close lettering,* "MOROCCO" 14¼ *mm. long.* (B) *spaced lettering,* "MOROCCO" 15¼ *mm. long.*

			A		B	
143	**124**	5 c. on ½d. grn. ..	0 3	0 3	†	
144	"	10 c. on 1d. scarlet	0 4	0 4	1 6	2 0
145	"	15 c. on 1½d. red-brown ..	0 6	0 6	†	
147	"	25 c. on 2½d. ultramarine ..	0 8	0 8	†	

III. FOR USE IN THE FRENCH ZONE OF SOUTHERN MOROCCO.

MOROCCO AGENCIES 25 CENTIMES

(F 1)

MOROCCO AGENCIES 1 FRANC

(F 2)

Contemporary stamps of Great Britain surcharged in French currency (value in "centimes" or "francs").

1917–24. *Surch. as Types* F **1** *or* F **2**, *in black or red* (R.). *W* **100.**

201 3 c. on ½d. green (R.) .. 0 4 0 6
202 5 c. on ½d. green 0 6 0 6
203 10 c. on 1d. scarlet 0 6 0 6
204 15 c. on 1½d. brown 0 8 0 8
205 25 c. on 2½d. blue 0 9 0 6
206 40 c. on 4d. slate-green .. 0 10 0 9
207 50 c. on 5d. yell.-brn. (1923) 2 0 2 0
208 75 c. on 9d. olive-grn. (1924) 2 0 2 0
209 1 fr. on 10d. turquoise .. 3 0 1 6

1924–32 *Surch. as Type* F **2**, *but closer vertical spacing.*

210 3 fr. on 2s. 6d. chocolate-brn. 4 0 2 6
210a 6 fr. on 5s. rose-red ('32) .. 10 0 5 0

1925–34. *Surch. as Types* F **1** *and* F **2**. *W* **111**

211 5 c. on ½d. green 0 6 0 6
212 10 c. on 1d. scarlet 0 6 0 6
213 15 c. on 1½d. red-brown .. 0 8 0 6
214 25 c. on 2½d. blue 0 8 0 6
215 40 c. on 4d. grey-green .. 0 9 0 8
216 50 c. on 5d. yellow-brown .. 1 0 1 0
217 75 c. on 9d. olive-green .. 1 3 0 10
218 90 c. on 9d. olive-green .. 1 3 1 3
219 1 fr. on 10d. turquoise .. 1 3 1 0
220 1 f. 50 c. on 1s. bistre .. 1 6 1 6

1935 (8 May). *Silver Jubilee stamps of Great Britain surch. as Type* S **4**, *but in French currency.*

221 **123** 5 c. on ½d. green (B.) .. 0 8 1 0
222 „ 10 c. on 1d. scarlet (B.) .. 1 9 3 0
223 „ 15 c. on 1½d. red-brn. (B.) 1 3 1 9
224 „ 25 c. on 2½d. blue (R.) .. 2 0 3 0

1935–37. *Harrison photo. ptgs. Surch. as Types* F **1** *or* F **2** (*1 fr.*).

225 **118** 5 c. on ½d. green .. 0 4 0 4
226 **119** 10 c. on 1d. scar. (2.3.36) 0 6 0 6
227 **118** 15 c. on 1½d. red-brown 2 6 2 9
228 **119** 25 c. on 2½d. ultram. ('36) 0 10 1 3
229 **120** 40 c. on 4d. deep grey-green (2.12.36) .. 0 6 0 8
230 **121** 50 c. on 5d. yell.-brn. ('36) 0 8 0 10
232 **122** 90 c. on 9d. deep olive-green (17.2.37) .. 0 8 1 0
233 „ 1 fr. on 10d. turquoise-blue (17.2.37) .. 0 9 1 0
233a „ 1 f. 50 on 1s. bistre-brn. (20.7.37) 1 0 1 3

1935–6. *Waterlow re-engraved ptgs. surch. as Type* F **2** (*but closer vertical spacing*).

234 **109** 3 fr. on 2s. 6d. choc. (No. 450) 4 0 4 0
235 „ 6 fr. on 5s. bright rose-red (No. 451) (17.6.36) .. 8 0 8 0

1936. *Stamps of Great Britain* (*King Edward VIII*). *Surch. as Type* S **5**, *but in French currency.*

236 **124** 5 c. on ½d. green .. 0 2 0 3
a. Bar through "POSTAGE" £25
237 „ 15 c. on 1½d. red-brown 0 3 0 4

IV. FOR USE IN THE INTERNATIONAL ZONE OF TANGIER.

Contemporary stamps of Great Britain overprinted "MOROCCO AGENCIES" or "TANGIER" only.

MOROCCO AGENCIES S

(T 1)

(A) Opt. 14 mm. long; ends of "s" cut off diagonally.

1914–31. *Stamps of King George V optd. with Type* T **1**, *in black. Wmk. T* **100.**

301 ½d. green 0 8 0 8
302 1d. scarlet 0 9 0 6
303 1½d. red-brown (1921) .. 1 8 1 3
304 2d. orange 1 6 1 3
305 3d. blue-violet (1921) .. 1 6 1 3
306 4d. grey-green (1921) .. 2 0 1 9
307 6d. reddish purple (1921) .. 3 6 3 6
308 1s. bistre (1917) 4 6 4 0

MOROCCO AGENCIES

(T 2)

Overprinted with Type T **2**.

(*a*) *Waterlow printing.*

309 2s. 6d. deep brown (1914) .. 32 6 35 0
a. Re-entry £30

(*b*) *De La Rue printings.*

310 2s. 6d. chestnut (1917) .. 30 0 25 0
a. Overprint double (1917) .. £22
311 2s. 6d. grey-brown 22 6 20 0

(*c*) *Bradbury-Wilkinson printings.*

312 2s. 6d. chocolate-brown .. 12 6 7 6
312a 5s. rose-red (1931) 25 0 27 6

MOROCCO AGENCIES S

(T 3)

(B) Opt. 15½ mm. long; ends of "s" cut off horizontally.

1925–36. *Stamps of King George V optd. with Type* T **1** (A) *or Type* T **3** (B). *W* **111.**

		A		B	
313	½d. green ..	2 0	2 0	0 6	0 8
315	1½d. chestnut ('31)	1 6	1 6	†	†
316	2d. orange ..	1 0	1 3	†	†
317	2½d. blue ..	2 6	2 0	40 0	25 0
317a	4d. grey-grn. (1.36)	†	†	20 0	30 0
318	6d. pur., O ('31)	4 0	4 6	2 6	2 6
319	1s. bistre ..	10 0	10 0	15 0	12 6

TANGIER

(T 4)

1927. *Optd. with Type* T **4**. *Wmk. T* **111.**

320 ½d. green 0 8 0 8
321 1d. scarlet 0 9 0 6
322 1½d. chestnut 1 3 1 3
323 2d. orange 1 0 1 0

1935 (8 May). *Silver Jubilee stamps of Great Britain.*

(*a*) *Optd. as Type* S **4**, *but without surch.*

324 **123** ½d. green (B.) 1 3 1 9
325 „ 1d. scarlet (B.) 3 0 4 6
326 „ 1½d. red-brown (B.) .. 10 0 15 0
327 „ 2½d. blue (R.) 17 0 22 6

TANGIER **TANGIER**

(T 5)

(*b*) *Optd. with Type* T **5**.

328 **123** ½d. green (B.) 1 3 1 9
329 „ 1d. scarlet (B.) 4 6 5 0
330 „ 1½d. red-brown (B.) .. 3 6 4 6

1934–37. *Stamps of King George V optd. "MOROCCO AGENCIES" only.*

(*a*) *Harrison photo. ptgs. optd. with Type* T **3**.

332 **119** 1d. scarlet 1 3 1 6
333 **118** 1½d. red-brown ('36) .. 5 0 7 6
334 **120** 2d. orange (11.5.36) .. 0 8 0 9
335 **119** 2½d. ultramarine (11.2.36) 4 6 4 0
336 **120** 3d. violet (2.3.36) .. 1 0 1 3
337 „ 4d. dp. grey-grn. (19.5.36) 1 3 1 3
338 **122** 1s bistre-brown ('36) .. 3 6 4 0

(*b*) *Waterlow re-engraved ptg. optd. with Type* T **2**.

339 **109** 2s. 6d. chocolate (No. 450) 12 6 15 0
340 „ 5s. bright rose-red (No. 451) (2.3.37) .. 22 6 25 0

(c) *Harrison photo. ptgs. optd. with Type* T **4.**

341	**118**	½d. green	0 4	0 6
342	**119**	1d. scarlet	1 6	1 9
343	**118**	1½d. red-brown	0 10	1 3

1936. *Stamps of King Edward VIII.* (a) *Optd.* " MOROCCO AGENCIES " *only, as in Type* S **5.**

(A) MOROCCO 14½ mm. long.
(B) MOROCCO 15¼ mm. long.

			A		B	
344	**124**	1d. scarlet	0 4	0 6	2 0	3 6
345	„	2½d. ultram.	0 8	0 10	5 0	6 6

(b) *Optd. as Type* T **4.**

346	**124**	½d. green	0 2	0 3
347	„	1d. scarlet	0 3	0 6
348	„	1½d. red-brown	0 6	0 6

NATAL.

1 2

(Embossed in plain relief on coloured wove paper.)

1857 (1 JUNE) (*the* 1d. *in* **1858**). *T* **1, 2,** *and similar types.*

1	1d. rose	—	£8 *to* £50
2	1d. buff	—	£8 *to* £50
3	1d. blue	—	£10 *to* £50
4	3d. rose	—	£5 *to* £25
5	6d. green	—	£12 *to* £60
6	9d. blue	—	£30 *to* £200
7	1s. buff	—	£35 *to* £225

Variety. Tête-bêche (pair).

8	3d. rose		

All the above have been reprinted more than once, and the early reprints of some values cannot always be distinguished with certainty from originals.

The stamps on surface-coloured paper, *P* 12½, are fiscals.

NOTE.—*The value of the above stamps depends so much on their dimensions and the clearness of the embossing that we now indicate the approximate range of price for each.*

6 7

(Recess. Perkins Bacon & Co.)

1859–60. *T* **6.** *No wmk. P* 14.

9	1d. rose-red	65 0	35 0
10	3d. blue	45 0	15 0

1861. *No wmk. Intermediate perf.* 14 *to* 16.

11	3d. blue	85 0	15 0

1862. *No wmk. Rough perf.* 14 *to* 16.

12	3d. blue	45 0	15 0
	a. Imperf. between (pair)	£30	
13	6d. grey	55 0	22 6

Variety. Imperf.

14	3d. blue	—	£20

1862. *Wmk. Small Star. Rough perf.* 14 *to* 16.

15	1d. rose-red	50 0	22 6

The 1d. and 3d. wmk. Star, *imperf.*, are only proofs, and are therefore not included. The 3d. wmk. Star, *perforated*, is believed to exist only with forged watermark.

(Printed by Messrs. De La Rue & Co.)

1863. *Thick paper. No wmk. P* 13.

18	1d. lake	35 0	17 6
19	1d. carmine-red	35 0	15 0

1864. *Wmk. Crown CC. P* 12½.

20	1d. brown-red	60 0	20 0
21	1d. rose	45 0	15 0
22	1d. bright red	47 6	15 0
23	6d. lilac	37 6	10 0
24	6d. violet	15 0	15 0

(Typo. De La Rue & Co.)

1867 (APRIL). *T* **7.** *Wmk. Crown CC. P* 14.

25	1s. green	60 0	20 0

1869 (23 AUG.). *Overprinted in the Colony. Horizontal overprint, in black. The* 1d. *and* 6d. *are T* **6,** *P* 12½, *and the* 1s. *T* **7,** *P* 14, *wmk. Crown CC.*; *the* 3d. *T* **6,** *no wmk.*

POSTAGE *Tall capitals.*

26	1d. rose	£10	65 0
27	1d. bright red	£12	65 0
28	3d. blue (No. 10)		
28a	3d. blue (No. 11)	£20	£12
28b	3d. blue (No. 12)	£15	85 0
29	6d. lilac	—	60 0
30	6d. violet	£18	45 0
31	1s. green	—	£50

Postage. 12½ *mm. long.*

32	1d. rose	£12	50 0
33	1d. bright red	£12	50 0
	a. Double	—	£25
34	3d. blue (No. 10)	—	£15
34a	3d. blue (No. 11)	£22	£8
34b	3d. blue (No. 12)	£20	80 0
35	6d. lilac	£12	40 0
36	6d. violet	£10	45 0
37	1s. green	—	£18

Postage. 13¾ *mm. long.*

38	1d. rose	£22	£5
39	1d. bright red	—	£5
40	3d. blue (No. 10)		
40a	3d. blue (No. 11)		
40b	3d. blue (No. 12)	£55	£16
41	6d. lilac	—	£5
42	6d. violet	£35	85 0
43	1s. green	—	£100

Postage. 14½ *to* 15½ *mm. long.*

44	1d. rose	£20	£8
45	1d. bright red	£20	£6
46	3d. blue (No. 10)		
46a	3d. blue (No. 11)	—	£15
46b	3d. blue (No. 12)	—	£12
47	6d. lilac	—	75 0
48	6d. violet	£50	75 0
49	1s. green	—	£100

POSTAGE. *With a stop.*

50	1d. rose	45 0	25 0
51	1d. bright red	£6	25 0
52	3d. blue (No. 10)	£10	55 0
53	3d. blue (No. 11)	75 0	30 0
54	3d. blue (No. 12)	£6	25 0
	a. Double	—	£40
54b	6d. lilac	70 0	35 0

55	6d. violet	60 0	20 0
56	1s. green	60 0	22 6

Two sets can be made with this overprint at the top or bottom of the stamp respectively. A few of the above have been chronicled with inverted or double overprints. The information about some of them is so meagre that we do not put them in our lists.

POSTAGE

(8)

1870. *No.* 25 *overprinted with* **T 8**, *in the colour given in brackets.*

57	1s. green (*carmine*)*	£175	
58	1s. green (*black*)	£100	
59	1s. green (*green*)	40 0	12 6

* For this stamp in orange see No. 107.

Variety. Overprint double.

59*a*	1s. green (*black*)	£180	£60

POSTAGE POSTAGE POSTAGE POSTAGE POSTAGE

(9) (10) (11)

1870–73. *T* **6** (*wmk. Crown CC, P* 12½) *overprinted at each side of the stamp as* **T 9**, *in the colour given.*

60	1d. bright red (*black*)	22 6	10 0
61	3d. bright blue (*red*)	25 0	15 0
62	6d. mauve (*black*)	70 0	22 6

1873 (July). *T* **7** (*wmk. Crown CC, P* 14) *overprinted with* **T 10** *up the centre, in black.*

63	1s. purple-brown	95 0	30 0

1874 (July). *No.* 21 *optd. with* **T 11**, *in black.*

65	1d. rose	90 0	30 0
	a. Overprint double		

NATAL POSTAGE / ONE PENNY

12

NATAL POSTAGE / THREE PENCE

13

NATAL POSTAGE / FOUR PENCE

14

NATAL POSTAGE / SIX PENCE

15

NATAL POSTAGE / FIVE SHILLINGS

16

(Typo. De La Rue & Co.)

1874–78. *T* **12** *to* **16**. *Wmk. Crown CC.* (*a*) *P* 14.

66	1d. dull rose	7 6	2 6
67	1d. bright rose	6 6	2 6
68	3d. blue	35 0	22 6
69	4d. brown (1878)	32 6	10 0
70	6d. lilac	17 6	5 0
71	5s. marone	£6	25 0
72	5s. rose	45 0	22 6
73	5s. carmine	20 0	15 0
	(*b*) *P* 12½.		
74	4d. brown	£10	17 6
	(*c*) *P* 14 × 12½.		
74*a*	3d. blue	£80	£55
	(*d*) *P* 15½ × 15.		
75	5s. marone	85 0	40 0

Nos. 71, 72, 73 and 75 normally have wmk. sideways.

POSTAGE (17) POSTAGE (18)

1875. *T* **6** (*wmk. Crown CC, P* 12½) *overprinted with* **T 17**, *in black.*

76	1d. rose	50 0	22 6
77	1d. bright red	£5	35 0

Variety. Overprint double.

78	1d. rose	£40	£30

T **6** (*P* 12½), *and* **7** (*P* 14), *overprinted with* **T 18**, 14½ *mm. long, without stop, in black. Wmk. Crown CC.*

81	1d. rose	30 0	20 0
82	1d. yellow	35 0	27 6
83	6d. violet	22 6	7 6
84	1s. green	40 0	12 6

Varieties. (i.) *Overprint double.*

84*a*	6d. violet	—	£35
85	1s. green	—	£10

(ii.) *Overprint inverted.*

86	1d. rose	£55	£20
87	6d. violet	£50	£12

½ HALF

(19)

1877 (13 Feb.). *No.* 66 *surch. in black, as* **T 19**.

There are several varieties of this surcharge, of which T 19 is an example. They may be divided as follows: (*a*) "½" is 4½ mm. high, "2" has straight foot; (*b*) as last, but "½" is 4 mm. high; (*c*) as last, but "2" has curled foot; (*d*) "½" is 3½ mm. high, "2" has straight foot; (*e*) as last, but "2" has curled foot; (*f*) as last, but "2" smaller. As the "½" and "HALF" were overprinted separately, they vary in relative position, and are frequently overlapping.

88	½d. on 1d. rose (*a*)	12 6	10 0
88*a*	½d. on 1d. rose (*b*)	90 0	
88*b*	½d. on 1d. rose (*c*)	60 0	
89	½d. on 1d. rose (*d*)	15 0	
89*a*	½d. on 1d. rose (*e*)	25 0	
89*b*	½d. on 1d. rose (*f*)	27 6	

Variety. "½" *double.*

89*c*	½d. on 1d. rose (*a*)		

POSTAGE

Half-penny

(21)

1877–79. *T* **6** *(wmk. Crown CC, P* 12½*) surch. as T* **21**, *in black.*

90 ½d. on 1d. yellow 10 0 10 0
91 1d. on 6d. violet 15 0 10 0
92 1d. on 6d. rose 35 0 22 6

Varieties. (i.) "PO TAGE."

92a ½d. on 1d. yellow £10
92b 1d. on 6d. violet £18
92c 1d. on 6d. rose .. ..

(ii.) "POS AGE."

92d ½d. on 1d. yellow £10

(iii.) *Surcharge inverted.*

93 ½d. on 1d. yellow £12 £10
94 1d. on 6d. rose .. .. — £10

(iv.) *Surcharge double.*

94a ½d. on 1d. yellow £12 £8
94b 1d. on 6d. rose .. .. — £16

(v.) *Surcharge double, one inverted.*

95 1d. on 6d. rose £12 £15

(vi.) *Surcharged four times.*

95a 1d. on 6d. rose £18 £8

(vii.) *Without surcharge (the lower stamp of a vertical pair).*

95b ½d. on 1d. yellow £45 £35

(viii.) "POSTAGE" *omitted (se-tenant with normal).*

95c ½d. on 1d. yellow £60

No. 95 is known with one surcharge showing variety (i.), "PO TAGE."

Other minor varieties exist in these surcharges.

23

(Typo. De La Rue & Co.)

1880 (13 Oct.). *T* **23**. *Wmk. Crown CC. P* 14.

96 ½d. blue-green 4 6 3 6
a. Imperf. between (vert. pair) ..

☞ *Wmk. Crown CA. P* 14 *(all Nos. from* 97 *to* 113 *inclusive).*

1882–85. *T* **23** *and* **12** *to* **15.**

97 ½d. blue-green 42 6 17 6
98 ½d. dull green 0 6 0 1
99 1d. rose 1 9 0 1
99a 1d. carmine 0 4 0 1
100 3d. blue 17 6 6 6
101 4d. brown 1 6 1 0
102 6d. mauve 2 6 1 3

ONE HALF-
PENNY.

(24)

TWO PENCE

(25)

1885 (26 Jan.). *No.* 99 *surch. with T* **24**, *in black.*

103 ½d. on 1d. rose 18 6 16 0

1886. *T* **13** *surcharged with T* **25**, *in black.*

104 2d. on 3d. grey 15 0 7 6

NATAL POSTAGE
TWO PENCE

26

(Typo. De La Rue.)

1887–89. *T* **26.**

105 2d. olive-green, Die I* 9 0 1 9
106 2d. olive-green, Die II 2 0 0 8

* The differences between Dies I and II are shown in the Introduction.

1888. *T* 7 *overprinted with T* **8**, *in carmine.*

107 1s. orange 5 0 2 6
a. Overprint double .. .. — £25

1889. *T* **13.** *Colour changed.*

108 3d. grey 3 0 2 6

TWOPENCE
HALFPENNY

(27)

1891. *T* **14** *surcharged with T* **27**, *in black.*

109 2½d. on 4d. brown 10 0 8 6
a. "TWOPENGE" 60 0 50 0
b. "HALFPENN" .. .. — £12
c. Surcharge double £15 £12
d. Surcharge inverted £18 £14

NATAL POSTAGE 2½d.

28

POSTAGE.

Half-Penny

(29)

POSTAGE.

(Varieties of long-tailed letters.)

(Typo. De La Rue.)

1891 (June). *T* **28.**

113 2½d. bright blue 1 0 0 6

1895 (12 March). *No.* 24 *surcharged with T* **29**, *in carmine.*

114 ½d. on 6d. violet 1 3 1 9
a. "Ealf-Penny" 15 0
b. "Half-Pennv" 8 6
c. No stop after "POSTAGE" 10 0
d. Long "P" 1 9
e. Long "T" 2 0
f. Long "A" 3 0
g. Long "P" and "T" .. 1 9
h. Long "P" and "A" .. 1 9 1 9
i. Long "T" and "A" .. 1 9 1 9
k. Long "P", "T" and "A" 2 6
l. Surcharge double, one vertical £24
la. Surcharge double, "Ealf Penny"
lb. Surcharge double, "Half-Pennv"

No. 114k is known without stop and also with comma instead of a stop after "POSTAGE."

HALF

30)

1895 (18 March). *No.* 99 *surch. with T* **30**.

125	HALF on 1d. rose	0 2	0 4

Varieties. (i.) *Surcharge double.*

125*a*	HALF on 1d. rose	—	£15

(ii.) "H" of "HALF" *with a longer limb on the left side.*

126	HALF on 1d. rose	15 0	

This occurs on the second, fourth, sixth, etc., stamps of the first vertical row of the right-hand pane. It was very soon corrected.

In some printings a broken "E" (with the top limb removed) appears to have been used instead of "L" in "HALF" on the last stamp in the sheet.

31

(Typo. De La Rue.)

1902–3. *Inscribed* "POSTAGE REVENUE". *P* 14. *T* **31**. *Wmk. Crown CA.*

127	½d. blue-green	0 6	0 1
128	1d. carmine	0 4	0 1
129	1½d. green and black	1 0	1 0
130	2d. red and olive-green ..	1 9	0 9
131	2½d. bright blue	2 6	1 9
132	3d. purple and grey	1 9	0 8
133	4d. carmine and cinnamon ..	3 6	4 0
134	5d. black and orange ..	3 6	4 0
135	6d. green and brown-purple	3 6	1 6
136	1s. carmine and pale blue ..	4 0	2 6
137	2s. green and bright violet ..	20 0	20 0
138	2s. 6d. purple	20 0	22 6
139	4s. deep rose and maize ..	40 0	40 0

32

(Typo. De La Rue.)

T **32**. *Wmk. Crown CC.*

140	5s. dull blue and rose ..	30 0	15 0
141	10s. deep rose and chocolate	50 0	25 0
142	£1 black and bright blue ..	90 0	50 0
143	£1 10s. green and violet ..	£12	60 0
144	£5 mauve and black ..	£45	
145	£10 green and orange ..	£200	
145*a*	£20 red and green	£850	£200

1904–8. *T* **31**. *Wmk. Mult. Crown CA.* *P* 14.

146	½d. blue-green	0 6	0 2
147	1d. rose-carmine	0 8	0 1
148	1d. deep carmine	1 0	0 3
149	2d. red and olive-green ..	1 9	0 9
152	4d. carmine and cinnamon ..	4 0	2 6
153	5d. black and orange (1908) ..	6 6	6 0
155	1s. carmine and pale blue ..	45 0	9 6
156	2s. dull grn. & bright violet ..	35 0	30 0
157	2s. 6d. purple	40 0	30 0

1908. *T* **32**. *Wmk. Mult. Crown CA.* *P* 14.

162	£1 10s. brown-orange and deep purple, C	£65	

1908–9. *T* **31** *and* **32** (5s. to £1), *but inscribed* "POSTAGE-POSTAGE". *Wmk. Mult. Crown CA.* *P* 14.

165	6d. dull and bright purple ..	7 0	4 0
166	1s. black/*green*	12 6	5 0
167	2s. purple & bright blue/*blue*	17 6	12 6
168	2s. 6d. black and red/*blue* ..	22 6	15 0
169	5s. green and red/*yellow* ..	40 0	35 0
170	10s. green and red/*green* ..	80 0	70 0
171	£1 purple and black/*red* ..	£15	£10

FISCALS USED FOR POSTAGE.

1869. *T* **1**. *Embossed on coloured wove, surfaced paper.* *P* 12½.

201	1d. yellow	50 0	80 0

1873 (July). *T* **7**. *Wmk. Crown CC.* *P* 14.

202	1s. purple-brown	10 0	55 0

1875. *T* **6**. *Wmk. Crown CC.* *P* 12½.

203	1d. yellow	7 6	12 0
204	6d. rose	15 0	27 6

41

(Typo. De La Rue.)

1903. *T* **41**. *Wmk. Crown CA.* *P* 14.

204*a*	5s. dull mauve & carmine ..	80 0	£6
205	£1 green	70 0	£5
206	£1 10s. dull mauve & blue ..	£10	£12
207	£5 green and red	£10	95 0
208	£10 green and blue	£15	£18

OFFICIAL STAMPS.

OFFICIAL

(51)

1904. *T* **31**, *wmk. Multiple Crown CA, overprinted with T* **51**, *in black.* *P* 14.

303	½d. blue-green	7 0	1 6
304	1d. carmine	1 6	1 0
305	2d. red and olive-green ..	15 0	12 6
306	3d. purple and grey ..	10 0	10 0
307	6d. green and brown-purple ..	22 6	22 6
308	1s. carmine and pale blue ..	50 0	45 0

The use of stamps overprinted as above was discontinued after 30 May, 1907. Stamps perforated with the letters "N.G.R." were for use on Government Railways.

Natal now uses the stamps of South Africa.

NAURU.

NAURU (1) NAURU (2)

1916 (Oct.)–**1923.** *Stamps of Great Britain* (1912–19) *overprinted in black.*

(*a*) *Overprint* 12½ *mm. long.* (*T* **1**.)

1	½d. green	0 3	0 4
	a. "NAUP.U"	£7	
2	1d. scarlet	0 4	0 6
	a. "NAUP.U"	£6	
3	1½d. red-brown (1923)	1 6	2 0
4	2d. orange (Die I.)	1 3	1 6
	a. "NAUP.U"	£7	

5	2d. orange (Die II.) (1923) ..	3	6	5	0
6	2½d. blue	1	6	2	0
	a. "NAUP.U"	£7			
7	3d. blue-violet	2	0	3	0
	a. "NAUP.U"	130	0		
8	4d. slate-green	2	6	3	0
	a. "NAUP.U"	£8			
9	5d. yellow-brown	3	0	3	6
	a. "NAUP.U"	£7			
10	6d. purple	3	6	4	0
	a. "NAUP.U"	£8			
11	9d. agate	5	0	5	0
12	1s. bistre-brown	5	0	6	0

(*b*) *Overprint* 13½ *mm. long.* (*T* 2.) (1923.)

13	½d. green	3	0	4	6
14	1d. scarlet	3	0	4	6
15	1½d. red-brown	3	0	4	6
16	2d. orange (Die II.)	8	6	10	0

NAURU

(3)

Overprinted with T 3 *in black or red* (R.).
Waterlow printing.

17	5s. rose-carmine	£40	
18	10s. deep blue (R.)	£75	

De La Rue printing.

19	2s. 6d. deep brown	£10		£12	
20	2s. 6d. chestnut-brown ..	30	0	35	0
21	2s. 6d. brown	35	0	37	6
22	5s. bright carmine	35	0	37	6
23	10s. pale blue (R.)	55	0	55	0

Bradbury-Wilkinson printing (1920).

24	2s. 6d. chocolate-brown ..	20	0	22	6
25	2s. 6d. grey-brown	15	0	17	6

4

(Recess. Commonwealth Treasury, Melbourne.)

1924-37. *T* 4. *No wmk.* *P* 11.

26	½d. chestnut	0	1	0	2
27	1d. green	0	2	0	3
28	1½d. scarlet	0	3	0	4
29	2d. orange	0	3	0	4
30	2½d. slate-blue	2	6	2	6
30*a*	2½d. greenish blue ('34) ..	1	3	1	6
30*b*	2½d. dull blue ('37)	0	3	0	6
31	3d. pale blue	0	4	0	6
32	4d. olive-green	0	5	0	8
33	5d. brown	0	6	1	0
34	6d. dull violet	0	7	1	0
35	9d. olive-brown	0	10	1	6
36	1s. brown-lake	1	1	2	0
37	2s. 6d. grey-green	2	8	5	0
38	5s. claret	5	3	10	0
39	10s. yellow	10	6	20	0

In 1937 the above issue appeared on shiny surfaced paper in shades differing slightly from those of earlier printings. No. 30*b* is on this surfaced paper.

For ½d. perf. 14, see No. 26*a*, under date 1947, in King George VI Catalogue.

HIS MAJESTY'S JUBILEE.

1910 - 1935

(5)

1935 (12 July). *Silver Jubilee. Surfaced paper T* 4 *optd. with T* 5.

40	1½d. scarlet	0	8	1	9
41	2d. orange	1	3	2	6
42	2½d. dull blue	2	0	5	0
43	1s. brown-lake	7	0	17	6

NEVIS.

1

2

3

4

The designs on the stamps refer to a medicinal spring on the island.

(Recess. Nissen & Parker, London.)

Types 1 *to* 4.

1861. *P* 13. (*a*) *Blued paper.*

1	1d. dull rose	£10		£5	
2	4d. rose	£25		£15	
3	6d. grey-lilac	£20		£22	
4	1s. green	£45		£18	

(*b*) *Greyish paper.*

5	1d. dull lake	30	0	37	6
6	4d. rose	90	0	90	0
7	6d. grey	80	0	60	0
8	1s. green	£8		£5	

1866. *White paper.* *P* 15.

9	1d. pale red	40	0	42	5
10	1d. deep red	50	0	40	6
11	4d. orange	75	0	55	0
12	4d. deep orange	90	0	55	0
13	1s. blue-green	£16		70	0
14	1s. yellow-green	£40		£10	
	a. Laid paper	—		£400	
	b. No. 9 on sheet with crossed lines on hill				

(Lithographed by transfer from the engraved plates. Nissen & Parker, London.)

1876. *P* 15.

15	1d. pale rose-red	17	6	30	0
	a. Imperf.	60	0		
16	1d. deep rose-red	25	0	40	0

17 1d. vermilion-red 20 0 32 6
a. Bisected .. .. ..
18 4d. orange-yellow £15 70 0
19 6d. grey £15 £15
20 1s. pale green 80 0 £8
a. Imperf. .. .. ..
b. Imperf. between (pair) ..
c. No. 9 on sheet with crossed lines on hill £16 £28
21 1s. deep green.. .. .. 80 0 £10

No. 9 on the sheet of the 1s., *deep* green, has not the distinct "crossed lines on hill" of Nos. 14b and 20c, but traces of the lines are visible.

RETOUCHES.

1d. *pale rose-red.*

i. No. 1 on sheet. Top of hill over kneeling figure redrawn by five thick lines and eight small slanting lines £15

ii. No. 1 on sheet. Another retouch. Three series of short vertical strokes behind the kneeling figure .. £18

iii. No. 3 on sheet. Right upper corner star and border below star retouched..

iv. No. 9 on sheet. Retouch in same position as on No. 3 but differing in detail ..

v. No. 12 on sheet. Dress of standing figure retouched by a number of horizontal and vertical lines ..

1878. *Lithographed.* P 11½.

22 1d. vermilion-red 40 0 50 0
a. Bisected .. .. ..
b. Imperf. 60 0
c. Imperf. between (pair) ..

5 (Die I)

(Typo. De La Rue & Co.)

1879-80. *T* 5. *Wmk. Crown CC.* P 14.

23 1d. lilac-mauve (1880) .. 20 0 22 6
a. Bisected (½d.) ..
24 2½d. red-brown 70 0 75 0

1882. *T* 5. *Wmk. Crown CA.* P 14.

25 1d. lilac-mauve 22 6 22 6
a. Bisected (½d.) .. .. — 85 0
26 2½d. red-brown 50 0 40 0
27 4d. blue 90 0 40 0

NEVIS. ½d.
(6)

1883. *Half* 1d., *No.* 25, *surcharged with T* 6 *for use as a Halfpenny.*

28 ½d. in *violet*, on half 1d., lilac-mauve £20 80 0
a. Double surcharge .. .. — £28
b. Surch. on half "REVENUE" stamp No. 54 .. ..
29 ½d. in *black*, on half 1d., lilac-mauve £12 65 0
a. Double surcharge .. .. — £40
b. Whole stamp with surcharge on right half only .. ..

1883-90. *T* 5. *Wmk. Crown CA.* P 14.

30 ½d. dull green (1883) 2 0 3 6
30*a* 1d. dull rose 16 6 15 0
31 1d. carmine (1884) 5 0 6 0
32 2½d. ultramarine (1884) .. 7 6 7 6
33 4d. grey (1884) 8 6 8 0
34 6d. green (1883) £20 £20
35 6d. chestnut (1886) 20 0 30 0
36 1s. pale violet (1890) .. 65 0 £15

FISCALS USED FOR POSTAGE.

Revenue (7) REVENUE (8)

1882. *Stamps of* 1876 *overprinted with T* 7.

51 1d. bright red 25 0
51*a* 1d. rose 25 0 15 0
52 4d. orange 35 0
53 6d. grey 45 0
53*a* 1s. green 50 0

Nos. 23, 27, *and* 34 *overprinted with T* 8.

54 1d. lilac-mauve 16 0 17 6
55 4d. blue 8 6 16 6
56 6d. green 12 6 37 6

For later issues see St. KITTS-NEVIS.

NEW BRITAIN.

See under **NEW GUINEA.**

NEW BRUNSWICK.

1. Royal Crown and heraldic flowers of the United Kingdom.

(Recess. Perkins, Bacon & Co.)

1851 (SEPT.). *T* 1. *Blue paper. Imperf.*

1 3d. bright red .. .. £30 £2 *to* £15
2 3d. dull red .. .. £22 £2 *to* £15
a. Bisected (1½d.) .. — £75
3 6d. yellow .. .. £60 £6 *to* £45
4 6d. olive-yellow .. £100 £12 *to* £75
a. Bisected (3d.) .. — £85

5	1s. reddish mauve	.. £350	£30 *to* £175
6	1s. dull mauve	.. £225	£25 *to* £150
	a. Bisected (6d.)	..	
	b. Quartered (3d.)	..	

Reprints of all three values were made in 1890 on thin, hard, white paper. The 3d. is bright orange, the 6d. and 1s. violet-black.

2

3

3*a*. Charles Connell.

4

6

7. King Edward VII as Prince of Wales.

(Recess. American Bank Note Co.)

1860 (15 MAY)–**1863**. *No wmk.* P 12.

7	2	1 c. brown-purple	.. ..	12	0	15	0
8	,,	1 c. purple ..	..	10	6	12	6
9	,,	1 c. dull claret ..	..	7	6	10	0
		a. Imperf. between (pair)	..	£15			
10	3	2 c. orange (1863)	..	6	6	12	6
11	,,	2 c. orange-yellow	..	4	6	12	0
12	..	2 c. deep orange ..	..	10	6	20	0
13	3*a*	5 c. brown ..		£175			
14	4	5 c. yellow-green..	..	4	0	5	0
15	,,	5 c. deep green ..	..	4	0	5	0
16	,,	5 c. sap-green ..	..	90	0	30	0
17	5	10 c. red	..	10	6	12	0
		a. Bisected (5 c.) ..	..	—		£25	
18	6	12½ c. indigo ..	..	10	6	12	6
19	7	17 c. black ..	..	12	6	15	0

In March, 1868, issues of the Dominion of Canada replaced those of New Brunswick.

NEWFOUNDLAND.

1

2

3

4

5

Royal Crown and heraldic flowers of the United Kingdom.

(Recess. Perkins, Bacon & Co.)

1857 (1 JAN.). *No wmk. Thick paper. Imperf.*

			Un.	*Used.*
1	1	1d. brown-purple ..	50 0	75 0
2	2	2d. scarlet-vermilion	£450	£35 *to* £200
3	3	3d. green (to deep) ..	£9	£20
4	4	4d. scarlet-vermilion	£300	£20 *to* £125
		a. Bisected (2d.) ..		
5	1	5d. brown-purple ..	£5	£8
6	4	6d. scarlet-vermilion	£300	£20 *to* £150
7	5	6½d. scarlet-vermilion	£65	£15 *to* £75
8	4	8d. scarlet-vermilion	£10	£5 *to* £30
		a. Bisected (4d.) ..	—	£150
9	2	1s. scarlet-vermilion	£400	£40 *to* £175
		a. Bisected (6d.) ..		

The 6d. and 8d. differ from the 4d. in many details, as does also the 1s. from the 2d.

1860. *No wmk. Thinner paper. Imperf.*

No.	Type	Description	Unused	Used
10	2	2d. orange-vermilion	£15	£7 to £25
11	3	3d. green (to deep) ..	60 0	
12	4	4d. orange-vermilion	£120	£8 to £45
		a. Bisected (2d.)	..	
13	1	5d. chocolate-brown	50 0	95 0
14	4	6d. orange-vermilion	£150	£6 to £40
15	2	1s. orange-vermilion	£600	£40 to £225
		a. Bisected (6d.)	..	

NOTE.—*The value of the rarer stamps varies so greatly, according to condition, that we have endeavoured to indicate a range of prices.*

The two undermentioned stamps are believed to be essays.

No.	Description	Unused
15*b*	6½d. orange-vermilion	..

Laid paper.

No.	Description	Unused	Used
16	1s. orange-vermilion ..	..	

1861–62. *New colours. No wmk. Imperf.*

No.	Type	Description	Unused	Used
17	1	1d. chocolate-brown ..	70 0	£10
17*a*	,,	1d. red-brown	£175	
18	2	2d. rose-lake..	£15	£18
19	4	4d. rose-lake	15 0	50 0
		a. Bisected (2d.) ..	..	
20	1	5d. red-brown	40 0	80 0
20*a*	,,	5d. brown	35 0	70 0
21	4	6d. rose-lake	15 0	40 0
		a. Bisected (3d.) ..	—	£80
22	5	6½d. rose-lake	40 0	£10
23	4	8d. rose-lake	40 0	£20
24	2	1s. rose-lake	17 6	75 0
		a. Bisected (6d.) ..	..	

The stamps of this issue are occasionally found with a watermark consisting of a part of the paper-maker's trademark, "STACEY WISE 1858."

Collectors are warned against buying bisected stamps of these issues without a reliable guarantee. The same warning applies to used specimens of the stamps which are worth less in unused condition, as many unused stamps have been provided with faked postmarks.

6. Codfish.

7. Seal on ice-floe.

8. Prince Consort.

9. Queen Victoria.

10 11. Queen Victoria.

(Recess. American Bank Note Co., New York.)

1866 (Jan.). *T* **6** *to* **11.** *P* 12.

(a) Thin yellowish paper.

No.	Description	Unused	Used
25	2 c. yellowish green	40 0	42 6
	a. Bisected (1 c.)	..	
26	5 c. brown	£18	£10
	a. Bisected (2½ c.)	..	
27	10 c. black	80 0	50 0
	a. Bisected (5 c.)	..	
28	12 c. red-brown	90 0	57 6
	a. Bisected (6 c.)	..	
29	13 c. orange-yellow	45 0	45 0
30	24 c. blue	17 6	20 0

(b) Medium white paper.

No.	Description	Unused	Used
31	2 c. bluish green (to deep) ..	30 0	25 0
32	10 c. black	60 0	30 0
33	12 c. chestnut	15 0	17 6
33*a*	24 c. blue	£22	£8

12. King Edward VII when Prince of Wales.

I.

(Recess. National Bank Note Co., New York.)

1868. *T* **12.** *P* 12.

No.	Description	Unused	Used
34	1 c. dull purple (I.)	27 6	30 0

14. Queen Victoria.

II.

(Recess. American Bank Note Co., New York.)

1868–73. *P* 12.

35	12	1 c. brn.-purple (II.) (1871)	35	0	30	0
36	14	3 c. vermilion (1870) ..	90	0	60	0
37	,,	3 c. blue (1873)	55	0	20	0
38	7	5 c. black	£6		85	0
39	14	6 c. rose (1870)	7	6	8	0

1876–79. *Rouletted.*

40	12	1 c. lake-purple (II.) (1877)	55	0	35	0
41	6	2 c. bluish green (1879) ..	50	0	30	0
42	14	3 c. blue (1877)	65	0	12	6
43	7	5 c. blue (1876)	60	0	12	6
		a. Imperf.				

In Type II the white oval frame line is unbroken by the scroll containing the words "ONE CENT"; the letters "N.F." are smaller and closer to the scroll, and there are other minor differences.

. King Edward VII
ıen Prince of Wales.

16. Codfish.

17

18. Seal on ice-floe.

(Recess. British-American Bank Note Co., Montreal.)

1880. *T* 15 *to* 18. *P* 12.

44		1 c. dull grey-brown	17	6	15	0
45		1 c. dull brown	10	0	8	6
45*a*		1 c. red-brown	10	0	8	6
46		2 c. yellow-green	20	0	15	0
47		3 c. pale dull blue	20	0	8	0
47*a*		3 c. bright blue	20	0	4	0
48		5 c. pale dull blue	35	0	10	0

19. Newfoundland dog. **20.** Atlantic brigantine.

(Recess. British-American Bank Note Co., Montreal.)

1887. *New colours and values.* *P* 12.

49	19	½ c. rose-red	1	6	4	0
49*a*	15	1 c. blue-green	5	0	3	0
50	,,	1 c. green	2	6	2	0
50*a*	,,	1 c. yellow-green	5	0	5	0
51	16	2 c. orange-vermilion ..	3	6	3	6
52	17	3 c. deep brown	12	6	6	6
53	18	5 c. deep blue	27	6	8	0
54	20	10 c. black	32	6	25	0

21. Queen Victoria.

(Recess. British-American Bank Note Co., Ottawa.)

1890. *T* 21. *P* 12.

55		3 c. deep slate	10	6	1	3
		a. Imperf.				
56		3 c. slate-grey (to grey) ..	10	6	1	3
		a. Imperf. between (pair) ..	£30			
57		3 c. slate-violet	10	0	3	6
58		3 c. grey-lilac	10	0	0	8
58*a*		3 c. brown-grey	10	6	4	0
58*b*		3 c. purple-grey	12	6	3	0

There is a very wide range of shades in this stamp, and those given only cover the main groups.

Stamps on pink paper are from a consignment recovered from the sea and which were affected by the salt water.

(Recess. British-American Bank Note Co., Montreal.)

1894. *Changes of colour.* *P* 12.

59	19	½ c. black	1	3	1	9
59*a*	18	5 c. bright blue	8	6	6	6
60	14	6 c. crimson-lake ..	8	0	8	6
61	9	12 c. deep brown	25	0	27	6

The 6 c. is printed from the old American Bank Note Company's plates.

1896–97. *Reissues.* *P* 12.

62	19	½ c. orange-vermilion ..	10	6	12	6
63	15	1 c. deep green	6	0	4	6
63*a*	,,	1 c. deep brown	15	0		
64	16	2 c. green	10	0	7	6
65	17	3 c. deep blue	10	6	7	6
65*a*	,,	3 c. chocolate-brown ..	30	0	30	0

The above have been misnamed as reprints. They were *reissued* for postal purposes. The colours are generally brighter than those of the original stamps.

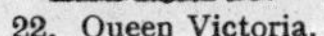

22. Queen Victoria.

23. Jean Cabot.

24. Cape Bonavista, the landfall of Cabot. **25.** Caribou hunting.

26. Mining (*horiz.*). **27.** Logging (*horiz.*).

28. Fishing (*horiz.*). **29.** Cabot's ship the "Matthew" leaving the Avon (*horiz.*).

30. Ptarmigan (*vert.*). **31.** Group of Seals (*horiz.*).

32. Salmon fishing (*horiz.*). **33.** Seal of the Colony. "Fisherman bringing gifts to Britannia" (*vert.*).

34. An iceberg off St. John's (*horiz.*). **35.** Henry VII (*vert.*).

(Recess. American Bank Note Co.)

1897 (24 June). *400th anniversary of the discovery of Newfoundland by Jean Cabot and the 60th year of Queen Victoria's reign.* T **22** *to* **35** (*various designs, dated* "1497–1897"). *P* 12.

66	1 c. green	1	6	1	9
67	2 c. bright rose	1	3	1	9
68	3 c. bright blue	5	0	1	9
69	4 c. olive-green	6	6	5	0
70	5 c. violet	7	6	7	6
71	6 c. red-brown	7	6	5	0
72	8 c. orange	15	0	12	6
73	10 c. sepia	17	6	15	0
74	12 c. deep blue	15	0	12	6
75	15 c. bright scarlet	12	6	10	6
76	24 c. dull violet-blue	17	6	17	6
77	30 c. slate-blue	25	0	25	0
78	35 c. red	55	0	60	0
79	60 c. black	25	0	22	6

The 60 c. surcharged "TWO—2—CENTS" in three lines is an essay made in December, 1918.

ONE CENT

(36)

ONE CENT

(37)

ONE CENT

(38)

1897 (Oct.). *T* 21 *surcharged with T* **36** *to* **38**.

(*a*) *In black.*

80	**36**	1 c. on 3 c. grey-purple	8	6	10	0
		a. Double surch., one diagonal	£135			
81	**37**	1 c. on 3 c. grey-purple	35	0	35	0
82	**38**	1 c. on 3 c. grey-purple	£16		£16	

This overprint is known on stamps of various shades.

(*b*) *In red and in black.*

82*a*	**36**	1 c. on 3 c. grey-purple	£100
82*b*	**37**	1 c. on 3 c. grey-purple	£275
82*c*	**38**	1 c. on 3 c. grey-purple	£650

(*c*) *In red only.*

82*d*	**36**	1 c. on 3 c. grey-purple	£90
82*e*	**37**	1 c. on 3 c. grey-purple	£185
82*f*	**38**	1 c. on 3 c. grey-purple	£550
		g. Type 38 double	

39. Prince Edward, now Duke of Windsor.

40. Queen Victoria.

41. King Edward VII when Prince of Wales.

42. Queen Alexandra when Princess of Wales.

43. Queen Mary when Duchess of York.

44. King George V when Duke of York.

(Recess. American Bank Note Co.)

1897–1918. *T* **39** *to* **44**. *P* 12.

83	½ c. olive (Aug., 1897)	0	8	0	6
84	1 c. carmine (Dec., 1897)	1	6	1	3
85	1 c. blue-green (June, 1898)	5	0	0	1
85*a*	1 c. yellow-green	1	0	0	1
	b. Imperf. between (pair)	£16			
86	2 c. orange (Dec., 1897)	1	3	2	6
87	2 c. scarlet (June, 1898)	4	0	0	4
88	3 c. orange (June, 1898)	2	0	0	1
	a. Imperf. between (pair)				
88*b*	3 c. red-orange/*bluish* (6.18)	7	6	4	6
89	4 c. violet (Oct., 1901)	8	6	6	0
90	5 c. blue (June, 1899)	8	0	3	0

Varieties. Imperf. (*pairs*).

91	½ c. olive	£18
92	2 c. scarlet	£20
93	3 c. orange	£25
93*a*	4 c. violet	£18

No. 88*b* was an emergency war-time printing made by the American Bank Note Co. from the old plate, pending receipt of the then current 3 c. from England.

45. Map of Newfoundland.

(Recess. American Bank Note Co.)

1908 (Sept.). *T* **45.** *P* 12.

94	2 c. lake	12	6	0	4

46. King James I. **49.** Guy's ship.

47. Arms of Colonisation Co. (*vert.*). **48.** John Guy (*vert.*).

50. Cupids (*horiz.*).

51. Sir Francis Bacon (*vert.*). **52.** View of Mosquito (*horiz.*).

53. Logging Camp (*horiz.*). **54.** Paper Mills (*horiz.*).

55. King Edward VII. (*vert.*). **56.** King George V. (*vert.*).

(Litho. Whitehead, Morris & Co., Ltd.)

1910 (15 Aug.). *T* **46** *to* **56** (*various designs dated* "1610–1910"). (*a*) *P* 12.

95	1 c. green	2	6	1	0
	a. "NFWFOUNDLAND" ..	50	0	60	0
	b. Imperf. between (horiz. pair)				
96	2 c. rose-carmine	1	9	0	8
97	3 c. olive	17	6	20	0
98	4 c. violet	18	0	20	0
99	5 c. bright blue	17	6	15	0
100	6 c. claret (A)	35	0	37	6
100*a*	6 c. claret (B)	40	0	40	0
101	8 c. bistre-brown	35	0	37	6
102	9 c. olive-green	25	0	27	6
103	10 c. purple-slate	35	0	37	6
104	12 c. pale red-brown	30	0	32	6
105	15 c. black	35	0	37	6

(A) In the first printing of the 6 c. the word "COLONIZATION" had the "z" reversed thus "ƨ"; in the later printing this was corrected (B).

(*b*) *P* 12 × 14.

106	1 c. green	1	9	1	9
	a. "NFWFOUNDLAND" ..	75	0		
	b. Imperf. between (pair) ..				
	c. As a, in pair imperf. between ..				
107	2 c. rose-carmine	3	0	0	4
	a. Imperf. between (pair) ..	£30			
108	5 c. bright blue (*perf.* 14 × 12) .	5	0	3	0

(*c*) *P* 12 × 11.

109	1 c. green	0	10	0	10
	a. Imperf. between (horiz. pair)	£18			
	b. Imperf. between (vert. pair) ..	£20			
	c. "NFWFOUNDLAND" ..	40	0	45	0
	d. As c, in pair imperf. vert. ..				

(*d*) *P* 12 × 11½.

110	2 c. rose-carmine				

(Dies eng. Macdonald & Sons. Recess. A. Alexander & Sons, Ltd.)

1911 (Feb.). *Types as Aug.* 1910, *but recess-printed.* *P* 14.

111	6 c. claret (B)	30	0	35	0
112	8 c. yellow-brown	55	0	60	0
113	9 c. sage-green	50	0	52	6
114	10 c. purple-black	55	0	60	0
115	12 c. red-brown	55	0	60	0
116	15 c. slate-green	60	0	65	0

57. Queen Mary. **58.** King George V.

59. Duke of Windsor when Prince of Wales. **60.** King George VI when Prince Albert.

61. Princess Mary, now Princess Royal. **62.** Prince Henry, now Duke of Gloucester.

63. Prince George, late Duke of Kent. **64.** Prince John.

65. Queen Alexandra. **66.** Duke of Connaught.

67. Seal of Newfoundland.

(Recess. Whitehead, Morris & Co.)

1911 (19 June). *Coronation issue. T* **57** *to* **66** (*various royal portraits*), *and* **67.**

(*a*) *P* 13½ × 14 (*comb*) *or perf.* 14 (*single line*).

117	1 c. yellow-green	2	6	0	6
117*a*	1 c. blue-green	1	9	0	2
118	2 c. carmine	1	9	0	2
118*a*	2 c. rose-red (*blurred impression*)	2	0	1	0
119	3 c. red-brown	42	6	42	6
120	4 c. purple	40	0	42	6
121	5 c. ultramarine	22	6	20	0
122	6 c. slate-grey	45	0	47	6
123	8 c. greenish blue	£8		£9	
123*a*	8 c. aniline blue	80	0	85	0
124	9 c. violet-blue	40	0	42	6
125	10 c. deep green	42	6	47	6
126	12 c. plum	40	0	42	6
127	15 c. lake	45	0	47	6

(*b*) *Imperf.*

128	15 c. lake (*pair, ungummed*) ..	£8			

The 2 c. rose-red, No. 118*a*, is a poorly executed war-time printing from the engraved plate.

68. Caribou.

(Recess. Whitehead, Morris & Co.)

1919 (2 Jan.). *Commemorative of the Newfoundland Contingent*, 1914–18. *T* **68.** *P* 14.

130	1 c. green	..	1	6	0	3
131	2 c. scarlet	..	2	0	0	6
131*a*	2 c. carmine-red	..	2	6	0	6
132	3 c. brown	..	3	0	0	3
132*a*	3 c. red-brown	..	2	6	0	3
133	4 c. mauve	..	6	0	1	6
133*a*	4 c. purple	..	6	6	1	9
134	5 c. ultramarine	..	6	0	1	3
135	6 c. slate-grey	..	20	0	20	0
136	8 c. bright magenta	..	20	0	20	0
137	10 c. deep grey-green	..	12	6	10	6
138	12 c. orange	..	25	0	25	0
139	15 c. indigo	..	22	6	22	6
139*a*	15 c. Prussian blue	..	37	6	37	6
140	24 c. bistre-brown	..	30	0	30	0
141	36 c. sage-green	..	35	0	35	0

Each value with "Trail of the Caribou" is inscribed with the name of a different action: 1 c. Suvla Bay; 3 c. Gueudecourt; 4 c. Beaumont Hamel; 6 c. Monchy; 10 c. Steenbeck; 15 c. Langemarck; 24 c. Cambrai; 36 c. Combles. Values 2 c., 5 c., 8 c., and 12 c., inscribed "Royal Naval Reserve, Ubique."

FIRST
TRANS-
ATLANTIC
AIR POST
April, 1919.

(69*a*)

Trans-Atlantic
AIR POST,
1919.
ONE DOLLAR.

(70)

1919 (12 April). *Air stamp. T* **68** *optd. with T* **69***a*, *by Robinson & Co. Ltd., at the offices of the "Daily News."*

142 3 c. brown £600 £400

These stamps franked correspondence carried by Mr. Hawker on his Atlantic flight. 18 were damaged and destroyed, 95 used on letters, 11 given as presentation copies, and the remaining 76 were sold in aid of the Marine Disasters Fund.

1919 (April). *T* **68**, *overprinted in MS.* "Aerial Atlantic Mail. J.A.R."

142*a* 3 c. brown .. ..

This provisional was made by the Postmaster, Mr. J. A. Robinson, for use on correspondence intended to be carried on the abortive Morgan-Raynham Trans-Atlantic flight. The mail was eventually delivered by sea.

1919 (9 June). *Air stamp. T* **31** *surch. with T* **70** *by J. W. Withers at the offices of the "Royal Gazette."*

143 $1 on 15 c. bright scarlet .. £12 £15
a. No comma after "AIR POST," £15 £18
b. As Var. a and no stop after "1919" £30 £35

These stamps were issued for use on the mail carried across the Atlantic by Alcock and Brown, and on other projected Trans-Atlantic flights.

THREE
CENTS

(71)

1920 (Sept.). *T* **33, 31,** *and* **34** *surcharged as T* **71**, *in black, by J. W. Withers.* (*2 c. on 30 c., with only one bar, at top of stamp.*)
(A) Bars of surcharge 10½ mm. apart.
(B) Bars 13½ mm. apart.

144 2 c. on 30 c. slate-blue .. 5 0 7 6
a. Surcharge inverted .. £30

145 3 c. on 15 c. bright scarlet (A) 45 0 50 0
a. Surcharge inverted .. £75
146 3 c. on 15 c. bright scarlet (B) 6 0 7 6
147 3 c. on 35 c. red 6 0 8 6
a. Surcharge inverted ..
b. Lower bar omitted .. £15
c. "THREE" omitted .. £125

Our prices for Nos. 147b and 147c are for stamps with lower bar or "three" entirely missing. The bar may be found in all stages of incompleteness and stamps showing broken bar are not of much value.

On the other hand, stamps showing either only the top or bottom of the letters "three" are scarce, though not as rare as No. 147c.

The 6 c. T **27**, surcharged "three cents," in red or black, is an essay. (*Price* £25.) The 2 c. on 30 c. with red surcharge is a colour trial. (*Price* £25.)

AIR MAIL
to Halifax, N.S.
1921.

(72)

1921 (16 Nov.). *Air stamp. T* **34** *optd. with T* **72.**

I. 2¾ *mm. between* "air" *and* "mail".

148 35 c. red (I) 60 0 65 0
a. No stop after "1921" .. 80 0 85 0
b. No stop and first "1" of "1921" below "f" of "Halifax" £15 £18
c. As No. 148, inverted .. £125
d. As No. 148a, inverted .. £125
e. As No. 148b, inverted .. £500

II. 1½ *mm. between* "air" *and* "mail".

148*f* 35 c. red (II) 85 0 95 0
g. No stop after "1921" .. £7 £8
h. No stop and first "1" of "1921" below "f" of "Halifax" £15 £18
i. As No. 148f, inverted .. £150
k. As No. 148g, inverted .. £175
l. As No. 148h, inverted .. £450

73. Twin Hills, Tor's Cove.

75. Statue of the Fighting Newfoundlander, St. John's.

74. South-West Arm, Trinity (*horiz.*).

76. Humber River (*vert.*).

77. Coast at Trinity (*vert.*).

78. Upper Steadies, Humber River (*horiz.*)

79. Quidi Vidi, near St. John's (*horiz.*).

80. Caribou crossing lake (*horiz.*).

81. Humber River Cañon (*vert.*).

82. Shell Bird Island (*horiz.*).

83. Mount Moriah, Bay of Islands (*horiz.*).

84. Humber River nr. Little Rapids (*vert.*).

85. Placentia (*horiz.*).

86. Topsail Falls (*vert.*).

(Recess. Whitehead, Morris & Co.)

1923 (9 July)–**1924.** *T* **73** *to* **86.** *P* 14 (*comb or line*).

No.	Description	Unused	Used
149	1 c. green	2 6	0 3
150	2 c. carmine..	3 6	0 3
151	3 c. brown	2 0	0 3
152	4 c. deep purple	4 0	0 10
153	5 c. ultramarine	6 6	1 3
154	6 c. slate	7 6	8 6
155	8 c. purple	8 6	8 0
156	9 c. slate-green	30 0	22 6
157	10 c. violet	8 6	7 6
157*a*	10 c. purple	10 0	8 6
158	11 c. sage-green	12 6	12 6
159	12 c. lake	12 6	12 6
160	15 c. Prussian blue	15 0	15 0
161	20 c. chestnut (28.4.24) ..	15 0	15 0
162	24 c. sepia (22.4.24)	£6	£7

Air Mail
DE PINEDO
1927

(87)

1927 (18 May). *Air stamp. T* **35** *optd. with T* **87**, *by Robinson & Co., Ltd.*

No.	Description	Unused	Used
163	60 c. black (R.)	£800	£200

For the mail carried by De Pinedo to Europe 300 stamps were overprinted, 230 used on correspondence, 66 presented to De Pinedo, Government Officials, etc., and 4 damaged and destroyed. Stamps without overprint were also employed.

88. Newfoundland and Labrador.

89. SS. *Caribou.*

90. King George V and Queen Mary.

91. Duke of Windsor when Prince of Wales.

92. Express train.

93. Hotel, St. John's.

94. Heart's Content.

95. Cabot Tower, St. John's.

War Memorial, St. John's.
96

G.P.O., St. John's.
97

98. Trans-Atlantic flight.

99. Colonial Building, St. John's.

100. Grand Falls, Labrador.

(Recess. Whitehead, Morris Ltd.)

1928 (3 Jan.)–**1929.** "*Publicity*" *issue. T* **88** *to* **100.** *P* 14, 13 × 13½ *or* 14 × 13½.

No.	Description	Unused	Used
164	1 c. deep green	0 8	0 6
165	2 c. carmine	1 9	0 6
166	3 c. brown	1 6	0 6
167	4 c. mauve	17 6	12 6
167*a*	4 c. rose-purple ('29) ..	6 6	3 6
168	5 c. slate-grey	7 6	2 0
169	6 c. ultramarine	6 6	7 0
170	8 c. red-brown	6 0	6 6
171	9 c. deep green	12 6	15 0
172	10 c. deep violet	15 0	6 0
173	12 c. carmine-lake	10 0	12 6
174	14 c. brown-purple (*T* 95) ..	10 0	6 6
175	15 c. deep blue	10 0	10 6
176	20 c. grey-black	12 6	7 6
177	28 c. deep green (*T* 97) ..	20 0	20 0
178	30 c. sepia	12 6	15 0

Perforations: P 14—1, 3, 5, 8, 9, 10, 12, 14, 15, 20, 28 and 30 c. P 13 × 13½—2, 3, 4, 5, 6, 10, 14 and 20 c. P 14 × 13½—8 and 30 c.

The above list is possibly incomplete.

THREE
CENTS

(101)

(Surcharged by Messrs. D. R. Thistle, St. John's.)

1929 (23 Aug.). *T* 78 *surcharged with T* 101.

179 3 c. on 6 c. slate (R.) 3 0 4 6
a. Surcharge inverted £30
b. Surcharge in black £35

W. (1 c.) P. W. (2 c.) P.

W. (3 c.) P.

W. (4 c.) P.

W. (5 c.) P.

W. (6 c.) P. W. (10 c.) P.

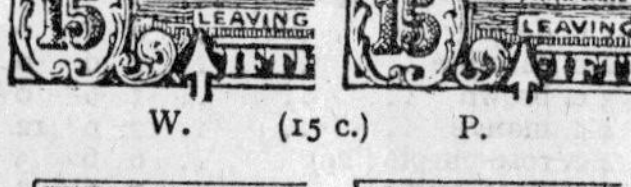

W. (15 c.) P.

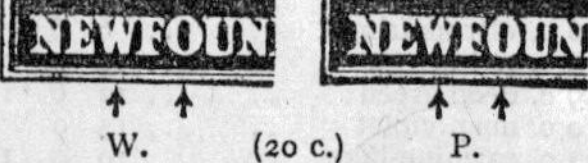

W. (20 c.) P.

W. " Whitehead, Morris " printing.
P. " Perkins, Bacon " printing.

1929-31. *" Perkins, Bacon " printing. Former types re-engraved. No wmk. P* 14 *or* 13½.

180 **88** 1 c. green (26.9.29) .. 1 0 0 3
a. Imperf. between (pair) .. £12
181 **89** 2 c. scarlet (10.8.29) .. 1 3 0 3
182 **90** 3 c. red-brown (10.8.29) .. 1 3 0 4
a. Imperf. .. ..
183 **91** 4 c. reddish pur. (26.8.29) 6 0 1 3
184 **92** 5 c. dp. grey-grn. (14.9.29) 5 0 1 9
185 **93** 6 c. ultram. (8.11.29) .. 15 0 15 0
188 **96** 10 c. violet (5.10.29) .. 10 0 5 0
189 **98** 15 c. blue (Jan. '30) .. 25 0 22 6
190 **99** 20 c. black (1.1.31) .. 35 0 25 0

Perforations: P 14—1, 6, and 20 c. P 13½—2, 3, 4, 5, 6, 10 and 15 c.

1930 (25 Sept.). *Air stamp. T* 68 *surcharged* " Trans-Atlantic / AIR MAIL / By B.M. / " Columbia " / September/1930 / Fifty Cents " *in seven lines, by Messrs. D. R. Thistle.*

191 50 c. on 36 c. sage-green .. £250 £175

Forgeries of this surcharge are known.

103. Aeroplane and dog-team.

Vickers-Vimy biplane and early sailing packet.
104

105. Routes of historic transatlantic flights.

106

(Recess. Perkins, Bacon & Co.)

1931. *Air stamps.* *T* **103** *to* **105.** *P* 14.

(*a*) *Without wmk.* (2.1.31).

No.	Description	Unused	Used
192	15 c. chocolate	10 6	12 6
	a. Imperf. between (horiz. pair)		
193	50 c. green	27 6	35 0
	a. Imperf. between (horiz. pair)		
194	$1 deep blue	65 0	75 0

(*b*) *Wmk. T* **106,** *sideways* (13.3.31).

No.	Description	Unused	Used
195	15 c. chocolate	8 0	10 0
	a. Pair; one with, one without wmk.	22 6	
196	50 c. green	55 0	60 0
	a. Imperf. between (horiz. pair)		
	b. Imperf.		
197	$1 deep blue	£5	£5
	a. Imperf. between (vert. pair)		

1931. "*Perkins, Bacon*" *printing* (*re-engraved types*). *Wmk. T* **106.** *P* 14 *or* $13\frac{1}{2}$.

No.	Type	Description	Unused	Used
198	**88**	1 c. green	1 6	0 6
199	**89**	2 c. scarlet	3 0	0 6
200	**90**	3 c. red-brown	5 0	0 6
201	**91**	4 c. reddish purple	8 0	1 3
202	**92**	5 c. deep grey-green	12 6	8 6
203	**93**	6 c. ultramarine (25.3.31)	40 0	40 0
204	**94**	8 c. chestnut (1.4.31)	27 6	27 6
205	**96**	10 c. violet	15 0	12 6
206	**98**	15 c. blue	45 0	45 0
207	**99**	20 c. black	45 0	17 6
208	**100**	30 c. sepia	45 0	40 0

107. Codfish.

108. King George V.

109. Queen Mary.

110. Duke of Windsor when Prince of Wales.

111. Caribou.

112. Princess Elizabeth.

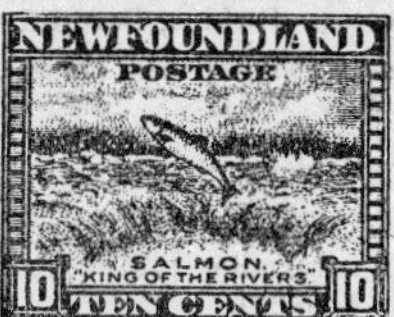

113. Salmon.

114. Newfoundland dog (*horiz.*).

115. Seal (*horiz.*).

116. Transatlantic Beacon (*horiz.*).

117. Sealing fleet (*horiz.*).

118. Fishing fleet (*horiz.*).

(Recess. Perkins, Bacon & Co.)

1932 (1 Jan.). *W* **106.** *P* $13\frac{1}{2}$ (15 c. $13\frac{1}{2}$ *or* 1).4

No.	Type	Description	Unused	Used
209	**107**	1 c. green	1 9	0 4
210	**108**	2 c. carmine	1 3	0 1
211	**109**	3 c. orange-brown	0 9	0 3
		a. Imperf.		
		b. Imperf. between (vert. pair)		
212	**110**	4 c. bright violet	10 0	2 6
213	**111**	5 c. marone	15 0	1 9
		a. Imperf.		
214	**112**	6 c. light blue	12 6	12 6
215	**113**	10 c. black-brown	2 6	1 3
		a. Imperf.		
216	**114**	14 c. black	4 0	4 6
217	**115**	15 c. claret	5 0	3 0
218	**116**	20 c. green	5 0	1 9
		a. Imperf.		
219	**117**	25 c. slate	8 6	5 0
		a. Imperf.		
220	**118**	30 c. ultramarine	47 6	52 6
		a. Imperf.		

For similar stamps perf $12\frac{1}{2}$ see Nos 276/289.

TRANS-ATLANTIC
WEST TO EAST
Per Dornier DO-X
May, 1932.
One Dollar and Fifty Cents

(119)

1932. *Air stamp.* *T* **105** *surch. as T* **119,** *by Messrs. D. R. Thistle.* *W* **106.** *P* 14.

No.	Description	Unused	Used
221	$1.50 on $1 deep blue (R.)	£20	£22
	a. Surcharge inverted	£250	

120. Queen Elizabeth, when Duchess of York.

121. Paper Mills.

122. Loading Iron Ore.

(Recess. Perkins, Bacon & Co.)

1932. *Colours changed, new values and designs. Wmk.* **T 106.** *P* 13½.

No.	Type	Description		Unused	Used
222	**107**	1 c. grey	.. ..	0 3	0 1
		a. Imperf.	.. ..		
223	**108**	2 c. green	.. ..	0 9	0 2
		a. Imperf.	.. ..		
224	**110**	4 c. carmine	.. ..	1 0	0 2
		a. Imperf.	.. ..		
		b. Imperf. between (vert. pair)	.. ..		
225	**111**	5 c. violet (Die I)	..	3 0	0 6
		a. Imperf.	.. ..		
		b. Die II	.. ..	2 6	0 3
226	**120**	7 c. red-brown	.. ..	2 6	2 0
227	**121**	8 c. red	.. ..	2 0	1 0
228	**122**	24 c. bright blue	..	4 0	4 6

Two dies exist of the 2 c. Die I was used for the stamp in carmine (No. 210) and both dies for No. 223. The differences, though numerous, are very slight.

There are also two dies of the 5 c., Die I being used for No. 213 only and both dies for the violet stamp.

In Die II the antler pointing to the "T" of "POSTAGE" is taller than the one pointing to the "S" and the individual hairs on the underside of the caribou's tail are distinct.

For similar stamps perf. 12½ see Nos. 276/289 in King George VI Catalogue.

(**123**) "L & S" = Land and Sea.

1933 (9 FEB.). *T* **103** *optd. with T* **123**, *by Messrs. D. R. Thistle. W* **106** *sideways. P* 14.

No.	Description		Unused	Used
229	15 c. chocolate	.. ..	6 0	5 0
	a. Pair; one with, one without wmk.	.. .. ..	37 6	

This overprint converted the air stamp into one for ordinary postal use.

124. Put to Flight.

125. Land of Hearts Delight.

126. Spotting the Herd.

127. News from Home.

128. Labrador.

(Recess. Perkins, Bacon & Co.)

1933 (31 MAY). *Air. Various horiz. designs. W* **106.** *P* 14 (*a*) *or* 11½ (*b*).

No.	Type	Description		Unused	Used
230	**124**	5 c. red-brown (*a*)	..	15 0	16 6
		a. Imperf.	.. ..		
231	**125**	10 c. orange-yellow (*b*)	..	20 0	22 6
		a. Imperf.	.. ..		
232	**126**	30 c. light blue (*a*)	..	60 0	65 0
233	**127**	60 c. green (*b*)	..	75 0	80 0
234	**128**	75 c. yellow-brown (*a*)	..	75 0	80 0

1933

GEN. BALBO
FLIGHT.
$4.50

(**129**)

(Surcharged by Robinson & Co., St. John's.)

1933 (24 JULY). *Air stamp. Balbo Transatlantic Mass Formation Flight. T* **128** *surcharged with T* **129.** *Wmk. T* **106.** *P* 14.

No.	Description	Unused	Used
235	$4.50 on 75 c. yellow-brown	£20	£25

130. Sir Humphrey Gilbert.

131. Compton Castle, Devon.

132. Gilbert Coat of Arms (*vert.*).

133. Eton College (*horiz.*).

134. Anchor token (*vert.*).

135. Gilbert commissioned by Elizabeth (*horiz.*)

136. Fleet leaving Plymouth, 1583 (*horiz.*).

137. Arrival at St. John's (*horiz.*).

138. Annexation, 5th August, 1583 (*horiz.*).

139. Royal Arms (*vert.*).

140. Gilbert in the *Squirrel* (*vert.*).

141. Map of Newfoundland (*horiz.*).

142. Queen Elizabeth (*vert.*).

143. Gilbert's statue at Truro (*vert.*).

(Recess. Perkins, Bacon & Co.)

1933 (3 AUG.). *350th Anniversary of the Annexation by Sir Humphrey Gilbert. Various designs, dated* "1583–1933". *W* **106.** *P* 13½ *or* 14.

No.	Type	Description		Unused	Used
236	**130**	1 c. slate	.. ..	1 0	0 10
		a. Imperf.	.. ..		
237	**131**	2 c. green	.. ..	1 6	1 0
		a. Imperf.	.. ..		
238	**132**	3 c. chestnut	.. ..	2 0	1 6
239	**133**	4 c. carmine	.. ..	2 6	0 9
		a. Imperf.	.. ..		
240	**134**	5 c. violet	.. ..	5 0	3 6
241	**135**	7 c. greenish blue	..	22 6	25 0
242	**136**	8 c. vermilion	.. ..	12 6	15 0
243	**137**	9 c. ultramarine	..	12 6	15 0
		a. Imperf.	.. ..		
244	**138**	10 c. brown-lake	..	12 6	8 0
		a. Imperf	.. ..		
245	**139**	14 c. grey-black	.. ..	30 0	17 6
246	**140**	15 c. claret	.. ..	30 0	13 6
247	**141**	20 c. grey-green	.. ..	22 6	25 0
248	**142**	24 c. marone	.. ..	65 0	70 0
		a. Imperf.	.. ..		
249	**143**	32 c. olive-black	.. ..	70 0	75 0

1935 (6 MAY). *Silver Jubilee. As T* **13** *of Antigua, inscr.* " NEWFOUNDLAND ". *Recess. B.W. & Co. Wmk. Mult. Script CA. P* 11 × 12.

250 4 c. rosine 1 3 1 0
251 5 c. bright violet 4 0 3 6
252 7 c. blue 4 6 5 0
253 24 c. olive-green 8 0 8 6

NEW GUINEA.

(LATE NEW BRITAIN.)

G.R.I. 2d. (1) G.R.I. 1s. (2)

I. STAMPS OF GERMAN NEW GUINEA.

To separate the printings, measure from the bottom of the " R " to the top of the " d " in the low values, or to the top of the figure of value in the large stamps.

1914 (OCT.). *Stamps of* 1900 *German Colonial issue (no wmk.), surcharged as T* **1** *or* **2** *(mark values), in black.*

FIRST PRINTING.

1914 (17 OCT.). " G.R.I." *and value* 6 *mm. apart*

1 1d. on 3 pf. brown 45 0 45 0
2 1d. on 5 pf. green 10 0 10 0
3 2d. on 10 pf. carmine .. 25 0 25 0
4 2d. on 20 pf. ultramarine .. 25 0 25 0
 a. "2d." double printed without the "G.R.I." £30
5 2½d. on 10 pf. carmine .. 30 0 35 0
6 2½d. on 20 pf. ultramarine .. 65 0 65 0
7 3d. on 25 pf. blk. & red/*yell.* .. £5 £5
8 3d. on 30 pf. blk. & oran./*buff* £5 £5
9 4d. on 40 pf. blk. & carmine .. £7 £8
 a. Surcharge double £40 £40
 b. Surcharge inverted .. ..
10 5d. on 50 pf. blk. & pur/*buff* .. £6 £7
11 8d. on 80 pf. blk. & carm./*rose* £16 £18
 a. No stop .. .. ..

" G.R.I." *and value* 3½ *to* 4 *mm. apart.*

12 1s. on 1 m. carmine £55 £55
13 2s. on 2 m. blue £55 £55
14 3s. on 3 m. violet-black .. £80 £80
15 5s. on 5 m. carmine and blk. £100 £110
 a. No stop after " I " .. ..

SECOND PRINTING.

1914 (16 DEC.). " G.R.I." *and value* 5 *mm. apart.*

16 1d. on 3 pf. brown 30 0 35 0
 a. Figure " 1 " omitted .. .. — £20
 b. Surcharge double .. ..
 c. Surcharge inverted .. ..
17 1d. on 5 pf. green 7 6 7 6
 a. " d " inverted .. .. — £20
 b. No stops after " G R I " .. — £12
 c. Surcharge double .. ..
 d. Small " I " 30 0 30 0
 e. " 1d." double £10
 f. " G.I.R. for " G.R.I." .. £70
18 2d. on 10 pf. carmine.. .. 10 0 10 0
 a. Surcharge double £30
 b. Surcharge double, one inverted
 c. Error. Surcharged " G.I.R. 3d."
 d. Stop before instead of after " G "
 e. Error. " 1d." for " 2d." and stop before " G " £45 £35
19 2d. on 20 pf. ultramarine .. 10 0 10 0
 a. " R " inverted £40 £30
 b. Surcharge double £40
 c. Surcharge double, one inverted — £55
 d. Error Surch. "G.R.I. 1d." — £55
20 2½d. on 10 pf. carmine 40 0 40 0
21 2½d. on 20 pf. ultramarine .. £15 £18
 a. Surcharge double, one inverted
22 3d. on 25 pf. black & red/*yellow* 80 0 80 0
 a. Surcharge " G.I.R." for "G.R.I." £85
23 3d. on 30 pf. blk. & orge./*buff* .. £5 £5
 a. " d " inverted .. .. — £45
 b. Surcharge double £45
 c. Surcharge double, one inverted £55
 d. Error. " 1d." for " 3d." .. £80
24 4d. on 40 pf. blk. & carm. .. 80 0 80 0
 a. Surcharge double, one inverted £55
25 5d. on 50 pf. blk. & pur./*buff* £6 £6
 a. Figure " 5 " omitted .. ..
 b. Surcharge double .. ..
 c. Surcharge double, one inverted
 d. " G.I.R." for " G.R.I."
26 8d. on 80 pf. blk. & carm./*rose* £6 £6
 a. Surcharge double, one inverted — £50
 b. Surcharge double .. ..
 c. Triple surcharge .. ..

" G.R.I." *and value* 5½ *mm. apart.*

27 1s. on 1 m. carmine £55 £55
28 2s. on 2 m. blue £60
 a. Surcharge double .. ..
29 3s. on 3 m. violet-black .. £80
30 5s. on 5 m. carm. & blk. .. £110

There appears to be also a third printing of most of the low values with 7½ mm. between the " G.R.I." and top of the " d."

The second printing is the only one we have had in full sheets. In this the surcharge is set up in a horizontal row of ten types, and this is repeated ten times down the sheet.

G.R.I. R. Rabaul (Deutsch Neuguinea) № 570

3

Registration Label, T 3, *surcharged and used for postage.*

3d. black and red/*buff*.

I. *With name of town in sans-serif letters and* " (Deutsch Neuguinea) ".

31 Rabaul 30 0 30 0
 a. " G.R.I. 3d." double .. ..
 b. No bracket before " Deutsch " ..
 c. Hyphen between " Deutsch " and " Neuguinea " £5
 d. No stop after " I " .. ..
32 Herbertshöhe 40 0 40 0
 a. " (Deutsch Neu-Guinea) " .. £5
33 Kieta (hyphen btwn. " Deutsch " and " Neuguinea ") .. 50 0 50 0
34 Käwieng (ditto) .. ..
 a. Without brackets .. — £5
 b. " Deutsch Neu-Guinea " ..
35 Manus £10
 a. " G.R.I. 3d." double .. ..

II. *With name of town in letters with serifs and* " (Deutsch-Neuguinea)" *hyphenated.*

36 Friedrich Wilhelmshafen .. 55 0 55 0
 a. No hyphen £10
37 Kawieng (no hyphen between " Deutsch " and " Neu-guinea ") 70 0 70 0
38 Manus .. ..

SERVICE STAMPS.

O. S.

G.R.I.

1d.

(4)

SPECIAL PRINTING.

"G.R.I." and value 3½ mm. apart. Overprinted as T 4.

40 1d. on 3 pf. brown 2 6 2 6
41 1d. on 5 pf. green 10 0 10 0

II. STAMPS OF MARSHALL ISLANDS.

1914 (16 DEC.). *Stamps of German Colonial issue surcharged as* T 1 *and* 2, *in black.*

"G.R.I." and value 5 mm. apart.

50 1d. on 3 pf. brown 12 6 12 6
 a. "1" with straight serif ..
 b. Surcharge inverted .. £40
51 1d. on 5 pf. green 12 6 12 6
 a. No stop after "d" .. ..
 b. "1" and "d" wider apart ..
52 2d. on 10 pf. carmine 4 6 4 6
 a. No stop after "G" .. ..
 b. Surcharge double ..
 c. Surcharge double, one inverted £55
53 2d. on 20 pf. ultram. 6 0 6 0
 a. No stop after "d" 20 0
 b. Surcharge double ..
 c. Surcharge double, one inverted £55
54 3d. on 25 pf. black and red/*yell.* £12 £12
 a. No stop after "d" £45 £45
 b. Surcharge double .. .. — £45
 c. Surcharge double, one inverted ..
55 3d. on 30 pf. blk. & orge./*buff* £10 £10
 a. No stop after "d" £30
56 4d. on 40 pf. blk. & carm. .. 60 0 60 0
 a. No stop after "d" £10 £10
 b. Surcharge inverted .. £40
57 5d. on 50 pf. blk. & purple/*buff* 80 0 80 0
 a. "5" only for "5d." ..
58 8d. on 80 pf. blk. & carm./*rose* £10 £12
59 1s. on 1 m. carmine £55 £55
 a. No stop after "I" .. ..
 b. Surcharge double .. ..
60 2s. on 2 m. blue £25 £25
 a. Surcharge double, one inverted — £90
 b. Large "S" after "2" ..
61 3s. on 3 m. violet-black .. £75 £75
 a. Surcharge double .. ..
 b. No stop after "I" .. ..
62 5s. on 5 m. carm. & black .. £110 £110
 a. Surcharge double, one inverted

G.R.I.

1d.

(5)

1915. *Nos.* 52 *and* 53 *further surcharged as in* T 5, *in black.*

63 "1" on 2d. on 10 pf. £5 £5
64 "1" on 2d. on 20 pf. £50 £50

The printing of the low values of the Marshall Islands is from the same setting as the second printing of the German New Guinea, but in the 2d. on 20 pf., the stop after "2d" on the 5th stamp has fallen out, and there is thus one row of ten stamps on each sheet without stop.

A few values have been found in Australia of the first printing, and probably others may exist.

The high values are *probably* the same setting as the German New Guinea second setting

III AUSTRALIAN STAMPS OVERPRINTED.

N. W.
PACIFIC
ISLANDS.
(6)

Stamps of the Australian Commonwealth overprinted in black or purple (P.), *as* T 6.

The purple overprint varies in intensity and can be distinguished more or less readily by looking at the back of the stamp.

N. W.
PACIFIC
ISLANDS.
(*a*)

N. W.
PACIFIC
ISLANDS.
(*b*)

N. W.
PACIFIC
ISLANDS.
(*c*)

The setting of the overprint consists of a block of 30 (6 × 5), and shows three varieties caused by the use of the two different types of "S" which occur in this fount of type. (*a*) Both "S S" normal. (*b*) First "S" with small head and large tail and second "S" normal. (*c*) Both "S S" with small head and large tail.

8

10

1915 (15 MARCH). T 5a *of Australian Commonwealth (King).* *Wmk.* T 8. P 14.

65 ½d. green (P.) (*a*) or (*c*) .. 0 7 0 7
 ,, (*b*) 1 2 1 2
 ,, (*strip of 3 vars.*) 3 0
66 ½d. bright green (P.) (*a*) or (*c*) 0 6 0 6
 ,, (*b*) .. 1 0 1 0
 ,, (*strip of 3 vars.*) 2 6
67 1d. pale rose (Die I) (*a*) or (*c*) 0 6 0 8
 ,, (*b*) .. 1 0 1 6
 ,, (*strip of 3 vars.*) 2 6
68 1d. dull red (Die I) (*a*) or (*c*) .. 1 0
 ,, (*b*) 2 0
 ,, (*strip of 3 vars.*) .. 4 6 4 6
69 1d. carm.-red (Die I) (*a*) or (*c*) 0 9 1 0
 ,, (*b*) 1 6 2 0
 ,, (*strip of 3 vars.*) 3 6
 d. Top of crown missing (*a*) .. — £5
69e 1d. carm.-red (Die II) (*a*) or (*c*) 15 0
 ,, (*b*) 30 0
 ,, (*strip of 3 vars.*) 75 0
 f. Top of crown missing (*a*) .. — £5
70 4d. yell.-oran. (*a*) or (*c*) .. 1 6 2 0
 ,, (*b*) 3 0 3 6
 ,, (*strip of 3 vars.*) 6 6
 d. Line through "FOURPENCE" 15 0 15 0
71 4d. orange-yell. (*a*) or (*c*) ..
 ,, (*b*) ..
 ,, (*strip of 3 vars.*)
72 5d. brown (*a*) or (*c*) .. 2 0 2 6
 ,, (*b*) 4 0 5 0
 ,, (*strip of 3 vars*) .. 8 0

T 1 *of Australian Commonwealth (Kangaroo).* *Wmk.* T 10. P 12.

73 2d. grey (P.) (*a*) or (*c*) .. 1 9 2 0
 ,, (*b*) 3 6 4 0
 ,, (*strip of 3 vars.*) 8
74 2½d. indigo (*a*) or (*c*) .. 2 0 2 6
 ,, (*b*) 4 0 5 0
 ,, (*strip of 3 vars.*) .. 10 0

No.	Description	Unused		Used	
75	2½d. indigo (P.) (*a*) or (*c*) ..	1	6	1	9
	„ (*b*)	3	0	3	6
	„ (*strip of 3 vars.*)	7	6		
76	3d. yell.-olive (P.) (*a*) or (*c*) ..	2	6	3	0
	„ (*b*)) ..	5	0	6	0
	„ (*strip of 3 vars.*)	10	0		
77	3d. greenish olive (P.) (*a*) or (*c*)				
	„ (*b*) ..				
	„ (*strip of 3 vars.*)				
78	6d. ultramarine (*a*) or (*c*) ..	6	0	7	6
	„ (*b*)	12	0	17	6
	„ (*strip of 3 vars.*)	30	0		
79	9d. violet (*a*) or (*c*)	25	0	30	0
	„ (*b*)	50	0		
	„ (*strip of 3 vars.*) ..				
80	9d. violet (P.) (*a*) or (*c*) ..	12	6	15	0
	„ (*b*)	25	0	30	0
	„ (*strip of 3 vars.*)	60	0		
81	1s. green (*a*) or (*c*)	22	6	25	0
	„ (*b*)	45	0	50	0
	„ (*strip of 3 vars.*) ..	£5			
82	1s. green (P.) (*a*) or (*c*) ..	17	6	20	0
	„ (*b*)	35	0	40	0
	„ (*strip of 3 vars.*)	70	0		
83	5s. grey & yell. (*a*) or (*c*) ..	£20			
	„ (*b*)	£40			
	„ (*strip of 3 vars.*) ..	£100			
84	10s. grey & pink (*a*) or (*c*) ..	20	0	25	0
	„ (*b*)	40	0	50	0
	„ (*strip of 3 vars.*)	90	0		
85	£1 brown & ultram. (*a*) or (*c*) ..	70	0	75	0
	„ (*b*)	£7		£8	
	„ (*strip of 3 vars.*)				

1915. (Oct.-Dec.). *T* **1** *of Australian Commonwealth. W* **8.** *P* 12.

No.	Description	Unused		Used	
86	2d. grey (*a*) or (*c*)	2	6		
	„ (*b*)	5	0	6	0
	„ (*strip of 3 vars.*) ..	12	6		
87	2½d. indigo (*a*) or (*c*)				
	„ (*b*)				
	„ (*strip of 3 vars.*) ..				
88	6d. ultram. (*a*) or (*c*)	1	6	2	0
	„ (*b*)	3	0	4	0
	„ (*strip of 3 vars.*) ..	6	0		
89	9d. violet (*a*) or (*c*)	1	3	1	9
	„ (*b*)	2	6	3	0
	„ (*strip of 3 vars.*) ..	5	6		
90	1s. emerald (P.) (*a*) or (*c*) ..	2	0	2	6
	„ (*b*)	4	0	4	6
	„ (*strip of 3 vars.*)	8	6		
91	2s. brown (*a*) or (*c*)	20	0	22	6
	„ (*b*)	40	0	45	0
	„ (*strip of 3 vars.*) ..	90	0		
92	5s. grey & yell. (*a*) or (*c*) ..	25	0	30	0
	„ (*b*)	50	0	60	0
	„ (*strip of 3 vars.*)	105	0		
93	5s. grey & yell. (P.) (*a*) or (*c*)	12	6	15	0
	„ (*b*) ..	25	0	30	0
	„ (*strip of 3 vars.*)	60	0		

11

1915 (Dec.)–**1916** (Aug.). *T* **1** *of Australian Commonwealth. W* **11.** *P* 12.

No.	Description	Unused		Used	
94	2d. grey (*a*) or (*c*)	0	9	1	0
	„ (*b*)	1	6	2	0
	„ (*strip of 3 vars.*) ..	3	6		
95	2d. grey (P.) (*a*) or (*c*) ..	4	0	4	6
	„ (*b*)	8	0	9	0
	„ (*strip of 3 vars.*)	17	6		
96	3d. yell.-olive (*a*) or (*c*) ..	1	3	1	6
	„ (*b*)	2	6	3	0
	„ (*strip of 3 vars.*)	5	0		
97	2s. brown (*a*) or (*c*)	8	6	12	6
	„ (*b*)	17	0	25	0
	„ (*strip of 3 vars.*)	34	0		
98	2s. red-brown (P.) (*a*) or (*c*) ..	4	0	6	0
	„ (*b*) ..	8	0	12	0
	„ (*strip of 3 vars.*)	16	0		
99	£1 brn. & ultram. (P.) (*a*) or (*c*)	30	0	40	0
	„ (*b*) ..	55	0	75	0
	„ (*strip of 3 vars.*)	£6			

One Penny

(11*a*)

1918. *Current issue surcharged locally with T* **11***a, in black.*

No.	Description	Unused		Used	
100	1d. on 5d. brown (*a*) or (*c*)	55	0	55	0
	„ (*b*) ..	90	0	70	0
	„ (*strip of 3 vars.*)	£10		£7	
101	1d. on 1s. green (*a*) or (*c*) ..	55	0	45	0
	„ (*b*)	90	0	65	0
	„ (*strip of 3 vars.*)	£10		£7	

1919–23. *As* 1915, *but new setting showing Type* (*a*) *of overprint only.* (*a*) *W* **8.**

No.	Description	Unused		Used	
102	½d. green	0	4	0	5
103	1d. carmine-red (Die I) ..	0	6	0	8
	a. Top of crown missing ..	50	0		
	b. Rosine. Rough paper, locally gummed (perfd. "O S") ..				
103*c*	1d. carmine-red (Die II) ..	15	0	10	0
	d. Top of crown missing ..	£5			
	e. Rosine. Rough paper, locally gummed (perfd. "O S") ..				
104	4d. yellow-orange	1	9	2	0
	a. Line through "FOURPENCE"				
105	5d. brown	1	3	1	6

(*b*) *W* **11.**

No.	Description	Unused		Used	
106	2d. grey	0	9	1	0
107	2½d. indigo	1	0	1	3
	a. "1" of "½" omitted ..	£30			
108	2½d. blue (1922)	2	0	3	0
109	3d. greenish olive	0	8	1	0
110	6d. ultramarine	0	9	1	3
111	6d. greyish ultram. (1923) ..	4	0	5	0
112	9d. violet	2	0	2	6
113	1s. emerald	2	0	3	0
114	1s. pale blue-green	4	6	5	6
115	2s. brown	4	0	6	0
116	5s. grey and yellow ..	10	0	15	0
117	10s. grey and bright pink ..	22	6	32	6
118	£1 brown and ultramarine ..	£15			

(*c*) *Wmk. Multiple Crown* "A" (*as T* 8).

No.	Description	Unused		Used	
119	½d. green	0	3	0	5

In this setting the foot of the "P" of "PACIFIC" is midway between the "I" and "S" of "ISLANDS." In variety (*a*) of the previous settings it is over the left portion of the "S."

1921–22. *T* **5***a of Australian Commonwealth W* **8.** *Colours changed.*

No.	Description	Unused		Used	
120	1d. bright violet	0	6	0	6
121	2d. orange	1	0	0	8
122	2d. scarlet	0	8	0	6
123	4d. violet	4	0	4	6
	a. "FOURPENCE" in thinner letters				
124	4d. ultramarine	9	0	10	0
	a. "FOURPENCE" in thinner letters	£10			

There are various settings (6 × 5 stamps) of the overprint T 6, as follows:—

No. 1. Horizontal rows 1 and 2 all Type (*a*). Row 3 all Type (*b*). Rows 4 and 5 all Type (*c*).

No. 2. As No. 1 except Row 5 in which types run (*a*) (*c*) (*c*) (*c*) (*b*) (*c*).

No. 2 A. A scarce variety of this setting has been found in the ½d. green, with the first stamp in the bottom row as Type (*c*), but otherwise as described.

Horizontal strips and pairs showing varieties (*a*) and (*c*), or (*b*) and (*c*) *se tenant* are of considerable rarity. Selections of those in stock will be sent to specialists on request.

The earliest printing of the 1d. and 2½d. values was made on sheets with margin attached on two sides, the later printings being on sheets from which the margins had been removed. In this printing the vertical distances between the overprints are less than in later printings, so that in the lower horizontal rows of the sheet the overprint is near the top of the stamp.

The settings used on King George stamps and on the Kangaroo type are similar, but the latter stamps being smaller the overprints are closer together in the vertical rows.

IV. TERRITORY OF NEW GUINEA.

12. Native village.

(Recess. Commonwealth Treasury, Melbourne.)

1925–28. *T* **12.** *P* 11.

No.	Description	s.	d.	s.	d.
125	½d. orange	0	6	0	8
126	1d. green	0	8	0	8
126*a*	1½d. orange-vermilion (1926)	0	9	0	9
127	2d. claret	0	9	0	9
128	3d. blue	1	0	1	3
129	4d. olive-green	1	9	1	9
130	6d. dull yellow-brown	5	0	5	6
130*a*	6d. olive-bistre (1927)	5	0	6	0
130*b*	6d. pale yellow-bistre ('28)	3	0	3	6
131	9d. dull purple (to violet)	4	6	5	0
132	1s. dull blue-green	4	6	5	0
133	2s. brown-lake	9	0	10	0
134	5s. olive-bistre	22	6	25	0
135	10s. dull rose	40	0	45	0
136	£1 dull olive-green	75	0	80	0

(13)

1931 (8 June). *Air stamps.* *T* **12** *overprinted with T* **13.** *P* 11.

No.	Description	s.	d.	s.	d.
137	½d. orange	0	6	0	8
138	1d. green	1	0	1	3
139	1½d. orange-vermilion	1	6	2	0
140	2d. claret	1	6	2	0
141	3d. blue	1	6	2	0
142	4d. olive-green	1	6	2	0
143	6d. pale yellow-bistre	2	0	2	6
144	9d. violet	2	6	3	0
145	1s. dull blue-green	5	0	5	0
146	2s. brown-lake	12	6	15	0
147	5s. olive-bistre	22	6	25	0
148	10s. bright pink	40	0	42	6
149	£1 olive-grey	80	0	85	0

14. Bird of Paradise. (Dates either side of value.) (15)

(Recess-printed by J. Ash, Melbourne.)

1931 (2 Aug.). *Tenth Anniversary of Australian Administration.* *T* **14.** *P* 11.

No.	Description	s.	d.	s.	d.
150	1d. green	0	6	0	6
151	1½d. vermilion	0	9	0	9
152	2d. claret	1	0	1	0
153	3d. blue	1	0	1	3
154	4d. olive-green	1	6	1	6
155	5d. deep blue-green	2	6	2	6
156	6d. bistre-brown	2	6	2	6
157	9d. violet	3	0	3	0
158	1s. pale blue-green	4	6	5	0
159	2s. brown-lake	7	6	8	6
160	5s. olive-brown	17	6	20	0
161	10s. bright pink	40	0	45	0
162	£1 olive-grey	85	0	90	0

1931 (2 Aug.). *Air stamps.* *T* **14** *optd. with T* **15.**

No.	Description	s.	d.	s.	d.
163	½d. orange	0	6	0	8
164	1d. green	0	6	0	8
165	1½d. vermilion	0	9	1	0
166	2d. claret	1	0	1	3
167	3d. blue	1	6	1	9
168	4d. olive-green	2	0	2	3
169	5d. deep blue-green	2	6	3	0
170	6d. bistre-brown	3	0	3	0
171	9d. violet	4	0	4	6
172	1s. pale blue-green	5	0	5	6
173	2s. dull lake	10	0	12	0
174	5s. olive-brown	15	0	17	6
175	10s. bright pink	45	0	50	0
176	£1 olive-grey	95	0	95	0

1932 (30 June)–**1934.** *T* **14** (*redrawn without dates*). *P* 11.

No.	Description	s.	d.	s.	d.
177	1d. green	0	6	0	3
178	1½d. claret	0	8	0	4
179	2d. vermilion	0	8	0	8
179*a*	2½d. green (14.9.34)	1	3	1	6
180	3d. blue	1	0	1	3
180*a*	3½d. aniline carm. (14.9.34)	1	9	2	3
181	4d. olive-green	1	3	1	9
182	5d. deep blue-green	1	9	2	3
183	6d. bistre-brown	1	9	2	3
184	9d. violet	2	6	3	0
185	1s. blue-green	3	6	4	0
186	2s. dull lake	7	6	7	6
187	5s. olive	22	6	22	6
188	10s. pink	40	0	30	0
189	£1 olive-grey	75	0	50	0

1932 (30 June)–**1934.** *Air stamps.* *T* **14.** (*redrawn without dates*), *overprinted with T* **15** *P* 11.

No.	Description	s.	d.	s.	d.
190	½d. orange	0	6	0	8
191	1d. green	0	9	1	0
192	1½d. claret	1	0	1	3
193	2d. vermilion	1	6	1	6
193*a*	2½d. green (14.9.34)	2	0	2	3
194	3d. blue	1	6	1	6
194*a*	3½d. aniline carm. (14.9.34)	2	6	3	0
195	4d. olive-green	2	0	2	6
196	5d. deep blue-green	2	6	3	0
197	6d. bistre-brown	2	6	3	0
198	9d. violet	3	0	4	0
199	1s. pale blue-green	4	0	4	6
200	2s. dull lake	7	6	7	6
201	5s. olive-brown	25	0	20	0
202	10s. pink	50	0	40	0
203	£1 olive-grey	90	0	60	0

16. Bulolo Goldfields.

(Recess. John Ash.)

1935 (1 May). *Air.* *P* 11.

No.	Type	Description	Unused	Used
204	16	£2 bright violet	£15	£6
205	„	£5 emerald-green	£35	£20

HIS MAJESTY'S
JUBILEE.
1910 — 1935

(17)

1935 (27 June). *Silver Jubilee. As Nos.* 177 *and* 179, *but shiny paper. Optd. with T* **17**.

No.	Description	Unused	Used
206	1d. green	1 9	3 6
207	2d. vermilion	3 6	5 0

OFFICIAL STAMPS.

O S (O 1)   O S (O 2)

1925–31. *T* **12** *optd. with Type* O **1**. *P* 11.

No.	Description	Unused	Used
O2	1d. green	0 6	0 8
O2*a*	1½d. orange-vermilion ('31) ..	0 7	0 9
O3	2d. claret	0 7	0 9
O4	3d. blue	0 10	1 0
O5	4d. olive-green	1 0	1 3
O6	6d. olive-bistre	2 6	3 0
O6*a*	6d. pale yellow-bistre ('31) ..	2 0	2 6
O7	9d. violet	2 6	3 0
O8	1s. dull blue-green	3 0	3 6
O9	2s. brown-lake	5 0	6 0

1931 (2 Aug.). *T* **14** *optd. with Type* O **2**. *P* 11.

No.	Description	Unused	Used
O10	1d. green	0 3	0 4
O11	1½d. vermilion	0 4	0 5
O12	2d. claret	0 6	0 8
O13	3d. blue	0 9	1 0
O14	4d. olive-green	1 0	1 6
O15	5d. deep blue-green	1 3	1 6
O16	6d. bistre-brown	1 6	2 0
O17	9d. violet	2 0	2 6
O18	1s. pale blue-green	3 0	4 0
O19	2s. brown-lake	6 6	7 6
O20	5s. olive-brown	15 0	17 6

1932 (30 June)–**1934.** *T* **14** (*redrawn without dates*), *overprinted with Type* O **2**. *P* 11.

No.	Description	Unused	Used
O21	1d. green	0 3	0 4
O22	1½d. claret	0 5	0 7
O23	2d. vermilion	0 6	0 8
O23*a*	2½d. green (14.9.34) ..	0 7	0 9
O24	3d. blue	0 9	1 0
O24*a*	3½d. aniline carm. (14.9.34)	1 0	1 3
O25	4d. olive-green	1 3	1 6
O26	5d. deep blue-green	1 6	2 0
O27	6d. bistre-brown	1 6	2 0
O28	9d. violet	2 0	2 6
O29	1s. pale blue-green	2 6	3 0
O30	2s. dull lake	5 0	6 0
O31	5s. olive-brown	12 6	15 0

NEW HEBRIDES.
(ANGLO-FRENCH CONDOMINIUM.)

NEW HEBRIDES CONDOMINIUM (1)   NEW HEBRIDES CONDOMINIUM (2)

1908–9. *T* 23 *and* 24 *of Fiji overprinted with T* **1**, *in black; on the bicoloured stamps the word* "FIJI" *obliterated by a bar in the colour of the word.* *P* 14.

(*a*) *Wmk. Multiple Crown CA.*

No.	Description	Unused	Used
1	½d. green & grey-green, O ('08)	2 0	2 6
2	1d. red, O	4 0	4 6
3	1s. green & carm., C (1909) ..	10 6	12 6

Variety. Vertical pair, one without overprint.

No.	Description	Unused	Used
3*a*	1d. red	£70	

(*b*) *Wmk. Crown CA.*

No.	Description	Unused	Used
4	½d. green & grey-green ('09) ..	22 6	25 0
5	2d. dull pur. and orange ..	5 0	5 0
6	2½d. dull pur. and blue/*blue* ..	3 0	3 6
7	5d. dull pur. and green ..	4 0	4 6
8	6d. dull pur. and carmine ..	4 0	5 0
9	1s. green and carmine ..	85 0	90 0

1911. *Types as last. Wmk. Multiple Crown CA. P* 14. *Optd. in London with T* **2**.

No.	Description	Unused	Used
10	½d. green, O	3 6	4 6
11	1d. red, O	10 0	10 6
12	2d. grey, O	1 9	2 6
13	2½d. bright blue, O	1 9	2 6
14	5d. dull pur. & olive-grn., C ..	3 0	3 6
15	6d. dull and deep purple, C ..	3 0	3 6
16	1s. black/*green*, C (R.) ..	4 0	5 0

3

(Recess-printed by Messrs. De La Rue & Co.)

1911 (Aug.)–**1912.** *T* **3**. *Wmk. Mult. Crown CA. P* 14.

No.	Description	Unused	Used
18	½d. green	0 6	0 8
19	1d. red	1 3	1 6
20	2d. grey	1 9	2 6
21	2½d. ultramarine	2 6	3 0
24	5d. sage-green	4 0	4 6
25	6d. purple	5 0	6 6
26	1s. black/*green*	8 6	10 0
27	2s. purple/*blue* (1912) ..	15 0	16 0
28	5s. green/*yellow* (1912) ..	32 6	37 6

1d.

(4)

1920. *T* **3** *surcharged with T* **4**, *in black.*

No.	Description	Unused	Used
30	1d. on 5d. sage-green	17 6	16 0
	a. Surcharge inverted	£50	£50
31	1d. on 1s. black/*green*	8 0	8 6
32	1d. on 2s. purple/*blue*	8 0	8 6
33	1d. on 5s. green/*yellow* ..	8 0	8 6

Stamps of French issue with similar surcharge.

(*a*) *Wmk. Mult. Crown CA.*

No.	Description	Unused	Used
34	2d. on 40 c. red/*yellow* ..	15 0	17 6

(*b*) *Wmk.* "R F" *in sheet.*

No.	Description	Unused	Used
35	2d. on 40 c. red/*yellow* ..	£12	£15

1921. *T* **3.** *Wmk. Mult. Script CA. P* 14.

No.	Description	Unused	Used
36	1d. scarlet	3 0	3 6
37	2d. slate-grey	4 0	4 6
39	6d. purple	4 6	5 0

1924. *T* 3 *surcharged as T* **4.**

No.	Description	Unused	Used
40	1d. on ½d. green (No. 18)	4 0	5 0
41	3d. on 1d. scarlet (No. 36)	4 0	5 0
42	5d. on 2½d. ultram. (No. 21)	5 0	6 0
	a. Surcharge inverted	£30	£30

5

(Recess-printed by Messrs. De La Rue & Co.)

1925. *T* **5.** *Wmk. Mult. Script CA. P* 14.

No.	Description	Unused	Used
43	½d. (5 c.) black	0 2	0 4
44	1d. (10 c.) green	0 3	0 4
45	2d. (20 c.) slate-grey	0 6	0 8
46	2½d. (25 c.) brown	0 9	1 0
47	5d. (50 c.) ultramarine	1 0	1 3
48	6d. (60 c.) purple	1 6	1 9
49	1s. (1.25 fr.) black/*emerald*	3 0	3 6
50	2s. (2.50 fr.) purple/*blue*	4 0	5 0
51	5s. (6.25 fr.) green/*yellow*	12 6	15 0

POSTAGE DUE STAMPS.

POSTAGE DUE

(D 1)

1925. *T* 5 *optd. with Type* D 1.

No.	Description	Unused	Used
D1	1d. (10 c.) green	—	1 0
D2	2d. (20 c.) slate-grey	—	1 0
D3	3d. (30 c.) red	—	1 0
D4	5d. (50 c.) ultramarine	—	1 0
D5	10d. (1 fr.) carmine/*blue*	—	1 0

Set of 5 un., 80s.

NEW REPUBLIC, SOUTH AFRICA.

(The territory of this ephemeral State was part of Zululand, but was subsequently annexed to the South African Republic as a new district, named Vrijheid. In January, 1903, the territory was annexed to the Colony of Natal.)

NIEUWE REPUBLIEK 1d 8 NOV 86 ZUID-AFRIKA.

1

Printed with a rubber handstamp on paper bought in Europe and sent out ready gummed and perforated.

1886 (Jan.)**-1887.** *T* **1.** *P* 11½.

(a) Black on yellow paper.

No.	Value	Date	Unused	Used
1	1d.	9 Jan 86	£12	

(b) Violet on yellow paper.

No.	Value	Date	Unused	Used
1a	1d.	9 Jan 86	6 6	8 6
2	1d.	13 Jan 86	25 0	
3	1d.	7 Mar 86		
4	1d.	17 Mar 86		
4a	1d.	14 Apl 86		
5	1d.	24 Apl 86		
6	1d	24 May 86		
7	1d.	30 Aug 86	4 0	6 0
8	1d.	6 Sep 86	5 0	
9	1d.	13 Oct 86	6 6	8 6
10	1d.	3 Nov 86		
11	1d.	13 Nov 86		
11a	1d.	24 Nov 86	7 6	
12	1d.	4 Jan 87		
13	1d.	17 Jan 87		
14	2d.	9 Jan 86	12 6	17 6
15	2d.	13 Jan 86	8 6	10 0
16	2d.	24 May 86		
17	2d.	30 Aug 86	8 6	
18	2d.	6 Sep 86	4 0	7 6
19	2d.	13 Oct 86	5 0	7 6
	a. "d" omitted			
20	2d.	24 Nov 86	7 6	10 0
21	2d.	4 Jan 87		
22	2d.	17 Jan 87		
23	3d.	13 Jan 86		
24	3d.	30 Aug 86	15 0	
25	3d.	6 Sep 86	27 6	
26	3d.	13 Oct 86	15 0	17 6
	a. "d" omitted			
27	3d.	24 Nov 86	20 0	25 0
28	3d.	17 Jan 87		
29	4d.	30 Aug 86	40 0	
30	4d.	6 Sep 86	27 6	
31	4d.	13 Oct 86	20 0	
32	6d.	21 May 86		
33	6d.	2 Jul 86		
34	6d.	30 Aug 86	20 0	
35	6d.	6 Sep 86	20 0	
36	6d.	13 Oct 86	20 0	22 6
37	9d.	13 Jan 86		
38	9d.	30 Aug 86	32 6	
39	9d.	6 Sep 86	20 0	
40	9d.	13 Oct 86	25 0	
41	1s.	30 Aug 86	45 0	
42	1s.	6 Sep 86	60 0	
43	1s.	13 Oct 86	45 0	
43a	1/s.	13 Oct 86		
44	1/6	30 Aug 86	55 0	
45	1/6	6 Sep 86	65 0	
45a	1s. 6d.	6 Sep 86		
46	1/6	13 Oct 86	90 0	
46a	1/6	26 Nov 86		
47	1s. 6.	13 Oct 86	50 0	
48	2s.	30 Aug 86	52 6	
49	2s.	6 Sep 86	60 0	
50	2s.	13 Oct 86	25 0	
51	2/6	13 Jan 86		
51a	2s. 6d.	20 Feb 86		
51b	2s. 6d.	7 Mar 86		
52	2s. 6d.	19 Aug 86		
53	2/6	30 Aug 86		
54	2/6	6 Sep 86	60 0	
55	2/6	13 Oct 86	70 0	
56	4/s.	17 Jan 87		
57	5s.	Jan 86	15 0	17 6
58	5s.	7 Mar 86	—	70 0
	a. "5" of "5s." omitted			
59	5s.	24 May 86		
60	5s.	6 Sep 86		
61	5s.	13 Oct 86	20 0	
62	5/6	20 Feb 86		
63	5/6	7 Mar 86	15 0	
63a	5s. 6d.	7 Mar 86	110 0	
64	7/6	13 Jan 86		
65	7/6	24 May 86	110 0	
65a	7s. 6d.	24 May 86		
65b	7s. 6d.	6 Sep 86		
66	10s.	6 Sep 86		
67	10s.	13 Oct 86	—	55 0
68	10s.	24 Nov 86		
69	10s. 6.	Jan 86		
69a	10s. 6d.	7 Jan 86		
70	10s. 6.	13 Oct 86	17 6	
71	13s.	24 Nov 86		
72	13s.	4 Jan 87		
73	£1	13 Jan 86		

74 £1 6 Sep 86 .. ..
75 £1 13 Oct 86 .. .. 65 0
76 30s. 13 Jan 86 .. ..
77 30s. 24 Nov 86 .. ..

(c) Violet on blue granite paper.

77a 1d. 20 Jan 86 .. ..
78 1d. 24 Jan 86 .. .. 12 6
79 1d. 21 May 86 .. ..
80 1d. 24 May 86 .. .. 7 6 7 6
81 1d. 26 May 86 .. .. 65 0
82 1d. Jun 30 86 .. .. 10 0 10 0
82a 1d. 6 Oct 86 .. ..
83 1d. 24 Nov 86 .. .. 25 0 15 0
a. "d" omitted .. £5
84 1d. 4 Jan 87 .. .. 7 6 8 6
85 1d. 17 Jan 87 .. ..
86 2d. 24 Jan 86 .. .. 20 0
87 2d. 7 Mar 86 .. ..
88 2d. 24 Apl 86 .. ..
89 2d. 24 May 86 .. .. 8 6 8 6
90 2d. 30 Aug 86 .. .. 7 6 8 6
91 2d. 13 Oct 86 .. .. 7 6 7 6
92 2d. 24 Nov 86 .. .. 15 0
a. "d" omitted .. £5
93 2d. 4 Jan 87 .. .. 10 0 7 6
94 2d. 20 Jan 87 .. ..
95 3d. 13 Oct 86 .. .. 7 6 10 0
96 4d. 24 May 86 .. ..
97 4d. 13 Oct 86 .. .. 17 6 17 6
98 4d. 24 Nov 86 .. .. 7 6 10 0
99 6d. 24 May 86 .. ..
100 6d. 6 Sep 86 .. .. 12 6 20 0
101 6d. 24 Nov 86 .. .. 20 0 20 0
102 9d. 6 Sep 86 .. ..
103 9d. 24 Nov 86 .. ..
103a 1s. 29 Apl 86 .. ..
104 1s. 21 May 86 .. .. 17 6 17 6
105 1s. 24 May 86 .. ..
106 1s. 6 Sep 86 .. .. 45 0
107 1s. 13 Oct 86 .. .. 20 0
108 1s. 24 Nov 86 .. .. 40 0 40 0
108a 1s. 6d. 2 Jul 86 .. ..
108b 1s. 6d. 6 Sep 86 .. ..
109 1/6 13 Oct 86 .. .. 85 0
110 1/6 24 Nov 86 .. ..
110a 2s. 21 May 86 .. ..
111 2s. 24 May 86 .. ..
112 2s. 13 Oct 86 .. .. 55 0
113 2s. 24 Nov 86 .. ..
114 2s. 6d. 19 Aug 86 .. .. 85 0
114a 2/6 19 Aug 86 .. .. 110 0
115 2/6 6 Sep 86 .. ..
116 4s. 17 Jan 87 .. ..
117 5s. 6d. 13 Jan 86 .. ..
117a 5/6 13 Jan 86 .. ..
118 5/6 13 Jan 87 .. ..
119 7/6 13 Jan 86 .. ..
120 7/6 13 Jan 87 .. ..
121 10s. Jan 86 .. ..
121a 10s. 13 Jan 86 .. ..
121b 10s. 2 Jul 86 .. ..
121c 10s. 6d. 7 Jan 86 .. ..
122 10s. 6d. 13 Jan 86 .. .. — 55 0
123 10s. 6. 2 Jul 86 .. ..
124 12s. 13 Jan 86 .. .. £12
125 13s. 17 Jan 87 .. .. £12
126 £1 13 Jan 86 .. .. £5
127 30s. 13 Jan 86 .. .. £6
128 30s. 17 Jan 87 .. .. £8

Varieties. Stamps printed tête-bêche (pairs).

128a 2s. (on *yellow*), 6 Sep 86 .. £25
129 30s. (on *yellow*), 24 Nov 86 ..
130 3d. (on *blue*), 13 Oct 86 .. £7
131 1s. (on *blue*), 21 May 86 .. £12
131a 1s. 6d. (on *blue*) 6 Sep 86 .. £15
131b 10s. (on *blue*), 2 Jul 86 .. £18

T 1, with Arms embossed. P 11½.

The motto on the embossed Arms is "EENDRAGT REGTVAARDIGHEID EN LIEFDE" (Union, Justice and Charity).

(a) Violet on yellow paper.

132 1d. 20 Jan 86 .. ..
133 1d. 10 Feb 86 .. ..
134 1d. 17 Mar 86 .. .. 40 0
135 1d. 14 Apl 86 .. .. 20 0
136 1d. 26 May 86 .. ..
137 1d. 28 May 86 .. ..
138 1d. 30 Jun 86 .. .. 10 0 12 6
139 1d. Jul 7 86 .. ..
140 1d. 4 Aug 86 .. .. 40 0
141 1d. 13 Sep 86 .. .. 35 0
142 1d. 6 Oct 86 .. .. 20 0 12 6
143 1d. 3 Nov 86 .. .. 6 0 7 6
144 1d. 2 Dec 86 .. .. 7 6 8 6
145 2d. 2 Dec 86 .. .. 8 6 10 0
146 2d. 20 Jan 87 .. ..
147 4d. 2 Dec 86 .. .. 60 0
148 4d. Dec 86 .. .. 15 0 20 0
149 6d. 2 Dec 86 .. .. 45 0
150 6d. Dec 86 .. .. 30 0

Varieties. Arms inverted.

151 1d. 20 Jan 86 .. .. 40 0
152 1d. 10 Feb 86 .. .. 40 0
153 1d. 14 Apl 86 .. .. 70 0
154 1d. 26 May 86 .. .. 50 0
155 1d. Jun 30 86 .. .. 20 0 20 0
156 1d. Jul 7 86 .. .. 60 0 60 0
157 1d. 13 Sep 86 .. .. 40 0
158 1d. 3 Nov 86 .. .. 20 0 20 0
159 1d. 2 Dec 86 .. 100 0
159a 1d. Jan 20 87 .. ..
160 2d. 24 Nov 86 .. ..
161 2d. 2 Dec 86 .. .. 17 6 20 0
162 2d. 20 Jan 87 .. ..
163 4d. Dec 86 .. .. 60 0 40 0

(b) Violet on blue granite paper.

164 1d. 20 Jan 86 .. 60 0
164a 1d. Jan 20 86 .. ..
165 1d. 10 Feb 86 .. ..
166 1d. 17 Mar 86 .. .. 60 0
167 1d. 14 Apl 86 .. .. 30 0
168 1d. 26 May 86 .. ..
169 1d. Jun 30 86 .. .. 40 0 25 0
170 1d. Jul 7 86 .. .. 10 0 12 6
171 1d. 4 Aug 86 .. ..
172 1d. 13 Sep 86 .. .. 50 0
173 1d. 6 Oct 86 .. .. 30 0
174 1d. 3 Nov 86 .. .. 7 6 10 0
175 1d. 2 Dec 86 .. .. 8 6
176 2d. 30 Aug 86 .. .. 30 0
177 2d. 2 Dec 86 .. .. 7 6 10 0
178 2d. 4 Jan 87 .. .. 30 0
179 2d. 20 Jan 87 .. .. 30 0

Varieties. Arms inverted.

180 1d. 10 Feb 86 .. .. 20 0
181 1d. 17 Mar 86 .. .. 50 0
182 1d. 26 Mar 86 .. .. 80 0
183 1d. 23 May 86 .. .. 75 0
184 1d. 26 May 86 .. .. 30 0 40 0
185 1d. Jul 7 86 .. .. 40 0 20 0
186 1d. 6 Oct 86 .. .. 50 0
187 1d. 3 Nov 86 .. .. 20 0 20 0
189 1d. 2 Dec 86 .. .. 35 0
190 2d. 30 Aug 86 .. ..
191 2d. 2 Dec 86 .. .. 30 0
191a 2d. 20 Jan 87 .. .. 60 0

Varieties. Arms embossed tête-bêche (pairs).

192 1d. (on *yellow*), 3 Nov 86 .. 50 0 50 0
193 1d. (on *yellow*), Jun 30 86 100 0 100 0
193a 1d. (on *blue*), 3 Nov 86 ..
194 2d. (on *blue*), 2 Dec 86 ..
195 4d. (on *yellow*), Dec 86 .. 100 0

1887 (Feb.). *With embossed Arms, but without date.*

(a) Blue granite paper.

196 1d. violet 5 0 6 0
a. Imperf. between (pair) ..
197 2d. violet 3 0 4 0
198 3d. violet 6 0 7 6
199 4d. violet 7 6 7 6
200 6d. violet 6 0 7 6
201 1/6 violet 6 0 7 6

Varieties. (i.) *Arms inverted.*

202	1d. violet	12 6	12 6
203	2d. violet	12 6	12 6
204	3d. violet	40 0	40 0
205	4d. violet	60 0	
206	6d. violet	60 0	
206*a*	1/6 violet		

(ii.) *Arms omitted.*

207	1d. violet	60 0	60 0
208	2d. violet	—	50 0

(iii.) *Stamps printed tête-bêche (pairs).*

209	1d. violet	£10	
209*a*	2d. violet	£10	
209*b*	3d. violet	£16	
209*c*	4d. violet	£10	

(iv.) *Arms tête-bêche (pairs).*

209*d*	1d. violet		
209*e*	3d. violet		
209*f*	4d. violet	£8	

1887 (March). *With embossed Arms, but without date.*

(*b*) *Yellow paper.*

	3d. violet	6 0	6 0
	a. Imperf. between (pair)		
211	4d. violet	7 6	6 0
212	6d. violet	5 0	6 0
213	9d. violet	6 0	7 6
214	1s. violet	7 6	7 6
215	1/6 violet	10 0	10 0
216	2s. violet	20 0	15 0
217	2/6 violet	12 6	12 6
218	3s. violet	30 0	30 0
219	4/s. violet	10 0	12 6
220	5s. violet	10 0	12 0
	a. Imperf. between (pair)		
221	5/6 violet	10 0	12 0
222	7/6 violet	15 0	15 0
223	10s. violet	10 0	10 0
	a. Imperf. between (pair)		
224	10/6 violet	12 6	12 6
	a. Imperf. between (pair)		
225	£1 violet	30 0	30 0
226	30s. violet	60 0	

Varieties. (i.) *Arms inverted.*

227	3d. violet	15 0	20 0
228	4d. violet	6 0	7 6
229	6d. violet	30 0	20 0
230	1s. violet	30 0	
231	2s. violet	—	40 0
232	2/6 violet	12 0	15 0
233	3s. violet	40 0	45 0
233*a*	5s. violet	—	65 0
234	7/6 violet		
235	10s. violet	12 6	
235*a*	10/6 violet		
236	£1 violet	30 0	

(ii.) *Arms omitted.*

237	2d. violet	6 0	
238	6d. violet		
239	2s. violet		
239*a*	4s. violet		
239*b*	4/- violet		
240	10s. violet	—	30 0

(iii.) *Arms tête-bêche (pairs).*

241	3d. violet		
242	6d. violet	£8	
243	7/6 violet		
244	10s. violet	70 0	

(iv.) *Stamps printed tête-bêche (pairs).*

245	3d. violet	£12	£12
246	£1 violet	£12	£12

NEW SOUTH WALES

SIMPLIFICATION (see p. xii)

Nos. 1 to 43e.

11, 25, 42. (Simplest.)
5, 11, 20, 25, 30, 33, 37, 42. (More advanced.)

Nos. 44 to 101.

48, 55, 58, 62, 64, 67, 74, 79. (Add further shades if desired.)
83, 85, 87. 88, 91 : 95 : 101.

Nos. 102 to 185.

103, 104, 106, 111, 114, 116, 120, 123, 126, 129. 131, 155, 133, 135, 156, 157, 160, 161, 162, 143, 145, 164, 167b, 167c, 152, 169, 170.
173. 175, 183.

Nos. 186 to 252.

191, 192, 194. 189, 202. 196, 197. 198, 199a, 201. 241, 203, 205.
207, 209, 210b, 211a, 214, 215, 216, 217, 218, 220a, 221.
222, 223f, 225g, 226c, 228a, 229b, 232, 243, 234, 235, 236, 237d.
238a, 239a. 244b, 245a, 246a : 247a, 250, 251b.

Nos. 253 to 360.

253, 256, 257, 304, 261, 262b, 305, 306, 308, 309, 268a, 312.
272, 273. 275, 276. 278, 280b. 282, 283, 284b. 285c, 298, 281. 287c, 287d.
299, 300, 301, 315, 292a, 296, 316. 328, 326.
331, 332, 333, 333d, 334, 335, 336, 337, 339, 340, 342b, 344, 345a, 346a.
349, 351, 352, 353, 354, 355, 356, 357, 348, 358, 359, 360.

Official Stamps.

401a, 402a, 404a, 405b, 406, 407a, 409, 410. 411b.
412, 413. 415b, 416b, 417, 419d, 421c, 424c, 425, 426c.
427. 428, 429, 430.
431, 432, 433, 434, 435, 436, 437, 438.
440, 441. 442, 443. 444, 448a, 445, 446, 447.

Postage Due Stamps.

One stamp of each value.

1 2

NOTE.—Prices for "Sydney Views" are for fine copies. Stamps showing the very early state of the plate, with large margins, are worth at least double, but medium specimens can be supplied at from one-third of the prices quoted, and poor copies for considerably less.

(Engraved by Mr. Robert Clayton, of Sydney.)

1850 (Jan.). T 1. *Plate I. No clouds.*

(*a*) *Soft yellowish paper.*

1	1d. crimson-lake	£150	£25
2	1d. carmine	£150	£18
3	1d. reddish rose	£150	£25
4	1d. brownish red	£175	£26

(*b*) *Hard bluish paper.*

5	1d. pale red	£175	£20
6	1d. dull lake	£175	£22

1850 (Aug.). *T* **2.** *Plate I, re-engraved by H. C. Jervis, commonly termed Plate II. With clouds.*

(*a*) *Hard toned yellowish paper.*

7	1d. vermilion	£95	£16
8	1d. dull carmine	£95	£14
	a. No trees on hill (No. 7) ..	£190	£28
	b. Hill unshaded (No. 8) ..	£190	£28
	c. Without clouds (No. 15) ..	£190	£28

(*b*) *Hard greyish or bluish paper.*

9	1d. crimson-lake	£100	£18
10	1d. gooseberry-red	£175	£25
11	1d. dull carmine	£110	£17
12	1d. brownish red	£120	£22
	a. No trees on hill (No. 7) ..	£175	£30
	b. Hill unshaded (No. 8) ..	£175	£30
	c. Without clouds (No. 15) ..	£175	£30

(*c*) *Laid paper.*

13	1d. carmine	£200	£30
14	1d. vermilion	£200	£30
	a. No trees on hill (No. 7) ..	—	£45
	b. Hill unshaded (No. 8) ..	—	£45
	c. Without clouds (No. 15) ..	—	£45

The varieties quoted with the letters "a," "b," "c" of course exist in each shade; the prices quoted are for the commonest shade, and the same applies to the following portions of this list.

The numbers given in brackets throughout indicate position on sheet.

3 4

A (Pl. I).

Illustrations A, B, C, and D are sketches of the lower part of the inner circular frame, showing the characteristic variations of each plate.

(Engraved by Mr. John Carmichael.)

1850 (1 Jan.). *Plate I. Vertical-lined background.* *T* **3.** (*a*) *Early impressions, full details of clouds, etc.*

15	2d. greyish blue	£300	£50
16	2d. deep blue	£275	£55
	a. Double lines on bale (No. 19) ..		

Intermediate impressions.

	b. 2d. greyish blue	—	£30
	c. 2d. deep blue	—	£35

T **4.** (*b*) *Later impressions, clouds, etc., mostly gone.*

17	2d. blue	£85	£10
18	2d. dull blue	£85	£10

1850 (end Jan.). *Stamps in the lower row partially retouched.*

19	2d. blue	£125	£10
20	2d. greyish blue	£100	£8

5 B (Pl. II).

(Plate entirely re-engraved by H. C. Jervis.)

1850 (Apr.). *T* **5.** *Plate II. Horizontal-lined background. Bale on left side supporting the seated figure, dated. Dot in centre of the star in each corner.*

(*a*) *Early impressions.*

21	2d. indigo	£225	£35
22	2d. lilac-blue	£300	£55
23	2d. grey-blue	£225	£30
24	2d. bright blue	£225	£30
	a. Fan as in Pl. III, but with shading outside (No. 1) ..	—	£45
	b. Fan as in Pl. III, but without shading, and inner circle intersects the fan (No. 2) ..	—	£45
	c. Pick and shovel omitted (No. 10)	—	£45
	d. "CREVIT" omitted (No. 13) ..	—	£60
	e. No whip (Nos. 4, 8, and 20) ..	—	£40

(*b*) *Worn impressions.*

25	2d. dull blue	£65	£8
26	2d. Prussian blue	£100	£9
	a. Fan as in Pl. III, but with shading outside (No. 1) ..	—	£18
	b. Fan as in Pl. III, but without shading, and inner circle intersects the fan (No. 2) ..	—	£18
	c. Pick and shovel omitted (No. 10)	—	£18
	d. "CREVIT" omitted (No. 13)	—	£20
	e. No whip (Nos. 4, 8, and 20) ..	—	£15

1850 (Aug.). *Bottom row retouched with dots and dashes in lower spandrels.*

27	2d. Prussian blue	£150	£12
28	2d. dull blue	£95	£8
	a. No whip (No. 20)	—	£15

C (Pl. III).

(Plate re-engraved a second time by H. C. Jervis.)

1850 (Sept.). *Plate III. Bale not dated and single-lined, except Nos.* 7, 10, *and* 12, *which are double-lined. No dots in stars.*

29	2d. ultramarine	£125	£12
30	2d. deep blue	£130	£10
	a. No whip (Nos. 15 and 19) ..	—	£17
	b. Fan with 6 segments (No. 20) ..	—	£17
	c. Double lines on bale (Nos. 7, 10, and 12)	—	£9

(Plate re-engraved a third time by H. C. Jervis.)

1851 (Jan.). *Plate IV. Double-lined bale, and circle in centre of each star.*

(*a*) *Hard bluish grey wove paper.*

31	2d. ultramarine	£95	£15
32	2d. Prussian blue	£135	£20
33	2d. bright blue	£135	£15
	a. Hill not shaded (No. 12) ..	—	£20
	b. Fan with 6 segments (No. 20) ..	—	£20
	c. No clouds (No. 22)	—	£20

(*b*) *Stout yellowish vertically laid paper.*

34	2d. ultramarine	£135	£15
35	2d. Prussian blue	£135	£16
	a. Hill not shaded (No. 12) ..	—	£18
	b. Fan with 6 segments (No. 20) ..	—	£18
	c. No clouds (No. 22)	—	£18

6 D (Pl. V).

(Plate re-engraved a fourth time by H. C. Jervis.)

1851 (APR.). *T* 6. *Plate V. Pearl in fan.*

(*a*) *Hard greyish wove paper.*

36	2d. ultramarine	£130	£15
37	2d. dull blue	£110	£12
	a. Pick and shovel omitted (No. 17)	—	£18
	b. Fan with 6 segments (No. 20) ..	—	£18

(*b*) *Stout yellowish vertically laid paper.*

38	2d. dull ultramarine	£195	£18
	a. Pick and shovel omitted (No. 17)	—	£30
	b. Fan with 6 segments (No. 20) ..	—	£30

7 8

(Engraved by Mr. H. C. Jervis.)

1850. *T* 7.

(*a*) *Soft yellowish wove paper.*

39	3d. yellow-green	£150	£16
40	3d. myrtle-green	£375	£50
41	3d. emerald-green	£185	£18
	a. No whip (Nos. 18 and 19) ..	—	£20
	b. "SIGIIIUM" for "SIGILLUM" (No. 23)	—	£22

(*b*) *Bluish to grey wove paper.*

42	3d. yellow-green	£125	£15
43	3d. emerald-green	£150	£18
	b. No whip (Nos. 18 and 19)	—	£15
	c. "SIGIIIUM" for "SIGILLUM" (No. 23)	—	£18

(*c*) *Yellowish to bluish laid paper.*

43*d*	3d. bright green	£300	£28
43*e*	3d. yellowish green	£300	£28
	f. No whip (Nos. 18 and 19) ..	—	£35
	g. "SIGIIIUM" for "SIGILLUM" (No. 23)	—	£40

(Designed by Mr. Manning; engraved on steel by Mr. John Carmichael, of Sydney.)

1851 (18 DEC.). *T* 8. *Imperf.*

(*a*) *Thick yellowish wove paper.*

		Un.	*Used.*
44	1d. carmine	£70	60 0 *to* £20
	a. No leaves right of "SOUTH" ..	—	£50
	b. Two leaves right of "SOUTH" ..	—	£30
	c. "WALE"	—	£50

1852. (*b*) *Bluish medium wove paper.*

45	1d. carmine	£28	20 0 *to* 75 0
46	1d. scarlet	£35	20 0 *to* 85 0
47	1d. vermilion	£30	20 0 *to* 75 0
48	1d. brick-red	£28	15 0 *to* 70 0
	a. No leaves right of "SOUTH" ..	—	£7
	b. Two leaves right of "SOUTH" ..	—	75 0
	c. "WALE"	—	£7

1852 (?). (*c*) *Thick vertically laid bluish paper.*

49	1d. orange-brown ..	£170	40 0 *to* £14
50	1d. claret	£170	35 0 *to* £12
	a. No leaves right of "SOUTH" ..	—	£22
	b. Two leaves right of "SOUTH" ..	—	£20
	c. "WALE"	—	£20

(Engraved on steel by Mr. John Carmichael.)

1851 (24 JULY). *T* 8. *Plate I.*

(*a*) *Thick yellowish wove paper.*

51	2d. ultramarine ..	£40	20 0 *to* 70 0

(*b*) *Fine impressions, blue to greyish medium paper.*

52	2d. ultramarine ..	£38	30 0 *to* £6
53	2d. chalky blue ..	£20	10 0 *to* 22 6
54	2d. dark blue	£20	12 6 *to* 27 6
55	2d. greyish blue ..	£20	7 6 *to* 17 6

(*c*) *Worn plate, blue to greyish medium paper.*

56	2d. ultramarine ..	£19	7 6 *to* 17 6
57	2d. Prussian blue ..	£11	10 0 *to* 22 6

(*d*) *Worn plate, blue wove medium paper.*

58	2d. ultramarine ..	£19	12 6 *to* 27 6
59	2d. Prussian blue ..	£13	7 6 *to* 20 0

9

(Plate II engraved by Mr. H. C. Jervis.)

1853 (OCT.). *T* . *Plate II. Stars in corners. Imperf.*

(*a*) *Bluish medium to thick wove paper.*

60	2d. deep ultramarine ..	£55	30 0 *to* 58 0
61	2d. indigo	£68	30 0 *to* 85 0
	a. "WAEES" (No. 23) ..	—	£14

(*b*) *Worn plate, hard blue wove paper.*

62	2d. deep Prussian blue	£65	30 0 *to* 75 0
	a. "WAEES" (No. 23) ..	—	£12

1855 (SEPT.). *Plate III, being Plate I re-engraved by H. C. Jervis. Background of crossed lines.*

(*a*) *Medium bluish wove paper.*

63	2d. Prussian blue ..	£22	7 6 *to* 22 6
	a. "WALES" covered with wavy lines (No. 3)	—	67 6

(*b*) *Stout white wove paper.*

64	2d. Prussian blue ..	£19	5 0 *to* 17 6
	a. "WALES" covered with wavy lines (No. 3)	—	65 0

(Engraved by John Carmichael.)

1852 (3 DEC.). *T* 8. *Imperf.*

(*a*) *Medium greyish blue wove paper.*

65	3d. deep green.. ..	£80	30 0 *to* £8
66	3d. green	£52	25 0 *to* £7
67	3d. dull yellow-green ..	£52	25 0 *to* £7
	a. "WAEES" (No. 37) ..	—	£9

(*b*) *Thick blue wove paper.*

69	3d. emerald-green ..	£72	35 0 *to* £12
71	3d. blue-green ..	£50	30 0 *to* £7
	a. "WAEES" (No. 37) ..	—	£8

1852 (APR.). *As T* 8. *Fine background. Imperf.*

(*a*) *Medium white wove paper.*

72	6d. vandyke-brown ..	—	£5 *to* £15
	a. "WALLS" (No. 8) ..		

(*b*) *Medium bluish grey wove paper.*

73	6d. vandyke-brown ..	£56	60 0 *to* £14
74	6d. yellow-brown ..	£56	60 0 *to* £14
75	6d. chocolate-brown ..	£56	80 0 *to* £16
76	6d. grey-brown ..	£56	60 0 *to* £14
	a. "WALLS" (No. 8) ..	—	£20

1853 (June). *Plate I re-engraved by H. C. Jervis. Coarse background. Imperf.*

77 6d. brown .. .. £70 80 0 *to* £15
78 6d. grey-brown .. .. £70 80 0 *to* £15

(Engraved by H. C. Jervis.)

1853 (May). *Medium bluish paper. Imperf.*

79 8d. dull yellow .. £140 80 0 *to* £20
80 8d. orange-yellow .. £180 80 0 *to* £20
81 8d. orange .. .. £180 80 0 *to* £20
a. No bow at back of head (No. 9) .. .. — £28
b. No leaves right of "SOUTH" (No. 21) — £28
c. No lines in spandrel (Nos. 12, 22, and 32) — £25

10

NOTE.—All watermarked stamps from No. 82 to No. 172 have double-lined figures, as T **10**.

1854 (Feb.). *T* **8**. *Wmk. "1", T* **10**. *Imperf. Yellowish wove paper.*

82 1d. red-orange 95 0 17 6
83 1d. orange-vermilion 95 0 17 6
a. No leaves right of "SOUTH" (Nos. 7 and 21) £16 55 0
b. Two leaves right of "SOUTH" (No. 15) £22 £6
c. "WALE" (No. 9) £22 £6

1854 (Jan.). *Plate III. Wmk.* "**2**". *Imperf.*

84 2d. ultramarine £40 52 6
85 2d. Prussian blue 85 0 5 0
86 2d. chalky blue 85 0 5 0
a. "WALES" partly covered .. £30 47 6

1854 (Mar.). *Wmk.* "**3**". *Imperf.*

87 3d. yellow-green 85 0 20 0
a. "WAEES" (No. 37) .. — 75 0
b. Error. Wmk. "2" .. .. — £65

13

(Engraved by Mr. John Carmichael.)

1856 (1 Jan.). *For Registered Letters. T* **13**. *No wmk. Imperf. Soft medium yellowish paper.*

88 (6d.) vermilion & Prussian blue £18 65 0
89 (6d.) salmon and indigo .. £25 80 0
90 (6d.) orange & Prussian blue £25 70 0
91 (6d.) orange and indigo .. £25 70 0

1859 (April). *Hard medium bluish wove paper, with manufacturer's wmk. in sans-serif, double-lined capitals across sheet and only showing portions of letters on a few stamps in a sheet.*

(*a*) *Imperf.*

92 (6d.) orange and Prussian blue £25 65 0
92*a* (6d.) verm. and Prussian blue £25 75 0

1860 (Feb.). (*b*) *P* 12.

93 (6d.) orange and Prussian blue £18 45 0
94 (6d.) orange and indigo .. £15 45 0

Coarse yellowish wove paper having the manufacturer's wmk. in Roman capitals.

(*a*) *P* 12.

95 (6d.) rose-red & Prussian blue £12 37 6
96 (6d.) rose-red and indigo .. — 70 0
97 (6d.) salmon and indigo ..

1862. (*b*) *P* 13.

98 (6d.). rose-red & Prussian blue £10 50 0

1863 (May). *Yellowish wove paper. Wmk.* "**6**". *P* 13.

99 (6d.) rose-red & Prussian blue 70 0 17 6
100 (6d.) rose-red and indigo .. £6 20 0
101 (6d.) rose-red and pale blue .. 40 0 17 6

14

(Printed in the Colony from plates engraved by Messrs. Perkins Bacon & Co.)

Two plates of the 2d. and 6d. were used. On Plate II of the 2d. the stamps are wider apart and more regularly spaced than on Plate I.

1856 (6 Apr.). *T* **14**. *Wmk.* "**1**" .. *Imperf.*

102 1d. orange-vermilion .. 65 0 22 6
103 1d. carmine-vermilion .. 65 0 20 0
104 1d. orange-red .. 55 0 20 0
a. Printed on both sides ..

1856 (7 Jan.). *T* **14**. *Plate I. Wmk.* "**2**". *Imperf.*

105 2d. light ultramarine .. 50 0 5 0
106 2d. Prussian blue 40 0 5 0
107 2d. dull blue 40 0 5 0
108 2d. cobalt-blue .. .. — 20 0
a. Error, wmk. "1" .. ..
b. Error, wmk. "5" .. £20 17 6
c. Error, wmk. "8" .. ..

1858. *Plate I, retouched.*

109 2d. dull blue .. .. .. — £12

1859 (Aug.). *Lithographic transfer of Plate I.*

110 2d. pale cobalt-blue .. .. — £25
a. Retouched .. ..

Plate II. Stamps printed wider apart.

110*b* 2d. blue .. .. .. — 15 0

1856 (10 Oct.). *As T* **14**. *Wmk.* "**3**". *Imperf.*

Un. *Used.*

111 3d. yellow-green .. £37 40 0 *to* £10
112 3d. bluish green .. £42 40 0 *to* £10
113 3d. dull green .. £42 40 0 *to* £10
a. Error, wmk. "2" .. — £130

In the 3d. the value is in block letters on a white ground.

15

17

19 21

1855 (1 Dec.). *Wmk.* "5". *Imperf.*

No.	Type	Description	Unused	Used
114	15	5d. dull green	£30	£12 *to* £35

1854 (Feb.). *Wmk.* "6". *Imperf.*

No.	Type	Description	Unused	Used
115	17	6d. deep slate	£10	32 6
116	"	6d. greenish grey	£8	27 6
117	"	6d. slate-green	£8	32 6
		a. Printed both sides		
118	"	6d. bluish grey	£15	47 6
119	"	6d. fawn	£10	75 0
120	"	6d. grey	£8	40 0
121	"	6d. olive-grey	£7	40 0
122	"	6d. greyish brown	£15	40 0

1859 (15 Aug.). *Error. Wmk.* "8".

No.	Type	Description	Unused	Used
123	17	6d. fawn	£50	50 0
124	"	6d. greyish brown	£50	80 0

1855 (1 Dec.). *Wmk.* "8". *Imperf.*

No.	Type	Description	Unused	Used
125	19	8d. golden yellow	£225	£15 *to* £60
126	"	8d. dull orange	£165	£12 *to* £45

1854 (Feb.). *Wmk.* "12". *Imperf.*

No.	Type	Description	Unused	Used
127	21	1s. rosy vermilion	£30	70 0
128	"	1s. pale red	£25	70 0
129	"	1s. brownish red	£30	55 0

1857 (20 June). *Error. Wmk.* "8".

No.	Type	Description	Unused	Used
130	21	1s. rosy vermilion	£100	60 0 *to* £10

1860 (Feb.)-**1863**. *Wmk. double-lined figure of value.* P 12.

No.	Type	Description	Unused	Used
131	14	1d. orange-red	100 0	12 6
		a. Imperf. between (pair)		
132	14	1d. scarlet	50 0	10 0
133	"	2d. chalky blue	50 0	7 6
134	"	2d. greenish blue	50 0	7 6
135	"	2d. Prussian blue	60 0	6 6
136	"	2d. dull blue	—	7 6
		a. Partially retouched	—	£22
		b. Error, wmk. "1"		
139	14	3d. yellow-green (1860)	£40	50 0
140	"	3d. blue-green	£10	35 0
141	15	5d. bluish green (1863)	85 0	30 0
142	"	5d. yellowish green (1863)	95 0	45 0
143	17	6d. grey-brown	£10	20 0
144	"	6d. olive-brown	£12	20 0
145	"	6d. greenish grey	£10	27 6
146	"	6d. fawn	£12	30 0
147	"	6d. mauve	£8	15 0
		a. Imperf.	—	£28
148	17	6d. violet	100 0	8 6
		a. Imperf. between (pair)		
149	19	8d. orange	£50	£10
150	"	8d. orange-red	£60	£12
151	"	8d. yellow		
152	21	1s. brownish red	£15	30 0
153	"	1s. rose-carmine	£8	35 0
		a. Imperf. between (pair)		

The perforated 2d. stamps from Plate I were printed after the return of the plate from London in March, 1861, where it had been repaired. The partially retouched stamps were probably old sheets printed before the plate was sent away, and perforated later.

1862–72. *Wmk. double-lined figure of value.* P 13.

No.	Type	Description	Unused	Used
154	14	1d. scarlet (1862)	35 0	8 6
155	"	1d. dull red	40 0	7 6
156	"	3d. blue-green (Dec., 1862)	30 0	10 0
157	"	3d. yellow-green	40 0	8 6
158	14	3d. dull green	15 0	7 6
		a. Wmk. "6", yellow-green (July, '72)	50 0	10 0
		b. Wmk. "6", dark green	50 0	12 6
159	15	5d. yellowish green (3.65)	67 6	22 6
160	"	5d. bluish green	30 0	12 6
161	"	5d. bright yellow-green	42 6	20 0
162	"	5d. sea-green	40 0	12 6
162a	"	5d. dark bluish green	23 6	15 0
163	17	6d. reddish purple (Pl. I, July, '62)	30 0	3 0
		a. Error, wmk. "5" (July '66)	£7	20 0
		b. Error, wmk. "12" (12.66)	85 0	7 6
164	17	6d. mauve	25 0	3 0
165	"	6d. purple (Pl. II, 1864)	25 0	3 6
166	"	6d. violet	27 6	4 0
167	"	6d. aniline mauve	—	80 0
167a	19	8d. deep orange	55 0	18 6
167b	"	8d. orange-yellow	55 0	16 6
167c	"	8d. bright yellow	55 0	15 0
168	21	1s. rose-carmine	40 0	6 0
169	"	1s. carmine	27 6	6 0
170	"	1s. crimson-lake	32 6	8 6

Perf. compound 12 × 13.

No.	Type	Description	Unused	Used
171	14	1d. scarlet	—	£35
172	"	2d. dull blue	—	80 0

23

1864 (June). T 14. W 23. P 13.

No.	Type	Description	Unused	Used
173		1d. pale red	22 6	20 0

24

25

(Designed by E. H. Corbould, R.I.)

1861–97. T 24. W 25. *Various perfs.*

No.	Description	Unused	Used
174	5s. dull violet, *perf.* 12 (1861)	£16	£6
175	5s. dull violet, *perf.* 13 (1863)	50 0	15 0
176	5s. aniline mauve, *p.* 13 ('72)	85 0	22 6
177	5s. rose-lilac, *perf.* 13 (1879)	70 0	17 6
178	5s. deep pur., *p.* 13 (1880–88)	60 0	15 0
179	5s. deep pur., *p.* 10 (1880–88)	80 0	10 0
180	5s. deep pur., *p.* 12 (1880–88)	30 0	12 6
181	5s. deep pur., *p.* 11 (1880–88)	22 6	8 0
182	5s. deep pur., *perf.* 12 × 10 (1880–88)	£10	27 6
183	5s. red-purple, *p.* 11, (1897)	15 0	8 6
184	5s. red-purple, *perf.* 12 (1897)	25 0	15 0
185	5s. red-pur., *p.* 11 × 12 (1897)	17 6	10 0
	a. Perf. 11× imperf. between (pair)		

26

28

29

A. Printed by Messrs. De La Rue & Co., and perf. 14 at Somerset House, London.

1862–65. *T* **26** *and* **28.** *P* 14.

(i) *Surfaced paper.* *W* **23.**

186 1d. dull red (Pl. I, 1 Apr., '64) 47 6 45 0

(ii) *Surfaced paper.* *No wmk.*

187 1d. dull red (Pl. II, Jan., '65) £6 37 6
188 2d. pale blue (Mar., '62) .. 85 0 45 0

B. Printed from the plates of Messrs. De La Rue & Co., in the Colony.

1862 (7 May). *T* **28.** *Wmk. double lined* "**2**".

189 2d. blue, *perf.* 13 .. .. 50 0 3 0
a. Perf. 12 .. .. .. 65 0 7 6
b. Perf. 12×13 .. ..

1864–65. *T* **26** *and* **28.** *W* **23.** *P* 13.

190 1d. dark red-brown (Plate I)
191 1d. brownish-red (Plate II) .. 10 0 1 6
192 1d. brick-red (Plate II) .. 10 0 1 6
a. Highly surfaced paper (1865)
194 2d. pale blue £8 6 6

Plates I and II were made from the same die; they can only be distinguished by the colour or by the marginal inscription. (See *N.S.W. Handbook*, p. 232.)

1865–66. *T* **26** *and* **28.** *Thin wove paper.* *No wmk.* *P* 13.

195 1d. brick-red £5 17 6
196 1d. brownish red .. .. — 13 6
197 2d. pale blue 40 0 3 6

1863–69. *T* **26** *and* **28.** *W* **29.**

198 1d. pale red, *perf.* 13 .. £5 16 6
199 2d. pale blue, *perf.* 12 ..
a. Perf. 13 .. .. .. 4 0 0 9
200 2d. cobalt-blue, *perf.* 13 .. 5 0 1 0
201 2d. Prussian blue, *perf.* 13 .. 15 0 3 0

1862 (Sept.). *T* **28.** *Wmk. double-lined* "**5**" *P* 13.

202 2d. dull blue 90 0 20 0

32

34

33

35

1867 (Sept.)–**1893.** *T* **32** *and* **34.** *W* **33** *and* **35**

203 4d. red-brown, *perf.* 13 .. 17 6 3 6
204 4d. pale red-brown, *perf.* 13 17 6 3 6
205 10d. lilac, *perf.* 13 .. .. 5 0 4 6
a. Imperf. between (pair) .. 100 0
206 10d. lilac (1893), *perf.* 11 .. 4 6 5 0
a. Perf. 10 .. .. .. 8 6 6 0
b. Perf. 10 and 11, compound .. 15 0 10 0
c. Perf. 12×11 .. .. — 30 0

36

37

38

NINEPENCE

(39)

From 1871 to 1903 the 9d. is formed from the 10d. by a *black* surcharge (T **39**), 15 mm. long on Nos. 219 to 220h, and 13½ mm. long on subsequent issues.

1871–84. *W* **36.**

207 **26** 1d. dull red (8.71), *perf.* 13 2 0 0 5
208 „ 1d. salmon, *perf.* 13 .. 2 0 0 8
a. Perf. 10 .. .. .. 25 0 6 0
b. Perf. 13×10 .. .. 10 0 0 9
209 **28** 2d. Pruss.-bl. (11.71), *p.* 13 2 3 0 8
a. Perf. 11×12, comb .. 50 0 8 6
210 **28** 2d. pale blue, *perf.* 13 .. 2 0 0 9
a. Perf. 10 .. .. .. 32 6 2 6
b. Perf. 13×10 .. .. 3 0 0 8
c. Surfaced paper, perf. 13 .. — 55 0
d. Perf. 12×13 .. .. — 45 0
211 **14** 3d. yell.-grn. (3.74), *p.* 13 .. 10 0 3 0
a. Perf. 10 .. .. .. 20 0 3 6
b. Perf. 11 .. .. ..
c. Perf. 12 .. .. ..
d. Perf. 10×12 .. .. £5 20 0
e. Perf. 12×11 .. ..
212 **14** 3d. bright green, *perf.* 10 18 6 4 0
a. Perf. 10×13 .. .. 27 6 12 0
213 **32** 4d. pale red-brn. (8.77), *perf.* 13 .. 16 6 8 6
214 „ 4d. red-brown, *perf.* 13 .. 10 0 3 6
a. Perf. 10 .. .. .. — 22 6
b. Perf. 13×10 .. .. 65 0 4 0
215 **15** 5d. bluish green (8.84), *p.* 10 7 6 6 0
a. Perf. 12 .. .. ..
b. Perf. 13×10 .. ..
c. Perf. 10×12 .. .. 17 6 7 6
216 **37** 6d. bright mve. (1.72), *p.* 13 5 0 0 6
217 „ 6d. pale lilac, *perf.* 13 .. 8 6 0 9
a. Perf. 10 .. .. .. — 10 0
b. Perf. 13×10 .. .. 22 6 3 0
218 **19** 8d. yell. (Mar., '77), *p.* 13 . 20 0 4 0
a. Perf. 10 .. .. .. 45 0 10 0
b. Perf. 13×10 .. .. £10 10 0
219 **34** 9d. on 10d. pale red-brown (Aug., '71), *perf.* 13 .. 8 6 4 0
220 „ 9d. on 10d. red-brn., *p.* 13 10 0 10 0
a. Perf. 10 .. .. .. 5 0 5 0
b. Perf. 12 .. .. .. 4 6 5 0
c. Perf. 11 .. .. .. 15 0 10 0
d. Perf. 10×12 .. .. 45 0 12 6
e. Perf. 10×11 .. .. 32 6 15 0
f. Perf. 12×11 .. .. 5 6 6 6
g. Perf. 11×12, comb .. 6 6 7 6
h. In black and blue, perf. 11 £8
221 **38** 1s. black (April, '76), *p.* 13 25 0 1 6
a. Perf. 10 .. .. .. — 8 6
b. Perf. 10×13 .. .. 35 0 5 0
c. Perf. 11 .. .. .. 90 0
d. Imperf. between (horiz. pair) — £5

Collectors should note that the classification of perforations is that adopted by the Royal Philatelic Society, London. "Perf. 12" denotes the perforation formerly called "11½, 12" and "perf. 13" that formerly called "12½, 13."

40

1882–93. *W* **40.**

No.	Type	Description				
222	**26**	1d. salmon (1882), *perf.* 10	4	0	0	9
		a. Perf. 13				
		b. Perf. 10×13	22	6	1	3
223	**26**	1d. orange *to* scarlet, *p.* 13				
		a. Perf. 10	2	6	0	6
		b. Perf. 10×13	22	6	10	0
		c. Perf. 10×12	—		10	0
		d. Perf. 10×11	—		22	6
		e. Perf. 12×11	90	0	32	6
		f. Perf. 11×12, comb ..	0	8	0	4
		g. Perf. 12×11½, comb ..				
		h. Perf. 11				
224	**28**	2d. pale blue (1882), *p.* 13	42	6	27	6
		a. Perf. 10	4	0	0	6
		b. Perf. 13×10	32	6	2	0
225	**28**	2d. Prussian blue, *perf.* 10	6	0	0	5
		a. Perf. 13×10	30	0	2	6
		b. Perf. 12				
		c. Perf. 11	—		12	6
		d. Perf. 12×11	£6			
		e. Perf. 12×10	—		5	0
		f. Perf. 10×11	90	0		
		g. Perf. 11×12, comb ..	0	9	0	2
226	**14**	3d. yell.-grn. (1886), *p.* 10	1	3	0	6
		a. Perf. 10×12	20	0	2	6
		b. Perf. 11	1	6	0	6
		c. Perf. 11×12	1	0	0	6
		d. Perf. 12	2	6	1	0
		da. Perf. 12×11	—		1	0
		e. Imperf. between (horiz. pair)	30	0		
		f. Imperf. (pair)	30	0		
227	**14**	3d. bluish green, *perf.* 10 ..	2	6	0	6
		a. Perf. 11	2	0	0	8
		b. Perf. 10×11	10	0	1	6
		c. Perf. 11×12	2	6	1	3
		d. Perf. 12×10	17	6	2	6
228	**14**	3d. emerald-grn. ('93), *p.* 10	5	0	3	6
		a. Perf. 10×11	18	6	2	6
		b. Perf. 12×10	—		10	0
229	**32**	4d. red-brn. (1882), *p.* 10 ..	16	6	2	6
		a. Perf. 10×12	—		22	6
		b. Perf. 11×12, comb ..	18	6	1	6
230	**32**	4d. dark brown, *perf.* 10 ..	20	0	3	0
		a. Perf. 12	—		40	0
		b. Perf. 10×12	£8		12	6
		c. Perf. 11×12	£6		35	0
		d. Perf. 11×12, comb ..	8	6	1	9
231	**15**	5d. dull grn. (1891), *perf.* 10	6	0	2	6
		a. Perf. 11×10	17	6	3	6
		b. Perf. 12×10	18	6	3	6
232	**15**	5d. bright green, *perf.* 10	15	0	4	0
		a. Perf. 11	—		6	6
		b. Perf. 10×11	22	6	6	0
		c. Perf. 12×10	37	6	4	6
	15	5d. blue-green, *perf.* 10 ..	5	6	2	0
		a. Perf. 12	5	6	2	0
		b. Perf. 11	2	6	1	6
		c. Perf. 10×11	17	6	3	0
		d. Perf. 11×12	2	6	1	0
		e. Imperf.	17	6		
234	**37**	6d. pale lilac (1882), *p.* 10	3	6	0	6
		a. Perf. 10×13				
		b. Perf. 10×12	10	0	2	0
235	**37**	6d. mauve, *perf.* 10 ..	4	6	0	5
		a. Perf. 12	16	6	3	0
		b. Perf. 11	£5		8	6
		c. Perf. 10×12	7	6	1	6
		d. Perf. 11×12	8	6	2	6
		e. Perf. 10×11	22	6	1	0
236	**19**	8d. yellow (1883), *perf.* 10	17	6	3	6
		a. Perf. 12	45	0	25	0
		b. Perf. 11	17	6	5	0
		c. Perf. 10×12	60	0	15	0
237	**38**	1s. black, *perf.* 10 (1883)	12	6	0	9
		a. Perf. 11	—		6	0
		b. Perf. 10×12	£13			
		c. Perf. 10×13	35	0	4	6
		d. Perf. 11×12, comb ..	6	6	0	9

41

1886–87. *T* **26** *and* **28.** *W* **41.**

No.	Description				
238	1d. scarlet, *perf.* 10	6	0	6	0
	a. Perf. 11×12, comb	2	0	1	6
239	2d. deep blue, *perf.* 10 ..	35	0	10	0
	a. Perf. 11×12, comb	4	6	2	6
	b. Imperf.				

1891 (Jul). *T* **14.** *Wmk.* "10" *as T* **35.** *P* 10.

No.	Description				
240	3d. green	6	6		
241	3d. dark green	1	3	1	9

42

1903–8. *T* **14** *and* **15.** *W* **42.**

No.	Description				
241*a*	3d. yellow-green, *perf.* 11 ..	5	0	1	0
	b. Perf. 12	3	6	1	6
	c. Perf. 11×12	2	6	0	8
242	3d. dull green, *perf.* 12 ..	15	0	5	0
	a. Perf. 11×12	6	0	1	6
243	5d. dark blue-green, *p.* 11×12	2	6	1	6
	a. Perf. 11	12	6	1	3
	b. Perf. 12	25	0	10	0

43

1885–86. *T* **43.** *W* **41.**

(i) *Overprinted* "POSTAGE", *in black.*

No.	Description				
244	5s. green and lilac, *perf.* 13				
	a. Perf. 10	—		£6	
	b. Perf. 12×10	50	0	42	6

245 10s. claret and lilac, *perf.* 13 ..
a. Perf. 12 .. .. .. 70 0 45 0
246 £1 claret and lilac, *perf.* 13 .. — £50
a. Perf. 12 .. .. .. £15 £8

(ii.) *Overprinted in blue.*

247 10s. claret and mauve, *perf.* 10 £12 85 0
a. Perf. 12 .. .. .. 27 6 16 6
b. Perf. 12×11 .. .. 85 0
248 £1 claret and rose-lilac, *perf.* 12×10 .. .. .. £30 £12

NSW

44

Overprinted " POSTAGE " *in blue.*

1894. *T* **43.** *Wmk. T* **44.**

249 10s. claret and mauve, *p.* 10 .. 85 0 22 6
249*a* 10s. claret and violet, *p.* 12 .. 37 6 15 0
b. Perf. 11 .. .. .. 35 0 25 0
c. Perf. 11×12 .. .. 37 0 25 0
250 10s. aniline crimson and violet, *perf.* 12×11 .. .. 35 0 27 6
a. Perf. 12 .. .. .. 60 0 30 0
250*b* £1 claret & violet, *p.* 12×11

1904. *T* **43**, *optd.* " POSTAGE " *in blue. Chalk-surfaced paper. W* **44.**

251 10s. rosine and violet, *perf.* 12 £11
a. Perf. 11 .. .. .. 55 0 35 0
b. Perf. 12×11 .. .. 35 0 12 6
252 10s. claret & viol., *p.* 12×11 60 0 25 0

45. View of Sydney. **46.** Emu.

47. Captain Cook. **48.** Queen Victoria and Arms of Colony.

49. Lyre bird.

50. Kangaroo.

1888-99. *Wmk. T* **40.**

253 **45** 1d. lilac, *perf.* 11×12 .. 0 3 0 1
a. Perf. 12×11½ 8 6 2 0
b. Perf. 12 .. .. 2 3 0 6
254 **45** 1d. mauve, *perf.* 11×12 0 3 0 1
a. Perf. 12×11½ 3 6 0 9
b. Perf. 12 .. .. 2 6 0 2
c. Imperf. between (pair), perf 11×12 .. ..
255 **46** 2d. Pruss.-bl., *p.* 11×12 0 8 0 1
a. Perf. 12×11½ 5 0 0 9
b. Perf. 12 .. .. 2 6 0 2
c. Imperf. 20 0
256 **46** 2d. chalky-bl., *p.* 11×12 0 6 0 1
a. Perf. 12×11½ .. ..
b. Perf. 12 .. .. 3 6 0 4
c. Perf. 11 .. ..
257 **47** 4d. purp.-brn., *p.* 11×12 1 9 0 5
a. Perf. 12×11½ 20 0 6 0
b. Perf. 12 .. .. 12 6 1 3
c. Perf. 11 .. ..
258 **47** 4d. red-brown, *p.* 11×12 2 0 0 4
a. Perf. 12×11½ 6 6 0 8
b. Perf. 12 .. .. 8 6 0 6
259 **47** 4d. orge.-brn., *p.* 12×11½ 6 0 1 0
260 **47** 4d. yell.-brn., *p.* 12×11½ 6 0 1 0
261 **48** 6d. carmine, *p.* 11×12 2 6 0 4
a. Perf. 12×11½ 9 0 1 9
b. Perf. 12 .. .. 3 0 1 9
262 **48** 6d. emerald-green, *perf.* 11×12 (1898) .. 7 0 5 6
a. Perf. 12×11½ 7 0 5 0
b. Perf. 12 .. .. 5 0 4 6
262*c* **48** 6d. orge.-yell., *p.* 11×12 (1899) 5 6 4 0
d. Perf. 12×11½ 4 6 1 9
e. Perf. 12 .. .. 7 6 5 0
263 **48** 6d. yellow, *perf.* 12×11½ 5 0 2 6
264 **49** 8d. lilac-rose, *p.* 11×12 4 0 2 6
a. Perf. 12×11½ 35 0 12 6
b. Perf. 12 .. .. 4 0 3 0
265 **49** 8d. magenta, *p.* 11×12 60 0 10 0
a. Perf. 12×11½ 6 0 3 0
b. Perf. 12 .. .. 8 0 3 6
266 **34** 9d. on 10d. red-brn. *perf.* 11×12 (1897) .. 6 6 6 6
a. Perf. 12 .. .. — 7 6
b. Perf. 11 .. .. 6 6 6 6
c. Double surcharge, perf. 11 £5 £5
267 **34** 9d. on 10d. orange-brn., *perf.* 12×11½ ..
268 **34** 10d. viol., *p.* 11×12(1897) 5 0 5 0
a. Perf. 12×11½ 4 0 4 0
b. Perf. 12 .. .. 10 0 10 0
c. Perf. 11 .. .. 10 0 10 0
269 **50** 1s. marone, *perf.* 11×12 (1889) 4 6 1 0
a. Perf. 12×11½ 6 6 1 6
b. Perf. 12 .. .. 12 6 1 6
270 **50** 1s. viol.-brn., *p.* 11×12 4 6 0 10
a. Perf. 12×11½ 25 0 2 6
b. Perf. 12 .. .. 25 0 1 0
c. Imperf. 30 0

All these perforations, with the exception of perf. 11, are from comb machines.

1888. *T* **45** *and* **46.** *Wmk. T* **41.** *P* 11×12 *comb.*

271 1d. lilac 6 0
272 1d. mauve 5 0 1 6
273 2d. Prussian blue 20 0 5 6

51. Map of Australia.

52. Portraits of the first Governor, Capt. Arthur Phillip, and of Lord Carrington, the Governor in 1888.

1888–89. *T* **51** *and* **52.** *Wmk. T* **25.** *P* 10.

274	5s. deep purple	47	6	20	0
275	5s. deep violet	35	0	17	6
276	20s. cobalt-blue	75	0	55	0

53

1890. *T* **51.** *Wmk. T* **53.**

277	5s. lilac, *perf.* 10	18	6	9	6
	a. Perf. 11	37	6	22	6
	aa. Imperf. between (horiz. pair) ..				
	b. Perf. 12	£10		15	0
	c. Perf. 10×11	£6		8	6
278	5s. mauve, *perf.* 10 ..	30	0	10	0
	a. Perf. 11	30	0	15	0

54

1890. *T* **52.** *Wmk. T* **54.**

279	20s. cobalt-blue, *perf.* 10 ..	65	0	37	6
	a. Perf. 11	90	0	22	6
	b. Perf. 11×10				
280	20s. ultramarine, *perf.* 11 ..	60	0	22	6
	a. Perf. 12	£8		50	0
	b. Perf. 11×12	45	0	20	0

55. Allegorical figure of Australia.

1890 (22 DEC.). *T* **55.** *Wmk. T* **40.**

281	2½d. ultramarine, *perf.* 11×12 *comb*	1	0	0	3
	a. Perf. 12×11½, comb ..	60	0		
	b. Perf. 12, comb	7	6	0	6

Halfpenny
(56)

SEVEN-PENCE HALFPENNY
(57)

1891 (5 JAN.). *T* **26, 37,** *and* **38** *surcharged a[s] T* **56** *and* **57,** *in black. Wmk. T* **40.**

282	½d. on 1d., grey, *perf.* 11×12 *comb*	0	6	0	5
	a. Surcharge omitted ..				
	b. Surcharge double				
283	7½d. on 6d. brown, *perf.* 10..	2	0	1	
	a. Perf. 11	2	6	1	
	b. Perf. 12	4	0	3	
	c. Perf. 11×12	2	0	1	
	d. Perf. 10×12	3	6	2	
284	12½d. on 1s. red, *perf.* 10 ..	5	0	4	0
	a. Perf. 11	5	6	4	0
	b. Perf. 11×12, comb ..	5	0	3	0
	c. Perf. 12×11½, comb ..	3	0	3	0
	d. Perf. 12, comb	6	0	4	0

58

1892 (21 MAR.)–**1899.** *T* **58.** *Die I. Narrow* "H" *in* "HALF". *W* **40.**

285	½d. grey, *perf.* 10	20	0	0	9
	a. Perf. 11	£6		1	6
	b. Perf. 10×12	55	0	3	0
	c. Perf. 11×12	0	4	0	1
	d. Perf. 12	1	0	0	1
286	½d. slate, *perf.* 11×12 (1897)	0	6	0	1
	a. Perf. 12×11½	0	3	0	2
	b. Perf. 12	0	6	0	2
287	½d. bluish grn., *p.* 11×12 ('99)	2	0		
	a. Perf. 12×11½	0	6	0	2
	b. Perf. 12	1	6	0	3

The perforations 11×12, 12×11½, 12, are from comb machines.

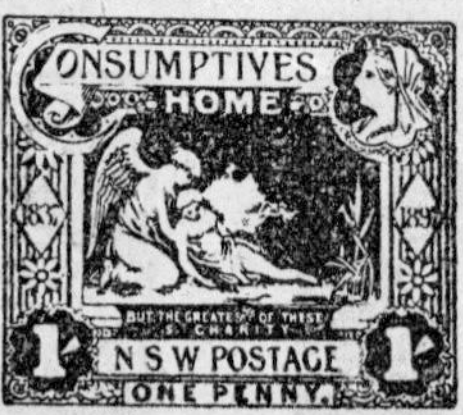

58*a*
Illustration reduced. Actual size 47×38 mm.

58*b*
Illustration reduced. Actual size 38×46 mm.

897. *Charity Stamps.* *T* **58***a and* **58***b.* *P* 11.

No.	Description	s.	d.	s.	d.
87*c*	1d. (1s.), green and brown	5	0	5	0
87*d*	2½d. (2s. 6d.), gold, carm. & bl.	35	0	35	0

These stamps, sold at 1s. and 2s. 6d. respectively, paid postage as 1d. and 2½d. stamps only, he difference being given to the funds of a onsumptives' Home.

59

60

61

Dies of the 1d.

Die I.

Die II.

1d. Die I.—The first pearl on the crown on the eft side is merged into the arch, the shading nder the fleur-de-lis is indistinct, the "s" of "WALES" is open.

Die II.—The first pearl is circular, the vertical hading under the fleur-de-lis clear, the "s" of "WALES" not so open.

Dies of the 2½d.

Die I.

Die II.

2½d. Die I.—There are 12 radiating lines in the star on the Queen's breast.

Die II.—There are 16 radiating lines in the star, the eye is nearly full of colour, and there are other minor points of difference.

1897–99. *Types* **59, 60** *and* **61.** *W* **40.**

No.	Description	s.	d.	s.	d.
288	1d. carmine (Die I), *p.* 11 × 12	1	6	0	5
	a. Perf. 12×11½	2	0	0	6
289	1d. scarlet (Die I), *p.* 11 × 12	1	3	0	4
	a. Perf. 12×11½	4	6	1	6
	b. Perf. 12	4	6	2	0
290	1d. rose-carmine (Die II), *p.* 11 × 12	1	6	0	1
	a. Perf. 12×11½	1	0	0	1
	b. Perf. 12	1	0	0	1
	c. Imperf. between (pair)				
291	1d. salmon-red (Die II), *perf.* 12 × 11½	1	0	0	3
	a. Perf. 12	3	6	0	9
292	2d. deep dull blue, *p.* 11 × 12	0	10	0	3
	a. Perf. 12×11½	0	9	0	4
	b. Perf. 12	2	0	0	6
293	2d. cobalt-blue, *perf.* 11 × 12	1	6	0	4
	a. Perf. 12×11½	2	0	0	3
	b. Perf. 12	3	0	0	4
294	2d. ultramarine, *perf.* 11 × 12	1	6	0	3
	a. Perf. 12×11½	0	8	0	1
	b. Perf. 12	1	0	0	4
	c. Imperf. between (pair)				
295	2½d. purple (Die I), *p.* 11 × 12	2	3	0	7
	a. Perf. 12×11½	5	0	0	9
	b. Perf. 11	4	0	1	6
296	2½d. deep violet (Die II), *perf.* 11 × 12	1	9	0	8
	a. Perf. 12×11½	6	6	1	3
	b. Perf. 12	1	6	1	0
297	2½d. Prussian blue, *p.* 11 × 12	6	6		
	a. Perf. 12×11½	2	3	0	8
	b. Perf. 12	2	6	1	0

The perforations 11 × 12, 12 × 11½, and 12 are from comb machines, the perforation 11 is from a single-line machine.

1899 (Oct.). *Chalk-surfaced paper.* *W* **40.** *P* 12 × 11½, *comb.*

No.	Type	Description	s.	d.	s.	d.
298	**58**	½d. blue-green (Die I)	0	4	0	1
		a. Imperf.	10	0	10	0
299	**59**	1d. carmine (Die II)	0	4	0	1
300	,,	1d. scarlet (Die II)	0	3	0	1
		a. Perf. 11				
301	**59**	1d. salmon-red (Die II)	0	4	0	1
		a. Imperf.	7	6	10	0
302	**60**	2d. cobalt-blue	0	6	0	2
		a. Imperf.	7	6		
303	**61**	2½d. Pruss. blue (Die II)	0	10	0	2
		a. Imperf.	15	0		
303*b*	**47**	4d. red-brown	2	0	0	8
		c. Imperf.	80	0		
304	**47**	4d. orange-brown	1	6	0	5
305	**48**	6d. deep orange	2	6	0	6
		a. Imperf.	25	0		
306	**48**	6d. orange-yellow	2	6	0	8
307	,,	6d. emerald-green	12	6		
		a. Imperf.	40	0		
308	**49**	8d. magenta	3	0	2	0
309	**34**	9d. on 10d. dull brown	2	6	2	0
		a. Surcharge double	80	0		
		b. Without surcharge	80	0		
310	**34**	10d. violet	4	0	3	6
311	**50**	1s. marone	2	6	0	9
		a. Perf. 12	—		27	6
312	**50**	1s. purple-brown	2	6	1	6
		a. Imperf.	40	0		

62. Lyre bird.

63

1902. *W* **42.** *P* 12 × 11½, *comb.*

No.	Type	Description	s.	d.	s.	d.
313	**58**	½d. blue-green (Die I)	2	6	0	1
		a. Perf. 12×11	2	0		
314	**59**	1d. carmine (Die II)	0	3	0	1
315	**60**	2d. cobalt-blue	0	6	0	1
316	**61**	2½d. dark blue (Die II)	1	0	0	2
317	**47**	4d. orange-brown	9	0	0	6
318	**48**	6d. yellow-orange	6	0	1	0
319	,,	6d. orange	4	6	1	0
320	,,	6d. orange-buff	3	0	1	0
321	**49**	8d. magenta	4	6	1	3
322	**34**	9d. on 10d., brownish orge.	2	6	3	0
323	,,	10d. violet	10	0	4	6
324	**50**	1s. marone	3	6	1	0
325	,,	1s. purple-brown	4	0	0	8
326	**62**	2s. 6d. green	10	0	4	6

1903. *T* **63.** *Wmk. double-lined* V *over Crown, Type* w. **10.**

327 9d. brown and ultramarine, *perf.* 12½ × 12½, *comb* .. 5 0 2 0
328 9d. brown and deep blue, *perf.* 12¼ × 12½, *comb* .. 5 0 2 0
329 9d. brown and blue, *perf.* 11 £15 4 0

Die II. Broad "H" in "HALF."

66

1905-10. *W* **66.** *P* 12 × 11½ *(comb) unless otherwise stated. Chalk-surfaced paper.*

330 **58** ½d. blue-green (Die I.) .. 2 0 0 6
 a. Perf. 11½ × 11 ..
331 **58** ½d. blue-green (Die II.) 0 4 0 2
 a. Perf. 11½ × 11 .. 1 0
332 **59** 1d. rose-carm. (Die. II.) 0 4 0 1
 a. Perf. 11½ × 11 .. 2 6
333 **60** 2d. deep ultramarine .. 0 6 0 1
 b. Perf. 11½ × 11 .. .. 1 0
333*d* **60** 2d. milky blue (1910) .. 0 9 0 1
 e. Perf. 11 .. .. 5 0
334 **61** 2½d. Prussian blue (Die II.) 1 3 0 4
335 **47** 4d. orange-brown .. 1 6 0 3
 a. Perf. 12 ..
336 **47** 4d. red-brown .. 3 0 1 0
337 **48** 6d. dull yellow .. 5 0 1 0
 a. Perf. 11½ × 11 .. 12 6
338 **48** 6d. orange-yellow .. 5 0 1 0
 a. Perf. 11½ × 11 .. 8 6
339 **48** 6d. deep orange .. 1 6 0 4
 a. Perf. 11 .. £15
339*b* **48** 6d. orange-buff .. 3 0 0 6
 c. Perf. 11½ × 11 .. 6 0
340 **49** 8d. magenta .. 4 6 1 6
341 ,, 8d. lilac-rose .. 5 0 3 0
342 **34** 10d. violet .. 6 6 4 6
 a. Perf. 11½ × 11 .. 4 6 3 6
 b. Perf. 11 .. 4 0 3 0
343 **50** 1s. maroné .. 3 0 0 6
344 ,, 1s. purple-brown (1908) 3 0 0 6
345 **62** 2s. 6d. blue-green .. 10 0 4 0
 a. Perf. 11½ × 11 .. 5 0 2 0
 b. Perf. 11 .. 7 6 6 0

67

T **52.** *W* **67.**

346 20s. cobalt-blue, *perf.* 11 .. 47 6
 a. Perf. 12 .. .. 42 6
 b. Perf. 11 × 12 .. .. — 42 6

1907. *T* **63.** *Wmk. double-lined* "A" *and Crow*
T w. **11.**

347 9d. brown & ultramarine, *p.* 12 × 12½, *comb* 3 6 1
 a. Perf. 11 .. .. 4 0 3
 b. Perf. 12½ × 11 ..
348 9d. yellow-brn. & ultramarine, *perf.* 12 × 12½, *comb* .. 3 0 0

1906. *Wmk. T* w. **11.** *P* 12 × 11½ *(comb) unle*
otherwise stated.

349 **58** ½d. blue-green (Die I.) .. 2 6 1
351 **59** 1d. dull rose (Die II.) .. 1 3 1
352 **60** 2d. cobalt-blue 0 8 0
 a. Perf. 11
353 **61** 2½d. Prussian blue (Die II.) 15 0
354 **47** 4d. orange-brown .. 4 6 4
355 **48** 6d. orange-buff 10 0 6
356 ,, 6d. dull yellow .. 8 6 5
357 **49** 8d. magenta 6 6 6
358 **34** 10d. violet, *perf.* 11 .. 10 0
359 **50** 1s. purple-brown .. 6 6 6
 a. Perf. 11
360 **62** 2s. 6d. blue-green .. 17 6 15

OFFICIAL STAMPS.

Various stamps overprinted

O S

(101)

There is a variety in this overprint, the spac between the letters being 8½ mm. instead 7½ mm. On the larger stamps (5s., etc.) th spacing is wider (11 to 14 mm.).

1879. *Overprinted with T* **101,** *in black or i red* (R.). *W* **36.**

401 **26** 1d. salmon, *perf.* 10 .. — 7
 a. Perf. 13 .. .. 6 0 1
 b. Perf. 10 × 13 .. 6 0 1
402 **28** 2d. blue, *perf.* 13 .. .. 6 0 0
 a. Perf. 10 × 13 .. 4 0 1
 b. Perf. 11 × 12 ..
 c. Perf. 10 .. .. 25 0 5
403 **14** 3d. green (R.), *perf.* 13 .. — 40
404 ,, 3d. yellow-green, *p.* 10 .. — 50
 a. Perf. 13 .. .. — 7
 b. Perf. 10 × 13 .. 20 0
 c. Wmk. "6", Perf. 13 .. — 15
405 **32** 4d. red-brown, *p.* 10 ..
 a. Perf. 13 .. .. — 2
 b. Perf. 10 × 13 .. 20 0 3
406 **15** 5d. green, *perf.* 10 .. 6 0 5
407 **37** 6d. pale lilac, *perf.* 10 ..
 a. Perf. 13 .. .. 30 0 3
 b. Perf. 10 × 13 .. 7
 c. Perf. 11 ..
408 **19** 8d. yellow (R.), *p.* 13 .. — 40
409 ,, 8d. yellow, *perf.* 10 .. — 6
 a. Perf. 13 .. .. — 6
410 **34** 9d. on 10d. brown, *p.* 10 100 0 100
411 **38** 1s. black (R.), *perf.* 10 .. — 7
 a. Perf. 13 .. .. — 5
 b. Perf. 10 × 13 .. — 3

1894 (30 June). *Wmk.* "10", *T* **35.**

412 **34** 10d. lilac, *perf.* 10 .. 20 0 20
 a. Perf. 11 × 10 .. £12

1880 (15 Feb.). *Wmk.* "5/–", *T* **25.**

413 **24** 5s. deep purple, *p.* 10 .. 40 0 15
 a. Perf. 11 .. .. 40 0 15
 b. Perf. 13 .. .. 80 0 50
 c. Perf. 10 × 12 .. 40 0 20

1882. *Stamps of same date.* *W* **40.**

414 **26** 1d. salmon, *perf.* 10 .. 1 0 0
 a. Perf. 10 × 13 .. 20 0 3
415 **26** 1d. aniline scarlet, *p.* 10 1 0 0
 a. Perf. 12 × 10 .. 15 0
 b. Perf. 11 × 12 .. 0 6 0
 c. Perf. 12 .. .. — 5

No.	Type	Description	Unused	Used
6	28	2d. blue, *perf.* 10	2 0	0 6
		a. Perf. 10×13	20 0	2 0
		b. Perf. 11×12	0 8	0 4
7	14	3d. yellow-green, *p.* 10	2 6	1 0
		a. Perf. 12	15 0	
		b. Perf. 10×11	5 0	3 0
		c. Perf. 10×12	3 0	2 0
8	14	3d. bluish green, *p.* 10	2 6	1 6
		a. Perf. 11		
		b. Perf. 12	25 0	
		c. Perf. 10×12	3 0	5 0
		d. Perf. 10×11	2 6	2 6
9	32	4d. red-brown, *p.* 10	6 0	2 0
		a. Perf. 12		
		b. Perf. 10×12	7 6	2 0
		c. Perf. 10×11	—	2 0
		d. Perf. 11×12	1 6	1 6
20	32	4d. dark brown, *p.* 10	4 0	2 0
		a. Perf. 12	—	10 0
		b. Perf. 10×12	15 0	2 0
		c. Perf. 11×12	1 0	1 0
21	15	5d. dull green, *p.* 10	10 0	7 6
		a. Perf. 11		
		b. Perf. 12	—	20 0
		c. Perf. 10×11	2 6	2 6
		d. Perf. 10×12	—	6 0
22	15	5d. blue-green, *perf.* 10	6 6	
		a. Perf. 11×10		
23	37	6d. pale lilac, *perf.* 10	3 6	1 6
		a. Perf. 11	6 0	1 6
		b. Perf. 12	—	5 0
		c. Perf. 10×12	—	40 0
		d. Perf. 10×13	—	6 0
		e. Perf. 11×12	20 0	7 6
		f. Perf. 11×10	7 6	
24	37	6d. mauve, *perf.* 10	2 6	0 9
		a. Perf. 12	—	3 0
		b. Perf. 10×11	3 6	2 0
		c. Perf. 10×12	1 6	1 3
		d. Perf. 11×12	—	5 0
25	19	8d. yellow, *perf.* 10	3 6	2 6
		a. Perf. 11	6 0	4 0
		b. Perf. 12	5 0	5 0
		c. Perf. 10×12	3 6	3 6
26	38	1s. black (R.), *perf.* 10	1 6	0 9
		a. Perf. 11		
		b. Perf. 10×13	—	5 0
		c. Perf. 11×12	1 6	1 0

Varieties in this issue may be found with the "O" sideways, or with double overprint.

Wmk. "N S W", *T* 41.

No.	Type	Description	Unused	Used
27	26	1d. scarlet, *perf.* 10	40 0	7 6

O S

(102)

887-90. *Long fiscal stamps, T* 43, *overprinted with T* 102, *in black.* "POSTAGE" *in blue. W* 41.

No.	Description	Unused	Used
28	10s. claret and mauve, *p.* 10	—	£50
	a. Perf. 12	—	£5

Overprinted with T 101, *in black.*

No.	Description	Unused	Used
29	10s. claret and mauve, *p.* 12	—	£8

O S

(103)

Overprinted with T 103, *in black.*

No.	Description	Unused	Used
30	20s. claret and rose-lilac, *perf.* 12×10	£100	£12

888-89. *Overprinted as T* 101, *in black.*

(i.) *W* 40.

No.	Type	Description	Unused	Used
31	45	1d. mauve, *p.* 11×12	0 3	0 1
		a. Perf. 12	0 6	0 4
32	45	1d. lilac, *p.* 11×12	0 3	0 1
		a. Perf. 12	0 9	0 6
33	46	2d. Prussian bl., *p.* 11×12	0 4	0 1
		a. Perf. 12	0 5	0 2
434	47	4d. pur.-brn. *p.* 11×12	1 6	0 8
		a. Perf. 12	6 0	1 0
		b. Perf. 11		
435	47	4d. red-brown, *p.* 11×12	0 8	0 4
		a. Perf. 12	5 0	0 9
436	48	6d. carmine, *p.* 11×12	1 0	0 5
		a. Perf. 12	6 0	1 3
437	49	8d. lilac-rose, *p.* 11×12	1 6	1 0
		a. Perf. 12	—	5 0
438	50	1s. marone, *p.* 11×12	2 3	0 6
		a. Perf. 12	4 6	1 3
439	50	1s. pur.-brn., *p.* 11×12	2 3	0 6
		a. Perf. 12	3 6	1 0

(ii.) *W* 41 (1889).

No.	Type	Description	Unused	Used
439*b*	45	1d. mauve, *p.* 11×12	—	45 0
439*c*	46	2d. blue, *p.* 11×12	£7	

1888–89. *T* **51** *and* **52** *optd. as T* **101.** *W* **25.** *P* 10.

No.	Description	Unused	Used
440	5s. deep purple (R.)	£10	£5
441	20s. cobalt-blue	£15	£5

1890 (FEB.). *As last, but W* **53** *and* **54.**

No.	Description	Unused	Used
442	5s. lilac, *perf.* 10	32 6	22 6
	a. Perf. 12	32 6	22 6
443	20s. cobalt-blue, *perf.* 10	£12	£5

1891–92. *Types of same date overprinted as T* **101.** *W* **40.**

No.	Type	Description	Unused	Used
444	26	½d. on 1d. grey, *p.* 11×12	25 0	10 0
445	55	2½d. ultram., *p.* 11×12	1 0	0 9
446	37	7½d. on 6d. brown, *p.* 10	3 0	3 0
447	38	12½d. on 1s. red, *p.* 11×12	4 0	4 0
		a. Perf. 10×12		
448	58	½d. grey, *perf.* 10	1 6	2 0
		a. Perf. 11×12	0 4	0 5
		b. Perf. 12×11½	6 6	
		c. Perf. 12	0 8	0 6

POSTAGE DUE STAMPS.

120

1891 (1 JAN.)–**1892.** *T* **120.** *W* **40.**

No.	Description	Unused	Used
501	½d. green, *perf.* 10	0 3	0 4
502	1d. green, *perf.* 10	0 5	0 6
	a. Perf. 11	0 3	0 3
	b. Perf. 12	12 6	7 6
	c. Perf. 10×12	—	3 0
	d. Perf. 10×11	1 6	0 9
	e. Perf. 11×12	0 7	0 6
503	2d. green, *perf.* 10	0 6	0 6
	a. Perf. 11	0 4	0 4
	b. Perf. 12		
	c. Perf. 10×12	12 6	6 6
	d. Perf. 10×11	3 6	2 0
	e. Perf. 11×12	1 0	1 0
504	3d. green, *perf.* 10	2 0	1 6
	a. Perf. 10×11	2 0	1 0
505	4d. green, *perf.* 10	4 6	2 6
	a. Perf. 11	—	2 6
	b. Perf. 10×11	1 6	0 9
506	6d. green, *perf.* 10	2 0	2 0
507	8d. green, *perf.* 10	4 0	2 0
508	5s. green, *perf.* 10	12 6	8 6
	a. Perf. 11	—	12 6
	b. Perf. 11×12		
509	10s. green, *perf.* 10	—	10 0
	a. Perf. 10×12	20 0	12 6
510	20s. green, *perf.* 10	—	15 0
	a. Perf. 12	£8	
	b. Perf. 10×12	40 0	20 0

1900. *T* 120. *Chalk-surfaced paper.* *W* 40.

511 ½d. emerald-green, *perf.* 11
512 1d. emerald-green, *perf.* 11 3 6 2 6
a. Perf. 12 .. .. ..
b. Perf. 11×12 .. .. 0 3 0 3
513 2d. emerald-green, *perf.* 11 .. 3 0 3 0
a. Perf. 11×12 .. .. 1 6 1 0
514 3d. emerald-green, *p.* 11×12 4 0 2 6
515 4d. emerald green, *perf.* 11 3 6 2 6

New South Wales now uses stamps of Australia.

NEW ZEALAND.

SIMPLIFICATION (see p. xii)

Nos. 1 to 142.
1, 2, 3. 4, 5, 6. 8, 10, 13.
35, 39, 40, 41, 43, 44.
97, 98, 99, 100. 107, 108, 106.
110, 111, 114, 115, 74, 117, 118, 119, 120, 75, 122, 125.
132. 133, 134, 136, 137, 138, 139. 140, 141.

Nos. 143 to 245.
Omit shades and perfs.
Disregard blued paper in 1874 issue.

Nos. 246 to 291.
Make one set of these two issues, selecting cheapest shades. Include marked shades if desired.

Nos. 292 to 448.
These fall into the following groups, in each of which perfs. and papers might be omitted where they occur, and only the most distinct shades taken :—

Wmk. 36*a*. 292 to 305. 314 to 332.
No wmk. 307 to 312. 313. 333 to 339.
Wmk. 41. 340 to 414. (Omit 418 to 423*a*.) 428 to 429*a*.
Exhibition. 424 to 427.
Reduced sizes, etc. 430, etc. 1d., 3d., 6d., and 1s. only.

Later Issues.
Omit perfs., papers and shades.

1

(Engraved by Humphrys and printed by Messrs. Perkins, Bacon & Co., London.)

Type 1.

1855 (18 July). *Wmk. Large Star, T* w. 1. *Imperf.*

1 1d. dull carm. (*white p.*) £375 £30 *to* £180
2 2d. dull blue (*blued p.*) £130 45 0 *to* £20
a. White paper .. — 60 0 *to* £32
3 1s. p. yell.-grn. (*blued p.*) £375 £10 *to* £80
a. Half of 1s. used as 6d. — £175
b. White paper .. £450 £75

Specimens of Nos. 2*a* and 3*b* are on paper which shows no blueing, but these no doubt come from sheets which were more or less blued in parts. These varieties must be in the identical shades of colour of the blued stamps. All 2d. and 1s. stamps, wmk. Star, dated prior to 1862, belong to this issue.

(Printed by J. Richardson, Auckland, N.Z.)

1855 (Nov.). *Blue paper. No wmk. Imperf.*

4 1d. red .. £120 £5 *to* £40
5 2d. blue .. £50 25 0 *to* £10
a. Without value .. ..
6 1s. green .. £140 £8 *to* £70
a. Half of 1s. used as 6d. — £95

These stamps on blue paper may occasionally be found wmk. double-lined letters, being portions of the paper-maker's name.

1857 (Jan.). *Wmk. Large Star. White paper similar to the issue of July,* 1855.

7 1d. dull orange .. .. — £600

This stamp is in the precise shade of the 1d. of the 1856 printing by Richardson on *no wmk.* white paper. An unsevered pair is known with Dunedin cancellation on a cover bearing arrival postmark of Auckland dated "19.1.1857."

1856-59. *Hard or soft white paper. No wmk.*

(*a*) *Imperf.*

8 1d. dull orange (1856) £18 20 0 *to* £8
9 2d. pale blue .. £16 15 0 *to* 75 0
10 2d. blue (1856) .. £14 15 0 *to* 75 0
11 2d. deep blue .. .. — 20 0 *to* 95 0
12 6d. bistre-brn. (Aug., '59) £30 40 0 *to* £10
13 6d. brown .. .. £20 20 0 *to* £8
14 6d. pale brown .. £25 35 0 *to* £9
15 6d. chestnut .. .. £90 £5 *to* £30
16 1s. dull emer.grn. ('56) £95 £5 *to* £40
17 1s. blue-green .. ..£140 £5 *to* £40

(*b*) *Pin-perf. about* 10.

18 1d. dull orange .. .. — £60
19 2d. blue .. .. .. — £50
20 6d. brown .. .. .. — £65
21 1s. blue-green .. .. .. — £100

(*c*) *Serrated perf.* 16.

22 1d. dull orange .. .. — £65
23 2d. blue .. .. .. — £75
24 6d. brown .. .. .. — £60
25 6d. chestnut .. .. .. — £95
26 1s. blue-green .. .. .. — £90

(*d*) *Rouletted* 7.

27 1d. dull orange .. .. — £60
28 2d. blue £150
29 6d. brown £50 £50
a. Imperf. between (pair)
30 1s. dull emerald-green .. — £85
31 1s. blue-green .. .. — £95

1862. (*e*) *P* 13.

31*a* 2d. pale blue £200 £85
32 6d. pale brown .. .. — £400

(Printed by John Davies at the G.P.O., Auckland, N.Z.)

1862 (Feb.). *Wmk. Large Star.* (*a*) *Imperf.*

33 1d. orange-vermilion 85 0 50 0
34 1d. vermilion 70 0 50 0
35 1d. carmine-vermilion .. 70 0 47 6
36 2d. deep blue (Plate I) .. 95 0 25 0
37 2d. slate-blue (Plate I) .. £25 £8
38 2d. greyish blue (Plate I) .. £6 30 0
39 2d. pale blue (Pl. I. worn state) 75 0 25 0
40 3d. brown-lilac 95 0 55 0
41 6d. black-brown £12 35 0
42 6d. brown £12 37 6
43 6d. red-brown £6 25 0
44 1s. green £15 75 0
45 1s. yellow-green £15 75 0
46 1s. deep green £20 £6

1862 (June) (*b*) *Rouletted* 7.

47 1d. orange-vermilion £38 £16
48 1d. vermilion £45 £14
49 2d. deep blue .. .. .. — £10
50 2d. slate-blue .. .. .. — £45
51 2d. pale blue £45 £9
52 3d. brown-lilac £55 £12

53 6d. black-brown £40 £10
54 6d. brown £35 £6
55 6d. red-brown £38 £5
56 1s. green .. .. .. — £15
57 1s. yellow-green .. .. — £15
58 1s. deep green .. .. — £35

1862 (Aug.). (*c*) *Serrated* 14 *or* 16.

59 1d. orange-vermilion .. .. — £38
60 2d. deep blue .. .. .. — £28
a. Imperf. between (pair) ..
61 2d. slate-blue .. .. ..
62 3d. brown-lilac .. .. — £42
63 6d. black-brown £50 £25
64 6d. brown £45 £25
65 1s. yellow-green £70

1862 (Aug.). (*d*) *Pin-perf.* 10.

66 2d. deep blue .. .. .. — £75
67 6d. black-brown .. .. — £75

The dates put to above varieties are the earliest that have been met with.

1862. *Wmk. Large Star.* P 13 (*at Dunedin*).

68 1d. orange-vermilion £15 82 6
69 1d. carmine-vermilion .. £18 80 0
70 2d. deep blue (Plate I) .. £15 65 0
71 2d. slate-blue (Plate I) .. — £85
72 2d. blue (Plate I) £10 40 0
73 2d. pale blue (Plate I) .. £14 40 0
74 3d. brown-lilac £28 75 0
75 6d. black-brown £16 35 0
a. Imperf. between (pair) ..
76 6d. brown £15 40 0
77 6d. red-brown £15 30 0
78 1s. dull green £15 90 0
79 1s. deep green £20 £6
80 1s. yellow-green £14 £5

1862. *Pelure paper. No wmk.* (*a*) *Imperf.*

1d. orange-vermilion .. £100 £15 *to* £60
2d. ultramarine .. £60 £7 *to* £30
2d. pale ultramarine £40 £5 *to* £25
84 3d. lilac .. £1800
85 6d. black-brown £30 50 0 *to* £20
86 1s. deep green .. £95 £6 *to* £25

The 3d. is known only unused.

(*b*) *Rouletted* 7.

87 1d. orange-vermilion ..
88 6d. black-brown .. £70 £7 *to* £25
89 1s. deep green .. £100 £15 *to* £55

(*c*) P 13.

90 1d. orange-vermilion £170 £30 *to* £70
91 2d. ultramarine .. £90 £8 *to* £35
92 2d. pale ultramarine .. £70 £5 *to* £25
93 6d. black-brown .. £70 60 0 *to* £15
94 1s. deep green .. £170 £8 *to* £25

(*d*) *Serrated* 16.

95 6d. black-brown £135

1863 (early). *Hard or soft white paper. No wmk.*
(*a*) *Imperf.*

96 2d. dull deep blue (*shades*) .. — £20

(*b*) P 13.

96*a* 2d. dull deep blue (*shades*) .. £65 £10

These stamps show slight beginnings of wear of the printing plate in the background to right of the Queen's ear, as one looks at the stamps. By the early part of 1864 the wear of the plate had spread, more or less, all over the background of the circle containing the head. The major portion of the stamps of this printing appears to have been consigned to Dunedin and to have been there perforated 13.

NZ

2

1864. *Wmk.* " N Z ", *T* **2.** (*a*) *Imperf.*

97 1d. carmine-vermilion £10 35 0 *to* 90 0
98 2d. p. blue (Pl. I worn) £30 45 0 *to* £7
99 6d. red-brown .. £120 £6 *to* £25
100 1s. green .. .. £25 35 0 *to* 90 0

(*b*) *Rouletted* 7.

101 1d. carmine-vermilion .. £170 £85
102 2d. pale blue (Plate I worn) £50 £17
103 6d. red-brown £90 £60
104 1s. green £35 £16

(*c*) P 13 (*at Dunedin*).

105 2d. pale blue (Plate I worn) £35 £15
106 1s. green £50 £18
a. Imperf. between (horiz. pair)

(*d*) P 12½ (*at Auckland*).

107 2d. pale blue (Plate I worn) .. 95 0 32 6
108 6d. red-brown £10 32 6
109 1s. yellow-green .. ..

1864–67. *Wmk. Large Star.* P 12½ (*at Auckland*).

110 1d. carmine-vermilion (1864) 37 6 15 0
111 1d. pale orange-vermilion 47 6 14 0
112 1d. orange 80 0 25 0
a. Imperf. Pale orge. Worn plate 80 0
113 2d. p. blue (Pl. I worn) (1864) 45 0 10 0
114 2d. dp. blue (Pl. II) (1866) .. 42 6 7 6
a. Imperf. between (pair) .. — £85
115 2d. blue (Plate II) 37 6 7 6
a. Retouched (Plate II) (1867) .. £10 45 0
b. Perf. 10×12½ (Plate II) .. — £170
c. Imperf. (Plate II) £6
d. Retouched. Imperf. .. £8
116 3d. brown-lilac (1864) .. £48 £30
117 3d. lilac 37 6 10 6
a. Imperf. £18 £6
118 3d. deep mauve £14 20 0
a. Imperf. £50 £18
119 4d. deep rose (1865) .. £8 47 6
120 4d. yellow (1865) 50 0 17 6
121 4d. orange £45 £25
122 6d. red-brown (1864) .. 55 0 10 0
122*a* 6d. brown 70 0 12 6
b. Imperf. (pale brown) .. £6
123 1s. deep green (1864) .. £25 47 6
124 1s. green 85 0 20 0
125 1s. yellow-green 50 0 16 6

1871. *Wmk. Large Star.* (*a*) P 10.

126 1d. brown £18 45 0

(*b*) P 10×12½.

127 1d. brown 55 0 12 6
128 2d. vermilion 90 0 17 6
a. Retouched £12 45 0
129 6d. deep blue £45 £12
130 6d. blue £30 £10
a. Imperf. between (vert. pair) .. £80

(*c*) P 12½.

131 1d. brown 25 0 10 0
132 1d. pale brown 25 0 10 0
a. Imperf. between (vert. pair) . — £40
133 2d. orange 37 6 10 0
a. Retouched £8 35 0
134 2d. vermilion 65 0 15 0
a. Retouched £12 50 0
135 6d. blue 45 0 15 0
136 6d. pale blue 40 0 15 0

In or about 1872 both 1d. and 2d. stamps were printed on some paper having a wmk. of script letters " W. T. & Co " (= Wiggins Teape & Co.) in the sheet, and other paper with the name " T. H. Saunders " in double-lined caps, in the sheet; portions of these letters are occasionally found on stamps.

1872. *No wmk.* P 12½.

137 1d. brown £12 45 0
138 2d. vermilion 40 0 15 0
a. Retouched £12 50 0
139 4d. orange-yellow £5 £15

1872. *Wmk.* "N Z", *T* **2.** *P* 12½.

140	1d. brown	—	£80
141	2d. vermilion	£10	42 6
	a. Retouched	£25	£6

1872. *Wmk. Lozenges, with the word* "INVICTA" *in double-lined capitals in middle of sheet. P* 12½.

142	2d. vermilion	£85	£20
	a. Retouched	—	£40

3

4

(Designed by John Davies. Die engraved on wood in Melbourne. Printed from electrotypes at Government Printing Office, Wellington.)

T **3.**

1873 (1 Jan.). *Wmk.* "N Z", *T* **2.**

143	½d. pale dull rose (*p.* 10) ..	14 0	14 0
144	½d. pale dull rose (*p.* 12½) ..	85 0	30 0
145	½d. pale dull rose (*p.* 12½ × 10)	65 0	27 6

No wmk.

146	½d. pale dull rose (*p.* 10) ..	12 6	10 0
147	½d. pale dull rose (*p.* 12½) ..	80 0	20 0
148	½d. pale dull rose (*p.* 12½ × 10)	65 0	32 6

As the paper used for Nos. 143–145 was originally intended for fiscal stamps which were more than twice as large, about one-third of the impressions fall on portions of the sheet showing no watermark, giving rise to varieties Nos. 146–148. In later printings of No. 151 a few stamps in each sheet are without watermark. These can be distinguished from No. 147 by the shade.

1875 (Jan.). *Wmk. Star, T* **4.**

149	½d. pale dull rose (*p.* 12½) ..	0 6	0 6
	a. Imperf. between (pair) ..	75 0	60 0
150	½d. pale dull rose (*p. nearly* 12)	3 6	0 8

1892 (June). *Wmk.* "*NZ and Star,*" *T* **12a.**

151	½d. bright rose (*shades*) (*p.* 12½)	0 3	0 2
	a. No wmk.	2 6	1 6

5

6

7

8

9

10

11

12

12a

(T **5–10** eng. by De La Rue & Co. T **11** and **12** des., eng. & plates by Bock & Cousins, Wellington. Typographed at the Government Printing Office, Wellington.)

T **5** *to* **12.**

1874 (1 Jan.). *W* **12a.**

A. *White paper.* (*a*) *P* 12½.

152	1d. lilac	5 0	1 0
	a. Imperf.		
153	2d. rose	7 6	0 9
154	3d. brown	40 0	25 0
155	4d. marone	—	12 6
156	6d. blue	35 0	5 0
157	1s. green	—	15 0

(*b*) *P* 11½, 12.

158	2d. rose	£12	£5

(*c*) *Perf. compound of* 12½ *and* 10.

159	1d. lilac	32 6	15 0
160	2d. rose	£20	40 0
161	3d. brown	60 0	22 6
162	4d. marone	£15	£6
163	6d. blue	60 0	17 6
164	1s. green	£15	25 0

(*d*) *Perf. nearly* 12 × 12½.

165	2d. rose	£10	£5

B. *Blued paper.* (*a*) *P* 12½.

166	1d. lilac	17 6	7 6
167	2d. rose	20 0	8 0
168	3d. brown	20 0	7 6
169	4d. marone	—	30 0
170	6d. blue	50 0	12 6

(*b*) *Perf. compound of* 12½ *and* 10.

172	1d. lilac	37 6	15 0
173	2d. rose	£22	50 0
174	3d. brown	50 0	20 0
175	4d. marone	£20	£7
176	6d. blue	45 0	20 0

1875. *Wmk. Large Star, T* w. **1.** *P* 12½.

178	1d. deep lilac	£10	25 0
179	2d. rose	30 0	7 6

1878. *Wmk. T* **12a.** *P* 12 × 11½.

180	1d. mauve-lilac	3 0	0 8
181	2d. rose	3 6	0 6

182	4d. marone	25	0	10	0
183	6d. blue	20	0	5	0
184	1s. green	30	0	10	6
185	2s. deep rose	90	0	90	0
186	5s. grey	90	0	90	0

This perforation is made by a horizontal "comb" machine, giving a gauge of 12 horizontally and about 11¾ vertically. Single specimens can be found apparently gauging 11½ all round or 12 all round, but these are all from the same machine.

13

14

15

16

17

18

19

20

21

22

(Engraved by Messrs. Bock & Cousins, Wellington, and typo. at the Government Printing Office.)

1882–97. *T* **13** *to* **22.** *W* **12a.**

(*a*) *P* 12×11½.

187	½d. black (1895)	6	0	6	0
188	1d. rose	0	4	0	1
	a. Imperf. between (pair)				
189	2d. lilac	0	8	0	1
	a. Imperf. between (pair)				
190	2½d. blue (1891)	6	6	1	3
191	2½d. ultramarine	7	6	1	3
192	2½d. pale ultramarine	5	0	1	3
193	3d. yellow	7	6	1	3
194	3d. orange	10	0	1	3
195	4d. green	4	0	0	6
196	5d. olive-black (1891)	6	0	3	0
197	6d. brown	6	0	0	6
	a. Imperf.				
198	8d. blue	8	0	4	0
199	1s. brown-red	10	0	1	6

(*b*) *P* 11.

200	½d. black	0	4	0	2
201	1d. rose	0	4	0	1
202	2d. bright purple	0	6	0	1
203	2½d. blue	1	6	0	10
204	3d. yellow	4	0	1	6
205	3d. pale orange	4	0	1	3
206	3d. deep orange	4	0	1	3
207	4d. green	2	6	0	6
208	5d. olive-black	5	0	4	0
209	6d. deep brown	3	0	0	9
210	6d. sepia	4	6	1	3
211	8d. blue	5	0	3	0
212	1s. brown-red	4	6	1	0

(*c*) *P* 10.

213	½d. black	0	6	0	4
214	1d. rose	0	3	0	1
215	2d. mauve-lilac	0	6	0	1
216	2½d. blue	4	6	0	8
217	2½d. ultramarine	5	0	1	0
218	3d. yellow	6	0	1	3
219	3d. pale orange	5	0	1	3
220	3d. deep orange	7	6	2	3
221	4d. green	5	0	0	8
222	5d. olive-black	5	0	1	9
223	6d. sepia	4	0	0	9
224	8d. blue	7	6	6	0
225	1s. brown-red	6	0	1	0

(*d*) *P* 10×11.

226	½d. black	0	9	0	2
227	1d. rose	1	0	0	2
228	2d. bright purple	1	3	0	2
229	2½d. ultramarine	6	0	1	3
230	3d. yellow	8	6	3	0
231	4d. green	35	0	3	6
232	5d. olive-black	7	6	3	0
233	6d. sepia	6	6	2	6
234	1s. brown-red	7	6	2	0

(*e*) *Perf. compound of* 12½ *and* 10.

235	1d. rose	40	0	40	0
236	2d. lilac	70	0	45	0
237	2½d. blue	90	0	75	0
238	3d. yellow	£10		92	6
239	5d. olive-black	£12		£8	
239a	6d. sepia	£10		£10	
240	1s. brown-red	£12		£12	

(*f*) *P* 12½.

241	1d. rose	£10		£8	
242	2d. lilac	£10		£5	
243	2½d. ultramarine	£12		£6	

(*g*) *Perf. nearly* 12×12½.

244	1d. rose	£7		£5	
245	6d. deep brown	£8		£7	

The dies of the 1d., 2d., 6d., and 8d. were retouched in 1891–92 and new plates made, but the differences are not sufficiently marked to enable us to catalogue them as separate varieties. The stamps perf. (*a*) and (*b*) are usually from the original plates, while those perf. (*c*), (*d*), and (*e*) are mostly from the new plates. Perf. (*d*) is also known 11×10 but stamps perforated thus are rare.

Stamps of this issue with advertisements printed on the back were issued in 1893.

23. Mount Cook or Aorangi.

24. Lake Taupo and Mount Ruapehu.

25. Pembroke Peak, Milford Sound.

28. Sacred Huia birds.

26. Lake Wakatipu and Mount Earnslaw, inscribed "WAKITIPU."

29. White Terrace, Rotomahana.

27. Lake Wakatipu and Mount Earnslaw, inscribed "WAKATIPU."

31. Apterix or Kiwi.

32. Native war canoe.

33. Pink Terrace, Rotomahana.

34. Kea and Kaka, or hawk-billed parrot.

30. Otira Gorge and Mount Ruapehu.

35. Milford Sound.

36. Mount Cook.

(Recess. ·Waterlow & Sons.)

1898 (5 April). *No wmk.* *P* 12 *to* 14, 14, 15, *and* 16.

No.	Type	Description	Unused	Used
246	**23**	½d. purple-brown ..	0 6	0 3
		a. Imperf. between (pair) ..	£7	£7
247	**23**	½d. purple-slate	0 6	0 3
248	,,	½d. purple-black ..	0 6	0 4
249	**24**	1d. blue and yellow-brn.	0 4	0 2
		a. Imperf. between (pair) ..	£8	£8
250	**24**	1d. blue and brown ..	0 6	0 2
251	**25**	2d. lake	0 10	0 3
		a. Imperf. between (pair) ..	£12	£12
252	**25**	2d. rosy lake	1 3	0 3
		a. Imperf. between (pair) ..	£12	£12
253	**26**	2½d. sky-blue ("WAKITIPU")	2 0	1 3
254	,,	2½d. blue ("WAKITIPU")	3 0	2 0
255	**27**	2½d. blue ("WAKATIPU")..	3 0	1 6
256	**27**	2½d. deep blue ("WAKATIPU")	3 6	2 0
257	**28**	3d. yellow-brown ..	2 0	1 6
258	**29**	4d. bright rose	4 6	4 0
259	,,	4d. lake-rose	4 0	3 9
260	,,	4d. dull rose	4 0	3 9
261	**30**	5d. sepia	30 0	25 0
262	,,	5d. purple-brown ..	5 0	3 0
263	**31**	6d. green	6 6	3 6
264	,,	6d. grass-green	15 0	6 0
265	**32**	8d. indigo..	12 0	7 6
266	,,	8d. Prussian blue ..	7 6	7 6
267	**33**	9d. purple	5 0	4 0
268	**34**	1s. vermilion	8 6	3 0
269	,,	1s. dull red	7 6	3 6
270	**35**	2s. grey-green	12 0	10 6
		a. Imperf. between (vert. pr.)	£15	
271	**36**	5s. vermilion	30 0	30 0

1899. *Printed by the Government Printer at Wellington.* "Waterlow" *paper. No wmk. P* 11.

No.	Type	Description	Unused	Used
272	27	2½d. blue	2 6	1 3
		a. Imperf. between (pair)	£6	£6
273	27	2½d. deep blue	2 0	1 0
274	28	3d. yellow-brown	1 0	0 6
		a. Imperf. between (pair)	£6	£6
275	28	3d. deep brown	1 6	0 6
276	30	5d. purple-brown	4 0	1 3
277	,,	5d. deep purple-brown	5 0	1 9
278	31	6d. yellow-green	11 0	11 0
279	,,	6d. deep green	5 6	5 0
280	32	8d. indigo	6 0	5 0
281	,,	8d. Prussian blue	6 0	4 0
282	33	9d. deep purple	4 0	4 0
283	,,	9d. rosy purple	5 0	5 0
284	34	1s. red	7 6	3 0
285	,,	1s. dull orange-red	7 6	3 0
286	,,	1s. dull brown-red	12 6	3 6
287	,,	1s. bright red	7 6	3 0
288	35	2s. blue-green	15 0	7 6
289	,,	2s. grey-green	15 0	7 6
290	36	5s. vermilion	35 0	25 0
291	,,	5s. carmine-red	50 0	35 0

36*a*

1900. *Waterlow paper. Wmk. double-lined* "N Z" *and Star, T* 36*a, sideways. P* 11.

No.	Type	Description	Unused	Used
292	13	½d. black	1 0	0 6
293	15	2d. bright purple	2 6	1 6

37. View of White Terrace, Rotomahana.

38*a*

38. Commemorative of the New Zealand contingent in the South African War.

(Printed in the colony.)

1900–1. *Wmk. T* 36*a. P* 11.

No.	Type	Description	Unused	Used
294	23	½d. deep green	0 6	0 3
294*a*	,,	½d. green	0 4	0 2
295	,,	½d. yellow-green	0 6	0 3
296	,,	½d. pale yellow-green	0 7	0 4
297	37	1d. lake	1 0	0 5
298	,,	1d. crimson	0 4	0 2
299	,,	1d. rose-red	0 6	0 3
		a. Imperf. between (pair)		
300	38	1½d. brown	6 0	2 6
		a. Imperf. between (pair)	£8	
		b. Imperf.	£5	
301	38	1½d. chestnut	1 6	0 9
302	,,	1½d. pale chestnut	1 6	0 9
303	38*a*	2d. dull violet	0 8	0 2
304	,,	2d. mauve	0 10	0 3
305	,,	2d. purple	0 8	0 2

The above ½d. stamps are slightly smaller than those of the previous printings. A new plate was made to print 240 stamps instead of 120 as previously, and to make these fit the watermarked paper the border design was redrawn and contracted, the centre vignette remaining as before. The stamp varies in shade from *very deep green* to *pale yellow-green.* The 2d. stamp is also from a new and smaller plate.

39. Lake Taupo and Mount Ruapehu.

40

1900. *No wmk. P* 11.

No.	Type	Description	Unused	Used
307	39	4d. indigo and brown	5 0	1 9
308	,,	4d. bright blue & chestnut	4 0	1 9
309	,,	4d. deep blue & bistre-brn.	3 0	1 6
310	31	6d. pale rose	4 6	1 3
		a. Imperf. between (pair)	75 0	
311	31	6d. rose-red	5 0	1 0
		a. Doubly printed	£12	
312	31	6d. scarlet	6 0	1 6
		a. Imperf. between (pair)	90 0	

(Recess. Waterlow & Sons.)

1901 (1 Jan.). *Commemorative of Universal Penny Postage. No wmk. P* 12 *to* 16.

No.	Type	Description	Unused	Used
313	40	1d. carmine	0 2	0 2
		a. Imperf. between (pair)	85 0	

Colonial prints.

1901 (Feb.). (i.) *Waterlow paper, thick and soft. W* 36*a.*

(*a*) *P* 11.

No.	Type	Description	Unused	Used
314	40	1d. carmine-lake	1 6	0 9
315	,,	1d. deep carmine	0 6	0 1
		a. Imperf. between (pair)	60 0	
316	40	1d. carmine	0 6	0 1

(*b*) *P* 14.

No.	Type	Description	Unused	Used
317	23	½d. green	1 6	0 10
318	40	1d. carmine	6 0	2 0
		a. Imperf. between (pair)	45 0	

(*c*) *Perf. compound of* 11 *and* 14.

No.	Type	Description	Unused	Used
319	23	½d. green	0 4	0 4
320	,,	½d. deep green	1 3	0 6
321	40	1d. carmine	£8	£8

(*d*) *P* 11 *and* 14 *mixed.*

The term "mixed" is applied to stamps from sheets which were at first perforated 14, or 14 and 11 compound, and either incompletely or defectively perforated. These sheets were patched on the back with strips of paper, and re-perforated 11 in those parts where the original perforation was defective.

No.	Type	Description	Unused	Used
322	23	½d. green	7 6	4 6
323	40	1d. carmine	£5	60 0

1901 (Dec.). (ii.) *Basted Mills, thin hard paper. W* 36*a.* (*a*) *P* 11.

No.	Type	Description	Unused	Used
324	23	½d. green	35 0	35 0
325	40	1d. carmine	40 0	30 0

(*b*) *Perf.* 14.

No.	Type	Description	Unused	Used
326	23	½d. green	2 6	1 9
327	40	1d. carmine	0 4	0 4
		a. Imperf. between (pair)	45	

(c) Perf. compound of 11 and 14.

328 **23** ½d. green 0 9 1 0
329 ,, ½d. deep green 1 3 1 6
330 **40** 1d. carmine 0 4 0 6

(d) Mixed perfs.

331 **23** ½d. green 40 0 30 0
332 **40** 1d. carmine 30 0 22 6

1902 (Jan.). (iii) *Cowan, thin hard paper. No wmk.* (a) *P* 11.

333 **23** ½d. green £6 80 0

(b) P 14.

334 **23** ½d. green 0 6 0 4
335 **40** 1d. carmine 0 6 0 4

(c) Perf. compound of 11 and 14.

336 **23** ½d. green £6 75 0
337 **40** 1d. carmine 10 0 10 0

(d) Mixed perfs.

338 **23** ½d. green £5 70 0
339 **40** 1d. carmine 35 0 30 0

41

1902 (April). (iv) *Cowan, thin hard paper. Wmk. single-lined "N Z" and Star, T* **41.**

(a) P 11.

340 **23** ½d. green 42 6 35 0
341 **40** 1d. carmine £10

(b) P 14.

341*a* **23** ½d. yellow-green 0 6 0 4
341*b* ,, ½d. pale yellow-green .. 0 8 0 4
342 ,, ½d. green 0 4 0 1
343 ,, ½d. deep green 0 4 0 1
a. Imperf. between (pair) .. 30 0
344 **40** 1d. carmine 0 3 0 1
a. Imperf. between (pair) .. 32 6
345 **40** 1d. pale carmine .. 0 3 0 1
345*a* ,, 1d. deep carmine .. 1 0 0 1

(c) Perf. compound of 11 and 14.

346 **23** ½d. green 5 0
347 ,, ½d. deep green 6 6
348 **40** 1d. carmine 10 0 10 0

(d) Mixed perfs.

349 **23** ½d. green 4 0 2 6
350 ,, ½d. deep green 4 6 3 0
351 **40** 1d. carmine 6 6 6 6
351*a* ,, 1d. pale carmine 6 6 6 6

1902–7. *W* **41.**

(a) P 11.

352 **27** 2½d. blue 3 6 2 6
353 ,, 2½d. deep blue (1905) .. 3 6 2 6
354 **28** 3d. yellow-brown .. 3 0 0 6
355 ,, 3d. bistre-brown .. 2 6 0 6
356 ,, 3d. pale bistre 3 0 0 10
357 **39** 4d. deep blue and deep brown/*bluish* .. 3 0 5 0
a. Imperf. between (pair) .. £6
358 **30** 5d. red-brown 12 0 5 0
359 ,, 5d. deep brown (1904) .. 8 0 3 0
360 ,, 5d. sepia (1906) 6 6 3 6
361 **31** 6d. rose 7 6 1 6
362 ,, 6d. rose-red 5 6 1 6
363 ,, 6d. rose-carmine .. 4 6 1 6
a. Imperf. between (pair) .. £7
364 **31** 6d. bright carm.-pink ('05) 30 0 3 0
365 ,, 6d. scarlet 8 0 2 6
366 **32** 8d. blue 4 6 3 0
367 ,, 8d. steel-blue (1904) .. 5 6 3 0
368 **33** 9d. purple 4 6 3 0
369 **34** 1s. brown-red 6 0 3 0
370 ,, 1s. bright red 8 6 3 0
371 **34** 1s. orange-red 7 0 2 0
372 ,, 1s. orange-brown .. 6 0 2 0
373 **35** 2s. green 11 0 6 6
374 ,, 2s. blue-green (1907) .. 14 6 6 6
375 **36** 5s. deep red 37 6 25 0
376 ,, 5s. vermilion (1906) .. 27 6 25 0

Variety. (*Mar.,* 1903.) *Laid paper. No wmk.*

377 **35** 2s. green 40 0 35 0

(b) P 14 (1903–9).

378 **38** 1½d. chestnut (1907) 2 6 2 6
379 **38*a*** 2d. grey-purple (1903) .. 1 3 0 8
380 ,, 2d. purple 0 8 0 4
a. Imperf. between (pair) ..
381 **38*a*** 2d. bright reddish purple 1 0 0 6
382 **27** 2½d. blue (1907) 2 6 1 6
383 ,, 2½d. deep blue 2 6 1 6
384 **28** 3d. bistre-brown .. 3 0 0 10
385 ,, 3d. bistre (1906) 3 6 0 10
386 ,, 3d. pale yellow-bistre .. 22 6
387 **39** 4d. deep blue and deep brown/*bluish* (1903) .. 5 6 2 0
a. Imperf. between (pair) .. 75 0
b. Centre inverted .. ..
388 **39** 4d. blue and chestnut/*bluish* (1906) .. 1 6 1 0
389 ,, 4d. blue and ochre-brown/*bluish* (1909) .. 3 6 2 0
390 **30** 5d. black-brown .. 12 6 4 0
391 ,, 5d. red-brown (1906) .. 4 0 1 9
392 **31** 6d. bright carm.-pink ('06) 15 0 2 6
393 ,, 6d. rose-carmine .. 25 0 3 6
394 **32** 8d. steel-blue (1907) .. 5 0 2 0
395 **33** 9d. purple (1906) .. 4 0 2 0
396 **34** 1s. orange-brown .. 11 0 2 6
397 ,, 1s. orange-red 8 0 2 0
398 ,, 1s. pale red (1907) .. 11 0 2 0
399 **35** 2s. green 10 0 5 0
400 ,, 2s. blue-green (1907) .. 10 6 6 0
401 **36** 5s. deep red 35 0 22 6
402 ,, 5s. dull red 30 0 20 0

(c) Perf. compound of 11 and 14.

403 **38*a*** 2d. purple (1903) .. 80 0 80 0
404 **31** 6d. rose-carmine (1907) .. 85 0 60 0
404*a* **32** 8d. steel-blue £12

(d) Mixed perfs.

405 **38** 1½d. chestnut £5 90 0
406 **38*a*** 2d. purple 45 0 40 0
407 **28** 3d. bistre-brown .. 85 0 75 0
408 **39** 4d. blue and chestnut/*bluish* ('04) £5 £5
409 ,, 4d. bl. & yell.-brn/*bluish* 75 0 75 0
410 **31** 6d. rose-carmine 75 0 55 0
411 ,, 6d. bright carmine-pink 75 0 55 0
412 **32** 8d. steel-blue £10 £8
413 **33** 9d. purple £10 £10
413*a* **35** 2s. blue-green £8 £8
414 **36** 5s. vermilion £12 £12

There are two sizes of paper used for the above stamps, viz.:—

(1) A sheet containing 240 wmks., with a space of 9 mm. between each.

(2) A sheet containing 120 wmks., with a space of 24 mm. between each vertical row.

Size (1) is used for the ½d., 1d., 2d., and 4d., and size (2) for 2½d., 5d., 9d., and 2s. The paper in each case exactly fits the plates, and has the watermark in register, though in the case of the 4d., the plate of which contains only 80 stamps, the paper is cut up to print it. The 3d., 6d., 8d., and 1s. are printed on variety (1), but with watermark sideways: by reason of this specimens from the margins of the sheets show parts of the words "NEW ZEALAND POSTAGE" in large letters, and some copies have no watermark at all. For the 1½d. and 5s. stamps variety (1) is also used, but two watermarks appear on each stamp. The 6d. also exists on paper with the words "LISBON SUPERFINE" wmkd. once in the sheet; the paper was obtained from Parsons Bros. (now the Parsons Trading Co.), an American firm with a branch at Auckland. *Price* 10s.

1904. *Printed from a new plate.* W **41.**

(*a*) *P* 14.

415 **40** 1d. rose-carmine 0 6 0 3
415*a* ,, 1d. pale carmine 0 6 0 3

(*b*) *P* 11.

415*b* **40** 1d. rose-carmine .. ..

(*c*) *Perf. compound of* 11 *and* 14.

416 **40** 1d. rose-carmine 20 0 15 0

(*d*) *Mixed perfs.*

417 **40** 1d. rose-carmine 15 0 10 0
417*a* ,, 1d. pale carmine 15 0 10 0

This plate has a minute dot almost in the centre of the spaces between the stamps in the horizontal rows, but it is frequently cut out by the perf.

In 1906 fresh printings were made from four new plates (*without* the minute dot mentioned above), two of which, marked in the margin "W 1" and "W 2", were supplied by Messrs. Waterlow Bros. and Layton, and the other two, marked in the margin "R 1" and "R 2", by Messrs. W. R. Royle & Sons. The intention was to note which pair of plates wore the best and produced the best results. The stamps were printed in *rose-carmine* on paper with *W* **41**; they are *perf.* 14 or *compound of* 11 *and* 14. These stamps can only be distinguished with certainty by marginal letters.

1906. *Printed from new plates by Waterlow & Royle (without the dot).* W **41.**

(*a*) *P* 14.

418 **40** 1d. deep rose-carmine .. 1 9 0 2
aa. Imperf. between (pair) .. 60 0
418*a* **40** 1d. aniline carmine .. 1 9 0 6
418*b* ,, 1d. rose-carmine .. 1 9 0 2

(*b*) *P* 11.

418*c* **40** 1d. bright rose-carmine .. 60 0

(*c*) *Perf. compound of* 11 *and* 14.

419 **40** 1d. rose-carmine 20 0

(*d*) *Mixed perf.*

419*a* **40** 1d. deep rose-carmine .. £5 35 0

1905–6. *Stamps supplied to penny-in-the-slot machines.* W **41.**

(i) "*Dot*" *plate of* 1904. (ii) *Waterlow reserve plate of* 1906.

(*a*) *Imperf. top and bottom; zigzag roulette* 9½ *on one or both sides, two large holes at sides.*

420 **40** 1d. rose-carmine (i) .. 60 0

(*b*) *As last but rouletted* 14½.

420*a* **40** 1d. rose-carmine (i) .. 65 0

(*c*) *Imperf. all round, two large holes each side.*

421 **40** 1d. carmine (i) 60 0
421*a* ,, 1d. carmine (ii) 60 0

(*d*) *Imperf. all round.*

422 **40** 1d. carmine (i) 60 0

(*e*) *Imperf. all round. Two small indentations on back of stamp.*

422*a* **40** 1d. carmine (ii) 45 0

(*f*) *Imperf. all round; two small pin-holes at sides.*

422*b* **40** 1d. carmine (ii) 45 0

1906 (May). *W* **41.** *P* 14×14½ (*comb machine*)

423 **40** 1d. bright rose-carmine .. 16 0 3 0
423*a* ,, 1d. rose-carmine 16 0 3 0

These 1d. stamps are known both with and without the small dot.

42. Te Arawa.

43. Maori Art.

44. Landing of Cook.

45. Annexation of New Zealand.

(Designed by L. J. Steele, Auckland, engraved by W. R. Bock, Wellington, and typo. at the Government Printing Office.)

1906 (Nov.). *Issue commemorative of the New Zealand Exhibition held at Christchurch.* T **42** *to* **45** (*various horiz. designs inscr.* "COMMEMORATIVE SERIES OF 1906"). *Wmk. single-lined* "N Z" *and Star,* T **41.** *P* 14.

424 ½d. emerald-green 17 6 20 0
425 1d. vermilion 17 6 20 0
426 3d. brown and blue 22 6 25 0
427 6d. pink and olive-green .. 70 0 80 0

1907. *T* **23.** *Wmk. single-lined* "N Z" *and Star,* T **41.** *P* 14.

428 ½d. green 3 0 1 3
429 ½d. yellow-green 3 0 1 3
429*a* ½d. deep yellow-green .. 2 6 2 0

The plate for above stamps has a minute dot similar to that for the 1d., as mentioned in first part of note after No. 417*a*. The ½d. stamps of 1907–8 are also printed from this plate, and also (perf. 14×15) from the plate without dot.

46

47 (T 28 reduced).

48 (T 31 reduced).

49 (T 34 reduced).

(Engraved and new plates (except 4d.) made by Messrs. Perkins, Bacon & Co.)

1907-8. *Wmk. single-lined* "N Z" *and Star,* T **41.**

(*a*) *P* 14.

430 **47** 3d. brown (1907) 6 0 3 0
431 **48** 6d. carmine-pink (1907) .. 3 6 1 6
432 ,, 6d. red 17 6 7 6

(*b*) *P* 14×13, 13½ (*comb machine*).

433 **23** ½d. green (1907) 3 6 1 9
434 ,, ½d. yellow-green 0 10 0 6
435 **47** 3d. brown 3 0 1 6
436 .. 3d. yellow-brown 4 6 1 6
437 **39** 4d. blue & yell.-brn./*bluish* 6 0 4 0
438 **48** 6d. pink £6 12 6
439 **49** 1s. orange-red (1907) .. 6 0 2 6

(*c*) *P* 14 × 15 (*comb machine*).

440	**23**	½d. yellow-green (1907)	1	0	0	1
441	**46**	1d. carmine	0	6	0	1
442	**47**	3d. brown	3	6	1	6
443	,,	3d. yellow-brown	4	6	1	9
445	**48**	6d. carmine-pink	3	6	1	6
446	**49**	1s. orange-red	6	6	2	6

Error. Imperf.

448	**23**	½d. green	85	0		

Stamps of T **47**, **48**, and **49** have a small dot as described in notes after Nos. 417*a* and 429*a*.

The stamps of T **46** are *surface-printed* and may be distinguished from those of T **40** by various differences. The rosettes in the upper corners are very much altered, the lines on the geographical globe are diagonal instead of vertical, and the words "UNIVERSAL POSTAGE" are slightly smaller. The paper is *chalk-surfaced*.

50 **51**

(Engraved by Messrs. Perkins, Bacon & Co. and typo. in New Zealand.)

1909. *T* **50** *and* **51**. *De La Rue chalky paper. Brownish gum. Wmk. single-lined* "N Z" *and Star, T* **41**. *P* 14 × 15, *comb machine*.

449	½d. yellow-green	0	3	0	1
450	1d. carmine	0	2	0	1

Stamps of ½d. and 1d. with blurred and heavy appearance are from booklets.

Variety. Imperf.

451	1d. carmine	90			

52

(Engraved by Messrs. W. R. Royle & Co., London, and recess-printed in New Zealand.)

1909–13. *T* 52 (*and similar types*). *Wmk. single-lined* "N Z" *and Star, T* **41**.

(*a*) *P* 14 × 14½, *comb machine*.

452	2d. mauve	2	0	0	6
453	2d. deep mauve	2	6	0	4
454	3d. chestnut	1	3	0	4
455	4d. orange-red	4	6	4	0
456	4d. orange-yellow (1912)	2	0	0	9
457	5d. brown	7	0	1	0
458	5d. red-brown	3	6	0	9
459	6d. carmine	2	6	0	6
460	6d. deep carmine (29.10.13)	3	0	0	6
461	8d. indigo-blue	3	6	1	0
461*a*	8d. deep bright blue	3	6	1	0
462	1s. vermilion	6	0	1	0

(*b*) *P* 14, *line machine*.*

463	3d. chestnut	6	0	1	3
464	4d. orange	3	6	1	3
465	5d. brown	6	6	2	0
466	5d. red-brown (15.9.11)	3	0	1	6
467	6d. carmine	4	0	1	3
468	8d. indigo-blue*	£15		£12	
469	1s. vermilion	7	6	2	3

* Stamps gauging even a fraction over 14 on the vertical sides are to be classed as perf. 14 × 14½ and not as 14.

See also No. 478 with sideways wmk.

AUCKLAND EXHIBITION, 1913.

(**59**)

1913. *T* **50**, **51**, *and* **52** *overprinted with T* **59**.

470	½d. green	17	6	20	0
471	1d. carmine	15	0	17	6
472	3d. chestnut (*perf.* 14 × 14½)	75	0	75	0
473	6d. carmine (*perf.* 14 × 14½)	70	0	75	0

These overprinted stamps were only available for letters in New Zealand and to Australia.

1915–16. *T* **52** (*and similar types*). *W* **41**. *P* 14 × 13½.

474	3d. chestnut	7	6	5	0
	a. Vert. pr., p. 14 × 13½ & 14 × 14½	25	0	25	0
475	5d. red-brown	2	6	0	6
	a. Vert. pr., p. 14 × 13½ & 14 × 14½	12	6	12	6
476	6d. carmine	10	0	7	6
	a. Vert pr., p. 14 × 13½ & 14 × 14½	30	0	30	0
477	8d. indigo-blue (Mar., 1916)	5	0	1	9
	a. Vert. pr., p. 14 × 13½ & 14 × 14½	20	0	20	0
477*b*	8d. deep bright blue	3	0	0	9
	c. Vert. pr., p. 14 × 13½ & 14 × 14½	15	0	15	0

This perforation may be met with in entire sheets, or in conjunction with the 14 × 14½ comb. In these cases the four top rows of the sheet are 14 × 13½, and the six lower rows show 14 × 14½.

On paper with widely spaced wmk. as used for 2½d. set of pictorial issue, and wmk. sideways (see note after No. 414). *P* 14.

478	8d. indigo-blue (Aug., 1916)	6	0	6	0
	a. No wmk.	20	0	20	0

60

(Designed by H. Linley Richardson, R.B.A.; plates made in London by Perkins, Bacon & Co. and stamps recess-printed in New Zealand.)

1915 (30 JULY). *T* **60**. *Wmk. single-lined* "N Z" *and Star, T* **41**. *P* 14 × 14½, *comb*. (*See note after* 490c.)

479	1½d. grey-slate	0	10	0	5
	a. Perf. 14 × 13½	0	9	0	5
	b. Vert. pair, 479/9a	5	0	5	0
480	2d. bright violet	4	6	3	0
	a. Perf. 14 × 13½	4	0	3	0
	b. Vert. pair, 480/80a	10	0	10	0
481	2½d. blue	1	9	0	9
	a. Perf. 14 × 13½	1	8	0	6
	b. Vert. pair, 481/1a	8	6	8	6
482	3d. chocolate	1	9	0	5
	a. Perf. 14 × 13½	1	6	0	5
	b. Vert. pair, 482/2a	8	6	8	6
483	4d. yellow	3	0	2	0
	a. Perf. 14 × 13½	3	0	2	3
	b. Vert. pair, 483/3a	12	6	12	6
484	4½d. deep green	3	0	1	9
	a. Perf. 14 × 13½	2	6	1	9
	b. Vert. pair, 484/4a	10	0	10	0

485 6d. carmine 2 6 0 3
a. Perf. 14×13½ 1 6 0 3
b. Vert. pair, 485/5a 10 0 10 0
486 7½d. red-brown 3 6 3 0
a. Perf. 14×13½ 2 9 2 0
b. Vert. pair, 486/6a 15 0 15 0
487 9d. sage-green 5 0 1 0
a. Perf. 14×13½ 2 6 0 9
b. Vert. pair, 487/7a 15 0 15 0
c. Imperf. three sides .. ..
d. Imperf. .. ..
e. Yellowish olive, P 14×13½ (Dec. 1925) 3 6 1 0
488 1s. vermilion 2 6 0 4
a. Perf. 14×13½ 4 6 0 8
b. Imperf. .. ..
c. Vert. pair, 488/8a 20 0 20 0
488*d* 1s. pale orange-red 7 6 3 6
e. Imperf. 50 0

The 1½d., 2½d., 4½d., and 7½d. have value tablets as shown in T 60. In the other values, the tablets are shortened, and the ornamental border at each side of the crown correspondingly extended.

1916. *T* **60.** *Colours changed.* *W* **41.** *P* 14×14½, *comb.*

489 2d. yellow (15 Jan.) 2 0 1 6
a. Perf. 14×13½ 2 0 1 6
b. Vert. pair, 489/9a 8 6 10 0
490 4d. bright violet (7 April) .. 1 0 0 4
a. Perf. 14×13½ 1 3 0 3
b. Imperf. £15
c. Vert. pair, 490/90a 8 6 8 6

The perfs. 14×14½ and 14×13½ may both be found on the same sheet, and blocks from the 4th and 5th rows would show both perforations *se-tenant*. (See note after No. 477c.)

Early sheets of the 1½d., 2½d., 4½d., 6d., 7½d., and 1s. are known with the perf. 14×13½ throughout.

Any stamps with the wmk. with perforations measuring 14×14 or nearly must be classed as 14×14½, this being an irregularity of the comb machine, and not a product of the 14-line machine.

1916 (Mar.–Aug.). *T* **60.** *On paper of pictorial issue, as* No. 478.

491 1½d. grey-slate (*p.* 14×14½) (Mar.) 1 9 1 0
a. No wmk. 4 0 4 0
492 1½d. grey-slate (*p.* 14×13½) .. 1 6 0 10
a. No wmk. 6 0 4 6
b. Vert. pair, 491/492 .. .. 5 0 5 0
c. As last. No wmk. 15 0 15 0
493 2d. yellow (*p.* 14) (June) .. 2 0 2 6
a. No wmk. 12 6 12 6
494 3d. chocolate (*p.* 14) (June) 2 0 2 0
a. No wmk. 12 6 12 6
495 6d. carmine (*p.* 14) (Aug.) .. 3 6 3 6
a. No wmk. 17 6 17 6

The 2d., 3d., and 6d. are found with the wmk. sideways only.

60*a*

60*b*

1916 (April). *T* **60***a*, *surface-printed from plates made locally. Die engraved by W. R. Bock, Wellington.* *W* **41.** *P* 14×15.

496 1½d. grey-black 1 0 0 1
497 1½d. black 1 0 0 2

Nos. 496 and 497 differ from No. 500 in many respects, particularly in the shading of the portrait, which is *diagonal* in the former and *horizontal* in the latter.

1915–19. *T* **60***b*, *surface-printed from steel plates made in London by Perkins, Bacon & Co. Chalky paper. Brownish gum.* *W* **41.** *P* 14×15.

498 ½d. green (July, 1915) .. 0 1 0 1
499 ½d. yellow-green 0 2 0 1
a. Very thick, hard, highly surfaced paper, white gum .. 1 9 1 6
500 1½d. slate (Sept., 1916) .. 0 6 0 1
501 1½d. orange-brown (Sept. 1918) 0 6 0 1
502 2d. yellow (Sept., 1916) .. 0 8 0 1
a. Imperf. 80 0
503 2d. pale yellow 0 10 0 1
504 3d. chocolate (May, 1919) .. 0 9 0 2

The note after No. 488e also applies to T **60***b*.

WAR STAMP
(**61**)

1915 (24 Sept.). *T* **60***b* *overprinted with T* **61**, *in black.* P 14×15.

505 ½d. green 0 2 0 2

62

63

64

65

66

67

(Plates made by Messrs. Perkins, Bacon & Co., Waterlow & Sons, and De La Rue & Co. Typographed by De La Rue & Co.)

1920 (27 Jan.). *T* **62** *to* **67**. *Issued to commemorate Victory and Peace.* *W* **41**. *P* 14.

506 ½d. green 1 0 0 3
507 ½d. pale yellow-green .. 1 0 0 3
508 1d. carmine-red 1 0 0 2
509 1d. bright carmine 1 6 0 2
510 1½d. brown-orange 2 0 0 2
511 3d. chocolate 7 6 4 0
512 6d. violet 10 0 5 0
513 1s. orange-red 25 0 20 0

The above stamps were placed on sale in London in November, 1919.

1921–22. *As July*, 1915. *Recess.* *P* 14×14½.

513*a* 5d. light blue.. .. .. 12 6 6 0
b. Perf. 14×13½ 1 9 0 4
c. Imperf. 60 0
514 5d. pale ultramarine .. 1 9 0 6
a. Perf. 14×13½ 1 6 0 6
b. Vert. pair, 514/14a 20 0
515 8d. indigo-blue (May, 1921).. 6 0 5 0
a. Perf. 14×13½ 6 0 5 0
b. Vert. pair, 515/15a 20 0 20 0
516 8d. red-brown (*p.* 14×13½) (Feb., '22) 2 6 0 8

2d. 2d.

TWOPENCE

(68)

1922. *T* **62** *surcharged with T* **68**, *in red.*

517 2d. on ½d. green 0 8 0 4

69

(Printed in New Zealand.)

1923. *T* **69**. *Chalky paper. Yellowish gum.* *W* **41**. *P* 14×15.

518 1d. carmine 0 6 0 1

This stamp was issued to celebrate the restoration of Penny Postage.

1924–25. *W* **41**. *P* 14×15.

(*a*) "*Jones*" *chalky paper, white gum.*

519 **60*b*** ½d. green 0 6 0 3
520 **51** 1d. deep carmine .. 0 7 0 3
a. Pale carmine. Unsurfaced paper 80 0
521 **69** 1d. carmine 0 10 0 3
522 **60*b*** 2d. dull yellow 4 6 2 6
523 „ 3d. deep chocolate .. 5 0 0 6

Only one half-sheet of No. 520a is known, due to faulty manufacture. This paper varies from thick to thin. It may be recognised by the watermark, as the letters "N Z" are larger than in the other papers and the "N Z" and Star are close together.

(*b*) "*De La Rue*" *medium, unsurfaced paper, brownish gum.*

524 **51** 1d. rose-carmine .. 3 0 3 0

(*c*) "*De La Rue*" *medium to thick chalky paper, brownish gum. Wmk. sideways.*

526 **51** 1d. bright carmine .. 0 10 1 0
a. No wmk. 3 6 4 0

Many stamps in the sheet of No. 526 are without watermark, while others show portions of "NEW ZEALAND POSTAGE" in double-lined capitals.

1925. *No wmk. but bluish* "*N Z and Star*" *lithographed on back.* *P* 14×15.

527 **60*b*** ½d. apple-green .. 0 6 0 4
a. "N Z" and Star colourless 5 0 5 0
528 **51** 1d. rose-carmine .. 0 6 0 4
a. "N Z" and Star in black . 15 0
b. "N Z" and Star colourless 40 0 30 0
529 **60*b*** 2d. yellow 3 6 4 6

1925–30. *As* 1924–5, *but* "*Cowan*" *thick opaque chalky paper, white gum.* *W* **41**.

530 **60*b*** ½d. green (*p.* 14×15) .. 0 3 0 1
a. Perf. 14 .. .. 0 3 0 1
531 **51** 1d. deep carm. (*p.* 14×15) 0 3 0 1
532 **60*b*** 1½d. orange-brn. (*p.*14)('30) 1 6 1 6
a. Perf. 14×15 .. .. 1 6 0 9
533 „ 2d. yellow (*p.* 14×15) .. 0 10 0 2
a. Perf. 14 ('30) 0 7 0 2
b. Imperf. 70 0
534 **60*b*** 3d. chocolate (*p.* 14×15) 1 0 0 1
a. Perf. 14 ('30) 1 3 0 3

This paper differs from the "Jones" paper of Nos. 519, etc., in being very opaque, so that the watermark as a rule is barely visible. The gum in the first supply was dull, and in later supplies shiny.

"*Cowan*" *unsurfaced paper.*

535 **69** 1d. carm.-pink (*p.* 14×15) 1 9 0 9

This is a medium soft paper similar to that on which the line-engraved stamps of T **60** were printed, with very shiny gum.

"*Wiggins Teape*" *thin, hard, chalk-surfaced paper.*

535*a* **51** 1d. rose-carm (*p.*14×15) 1 3 0 6
535*b* **60*b*** 1½d. orange-brown (*p.* 14) 2 0 1 6
535*c* „ 2d. yellow (*p.* 14×15) .. 1 6 1 0
d. Perf. 14 .. .. 0 8 0 4

This paper is not unlike the "Cowan" surfaced paper but has a distinct metallic ring when bent and released.

70

(Designed by H. Linley Richardson, R.B.A. Engraved by line-etching process and typo at Government Printing Office, Wellington.)

1925 (17 Nov.). *Dunedin Exhibition.* *T* **70.** *Thick chalky paper.* *W* **41.** *P* 14 × 15.

536	½d. yellow-green/*green* ..	2	6	2	6
537	1d. carmine/*rose* ..	3	0	3	0
538	4d. mauve/*pale mauve* ..	20	0	22	6
	a. "POSTAGF" at right ..	£5		£5	

71 72

1926. *T* **71** (1d.) *and* **72.** *W* **41.** *P* 14.

539	1d. rose-carmine (12.11.26) ..	0	2	0	1
	a. Perf. 14 × 15	0	4	0	2
	b. Imperf.				
540	2s. deep blue	15	0	5	0
541	3s. mauve	25	0	12	6

The 2s. and 3s. are on "Jones" paper.

As last. "Cowan" paper.

542	2s. light blue	10	0	2	0
	a. Imperf.				
543	3s. pale mauve	20	0	17	6

73. Nurse.

(Typo. Govt. Printing Office, Wellington.)

1929–30. *Anti-Tuberculosis Fund.* *T* **73** (*and similar type*). *W* **41.** *P* 14.

(*a*) *Inscribed* "HELP STAMP OUT TUBERCULOSIS."

544	1d. + 1d. scarlet (11.12.29)	10	0	10	6

(*b*) *Inscribed* "HELP PROMOTE HEALTH."

544*a*	1d. + 1d. scarlet (29.10.30) ..	15	0	16	6

73a

(Des. H. L. Richardson. Typo. Govt. Ptg. Office.)

1931–38. *Types as* **73***a* (*various frames*). *W* **41.** *P* 14.

544*b*	1s. 3d. lemon ('31) ..	2	6	3	6
544*c*	1s. 3d. orange-yellow ('32)	2	0	0	6
544*d*	2s. 6d. brown	4	0	0	9
544*e*	4s. red ('32)	6	6	1	3
544*f*	5s. green	8	0	2	0
544*g*	6s. carmine-rose ('32) ..	10	0	2	0
544*h*	7s. blue	11	6	2	6
544*i*	7s. 6d. olive-grey ('32) ..	8	0	3	0
544*k*	8s. slate-violet	13	0	4	0
544*l*	9s. orange	9	6	5	0
544*m*	10s. carmine-lake	16	0	6	0
544*n*	12s. 6d. purple ('35) ..	12	6	8	0
544*o*	15s. olive-green ('32) ..	24	0	12	6
544*p*	£1 pink ('32)	32	6	17	6
544*q*	25s. greenish blue ('38) ..	40	0	20	0
544*r*	30s. brown ('36)	47	6	22	6
544*s*	35s. orange-yellow ('37) ..	35	0	20	0
544*t*	£2 violet ('33)	40	0	22	6
544*u*	£2 10s. red ('36)	50	0	30	0
544*v*	£3 green ('32)	60	0	35	0
544*w*	£3 10s. rose ('39)	70	0		
544*x*	£4 light blue	80	0	40	0
544*y*	£4 10s. olive-grey ('39) ..	90	0		
544*z*	£5 blue ('32)	£5		65	0

We do not list values above £5 as they are mainly employed for revenue purposes.

35/-

(**73***b*)

1939–40. *Types as* **73***a* *surch. as T* **73***b*.

545	3/6 on 3s. 6d. grey-green ..	7	6	7	6
545*a*	5/6 on 5s. 6d. lilac	10	0	10	0
545*b*	11/- on 11s. yellow	20	0	20	0
545*c*	22/- on 22s. scarlet	40	0	40	0
545*d*	35/- on 35s. orge.-yell. ('39)	35	0	35	0

For Types as **73***a* with Multiple wmk. see King George VI Catalogue.

74. Smiling Boy.

(Des. L. C. Mitchell. Dies and plates, Perkins, Bacon. Typo. Govt. Ptg. Office, Wellington.)

1931 (31 Oct.). *Health Stamps.* *T* **74.** *W* **41.** *P* 14½ × 14.

546	1d. + 1d. scarlet	60	0	60	0
547	2d. + 1d. blue	75	0	75	0

75. Lake Manapouri.

(Des. L. C. Mitchell. Typo. Govt. Ptg. Office.)

1931 (11 Nov.). *Air stamps.* *T* **75.** *W* **41.** *P* 14 × 14½.

548	3d. chocolate	6 0	4 6
	a. Perf. 14×15	75 0	
549	4d. blackish purple	6 0	4 0
550	7d. brown-orange	17 6	12 0

FIVE PENCE

(76)

1931 (18 Dec.). *Air stamp.* *T* **75**, *surch. with T* **76.**

551	5d. on 3d. green (R.)	6 0	4 6

77. Hygeia—Goddess of Health.

(Designed by R. E. Tripe and W. J. Cooch. Engraved by H. T. Peat. Recess-printed at Govt. Printing Office, Wellington.)

1932 (18 Nov.). *Health stamp.* *T* **77.** *W* **41.** *P* 14.

552	1d.+1d. carmine	30 0	30 0

78. The Path to Health.

(Des. S. J. Berry, Eng. H. T. Peat. Recess-printed at Govt. Printing Office, Wellington.)

1933 (8 Nov.). *Health stamp.* *T* **78.** *W* **41.** *P* 14.

553	1d.+1d. carmine	15 0	15 0

TRANS-TASMAN
AIR MAIL
"FAITH IN AUSTRALIA."

(79)

1934 (Feb.). *Air stamp.* *T* **75** *in new colour optd. with T* **79.** *W* **41.** *P* 14 × 14½.

554	7d. light blue (B.)	17 6	17 6

80. Crusader.

(Des. S. J. Berry. Recess. De La Rue & Co.)

1934 (26 Oct.). *Health stamp.* *W* **41.** *P* 14 × 13½.

555	**80** 1d.+1d. carmine	15 0	15 0

81. Pied fantail.

82. Kiwi.

83. Maori woman.

84. Maori carved house

85. Mt. Cook.

86. Maori girl.

87. Mitre Peak.

88. Swordfish.

89. Harvesting.

90. Tuatara lizard.

91. Maori panel.

92. Tui.

93. Capt. Cook at Poverty Bay.

94. Mt. Egmont.

Die I Die II

(Des. J. Fitzgerald (½d. and 4d.), C. H. and R. J. G. Collins (1d.), M. Matthews (1½d.), H. W. Young (2d.), L. C. Mitchell (2½d., 3d., 8d., 1s. and 3s.), W. J. Cooch and R. E. Tripe (5d.), T. I. Archer (6d.), I. F. Calder (9d.) and I. H. Jenkins (2s.).)

(Litho. Waterlow & Sons (9d.). Recess. De La Rue & Co. (remainder).)

1935 (1 May). *W* **41.** *P* 14×13½ (*½d., 1d., 1½d., 2d., 3d., 8d. and 1s.*), 13½×14 (*1d., 1½d., 2½d., 5d., 6d., 2s. and 3s.*), 13–14×13½ (*2½d., 5d., 2s. and 3s.*), 14 (*4d.*) *or* 14×14½ (*9d.*).

556	**81**	½d. bright green	0	4	0	1
557	**82**	1d. scarlet (Die I) ..	0	6	0	1
		a. Deepened die (Die II) ..	0	9	0	1
558	**83**	1½d. red-brown	2	6	1	0
559	**84**	2d. orange	1	6	0	4
560	**85**	2½d. chocolate and slate	1	9	1	0
561	**86**	3d. brown	2	6	0	6
562	**87**	4d. black and sepia ..	1	9	0	7
563	**88**	5d. ultramarine	2	0	1	6
564	**89**	6d. scarlet	2	6	0	10
565	**90**	8d. chocolate	3	6	2	6
566	**91**	9d. scarlet and black ..	3	6	0	10
567	**92**	1s. deep green	15	0	2	5
568	**93**	2s. olive-green	12	6	5	0
569	**94**	3s. choc. and yellow-brn.	15	0	10	0

In the 2½d., 5d., 2s. and 3s. perf. 13–14×13½ the horizontal perforations of each stamp are in two sizes, one half of each horizontal side measuring 13 and the other 14.

For 9d. typographed and similar stamps with Multiple wmk. see King George VI Catalogue. In these the wmk. units are arranged alternately in horizontal rows closely spaced and are continued into the sheet margins.

In T **41** the wmk. units are in vertical columns widely spaced and the sheet margins are unwatermarked or wmkd. "NEW ZEALAND POSTAGE" in large letters.

95. Bell Block Aerodrome.

(Des. S. J. Berry. Eng. Stamp Printing Office, Melbourne. Recess. Govt. Printing Office, Wellington.)

1935 (4 May). *Air.* *W* **41.** *P* 14.

570	**95**	1d. carmine	0	8	0	6
571	,,	3d. violet	2	0	1	6
572	,,	6d. blue	2	6	2	0

96

(Frame by S. J. Berry. Recess. Bradbury Wilkinson & Co.)

1935 (7 May). *Silver Jubilee.* *W* **41.** *P* 11×11½.

573	**96**	½d. green	0	6	0	6
574	,,	1d. carmine	0	10	0	4
575	,,	6d. red-orange	15	0	16	0

97. "The Key to Health."

(Des. S. Hall. Recess. J. Ash, Melbourne.)

1935 (30 Sept.). *Health Stamp.* *W* **41.** *P* 11.

576	**97**	1d.+1d. scarlet	3	6	3	6

99. N.Z. Soldier at Anzac Cove.

(Recess. John Ash, Melbourne.)

1936 (27 Apr.). *Charity. 21st Anniv. of "Anzac" Landing at Gallipoli. W* **41.** *P* 11.

591	**99**	½d.+½d. green	0	6	0	8
592	„	1d.+1d. scarlet	0	8	1	0

100. Wool.

101. Butter. **102.** Sheep.

103. Apples. **104.** Exports.

(Des. L. C. Mitchell. Recess. J. Ash, Melbourne.)

1936 (1 Oct.). *Congress of British Empire Chambers of Commerce, Wellington. N.Z. Industries Issue. T* **100** *to* **104** *(various horiz. designs, inscr.* "CHAMBER OF COMMERCE" *etc.). W* **41.** *P* 11½.

593	**100**	½d. emerald green	0	5	0	6
594	**101**	1d. scarlet	0	6	0	8
595	**102**	2½d. blue	3	6	4	6
596	**103**	4d. violet	2	0	3	0
597	**104**	6d. red-brown	3	6	4	6

105. Health Camp.

(Des. S. J. Berry. Recess. J. Ash, Melbourne.)

1936 (2 Nov.). *Health Stamp. W* **41.** *P* 11.

598	**105**	1d.+1d. scarlet	2	6	2	6

EXPRESS DELIVERY STAMPS

E 1

1903–20. *Type* **E 1.** *Value in centre in first colour. Wmk. single-lined* "N Z" *and Star, T* **41.** *P* 11.

E1	6d. red and violet	2	6	1	9
E2	6d. orange-red & violet (1920)	2	6	1	9

1926–39. *Type* **E 1,** *but Cowan thick opaque paper. W* **41.** *(a) P* 14 × 14½.

E3	6d. vermilion & bright violet	1	6	1	6

(b) *P* 14 × 15.

E4	6d. carmine and bright violet	3	0	3	6
E5	6d. verm & bright vio. ('39)	2	6	3	0

POSTAGE DUE STAMPS.

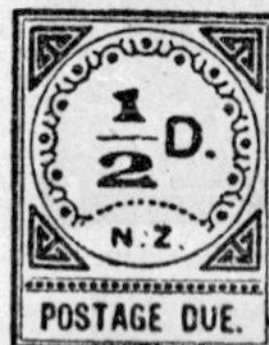

D 1

(I.)

N.Z.

(II.)

3D. (a) 5D. (b)

1899 (Dec.). *Type* **D 1.** *Value in centre in second colour. W* **12a.** *P* 11. *Two types of frame, two types of* "D." *in values (a) and (b).*

Type I. *Circle of* 14 *ornaments,* 17 *dots over* "N.Z.", "N.Z." *large.* (a) *Large* "D."

801	½d. green and carmine	0	9	0	9
802	8d. green and carmine	4	0	4	0
803	1s. green and carmine	4	6	4	6
804	2s. green and carmine	7	6	7	6

To avoid further subdivision the 1s. and 2s. are placed with the *pence* values, although the two types of "D" do not apply to the higher values.

Variety. No stop after "D"

805	½d. green and carmine	22	6	22	6

(b) *Small* "D."

806	5d. green and carmine	1	6	1	6
807	6d. green and carmine	1	6	1	6
808	10d. green and carmine	4	0	4	0

Type II. *Circle of* 13 *ornaments,* 15 *dots over* "N.Z.", "N.Z." *small.* (a) *Large* "D."

809	½d. green and vermilion	0	4	0	5
810	1d. green and vermilion	0	8	0	4
811	2d. green and vermilion	1	0	0	6
812	3d. green and vermilion	0	10	0	6

Variety. No stop after "D"

813	½d. green and vermilion	17	6	20	0

(b) *Small* "D."

814	1d. green and vermilion	0	6	0	4
815	2d. green and vermilion	1	6	0	6
816	4d. green and carmine	1	3	0	8

D 2

(Typo. Govt. Printing Office.)

1902-6. *Type* **D 2.** *Centre in first colour. No wmk.* P 11.

817	½d. red and deep green (1902)	0	6	0	6

Wmk. "*N Z*" *and Star, T* **41**, *sideways.*

(*a*) *P* 11.

818	½d. red and green (1902) ..	0	4	0	4
819	1d. red and green	2	6	2	6
820	2d. red and green	27	6	22	6

(*b*) *P* 14.

821	1d. carmine and green (1904)	1	3	0	10
822	2d. carmine and green (1904)	1	6	1	0

1910. *Type* **D 2.** *W* **41.** *P* 14.

823	1d. rose-pink and green ..	0	8	0	3
824	2d. rose-pink and green ..	0	10	0	6

1913. *Type* **D 2.** *Chalky paper. W* **41.** *P* 14×15.

824*a*	½d. carmine and green ..	0	2	0	2
825	1d. carmine and green ..	0	6	0	3
826	2d. carmine and green ..	1	3	0	3

1924. *Type* **D 2.** "*Jones*" *chalky paper. White gum. W* **41.** *P* 14×15.

827	½d. carmine and green ..	3	6	3	6

1925. *Type* **D 2.** *No wmk., but bluish* "*N Z*" *and Star lithographed on back. P* 14×15.

829	½d. carmine and green ..	0	6	0	6
830	2d. carmine and green ..	1	0	1	0

1925-32. *Type* **D 2.** *Wmk.* "*N Z*" *and Star.* "*Cowan*" *thick opaque chalky paper. White gum.*

(*a*) *P* 14×15.

830*a*	½d. carmine and green ('30) ..	0	1	0	2
831	1d. carmine and green ..	0	3	0	2
832	2d. carmine and green ..	0	6	0	3

(*b*) *P* 14.

833	½d. carmine and green ('26) ..	0	3	0	2
834	1d. rose and pale yellow-grn.	0	6	0	1
835	2d. carmine and green ('32) ..	1	0	0	4
836	3d. carmine and green ('28) ..	1	6	0	6

OFFICIAL STAMPS.

1892-1901. *Contemporary issues overprinted* "*O. P. S. O.*" *diagonally. W* **12a.**

Violet overprint.

O40	**3**	½d. rose (*p.* 12½)	80	0		

Rose or magenta overprint.

O41	**13**	½d. black (*p.* 10×11) ..	65	0		
O42	,,	½d. black (*p.* 10) ..	65	0		
O43	**14**	1d. rose (*p.* 12×11½) ..	70	0		
O44	,,	1d. rose (*p.* 11)	65	0		
O45	**15**	2d. purple (*p.* 11) ..	60	0		
O46	,,	2d. purple (*p.* 10) ..	60	0		
O47	**16**	2½d. ultram. (*p.* 10×11) ..	65	0		
O48	,,	2½d. ultram. (*p.* 10) ..	80	0		
O49	**19**	5d. olive-blk. (*p.* 12×11½)	70	0		
O50	**20**	6d. brown (*p.* 12×11½) ..	75	0		

Violet overprint. P 11.

O52	**40**	1d. carm. (*wmk. T* **36a**)	50	0		
O52*a*	**26**	2½d. blue (*no wmk.*)	£5			
O53	**27**	2½d. blue (*wmk. T* **41**) ..	65	0		
O53*a*	,,	2½d. blue (*no wmk.*) ..	80	0		
O54	**30**	5d. brown *no wmk.*) ..	£5			
O55	**32**	8d. blue (*no wmk.*) ..	£5			
O55*a*	**33**	9d. purple	£7			
		b. Perf. 14, 15 (No. 267) ..	£7			
O56	**35**	2s. green (*wmk. T* **41**) ..	£8			

Green overprint. P 11.

O57	**30**	5d. brown (*no wmk.*) ..	£5			

The letters signify "On Public Service Only." and stamps so overprinted were used by the Post Office Department on official correspondence between the department and places abroad.

OFFICIAL

(O 3)

1907. *Stamps of* 1902-7 (*W* **41.** *P* 14) *overprinted with Type* O 3 (*vertically upwards*) *in black.*

O59	½d. yellow-green	0	8	0	2
O60	1d. carmine	1	0	0	1
O61	2d. purple	0	9	0	2
O62	2d. bright purple	0	9	0	2
O63	3d. bistre-brown	2	9	1	0
O64	6d. pink	12	6	2	0
	a. Imperf. between (pair) ..	£20			
O65	1s. red	9	0	2	6
O66	2s. blue-green	6	0	6	6
	a. Imperf. between (pair) ..	£20			
O67	5s. deep red	10	0	10	0
O68	£1 rose (No. F 164)	80	0	80	0

1908. *T* **23, 46** *and* **48.** *W* **41.** *Overprinted as Type* O 3.

O69	½d. green (*p.* 14×15) ..	2	0	0	4
O70	1d. carmine (*p.* 14×15) ..	5	0	0	1
O71	6d. pink (*p.* 14×15)	15	0	2	0
O72	6d. pink (*p.* 14×13, 13½) ..	15	0	2	0

1910-16. *T* **50** *and* **51** *overprinted as Type* O 3. *W* **41.** *P* 14×15.

O73	½d. yellow-green	0	2	0	1
O74	1d. carmine	0	3	0	1

T **52** (*and similar type*), *overprinted as Type* O 3. *W* **41.** *P* 14×14½.

O78	3d. chestnut	1	3	0	4
	a. Perf. 14×13½	17	0	6	0
	b. Vert. pair, O78/8a	32	6	32	6
O79	6d. carmine	3	0	0	6
O80	6d. deep carmine	2	6	0	4
O81	1s. vermilion	3	0	1	6

1913-14. *T* **154.** *W* **41.** *P* 14. *Overprinted as Type* O 3.

O81*a*	2s. blue (30.9.14)	5	0	3	6
O82	5s. yellow-green (13.6.13) ..	12	6	7	6

The overprint on these last and on No. O 69 is from a new set of type, giving a rather sharper impression than Type O 3, but otherwise resembling it so closely as to make further illustration useless.

1915-22. *T* **60b** *and* **60a** *overprinted as Type* O 3. *Wmk. T* **41.** *P* 14×15.

O83	½d. green (Oct. 12, 1915) ..	0	2	0	1
O84	1½d. slate (*local plate*), (June, '16)	1	0	0	3

T **52** *optd. as Type* O 3 *in red.* P 14×14½.

O85	8d. indigo-blue (May, '16) ..	2	6	1	6
	a. Perf. 14×13½ ..	3	6	1	6
	b. Vert. pair, O85/5a	10	0	10	0

T **60** *overprinted as Type* O 3. *P* 14×14½.

O86	3d. chocolate (May, 1916)	2	6	0	6
	a. Perf. 14×13½	3	0	0	6
	b. Vert. pair, O86/6a	9	6	9	6
O87	6d. carmine (June, 1916) ..	1	3	0	4
	a. Perf. 14×13½	1	0	0	6
	b. Vert. pair, O87/7a	10	0	10	0
O88	8d. red-brn. (*p.* 14×13½) ('22)	4	6	4	0
O89	1s. vermilion (Sept., 1916)	2	0	0	6
	a. Perf 14×13½	2	6	1	3
	b. Vert. pair, O89/9a	12	6	12	6
O90	1s. pale orange-red ..	7	6	4	6

1916. *T* **60** *optd. as Type* O **3**, *on pictorial issue paper. Wmk. sideways. P* 14.

O93 3d. chocolate 1 6 2 0
a. No wmk. 10 0 10 0

1916–19. *T* **60***b*. *P* 14×15. *Overprinted as Type* O **3**.

O94 1½d. slate (Dec. '16) .. 0 9 0 2
O95 1½d. chestnut-brown (4.'19) 0 6 0 3
O96 2d. yellow (April, '17) .. 0 6 0 2
O97 3d. chocolate (Nov., '19) .. 1 0 0 6

1919–30. *T* **154** *optd. as Type* O **3**. *W* **41**. *P* 14½×14.

O98 2s. deep blue 4 6 4 0
a. No stop after "OFFICIAL" 30 0 30 0
O99 5s. yellow-green 10 0 10 0
a. No stop after "OFFICIAL" 40 0 30 0

1925. *T* **60** *optd. as Type* O **3**. *P* 14×13½.

O100 4d. red-violet 1 3 0 3
a. Violet. Perf. 14×14½ .. 0 10 0 2
O101 9d. sage-green 1 6 0 9

1925–31. *Overprinted as Type* O **3**. "Jones" *chalky paper. White gum. W* **41**. *P* 14×15.

O102 **60***b* ½d. green 0 6 0 4
O103 **51** 1d. deep carmine .. 0 8 0 4
O104 **60***b* 3d. deep chocolate .. 1 9 0 6

No wmk. but bluish "N Z" *and Star lithographed on back.*

O105 **51** 1d. carmine-pink .. 0 9 1 0

"Cowan" *thick, opaque, chalky paper. White gum.*

O106 **60***b* ½d. green (*p.* 14×15) 0 2 0 1
a. Perf. 14 .. .. 0 3 0 1
b. No stop after "OFFICIAL" (Perf. 14) 2 6 2 6
O107 **51** 1d. deep carmine .. 0 8 0 2
O108 **60***b* 1½d. orge.-brn. (*p.* 14) ('30) 0 6 0 4
a. No stop after "OFFICIAL" .. 6 6 6 6
b. Perf. 14×15 .. .. 0 6 0 4
O109 **60***b* 2d. yellow (*p.* 14) ('31) 0 6 0 3
a. No stop after "OFFICIAL" .. 5 0 5 0
O110 **60***b* 3d. chocolate (*p.* 14×15) 1 0 0 2
a. No stop after "OFFICIAL" .. 12 6 12 6
b. Perf. 14 .. .. 0 9 0 2
c. Ditto, no stop after "OFFICIAL" .. 12 6 12 6

1927. *T* **71** *overprinted as Type* O **3**.

O111 1d. rose-carmine (*p.* 14) .. 0 4 0 1
a. No stop after "OFFICIAL" 2 6 2 6
b. Perf. 14×15 .. .. 0 3 0 2

No. 542 *overprinted as Type* O **3**.

O112 2s. light blue 5 0 5 6

1933. *No.* 544 *f.* (*Type as* **73***a*) *optd. as Type* O **3**.

O113 5s. green 20 0 25 0

Official

(O **4**)

1936 (1 Apr.)**–38.** *Pictorial issue optd. horiz. with Type* O **4**. *W* **41** (*Single* "NZ" *and Star*).

O115 **82** 1d. scarlet (Die I) (*p.* 14×13½) .. 1 0 0 2
O116 **83** 1½d. red-brn. (*p.* 14×13½) 1 3 0 9
O122 **92** 1s. dp. grn. (*p.* 14×13½) 5 0 4 0
O123 **73***a* 5s. green (Dec. '38) (*p.* 14) 10 0 8 6

The watermark of No. O123 is almost invisible.

PROVISIONALS ISSUED AT REEFTON AND USED BY THE POLICE DEPARTMENT.

1907 (Jan.). *Current stamps of* 1906, *overwritten* "Official," *in red ink, and marked* "Greymouth—PAID—3" *inside a circular postmark-stamp. P* 14.

P1 ½d. green .. .. .. — £8
P2 1d. carmine .. .. .. — £10
P3 2d. purple .. .. .. — £10
P4 3d. bistre .. .. .. — £12
P5 6d. pink .. .. .. — £25
P6 1s. orange-red .. .. — £35
P7 2s. green .. .. .. — £140

LIFE INSURANCE DEPARTMENT.

S **1**. Lighthouse.

(Designed by W. B. Hudson. Engraved by A. E. Cousins. Printed in New Zealand.)

1891 (2 Jan.). *Type* S **1**. *W* **12***a*.

(*a*) *P* 12×11½.

1001 ½d. bright purple 4 0 0 6
1002 1d. blue 4 0 0 9
1003 2d. brown-red 4 6 0 6
1004 3d. deep brown 15 0 4 6
1005 6d. green 25 0 5 0
1006 1s. rose 30 0 12 6

(*b*) *P* 10.

1007 ½d. bright purple 6 0 2 6
1008 1d. blue 3 6 1 6
1009 2d. lake 7 6 1 6

(*c*) *P* 10 *and* 11 *compound.*

1010 ½d. bright purple 15 0 6 6
1011 1d. blue 6 0 2 6

(*d*) *P* 11.

1012 ½d. bright purple 2 0 0 2
1013 1d. blue 1 3 0 2
1014 2d. brown-red 2 6 0 4
1015 2d. chocolate 40 0 6 0

1902–4. *Type* S **1**. *W* **41**. (*a*) *P* 11.

1019 ½d. bright purple 4 0 0 2
1020 1d. blue 4 6 0 4
1021 2d. brown-red 2 0 0 6

(*b*) *P* 11 *and* 14 *compound.*

1021*a* ½d. bright purple .. ..
1022 1d. blue 7 6 3 0

Nos. 1019, 1020 and 1022 are also known without watermark from the margins of the sheets.

S **2**

1905 (Dec.)–**1906.** *Type* S **2.** (*Design redrawn.* "V.R." *omitted.*) *W* **41.** (*a*) *P* 11.

No.	Description	Unused	Used
1023	2d. brown-red	25 0	10 0
	(*b*) *P* 14.		
1024	1d. blue	12 6	5 0
	(*c*) *Perf. compound of* 11 *and* 14.		
1025	1d. blue	40 0	35 0

1913–37. *Type* S **2.** *W* **41.** *New values and colours.* (*a*) *P* 14×15.

No.	Description	Unused	Used
1026	½d. green	0 4	0 2
	a. Yellow-green ('25)	0 1	0 1
1027	1d. carmine	0 10	0 4
	a. Red	1 6	0 6
	b. Carmine-pink ('25)	0 9	0 2
1029	1½d. black (1917)	4 0	1 0
1030	1½d. chestnut-brown (1919)	0 3	0 2
1031	2d. bright purple	3 6	1 9
1031*a*	2d. yellow (1920)	0 6	0 4
1032	3d. yellow-brown	1 0	1 3
1033	6d. carmine-pink	0 10	0 8
	(*b*) *P* 14.		
1034	½d. yellow-green ('26)	1 0	0 4
1036	1d. scarlet ('31)	0 4	0 1
1037	2d. yellow ('37)	0 4	0 4
1038	3d. brown-lake ('31)	0 5	0 5
1039	6d. pink ('25)	2 0	1 6

In the 1½d. the word "POSTAGE" is in both the side-labels instead of at left only.

POSTAL FISCALS.

151

152

153

1882 (1 April). *T* **151** (*1d. to 8d.*) *and* **152.** *Wmk.* "N Z", *T* **153**, *Large Star, or impressed monogram* "N Z". (*a*) *Imperf.*

No.	Description	Unused	Used
F 1	1d. lilac and red	10 0	10 0
F 2	1d. blue and red	10 0	6 0
F 3	4d. green and black	7 6	10 0
F 4	6d. brown and blue	12 6	10 0
F 5	8d. blue and black	10 0	10 0
F 6	1s. purple and red	20 0	12 6
F 7	1s. 4d. brown and blue	—	20 0
F 8	1s. 6d. blue and black	—	15 0
F 9	1s. 8d. drab and blue	30 0	20 0
F10	2s. red and green	30 0	
F11	2s. 4d. green and black		
F12	2s. 6d. brown and blue	—	15 0
F13	2s. 8d. blue and black	—	30 0
F14	3s. lilac and red	20 0	20 0
F15	3s. 4d. brown and blue	22 6	20 0
F16	3s. 6d. blue and black		
F17	3s. 8d. drab and blue	20 0	
F18	4s. red and green	—	20 0
F19	4s. 4d. green and black		
F20	4s. 6d. drab and blue		
F21	4s. 8d. blue and black		
F22	5s. 4d. drab and green		
F23	6s. carmine and blue	25 0	
F24	6s. 4d. pale blue and red		
F25	6s. 8d. blue and black	25 0	25 0
F26	7s. 6d. blue and black	—	12 6
F28	9s. violet and red	30 0	
F29	9s. 6d. blue and black	—	20 0
F30	10s. red and green	25 0	15 0
F31	15s. red and grey	—	20 0
F32	£1 red-brown and blue	30 0	
F33	£1 5s. red and grey	—	15 0
F34	30s. red and green	—	10 0
F35	35s. grey-blue and red	—	15 0
F36	40s. red and green	—	20 0
F37	90s. red and green		

Varieties. Wmk. Large Star.

No.	Description	Unused	Used
F38	17s. 6d. blue and black	£9	40 0
F39	27s. 6d. blue and black	£8	60 0

Several varieties are known *percé en scie.*

(*b*) *P* 10, 12½, *and compound.*

No.	Description	Unused	Used
F 40	1d. lilac and green	1 6	3 0
F 41	1d. mauve and green	2 0	3 0
F 42	1d. blue and brown		
F 44	1d. slate and green	5 0	5 0
F 45	1d. dull purple and green	5 0	
F 46	2d. green and red	6 0	6 0
F 48	4d. green and black	5 0	5 0
F 49	6d. grey-brown and blue	5 0	
F 50	6d. red-brown and blue	5 0	4 0
F 51	8d. blue and black	5 0	4 0
F 52	8d. blue and red	7 6	
F 53	1s. mauve and blue	5 0	2 6
F 54	1s. mauve and green	6 0	6 0
F 55	1s. purple and green	10 0	10 0
F 56	1s. 4d. brown and blue	30 0	
F 58	2s. rose and blue	12 6	
F 59	2s. 4d. green and black		
F 60	2s. 6d. brown and blue	7 6	6 0
F 61	2s. 6d. red-brown & blue	10 0	5 0
F 63	3s. mauve and green	—	20 0
F 64	3s. 4d. brown and blue	12 6	12 6
F 65	4s. carmine and blue	15 0	10 0
F 67	5s. dull violet and green	—	5 0
F 68	5s. mauve and blue	—	7 6
F 70	6s. red-brown and blue	10 0	
F 71	6s. carmine and blue	—	7 6
F 72	6s. 8d. blue and rose	15 0	
F 74	7s. violet and red		
F 76	7s. 6d. blue and black	—	7 6
F 78	8s. brown and blue		
F 80	9s. violet and red	—	30 0
F 82	10s. red-brown and green	—	15 0
F 83	10s. carmine and blue	—	6 0
F 84	12s. 6d. brown	—	10 0
F 85	15s. mauve and blue	—	10 0
F 86	15s. grey and red	—	15 0
F 87	20s. rose and blue		
F 88	£1 pink	30 0	7 6
F 89	£1 2s. 6d. brown & blue	—	40 0
F 91	£1 5s. grey and red	—	35 0
F 92	£1 10s. brown and green	60 0	
F 93	£1 10s. red and green	—	40 0
F 95	£2 orange and green	—	35 0
F 96	£2 10s. pink and blue	—	50 0
F 97	£3 pink and blue	—	50 0
F 98	£3 red-brown and green	—	50 0
F 99	£4 red-brown and green	—	45 0
F100	£5 carmine and blue	—	60 0
F101	£10 red-brown and green	—	60 0

154

T **154.** *Value on white labels. Wmk.* " NZ " *and Star. T* **12a** *or* " NZ " *T* **153.** *P* 12½, 13 *or P* 11½, 12, *or P* 11.

No.	Description	Unused	Used
F102	4d. red-brown	—	60 0
F103	6d. marone	60 0	60 0
F104	8d. green (*wmk.* " NZ ") ..	—	7 6
F105	1s. rose	—	5 0
F106	1s. rose (*wmk.* " NZ ")	7 6	5 0
F107	2s. blue	2 6	0 6
F108	2s. 6d. grey-brown ..	3 0	0 9
F109	3s. mauve	4 0	0 9
F110	4s. brown-rose	6 0	2 6
F111	4s. dull purple	10 0	6 0
F112	4s. dull claret	6 0	2 0
F113	5s. green	6 0	0 6
F114	6s. rose	8 0	2 0
F114a	6s. rose (*wmk.* " NZ ") ..	—	4 0
F115	7s. blue	10 0	3 6
F116	7s. 6d. sepia	—	5 0
F117	8s. blue	12 0	4 0
F117a	8s. blue (*wmk.* " NZ ") ..		
F118	9s. orange	10 0	5 0
F119	9s. orange (*wmk.* " NZ ")	—	7 6
F120	10s. Venetian red	12 0	1 6
F121	10s. Venetian red (*wmk.* "NZ")	—	4 6
F122	15s. green	—	7 0
F123	15s. green (*wmk.* " NZ ") ..	—	12 0
F125	£1 rose	30 0	3 0
F126	£1 rose (*wmk.* " NZ ")		
F127	25s. blue	—	15 0
F128	25s. blue (*wmk.* " NZ ") ..	—	20 0
F129	30s. brown	—	12 6
F130	35s. yellow	—	20 0
F131	£2 bright purple	—	7 6
F132	£2 10s. red-brown ..	—	15 0
F133	£3 green	—	12 0
F134	£3 10s. rose	—	45 0
F135	£4 ultramarine	—	35 0
F136	£4 10s. olive-brown ..	—	35 0
F137	£5 blue	—	10 0
F137a	£5 blue (*wmk.* " NZ ") ..	—	35 0
F138	£6 orange-red	—	25 0
F139	£7 Venetian red	—	25 0
F140	£8 green	—	20 0
F141	£9 rose	—	50 0
F142	£10 blue	—	30 0

Error. With " COUNTERPART " *inscribed above lower label.*

No.	Description	Unused	Used
F143	2s. 6d. brown (1901) ..	15 0	20 0

All values under 15s. are T **154**. The 15s. to £2 10s. are of a slightly different type. The £3 to £5 have the head in a rectangle; the higher values have the head in a hexagon

155

156

T **155** (*for* 1d.) *and various designs* (*small rectangular as T* **156**) *for other values. Wmk. T* **12a.** *P.* 11½, 12.

No.	Description	Unused	Used
F144	1d. lilac	8 6	7 6
F145	1d. blue	1 6	0 9
F146	1s. green (LAND & DEEDS)	10 0	7 6
F147	1s. grn. & red (LAW COURTS)	10 0	12 6
F148	2s. rose & blue (LAW COURTS)	30 0	

1903–4. *T* **154,** *etc. Wmk. single-lined* "NZ" *and Star, T* **41.** *P* 11.

No.	Description	Unused	Used
F149	2s. 6d. brown	5 0	2 0
F150	3s. mauve	6 0	2 6
F151	4s. rose	12 6	3 0
F152	6s. rose	14 0	4 0
F152a	7s. pale blue	17 6	5 0
F153	10s. brown	20 0	6 0
F154	£1 rose	40 0	10 0

1906–14. *T* **154,** *etc. W* **41.** (*a*) *P* 14.

No.	Description	Unused	Used
F155	2s. blue, C (1914) ..	4 6	0 8
F156	2s. 6d. brown, OC ..	4 0	1 3
F157	3s. mauve, OC	6 0	1 6
F158	4s. Venetian red, O ..	7 6	2 6
F159	5s. green, C	10 0	2 0
F159a	6s. rose, O	12 6	3 6
F160	7s. blue, OC	15 0	4 0
F160a	7s. 6d. sepia, OC ..	15 0	3 0
F161	8s. blue, OC	15 0	4 6
F162	9s. orange, O	17 6	4 6
F163	10s. brown, OC	20 0	4 6
F163a	15s. green, O	30 0	6 6
F164	£1 rose, OC	35 0	12 0
F165	£2 violet	—	30 0

(*b*) *P* 14½ × 14 (*chalk-surfaced paper*).

No.	Description	Unused	Used
F166	2s. blue	4 0	0 6
F167	2s. 6d. brown	3 6	0 9
F168	3s. bright mauve	6 0	1 6
F169	4s. Venetian red	6 0	2 0
F170	5s. yellow-green (1913) ..	7 6	2 0
F171	6s. rose (1913)	10 0	3 0
F172	7s. blue	11 6	3 6
F173	8s. blue (1913)	12 6	4 0
F173a	9s. orange	17 6	6 6
F174	10s. brown	17 6	4 0
F174a	12s. 6d. purple	25 0	15 0
F175	15s. green	25 0	15 0
F176	£1 rose	30 0	8 6
F177	£2 violet	50 0	

Later printings of some values were on "Jones," " Cowan," or " Wiggins Teape " paper.

NOTE. While there are still differences of opinion as to the status of the stamps of T **151** and **152**, stamps of T **154** and in the arms design formerly listed as T **157** (now T **73a**), were authorized to be accepted in prepayment of postage and were, in fact, with a few exceptions, the only postage stamps of high denomination in existence.

This differentiates them sharply from most other stamps listed under the heading " Postal Fiscals " in this catalogue, the use of these others being mainly for revenue purposes and their postal use exceptional.

In regard to stamps of T **154** the only point of difficulty is whether all values should be regarded as postage stamps in the fullest sense, or only those which were generally used for postal purposes. We have therefore left these stamps in this section of the list until there has been opportunity for fuller discussion on this point but we have transferred the stamps in the Arms design, formerly listed as Nos. F178 to F207, to the list of postage stamps, as there can be no question as to their right to that position.

ANTARCTIC EXPEDITIONS.

KING EDWARD VII LAND.

1908. *Shackleton Expedition. T* **40** *of New Zealand* (*p.* 14), *overprinted.* " King Edward VII Land " *in two lines, reading up.*

No.	Description	Unused	Used
A1	1d. carmine (No. 344) (G.) ..	20 0	20 0

VICTORIA LAND.

1911. *Scott Expedition. T* **50** *and* **51** *of New Zealand overprinted* "VICTORIA LAND." *in two lines, in black.*

A2	½d. green	—		45	0
A3	1d. carmine	20	0	20	0
	a. No stop after "LAND" ..				

These issues were made under authority of the New Zealand Postal Department and, while not strictly necessary, they actually franked correspondence to New Zealand.

BRITISH POSSESSIONS UNDER THE CONTROL OF NEW ZEALAND.

AITUTAKI.

AITUTAKI.
1

Ava Pene.
2 (½d.)

Tai Pene.
3 (1d.)

Rua Pene Ma Te Ava.
4 (2½d.)

Toru Pene.
5 (3d.)

Ono Pene.
6 (6d.)

Tai Tiringi.
7 (1s.)

1903. *T* **23, 40, 27, 28, 31,** *and* **34** *of New Zealand, wmk. single-lined* "N Z" *and Star, T* **41**, *overprinted with name at top, T* **1**, *and surcharged with values at foot, T* **2** *to* **7**, *in red* (*R.*) *or blue* (*B.*).

(*a*) *P* 14.

1	½d. green (R.)	2	6	3	6
2	1d. carmine (B.) ..	3	6	4	6
3	2½d. blue (R.)	4	0	4	6
	a. "Ava" without stop	30	0	40	0

(*b*) *P* 11.

5	2½d. blue (R.)	4	0	4	6
	a. "Ava" without stop	40	0	50	0
7	3d. yellow-brown (B.)	4	0	4	6
8	6d. rose-red (B.) ..	5	0	5	6
9	1s. bright red (B.) ..	16	0	20	0
	a. "Tiringi" without stop	60	0	80	0
10	1s. orange-red (B.) ..	22	6	25	0
	a. "Tiringi" without stop	75	0	£6	

AITUTAKI.

Ono Pene.
(7*a*)

1912–16. *T* **50, 51,** *and* **52** *of New Zealand surcharged, the ½d. and 1d. as above, the 6d. and 1s. as T 7a.*

11	½d. green (R.)	0	8	1	0
12	1d. carmine (B.) (1913)	1	0	1	6
14	6d. carm. (B.) (*p.* 14×14½) ('16)	5	0	7	6
15	1s. verm. (B.) (*p.* 14×14½) ('14)	12	6	12	6

1916–17. *T* **60** *surch. as T 7a. P* 14×14½.

23	6d. carmine (B.) (June, '16) ..	5	6	7	6
	a. Perf. 14×13½	6	6	8	6
	b. Vert. pair, 23/3a ..	30	0	40	0
25	1s. vermilion (B) (Mar., '17) ..	7	6	10	0
	a. Perf. 14×13½	7	6	12	0
	b. Vert. pair, 25/25a ..	35	0	45	0
	c. "Tai" without dot ..	32	6	42	6
	d. "Tiringi" no dot on second "i"	45	0	55	0
	e. "Tiringi" no dot on third "i"	55	0	65	0

1917–18. *T* **60** *overprinted* "AITUTAKI." *only, as in T 7a. P* 14×14½.

27	2½d. blue (R.) (Dec., '18) ..	1	6	1	6
	a. Perf. 14×13½	1	9	2	0
	b. Vert. pair, 27/7a ..	5	0	6	0
28	3d. chocolate (B.) (Jan., '18) ..	3	0	3	6
	a. Perf. 14×13½	3	6	4	0
	b. Vert. pair, 28/8a ..	12	6	15	0
29	6d. carmine (B.) (Dec., '17) ..	3	6	4	0
	a. Perf. 14×13½	3	0	4	0
	b. Vert. pair, 29/9a ..	10	0	12	6
30	1s. vermilion (B.) (Dec., '17) ..	3	0	4	0
	a. Perf. 14×13½	3	6	4	6
	b. Vert. pair, 30/30a ..	15	0	17	6

1917–20. *T* **60*b*** *and* **51**, *surface-printed, optd.* "AITUTAKI" *only, as in T 7a. Wmk.* "N Z" *and Star, T* **41**. *P* 14×15.

31	½d. green (R.) (Feb., '20) ..	0	4	0	6
32	1d. carmine (B.) (May, '20) ..	0	6	0	9
33	1½d. slate (R.) (Nov., '17) ..	1	3	1	9
34	1½d. oran.-brn. (R.) (Feb., '19)	0	8	0	10
35	3d. chocolate (B.) (July, '19) ..	2	0	2	6

(Des. and recess. Perkins, Bacon & Co.)

1920 (Aug.). *As T* **10** *to* **15** *of Cook Islands, but inscr.* "AITUTAKI". *No wmk. P* 14.

36	½d. black and deep green ..	1	6	2	0
	a. Imperf.				
37	1d. black and dull carmine ..	2	0	2	6
38	1½d. black and sepia ..	1	6	2	0
39	3d. black and deep blue ..	2	0	2	6
40	6d. red-brown and slate ..	3	6	4	0
	a. Centre inverted ..	£125			
41	1s. black and purple	6	0	7	0
	a. Imperf.				

(Nos. 42–44. Recess. Govt. Printing Office, Wellington.)

1927. *As Nos.* 36/37, *but wmk.* "N Z" *and Star, T* **41**. *P* 14.

42	½d. black and green	1	0	1	6
43	1d. black and deep carmine ..	1	6	2	0

1927. *As T* **16** *of Cook Islands, but inscr.* "AITUTAKI". *Wmk.* "N Z" *and Star, T* **41**. *P* 14.

44	2½d. black and dull blue ..	3	0	3	6

Cook Islands stamps superseded those of Aitutaki on 15 March, 1932.

NIUE.

NIUE
(1)

T **23, 27,** *and* **40** *of New Zealand, overprinted or surcharged.*

1902. *Handstamped with T* **1**, *in green or bluish green. Waterlow paper. Wmk. double-lined* "N Z" *and Star, T* **36*a***. *P* 11.

1	1d. carmine	£6	£6

A few overprints were made with a *greenish violet* ink.

NIUE.
½ PENI.
(2)

NIUE.
TAHA PENI.
3 (1d.)

NIUE.
2½ PENI.
(4)

1902. *Type-set surcharges, T* **2, 3,** *and* **4.** *½d. and 2½d. in red, 1d. in blue.*

(1) *Waterlow paper. No wmk. P* 11.

2 2½d. blue 1 6 2 0
3 2½d. blue "PENI" without stop 20 0 25 0

(2) *Basted Mills paper. Wmk. double-lined "N Z" and Star, T* **36a.** (*a*) *Perf.* 14.

4 ½d. green 0 9 1 0
5 ½d. deep green 1 0 1 6
6 ½d. grn., spaced "U" and "E" 1 6 2 0
7 ½d. green, surcharge inverted .. 60 0 70 0
8 1d. carmine 3 6 4 0
9 1d. carmine, spaced "U" and "E" 10 0 10 0
10 1d. carmine "PENI" without stop 45 0 52 6
11 1d. carmine, last two varieties on same stamp 50 0 60 0

(*b*) *P* 11 *and* 14 *compound.*

12 1d. carmine 0 8 0 10
13 1d. carmine spaced "U" and "E" 2 0 2 6
14 1d. carmine "PENI" without stop 6 0 8 6
15 1d. carmine, last two varieties on same stamp 25 0 35 0

(*c*) *Mixed perfs.*

15*a* ½d. green 70 0
16 1d. carmine £6

(3) *Cowan paper. Wmk. single-lined "N Z" and Star, T* **41.** (*a*) *P* 14.

17 ½d. green 0 6 0 8
18 ½d. grn., spaced "U" and "E" 1 3 1 9
19 1d. carmine 0 6 0 8
a. Surcharge double .. £14
20 1d. carmine, spaced "U" and "E" 7 0 8 0
21 1d. carmine, "PENI" without stop 7 0 8 0
22 1d. carmine, last two varieties on same stamp 16 0 18 6

(*b*) *Mixed perfs.*

22*a* ½d. green £8
23 1d. carmine 60 0
a. Spaced "U" and "E" ..

NIUE.
5

Tolu e Pene.
6 (3d.)

Ono e Pene.
7 (6d.)

Taha e Sileni.
8 (1s.)

1903–4. *T* **28, 31, 34** *overprinted with name at top, T* **5,** *and values at foot, T* **6, 7,** *and* **8,** *respectively, in blue. Wmk. single-lined "N Z" and Star, T* **41.** *P* 11.

24 3d. yellow-brown 4 0 5 0
25 6d. rose-red 6 0 7 0
26 1s. brown-red 70 0 90 0
27 1s. bright red 8 6 12 6
28 1s. orange-red 17 6 20 0

Error. "Tahae" *for* "Taha e."

29 1s. brown-red £14

NIUE.
½ PENI.
(9)

1911 (Nov.). *T* **50** *surcharged with T* **9.**

30 ½d. green (C.) 0 6 0 8

T **52** *overprinted with name at top as T* **5,** *and values at foot as T* **7** *and* **8,** *in blue. P* 14×14½.

31 6d. carmine 3 0 4 0
32 1s. vermilion 6 0 7 0

1915. *T* **27,** *but wmkd.* "N Z" *and Star, T* **41.** *Surch. as T* **4.** *P* 14.

33 2½d. deep blue (R.) 2 6 3 6
a. "NIUE" 1¼ mm. high .. 20 0

1917. *T* **51** *and* **60** *surch. as T* **3,** *in deep brown* (1d.) *or* "NIUE" *as T* **5** *and value as T* **6** *in blue* (3d.).

34 1d. carmine 5 0 6 0
a. No stop after "Peni" .. 50 0
35 3d. chocolate (*p.* 14×14½) .. 50 0 60 0
a. No stop after "Pene" ..
b. Perf. 14×13½ 62 6 70 0
c. Vert. pair, 35/5b £8

NIUE.
(10)

1917–20. *T* **51, 60** (*P* 14×14½, *etc.*) *and* **154,** *overprinted with T* **10.**

37 1d. carmine (B.) 0 6 0 8
38 2½d. blue (R.) 1 0 1 3
a. Perf. 14×13½ 1 3 1 6
b. Vert. pair, 38/8a 5 0 6 0
39 3d. chocolate (B.) 2 3 2 6
a. Perf. 14×13½ 2 3 3 0
b. Vert. pair, 39/9a 12 6 15 0
40 6d. carmine (B.) 1 9 2 3
a. Perf. 14×13½ 1 9 2 3
b. Vert. pair, 40/40a 8 6 10 6
41 1s. vermilion (B.) 4 0 4 6
a. Perf. 14×13½ 4 0 4 6
b. Vert. pair, 41/1a 12 6 15 0
42 2s. blue (R.) (*p.* 14½×14) .. 6 0 7 6
43 5s. green (R.) (*p.* 14, 14½) .. 15 0 17 6
a. Perf. 14½×14 .. .. 10 0 12 6

1917–20. *T* **60b,** *surface printed, optd. with T* **10.** *Wmk.* "N.Z" *and Star, T* **41.** *P* 14×15.

44 ½d. green (R.) 0 4 0 6
45 1½d. slate (R.) 1 0 1 6
46 1½d. orange-brown (R.) .. 0 8 0 10
47 3d. chocolate (B.) 1 6 2 0

(Designed, engraved and printed by Messrs. Perkins, Bacon & Co., Ltd.)

1920 (Aug.). *As T* **10** *to* **15** *of Cook Is., but inscr.* "NIUE." *No wmk. P* 14.

48 ½d. black and green .. 1 0 1 3
49 1d. black and dull carmine .. 1 6 2 0
a. Imperf. .. .. ..
50 1½d. black and red 2 0 2 6
51 3d. black and blue 2 0 2 6
52 6d. red-brown and green .. 2 6 3 0
a. Centre inverted £135
b. Imperf. .. .. ..
53 1s. black and sepia 5 0 6 0

1923. *T* **154** *of New Zealand, overprinted with T* **10** *in blue.*

54 2s. 6d. pale chocolate 5 0 7 6
55 10s. claret 22 6 25 0
56 £1 bright carmine-rose .. 42 6 50 0

(Recess. Govt. Printing Office, Wellington.)

1925–27. *Pictorial types as* 1920, *but wmk.* "N Z" *and Star, T* **41.**

57 ½d. black and green (1927) 1 0 1 3
58 1d. black and deep carmine .. 1 3 1 6

1927. *T* **72** *of New Zealand overprinted as T* **10.** "*Jones*" *paper.*

63 2s. deep blue (R.) 7 0 8 6

As last. "*Cowan*" *paper.*

64 2s. light blue (R.) 3 6 4 0

(Recess. Govt. Printing Office, Wellington.)

1927. *As T* **16** *and* **17** *of Cook Islands, but inscr.* "NIUE". *Wmk.* "N Z" *and Star, T* **41.** *P* 14

65 2½d. black and blue 2 0 2 6
66 4d. black and violet.. .. 2 6 3 0

1931. *No.* 50 *surch. as T* **18** *of Cook Is.*

67 2d. on 1½d. black and red .. 2 6 2 6

1931–32. *Types as* **73a** *of New Zealand (various frames), overprinted as T* **10.** *Wmk.* "N Z" *and Star, T* **41.** *P* 14.

68 2s. 6d. brown (B.) 5 0 6 6
69 5s. green (R.) 10 0 11 6
70 10s. carmine-lake (B.) 20 0 22 6
71 £1 pink (B.) 35 0 37 6

(Designed by L. C. Mitchell. Recess-printed by Messrs. Perkins, Bacon & Co., Ltd.)

1932 (16 MAR.). *As T* **19** *to* **25** *of Cook Is., but frames altered to include the name* "NIUE" *as well as* "COOK ISLANDS." *No wmk. P* 13.

72 ½d. black and emerald .. 1 0 1 0
a. Perf. 14×13 .. .. .. 35 0
73 1d. black and deep lake .. 1 0 1 3
74 2d. black and red-brown .. 0 10 1 0
75 2½d. black and slate-blue .. 2 0 2 6
76 4d. black and greenish blue .. 3 6 4 0
a. Perf. 14 .. .. .. 2 0 2 6
77 6d. black & orange-vermilion 2 0 2 6
78 1s. black and purple (*p.* 14) 5 0 6 0

(Recess-printed from Perkins, Bacon's plates at the Govt. Ptg. Office, Wellington, N.Z.)

1932–36. *Pictorial types as* 1932, *but wmk.* "N Z" *and Star, T* **41.** *P* 14.

79 ½d. black and emerald .. 0 2 0 3
80 1d. black and deep lake .. 0 3 0 4
81 2d. black & yell.-brn. (1.4.36) 0 4 0 6
82 2½d. black and slate-blue .. 0 5 0 8
83 4d. black and greenish blue .. 0 8 1 0
84 6d. black and red-orge. (1.4.36) 1 0 1 3
85 1s. black and purple (1.4.36) 2 6 3 0

1935 (7 MAY). *Silver Jubilee. Designs as Nos.* 80, 82 *and* 84 *(colours changed) optd. as T* **26** *of Cook Is. (wider vertical spacing on 6d.). Wmk.* "N Z" *and Star, T* **41.** *P* 14.

86 1d. red-brown and lake .. 0 10 2 0
a. Narrow "K" in "KING" .. 2 6
b. Narrow "B" in "JUBILEE" 2 6
87 2½d. dull and deep blue (R.) .. 3 6 10 0
a. Narrow first "E" in "GEORGE" 7 6
b. Imperf. between (vert. pair) .. £35
88 6d. green and orange .. 15 0 25 0
a. Narrow "N" in "KING" .. 25 0

For illustrations of varieties, see Cook Islands.

PENRHYN ISLAND.

PENRHYN ISLAND.
½ PENI.
(1)

PENRHYN ISLAND.
TAI PENI.
2 (1d.)

PENRHYN ISLAND.
2½ PENI.
(3)

1902. *T* **23, 40,** *and* **27** *of New Zealand surcharged with T* **1, 2,** *and* **3.** *½d. and 2½d. in red, 1d. in brown.*

(1) *Waterlow paper. No wmk. P* 11.

1 2½d. blue 1 6 2 0
2 2½d. blue "½" and "P" spaced 2 0 3 0

(2) *Basted Mills paper. Wmk. double-lined* "N Z" *and Star, T* **36a.** (a) *P* 11.

3 1d. carmine 65 0 80 0

(b) *P* 14.

4 ½d. green 0 8 0 10
a. No stop after "ISLAND" .. 35 0 45 0
5 1d. carmine 0 9 1 0
6 1d. pale carmine 0 8 1 0

(c) *P* 11×14.

8 1d. carmine 40 0 50 0

(d) *Mixed perfs.*

9 1d. carmine £6

(3) *Cowan paper. Wmk. single-lined* "N Z" *and Star, T* **41.** *½d. overprinted in red, 1d. in blue.* (a) *P* 14.

10 ½d. green 0 6 0 8
a. No stop after "ISLAND" .. 27 6 40 0
11 1d. carmine 0 6 0 8
a. No stop after "ISLAND" .. 15 0 20 0

(b) *Mixed perfs.*

12 ½d. green £6 £7
13 1d. carmine 35 0 45 0

PENRHYN ISLAND.
(4)

Toru Pene.
5 (3d.)

Ono Pene.
6 (6d.)

Tahi Silingi.
7 (1s.)

1903. *T* **28, 31, 34** *overprinted with name at top, T* **4,** *and values at foot, T* **5, 6** *and* **7,** *respectively, in blue. Wmk. single-lined* "N Z" *and Star, T* **41.** *P* 11.

14 3d. yellow-brown 2 0 2 6
15 6d. rose-red 5 0 6 0
16 1s. brown-red 10 0 12 6
17 1s. bright red 10 0 12 6
18 1s. orange-red 15 0 17 6

1914–15. *T* **50** *surcharged with T* **1** *in carmine (C.), or vermilion (V.), and T* **52** *optd. with T* **4** *at top, and surcharged with T* **6** *or* **7** *at foot, all in blue (B.).*

19 ½d. yellow-green (C.) (7.14) .. 0 9 1 0
a. No stop after "ISLAND" .. 25 0 27 6
b. No stop after "PENI" .. 30 0 35 0
20 ½d. yellow-green (V.) (3.15) .. 0 6 0 9
a. No stop after "ISLAND" .. 17 6 22 6
b. No stop after "PENI" .. 27 6 32 6
22 6d. carmine (B.) (Aug., '14) .. 3 6 4 0
23 1s. vermilion (B.) (Sept., '14) 5 0 6 0

1917–20. *Contemporary stamps of N.Z., T* **60** *(P* 14×14½, *etc.), optd. with name only, T* **4,** *in blue or red (R.).*

24 2½d. blue (R.) (Oct., '20) .. 1 0 1 3
a. No stop after "ISLAND" .. 22 6 32 6
b. Perf. 14×13½ 1 6 1 9
c. Vert. pair, 24/4b 6 0 7 6
25 3d. chocolate (June, '18) .. 2 6 3 0
a. Perf. 14×13½ 2 6 3 6
b. Vert. pair, 25/5a 12 6 15 0
26 6d. carmine (Jan., '18) .. 2 0 2 6
a. No stop after "ISLAND" .. 30 0 40 0
b. Perf. 14×13½ 2 0 2 6
c. Vert. pair, 26/6b 10 0 12 6
27 1s. vermilion (Dec., '17) .. 3 0 3 6
a. No stop after "ISLAND" .. 35 0 45 0
b. Perf. 14×13½ 4 0 5 0
c. Vert. pair, 27/7b 12 6 15 0

1917–20. *T* **60b,** *surface-printed, optd. as T* **4,** *in red (R.) or in blue (B.). Wmk.* "N Z" *and Star, T* **41.** *P* 14×15.

28 ½d. green (R.) (Feb., '20) .. 0 4 0 6
a. No stop after "ISLAND" .. 20 0 30 0
29 1½d. slate (R.) (Nov., '17) .. 1 9 2 3
30 1½d. orange-brown (R.) (2.19) 0 7 0 9
31 3d. chocolate (B.) (July, '19) 1 3 1 6

(Designed, engraved and printed by Perkins, Bacon & Co., Ltd.)

1920 (AUG.). *Pictorial types as Aitutaki. No wmk. P* 14.

32 ½d. black and emerald .. 0 10 1 0
a. Centre inverted £100
b. Imperf. .. .. ..

33 1d. black and deep red .. 1 6 2 0
 a. Centre inverted £125
34 1½d. black and deep violet .. 1 6 2 0
 a. Imperf. .. .. ..
35 3d. black and red .. 2 0 2 6
36 6d. red-brown and sepia .. 2 6 3 0
37 1s. black and slate-blue .. 5 0 6 0
 a. Imperf. .. .. ..

(Recess. Govt. Printing Office, Wellington.)

1927–29. *As* **T 10, 11** *and* **16** *of Cook Islands, but inscribed* "PENRHYN". *Wmk.* "N Z" *and Star,* **T 41.** *P* 14.

38 ½d. black and green .. 1 0 1 6
39 1d. black and deep carmine .. 2 0 2 6
40 2½d. red-brown and dull blue .. 2 6 3 0

Cook Islands stamps superseded those of Penrhyn Island on 15 March, 1932.

(For stamps of New Zealand overprinted "**RAROTONGA**" see Cook Islands, and for stamps overprinted "**SAMOA**" see list under that heading.)

NIGER COAST PROTECTORATE.

This district was known as the "OIL RIVERS PROTECTORATE" from 5 June, 1885, till 12 May, 1893, when the name was altered to the "NIGER COAST PROTECTORATE."

BRITISH
PROTECTORATE

OIL RIVERS

(1)

1892 (July). *Stamps of Great Britain* (1881 *and* 1887 *issues*) *overprinted in London, by Messrs. De La Rue & Co., with* **T 1**, *in black.*

1 ½d. vermilion 4 0 5 0
2 1d. lilac 4 0 5 0
 a. Bisected (½d.)
3 2d. green and carmine .. 5 0 6 0
 a. Bisected (1d.)
4 2½d. purple/*blue* 4 0 4 6
5 5d. dull purple and blue .. 5 0 5 6
6 1s. green 17 6 16 0

Variety. Overprint reversed "OIL RIVERS" *at top.*

6a 1d. lilac £55

Control letters. ½d. E, K, L, M.
 1d. L, N, O, P, Q.

The above stamps variously surcharged.

(2)

1893 (3 Sept.). *As* **T 2.**

7 ½d. in *red*, on half of 1d. .. 45 0 45 0
 a. Surcharge inverted
 b. Surcharge reversed (left to right)
 c. Straight top to "1" in "½" .. £7
8 ½d. in *violet* on half of 1d. .. £90

Nos. 7 and 8 exist *se-tenant.*

HALF PENNY.

(3)

HALF PENN.Y

(4)

1893 (Dec.). *With* **T 3.**

9 ½d. in *violet*, on 2d. £8 £8
 a. Surcharge inverted
 b. Surcharge diagonal
 c. Surcharge sideways
 d. Surcharge vertical
10 ½d. in *green*, on 2½d. £8 £8
11 ½d. in *vermilion*, on 2½d.
12 ½d. in *carmine*, on 2½d. .. £8 £8
 a. Surcharge omitted (in pair)
13 ½d. in *blue*, on 2½d. £9 £9
14 ½d. in *black*, on 2½d. .. £75
 a. Surcharge inverted ..
 b. Surcharge diagonal, inverted
15 ½d. in *bluish black*, on 2½d. .. £70
15a ½d. in *violet*, on 2½d.

With **T 4.**

15b ½d. in *violet*, on 2d. £18 £12
15c ½d. in *vermilion*, on 2½d. .. 85 0 75 0
 d. Surcharge inverted
 e. Surcharge double .. .. — £40
 f. Surcharge diagonal .. £40
 g. Surcharge omitted (in pair)
 h. Surcharge sideways
 i. Surcharge vertical ..

In **T 4** the "P" and "Y" are raised. There is no stop after "PENNY", and the space between the words is ½ mm. greater than in **T 3.** The stop before the "Y" only shows in clearly printed copies.

Half Penny

(5)

HALF PENNY.

(6)

With **T 5.**

16 ½d. in *violet*, on 2d. £7 £7
 a. Surcharge double
 b. Surcharge sideways
 c. Bar omitted
17 ½d. in *vermilion*, on 2½d. .. 85 0 85 0
 a. Surcharge double
 b. Surcharge sideways
 c. Surcharge inverted
 d. Surcharge diagonal
18 ½d. in *blue* on 2½d. £140 £100
19 ½d. in *green*, on 2½d. £5 £5
 a. Bar omitted £15
20 ½d. in *carmine*, on 2½d.
21 ½d. in *violet*, on 2½d. ..

With **T 6.**

22 ½d. in *violet*, on 2d. £6 £6
23 ½d. in *blue*, on 2d. £20 £18
 a. Surcharge double
24 ½d. in *vermilion*, on 2½d. .. £17 £17
25 ½d. in *blue*, on 2½d. £8 £8
26 ½d. in *green*, on 2½d. £8 £8
 a. Surcharge double
27 ½d. in *violet*, on 2½d. .. £65

HALF PENNY

(7)

One Shilling

(8)

With **T 7.**

28 ½d. in *green*, on 2½d. £7 £7
29 ½d. in *vermilion*, on 2½d. .. £90

With T 8.

No.	Description		Unused	Used
30	1s. in *violet*, on 2d. ..	..	£12	£12
	a. Surcharge inverted ..	..	£70	
	b. Surcharge sideways ..	..	£70	
31	1s. in *vermilion*, on 2d.	..	£14	£14
	a. Surcharge inverted ..	..		
	b. Surcharge diagonal ..	..		
32	1s. in *black*, on 2d. (I)	..	£150	
	a. Surcharge inverted ..	..		
	b. Surcharge sideways ..	..		
32*c*	1s. in *black*, on 2d. (II)	..	£150	

In Type I of the 1s. surcharge the letters "l" of "Shilling" are in line with the downstrokes of the "n" of "One". In Type II the second "l" is below the space between the downstrokes of the "n".

Various types of the surcharges on Nos. 9 to 32 were printed on the same sheet, and different types in different colours may be found *se tenant*. These are of great rarity.

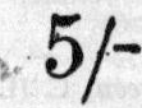

(9)

As T 9.

No.	Description		Unused	Used
33	5s. in *violet*, on 2d.	..	£100	
	a. Surcharge inverted ..	..		
	b. Surcharge sideways ..	..		
	c. Surcharge diagonal ..	..		
34	10s. in *vermilion*, on 5d.	..	£80	
	a. Surcharge inverted ..	..		
	b. Surcharge sideways ..	..		
35	20s. in *violet*, on 1s.	..	£550	
	a. Surcharge inverted ..	..		
36	20s. in *vermilion*, on 1s.	..	£1,000	
37	20s. in *black*, on 1s. ..	..		

10

(Designed by G. D. Drummond. Recess. Waterlow & Sons, Ltd.)

1893 (Nov. (?)) *T* 10 *and similar types. No wmk. P* 14, 15, *and* 12 *to* 15 *in various combinations.*

No.	Description		Unused	Used
38	½d. vermilion ..	..	5 0	5 0
39	1d. pale blue ..	..	8 6	8 6
40	1d. dull blue ..	..	6 0	7 6
	a. Bisected, and half used for ½d..	..	—	45 0
41	2d. green ..	..	22 6	25 0
	a. Imperf. between (pair)	..		
42	2½d. carmine-lake ..	..	3 6	4 0
43	5d. grey-lilac ..	..	7 0	7 6
44	5d. lilac ..	..	12 0	15 0
45	1s. black ..	..	25 0	27 6

All values exist perf. 14 and perf. 15. There were three printings of each value, in June, 1893, late in 1893, and early in 1894.

½ (16) 1 (17)

1894. *Provisionals. Issued at Opobo.*

May–Aug. *Nos.* 39 *and* 40 *bisected vertically and surcharged with T* 16, *in red.*

No.	Description		Unused	Used
46	"½" on half of 1d. dull blue (May) ..	..	£33	£10
47	"½" on half of 1d., pale blue (Aug.) ..	..	£35	£8
	a. Surcharge tête-bêche (pair) ..			

(June–Oct.). *No.* 3 *bisected vertically and surcharged with T* 17 (12 *mm. high*), *in vermilion.*

No.	Description		Unused	Used
48	"1" on half of 2d. green and carmine ..	..	£18	£9
	a. Surcharge double ..	..	—	£40

Variety. Smaller "1" (4¾ *mm. high*).

No.	Description		Unused	Used
49	"1" on half of 2d. green and carmine ..	..		

18

(Recess. Waterlow & Sons, Ltd.)

1894 (May). *T* 18 *and similar types. No wmk. P* 14, 15, *and* 12 *to* 15 *in various combinations.*

No.	Description		Unused	Used
50	½d. yellow-green ..	..	1 3	1 3
50*a*	½d. dark green..	..	1 9	1 9
51	1d. orange-vermilion ..	..	4 0	4 0
52	1d. vermilion ..	..	2 6	3 0
	a. Bisected diagonally (½d.)	..	—	22 6
53	2d. lake ..	..	3 0	3 0
54	2½d. blue ..	..	7 6	6 0
55	2½d. pale blue ..	..	6 0	6 0
56	5d. purple ..	..	4 0	5 0
57	5d. deep violet ..	..	4 0	5 0
58	1s. black ..	..	6 0	7 0

All values exist perf. 15, and all, except the 5d., perf. 14.

1894 (Aug.-Oct.). *Provisionals.*

A. *Issued at Opobo* (Aug.-Oct.).

No. 52, *bisected, surch. with T* 16, *in black* (Bk.) *violet* (V.), *or blue* (Bl.).

No.	Description	Unused	Used
59	½ on half of 1d. vermilion (Bk.)	£45	£15
60	½ on half of 1d. vermilion (V.)	£45	£15
61	½ on half of 1d. vermilion (Bl.)	£40	£12

The stamp is found divided down the middle and also diagonally.

ONE

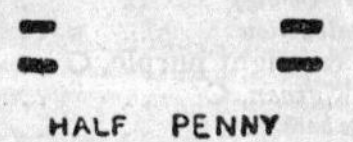

HALF PENNY

(24)

B. *Issued at Old Calabar* (10 Aug.).

No. 54 *surcharged with T* 24, *and two bars through value at foot, in black.*

No.	Description		Unused	Used
62	½d. on 2½d. blue ..	..	£10	£6
	a. Surcharge double ..	..	—	£45
	b. "OIE" for "ONE"	..	—	£32

(Recess. Waterlow & Sons, Ltd.)

1897 (Mar.)-**1898.** *Types as before and similar types for* 6*d.*, 2*s.* 6*d. and* 10*s. Wmk. Crown CA. P* 14, 15 *and* 12 *to* 15 *in various combinations.*

No.	Description		Unused	Used
64	½d. green ..	..	1 0	1 0
65	1d. orange-vermilion ..	..	1 9	2 0

66	2d. lake	3 0	3 6
67	2½d. slate-blue	2 6	3 6
67*a*	5d. red-violet	10 6	10 6
68	5d. purple	6 6	7 0
69	6d. yellow-brown (June, 189	7 0	7 0
70	1s. black	8 0	8 0
71	2s. 6d. olive-bistre	20 0	22 6
72	10s. deep violet (June, 1898)..	55 0	57 6
73	10s. bright violet (June, 1898)	40 0	45 0

All values exist perf. 14 and all except the 5d. and 1s. (possibly), perf. 15, the latter perf. being the scarcer except in the 6d.

Owing to a temporary shortage in Southern Nigeria, the above issue was again put into use during 1902, all stamps being perf. 14, probably from the last printing made.

On 28th December, 1899, the territory occupied by the Royal Niger Company was taken over by the Imperial Government, and with Lagos and the Niger Coast Protectorate was divided into two Administrations, Northern and Southern Nigeria, later merged in Nigeria.

NIGERIA.

(Comprising the Combined Territories of Northern and Southern Nigeria and Lagos.)

1

2

(Typo. De La Rue & Co.)

1914–26. *T* **1** *and* **2** (*3d., 4d., 6d., 5s., and £1*). *Wmk. Mult. Crown CA. P* 14.

1	½d. green, O	0 5	0 2
2	1d. carmine-red, O	0 6	0 2
3	1d. scarlet, O (1917)	1 3	0 2
4	2d. grey, O	1 6	0 6
5	2d. slate-grey, O	1 9	0 6
6	2½d. bright blue, O	1 9	1 9
7	3d. purple/*yellow*, C	4 6	1 0
	a. White back	1 9	1 0
	b. On lemon	8 0	3 0
	c. On orange-buff	3 6	1 3
	d. On pale yellow	3 6	1 0
8	4d. black and red/*yellow*, C ..	6 6	3 0
	a. White back	2 6	2 6
	b. On lemon	6 0	4 0
	c. On orange-buff	4 0	1 3
	d. On pale yellow	8 0	4 0
9	6d. dull & bright purple, C ..	3 0	1 6
10	1s. black/*green*, C	6 0	1 6
	a. White back	4 0	3 0
	b. On blue-green, olive back ..	13 6	2 0
	c. On emerald surface	11 0	2 6
	d. On emerald back	5 0	1 3
11	2s. 6d. black & red/*blue*, C ..	11 0	3 6
12	5s. green and red/*yellow*, C ..	20 0	8 6
	a. White back	16 6	17 6
	b. On lemon	32 6	13 6
	c. On orange-buff	20 0	
	d. On pale yellow	27 6	
13	10s. green and red/*green*, C ..	40 0	16 6
	a. White back	52 6	32 6
	b. On blue-green, olive back ..	£13	55 0
	c. On emerald surface	75 0	20 0
	d. On emerald back	32 6	16 0
14	£1 purple and black/*red*, C ..	65 0	70 0
	a. Die II ('26)	70 0	

1921–32. *T* **1** *and* **2.** *Wmk. Mult. Script CA. P* 14.

15	½d. green, O (Die I) (1921) ..	0 5	0 4
	a. Die II (May '25)	0 4	0 2
16	1d. rose-car., O (Die I) ('21) ..	0 8	0 2
	a. Die II (May '25)	0 4	0 1
17	2d. grey, O (Die I) (May '21)	4 0	1 6
	a. Die II ('24)	3 0	0 8
18	2½d. brt. blue, O (Die I) (May '21)	2 3	1 9
19	4d. black and red/*pale yellow*, C (Die II) (Oct. '23) ..	2 0	1 3
	a. Die I (Aug. '32)	3 0	1 6
20	6d. dull & bright purple, C (Die I) (May '21)	6 0	1 9
	a. Die II (July '24)	2 0	1 3
21	1s. black/*emerald*, C (Die II) (July '24)	5 0	1 9
22	2s. 6d. black and red/*blue*, C (Die II) (June '25) ..	10 0	10 0
	a. Die I (Aug. '32)	25 0	22 6
23	5s. green and red/*yellow*, C (Die II) (Oct. '26) ..	17 6	17 6
	a. Die I (Aug. '32)	30 0	30 0
24	10s. green & red/*green*, C (Die II) (Aug. '27)	35 0	37 6
	a. Die I (Aug. '32)	60 0	65 0

1924–32. *T* **1** *and* **2**, *new value* (1½d. *T* **2**) *and colours changed. Wmk. Mult. Script CA. P* 14.

25	1½d. orange, O (Die II) (Apr. '31)	1 3	0 4
26	2d. chestnut, O (1.10.27) ..	3 0	1 3
27	2d. chocolate, O (Die I) (Mar. '32)	1 9	0 6
	a. Die II (1.7.28)	1 0	0 5
28	3d. brt. vio., O (Die I) (Jan. '24)	3 6	1 6
	a. Die II (May '25)	1 9	0 10
29	3d. bright blue, O (Apr. '31)	2 6	1 0

1935 (6 May). *Silver Jubilee. As T* **13** *of Antigua, inscr.* "NIGERIA". *Recess. W'low. & Sons. Wmk. Mult. Script CA. P* 11 × 12

30	1½d. ultramarine and grey ..	0 6	0 5
31	2d. green and indigo ..	1 9	2 0
32	3d. brown and deep blue ..	3 6	4 0
33	1s. slate and purple	10 6	12 0

3. Apapa Wharf.

4. Cocoa.

5. Tin Dredger. **6.** Timber Industry.

7. Fishing Village. **8.** Cotton Ginnery.

9. Habe Minaret. **10.** Fulani Cattle.

11. Victoria-Buea Road.

12. Oil Palms. **13.** Niger at Jebba.
14. Canoe Pulling.

(Recess. De La Rue & Co. Ltd.)

1936 (1 Feb.). *T* **3** *to* **14** (*various vert.* (*T* **3** *to* **10**) *or horiz.* (*others*) *designs*). *Wmk. Mult. Script CA.* (*a*) *P* 11½ × 13.

No.	Type	Description	Unused		Used	
34	**3**	½d. green	0	2	0	2
35	**4**	1d. carmine	0	6	0	2
36	**5**	1½d. brown	0	8	0	4
		a. Perf. 12½×13½	40	0	2	6
37	**6**	2d. black	1	6	0	6
38	**7**	3d. blue	2	6	1	6
		a. Perf. 12½×13½	£6		40	0
39	**8**	4d. red-brown	2	0	2	6
40	**9**	6d. dull violet	2	0	2	0
41	**10**	1s. sage-green	6	0	5	0

(*b*) *P* 14.

No.	Type	Description	Unused		Used	
42	**11**	2s. 6d. black & ultramarine	12	6	12	6
43	**12**	5s. black and olive-green ..	22	6	17	6
44	**13**	10s. black and grey ..	45	0	62	6
45	**14**	£1 black and orange ..	£6		£7	

NORTH BORNEO.

PRINTERS. The stamps of this country up to 1894 were designed by Mr. Thos. Macdonald and lithographed by Messrs. Blades, East and Blades, London.

1

8 Cents
(2)

EIGHT CENTS
(3)

1883. *T* **1**. *P* 12.

No.	Type	Description	Unused		Used	
1		2 c. red-brown..	10	0	12	6

The figure "2" varies in size.

1883. *No.* 1 *surcharged in black.*

No.	Type	Description	Unused		Used	
2	**2**	c. on 2 c. red-brown ..	£22		£16	
3	**3**	8 c. on 2 c. red-brown ..	£8		80	0

Variety. Surcharge double.

No.	Type	Description	Unused		Used	
3a	**3**	8 c. on 2 c. red-brown ..				

There is grave doubt as to the authenticity of No. 2.

> **NOTE.**—Prices are now indicated (in a third price column, in brackets, or by notes below certain issues) for remainders of the stamps of North Borneo cancelled with black bars, where these exist.
>
> It should be noted, however, that a postmark of this form was in general use for postal purposes for many years, and is, we believe, still used at one or two of the smaller post-offices.

4

5

1883. *T* **4** *and* **5**. *P* 14.

No.	Description	Unused			Used	
4	50 c. violet	52	6	—	22	6
	a. Error. "FIFTY" ..	£12		—	£6	
5	$1 scarlet	32	6	—	17	6

1884. *T* **1**. *P* 12.

No.	Description	Unused		Used	
6	4 c. pink	10	6	16	0
7	8 c. pale green	15	0	15	0

1886. *T* **1**. *P* 14.

No.	Description	Unused		Used	
8	½ c. magenta	22	6		
9	1 c. orange	£12			
	a. Imperf.	22	0		
10	2 c. brown	8	0	8	0
	a. Imperf. between (pair) ..	£8			
11	4 c. pink	15	0	15	0
12	8 c. green	15	0	15	0
13	10 c. blue	15	0	17	6
	a. Imperf.	70	0		

and Revenue
(6)

3 CENTS
(7)

3 CENTS
(8)

1886. *Nos.* 8 *and* 13 *overprinted with T* **6**.

No.	Description	Unused		Used	
14	½ c. magenta	40	0	40	0
15	10 c. blue	75	0	75	0

1886. *T* **1** *surcharged in black.* (*a*) *P* 12.

No.	Type	Description	Unused		Used	
16	**7**	3 c. on 4 c. pink	75	0	75	0
17	**8**	3 c. on 4 c. pink				
18	**7**	5 c. on 8 c. green	£5		£5	

(*b*) *P* 14.

No.	Type	Description	Unused		Used	
19	**7**	3 c. on 4 c. pink	30	0	35	0
20	**8**	3 c. on 4 c. pink	£10			
21	**7**	5 c. on 8 c. green	35	0	40	0

Variety. Surcharge inverted.

No.	Type	Description	Unused		Used	
21a	**7**	5 c. on 8 c. green	£30			

9

10

11

12

13

1886-87. *T 9 (½ c. to 10 c.) to 13.*

(a) P 14.

No.	Description		
21*b*	½ c. magenta	12 0	
22	½ c. rose	6 6	7 0
	a. Imperf.	12 0	
23	1 c. orange-yellow	5 0	5 0
	a. Imperf. between (pair)		
	b. Imperf.	12 0	
24	1 c. orange	2 6	2 6
	a. Imperf.	6 6	
25	2 c. brown	3 0	3 6
	a. Imperf.	4 6	
26	4 c. pink	2 0	2 6
	a. Imperf.	4 6	
	b. Imperf. between (pair)		
27	8 c. green	4 0	4 0
	a. Imperf.	8 0	
28	10 c. blue	6 0	7 0
	a. Imperf. between (pair)		
	b. Imperf.	14 0	
29	25 c. indigo (c. 25s.)	55 0	
	a. Imperf. between (pair)		
	b. Imperf. (c. 25s.)	35 0	
30	50 c. violet (c. 25s.)	35 0	
	a. Imperf. (c. 15s.)	22 6	
31	$1 scarlet (c. 30s.)	67 6	
	a. Imperf. (c. 20s.)	30 0	
32	$2 sage-green (c. 35s.)	55 0	
	a. Imperf. (c. 30s.)	45 0	

Error on sheet of 4 c.

No.	Description		
33	1 c. pink (strip of 3 with error in centre)	60 0	80 0
	a. Imperf. between (pair)		
	b. Imperf.	£100	

(b) P 12.

No.	Description		
34	½ c. magenta	£8	
35	1 c. orange	55 0	55 0

14

15

1889. *T 14 and 15.* *P 14.*

No.	Description			
36	$5 bright purple	32 6	32 6	7 6
	a. Imperf.	32 6	—	20 0
37	$10 brown	52 6	52 6	25 0
	a. Imperf.	—	—	25 0

Variety. "DOLLAPS" *for* "DOLLARS."

No.	Description			
37*b*	$10 brown	£25	—	£12
	c. Imperf.	£25	—	£15

16

1889-92. *T 16.* *P 14.*

No.	Description			
38	½ c. magenta	6 0	6 0	—
38*a*	½ c. rose	1 0	2 0	0 4
39	1 c. orange	1 0	1 6	0 6
40	2 c. brown	6 0	6 0	0 9
41	2 c. lake-brown	1 6	1 3	0 6
42	3 c. violet	3 6	3 6	0 8
43	4 c. rose-pink	3 0	3 0	0 6
	a. Imperf. between (pair)			
44	5 c. slate	3 0	3 6	0 8
	a. Imperf. between (pair)			
44*b*	6 c. lake (1892)	4 6	5 0	1 0
45	8 c. blue-green	4 6	4 0	0 9
45*a*	8 c. yellow-green	9 0	9 0	1 9
46	10 c. blue	5 0	5 0	1 0
46*a*	10 c. dull blue	4 6	4 6	1 0

This set also exists imperf. *Price 3s. per stamp unused; 2s. 6d. cancelled.*

17

18

19

20

1888. *T 17 to 20 (10 to 13 redrawn).* *P 14.*

No.	Description			
47	25 c. indigo	5 0	—	1 3
	a. Imperf.	40 0	—	3 0
48	50 c. violet	9 0	—	1 3
	a. Imperf.	50 0	—	3 0
49	$1 scarlet	9 0	—	1 6
	a. Imperf.	50 0	—	4 6

50 $2 dull green .. 22 6 — 3 0
a. Imperf. .. .. 60 0 — 6 0

The new 25 c. has the inscription "BRITISH NORTH BORNEO" in taller capitals. In the 50 c. the "o" of the numerals "50" in the two upper corners is square-shaped at the top and bottom instead of being oval. The 1 dollar has 14 pearls instead of 13 at each side, and on the 2 dollars the word "BRITISH" measures 10½ to 11 mm. in length in place of 12 mm.

Two Cents.
(21)

1890 *No. 47 surcharged, in red, as T 21.*

51 2 c. on 25 c. indigo 30 0 30 0
52 8 c. on 25 c. indigo 45 0 47 6

Variety. Surcharge inverted.

53 2 c. on 25 c. indigo £12 £8

6 cents. (22) **1 cent.** (23)

1891–92. *Various stamps surcharged with T 22 in black.*

54 6 c. on 8 c. (No. 27) £100
55 6 c. on 8 c. (No. 45a) .. 7 6 8 0
56 6 c. on 10 c. (No. 28) .. 12 0 12 0
57 6 c. on 10 c. (No. 46) .. 22 6 22 6

Varieties. (i.) *Letters misplaced.*

58 6 cents on 8 c. (No. 45) .. 85 0
59 6 cetns on 8 c. (No. 45) .. £5 £5

(ii.) *Large "s" in "cents."*

59a 6 c. on 8 c. (No. 27) ..
59b 6 c. on 8 c. (No. 45) .. 37 6
59c 6 c. on 10 c. (No. 28) .. 50 0 50 0
59d 6 c. on 10 c. (No. 46) .. 72 6 72 6

(iii.) *Surcharge inverted.*

60 6 c. on 8 c. (No. 45) .. £12
61 6 c. on 10 c. (No. 28) .. 70 0

(iv.) *Surcharge treble.*

62 6 c. on 10 c. (No. 28) ..

1892–93. *Nos. 43, 44, and 47 surcharged as T 23, in red.* (*On No. 65 "Cents" with capital "C," as in T 21.*)

63 1 c. on 4 c. pink 10 0 10 6
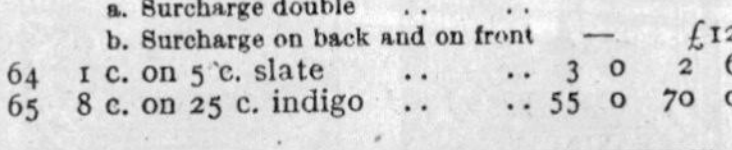
a. Surcharge double .. ..
b. Surcharge on back and on front — £12
64 1 c. on 5 c. slate 3 0 2 6
65 8 c. on 25 c. indigo 55 0 70 0

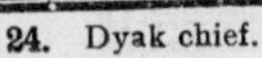
24. Dyak chief.

25. "Roussa" or Malay stag.

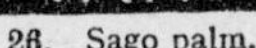
26. Sago palm.

27. Argus pheasant.

28. Arms of the Company.

29. Malay dhow.

30. Crocodile.

31. View of Mount Kinabalu.

32. Arms of the Company with supporters.

(Recess. Waterlow & Sons.)

1894. *T 24 to 32. P 15.*

66 1 c. black and olive-bistre .. 1 3 1 3
a. Imperf. between (pair) ..
b. Perf. 14 .. .. .. 1 9 2 0
c. Perf. 14×13½ .. ..
d. Perf. 14, comp. 12–13 .. 4 6 4 6
67 1 c. black and bistre-brown .. 1 6 1 6
a. Perf. 14 .. .. .. 1 0
b. Perf. 14, comp. 12–13 .. — 4 0

No.	Description	Unused	Used
68	2 c. black and rose-lake	3 0	3 0
	a. Imperf. between (pair)	65 0	
	b. Perf. 14		
69	2 c. black and lake	1 6	1 9
	a. Perf. 14	2 6	3 0
	b. Perf. 14, comp. 12–13	3 6	
	c. Imperf. between (pair)		
70	3 c. olive-green and mauve	1 3	1 9
	a. Imperf. between (pair)		
71	3 c. olive-grn. & violet (*p.* 14)	3 0	3 0
72	5 c. black and vermilion	1 6	2 6
	a. Imperf. between (pair)	65 0	
	b. Perf. 14	—	2 6
	c. Perf. 14, comp. 12–13	—	4 6
73	6 c. black and bistre-brown	3 0	3 0
	a. Perf. 14	1 0	1 9
	b. Perf. 14, comp. 12–13	—	4 0
	c. Perf. 14×15		
	d. Imperf. between (pair)		
74	8 c. black and dull purple	1 0	2 6
	a. Imperf. between (vert. pr.) (perf. 15)		
	b. Perf. 14	1 0	2 0
	c. Imperf. between (vert. pr.) (perf. 14)	87 6	67 6
	d. Perf. 14, comp. 12–13		
75	12 c. black and blue	8 0	8 0
	a. Perf. 14	8 0	
76	12 c. black and ultramarine	8 0	8 0
	a. Perf. 14	2 6	
	b. Imperf. between (pair)		
78	18 c. black and deep green	5 0	6 6
	a. Perf. 14	6 6	6 6
79	24 c. blue and rose-lake	6 0	7 0
	a. Imperf. between (pair) (*canc.* 60s.)		
	b. Perf. 14	5 0	6 0

NOTE.—The prices in the used column are for postally used stamps with circular postmark. Stamps cancelled with bars can be supplied at about one-third of these prices.

32*a*

32*b*

32*c*

32*d*

(Printed by Messrs. Blades, East & Blades.)

T 32*a to* 32*d, and T* 14 *and* 15, *but inscribed* "THE STATE OF NORTH BORNEO." *P* 14.

No.	Description			
81	25 c. indigo	8 0	9 0	1 3
	a. Imperf.	—	—	2 6
82	50 c. violet	12 6	12 6	1 6
	a. Imperf.	—	—	3 0

No.	Description			
83	$1 scarlet	12 6	12 6	2 6
	a. Perf. 14×11	£8		
	b. Imperf.	20 0	—	10 0
	c. Printed both sides	20 0	—	—
84	$2 dull green	30 0	30 0	2 6
	a. Imperf.	—	—	5 0
85	$5 bright purple	40 0	40 0	7 6
	a. Imperf.	—	—	15 0
86	$10 brown	65 0	60 0	10 0
	a. Imperf.	—	—	20 0

4

CENTS

33. (3½ mm. between lines of surcharge.)

1895 (June). *No.* 83 *surcharged as T* **33.**

No.	Description			
87	4 cents on $1 scarlet	2 6	3 0	1 6
	a. Surcharge double			
88	10 cents on $1 scarlet	2 6	2 6	1 3
89	20 cents on $1 scarlet	4 0	4 0	1 6
90	30 cents on $1 scarlet	4 0	4 0	1 6
91	40 cents on $1 scarlet	6 0	6 0	2 6

For 4 c. on $1 with wider spacing see No. 121.

34

35

36

37. Orang-Utan.

38

39

40

41. Bruang or honey-bear.

42

43. Borneo railway train.

44

45

(Recess. Waterlow & Sons.)

1897-1902. *T* **34** *to* **45.** *New frames.* *P* 14.

No.	Description	Unused	Used
92	1 c. black and bistre-brown ..	2 6	2 6
	a. Perf. 15	1 0	1 3
	b. Perf. 14, comp. 12–13 ..	8 0	
	c. Perf. 13½	5 0	5 0
	d. Perf. 13½×14		
	e. Imperf. between (pair) ..		
93	1 c. black and ochre ..	4 0	4 6
	a. Perf. 15	1 6	1 9
94	2 c. black and lake	2 6	2 6
	a. Perf. 15	2 6	2 6
	b. Perf. 13½	—	3 6
	c. Perf. 14, comp. 12–13 ..	—	3 6
95	2 c. black and green ..	2 0	2 0
	a. Perf. 15	—	2 6
	b. Perf. 14, comp. 12–13 ..	—	4 0
	c. Imperf. between (pair) ..		
96	3 c. green and rosy mauve ..	3 6	3 6
	a. Perf. 15	8 0	8 0
	b. Perf. 14, comp. 12–13 ..	14 0	14 0
	c. Perf. 13½	—	7 0
97	3 c. grn. & dull mauve (*p.* 15)	2 6	3 0
98	4 c. black and green (1900) ..	1 6	1 9
99	4 c. black & carmine (1900) ..	1 9	2 0
	a. Perf. 16	—	8 0
	b. Perf. 15	3 0	3 0
	c. Perf. 14, comp. 12–13 ..	4 0	4 6
100	5 c. blk. & orange-vermilion	2 6	3 0
	a. Perf. 15	3 0	3 0
	b. Perf. 14, comp. 12–13 ..	5 0	5 6
101	6 c. black & bistre-brown ..	2 6	3 0
	a. Perf. 15	2 6	3 0
	b. Perf. 13½		
102	8 c. black & brown-purple ..	4 0	
	a. Perf. 16	—	5 0
	b. Perf. 15	3 6	4 0
	c. Imperf. between (pair) ..		
103	8 c. black and brown ..	3 6	
	a. Perf. 15	4 6	
104	10 c. deep brown & slate-lilac (1902)	4 6	5 0
	a. Imperf. between (vert. pair) ..		
105	10 c. brn. & grey-lilac (1902) ..	6 0	6 6
106	12 c. black and dull blue ..	8 0	6 6
	a. Imperf. between (pair) ..		
	b. Perf. 15	8 0	6 0
	c. Perf. 14, comp. 12–13 ..	—	25 0
107	16 c. green & chestnut (1902)	4 6	6 0
	a. Perf. 15		
108	18 c. black & green (*perf.* 16) ..	5 0	5 6
	a. Imperf. between (vert. pair) ..	—	80 0
109	24 c. blue and lake	6 0	6 6
	a. Perf. 14, comp. 12–13 ..	—	10 0
	b. Perf. 13½	8 0	

In the above the 18 c. has "POSTAL REVENUE" instead of "POSTAGE AND REVENUE," and the 24 c. has these words omitted. These stamps were replaced by others with corrected inscriptions.

NOTE.—Stamps cancelled to order can be supplied at about one-third the prices quoted above for postally used specimens, except in the case of some of the scarcer perforation varieties.

46

47

T **46** *and* **47.** *Corrected inscriptions.* *P* 14.

No.	Description	Unused	Used
110	18 c. black and green ..	4 0	5 0
	a. Perf. 15	10 6	8 0
	b. Perf. 14, comp. 13½ ..		

111 24 c. blue and lake 6 0 6 6
a. Perf. 16 .. .. .. 8 0 5 6
b. Perf. 15 .. .. .. 5 6
c. Perf. 14, comp. 13½ ..

NOTE.—Price note after No. 109 applies here.

4 CENTS

BRITISH PROTECTORATE.

48. (4½ mm. between lines of surcharge.) (49)

1899. *Contemporary stamps surcharged with T 48, in black. P 14.*

112 4 c. on 5 c. (No. 100) .. 3 6 3 6
a. Perf. 14, comp. 12–13 .. — 4 6
113 4 c. on 6 c. (No. 101) .. 4 6 4 6
a. Perf. 15 .. .. 5 0
114 4 c. on 8 c. (No. 102b) (p. 15) 4 6 4 6
115 4 c. on 12 c. (No. 106b) (p. 15) 4 6 4 6
a. Imperf. between (pair) ..
116 4 c. on 18 c. (No. 110a) (p. 15) 4 6 4 6
117 4 c. on 24 c. (No. 111b) (p. 15) 4 6 4 6
a. Perf. 16 .. .. .. 14 0
b. Perf. 14, comp. 12–13 .. 5 6
c. Perf. 13½×14 .. ..
118 4 c. on 25 c. (No. 81) .. 4 6 5 0
a. Perf. 13½ .. ..
b. Imperf. between (pair) ..
119 4 c. on 50 c. violet (No. 82) ..
120 4 c. on 50 c. mauve 4 6 5 0
121 4 c. on $1 (No. 83) 4 6 5 0
122 4 c. on $2 (No. 84) 4 6 5 0
123 4 c. on $5 (No. 85) 7 0 7 0
124 4 c. on $10 (No. 86) 7 0 7 0

1900 (?) *Surch. as T 48 but 8½ mm. between lines of surcharge. P 14.*

125 4 c. on $5 (No. 85) 5 0 5 0
126 4 c. on $10 (No. 86) .. 5 0 5 0

No. 121 differs only from No. 87 in having the "4" and "cents" wider apart.

1901–5. *Contemporary stamps overprinted as T 49 in the colour given below in italics. P 14.*

127 1 c. (No. 92), *red* 1 0 1 0
a. Perf. 15 .. .. .. 1 3 1 6
b. Perf. 13½ 1 9 1 9
128 2 c. (No. 95), *red* 1 6 1 3
a. Perf. 16 .. .. .. 1 0 1 3
b. Perf. 15 .. .. .. 2 0 1 9
c. Perf. 13½ .. .. .. — 2 6
129 3 c. (No. 96), *black* 1 9 2 6
a. Perf. 15 .. .. .. 2 6 2 6
b. Perf. 15×14 .. ..
130 4 c. (No. 99), *green* 1 9 1 3
a. Perf. 15 .. .. .. 3 0 2 6
b. Perf. 13½ 3 6 3 0
131 5 c. (No. 100), *green* .. — 2 0
a. Perf. 15 .. .. 2 0 2 6
b. Perf. 13½ .. ..
132 6 c. (No. 101), *red* 2 6 3 0
a. No stop after "Protectorate" 14 0 14 0
b. Perf. 16 .. .. .. 2 0 2 6
c. Perf. 13½ .. .. — 2 6
133 8 c. (No. 102), *blue* 2 0 2 6
a. Perf. 13½ No stop after "Protectorate" 16 0 16 0
b. Perf. 14, comp. 12–13 .. — 7 0
c. Perf. 13½×14 ..
134 10 c. (No. 104), *red* 4 0 4 6
a. Perf. 15 .. .. 5 0 4 6
b. Perf. 13½ .. .. — 6 0
c. Perf. 13½. No stop after "Protectorate" ..
d. Overprint double 87 6
135 12 c. (No. 106), *red* 4 6 5 0
a. Perf. 13½ 5 0 5 6
136 16 c. (No. 107), *black* .. 5 6 4 6
a. Perf. 15 .. .. .. 5 0 5 6
b. Perf. 14, comp. 12–13 .. — 5 6
c. Perf. 13½×14 .. .. — 8 0
d. Perf. 14×13½ 8 0 6 6
137 18 c. (No. 110), *red* 4 6 4 6
a. No stop after "Protectorate"
b. Perf. 13½ .. .. .. — 8 0
138 24 c. (No. 111), *black* .. 4 6 4 6
a. Perf. 15 .. .. .. 5 0 5 0
b. Imperf. between (pair) ..
c. Perf. 13½ .. .. .. — 7 0
139 25 c. (No. 81), *red* (c. 1/6) .. 5 0 5 6
a. No stop after "Protectorate" 20 0
b. Overprints tête-bêche (pair) .. £18
c. Overprint inverted £14
140 50 c. (No. 82), *red* (c. 2/3) .. 6 6 7 0
a. No stop after "Protectorate" 27 6 27 6
141 $1 (No. 83), *red* 32 6 32 6
142 $1 (No. 83), *blk.* ('03) (c. 10/–) 32 6 32 6
a. Imperf. between (vert. pair) £7
b. Overprint double ..
143 $2 (No. 84), *red* (1905) (c. 12/6) 37 6 37 6
a. Overprint double .. ..
144 $5 (No. 85), *red* (c. 14/–) .. 42 6 42 6
145 $10 (No. 86), *red* (c. 25/–) .. 80 0 80 0
a. Overprint inverted .. ..

There was more than one setting of the overprint for some of the values. Full sheets of the 6 c. and 8 c. are known, without stop throughout.

NOTE.—Nos. 127 to 138 cancelled to order can be supplied at about one-third of the prices quoted for postally used specimens. Prices for Nos. 139 to 145, cancelled, are given in brackets.

4 cents (50)

1904–5. *Contemporary stamps surcharged locally with T 50, in black. P 15.*

146 4 c. on 5 c. (No. 100a) .. 4 0 4 0
147 4 c. on 6 c. (No. 101a) .. 4 0 4 0
a. Surcharge inverted .. 85 0
148 4 c. on 8 c. (No. 102b) 4 0 4 0
a. Surcharge inverted .. £8
149 4 c. on 12 c. (No. 106b) .. 4 0 4 0
a. Perf. 14 .. .. 4 6 4 6
b. Perf. 14, comp. 12 ..
150 4 c. on 18 c. (No. 110a) .. 4 0 4 0
151 4 c. on 24 c. (No. 111b) .. 4 6 4 6
a. Perf. 16 .. .. 4 6 4 6
b. Perf. 14 .. .. 5 0 5 0
152 4 c. on 25 c. (No. 81) (p. 14) 4 6 4 6
153 4 c. on 50 c. (No. 82) (p. 14) 4 6 4 6
154 4 c. on $1 (No. 83) (p. 14) .. 4 6 4 6
155 4 c. on $2 (No. 84) (p. 14) .. 4 6 4 6
156 4 c. on $5 (No. 85) (p. 14) .. 4 6 4 6
157 4 c. on $10 (No. 86) (p. 14) .. 4 6 4 6
a. Surcharge inverted .. £12

51. Tapir. 52. Traveller's-tree.
53. Railroad at Jesselton (*horiz.*).
54. The Sultan of Sulu, his staff and W. C. Cowie, first Chairman of the Company (*horiz.*).
55. Asiatic Elephant (*horiz.*). 56. Rhinoceros (*vert.*)

57. Ploughing with Buffalo (*horiz.*). **58.** Wild Boar (*vert.*).

59. Cockatoo (*vert.*). **60.** Hornbill (*vert.*).

61. Wild Bull (*vert.*). **62.** Megapod (*a large bird*) (*horiz.*).

(Recess. Waterlow & Sons, Ltd.)

1909 (July)–**1922.** *Centres in black.* *P* 14.

No.	Type	Stamp			
158	**51**	1 c. chocolate-brown	0 8	0 4	0 1
		a. Perf. 15	2 0	2 0	—
159	,,	1 c. brown ..	—	0 6	—
		a. Perf. 15	2 0	2 0	0 6
160	**52**	2 c. green	0 8	0 4	0 1
		a. Imperf. between (pair)			
		b. Perf. 15	0 10	0 4	—
161	**53**	3 c. lake	1 6	0 6	0 2
162	,,	3 c. rose-lake ..	1 9	0 8	0 2
		a. Perf. 15	—	—	0 4
163	,,	3 c. green (1922) ..	0 8	0 3	—
164	**54**	4 c. scarlet ..	1 0	0 8	0 2
		a. Perf. 13½ ..	—	0 10	—
		b. Perf. 15	6 0	3 6	0 2
165	**55**	5 c. yellow-brown ..	1 0	0 8	0 3
		a. Perf. 15			
166	,,	5 c. dark brown ..			
167	**56**	6 c. olive-green ..	1 9	0 9	0 2
		a. Perf. 15	10 0	—	0 3
168	,,	6 c. apple-green ..	1 9	1 0	—
169	**57**	8 c. lake	1 6	1 3	0 4
		a. Perf. 15			
170	**58**	10 c. pale blue ..	2 6	1 6	0 4
		a. Perf. 15	3 6	3 6	—
		b. Perf. 14×13½ ..			
		c. Perf. 13½ ..	—	3 0	—
171	,,	10 c. bright-blue ..	2 0	1 6	—
172	,,	10 c. dull blue ..	1 9	1 0	—
		a. Perf. 15	2 6	1 9	—
173	**59**	12 c. deep blue ..	2 0	1 6	0 8
		a. Perf. 15			
174	**60**	16 c. red-brown ..	2 0	2 0	0 6
		a. Perf. 13½ ..			
175	**61**	18 c. blue-green ..	8 0	9 0	0 9
176	**62**	24 c. mauve ..	4 0	2 6	0 6

For this issue perf. 12½ see Nos. 277, etc.

20

CENTS

(63)

1909 (Aug.). *T* **61** *surcharged with T* **63.**

177	20 c. on 18 c. blue-green (R.)	3 6	1 6
	a. Perf. 15		

64

65

1911. *T* **64** *and* **65** ($5 *and* $10). *Centres in black.* *P* 14.

178	25 c. green	3 0	3 6
	a. Perf. 15		
	b. Imperf.	25 0	
179	50 c. steel-blue	5 0	5 0
	a. Perf. 15	4 0	4 6
	b. Imperf.	22 6	
180	$1 chestnut	8 0	6 0
	a. Perf. 15	8 0	8 0
	b. Imperf.	8 6	
181	$2 lilac	15 0	10 0
182	$5 lake	30 0	25 0
	a. Perf. 13½		
	b. Imperf.	18 6	
183	$10 brick-red	47 6	
	a. Imperf.	25 0	

BRITISH

PROTECTORATE

(66)

2

cents

(67)

1912. *Nos.* 85 *and* 86 *overprinted with T* **66.**

184	$5 brt. pur. (R.) (*canc.* 12/6)	£8
185	$10 brown (R.) (*canc.* 10s.) ..	£8

1916. *Stamps of* 1909–22 *surcharged as T* **67** *in black or in red* (R.). *P* 14.

186	2 c. on 3 c. black & rose-lake	7 0	7 6
	a. "s" inverted	50 0	
187	4 c. on 6 c. blk. & olive-grn. (R.)	5 6	6 6
	a. "s" inverted	55 0	55 0
	b. "s" inserted by hand		
188	10 c. on 12 c. black and deep blue (R.)	8 0	8 0
	a. "s" inverted	40 0	40 0

(68)

1916 (May). *Stamps of North Borneo,* 1909–11, *optd. with T* **68.** *P* 14. *All centres in black.*

(*a*) *Cross in vermilion.*

189	1 c. brown	8 0	8 6
190	2 c. green	25 0	27 6
	a. Perf. 15	25 0	27 6
191	3 c. rose-lake	18 6	22 6
192	4 c. scarlet	8 6	9 0
193	5 c. yellow-brown ..	18 6	20 0
194	6 c. apple-green	20 0	20 0
195	8 c. lake	20 0	20 0
196	10 c. pale blue..	22 6	25 0
197	12 c. deep blue	30 0	32 6
198	16 c. red-brown	30 0	32 6
199	20 c. on 18 c. blue-green ..	30 0	32 6
200	24 c. dull mauve	37 6	40 0
201	25 c. green (*p.* 15)	£6	£7

(*b*) *Cross in carmine.*

202	1 c. brown	4 6	5 0
203	2 c. green	8 0	8 6
204	3 c. rose-lake	8 0	8 6
205	5 c. yellow-brown ..	14 0	14 6
206	6 c. apple-green	14 0	14 6
207	8 c. lake	14 0	14 6
208	10 c. pale blue..	14 0	14 6
209	12 c. deep blue	30 0	32 6
210	16 c. red-brown	30 0	32 6
211	20 c. on 18 c. blue-green ..	30 0	32 6
212	24 c. dull mauve	30 0	32 6
213	25 c. green (*p.* 15)	£6	£7

RED CROSS

TWO CENTS

(69)

1918. *Stamps of* 1909–11 *surcharged as T* **69**, *in black.* *P* 14.

(A) *Lines of surcharge* 9 *mm. apart.*

214	1 c. brown	2 6	3 6
	a. Imperf. between (pair) ..	45 0	
215	2 c. green	1 0	1 3
216	3 c. rose-red	3 6	4 0
	a. Imperf. between (pair) ..		
	b. Perf. 15	40 0	
217	3 c. dull rose-carmine ..	£9	
218	4 c. scarlet	1 0	1 3
	a. Surcharge inverted	£16	
219	5 c. deep brown	4 0	5 0
220	5 c. pale brown	40 0	
221	6 c. olive-green	4 0	5 0
	a. Perf. 15	£8	
222	8 c. lake	4 0	5 0
223	10 c. pale blue	6 0	7 0
224	12 c. deep blue	6 0	7 0
	a. Surcharge inverted		
225	16 c. deep claret	6 0	7 0
226	24 c. mauve	6 0	7 0

(B) *Lines of surcharge* 13 *mm. apart.*

227	2 c. green	20 0	22 6
228	6 c. olive-green	£10	
229	25 c. green	12 0	14 0
230	50 c. steel-blue	12 0	14 0
231	$1 chestnut	35 0	40 0
232	$2 lilac	35 0	40 0
233	$5 lake	£17	£17
234	$10 brick-red	£17	£17

The above stamps were dispatched from London in three consignments, of which two were lost through enemy action at sea.

These stamps were sold at face value, plus 2 c. on each stamp, and this 2 c. went to the Red Cross Society.

+

FOUR CENTS

(70)

1919. *Stamps of* 1909–11 *surcharged with T* **70**, *in red.* *P* 14.

235	1 c. chocolate	1 0	1 3
236	2 c. green	1 0	1 3
237	3 c. rose-lake	1 0	1 3
238	4 c. scarlet	1 6	1 9
239	5 c. brown	2 0	2 6
240	6 c. apple-green	3 0	3 6
	a. Imperf. between (pair) ..		
241	8 c. lake	3 0	3 6
242	10 c. bright blue	4 0	4 6
243	12 c. deep blue	3 6	4 0
244	16 c. red-brown	5 0	6 0
245	24 c. mauve	7 0	7 6
246	25 c. yellow-green	8 0	9 0
247	25 c. blue-green	16 6	17 6
248	50 c. steel-blue	10 0	12 0
249	$1 chestnut	15 0	17 6
250	$2 lilac	30 0	32 6
251	$5 lake	£12	£12
252	$10 brick-red	£12	£12

Nos. 235/52 were sold at face, plus 4 c. on each stamp for Red Cross Funds.

MALAYA-BORNEO

EXHIBITION

1922.

(71)

1922. *Stamps of* 1909–11 *overprinted as T* **71**. *P* 14.

253	1 c. brown (R.)	3 6	4 0
	a. Error. "BORHEO" ..	£14	
	b. Perf. 15	3 6	4 0
	c. Stop after "EXHIBITION"	15 0	
	d. Stop after "EXHIBITION" perf. 15	25 0	
	e. Error. "BORNEQ." ..	£10	
	f. Error. Overprint in blue ..		
254	1 c. orange-brown (R.) ..	4 0	4 6
255	2 c. green (R.)	1 9	2 6
	a. Stop after "EXHIBITION"	8 6	
256	3 c. rose-lake (B.)	2 0	2 6
	a. Stop after "EXHIBITION"	12 6	
257	4 c. scarlet (B.)	2 0	2 6
	a. Stop after "EXHIBITION"	8 6	
258	5 c. orange-brown (B.) ..	2 6	3 0
	a. Imperf. between (pair) ..		
	b. Stop after "EXHIBITION"	8 6	
259	5 c. chestnut (B.)	2 6	3 0
260	6 c. apple-green (R.) ..	2 6	3 0
	a. Stop after "EXHIBITION"	8 6	
261	8 c. dull rose (B.)	2 6	3 0
262	8 c. deep rose-lake (B.) ..	2 6	3 6
	a. Stop after "EXHIBITION"	12 6	
263	10 c. pale blue (R.)	2 6	3 6
	a. Perf. 15	25 0	
	b. Stop after "EXHIBITION"	12 6	
264	10 c. bright blue (R.) ..	3 0	3 6
	a. Stop after "EXHIBITION"	12 6	
265	12 c. deep blue (R.)	2 6	3 6
	a. Stop after "EXHIBITION"	17 6	
266	12 c. deep bright blue (R.) ..	17 6	
267	16 c. red-brown (B.)	3 6	4 0
	a. Stop after "EXHIBITION"	20 0	
	b. Overprint in red		
268	20 c. on 18 c. blue-green (B.) ..	9 0	10 0
	a. Stop after "EXHIBITION"	70 0	
	b. Error "ALAYA"		
269	20 c. on 18 c. blue-green (R.) ..	52 6	
	a. Stop after "EXHIBITION"	£10	
270	24 c. mauve (R.)	4 0	4 6
	a. Stop after "EXHIBITION"	25 0	
271	24 c. lilac (R.)	4 6	5 0
	a. Stop after "EXHIBITION"	25 0	
272	24 c. reddish lilac (R.) ..	6 0	7 0
273	25 c. blue-green (R.)	6 0	7 0
	a. Stop after "EXHIBITION"	32 6	
274	25 c. yellow-green (R.) ..	9 0	10 0
	a. Stop after "EXHIBITION"	35 0	
	b. Perf. 15	35 0	
	c. Perf. 15. Stop after "EXHIBITION"		
	d. Perf. 15. Overprint double ..	£12	
275	50 c. steel-blue (R.)	8 0	9 0
	a. Stop after "EXHIBITION"	50 0	
	b. Perf. 15	42 6	
	c. Perf. 15. Stop after "EXHIBITION"		

THREE

CENTS

(72)

1923. *T* **54** *surcharged with T* **72**, *in black.*

276	3 c. on 4 c. black & scarlet ..	2 6	1 6

1927. *As* 1909–22 (*T* **51**, *etc.*), *but perf.* 12½. *Centres in black.*

277	1 c. chocolate-brown ..	0 2	0 2
	a. Imperf. between (horiz. pair)	80 0	
278	2 c. claret	0 2	0 2
279	3 c. green	0 4	0 2

No.	Description	Unused	Used
280	4 c. scarlet	0 4	0 2
	a. Imperf. between (vert. pair)	50 0	
	b. Imperf. between (horiz. pair)	75 0	
281	5 c. yellow-brown	0 4	0 6
282	6 c. olive-green	0 4	0 6
283	8 c. carmine	0 6	0 6
284	10 c. pale blue	0 8	0 5
285	12 c. deep blue	1 0	0 10
286	16 c. red-brown	1 9	2 6
287	20 c. on 18 c. blue-green (R.)	1 6	1 3
288	24 c. violet	3 0	3 0
289	25 c. green	2 0	2 0
290	50 c. steel-blue	4 0	4 0
291	$1 chestnut	6 6	7 6
292	$2 mauve	15 0	17 6
293	$5 lake	30 0	32 6
294	$10 orange-red	55 0	65 0

73. Head of a Murut.

74. The Orang-Utan (*vert.*). **75.** Dyak Warrior (*vert.*).

76. Mount Kinabalu.

77. The Clouded Leopard (*horiz.*).

78, 80. Arms of the Company (*vert.*).

79. Arms of the Company (*horiz.*).

(Recess. Waterlow & Sons, Ltd.)

1931 (1 Jan.). *Fiftieth Anniversary of British North Borneo Company's Foundation. Various designs, dated* "1881–1931". *P* 12½.

No.	Type	Description	Unused	Used
295	73	3 c. black and blue-green	6 0	7 6
296	74	6 c. black and orange	6 0	7 6
297	75	10 c. black and scarlet	6 0	7 6
298	76	12 c. black and ultram.	12 6	15 0
299	77	25 c. black and violet	22 6	25 0
300	78	$1 black & yellow-green	35 0	40 0
301	79	$2 black and chestnut	60 0	60 0
302	80	$5 black and purple	£7	£8

POSTAL FISCALS.

Three Cents Revenue

(F 1)

Ten Cents. Revenue

(F 2)

1886. *Regular issues surch. as Type* **F 1** *or* **F 2.**

No.	Description	Unused	Used
F1	3 c. on 4 c. pink (No. 6)	20 0	25 0
F2	5 c. on 8 c. green (No. 7)	20 0	25 0
F3	10 c. on 50 c. violet (No. 4)	30 0	30 0

POSTAGE DUE STAMPS.

NOTE.—Postage Due stamps cancelled to order can be supplied at about one-third of the prices quoted for postally used specimens. The issues of 1923 to date have not been thus cancelled.

POSTAGE DUE

(D 1)

1895. *Stamps of* 1894 *overprinted with Type* **D 1,** *in black. P* 15.

A. *Vertically* (*reading upwards*).

No.	Description	Unused	Used
D1	2 c. black and rose-lake	4 0	4 6
D2	2 c. black and lake	3 6	4 0
D3	3 c. olive-green & mauve	3 0	3 6
D4	5 c. black and vermilion	3 6	4 0
	a. Stop after "DUE"	18 6	
	b. Perf. 14	—	6 0
	c. Perf. 14, comp. 12–13	—	6 0
D5	6 c. black & bistre-brown	3 0	3 6
	a. Perf. 14	—	4 0
D6	18 c. black and deep green	9 0	10 6
	a. Overprint reading downwards		

B. *Horizontally.*

No.	Description	Unused	Used
D 7	8 c. black and dull purple	4 6	5 0
	a. Overprint double		
	b. Overprint inverted, perf. 14		
D 8	12 c. black and blue	—	8 0
	a. Overprint double		
	b. Perf. 14	5 6	6 6
D 9	12 c. blk. & ultram. (*perf.* 14)	8 0	
D10	18 c. black and deep green	10 6	
	a. Overprint inverted		
	b. Perf. 14	12 6	12 6
D11	24 c. blue and rose-lake	—	10 6
	a. Perf. 14	4 6	5 6

1897. *Stamps of* 1897 *overprinted with Type* **D 1.** *P* 15.

A. *Vertically.*

No.	Description	Unused	Used
D12	2 c. black and lake	2 6	3 0
	a. Perf. 14	3 6	

B. *Horizontally.*

No.	Description	Unused	Used
D13	2 c. black and lake	3 6	4 0
D14	8 c. black & brown-purple	4 0	4 6
	a. Stop after "DUE"	8 0	8 0

1901. *Issue of* 1897–1902 *optd. with Type* **D 1.** *P* 14.

A. *Vertically.*

No.	Description	Unused	Used
D15	2 c. black and green	2 0	2 6
	a. Perf. 14×13½		
	b. Perf. 14, comp. 12–13	—	3 6
	c. Perf. 16		
D16	3 c. green and rosy mauve	2 6	3 0
	a. Stop after "DUE"	10 0	
	b. Perf. 15	2 0	2 6
	c. Overprint double		
	d. Opt. double. Stop after "DUE"		
D17	3 c. grn. & dull mve. (*p.* 15)	3 6	4 0
D18	4 c. black and carmine	1 9	1 9
	a. Perf. 13½	1 9	2 6
D19	5 c. black & orange-verm.	1 9	2 6
	a. Perf. 15	—	2 6
	b. Stop after "DUE"		
D20	6 c. black & bistre-brown	—	2 6
	a. Perf. 15	1 9	2 6
	b. Perf. 14, comp. 12–13		
D21	8 c. black & brown (*p.* 15)	2 6	2 9
D22	12 c. black & dull blue	2 6	2 9
	a. Perf. 15		
D23	18 c. black & green (No. 108)		
D24	18 c. black & green (No. 110)	3 6	3 9
	a. Perf. 14, comp. 12–13	—	3 6
D25	24 c. blue and lake (No. 109)	—	3 6
D26	24 c. blue and lake (*perf.* 15) (No. 111*b*)	3 0	3 6

B. *Horizontally.*

D27 2 c. black and green .. 4 6
D28 8 c. blk. & brown (*perf.* 15) 8 0
a. Stop after "DUE" ..

1904-5. *Stamps of* 1901-4 *overprinted* "British Protectorate," *further overprinted with Type* D 1, *in black.*

A. *Vertically.*

D29 2 c. black & green (*perf.* 16)
D30 3 c. grn. & rosy mve. (*perf.* 14)
D31 5 c. blk. & orge.-ver. (*p.* 15)
D32 8 c. black & brown (*perf.* 14)
D33 24 c. blue & lake (*perf.* 14) ..

B. *Horizontally, at top of stamp.*

D34 2 c. black & green (*perf.* 15)
a. Perf. 16 .. .. ..
D35 4 c. black & car. (*perf.* 14) — 10 0

C. *Horizontally, at centre of stamp.* P 14.

D36 2 c. black and green .. 1 9 0 8
a. Perf. 15 .. .. £5
D37 3 c. olive.-grn. & rosy mve... 1 9 1 3
a. Perf. 15 .. .. — 4 6
D38 4 c. black and carmine .. 1 9 2 6
a. Overprint double 47 6
b. Perf. 15 .. .. 1 9 2 6
D39 5 c. black & orge.-vermilion 3 0 1 3
a. Perf. 15 .. .. 3 6 3 6
b. Perf. 13½ .. .. .. — 4 0
D40 6 c. black & bistre-brown .. 2 6 1 0
a. Overprint inverted
b. No stop after "PROTECTORATE" .. ..
c. Perf. 16 .. .. .. 6 0
D41 8 c. black and brown .. 3 0 1 9
a. No stop after "PROTECTORATE" (*p.* 13½) 22 6 22 6
D42 10 c. brown and slate-lilac .. 6 0 3 0
a. No stop after "PROTECTORATE" ..
D43 12 c. black and blue .. 4 6 5 6
D44 16 c. green and chestnut .. 4 6 1 6
D45 18 c. black and green .. 4 6 5 6
a. Overprint double .. ..
D46 24 c. blue and lake 4 6 5 6
a. Overprint double .. ..

D. *Horizontally. Overprinted locally, with stop after* "DUE."

D47 1 c. blk. & bistre-brn. (*p.* 14) 5 6
a. With raised stop after "DUE" 8 0

1920-31. *Stamps of* 1909-22, *overprinted with Type* D 1. P 14.

A. *Horizontally at top of stamp.*

D48 4 c. black & scarlet (1920) 20 0 7 6

B. *Horizontally towards foot of stamp.*

D49 2 c. black and green .. 0 9 0 9
a. Perf. 15 .. .. .. 1 6
b. Perf. 13½ 15 0
D50 3 c. black and green .. 0 6 0 6
D51 4 c. black and scarlet .. 0 6 0 3
D52 5 c. black and yellow-brown 0 8 0 6
D53 6 c. black and olive-green .. 0 8 0 6
D54 8 c. black and rose-lake .. 0 8 0 6
D55 10 c. black and pale blue .. 1 0 0 9
a. Perf. 15 .. .. .. 40 0
D56 12 c. black and deep blue .. 1 6 1 6
D56*a* 16 c. black and brown-lake .. 1 6 1 6
b. Black and red-brown .. 16 0

1926-31. *As* 1920-31, *but perf.* 12½.

D57 2 c. black and claret .. 0 2 0 2
D58 3 c. black and green .. 0 2 0 2
D59 4 c. black and scarlet .. 0 3 0 2
D60 5 c. black and yellow-brown 0 4 0 4
D61 6 c. black and olive-green .. 0 6 0 2
D62 8 c. black and carmine .. 0 8 0 4
D63 10 c. black and blue .. 0 10 1 0
D64 12 c. black and deep blue .. 1 3 1 3
D65 16 c. black & red-brown ('31) 2 0 2 3

NORTHERN NIGERIA.

PRINTERS. All issues were typographed by De La Rue & Co.

1  2

1900 (MAR.). T 1 *and* 2 (5*d. and* 6*d.*). *Wmk. Crown CA.* P 14.

1 ½d. dull mauve and green .. 0 9 1 0
2 1d. dull mauve and carmine .. 1 6 1 6
3 2d. dull mauve and yellow .. 10 0 10 6
4 2½d. dull mauve and ultram. .. 14 6 15 0
5 5d. dull mauve and chestnut .. 14 0 14 0
6 6d. dull mauve and violet .. 15 0 16 0
7 1s. green and black 25 0 27 6
8 2s. 6d. green and ultramarine 60 0
9 10s. green and brown .. £10

3  4

1902 (1 JULY). *Wmk. Crown CA.* P 14.

10 3 ½d. dull purple and green 0 6 0 7
11 „ 1d. dull purple and carmine 1 0 1 3
12 „ 2d. dull purple and yellow 3 6 4 0
13 „ 2½d. dull purple & ultram. .. 1 9 1 9
14 4 5d. dull purple & chestnut 7 0 7 6
15 „ 6d. dull purple & violet .. 9 0 6 0
16 3 1s. green and black .. 8 0 8 0
17 „ 2s. 6d. green and ultram. .. 25 0 27 6
18 „ 10s. green and brown .. 45 0 37 6

1904 (APRIL). *Wmk. Multiple Crown CA.* P 14.

19 3 £25 green and carmine, O .. £400

1905 (AUG.-OCT.) *Wmk. Mult. Crown CA.* P 14.

20 3 ½d. dull purple & green, OC 1 6 1 6
21 „ 1d. dull purple & carm., OC 1 6 0 8
22 „ 2d. dull purple & yell., OC 4 0 3 6
23 „ 2½d. dull purple & ultram., O 8 6 9 0
24 4 5d. dull pur. & chest., OC 10 6 12 0
25 „ 6d. dull pur. & violet, OC 10 6 8 0
26 3 1s. green and black, OC 15 0 16 0
27 „ 2s. 6d. green & ultram., OC 27 6 30 0

1910-11. *Wmk. Mult. Crown CA.* P 14.

28 3 ½d. green, O (Apr. '10) .. 0 6 0 7
29 „ 1d. carmine, O (Jan. '10) 0 8 0 4
30 „ 2d. grey, O (Oct. '11) .. 4 0 4 6
31 „ 2½d. blue, O (Oct. '10) .. 3 0 3 6
32 4 3d. pur./*yell.*, C (Sept. '11) 2 0 2 0
34 „ 5d. dull pur. & olive-green, C (Feb. '11) 3 0 3 6
35 „ 6d. dull pur. and purple, C (Nov. '10) 6 0 5 0
35*a* „ 6d. dull & brt. pur., C ('11) 4 0 4 0

36	3	1s. black/*grn.*, C (Nov. '10)	6	0	6	0
37	,,	2s. 6d. black and red/*blue*, C (Mar. '11)	12	6	12	0
38	4	5s. green and red/*yellow*, C (Sept. '11)	17	6	15	0
39	3	10s. green & red/*green*, C (Mar. '11)	45	0	30	0

5

6

1912. *T* **5** *and* **6** (*3d., 4d., 5d., 6d., 9d., 5s., and £1*). *Wmk. Mult. Crown CA. P 14.*

40	½d. deep green, O	0	9	1	0
41	1d. red, O	1	0	0	4
42	2d. grey, O	1	6	1	9
43	3d. purple/*yellow*, C	2	3	2	3
44	4d. black and red/*yellow*, C ..	2	9	2	9
45	5d. dull pur. & olive-green, C	5	6	6	0
46	6d. dull & bright purple, C ..	4	6	5	0
47	9d. dull purple & carmine, C	5	6	6	0
48	1s. black/*green*, C	7	0	5	0
49	2s. 6d. black and red/*blue*, C	13	6	13	6
50	5s. green and red/*yellow*, C ..	27	6	25	0
51	10s. green and red/*green* C ..	50	0	35	0
52	£1 purple and black/*red*, C ..	85	0	65	0

Since 1 January, 1914, Northern Nigeria has formed part of NIGERIA.

NORTHERN RHODESIA.

1

2

(Die eng. W. G. Fairweather. Recess. Waterlow and Sons, Ltd.)

1925 (1 APRIL)–**1929.** *T* **1** *and* **2** (*shilling values*). *Views in second colour. Wmk. Mult. Script CA. P 12½.*

1	½d. green	0	3	0	4
2	1d. brown	0	5	0	2
3	1½d. carmine-red	1	0	1	0
4	2d. yellow-brown	0	9	0	6
5	3d. ultramarine	1	9	1	3
6	4d. violet	2	6	1	6
7	6d. slate-grey	3	0	1	0
8	8d. rose-purple	6	6	7	6
9	10d. olive-green	8	0	9	0
10	1s. black & yellow-brown ..	7	0	4	0
11	2s. ultramarine and brown ..	22	6	25	0
12	2s. 6d. green and black ..	17	6	10	0
13	3s. blue and violet ('29) ..	20	0	18	6
14	5s. violet and slate-grey ..	37	6	37	6
15	7s. 6d. black and rose-pur ..	55	0	65	0
16	10s. black and green	55	0	65	0
17	20s. rose-pur. & carmine-red ..	110	0	£6	

1935 (6 MAY). *Silver Jubilee. As T* **13** *of Antigua, inscribed* "NORTHERN RHODESIA". *Recess. D.L.R. & Co. Wmk. Mult. Script C.A. P 13½ × 14.*

18	1d. light blue and olive-green ..	0	6	0	6
19	2d. green and indigo	2	0	1	9
20	3d. brown and deep blue ..	4	0	5	0
21	6d. slate and purple	8	6	9	0

POSTAGE DUE STAMPS.

D 1. (Typo. De La Rue & Co.)

1929. *T* **D 1.** *Wmk. Mult. Script CA. P 14.*

D1	1d. black	0	2	0	3
D2	2d. black	0	3	0	5
D3	3d. black	0	5	0	7
D4	4d. black	0	6	0	8

NORTH-WEST PACIFIC ISLANDS.

See NEW GUINEA.

NOVA SCOTIA.

1

2

Royal Crown and heraldic flowers of the United Kingdom.

(Recess. Messrs. Perkins Bacon & Co.)

1851 (1 SEPT.). (*1d. on* 12 MAY, **1853**). *T* **1** (*1d.*) *and* **2** (*other values*). *Bluish paper. Imperf.*

1 1d. red-brown .. .. £35 70 0 *to* £20
a. Bisected (½d.) ..

2	3d. deep blue	£15	35 0 to £8
	a. Bisected (1½d.) ..	—	£25
3	3d. bright blue ..	£15	35 0 to 95 0
	a. Bisected (1½d.) ..	—	£25
4	3d. pale blue	£15	35 0 to 95 0
5	6d. yellow-green ..	£40	80 0 to £25
	a. Bisected (3d.) ..	—	£40
	b. Quartered (1½d.) ..		
6	6d. deep green ..	£75	£8 to £30
	a. Bisected (3d.) ..	—	£40
	b. Quartered (1½d.) ..		
7	1s. cold violet.. ..	£275	£35 to £150
	a. Bisected (6d.) ..		
	b. Quartered (3d.) ..		
8	1s. purple	£250	£35 to £130

The stamps formerly catalogued on almost white paper are probably some from which the bluish colour has been discharged.

As the value of these stamps depends entirely on condition, the prices quoted for unused are for fair average specimens only.

Reprints of all four values were made in 1890 on thin, hard, white paper. The 1d. is brown, the 3d. blue, the 6d. deep green, and the 1s. violet-black.

3

4 5

(Engraved and printed by the American Bank Note Co., New York.)

1860–63. *T* **3** (*1 c. to 5 c.*), **4** (*8½ c. and* 10 *c.*), *and* **5**. *P* 12.

(*a*) *Yellowish wove paper.*

9	1 c. jet-black	3 6	7 6
	a. Bisected		
10	1 c. grey-black	3 0	10 0
11	2 c. grey-purple	30 0	20 0
11a	2 c. purple	60 0	17 6
12	5 c. blue	75 0	15 0
13	5 c. deep blue	65 0	15 0
14	8½ c. deep green	7 6	
15	8½ c. yellow-green	5 0	
16	10 c. scarlet	30 0	17 6
17	12½ c. black	15 0	10 0
17a	12½ c. greyish black	—	15 0

(*b*) *White paper.*

18	1 c. black	7 6	15 0
	a. Imperf. between (horiz. pair)	£15	
19	1 c. grey	10 0	20 0
20	2 c. dull purple	6 6	12 6
21	2 c. purple	5 0	12 6
22	2 c. grey-purple	5 0	12 6
	a. Bisected	—	£60
23	2 c. slate-purple	6 0	12 6
24	5 c. blue	40 0	8 0
25	5 c. deep blue	40 0	9 0
26	8½ c. deep green	50 0	50 0
27	10 c. scarlet	10 0	22 6
28	10 c. vermilion	15 0	25 0
	a. Bisected	—	£35
29	12½ c. black	50 0	10 0

Since 1868 Nova Scotia has used stamps of the Dominion of Canada.

NYASALAND PROTECTORATE.

(Formerly British Central Africa.)

B.C.A.

(1)

1891 (April)–**1895.** *Stamps of Rhodesia overprinted as T* **1**, *in black. P* 14, 14½.

1	1	1d. black	1 0	1 3
2	4	2d. sea-green and vermilion	1 9	2 6
3	„	4d. reddish chestnut & blk.	2 6	3 0
4	1	6d. ultramarine	8 6	7 6
5	„	6d. deep blue	6 0	6 0
6	4	8d. rose-lake & altram. ..	8 6	7 6
6a	„	8d. red and ultramarine ..	7 6	7 6
7	1	1s. grey-brown	6 0	6 0
8	„	2s. vermilion	15 0	15 0
9	„	2s. 6d. grey-purple ..	15 0	15 0
10	4	3s. brown & green (10.'95)	15 0	14 0
11	„	4s. grey-blk. & ver. (2.'93)	15 6	15 6
12	1	5s. orange-yellow	22 6	22 6
13	„	10s. deep green	50 0	52 6
14	2	£1 deep blue	£12	£10
15	„	£2 rose-red	£18	
16	„	£5 sage-green	£20	
17	„	£10 brown	£35	

The overprint varies on values up to 10s. Sets may be made with *thin* or *thick* letters.

B.C.A.
FOUR
SHILLINGS.

(2)

ONE PENNY.

(4)

1892–93. *Stamps of Rhodesia surch. as T* **2**.

18	4	3s. on 4s. grey-blk. & verm.	£6	£6
19	1	4s. on 5s. orange-yellow ..	60 0	60 0

The 4s. was issued in Aug., 1892, the 3s. in Oct., 1893.

1895. *No.* 2 *surch. at Cape Town with T* **4**.

20	4	1d. on 2d. sea-grn. & verm.	15 0	15 0
		a. Surcharge double	£15	

Specimens are known with double surcharge, without stop after "Penny". These are from a trial printing made at Blantyre, but it is believed that they were not issued to the public.

Supporters, typical of labour, depict Makalolo chieftains.

5 6

(Typo. De La Rue and Co.)

1895. *Centres in black. No wmk. P* 14.

21	5	1d. black	6 0	6 0
22	„	2d. green	12 0	8 6
23	„	4d. reddish buff	12 6	10 0
24	„	6d. blue	10 0	7 6

No.	Type	Description	Unused	Used
25	5	1s. rose	30 0	20 0
26	6	2s. 6d. bright magenta	55 0	55 0
27	„	3s. yellow	50 0	15 0
28	„	5s. olive	70 0	52 6
29	„	£1 yellow-orange	£18	£10
30	„	£10 orange-vermilion	£65	
31	„	£25 blue-green	£130	

1896 (Feb.). *T* **5** (*wmk. Crown CA*) *and* **6** (*wmk. Crown CC*). *Centres in black. P* 14.

No.	Type	Description	Unused	Used
32	5	1d. black	4 0	4 0
33	„	2d. green	7 6	6 6
34	„	4d. orange-brown	8 6	7 6
35	„	6d. blue	8 6	7 6
36	„	1s. rose	17 6	17 6
37	6	2s. 6d. magenta	47 6	45 0
38	„	3s. yellow	35 0	25 0
39	„	5s. olive	60 0	60 0
40	„	£1 blue	£20	
41	„	£10 orange	£65	
42	„	£25 green	£150	

7

8

1897 (Aug.). *T* **7** (*wmk. Crown CA*) *and* **8** (*wmk. Crown CC*). *Centres in black. P* 14.

No.	Type	Description	Unused	Used
43	7	1d. ultramarine	0 10	0 6
44	„	2d. yellow	1 3	0 10
45	„	4d. carmine	3 0	3 0
46	„	6d. green	3 6	3 6
47	„	1s. dull purple	6 0	4 6
48	8	2s. 6d. ultramarine	25 0	22 6
49	„	3s. sea-green	52 6	47 6
50	„	4s. carmine	25 0	22 6
50a	„	10s. olive-green	65 0	37 6
51	„	£1 dull purple	70 0	45 0
52	„	£10 yellow	£70	£25

ONE

PENNY

(9)

No. 49 *surcharged with T* **9**, *in red.*

No.	Description	Unused	Used
3	1d. on 3s. black and sea-green	2 6	2 6
	a. Error "PNNEY"	£40	
	b. Error "PENN"	£20	
	c. Double surcharge	£20	

10

1898 (11 Mar.). *T* **10**. *Imperf.*

Setting I. *The vertical frame lines of the stamps cross the space between the two rows of the sheet.*

(i.) *With the initials "J.G." or "J.T.G." on the back in black ink.*

No.	Description	Unused	Used
54	1d. vermilion and grey-blue	—	40 0
	a. Without the initials		
	b. Without the initials and centre inverted	£100	

(ii.) *With a control number and letter, or letters printed in plain relief at the back.*

No.	Description	Unused	Used
55	1d. vermilion and grey-blue	—	42 6

Setting II. *The vertical frame lines do not cross the space between the rows.*

As No. 55.

No.	Description		Unused	Used
55a	1d. vermilion and pale ultram.		—	12 6
56	1d. vermilion and deep ultram.		—	12 6
	a. Without number and letters at back		£7	22 6

1898 (June). *T* **10**. *Setting* II. *P* 12.

No.	Description	Unused	Used
57	1d. vermilion & pale ultram.	£9	4 0
57a	1d. vermilion & deep ultram.	—	5 0
	b. Without number and letters at back	—	10 0

The two different settings of these stamps are each in 30 types, *vide* article in *London Philatelist*, August, 1914, by Sir Edward Bacon, K.C.V.O.

1901. *T* **7**. *Wmk. Crown CA. P* 14.

No.	Description	Unused	Used
57c	1d. dull pur. & carmine-rose	0 9	0 6
57d	4d. dull pur. & olive-green	7 6	6 0
58	6d. dull pur. & brown	10 0	8 6

11

12

(Typo. De La Rue & Co.)

1903–4. *T* **11** (*Wmk. Crown CA*) *and* **12** (*Wmk. Crown CC*). *P* 14.

No.	Type	Description	Unused	Used
59	11	1d. grey and carmine	1 3	0 6
60	„	2d. dull & bright purple	4 0	2 6
61	„	4d. grey-green and black	6 0	5 0
62	„	6d. grey & reddish buff	7 6	5 0
62a	„	1s. grey and blue	12 0	10 6
63	12	2s. 6d. grey-green & grn.	25 0	17 6
64	„	4s. dull & bright purple	32 6	25 0
65	„	10s. grey-green and black	50 0	50 0
66	„	£1 grey and carmine	£8	£8
67	„	£10 grey and blue	£75	£75

1907. *T* **11**. *Wmk. Mult. Crown CA. P* 14.

No.	Description	Unused	Used
68	1d. grey and carmine, C	1 3	0 8
69	2d. dull and bright purple, C	£250	
70	4d. grey-green and black, C	£250	
71	6d. grey and reddish buff, C	40 0	40 0

By an order in Council, 6 July, 1907, the name of the territory was altered to "NYASALAND PROTECTORATE."

13

14

(Typo. De La Rue & Co.)

1908 (22 JULY). *Wmk. Crown CA. P* 14.

No.	T		Unused	Used
72	13	1s. black/*green*, C	8 6	8 6

Wmk. Mult. Crown CA. P 14.

No.	T		Unused	Used
73	13	½d. green, O	1 6	1 3
74	,,	1d. carmine, O	1 9	1 0
75	,,	3d. purple/*yellow*, C	6 0	2 6
76	,,	4d. black and red/*yellow*, C	4 0	3 6
77	,,	6d. dull pur. & brt. pur., C	6 0	4 0
78	14	2s. 6d. black & red/*blue*, C	18 0	18 0
79	,,	4s. carmine and black, C	35 0	35 0
80	,,	10s. green and red/*green*, C	60 0	60 0
81	,,	£1 purple and black/*red*, C	£12	£12
82	,,	£10 purple & ultramarine, C	£75	

15

16

(Typo. De La Rue & Co.)

1913 (1 JUNE)–**1918.** *T* **15** *and* **16** (2s. 6d., *etc.*). *Wmk. Mult. Crown CA. P* 14.

No.		Unused	Used
83	½d. green, O	0 4	0 3
84	½d. blue-green, O (1918)	0 5	0 3
85	1d. carmine-red, O	0 8	0 3
86	1d. scarlet, O (1916)	0 6	0 3
87	2d. grey, O (1916)	1 9	0 9
88	2d. slate, O	1 9	0 9
89	2½d. bright blue, O	0 10	1 0
90	3d. purple/*yellow*, C (1914)	2 6	1 6
	a. On pale yellow	3 0	2 9
91	4d. black and red/*yellow*, C	3 0	0 10
	a. On lemon	55 0	
	b. On pale yellow	3 6	
92	6d. dull & bright purple, C	2 6	1 6
92*a*	6d. dull pur. & bright vio., C	2 6	1 6
93	1s. black/*green*, C (1918)	6 0	3 0
	a. On blue-green, olive back	5 0	3 0
	b. On emerald back	3 0	3 6
94	2s. 6d. blk. & red/*blue*, C ('18)	10 0	10 0
95	4s. carmine & black, C ('18)	17 6	20 0
96	10s. green & red/*grn.*, C ('18)	30 0	32 6
97	10s. pale grn. & red/*green*, C	50 0	50 0
98	£1 purple & blk./*red*, C ('18)	70 0	75 0
99	£10 purple & blue, C (1914)	£25	

1921–30. *T* **15** *and* **16** (2s., *etc.*). *Wmk. Mult. Script CA. P* 14.

No.		Unused	Used
100	½d. green, O	0 4	0 4
101	1d. carmine, O	0 6	0 4
102	1½d. orange, O	0 8	0 8
103	2d. grey, O	0 8	0 4
105	3d. purple/*pale yellow*, C	1 0	1 0
106	4d. black & red/*yellow*, C	1 9	2 0
107	6d. dull and bright purple, C	1 9	1 3
108	1s. black/*emerald*, C ('30)	4 0	4 0
109	2s. purple and blue/*blue*, C	7 6	8 0
110	2s. 6d. blk. & red/*blue*, C ('24)	8 0	10
111	4s. carmine and black, C	15 0	17 6
112	5s. green & red/*yellow*, C ('29)	20 0	22 6
113	10s. green and red/*green*, C	40 0	42 6

17. King George V and Symbol of the Protectorate.

(Des. Major H. E. Green, D.S.O., O.B.E. Recess. Waterlow.)

1934 (JUNE)–**1935.** *T* **17.** *Wmk. Mult. Script CA. P* 12½.

No.		Unused	Used
114	½d. green	0 3	0 3
115	1d. brown	0 6	0 3
116	1½d. carmine	1 0	1 3
117	2d. pale grey	2 0	1 0
118	3d. blue	2 0	1 3
119	4d. bright magenta (20.5.35)	4 0	4 6
120	6d. violet	5 0	4 0
121	9d. olive-bistre (20.5.35)	8 6	10 0
122	1s. black and orange	10 0	8 6

1935 (6 MAY). *Silver Jubilee. As T* **13** *of Antigua, inscr.* "NYASALAND". *Recess. W'low & Sons. Wmk. Mult. Script CA. P* 11×12.

No.		Unused	Used
123	1d. ultramarine and grey	0 8	1 3
124	2d. green and indigo	4 0	4 6
125	3d. brown and deep blue	8 6	10 0
126	1s. slate and purple	20 0	22 6

For stamps of Nyasaland overprinted "N.F." see TANGANYIKA.

ORANGE FREE STATE.

(CALLED ORANGE RIVER COLONY, 1900–1910).

SIMPLIFICATION (see p. xii)

Type I unsurcharged.

48, 84, 2, 68, 49, 51, 18, 5, 7, 9, 87, 20.

Type I surcharged.

13, 24, 36, 39, 53, 54, 67, 69, 77, 82a, 83. (Add other surch. types if desired.)

V.R.I. overprints.

101 to 110 (less 105). 156 to 166 (less 160). (214 to 223 can be included if desired.)

I. INDEPENDENT REPUBLIC.

All stamps are perf. 14. *All surcharges are in black.*

1

(Typo. De La Rue & Co.)

1868 (1 JAN.)–**1890.** *T* **1.**

No.		Unused	Used
1	1d. pale brown	1 6	0 6
2	1d. red-brown	1 6	0 6

		Unused	Used
3	1d. deep brown	2 0	0 6
4	6d. pale rose (1868)	10 0	3 6
5	6d. rose (1871)	3 6	3 0
6	6d. rose-carmine (1877)	12 6	3 0
7	6d. bright carmine (1890)	3 0	1 6
8	1s. orange-buff	8 6	5 0
9	1s. orange-yellow	3 0	1 0

4 (a) 4 (b) 4 (c) 4 (d)

1877. *No. 6 surcharged as above.*

10	4 on 6d. rose-carmine (a)	50 0	25 0
11	4 on 6d. rose-carmine (b)	£10	50 0
12	4 on 6d. rose-carmine (c)	45 0	20 0
13	4 on 6d. rose-carmine (d)	35 0	15 0

Varieties. (i.) *Surcharge inverted.*

14	4 on 6d. rose-carmine (a)	—	£16
15	4 on 6d. rose-carmine (b)	—	£22
16	4 on 6d. rose-carmine (c)	—	£9
17	4 on 6d. rose-carmine (d)	—	£11

(ii.) *Surcharge double, one inverted.*

17a	4 on 6d. rose-carmine (a and c)	—	£26
17b	4 on 6d. rose-carmine (b and d)	—	£26

1878 (July). *T* 1.

18	4d. pale blue	7 6	2 6
19	4d. ultramarine	10 0	5 0
20	5s. green	15 0	12 0

1d. (a) 1d. (b) 1d. (c) 1d. (d) 1d. (e)

1881 (June). *No. 20 surcharged as above, with a heavy black bar cancelling the old value.* (a) *Small "1" and "d."* (b) *Sloping serif.* (c) *Same size as* (b), *but "1" with straight horizontal serif.* (d) *Taller "1," with horizontal serif.* (e) *Same size as* (d), *but with sloping serif and thin line at foot.*

21	1d. on 5s. green (a)	35 0	15 0
22	1d. on 5s. green (b)	20 0	15 0
23	1d. on 5s. green (c)	30 0	20 0
24	1d. on 5s. green (d)	17 6	15 0
25	1d. on 5s. green (e)	75 0	

There are two varieties of No. 24—one with an antique "d," the other with a Roman "d."

Varieties. (i.) *Surcharge inverted.*

27	1d. on 5s. green (b)	—	£16
28	1d. on 5s. green (c)	—	£22
29	1d. on 5s. green (d)	—	£12
30	1d. on 5s. green (e)	—	£22

(ii.) *Surcharge double.*

32	1d. on 5s. green (b)	—	£16
33	1d. on 5s. green (c)		
34	1d. on 5s. green (d)	—	£22
35	1d. on 5s. green (e)		

No. 21 was the first printing in one type only. Nos. 22 to 25 constitute the second printing about a year later, and are all found on the same sheet; and as certain varieties are known with surcharge inverted and double, all probably exist.

Owing to defective printing, specimens may be found with the obliterating bar at the top of the stamps and others without the bar.

½d

1882 (Aug.). *No. 20, surcharged "½d." as above, and with a thin black line cancelling old value.*

36	½d. on 5s. green	3 0	3 6

Varieties. (i.) *Surcharge double.*

37	½d. on 5s. green	£12	£10

(ii.) *Surcharge inverted.*

37a	½d. on 5s. green		

(iii.) *Surcharge double, both inverted.*

37b	½d. on 5s. green		

3d (a) 3d (b) 3d (c) 3d (d) 3d (e)

1882. *No. 19 surcharged as above with thin black line cancelling value.*

38	3d. on 4d. ultramarine (a)	30 0	25 0
39	3d. on 4d. ultramarine (b)	20 0	15 0
40	3d. on 4d. ultramarine (c)	20 0	17 6
41	3d. on 4d. ultramarine (d)	25 0	15 0
42	3d. on 4d. ultramarine (e)	65 0	40 0

Varieties. Surcharge double

43	3d. on 4d. ultramarine (a)	—	£22
44	3d. on 4d. ultramarine (b)	—	£22
45	3d. on 4d. ultramarine (c)	—	£20
46	3d. on 4d. ultramarine (d)	—	£16
47	3d. on 4d. ultramarine (e)	—	£22

1883–84. *T* 1.

48	½d. chestnut	0 9	0 6
49	2d. pale mauve	3 6	0 4
50	2d. bright mauve	3 6	0 4
51	3d. ultramarine	5 0	3 0

For 1d. purple, see No. 68.

2d (a) 2d (b)

1888 (Oct.). *No. 51 surcharged as above.*

(a) *Wide "2."* (b) *Narrow "2."*

52	2d. on 3d. ultramarine (a)	15 0	12 6
53	2d. on 3d. ultramarine (b)	6 0	4 0

Varieties. Surcharge inverted.

53a	2d. on 3d. ultramarine (a)	—	£16
53b	2d. on 3d. ultramarine (b)	—	£11

A variety exists having "2" with a curly tail.

1d (a) 1d (b) Id (c)

1890 (Dec.)–**1891** (Mar.). *Nos.* 51 *and* 19 *surcharged as above.*

54	1d. on 3d. ultramarine (a)	1 0	1 3
55	1d. on 3d. ultramarine (b)	3 6	3 0
57	1d. on 4d. ultramarine (a)	15 0	4 0
58	1d. on 4d. ultramarine (b)	20 0	15 0
59	1d. on 4d. ultramarine (c)	£12	£10

Varieties. (i.) *Surcharge double.*

60	1d. on 3d. ultramarine (a)	60 0	
61	1d. on 3d. ultramarine (b)	70 0	
61a	1d. on 3d. ultramarine (a) & (b)	70 0	
63	1d. on 4d. ultramarine (a)	90 0	70 0
64	1d. on 4d. ultramarine (b)	£5	
65	1d. on 4d. ultram. (a) & (b)		

(ii.) *"1" and "d" wide apart.*

66	1d. on 3d. ultramarine (a)	£8	£5

The settings of the 1d. on 3d. and on 4d. are not identical. The variety (c) does not exist on the 3d.

2½d.

1892 (Oct.). *No. 51 surcharged as above.*

67	2½d. on 3d. ultramarine	1 3	1 6

Variety. No stop after "d".

67a	2½d. on 3d. ultramarine	20 0	

1894 (Sept.). *T* 1. *Colour changed.*

68	1d. purple	0 4	0 2

½d (a) ½d (b) ½d (c)

½d (d) ½d (e) ½d (f) ½d (g)

1896 (Nov.). *No.* 51 *surcharged as above.*

No.			
69	½d. on 3d. ultramarine (*a*) ..	1 6	2 0
70	½d. on 3d. ultramarine (*b*) ..	3 0	3 6
71	½d. on 3d. ultramarine (*c*) ..	6 6	6 6
72	½d. on 3d. ultramarine (*d*) ..	5 0	5 6
73	½d. on 3d. ultramarine (*e*) ..	5 0	5 0
74	½d. on 3d. ultramarine (*f*) ..	2 6	3 0
75	½d. on 3d. ultramarine (*g*) ..	1 6	2 0

Types (*a*) and (*e*) differ from types (*b*) and (*f*) respectively, in the serifs of the "1", but owing to faulty overprinting this distinction is not always clearly to be seen.

Variety. Surcharge double.

76	½d. on 3d. ultramarine ..	10 0	10 0

The double surcharges are often different types, but are always type (*g*), or in combination with type (*g*).

Halve Penny.

1896. *No.* 51 *surcharged as above.*

77	½d. on 3d. ultramarine ..	0 4	0 4

Varieties. (i.) *Errors in setting.*

78	½d. on 3d. (no stop) ..	15 0	15 0
79	½d. on 3d. ("Peuny") ..	15 0	15 0
80	½d. on 3d. (no bar) ..	6 0	6 0

(ii.) *Surcharge inverted.*

81	½d. on 3d. ..	30 0	
81*a*	½d. on 3d. (no stop) ..		
81*b*	½d. on 3d. ("Peuny") ..		

(iii.) *Surcharge double, one inverted.*

81*c*	½d. on 3d. (Nos. 77 and 81) ..	£6	£6
81*d*	½d. on 3d. (Nos. 77 and 81*a*) ..	£20	
81*e*	½d. on 3d. (Nos. 77 and 81*b* ..	£25	
81*f*	½d. on 3d. (Nos. 81 and 78) ..		
82	½d. on 3d. (Nos. 81 and 79) ..	—	£25

Nos. 69 *to* 75 *additionally surcharged as last.*

82*a*	"Halve Penny" on No. 69 ..	45 0	
82*b*	"Halve Penny" on No. 70 ..	80 0	
	ba. "Peuny" for "Penny" ..	£35	
	bb. No bar ..	£10	
82*c*	"Halve Penny" on No. 71 ..	£5	
82*d*	"Halve Penny" on No. 72 ..		
82*e*	"Halve Penny" on No. 73 ..	£5	
82*f*	"Halve Penny" on No. 74 ..	£5	
82*g*	"Halve Penny" on No. 75 ..	55 0	
	ga. No stop ..	£27	
	gb. No bar ..	£27	

Surcharge double.

82*k*	"Halve Penny" on No. 76 ..	£20	
	ka. No bar ..	£25	

2½

No. 51 *surcharged as above.*

(*a*) *As in illustration.*

(*b*) *With Roman* "1" *and antique* "2" *in fraction.*

83	2½ on 3d. ultramarine (*a*) ..	1 6	1 6
83*a*	2½ on 3d. ultramarine (*b*)	100 0	45 0

1897–1900. *T* **1.**

84	½d. yellow ..	0 5	0 5
85	½d. orange ..	0 10	0 5
87	1s. brown ..	4 6	5 0

The 6d. blue was prepared for use in the Orange Free State, but had not been brought into use when the stamps were seized in Bloemfontein. A few have been seen without the "V.R.I." overprint, but they were not authorized or available for postage.

II. BRITISH OCCUPATION.

V. R. I.

4d
(31)

1900 (March). *The previous issues of Orange Free State surcharged by Messrs. Curling at Bloemfontein, as T* **31**, *in black.*

The 3d. *stamps, which had already been surcharged* 2½d., *before they were taken over by the British Government, only had the letters* "V.R.I." *overprinted.*

I. First Printings of Each Value with Stops after the Letters on the Line.

101	½d. orange ..	0 9	0 9
102	1d. purple ..	0 9	1 0
103	2d. bright mauve ..	0 9	1 0
104	2½ on 3d. ultram., var. (*a*) ..	2 6	3 6
105	2½ on 3d. ultram., var. (*b*) ..	£6	£6
106	3d. ultramarine ..	1 0	1 0
107	4d. ultramarine ..	3 0	4 0
108	6d. bright carmine ..	35 0	35 0
109	6d. blue ..	1 6	2 0
110	1s. brown ..	1 6	2 0
111	5s. green ..	20 0	22 6

Errors. Stamps of 1868 (*old colours*) *surcharged.*

112	1d. brown ..	£6	£6
113	1s. orange-yellow ..	—	£15

Varieties. (i) *No stop after* "V."

114	½d. orange ..	20 0	20 0
115	1d. purple ..	25 0	25 0
116	2d. bright mauve ..	12 6	12 6
117	2½ on 3d. ultramarine (*a*) ..	60 0	60 0
118	3d. ultramarine ..	10 0	10 0
119	4d. ultramarine ..	40 0	40 0
120	6d. bright carmine ..	£12	250 0
121	6d. blue ..	30 0	30 0
122	1s. brown ..	25 0	25 0
123	5s. green ..	£15	£10

(ii.) *No stop after* "R."

124	1d. purple ..		
125	2d. bright mauve ..		

(iii.) *No stop after* "I."

126	½d. orange ..	£6	£6
127	2d. bright mauve ..		

(iv.) *Figure of value omitted.*

128	½d. orange ..	£8	£8
129	1d. purple ..	150 0	
130	6d. bright carmine ..	£12	£12
131	6d. blue ..	50 0	65 0
132	1s. brown ..	95 0	95 0
	a. Spaced stop after "s" ..	95 0	
133	5s. green ..	£35	

(v.) *Letter " I " of " V.R.I." omitted.*

134 ½d. orange .. ..
135 1d. purple 50 0 50 0
a. Stop after " R " omitted .. 80 0 80 0

There are two varieties of No. 135—one with raised stop after " R " (and the letters " V.R." closer together than in normal overprint), the other (135*a*) without stop after " R."

(vi.) *" V.R.I." omitted.*

136 ½d. orange £10
137 1d. purple £12
138 2d. bright mauve £12
139 6d. blue .. ..
140 1s. brown £8 £6

(vii.) *" d " omitted.*

141 1(d.) purple £15

(viii.) *Value omitted.*

142 (½d.) orange £7
143 (1d.) purple £6
144 (1s.), brown .. .. .. — £8

(ix.) *Small " ½."*

145 ½d. orange 60 0 60 0

(x.) *Inverted stop after " R."*

146 1d. purple £10
147 5s. green £20

(xi.) *Raised stop after " s."*

148 1s. brown 10 0 10 0

(xii.) *Wider space between figure and letter of value.*

149 1d. purple £6 £6
150 1s. brown £5
151 5s. green £6 £6

(xiii.) *" V " and " R " close.*

152 1d. purple .. .. ..

(xiv.) *Surcharge double.*

153 ½d. orange 60 0

(xv.) *Surcharge omitted.*

154 1d. purple £15
155 3d. ultramarine .. ..

These stamps can only be distinguished when joined to a stamp *with* surcharge. Some values may be found with the overprint shifted up or down, so that the value appears above " V.R.I." ; or sideways, showing part of two overprints.

All values of this set are found with a rectangular stop instead of an oval stop after " R " of " V.R.I."

V. R. I.

½d

32 (Thin " V.")

II. SUBSEQUENT PRINTINGS IN WHICH THE NORMAL TYPE HAS ALL STOPS ABOVE THE LINE, AS SHOWN IN T 32.

156 ½d. orange 0 2 0 3
157 1d. purple 0 3 0 3
158 2d. bright mauve 0 6 0 6
159 2½ on 3d. ultram., var. (*a*) £5 £5
160 2½ on 3d. ultram., var. (*b*) £40
161 3d. ultramarine 0 6 0 9
162 4d. ultramarine 1 6 2 6
163 6d. bright carmine 25 0 25 0
164 6d. blue 1 6 1 3
165 1s. brown 1 9 2 0
166 5s. green 5 0 5 0

The shades of the 1d. and 2d. stamps vary considerably in these printings.

Varieties. (i.) *Stops on the line and above the line, mixed.*

167 ½d. orange 3 0 3 6
168 1d. purple 3 0 3 0
169 2d. bright mauve 7 6 10 0
169*a* 2½ on 3d. ultram., var. (*a*)
170 3d. ultramarine 10 0 12 6
171 4d. ultramarine 10 0
172 6d. bright carmine £5 £5
173 6d. blue 10 0 12 6
174 1s. brown 15 0
175 5s. green £18 £18

(ii.) *Stops on the line (one stamp on each pane) with stamp with stops above the line (pair).*

176 ½d. orange 12 0 12 0
177 1d. purple 25 0 25 0
178 2d. bright mauve 15 0 15 0
179 3d. ultramarine 22 0 22 0
180 4d. ultramarine 25 0 25 0
181 6d. bright carmine £12
182 6d. blue 25 0 25 0
183 1s. brown 30 0 30 0
184 5s. green £45

(iii.) *No stop after " V."*

185 ½d. orange 3 6 6 6
186 1d. purple 7 6 7 6
187 3d. ultramarine £10
188 6d. ultramarine .. ..
189 1s. brown .. .. ..

(iv.) *No stop after " R."*

190 1d. purple 15 0 15 0
191 3d. ultramarine .. ..
192 1s. brown .. .. ..

(v.) *No stop after " I."*

193 ½d. orange 40 0 40 0
194 1d. purple 20 0 25 0

(v*a*.) *No stops after " V " and " I."*

194*a* 1d. purple .. .. ..

(vi.) *" V " of " V.R.I." omitted.*

195 ½d. orange .. .. .. £12 10s.

(vii.) *" I " of " V.R.I." omitted.*

196 3d. ultramarine .. .. £15 15s.

(viii.) *" s " of value omitted.*

197 1 (s.), brown 80 0

(ix.) *Surcharge all inverted.*

198 1d. purple £10
199 2d. bright mauve £10

(x.) *Surcharge double.*

200 1d. purple 85 0 60 0
201 3d. ultramarine £15
a. Double, one surch. diagonal ..

(xi.) *Surcharge omitted (in pair with normal).*

202 1d. purple .. .. ..

This variety is from the junction of right and left panes, the right pane being without surcharge.

(xii.) *Short " 1 " in " 1d."*

203 1d. purple £5 95 0

(xiii.) *Short top to " 5."*

204 5s. green 90 0 90 0

(xiv.) *Small " ½."*

205 ½d. orange (No. 156) .. 20 0 22 6
206 ½d. orange (No. 167) .. 20 0 22 6
207 ½d. orange (No. 176) ..

(xv.) *Wide space between " V " and " R ".*

208 ½d. orange .. .. ..
209 1d. purple .. .. .. — £6

(xvi.) *Wide space between " R " and " I ".*

210 1d. purple 50 0

(xvii.) *Wide space between figure and letter of value.*

211 1d. purple .. .. ..

(xviii.) "I" of "V.R.I." *raised.*

212 2d. bright mauve .. ..

Error. Stamp of 1868 (*old colour*) *surcharged with* T 32.

213 1s. orange-yellow £12

V. R. I.

½d

33 (Thick "V.")

(xix.) *Thick* "V," *stops raised* (*T* 33).

214 ½d. orange 0 3 0 4
215 1d. purple 0 4 0 4
216 2d. bright mauve 1 0 1 6
217 2½ on 3d. ultramarine (*a*) .. £30
218 2½ on 3d. ultramarine (*b*) ..
219 3d. ultramarine 2 6 3 0
220 6d. carmine £20
221 6d. blue 4 6 6 6
222 1s. brown 5 0 6 6
223 5s. green 10 0 10 0

(xix*a*.) *Thick* "V" *and inverted* "1" *for* "I."

224 1d. purple 20 0 25 0
225 2d. bright mauve 30 0 30 0
226 3d. ultramarine £5 60 0

(xix*b*.) *Thick* "V." *No stops after* "R" *and* "I."

227 1d. purple £5 50 0

(xix*c*.) *Thick* "V." *No stop after* "R."

228 1d. purple 50 0 50 0

(xix*d*.) *Thick* "V." *Surcharge double.*

229 1d. purple .. .. .. — £10

Stamps with thick "V" occur in certain positions in *later* settings of the type with stops above the line (T 32). *Earlier* settings with stops above the line have all stamps with thin "V."

Some confusion has hitherto been caused by the listing of certain varieties as though they occurred on stamps with thick "V," whereas they occur in panes of the thick "V" settings, but on stamps showing the normal thin "V."

All varieties which occur on stamps with thin "V" are now shown under that heading, whether they occur in panes of the thick "V" settings or not.

As small blocks of unsurcharged Free State stamps could be handed in for surcharging, varieties thus occur which are not found in the complete settings.

III. BRITISH COLONY.

ORANGE
RIVER
COLONY.

(34)

1900–2. *Cape of Good Hope stamps* (*T* 17 *and* 15 *wmk. Cabled Anchor.* P 14) *optd. with* T 34. *in black.*

230 ½d. green (Oct., 1900) .. 0 2 0 3
231 1d. carmine (July, 1902) .. 0 4 0 4
232 2½d. ultramarine (Aug., 1900) 0 6 0 8

Varieties. (i) *Stop after* "COLONY" *omitted.*

233 ½d. green 10 0 12 6
234 1d. carmine 15 0 17 6
235 2½d. ultramarine 30 0 35 0

In the ½d. and 2½d. this was the first stamp in the left lower pane, in the 1d. it is the twelfth stamp in the right lower pane. This was corrected in later printings.

(ii) *Overprint double.*

236 ½d. green .. .. ..

Varieties also exist in which the "E" of "ORANGE" has been printed lower than the other letters of the word.

4d
—
(35)

1902 (Mar.). *The* 6d. (No. 164), *surcharged with* T 35 *in red.*

237 4d. on 6d. blue 1 0 1 6

Varieties. (i) *No stop after* "R".

238 4d. on 6d. blue 30 0 35 0

(ii) *No stop after* "I".

239 4d. on 6d. blue .. ..

(iii) *Thick* "V".

240 4d. on 6d. blue 1 6 2 6

(iv) *Thick* "V" *and inverted* "1" *for* "I".

241 4d. on 6d. blue 5 0 6

E. R. I.

6d

(36)

One
Shilling
*

(37)

Stamps of the Orange Free State surcharged.

1902 (Aug.). *With* T 36, *in black.*

242 6d. blue 2 0 2 6
a. Surcharge double, one inverted £22
b. Wide space between "6" and "d" £6 12 6

1902 (Oct.). *With* T 37 *in orange.*

243 1s. on 5s. green 6 0 6 0

Varieties. (i) *Thick* "V".

244 1s. on 5s. green 12 0 10 0

(ii) *Short top to* "5".

245 1s. on 5s. green £8 50 0

(iii) *Surcharge double.*

246 1s. on 5s. green ..

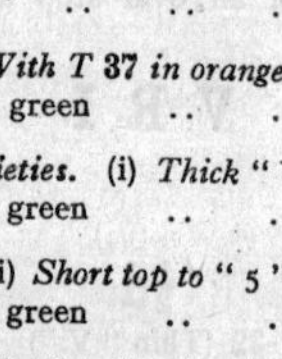

38. Head of King Edward VII, with springbok and gnu beneath.

(Typo. De La Rue & Co.)

1903-4. *T* 38. *Wmk. Crown CA.* *P* 14.

No.	Description				
247	½d. yellow-green	0	8	0	3
248	1d. scarlet	0	5	0	3
249	2d. brown	2	6	1	9
250	2½d. bright blue	1	3	1	6
251	3d. mauve	2	6	0	8
252	4d. scarlet and sage-green	5	0	4	6
	a. Error "IOSTAGE"	£20			
253	6d. scarlet and mauve	3	6	1	6
254	1s. scarlet and bistre	8	0	2	6
255	5s. blue and brown (1904)	26	6	20	0

Several of the above values are found with the overprint "C.S.A.R.", in black, for use by the Central South African Railways.

1905-7. *T* 38. *Wmk. Multiple Crown CA.* *P* 14.

No.	Description				
256	½d. yellow-green (1907)	0	6	0	4
257	1d. scarlet	0	5	0	2
258	4d. scarlet and sage-green	5	0	3	0
	a. Error "IOSTAGE"	80	0	80	0
259	1s. scarlet and bistre	20	0	5	0

POSTCARD STAMPS.

Postage stamps of Type 1 (tree), of several denominations, surcharged or unsurcharged, overprinted with Arms similar to above illustration, and in some cases surcharged in addition, were for use on postcards, the overprinting being done after the stamps were affixed to the cards.

FISCAL STAMPS USED FOR POSTAGE.

F 1

(Typo. De La Rue & Co.)

1882-86. *Type* F 1. *P* 14.

No.	Description				
F1	6d. pearl-grey	1	6	5	0
F2	6d. purple-brown	—		5	0

F 2

Type F 2. *P* 14.

No.	Description				
F 3	1s. purple-brown	2	0	10	0
F 4	1s. pearl-grey	—		20	0
F 5	1s. 6d. blue	3	6	2	0
F 6	2s. magenta	3	6	2	0
F 7	3s. chestnut	4	6	20	0
F 8	4s. grey				
F 9	5s. rose	3	6		
F10	6s. green	—		20	0
F11	7s. violet				
F12	10s. orange	10	0		
F13	£1 purple	15	0		
F14	£2 red-brown	10	0		
F15	£5 green	30	0	10	0

ZES PENCE.

(F 3)

Type F 2 *surcharged with Type* F 3, *in black.*

No.	Description				
F16	6d. on 4s. grey				
F17	6d. on 8s. yellow	50	0		

Postage stamps overprinted for use as Telegraph stamps and used postally were formerly given, but as the bulk of those found have been undoubtedly used for telegraph purposes, and the overprints are so varied as to render it impossible to say with accuracy which stamps were genuinely used for postal purposes, these stamps are now omitted.

Stamps of the UNION OF SOUTH AFRICA are now in use.

PALESTINE.

OCCUPIED ENEMY TERRITORIES (MILITARY) ADMINISTRATION.

1 (2)

(Printed by photo-lithography by the Typographical Dept., Survey of Egypt, Giza, Cairo.)

1918 (10 FEB.). *Wmk. Royal Cypher in column* (*T* 100 *of Great Britain*). *Ungummed. Roul.* 20

No.	Type	Description				
1	1	1 p. indigo	80	0	70	0
		a. Deep blue	70	0	50	0
		b. Blue	80	0	70	0

Control. A 18. (Prices, corner block of 4: No. 1, £18. No. 1a, £15. No. 1b, £18.)

1918 (16 FEB.). *As last* (*issued, without gum*), *surcharged with T* 2.

No.	Type	Description				
2	1	5 m. on 1 p. cobalt-blue	80	0	£5	
		a. Error. "MILLILMES" (No. 10 in sheet)	£80			

Control. B 18 A. (Corner block, £25.)

1918 (5 MAR.). *As* No. 1, *but colour changed and on gummed paper.*

No.	Type	Description				
3	1	1 p. ultramarine	1	3	1	3

Control. C 18. (Corner block, 35s.)

1918 (5 MAR. *and* 13 MAY). *No.* 3 *surcharged with T* 2. *Gummed paper.*

No.	Type	Description				
4	1	5 m. on 1 p. ultramarine	3	6	1	9
		a. Error. Arabic surcharge wholly or partly missing (No. 11 in sheet)	£6			

Controls. C 18 B (Mar.) (Corner block, £20.)
D 18 C (May). (Corner block, £5.)

3

(Typographed by the Stamping Dept., Board of Inland Revenue, Somerset House, London.)

1918 (16 July–27 Dec.). *Wmk. Royal Cypher in column. P* 15×14.

No.	Type					
5	3	1 m. sepia (16 July) ..	0	1	0	1
		a. Deep brown	0	1	0	1
6	,,	2 m. blue-green (16 July) ..	0	2	0	3
		a. Deep green	0	2	0	2
7	,,	3 m. yellow-brown (17 Dec.)	0	3	0	3
		a. Chestnut	7	6	1	6
8	,,	4 m. scarlet (16 July) ..	0	4	0	4
9	,,	5 m. yellow-orange (25 Sept.)	0	4	0	3
		a. Orange	1	0	0	6
10	,,	1 p. deep indigo (9 Nov.) ..	0	6	0	3
11	,,	2 p. pale olive (16 July) ..	1	3	1	3
		a. Olive	1	3	1	3
12	,,	5 p. purple (16 July) ..	1	6	2	6
13	,,	9 p. ochre (17 Dec.) ..	6	0	4	0
14	,,	10 p. ultramarine (17 Dec.)	6	0	4	6
15	,,	20 p. pale grey (27 Dec.) ..	16	0	17	6
		a. Slate-grey	25	0	15	0

There are two sizes of the design of this issue:

19×23 *mm.* 1, 2, and 4 m., and 2 and 5 p.
18×21½ *mm.* 3 and 5 m., and 1, 9, 10, and 20 p.

There are numerous minor plate varieties in this issue, such as stops omitted in "E.E.F.", malformed Arabic characters, etc.

Originally issued by the Military Authorities for use of the civil population in occupied enemy territories (including at one time or another, a large part of Asia Minor), these stamps were used in Palestine until superseded by the following issue. They were finally demonetised on 1 May, 1922.

CIVIL ADMINISTRATION UNDER BRITISH HIGH COMMISSIONER.
(1 July, 1920.)

فلسطين   فلسطين

PALESTINE   PALESTINE

פלשתינה א״י   פלשתינה א״י

(4)   (5)

(Overprinted at the Greek Orthodox Convent, Jerusalem.)

1920 (1 Sept.). *Optd. with T* **4**. (*Arabic* 8 *mm. long.*) (*a*) *P* 15×14.

No.	Type					
16	3	1 m. sepia	0	4	0	4
17	,,	2 m. blue-green	4	0	2	6
18	,,	3 m. chestnut	1	9	1	6
		a. Error. Overprint inverted	£25		£30	
19	,,	4 m. scarlet	0	8	0	6
20	,,	5 m. yellow-orange ..	7	6	2	6
21	,,	1 pi. deep indigo (Silver) ..	0	9	0	8
22	,,	2 pi. deep olive	1	3	1	3
23	,,	5 pi. deep purple	2	0	2	6
24	,,	9 pi. ochre	6	0	7	6
25	,,	10 pi. ultramarine ..	7	6	8	0
26	,,	20 pi. pale grey	12	6	15	0

(*b*) *P* 14.

No.	Type					
27	3	2 m. blue-green	0	4	0	4
28	,,	3 m. chestnut	40	0	50	0
29	,,	5 m. orange	0	9	0	6

An error, consisting of the two Hebrew characters at left transposed, is so far only known on the 2, 5, 9, 10 and 20 pi., though it existed in sheets of all values as first printed.

1920 (22 Sept.)–**1921** (21 June). *Optd. with T* **5***. (*Arabic* 10 *mm. long.*)

(*a*) *P* 15×14.

No.	Type					
30	3	1 m. sepia	0	4	0	5
31	,,	2 m. blue-green	3	6	1	0
32	,,	3 m. yellow-brown	0	6	0	6
33	,,	4 m. scarlet	0	8	0	6
34	,,	5 m. yellow-orange ..	1	3	0	3
35	,,	1 p. deep indigo (Silver)	£15		2	6
36	,,	2 p. olive	40	0	12	6
37	,,	5 p. deep purple	15	0	2	6

(*b*) *P* 14.

No.	Type					
38	3	1 m. sepia	£15		£20	
39	,,	2 m. blue-green	2	0	2	0
40	,,	4 m. scarlet	12	6	17	6
41	,,	5 m. orange	90	0	10	0
		a. Yellow-orange ..	2	0	2	6
42	,,	1 p. deep indigo (Silver) ..	17	6	3	6
43	,,	5 p. purple	65	0	85	0

* In this setting the Arabic and Hebrew characters are badly worn and blunted, the Arabic "s" and "T" are joined (i.e. there is no break in the position indicated by the arrow in our illustration); the letters of "PALESTINE" are often irregular or broken; and the space between the two groups of Hebrew characters varies from 1 mm. to over 1⅜ mm.

(*For clear, sharp overprint, see Nos.* 47 *to* 59.)

فلسطين

PALESTINE

פלשתינה א״י

(6)

1920 (6 Dec.). *Provisionally optd. with T* **6**. (*Opt. measures* 19 *mm. vertically instead of* 20 *mm. and the word* "PALESTINE" *is only* 6 *mm. from Hebrew.*)

(*a*) *P* 15×14.

No.	Type					
44	3	3 m. yellow-brown	27	6	32	6

(*b*) *P* 14.

No.	Type					
45	3	1 m. sepia	10	0	12	6
46	,,	5 m. orange	90	0	40	0

1921 (29 May–4 Aug.). *Optd. as T* **5***.

(*a*) *P* 15×14.

No.	Type					
47	3	1 m. sepia	0	8	0	6
48	,,	2 m. blue-green	1	3	0	9
49	,,	3 m. yellow-brown	10	0	3	6
		a. "PALESTINE" omitted				
50	,,	4 m. scarlet	6	6	1	0
51	,,	5 m. yellow-orange ..	8	6	0	9
52	,,	1 p. deep indigo (Silver) ..	5	0	0	8
53	,,	2 p. olive	10	0	3	0
54	,,	5 p. purple	80	0	12	6
55	,,	9 p. ochre	40	0	50	0
56	,,	10 p. ultramarine	30	0	8	6
57	,,	20 p. pale grey	45	0	30	0

(*b*) *P* 14.

58	3	1 m. sepia	—	£50
59	,,	20 p. pale grey	—	£75

* In this setting the Arabic and Hebrew characters are sharp and pointed as in T 6; there is usually a break between the Arabic "s" and "T" though this is sometimes filled with ink; and the whole overprint is much clearer. The space between the two groups of Hebrew characters is always 1¾ mm. (*cf. note below* No. 43).

فلسطين

PALESTINE

פלשתינה א"י

(7)

(Overprinted by the Stamping Dept., Board of Inland Revenue, Somerset House, London.)

1921. *Optd. with* T 7 ("PALESTINE" *in sans-serif letters*). *Wmk. Royal Cypher in column. P* 15×14.

60	3	1 m. sepia	0	3	0	3
61	,,	2 m. blue-green	0	3	0	4
62	,,	3 m. yellow-brown	0	6	0	4
63	,,	4 m. scarlet	0	6	0	3
64	,,	5 m. yellow-orange ..	0	6	0	2
65	,,	1 p. bright turquoise-blue	1	0	0	3
66	,,	2 p. olive	1	6	0	6
67	,,	5 p. deep purple	4	0	3	0
68	,,	9 p. ochre	8	6	4	6
69	,,	10 p. ultramarine	30	0	35	0
70	,,	20 p. pale grey	£5		£7	

فلسطين

PALESTINE

פלשתינה א"י

(8)

(Printed and overprinted by Waterlow & Sons, Ltd., from new plates.)

1922. T 3 (*redrawn*), *optd. with* T 8. *Wmk. Mult. Script CA.* (*a*) *P* 14.

71	3	1 m. sepia	0	2	0	3
		a. Deep brown	0	3	0	3
		b. Overprint inverted ..	—		£65	
		c. Overprint double ..	£10			
72	,,	2 m. yellow	0	2	0	1
		a. Orange-yellow	0	4	0	2
73	,,	3 m. greenish blue	0	4	0	2
74	,,	4 m. carmine-pink	0	3	0	2
		a. Very thin paper	12	6	12	6
75	,,	5 m. orange	0	4	0	1
76	,,	6 m. blue-green	0	6	0	3
77	,,	7 m. yellow-brown	0	6	0	3
78	,,	8 m. scarlet	0	8	0	3
79	,,	13 m. ultramarine	1	3	0	3
80	,,	1 p. grey	0	8	0	2
81	,,	2 p. olive	1	6	0	5
		a. Overprint inverted ..	£25		£30	
		b. Ochre	£6		1	6
82	,,	5 p. deep purple	3	6	0	10
82*a*	,,	9 p. ochre	£75		£8	
83	,,	10 p. light blue	35	0	1	9
		a. "E.F.F." for "E.E.F." in bottom panel	£40		£40	
84	,,	20 p. bright violet	90	0	37	6

(*b*) *P* 15×14.

86	3	5 p. deep purple	20	0	1	0
87	,,	9 p. ochre	10	0	3	6
88	,,	10 p. light blue	8	6	1	6
		a. "E.F.F." for "E.E.F." in bottom panel	£25		£25	
89	,,	20 p. bright violet	17	6	6	6

In this issue the design of all denominations is the same size, viz. 18 mm. × 21½ mm. Varieties may be found with one or other of the stops between "E.E.F." missing.

9. Rachel's Tomb.

10. Dome of the Rock.

11. Citadel, Jerusalem.

12. Sea of Galilee.

(Designed by F. Taylor. Plates made and stamps printed by Harrison & Sons, Ltd.)

1927–44. *Wmk. Mult. Script CA. P* 13½×14½ (2 *m. to* 20 *m.*) *or* 14.

90	9	2 m. greenish blue ..	0	2	0	1
91	,,	3 m. yellow-green ..	0	2	0	1
92	10	4 m. rose-pink	2	6	1	0
93	11	5 m. orange	0	3	0	1
		a. From coils. Perf. 14½×14 ('36)	1	6	0	6
		b. Yellow (Dec. '44) ..	0	3	0	1
94	10	6 m. pale green	2	0	0	3
		a. Deep green	0	3	0	1
95	11	7 m. scarlet	3	6	0	6
96	10	8 m. yellow-brown ..	3	0	2	0
97	9	10 m. slate	1	0	0	3
		b. Grey ('44)	0	4	0	1
98	10	13 m. ultramarine ..	4	6	0	4
99	11	20 m. dull olive-green ..	0	8	0	2
		a. Bright olive-green (Dec. '44)	0	7	0	2
100	12	50 m. deep dull purple ..	3	0	0	4
		a. Bright pur. (Dec. '44) ..	1	4	0	4
101	,,	90 m. bistre	50	0	40	0
102	,,	100 m. turquoise-blue ..	2	9	0	9
103	,,	200 m. deep violet ..	5	6	2	6
		a. Bright violet (1928) ..				
		b. Blackish vio. (Dec. '44) ..	5	6	2	6

For 5 m. yellow and 10 m., perf. 14½×14, see King George VI Catalogue.

Two sets may be made of the above issue; one on thin paper, and the other on thicker paper with a ribbed appearance.

2 m. stamps in the grey colour of the 10 m. are changelings as also are 50 m. stamps in blue.

1932–44. *New values and colours. Wmk. Mult. Script CA. P* 13½×14½ (4 *m. to* 15 *m.*) *or* 14.

104	10	4 m. purple	0	2	0	1
105	11	7 m. deep violet ..	0	3	0	2
106	10	8 m. scarlet	0	3	0	1
107	,,	13 m. bistre	0	6	0	1
108	,,	15 m. ultramarine ..	0	6	0	1
		a. Grey-blue (Dec. '44) ..	0	6	0	1

POSTAL FISCALS.

Type-set stamps inscribed "O.P.D.A." or "H.J.Z."; British 1d. stamps (No. 336); and Palestine stamps overprinted with one or other of the above groups of letters, or with the word "Devair", with or without surcharge of new value, are fiscal stamps. They are known used as postage stamps, alone, or with other stamps to make up the correct rates, and were passed by the postal authorities, although they were not definitely authorised for postal use.

POSTAGE DUE STAMPS.

D 1

(Typographed at Jerusalem.)

1923. *P* 11.

No.	Type	Description	Unused	Used
D1	D 1	1 m. yellow-brown	0 6	0 9
		a. Imperf.	£6	
		b. Imperf. between (horiz. pair)	£15	
D2	"	2 m. blue-green	0 9	0 6
D3	"	4 m. scarlet	1 0	0 9
D4	"	8 m. mauve	1 6	1 0
		a. Imperf	£6	
D5	"	13 m. steel-blue	2 0	1 6
		a. Imperf. between (horiz. pair)	£20	

Perfectly centered and perforated stamps of this issue are worth considerably more than the above prices, which are for average specimens.

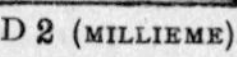

D 2 (MILLIEME).

D 3 (MIL.).

(Types D 2 *and* D 3. Typo. De La Rue & Co.)

1924 (1 Dec.). *Wmk. Mult. Script CA.* *P* 14.

No.	Type	Description	Unused	Used
D 6	D 2	1 m. deep brown	0 4	0 3
D 7	"	2 m. yellow	0 5	0 3
D 8	"	4 m. green	0 6	0 3
D 9	"	8 m. scarlet	1 0	0 6
D10	"	13 m. ultramarine	2 0	1 0
D11	"	5 pi. violet	5 0	2 0

1928–33. *Wmk. Mult. Script CA.* *P* 14.

No.	Type	Description	Unused	Used
D12	D 3	1 m. brown	0 1	0 2
D13	"	2 m. yellow	0 1	0 2
D14	"	4 m. green	0 2	0 3
D14*a*	"	6 m. orange-brown ('33)	0 3	0 3
D15	"	8 m. carmine	0 4	0 4
D16	"	10 m. pale grey	0 4	0 4
D17	"	13 m. ultramarine	0 6	0 9
D18	"	20 m. pale olive-green	0 8	1 0
D19	"	50 m. violet	1 6	1 6

PAPUA.

(BRITISH NEW GUINEA.)

SIMPLIFICATION (see p. xii)

Nos. 1 to 51.

9, 10, 3, 12, 5, 14, 7, 8.
30, 31, 32, 27, 23, 24, 25, 26.
40, 41, 42, 38, 43, 44, 45, 46.

Later Issues.

Omit dies, perfs. and shades.

1 "Lakatoi" (native canoe) with Hanuabada village in the background.

2 (Horizontal).

(Recess. De La Rue & Co.)

1901–5. *T* **1**. *Wmk. Mult. Rosettes, T* **2**. *P* 14.

No.	Description	Unused	Used
	I. *Thick paper. Wmk. horizontal.*		
1	½d. black and yellow-green	3 6	4 6
2	1d. black and carmine	2 6	4 6
3	2d. black and violet	2 6	4 0
4	2½d. black and ultramarine	16 0	22 0
5	4d. black and sepia	22 6	27 6
6	6d. black and myrtle-green	27 6	32 6
7	1s. black and orange	37 6	45 0
8	2s. 6d. black and brown	£12	£12
	II. *Thick paper. Wmk. vertical.*		
9	½d. black and yellow-green	2 0	2 6
10	1d. black and carmine	2 6	3 6
11	2d. black and violet	5 0	6 6
12	2½d. black and ultramarine	12 6	15 0
13	4d. black and sepia	30 0	35 0
14	6d. black and myrtle-green	20 0	25 0
14*a*	1s. black and orange	45 0	52 6
14*b*	2s. 6d. black and brown	£18	
	III. *Thin paper. Wmk. horizontal.*		
14*c*	½d. black and yellow-green	42 6	45 0
14*d*	2½d. black and ultramarine	£5	80 0
14*e*	2½d. black and dull blue	£5	80 0
	IV. *Thin paper. Wmk. vertical.*		
15	½d. black and yellow-green	2 0	2 9
16	1d. black and carmine	—	25 0
17	2d. black and violet	20 0	16 0
18	2½d. black and ultramarine	75 0	85 0
18*a*	2½d. black and dull blue	£5	£6
19	4d. black and sepia	60 0	60 0
20	6d. black and myrtle-green	£8	£10
21	1s. black and orange	£8	£10
22	2s. 6d. black and brown	£12	£12

The twentieth and twenty-eighth stamps of some values show a variety known as "white leaves" caused by a wearing of the plate; the values most affected are the ½d., 2d., 2½d., and 1s.

Papua.

(3)

1906 (8 Nov.). *T* **1** *optd.* *P* 14.

A. *With T* **3** (*large opt.*), *at Port Moresby.*

I. *Thick paper. Wmk. horizontal.*

No.	Description	Unused	Used
23	4d. black and sepia	£5	£6
24	6d. black and myrtle-green ..	20 0	25 0
25	1s. black and orange ..	15 0	17 6
26	2s. 6d. black and brown ..	30 0	40 0

II. *Thick paper. Wmk. vertical.*

No.	Description	Unused	Used
27	2½d. black and ultramarine ..	4 0	5 6
28	4d. black and sepia	£5	£6
29	6d. black and myrtle-green ..	25 0	30 0
29*a*	1s. black and orange ..	£7	£6
29*b*	2s. 6d. black and brown ..	£16	

III. *Thin paper. Wmk. vertical.*

No.	Description	Unused	Used
30	½d. black and yellow-green ..	2 6	3 6
31	1d. black and carmine ..	8 6	10 6
32	2d. black and violet	3 6	4 0

Papua.

(4)

B. *With T* **4** (*small opt.*), *at Brisbane.*

I. *Thick paper. Wmk. horizontal.*

No.	Description	Unused	Used
34	½d. black and yellow-green ..	40 0	45 0
35	2½d. black and dull blue ..	50 0	50 0
36	1s. black and orange.. ..	55 0	55 0
37	2s. 6d. black and brown ..	10 0	10 6

Varieties. (i) *Opt. reading downwards.*

No.	Description	Unused	Used
37*a*	2s. 6d. black and brown (*pair*)	£60	

(ii) *Opt. double.*

No.	Description	Unused	Used
37*b*	2s. 6d. black and brown ..	—	£15

II. *Thick paper. Wmk. vertical.*

No.	Description	Unused	Used
38	2½d. black and ultramarine ..	3 6	4 6
38*a*	1s. black and orange	17 6	20 0
38*b*	2s. 6d. black and brown ..		

Variety. Opt. double.

No.	Description	Unused	Used
38*c*	2½d. black and ultramarine ..		

III. *Thin paper. Wmk. horizontal.*

No.	Description	Unused	Used
38*d*	½d. black and yellow-green..	40 0	50 0
39	2½d. black and ultramarine ..	12 6	15 0
39*a*	2½d. black and dull blue ..	30 0	32 6

Variety. Opt. double.

No.	Description	Unused	Used
39*b*	2½d. black and ultramarine ..		

IV. *Thin paper. Wmk. vertical.*

No.	Description	Unused	Used
40	½d. black and yellow-green ..	2 6	3 0
41	1d. black and carmine ..	2 0	4 0
42	2d. black and violet	2 0	3 6
43	4d. black and sepia	9 0	12 0
44	6d. black and myrtle-green ..	12 6	16 0
45	1s. black and orange.. ..	12 6	16 0
46	2s. 6d. black and brown ..	6 0	12 0

Varieties. (i) *Opt. double.*

No.	Description	Unused	Used
48	½d. black and yellow-green ..		
49	6d. black and myrtle-green ..	£30	

(ii) *Opt. reading upwards.*

No.	Description	Unused	Used
51	1d. black and carmine (*pair*)	£15	£15

In the setting of this overprint Nos. 10, 16, and 21 have the "p" of "Papua" with a defective foot or inverted "d" for "p", and in No. 17 the "pua" of "Papua" is a shade lower than the first "a".

Minor varieties in the sheets can be supplied at following rates above normal for each value :—

"d" for "p", twice normal.

"White leaves," twice normal.

5

1907–10. *Centres in black. Lithographed in Melbourne.* *T* **5** (*small* "PAPUA").

I. *Wmk. Crown over A. Type* w. **11** *upright.*

(*a*) *P* 11.

No.	Description	Unused	Used
52	1d. rose (June, 1908) ..	1 6	2 0
53	2d. purple (Oct., 1908) ..	6 0	7 6
54	2½d. bright ultram. (July, '08)	7 6	10 0
55	2½d. pale ultramarine ..	3 0	4 0
56	4d. sepia (Nov., 1907) ..	3 0	5 0
57	6d. myrtle-green (April, 1908)	12 6	15 0
58	1s. orange (Oct., 1908) ..	10 0	12 6

(*b*) *P* 12½.

No.	Description	Unused	Used
59	2d. purple (Oct., 1908) ..	5 0	6 6
59*a*	2½d. bright ultramarine ..	17 6	25 0
60	2½d. pale ultramarine (7.08) ..	20 0	25 0
61	4d. sepia (Nov., 1907) ..	6 0	6 6
63	1s. orange (Jan., 1909) ..	47 6	57 6

II. *Wmk. sideways.* (*a*) *P* 11.

No.	Description	Unused	Used
64	½d. yellow-green	1 3	2 6
64*a*	½d. deep green..	5 6	6 6
65	1d. carmine (Jan., 1910) ..	2 0	3 0
66	2d. purple (Feb., 1910) ..	3 0	3 6
68	2½d. dull blue (Jan., 1910) ..	3 6	4 6
69	4d. sepia (Jan., 1910).. ..	2 0	4 0
70	6d. myrtle-green (Dec., 1909)	4 0	5 6
71	1s. orange (Mar., 1910) ..	6 0	7 6

(*b*) *P* 12½.

No.	Description	Unused	Used
72	½d. yellow-green (Dec., 1909)	1 6	2 6
73	½d. deep green (1910).. ..	8 0	11 6
74	1d. carmine (Dec., 1909) ..	3 0	4 0
75	2d. purple (Jan., 1910) ..	2 6	3 6
76	2½d. dull blue	2 0	3 6
77	2½d. ultramarine	20 0	25 0
78	6d. myrtle-green	£22	
79	1s. orange	3 0	6 0

(*c*) *P* 11 × 12½.

No.	Description	Unused	Used
79*a*	½d. yellow-green		
80	2d. purple	£12	
80*a*	4d. sepia		

There is a variety of this type showing a white line or "rift" in the clouds, which occurs on the twenty-third stamp of the sheet. Many of these can be supplied at four times the normal price.

The varieties showing white leaves are also to be found in the case of those values where they occurred in the original plate.

7

Type I.

Type II.

T **7** (*large* " PAPUA "). *Centres in black.*

I. *Wmk. upright.* (*a*) *P* 11.

81	½d. yellow-green (1907) ..	0 10	1 3

(*b*) *P* 12½ (1910).

82	½d. green	1 0	1 6
83	1d. carmine	2 0	2 6
84	2d. dull purple	1 6	2 6
	a. " C " for " O " in POSTAGE	27 6	32 6
85	2½d. blue-violet	3 6	5 0
86	4d. sepia	3 6	6 0
87	6d. myrtle-green	3 6	4 0
88	1s. deep orange	3 0	4 0
89	2s. 6d. brown (Type I) ..	7 0	7 6
90	2s. 6d. brown (Type II) ..	7 0	7 6

The three types of the 2s. 6d. (Nos. 89, 90 and 91) can be distinguished by the shape of the numerals and the thickness of the dividing stroke between them, that of Type I being thicker and more uneven, whilst that of Type II is very thin and sharp. In Type III (No. 91, distinguishable also by wmk. and perf.) the numerals are very thin. Type II is a transfer from the original engraved plate, while in Types I and III the figures of value were redrawn.

II. *Wmk. sideways.* *P* 11.

91	2s. 6d. chocolate (Type III) ('08)	15 0	17 6

8

1911–15. *T* **5**, *printed in one colour. Typographed at the Commonwealth Printing Works, Melbourne.* *W* **8** *sideways.*

(*a*) *P* 12½. (1911.)

93	½d. yellow-green	1 6	1 9
93*a*	½d. green	0 8	0 9
94	1d. rose-pink	1 0	1 3
95	2d. bright mauve	0 10	1 0
96	2½d. bright ultramarine ..	3 0	4 0
96*a*	2½d. dull ultramarine ..	3 6	4 6
97	4d. pale olive-green ..	2 0	2 6
98	6d. orange-brown	3 6	3 6
99	1s. yellow	5 0	5 0
100	2s. 6d. rose-carmine ..	8 0	10 0

(*b*) *P* 14. (June, 1915.)

101	1d. rose-pink	7 6	8 6
102	1d. pale scarlet	6 6	7 6

1916. *T* **5**. *Typo. Colour changed, and new values.* *W* **8** *sideways.* *P* 14.

103	1d. black and carmine-red	0 8	0 4
104	3d. blk. and bright blue-grn.	0 10	1 0
105	5s. black and deep green ..	15 0	17 6

ONE PENNY

(9)

1918. *Stamps of* 1911 *surcharged with T* **9**.

106	1d. on ½d. yellow-green ..	0 8	0 10
107	1d. on 2d. bright mauve ..	4 0	6 0
108	1d. on 2½d. ultramarine ..	1 6	4 0
109	1d. on 4d. pale olive-green	1 9	4 0
110	1d. on 6d. orange-brown ..	6 6	8 0
111	1d. on 2s. 6d. rose-carmine	2 0	4 6

1919 (Mar.)–**1931.** *T* **5**. *W* **8**. *P* 14. *Typographed by T. S. Harrison, A. J. Mullett or J. Ash, Printers to the Commonwealth Government.*

112	½d. myrtle and apple-green	0 3	0 4
113	1d. black and red	0 4	0 6
113*a*	1½d. pale ultram. & brn. ('25)	0 8	0 8
	b. " POSTACE " for " POSTAGE " at right	7 6	8 6
114	2d. chocolate and purple ..	1 6	1 6
114*a*	2d. chocolate & lake-red('31)	7 6	5 0
114*b*	2d. chocolate and claret('31)	1 0	0 10
115	2½d. myrtle and ultramarine	2 6	2 9
116	4d. brown and orange ..	1 6	1 9
116*a*	5d. bluish slate & pale brn. ('31)	2 6	3 0
116*b*	6d. dull and bright purple..	2 0	2 6
	c. " POSTACE " for " POSTAGE " at left	25 0	
117	1s. sepia and olive-green ..	5 0	5 0
118	2s. 6d. marone & bright pink (*Ash*)	10 0	10 6
118*a*	2s. 6d. marone and pale pink (*Harrison*)	16 0	
119	10s. grn. & pale ultram. ('25)	35 0	40 0

Ash printings in the above and subsequent issues, where not otherwise described, can often, but not always, be distinguished from others by the white paper on which they are printed.

AIR MAIL

(10)

1929–30. *Air stamps.* *T* **5** *overprinted with T* **10**. *W* **8**. *P* 14.

(*a*) *Ash printing. White paper.*

120	3d. black & bright blue-green	3 0	3 6
	aa. Opt. omitted in horiz. pair with normal	£100	
	ab. Ditto, but vertical pair	£100	
	ac. Overprint vertical, on back ..	£100	
	ad. Overprints tête-bêche (pair) ..	£50	

(*b*) *Cooke printing. Yellowish paper.*

120*a*	3d. black & bright blue-green	3 6	4 0
	ae. Opt. omitted in vert. pair with normal	£100	

(*c*) *Harrison printing. Yellowish paper.*

120*b*	3d. sepia-black & bright blue-green	50 0	55 0

(11)

1930 (15 Sept.). *Air stamps.* *T* **5** *overprinted with T* **11**, *in carmine.*

121	3d. black & blue-green (*Ash*)	1 9	2 6
	a. Harrison printing	£10	
122	6d. dull & bright purp. (*Ash*)	3 6	4 0
	a. " POSTACE " for " POSTAGE " at left (*Ash*) ..	25 0	
	b. Harrison printing	3 6	4 0
	ba. Ditto, " POSTACE " error ..	30 0	
123	1s. sepia & olive-green (*Ash*)	7 6	8 0
	a. Harrison printing	30 0	
	ab. Overprint inverted	£85	

TWO PENCE

(12)

1931 (1 JAN.). *T* **5** *surcharged with T* **12.**

124	2d. on 1½d. ultram. & brown (*Ash*)	1	3	1	6
	a. "POSTACE" for "POSTAGE" at right	20	0		
	b. Mullett printing	7	6		
	c. "POSTACE" error (*Mullett*)	60	0		

The scarcer Mullett printing (No. 124*b*), is distinguishable by its lighter shades—the centre being a very pale ultramarine, and the frame a paler brown.

5d.

FIVE PENCE

(13)

1931. *T* **5** *surcharged as T* **13** (*variously spaced*). *W* **8.** *P* 14.

125	5d. on 1s. sepia & olive-green	2	0	2	6
126	9d. on 2s. 6d. marone & pink (*Ash*)	5	0	6	0
	a. Harrison printing	4	6	5	0
127	1s. 3d. on 5s. blk. & deep grn.	5	0	6	0

14

1932. *T* **5.** *W* **14.** *P* 11.

128	9d. lilac and violet	3	0	3	6
129	1s. 3d. lilac & pale greenish bl.	5	0	6	0

15. Motuan Girl.

16. A Chieftain's Son.

17. Tree Houses.

18. Bird of Paradise.

19. Papuan Dandy.

20. Native Mother and Child.

21. Masked Dancer. **22.** Papuan Motherhood.

23. Papuan shooting fish. **24.** *Dubu*—or Ceremonial Platform.

25. "Lakatoi." **26.** Papuan Art.

27. Pottery Making. **28.** Native Policeman.

29. Lighting a Fire. **30.** Delta House.

(Designed by F. E. Williams (2s. and £1 and frames of other values), and E. Whitehouse (2d., 4d., 6d., 1s., and 10s.); remaining central designs from photographs taken by Messrs. F. E. Williams and Gibson. Recess. John Ash, Melbourne.)

1932 (14 Nov.). *Various designs* (*T* **22** *and* **24** *are shaped as T* **18**; *T* **29** *as T* **20**; *others as T* **15**). *No wmk.* *P* 11.

130	**15**	½d. black and orange ..	0	2	0	3
131	**16**	1d. black and green ..	0	4	0	5
132	**17**	1½d. black and lake ..	0	6	0	8
133	**18**	2d. red	0	8	0	6
134	**19**	3d. black and blue ..	1	0	1	3
135	**20**	4d. olive-green	1	3	1	9
136	**21**	5d. black and slate-green	1	6	1	9
137	**22**	6d. bistre-brown ..	2	0	2	0
138	**23**	9d. black and violet ..	3	0	3	6
139	**24**	1s. dull blue-green ..	3	6	3	6
140	**25**	1s. 3d. black & dull purple	5	0	5	0
141	**26**	2s. black and slate-green	7	6	8	0
142	**27**	2s. 6d. black & rose-mve.	9	0	10	0
143	**28**	5s. black and olive-brown	17	6	20	0
144	**29**	10s. violet	35	0	37	6
145	**30**	£1 black and olive-grey	70	0	75	0

31. Hoisting the Union Jack.

32. Scene on H.M.S. *Nelson.*

(Recess. J. Ash, Melbourne.)

1934 (6 Nov.). *50th Anniv. of Declaration of British Protectorate. P 11.*

No.	Type	Description	Unused	Used
146	31	1d. green	3 0	4 0
147	32	2d. scarlet	5 0	6 0
148	31	3d. blue	10 0	12 6
149	32	5d. purple	20 0	25 0

HIS MAJESTYS JUBILEE.

1910 1935

(33)

HIS MAJESTY'S JUBILEE.

1910 — 1935

(34)

1935 (9 July). *Silver Jubilee. Optd. with T* 33 *or* 34 (*2d.*).

No.	Type	Description	Unused	Used
150	16	1d. black and green ..	0 6	0 10
151	18	2d. scarlet	1 6	2 0
152	19	3d. black and blue ..	4 0	6 0
153	21	5d. black and slate-green	8 0	16 6

OFFICIAL STAMPS.

Stamps Perforated "O S."

We have a number of these in stock with the initials perforated through the stamps. We do not catalogue such varieties, but can send selections to collectors who are interested in them. In most cases the prices are those of used copies of the corresponding number in Catalogue.

O S

(O 1)

(Typo. by T. S. Harrison (1d. and 2s. 6d.) and J. Ash.)

1931 (29 July). *T* 5 *overprinted with Type* O 1. *W* 8. *P* 14.

No.	Description	Unused	Used
O 1	½d. myrtle and pale olive ..	0 2	0 4
O 2	1d. black and red	0 3	0 4
O 3	1½d. pale ultramarine & brn.	0 6	0 9
	a. "POSTACE" for "POSTAGE" at right	12 6	15 0
O 4	2d. chocolate and claret ..	0 8	0 10
O 5	3d. black and blue-green ..	0 9	1 0
O 6	4d. brown and orange ..	1 0	1 3
O 7	5d. bluish slate & pale brown	1 6	2 0
O 8	6d. dull and bright purple ..	1 9	2 6
	a. "POSTACE" for "POSTAGE" at left	20 0	25 0
O 9	1s. sepia and olive-green ..	3 0	4 0
O10	2s. 6d. marone & pink (*Ash*)	8 6	12 0
	a. Harrison printing	9 6	12 6

1932. *T* 5 *overprinted with Type* O 1. *W* 14. *P* 11.

No.	Description	Unused	Used
O11	9d. lilac and violet ..	2 6	3 6
O12	1s. 3d. lilac & pale grnish blue	3 6	4 6

PRINCE EDWARD ISLAND.

— SIMPLIFICATION (see p. xii) —

Nos. 1 to 47a.

9, 12, 14, 16, 18, 20 : 28, 30, 31.
32. 44, 38, 37, 39, 41, 42.

1

2

3

4

5

6

(Electrotyped and printed by Mr. Charles Whiting, Beaufort House, Strand, London.)

T 1 *to* 6.

1861 (1 Jan.). *Yellowish toned paper. P* 9.

No.	Description	Unused	Used
1	2d. rose	75 0	55 0
	a. Imperf. between (pair) ..		
	b. Bisected (1d.) ..		
2	2d. rose-carmine	80 0	60 0
3	3d. blue	£16	£12
	a. Bisected (1½d.)		
4	6d. yellow-green	£15	£8

Rouletted.

No.	Description	Unused	Used
5	2d. rose		

The 2d. and 3d., perf. 9, were authorised to be bisected and used for half their nominal value.

1862. *Yellowish toned paper. P* 11.

No.	Description	Unused	Used
6	1d. brown-orange	50 0	£10
7	9d. bluish lilac	85 0	40 0
8	9d. dull mauve	85 0	45 0

1863–68. *Yellowish toned paper.* (*a*) *P* 11½–12.

No.	Description	Unused	Used
9	1d. yellow-orange	25 0	30 0
	a. Bisected (½d.)		
	b. Imperf.		
	c. Imperf. between (horiz. pair) ..		
10	1d. orange-buff	40 0	45 0
11	1d. yellow	40 0	40 0
12	2d. rose	15 0	17 6
	a. Imperf. between (pair) ..		
	b. Bisected (1d.)		

13 2d. deep rose 15 0 17 6
14 3d. blue 30 0 30 0
a. Imperf. between (pair) .. ..
b. Bisected (1½d.) .. ..
15 3d. deep blue 35 0 27 6
16 4d. black 75 0 75 0
17 6d. yellow-green 50 0 35 0
a. Bisected (3d.) .. ..
18 6d. blue-green (1868) 25 0 50 0
19 9d. lilac 30 0 40 0
20 9d. reddish mauve 17 6 22 6
a. Imperf. between (pair) .. £25
b. Bisected (4½d.) .. ..

(*b*) *Perf. compound of* 11 *and* 11½–12.

21 1d. yellow-orange £9 90 0
22 2d. rose £9 65 0
23 3d. blue £12 95 0
24 4d. black £22 £16
25 6d. yellow-green £12 £8
26 9d. reddish mauve £16 £12

1867–68. *Coarse wove bluish white paper. P* 11½–12.

27 2d. rose 5 0 16 0
28 2d. rose-pink 4 0 16 0
a. Variety "TWO" 80 0
29 3d. pale blue 7 6 27 6
30 3d. blue 7 6 27 6
31 4d. black 5 0 75 0
a. Imperf. between (pair) .. £16
b. Bisected (2d.) .. ..
c. Perf. compound 11 and 11½–12

7

(Engraved and printed by the British-American Bank Note Co., of Montreal and Ottawa.)

1870 (1 June). *T* **7.** *P* 12.

32 4½d. (3d. stg.), yellow-brown .. 22 6 27 6
33 4½d. (3d. stg.), deep brown .. 25 0 27 6

8

9

10

11

12

13

(Electrotyped and printed by Mr. Charles Whiting, London.)

1872 (1 Jan.). *T* **8** *to* **13.** (*a*) *P* 11½–12.

34 1 c. orange 7 6
a. Imperf. 65 0
35 1 c. yellow-orange 7 6 27 6
36 1 c. brown-orange 9 0 27 6
37 3 c. rose 17 6 17 6
a. Stop between "PRINCE EDWARD" 30 0 35 0
b. Bisected 1½ c. .. ..
c. Imperf. between (pair) .. £25

(*b*) *Perf.* 12 *to* 12¼, *large holes.*

38 2 c. blue 6 0 37 6
a. Bisected (1 c.) .. ..
39 4 c. yellow-green 4 0 27 6
a. Imperf. .. £16
40 4 c. deep green 6 0 25 0
41 6 c. black 4 0 32 6
a. Bisected (3 c.) .. .. — £40
b. Imperf. between (vert. pair) .. £18
42 12 c. reddish mauve 5 0 75 0

(*c*) *P* 12½–13, *smaller holes.*

43 1 c. orange 35 0
44 1 c. brown-orange 7 6 25 0
45 3 c. rose 35 0 27 6
a. Stop between "PRINCE EDWARD" 55 0 55 0
45*b* 6 c. black .. .. .. — £22

(*d*) *Perf. compound of* (*a*) *and* (*c*) 11½–12 × 12½–13.

46 1 c. orange 60 0 95 0
47 3 c. rose 95 0 75 0
a. Stop between "PRINCE EDWARD" £22 £16

The stamps were withdrawn 1 July, 1873, when the colony was admitted as a province into the Dominion of Canada.

QUEENSLAND,

SIMPLIFICATION (see p. xii)

Nos. 1 to 127.

1, 2, 3. 4, 5, 6. 14, 15, 16, 17, 19, 20.
36, 37, 32, 27, 29, 49. 51, 52, 55, 58.
59, 62, 64, 65, 67, 68, 70, 72, 73.
94, 96, 100, 101, 102, 105, 109.
116, 117. 118, 120, 121, 123, 125, 127.

Nos. 128 to 165.—

133, 135. 136, 138, 140, 142, 143, 146, 147, 148, 150.
151. 152, 157, 158, 155, 160. 161 to 165.

Nos. 166 to 309.

167, 168, 192, 169, 194, 170, 172, 174, 197.
219, 202, 204, 205: 223, 206: 227, 228, 207. 184, 185, 191.
208, 210, 212, 213, 215. 229.
231, 232, 235, 236, 237, 238, 241, 244, 246, 250, 252, 253, 254.
256, 257. 262. 264*a*, 264*b*. 266. 272, 273: 275, 277, 279, 280.
283. 287, 288, 290, 291, 293, 294, 295, 296, 299, 300.

From 26 January, 1860, to 1 November, 1860, current stamps of New South Wales were used in Queensland. The stamps so used were the 1d., 2d. and 3d. diademed heads, the large square 6d., 8d. and 1s., and the "registered" stamp. Such stamps bearing a Queensland postmark may be included in a collection of the stamps of this country.

1

1*a*

(Dies engraved by Wm. Humphrys, and plates made by Perkins, Bacon & Co.)
Printed and perforated in London.

1860 (1 Nov.). *T* **1.** *Wmk. Large Star, T* **1a.** *Imperf.*

1	1d. carmine-rose	£40	£6 *to* £35
2	2d. blue	£175	£25 *to* £100
3	6d. green	£150	£8 *to* £50

1860 (Nov.). *T* **1.** *W* **1a.** *Perf. clean-cut* 14–15½.

4	1d. carmine-rose (1.11.1860)	£80	£20
5	2d. blue (1.11.1860)	£16	50 0
	a. Imperf. between (pair)		
6	6d. green (15.11.1860)	£15	45 0

2

1860–61. *T* **1.** *Wmk. Small Star, T* **2.** *Perf. clean-cut* 14–15½.

7	2d. blue	£22	£8
	a. Imperf. between (horiz. pair)	—	£35
8	3d. brown (15 April, 1861)	£12	75 0
9	6d. green	£26	70 0
10	1s. violet (15 Nov., 1860)	£22	80 0
11	"REGISTERED," olive-yellow (January, 1861)	£12	75 0
	a. Imperf. between (pair)		

The perforation of the 3d. is that known as "intermediate between clean-cut and rough."

1861 (July (?)). *T* **1.** *W* **2.** *Clean-cut perf.* 14.

12	1d. carmine-rose	90 0	40 0
13	2d. blue	£15	37 6

1861 (Sept.). *T* **1.** *W* **2.** *Rough perf.* 14–15½.

14	1d. carmine-rose	45 0	30 0
15	2d. blue	85 0	17 6
	a. Imperf. between (pair)		
16	3d. brown	20 0	27 6
	a. Imperf. between (pair)		
17	6d. deep green	£10	30 0
18	6d. yellow-green	£12	30 0
19	1s. violet	£20	65 0
20	"REGISTERED," orange-yellow	20 0	25 0

(Printed and perforated in Brisbane.)

1862–63. *T* **1.** *Thick toned paper. No wmk.* (*a*) *Rough pin-perf.* 13.

21	1d. Indian red (16.12.1862)	£25	55 0
22	1d. orange-vermilion (2.1863)	60 0	20 0
	a. Imperf.	—	100 0
	b. Imperf. between (pair)		
23	2d. blue (16 Dec., 1862)	50 0	15 0
24	2d. pale blue	£6	30 0
	a. Imperf.	—	100 0
	b. Imperf. between (horiz. pair)		
25	3d. brown	50 0	35 0
26	6d. apple-green (17.4.1863)	85 0	12 6
27	6d. yellow-green	65 0	10 0
	a. Imperf. between (horiz. pair)		
28	6d. blue-green	£5	30 0
	a. Imperf.	—	£8
29	1s. grey (14 July, 1863)	70 0	12 6
	a. Imperf. between (horiz. pair)		
	b. Imperf. between (vert. pair)		

(*b*) *P* 12½ *square holes* × *rough pin-perf.* 13 (1867).

30	1d. orange-vermilion	50 0	25 0
31	2d. blue	60 0	20 0
32	3d. brown	60 0	20 0
33	6d. apple-green	—	30 0
34	6d. yellow-green	—	30 0
35	1s. grey	£6	35 0
	a. Imperf. between (horiz. pair)		

(*c*) *P* 13 *round holes* (1867).

36	1d. orange-verm. (9.8.1867)	50 0	20 0
37	2d. blue (30 March, 1867)	60 0	8 6
38	2d. pale blue	£8	
	a. Imperf. between (horiz. pair)		
38*b*	3d. brown		
39	6d. apple-green (8.7.1867)	£5	9 0
40	6d. yellow-green	£5	10 6

(*d*) *P* 12½ *square holes* × *perf.* 13 *round holes* (1867)

41	1d. orange-vermilion	—	65 0
42	2d. blue		
43	6d. yellow-green		

1864–65. *T* **1.** *Wmk. Star, T* **2.** (*a*) *Rough pin-perf.* 13.

44	1d. orange-verm. (Jan. 1865)	60 0	20 0
	a. Imperf. between (horiz. pair)	£25	
45	2d. pale blue (Jan., 1865)	70 0	15 0
46	2d. deep blue	80 0	17 6
	a. Imperf. between (vert. pair)		
	b. Bisected (1d.)		
47	6d. yellow-green (Jan., 1865)	£6	20 0
48	6d. deep green	£9	22 6
49	"REGISTERED," orange-yellow (June 21, 1864)	37 6	25 0
	a. Double printed		
	b. Imperf.		

(*b*) *P* 12½ *square holes* × *rough pin-perf.* 13.

50	1d. orange-vermilion	90 0	60 0

1866 (24 Jan.). *T* **1.** *Wmk.* "QUEENSLAND/POSTAGE—POSTAGE/STAMPS—STAMPS" *in three lines in script capitals between wavy lines. Single stamps only show a portion of one or two letters of this wmk. Rough pin-perf.* 13.

51	1d. orange-vermilion	£6	22 6
52	2d. blue	45 0	9 6

1866 (24 Sept). *Lithographed on thick paper. No wmk. P* 13, *round holes.*

53	4d. slate	£6	27 6
55	4d. lilac	45 0	12 6
56	4d. reddish lilac	45 0	17 6
57	5s. bright rose	£10	75 0
58	5s. pale rose	£6	60 0
	a. Imperf. between (vert. pair)		

The "four pence" is from a transfer taken from the 3d. die, and the 5s. was taken from the 1s. die, the final "s" being added. The alteration in the values was made by hand on the stone, and there are many varieties, such as tall and short letters in "FOUR PENCE," some of the letters of "FOUR" smudged out, and differences in the position of the two words. With sufficient material these stamps could certainly be plated.

5

1868–74. *Wmk. small truncated Star, T 5 on each stamp, and the word "*QUEENSLAND*" in single-lined Roman capitals four times in each sheet.* (*a*) *P* 13.

No.		Unused		Used	
59	1d. orange-verm. (18.1.1871)	50	0	5	0
60	2d. pale blue	55	0	5	0
61	2d. blue (3 April, 1868) ..	20	0	3	3
62	2d. bright blue	45	0	3	0
63	2d. greenish blue	85	0	3	6
64	2d. dark blue	60	0	5	0
	a. Imperf.				
65	3d. olive-brown (27.2.1871) ..	85	0	7	6
66	3d. greenish brown	£6		8	6
67	3d. brown	85	0	9	6
68	6d. yellow-grn. (10.11.1871) ..	£8		12	0
69	6d. green	£8		12	0
70	6d. deep green..	£10		22	6
71	1s. dull claret (13.11.1872) ..	£25		65	0
72	1s. brownish grey	£25		55	0
73	1s. mauve (19.2.1874) ..	£12		42	6

(*b*) *P* 12 (*about Feb.*, 1874).

No.		Unused		Used	
74	1d. orange-vermilion	—		40	0
75	2d. blue	—		45	0
76	3d. greenish brown				
77	3d. brown	—		£18	
78	6d. deep green..	—		40	0
79	1s. mauve	—		60	0

(*c*) *P* 13 × 12.

No.		Unused		Used	
80	1d. orange-vermilion	—		£10	
81	2d. blue	—		40	0
82	3d. brown	—		£25	

Reprints were made in 1895 of all five values on the paper of the regular issue, and perforated 13; the colours are:—1d. orange and orange-brown, 2d. dull blue and bright blue, 3d. deep brown, 6d. yellow-green, 1s. red-violet and dull violet. The "Registered" was also reprinted with these on the same paper, but perforated 12.

6

6*a*

Wmk. Crown and Q, T 6.

(*4d., lithographed. Other values recess-printed.*)

1868–75. (*a*) *P* 13.

No.		Unused		Used	
83	1d. oran.-verm. (10.11.1868) ..	50	0	6	0
	a. Imperf.				
84	1d. pale rose-red (4.11.1874) ..	60	0	12	6
85	1d. deep rose-red	80	0	11	6
86	2d. pale blue (4.11.1874) ..	50	0	2	6
87	2d. deep blue (20.11.1868) ..	40	0	2	6
	a. Imperf.	£7			
	b. Imperf. between (vert. pair) ..				
88	3d. brown (11.6.1875) ..	65	0	15	0
89	4d. yellow (1.1.1875)	£25		60	0
90	6d. deep green (9.4.1869)	100	0	12	6
91	6d. yellow-green	75	0	8	0
92	6d. pale apple-grn. (1.1.1875)	120	0	12	6
	a. Imperf.				
93	1s. mauve	—		55	0

1876–78. (*b*) *P* 12.

No.		Unused		Used	
94	1d. deep orange-vermilion ..	35	0	6	6
95	1d. pale orange-vermilion ..	45	0	6	0
	a. Imperf. between (vert. pair) ..				
96	1d. rose-red	50	0	8	6
97	1d. flesh	60	0	15	0
98	2d. pale blue	80	0	22	6
99	2d. bright blue	10	0	1	6
100	2d. deep blue	15	0	2	0
101	3d. brown	40	0	12	6
102	4d. yellow	£15		15	0
103	4d. buff	£15		15	0
104	6d. deep green	£6		10	0
105	6d. green	90	0	6	6
106	6d. yellow-green	£5		7	6
107	6d. apple-green	£6		12	0
108	1s. mauve	40	0	10	0
109	1s. purple	£5		6	6
	a. Imperf. between (pair) ..				

(*c*) *P* 13 × 12.

No.		Unused		Used	
110	1d. orange-vermilion				
111	2d. deep blue				
112	4d. yellow				
113	6d. deep green				

(*d*) *P* 12½ *square holes* × 13 *round holes.*

No.		Unused		Used	
114	1d. orange-vermilion				
115	2d. blue	—		130	0

1879. *No wmk. P* 12.

No.		Unused		Used	
116	6d. pale emerald-green ..	£10		37	6
	a. Imperf. between (horiz. pair) ..	—		£30	

Lilac burelé band at back.

No.		Unused		Used	
117	1s. mauve (*fisc.-canc.* 20/–) ..	90	0	60	0

The *burelé* is usually very indistinct.

Reprints exist of the 1d., 2d., 3d., 6d. and 1s. on thicker paper and in different shades from the originals.

1881. *Lithographed from transfers from the 1s. die. Wmk. Crown and Q, T 6a. P* 12.

No.		Unused		Used	
118	2s. pale blue (6 April, 1881) ..	55	0	35	0
119	2s. blue (*fisc.-canc.* 5/–) ..	40	0	30	0
120	2s. deep blue	60	0	20	0
121	2s. 6d. dull scarlet (28.8.1881)	65	0	45	0
122	2s. 6d. brt. scar. (*fisc.-c.* 7/6)	50	0		
123	5s. pale yell.-ochre (28.8.1881)	40	0	30	0
124	5s. yellow-ochre	40	0	35	0
125	10s. reddish brown (Mar., 1881)	£9		80	0
	a. Imperf.	£10			
126	10s. bistre-brown	£10		80	0
127	20s. rose (*fisc.-canc.* 10/–) ..	£7		60	0

Of the 2s. and 20s. stamps there are five types of each, and of the other values ten types of each.

7

DIE I.

DIE II.

Dies I. and II. occur in the same sheeet.

DIE I. The white horizontal inner line of the triangle in the upper right-hand corner merges into the outer white line of the oval above the "L."

DIE II. The same line is short and does not touch the inner oval.

1879-80. *T* 7. *P* 12.

(*a*) *Wmk. Crown and Q, T* 6.

128 1d. reddish brown (Die I.) .. 52 6 8 6
129 1d. orange-brown (Die I) .. 65 0 8 6
130 1d. reddish brown (Die II.) .. 65 0 8 6
a. Error. "QOEENSLAND" ..
131 2d. blue (Die I.) 65 0 6 0
a. Error. "PENGE" .. ..
132 4d. orange-yellow £15 22 6

The variety "QO" is No. 48 in the first arrangement, and No. 44 in a later arrangement on the sheets. The "PENGE" error is No. 116 on Plate I.

(*b*) *No wmk., with lilac burelé band on back.*

133 1d. reddish brown (Die I.) .. — 55 0
134 1d. reddish brown (Die II.) .. £20 £5
a. Error. "QO" .. .. — £40
135 2d. blue (Die I.) £28 30 0
a. Error. "PENGE" .. .. — £16

(*c*) *Wmk. Crown and Q, T* 6*a*.

136 1d. reddish brown (Die I.) .. 6 6 3 0
a. Imperf. between (pair) .. — £7
137 1d. reddish brown (Die II.) .. 15 0 4 6
a. Error. "QO" £5
b. Imperf. between (pair) .. — £7
138 1d. dull orange (Die I.) .. 6 6 4 0
139 1d. dull orange (Die II.) .. 5 0 4 0
a. Error. "QO" 75 0 40 0
140 1d. scarlet (Die I.) 4 0 1 6
141 1d. scarlet (Die II.) 7 6 2 6
a. Error. "QO" 80 0 45 0
142 2d. bright blue (Die I.) .. 18 6 2 6
143 2d. grey-blue (Die I.) .. 10 0 1 9
a. Error. "PENGE" .. .. — 100 0
b. Imperf. between (pair) ..
144 2d. pale blue (Die II.) .. 22 6 5 0
a. "TW" joined 15 0 2 0
145 2d. deep blue (Die II.) .. 22 6 8 0
a. "TW" joined 15 0 1 6
146 4d. orange-yellow 12 6 3 0
a. Imperf. between (pair) ..
147 6d. deep green 12 0 3 6
a. Imperf. between (pair) ..
148 6d. yellow-green 17 6 3 6
149 1s. deep violet 15 0 5 0
150 1s. pale lilac 10 0 5 0

All these values have been seen imperf. and unused, but we have no evidence that any of them were used in this condition.

The above were printed in sheets of 120, from plates made up of 30 groups of four electrotypes. There are four different types in each group, and two such groups of four are known of the 1d. and 2d., thus giving eight varieties of these two values. There was some resetting of the first plate of the 1d., and there are several plates of the 2d.; the value in the first plate of the latter value is in thinner letters, and in the last plate three types in each group of four have the "TW" of "TWO" joined, the letters of "PENCE" are larger and therefore much closer together, and in one type the "O" of "TWO" is oval, that letter being circular in the other types.

Half-penny

(8)

1880 (21 Feb.). *Nos.* 136 *and* 137 *surcharged with T* 8, *vertically in black.*

151 ½d. on 1d. reddish brown (Die I.) 50 0 40 0
151*a* ½d. on 1d. reddish brown (Die II.) £50
b. Error, "QO" .. .. — £35

9

11

(Recess. Bradbury, Wilkinson & Co.)

1882-86. *T* 9. *Engraved.*

A. *Thin paper. W* 6 *twice sideways. P* 12.

152 2s. bright blue 15 0 10 0
153 2s. 6d. vermilion 30 0 15 0
154 5s. rose 25 0 12 6
155 10s. brown 30 0 30 0
156 £1 deep green 65 0 55 0

B. *Thin paper. W* 6*a twice sideways. P* 12.

157 2s. 6d. vermilion 20 0 15 0
158 5s. rose 22 6 10 0
159 10s. brown £6 40 0
160 £1 deep green 35 0 30 0

C. *Thick paper. Wmk. Large Crown and Q, T* 11. *P* 12.

161 2s. bright blue 35 0 15 0
162 2s. 6d. vermilion 12 6 12 6
163 5s. rose 15 0 15 0
164 10s. brown 22 6 22 6
165 £1 deep green 40 0 15 0

11*a*

12

1882-83. *T* 11*a*. *Wmk. Crown and Q, T* 6*a*. (*a*) *P* 12.

166 1d. pale vermilion-red .. 3 0 0 6
167 1d. deep vermilion-red .. 3 0 0 4
168 2d. blue 4 6 0 4
169 4d. pale yellow 7 6 0 6
170 6d. green 3 6 0 6
171 1s. violet 15 0 2 6
172 1s. lilac 4 0 1 0
173 1s. deep mauve 4 0 1 0
174 1s. pale mauve 5 0 1 0

Variety. Lettered "PENGE."

175 4d. pale yellow .. .. — 40 0

(*b*) *P* 9½×12.

176 1d. pale red 70 0 30 0
177 2d. blue £10 45 0
178 1s. mauve 90 0 35 0

The above were printed from plates made up of groups of four electrotypes as previously. In the 1d. the words of value are followed by a full stop. There are four types each of the 4d., 6d., and 1s., eight types of the 1d., and twelve types of the 2d.

1887-89. *T* 12. *W* 6*a*. (*a*) *P* 12.

179 1d. vermilion-red 2 6 0 6
a. Imperf. 15 0
180 2d. blue 6 0 0 3
181 2s. deep brown 27 6 20 0
182 2s. pale brown 22 6 17 6

(b) P 9½ × 12.

No.	Description				
183	2d. blue	£12		30	0

These are from new plates; four types of each value grouped as before. The 1d. is without stop. In all values, No. 2 in each group of four has the "L" and "A" of "QUEENSLAND" joined at the foot, and No. 3 of the 2d. has "P" of word "PENCE" with a long downstroke. Varieties are known (*perf.* 12) in which the "P" has been made normal, probably by hand on the plate.

In T 12 the shading lines do not extend entirely across, as in T 11*a*, thus leaving a white line down the front of the throat and point of the bust.

13

14

1890–94. *T* **13** (½*d.*), **14** (2½*d.*), **11*a*** (4*d. and* 6*d.*), *and* **12** (*other values*). *W* **6*a*.** *P* 12½, 13 (*comb machine*).

No.	Description				
184	½d. pale green	1	6	0	8
185	½d. deep green	1	6	0	8
186	½d. deep blue-green ..	1	9	0	10
187	1d. vermilion-red	0	6	0	2
188	2d. blue (old plate)	4	0	0	4
189	2d. pale blue (old plate) ..	2	6	0	3
190	2d. pale blue (retouched plate)	2	0	1	0
191	2½d. carmine	2	0	0	6
192	3d. brown	2	0	1	0
193	4d. yellow	3	6	1	6
194	4d. orange	4	0	1	6
195	4d. lemon	7	6	2	0
196	6d. green	4	0	1	3
197	2s. red-brown	10	0	4	0
198	2s. pale brown	11	0	6	6

Varieties. Lettered "PENGE".

No.	Description				
199	4d. yellow	15	0		
200	4d. orange	25	0	10	0
201	4d. lemon				

The 1d. vermilion-red is known *imperf.*

This issue is perforated by a new vertical-comb machine, gauging about 12¾ × 12¾. The 3d. is from a plate similar to those of the last issue, No. 2 in each group of four types having "L" and "A" joined at the foot. The ½d. and 2½d. are likewise in groups of four types, but the differences are very minute. In the ½d. the watermark is sideways. In the retouched plate of the 2d. the letters "L" and "A" no longer touch in No. 2 of each group, and the "P" in No. 3 is normal.

1894–95. *T* **12** (1*d. and* 2*d.*) *and* **11*a*** (1*s.*).

A. *Thick paper. Wmk. Large Crown and Q. T* **11.** (*a*) P 12½, 13.

No.	Description				
202	1d. vermilion-red	2	0	0	6
203	1d. red-orange	1	6	0	8
204	2d. blue (retouched plate) ..	1	0	0	8

(*b*) *P* 12.

No.	Description				
205	1s. mauve	5	0	4	0

B. *Unwmkd. paper; with blue burelé band at back. P* 12½, 13.

No.	Description				
206	1d. deep vermilion-red ..	0	6	0	6

C. *Thin paper. Crown and Q faintly impressed. P* 12½, 13.

No.	Description				
207	2d. blue (retouched plate) ..	3	0		

15

16

17

18

1895–96. *T* **15, 16** (1*d. and* 2*d.*), **17** *and* **18.** *P* 12½, 13.

A. *Watermark Crown and Q, T* **6*a*.**

No.	Description				
208	½d. green	0	6	0	4
209	½d. deep green	0	6	0	4
210	1d. orange-red	1	3	0	3
211	1d. pale red	1	3	0	3
212	2d. blue	0	10	0	1
213	2½d. carmine	3	0	2	0
214	2½d. rose	2	6	1	9
215	5d. purple-brown	3	6	1	6

Variety. Printed both sides.

No.	Description				
216	½d. deep green	20	0		

P 12.

No.	Description				
217	1d. red				
218	2d. blue	—		10	0

B. *Thick paper. Wmk. Large Crown and Q, T* **11** (*portion only showing on each stamp*). (*a*) *P* 12½, 13.

No.	Description				
219	½d. green	0	8	0	8
220	½d. deep green	0	8	0	8

(*b*) *P* 12.

No.	Description				
221	½d. green	10	0		
222	½d. deep green	10	0		

C. *No wmk.; with blue burelé band at back.*

(*a*) *P* 12½, 13.

No.	Description				
223	½d. green	0	4	0	5
224	½d. deep green	0	9		

(*b*) *P* 12.

No.	Description				
225	½d. green	15	0		

Variety without the burelé band.

(*a*) *P* 12½, 13.

No.	Description				
226	½d. green	40	0		

(*b*) *P* 12.

No.	Description				
226*a*	½d. green	60	0		

These are from the margins of the sheet.

D. *Thin paper. with Crown and Q faintly impressed. P* 12½, 13.

No.	Description				
227	½d. green	1	0	1	0
228	1d. orange-red	1	9	1	3

The above are in groups of four as before, but the four types show no prominent differences.

19

1896. *T* **19.** *Wmk. Crown and Q, T* **6a.** *P* 12½, 13.

229	1d. vermilion	0	8	0	2

20

21

22

23

24

25

1897–1907. *T* **20, 21** (*1d., 2d., 3d., 4d. and 6d.*), **22** *to* **25.** *Figures in all corners.* *W* **6a.**

(*a*) P 12½, 13.

231	½d. deep green	0	8	0	8
232	1d. orange-vermilion ..	0	4	0	1
233	1d. vermilion	0	4	0	1
234	2d. blue	0	8	0	2
235	2d. deep blue..	0	6	0	2
236	2½d. rose	2	9	2	6
237	2½d. purple/*blue*	1	6	0	8
238	2½d. brown-purple/*blue* ..	1	3	0	6
239	2½d. slate/*blue*	6	6	5	0
240	3d. brown	2	9	1	0
241	3d. deep brown	1	9	1	0
242	3d. reddish brown (1906) ..	1	9	1	0
243	3d. grey-brown (1907) ..	2	9	1	0
244	4d. yellow	2	0	0	8
245	4d. yellow-buff	2	0	0	8
246	5d. purple-brown	1	6	1	3
247	5d. dull brown (1906) ..	2	0	2	0
248	5d. black-brown (1907) ..	2	9	2	6
249	6d. green	1	6	0	6
250	6d. yellow-green	1	6	0	6
251	1s. pale mauve	4	0	1	9
252	1s. dull mauve	3	6	1	9
253	1s. bright mauve	6	6	2	0
254	2s. turquoise-green	8	6	6	0

(*b*) P 12.

255	½d. deep green				

The 1d. formerly catalogued *perf.* 12×9½, is now omitted, as later information shows that it was printed outside the Government Printing Office and was not an official issue.

1899. *T* **21.** *W* **6a.** (*a*) *Zigzag roulette in black.* (*b*) *The same but plain.* (*c*) *Roulette* (*a*) *and also* (*b*). (*d*) *Roulette* (*b*) *and perf.* 12½, 13. (*e*) *Roulette* (*a*) *and perf.* 12½, 13. (*f*) *Compound of* (*a*), (*b*), *and perf.* 12½, 13.

256	1d. vermilion (*a*)	6	0	6	0
257	1d. vermilion (*b*)	1	3	1	6
258	1d. vermilion (*c*)	5	0		
259	1d. vermilion (*d*)	1	6	1	9
260	1d. vermilion (*e*)	30	0		
261	1d. vermilion (*f*)	50	0		

26

26a

1899–1906. *T* **26.** *W* **6a.** *P* 12½, 13.

262	½d. deep green	0	4	0	3
263	½d. grey-green	0	4	0	3
264	½d. pale green (1906)	0	6	0	6

The stamps of this type, *without wmk.*, are proofs.

1900. *Charity stamps.* *T* **26a** *and horiz. design showing Queen Victoria in medallion, inscr.* "PATRIOTIC FUND 1900". *W* **6.** *P* 12.

264*a*	1d. (1s.) claret	17	6	17	6
264*b*	2d. (2s.), violet	35	0	35	0

These stamps, sold at 1s. and 2s. respectively, paid postage as 1d. and 2d. stamps only, the difference being contributed to a Patriotic Fund.

27

QUEENSLAND

(a)

QUEENSLAND

(*b*)

(Engraved and printed in Melbourne, Victoria.)

1903. *T* **27.** *Dates on stamps are those at which the various colonies were established. Name, lower value tablet, and values in upper corner in second colour. Two varieties of* "QUEENSLAND" (*a*) *and* (*b*). *The letters in* (*a*) *are smaller than in* (*b*). *Wmk. V and Crown, Type* w. **10.** *P* 12½.

265	9d. brown & ultramarine (*a*) ..	3	6	2	6
266	9d. brown & ultramarine (*b*) ..	3	6	2	6

1903. *T 26 and 21. W 6a. P 12.*

No.		Description				
267		½d. green	0	8	0	8
268		1d. vermilion	2	0	1	6
269		2d. blue	—		8	6

1905. *Reissue of T 9. Engraved. P 12½, 13 (irregular).*

No.		Description				
270		2s. 6d. vermilion	50	0	20	0
271		£1 deep green				

1906–10. *Lithographed.*

A. *T 9. Wmk. Crown and Q, T 6a, twice sideways. (a) P 12.*

No.		Description				
272		5s. rose	35	0	20	0
273		£1 deep green	70	0	30	0

(*b*) *P 12½, 13 (irregular).*

No.		Description				
274		£1 deep green	—		50	0

29

30

B. *T 9. Wmk. T 29, twice sideways. P 12½, 13 (irregular).*

No.		Description				
275		2s. 6d. vermilion	18	6	14	0
276		2s. 6d. dull orange (1910)	26	6	20	0
277		5s. rose	18	6	12	6
278		5s. deep rose	22	6	17	6
279		10s. deep brown	30	0	25	0
280		£1 bluish green	60	0	50	0
280a		£1 deep green				

1907. *T 30 (T 21 redrawn). Wmk. Crown and Q, T 6a. P 12½, 13.*

No.		Description				
281		2d. blue	2	9	1	3

The head has been redrawn, the top of the crown being made higher, so that it touches the frame, as do also the back of the chignon and the point of the bust. The forehead has been filled in with lines of shading, and the figures in the corners appear to have been redrawn also.

T 27. Wmk. Crown and double-lined A, Type w. 11. *(a) P 12 × 12½.*

No.		Description				
282		9d. brown and ultramarine (*a*)	20	0	5	0
283		9d. brown and ultramarine (*b*)	3	6	2	0
284		9d. pale brown and blue (*b*)	4	6	2	6

(*b*) *P 11 (1912).*

No.		Description				
285		9d. brown and blue (*b*)	—		£7	

32

T 32 is a second redrawing of T 21. The forehead is again plain, and though the top of the crown is made higher, it does not touch the frame; but the point of the bust and the chignon still touch. The figure in the right lower corner does not touch the line below, and has not the battered appearance of that in the first redrawn type. The stamps are very clearly printed, the lines of shading being distinct.

1908. *Wmk. Crown and single-lined A, T 29.*

(*a*) *P 12½, 13.*

No.	Type	Description				
286	26	½d. deep green	0	10	0	6
287	,,	½d. deep blue-green	0	6	0	4
288	21	1d. vermilion	0	6	0	1
		a. Variety. Imperf.	75	0		
289	30	2d. blue	1	0	0	3
290	32	2d. bright blue	0	10	0	2
291	21	3d. pale brown	3	0	1	0
292	,,	3d. bistre-brown	3	0	1	0
293	,,	4d. yellow	5	6	2	6
294	,,	4d. grey-black	1	9	1	6
295	23	5d. dull brown	3	6	1	6
295a	,,	5d. sepia	7	6	3	0
296	21	6d. yellow-green	3	6	1	6
297	,,	6d. bright green	4	0	1	6
298	24	1s. violet	6	0	3	6
299	,,	1s. bright mauve	5	6	3	6
300	25	2s. turquoise-green	10	0	6	0

(*b*) *P 13 × 11 to 12½.*

No.	Type	Description				
301	26	½d. deep green				
302	21	1d. vermilion	0	6	0	6
303	32	2d. blue	2	0		
304	21	3d. bistre-brown	1	3	1	3
305	,,	4d. grey-black	6	0		
306	23	5d. dull brown	3	6		
307	21	6d. yellow-green	7	6		
308	24	1s. violet	15	0		

The perforation (*b*) is from a machine introduced to help cope with the demands caused by the introduction of penny postage. The three rows at top (or bottom) of the sheet show varieties gauging 13 × 11½, 13 × 11, and 13 × 12 respectively; these can be supplied in strips of three showing the three variations.

1911. *T 21. W 29. Perf. irregular compound, 10½ to 12½.*

No.		Description				
309		1d. vermilion				

This was from another converted machine, formerly used for perforating Railway stamps. The perforation was very unsatisfactory and only one or two sheets were sold.

POSTAL FISCALS.

51

52

T 51. P 13.

A. *No wmk.*

No.	Description				
401	1d. blue	8	6		
402	6d. deep violet	—		17	6
403	1s. blue-green				
404	2s. brown	—		25	0
405	2s. 6d. dull red	—		10	0
406	5s. yellow				
407	10s. green	25	0		
408	20s. rose				

B. *W 52.*

No.	Description				
409	1d. blue	2	0	10	0
410	6d. deep violet	—		15	0
411	6d. blue				
412	1s. blue-green	5	0		
413	2s. brown				
414	10s. green				
415	20s. rose				

53

54

Type **53.** *P* 12 *or* 13.

A. *Wmk. Large Crown and Q, T* **52.**

416	1d. mauve	1	0	1	6
417	6d. red-brown	2	0	3	0
418	1s. green	2	0	3	0
419	2s. blue	3	0	2	6
420	2s. 6d. brick-red	6	0	6	6
421	5s. orange-brown	7	6	6	0
422	10s. brown	—		17	6
423	20s. rose	—		35	0

B. *No wmk. With blue burelé band at back.*

424	1d. mauve	2	6		
425	6d. red-brown	3	6		
426	6d. mauve	5	0		
427	1s. green	3	6	4	6
428	2s. blue	6	0	5	0
429	2s. 6d. vermilion				
430	5s. yellow-brown	—		12	6
431	10s. brown	—		20	0
432	20s. rose	—		25	0

T **54.** *P* 12.

A. *No wmk. With lilac burelé band on back.*

433	1d. violet	—		3	0

B. *Wmk. Crown and Q, T* **6.**

434	1d. violet	1	0	1	3

55

T **55.** *Wmk. Crown and Q, T* **6,** *sideways. P* 12.

435	6d. green	8	6	25	0
436	5s. carmine	17	6	25	0
437	10s. brown	30	0		

Australian stamps are now used in Queensland.

RHODESIA.

(Formerly British South Africa Company.)

— SIMPLIFICATION (see p. xii) **—**

Nos. 119 to 185.

119, 121, 123, 125, 129, 131a, 133, 134, 137, 139, 140, 141a, 144, 145, 146, 148, 149, 151, 152, 153, 154, 155a, 157, 158, 160, 160b, 163, 165.

Nos. 186 to 322.

186, 188b, 190, 192, 193, 194, 195, 286, 197, 256, 291, 201, 208, 223, 260, 225, 227, 265, 295, 230, 268, 247, 270, 233, 272, 301, 236, 274a, 304, 239, 276, 306, 252, 241, 242, 243, 280, 281.

1

2

(Recess. Bradbury, Wilkinson & Co.)

1890 (Dec.). *T* **1** (*1d. to 10s.*) *and* **2** (*higher values*). *Thin wove paper. P* 14, 14½.

1	1d. black	1	0	0	8
2	6d. ultramarine	16	0	7	6
3	6d. deep blue..	3	6	2	0
4	1s. grey-brown	10	0	5	6
5	2s. vermilion	15	0	16	0
6	2s. 6d. grey-purple	16	0	15	0
7	2s. 6d. purple	17	0	15	0
8	5s. orange-yellow	32	6	25	0
9	10s. deep green	40	0	50	0
10	£1 deep blue (*fisc.-c.* 5s.) ..	80	0	55	0
11	£2 rose-red (*fisc.-c.* 10s.)* ..	95	0	50	0
12	£5 sage-green (*fisc.-c.* 5s.) ..	£18		75	0
13	£10 brown (*fisc.-c.* 5s.) ..	£28		95	0

* For later printing of the £2 see No. 74.

Great caution is needed in buying the high values in either used or unused condition, many stamps offered being revenue stamps cleaned and re-gummed or with forged postmarks.

The following sheet watermarks are known in the issues of 1890 and 1891–4. (1) William Collins, Sons & Co's. paper watermarked with the firm's monogram, and "PURE LINEN WOVE BANK" in double-lined capitals. (2) As (1) with "EXTRA STRONG" and "139" added. (3) Paper by Wiggins, Teape & Co., watermarked "W T & Co" in script letters in double-lined wavy border. (4) The same firm's paper, watermarked "1011" in double-lined figures. (5) "WIGGINS TEAPE & CO LONDON" in double-lined block capitals. Many values can also be found on a slightly thicker paper without wmk. but single specimens are not easily distinguishable

½d.

(3)

1891 (Mar.). *Nos.* 2 *and* 4 *surcharged as T* **3.**

14	½d. on 6d. ultramarine ..	40	0	40	0
15	2d. on 6d. ultramarine ..	70	0	75	0
16	4d. on 6d. ultramarine ..	80	0	82	6
17	8d. on 1s. grey-brown ..	90	0	92	6

4

5

(T **4**. Recess. Bradbury, Wilkinson & Co.)

1891–94. *T* **4**. *Value typo. in second colour. Thin wove paper (wmks. as note after No.* 13). *P* 14, 14½.

18	½d. dull blue and verm. (4.'91)	1	6	1	0
19	½d. deep blue and vermilion	1	6	0	6
20	2d. sea-green & verm. (4.'91)	3	0	1	0
21	3d. grey-blk. & grn. (12.'91)	2	6	2	6
22	4d. chestnut & black (4.'91) ..	3	6	2	6
23	8d. rose-lake & ultram. (4.'91)	5	0	7	0
24	8d. red and ultramarine ..	3	6	4	0
25	3s. brown & green (3.'94) ..	35	0	30	0
26	4s. grey-black & ver. (3.'93) ..	22	6	22	6

(Printed by Messrs. Perkins, Bacon & Co. from the Bradbury, Wilkinson plates.)

1895. *T* **4**. *Thick soft wove paper. P* 12½.

27	2d. green and red	4	0	3	0
28	4d. yellow-brown & black ..	5	0	3	6
	a. Imperf. (pair)	£18			

(Centre recess; value typo; by Perkins, Bacon & Co.)

1896–97. *T* **5**. *Wove paper. P* 14.

DIE I. PLATES 1 AND 2.

This die has a small dot to the right of the tail of the right-hand supporter in the coat of arms. Body of lion only partly shaded; in Die II it is heavily shaded all over.

29	1d. scarlet and emerald ..	3	6	1	0
30	2d. brown and mauve ..	4	6	1	9
31	3d. chocolate & ultramarine ..	2	0	1	6
32	4d. ultramarine and mauve ..	3	6	4	0
	a. Imperf. between (pair) ..				
33	6d. mauve and pink	10	0	3	6
34	8d. green and mauve/*buff* ..	3	6	3	0
	a. Imperf. between (pair)				
35	1s. green and blue ..	4	6	2	6
36	3s. green and mauve/*blue* ..	12	6	12	6
37	4s. red and blue/*green* ..	10	0	12	0

Varieties. Imperf.

38	8d. green & mauve/*buff* (*pair*)	£35	
39	3s. green & mauve/*blue* (*pair*)	£60	

DIE II. PLATES 3 AND 4.

41	½d. slate and violet	1	0	1	6
42	1d. scarlet and emerald ..	0	9	1	0
43	2d. brown and mauve ..	2	6	2	0
44	4d. ultramarine and mauve ..	16	0	3	0
45	4d. blue and mauve	1	3	0	8
46	6d. mauve and rose	2	6	1	0
47	2s. indigo and green/*buff* ..	6	6	5	0
48	2s. 6d. brown & pur. /*yellow* ..	12	0	8	0
49	5s. chestnut and emerald ..	10	0	6	6
50	10s. slate & vermilion/*rose* ..	27	6	17	6

PROVISIONALS *used at Bulawayo during the Matabele rebellion.*

One Penny

(6)

THREE PENCE.

(7)

1896 (APRIL). *Stamps of the Company surcharged at Bulawayo with T* **6** *and* **7**, *in black.*

51	**6**	1d. on 3d. (No. 21)	£12	£12
52	,,	1d. on 4s. (No. 26	£10	£7
53	**7**	3d. on 5s. (No. 8)	90 0	90 0

Varieties. (i.) "P" *in* "Penny" *inverted.* (ii.) "y" *in* "Penny" *inverted.* (iii.) *Single bar through original value.* (iv.) "R" *in* "THREE" *inverted.* (v.) "T" *in* "THREE" *inverted.*

54	**6**	1d. on 3d. (i.)		
54*a*	,,	1d. on 4s. (i.)		
55	,,	1d. on 4s. (ii.)		
55*a*	,,	1d. on 4s. (iii.)	£35	
56	**7**	3d. on 5s. (iv.)	£200	
57	,,	3d. on 5s. (v.)		

BRITISH

SOUTH AFRICA

COMPANY.

(8)

1896 (22 MAY). *Contemporary Cape of Good Hope stamps overprinted by Argus Printing Co., Cape Town, with T* **8**, *in black. Wmk. Anchor* (3*d. wmk. Crown CA*). *P* 14.

58	½d. grey-black (No. 48) ..	3	6	3	0
59	1d. rose-red (No. 58)	4	0	3	6
60	2d. deep bistre (No. 50*a*) ..	6	6	5	6
61	3d. pale claret (No. 40) ..	8	6	8	6
62	4d. blue (No. 51)	7	6	6	6
63	6d. deep purple (No. 52*a*) ..	17	6	17	6
64	1s. yellow-ochre (No. 65) ..	35	0	35	0

Error. "COMPANY" *omitted.*

65	4d. blue	£175	

9

(Recess. Waterlow & Sons.)

1897. *T* **9**. *New plates from a redrawn design. Centre in first colour. P* 13½ *to* 16.

66	½d. grey-black and purple ..	1	9	2	0
67	1d. scarlet and emerald ..	2	6	2	6
68	2d. brown and mauve	1	0	1	0
69	3d. brown-red and slate-blue ..	2	6	1	0
	a. Imperf. between (pair) ..	£24			
70	4d. ultramarine and claret ..	1	9	1	0
	a. Imperf. between (pair) ..				
71	6d. dull purple and pink ..	2	0	2	0
72	8d. green and mauve/*buff* ..	5	6	5	0
	a. Imperf. between (pair) ..	—		£22	
73	£1 black & red-brown/*green* ..	60	0	60	0

In T **5** the scrolls above the words "Justice" and "Freedom" pass behind the right leg of the supporting animals. In T **9** the scrolls do not touch the leg.

(Printed by Messrs. Waterlow & Sons from the Bradbury, Wilkinson plate.)

1897 (JAN.). *T* **2**. *P* 15.

74	£2 rosy red	£8	75	0

10

11

12

(Recess. Waterlow & Sons.)

1898–1908. *No wmk.* *P* 13½ *to* 16.

No.	Type	Description	Unused	Used
75	**10**	½d. yellow-green	0 5	0 3
		a. Imperf. between (pair)	£6	
		b. Imperf. (pair)	£10	
76	,,	½d. deep green	15 0	0 5
77	,,	1d. rose	0 5	0 1
		a. Imperf. (pair)	£20	£13
		b. Imperf. between (pair)	£6	
78	,,	1d. red	2 6	0 1
		a. Imperf. between (pair)	60 0	
		b. Imperf. (pair)	£6	
79	,,	2d. brown	0 9	0 3
80	,,	2½d. pale dull blue (1903)	1 3	0 8
		a. Imperf. between (pair)	£8	
81	,,	3d. claret (1908)	6 0	3 0
		a. Imperf. between (pair)	£14	
82	,,	4d. olive	3 6	1 0
		a. Imperf. between (pair)	£16	
83	,,	6d. mauve	4 6	2 6
83*a*	,,	6d. reddish purple	6 6	3 6
84	**11**	1s. bistre-buff	3 6	1 6
		a. Imperf. between (pair)	£22	
84*b*	,,	1s. olive-bistre	£5	
		c. Imperf. (pair)		
		d. Imperf. between (horiz. pair)		
85	,,	2s. 6d. bluish grey (Nov., 1906)	10 0	6 0
		a. Imperf. between (pair)	£20	£12
86	,,	3s. deep violet (May, 1908)	5 0	5 0
87	,,	5s. orange (July, 1901)	10 0	7 0
88	,,	7s. 6d. black (Nov., 1901)	22 6	15 0
89	,,	10s. dull grn. (May, 1908)	10 0	14 6
90	**12**	£1 grey-purple (July, '01) (*fisc.-canc.* 5/–)	40 0	27 6
91	,,	£2 brown (May, 1908)	£6	35 0
92	,,	£5 deep blue (July, 1901)	£20	80 0
93	,,	£10 lilac (7.01) (*fisc.-c.* 7/6)	£35	£5

13. Victoria Falls.

(Recess. Waterlow & Sons.)

1905 (13 July). *Issue commemorating the visit of the British Association to Rhodesia and the opening of the Victoria Falls Bridge across the Zambesi.* *T* **13.** *No wmk.* *P* 13½ *to* 15.

No.	Description	Unused	Used
94	1d. red	2 6	3 0
95	2½d. deep blue	7 6	8 0
96	5d. claret	17 6	17 6
97	1s. blue-green	20 0	22 6
	a. Imperf. between (pair)	£50	
	b. Imperf.		
98	2s. 6d. black	32 6	35 0
99	5s. violet	32 6	37 6

RHODESIA.

(14)

1909 (15 April). *T* **10, 11** *and* **12,** *overprinted as T* **14** (*stop after* "RHODESIA"), *in black.* *No wmk.* *P* 14 *or* 15.

No.	Description	Unused	Used
100	½d. green	0 4	0 3
	a. No stop after "RHODESIA"	20 0	5 0
101	1d. carmine-red	0 5	0 2
	a. No stop	40 0	5 0
	b. Imperf. between (pair)	£6	
101*c*	1d. scarlet	5 0	0 4
	d. Imperf. between (pair)	£8	
102	2d. brown	1 3	1 3
	a. No stop	25 0	15 0
103	2½d. pale dull blue	1 3	0 6
	a. No stop	17 6	5 0
104	3d. claret	2 9	2 3
	a. No stop	60 0	40 0
105	4d. olive	4 0	2 6
	a. No stop	20 0	17 6
106	6d. dull purple	4 6	2 6
	a. No stop	32 6	12 6
106*b*	6d. reddish purple	2 6	1 9
107	1s. bistre-buff	4 6	2 6
	a. No stop	20 0	15 0
108	2s. 6d. bluish grey	7 6	6 6
	a. No stop	17 6	17 6
109	3s. deep violet	7 6	8 6
110	5s. orange	10 0	12 6
	a. No stop	30 0	32 6
111	7s. 6d. black	20 0	15 0
112	10s. dull green	25 0	17 6
	a. No stop	£6	
113	£1 grey-purple	70 0	40 0
	a. Vertical pair, one with and one without overprint	£50	
	b. Overprint in violet	£10	£10
113*c*	£2 brown (*bluish paper*)	£40	£10

In some values the no-stop variety occurs in every stamp in a vertical row of a sheet, in other values only once in a sheet. Other varieties, such as no serif to the right of apex of "A," no serif to top of "R," etc., exist in some values.

RHODESIA.
5d

(15)

RHODESIA.
TWO SHILLINGS.

(16)

1909 (April)–**1911.** *T* **10** *and* **11** *surcharged as T* **15** *and* **16** (2*s.*), *in black.*

No.	Description	Unused	Used
114	5d. on 6d. reddish purple	6 0	4 0
	a. Surcharge in violet	12 0	
115	5d. on 6d. dull purple	5 0	3 0
116	7½d. on 2s. 6d. bluish grey	4 6	3 6
	a. Surcharge in violet	12 0	6 0
117	10d. on 3s. deep violet	6 0	5 0
	a. Surcharge in violet	5 0	4 0
118	2s. on 5s. orange	12 6	7 6

In the 7½d. and 10d. surcharges, the bars are spaced as in T **16.**

17

(Recess. Waterlow & Sons, Ltd.)

1910 (11 Nov.)–**1916.** *T* 17. *No wmk.* (*a*) *P* 14.

No.	Description	Unused	Used
119	½d. yellow-green	0 9	0 5
	a. Imperf.	£9	
120	½d. bluish green	3 0	0 6
121	½d. olive-green	2 6	0 4
122	½d. dull green (1916)	1 6	2 6
123	1d. bright carmine	1 0	0 3
	a. Imperf. between (pair)	£14	
124	1d. carmine-lake	2 6	0 4
125	1d. rose-red	2 6	0 4
126	2d. black and grey	3 0	1 6
127	2d. black-pur. & slate-grey	£7	
128	2d. black & slate-grey	2 6	1 6
129	2d. black and slate	1 6	1 6
130	2d. black & grey-black	2 0	1 9
131	2½d. ultramarine	6 6	4 0
131*a*	2½d. bright ultramarine	3 6	5 0
132	2½d. dull blue	4 0	3 6
133	2½d. chalky blue	4 6	3 6
134	3d. purple and ochre	6 0	2 6
135	3d. purple & yell.-ochre	7 6	2 0
136	3d. magenta & yellow-ochre	25 0	6 6
137	3d. violet and ochre	12 6	6 0
138	4d. greenish black & orange	17 6	9 0
139	4d. brown-pur. & orange	12 6	6 0
140	4d. black and orange	5 0	3 6
141	5d. purple-brn. & olive-grn.	17 6	7 6
141*a*	5d. purple-brn. & olive-yell.	6 0	3 6
142	5d. purple-brn. & ochre (*error*)	£12	80 0
143	5d. lake-brown and olive	25 0	15 0
144	6d. red-brown and mauve	5 0	2 6
145	6d. brown and purple	5 0	2 6
145*a*	6d. bright chestnut & mauve	35 0	6 6
146	8d. black and purple	17 6	15 0
147	8d. dull purple & purple	20 0	10 0
148	8d. greenish black & purple	20 0	10 0
149	10d. scarlet & reddish mauve	6 0	6 0
150	10d. carm. and deep purple	10 0	6 6
151	1s. black and deep blue-grn.	5 0	3 6
152	1s. black & pale blue-green	5 0	3 0
152*a*	1s. purple-black & blue-grn.	—	20 0
153	2s. black & ultramarine	10 0	12 6
154	2s. black & dull blue	40 0	12 6
154*a*	2s. purple-black & ultram.	£9	25 0
155	2s. 6d. black and lake	30 0	
155*a*	2s. 6d. black and crimson	35 0	35 0
156	2s. 6d. sepia & deep crimson	£7	
157	2s. 6d. black & rose-carmine	35 0	30 0
158	3s. green and violet	20 0	25 0
159	5s. vermilion & deep green	35 0	
160	5s. scarlet & pale yell.-grn.	22 6	27 6
160*a*	5s. crimson and yellow-grn.	60 0	
160*b*	7s. 6d. carmine & pale blue	40 0	
161	7s. 6d. carmine & light blue	32 6	35 0
162	7s. 6d. carmine & brt. blue	£6	
163	10s. deep myrtle & orange	70 0	75 0
164	10s. blue-green & orange	£8	
165	£1 carm.-red & bluish black	£9	£10
166	£1 rose-scarlet & bluish blk.	£10	
166*a*	£1 crimson & slate-black	£12	£12
166*b*	£1 scarlet and reddish mauve (*error*)	£60	

(*b*) *P* 15.

No.	Description	Unused	Used
167	½d. blue-green	50 0	1 0
168	½d. yellow-green	50 0	1 9
169	½d. apple-green	75 0	3 0
170	1d. carmine	45 0	0 8
171	2d. black and grey-black	55 0	4 0
172	2½d. ultramarine	25 0	8 0
173	3d. purple & yellow-ochre	£9	8 0
174	4d. black and orange	15 0	8 0
175	5d. lake-brown & olive-green	60 0	30 0
176	6d. brown and mauve	60 0	15 0
177	1s. black and blue-green	60 0	10 0
178	2s. black and dull blue	£14	65 0
179	£1 red and black	£35	£18

(*c*) *P* 15×14 *or* 14×15.

No.	Description	Unused	Used
179*a*	½d. yellow-green (*p.* 14×15)		
180	3d. purple & ochre (*p.* 14×15)	£25	£10
181	4d. black & orge. (*p.* 15×14)	£8	
181*a*	1s. blk. & blue-grn. (*p.* 14×15)	—	£20

(*d*) *P* 13½.

No.	Description	Unused	Used
182	½d. yellow-green	60 0	15 0
183	1d. bright carmine	80 0	16 0
184	2½d. ultramarine	12 6	15 0
185	8d. black and purple	22 6	25 0

Minor plate varieties in T 17 are:—½d. Double dot below "D" in right-hand value tablet. 2d. to £1. Straight stroke in Queen's right ear.

18

(Recess. Waterlow & Sons, Ltd.)

1913–22. *T* 18. *No wmk.*

(i.) *From single working plates.* (*a*) *P* 14.

No.	Description	Unused	Used
186	½d. blue-green	1 6	0 2
	a. Imperf. between (pair)	£8	
187	½d. deep green	1 0	0 1
188	½d. yellow-green	1 0	0 3
	a. Imperf. between (pair)	£15	
188*b*	½d. dull green	0 8	0 1
189	½d. bright green	1 6	0 2
190	1d. rose-carmine	0 6	0 2
	a. Imperf. between (pair)	£10	
191	1d. carmine-red	1 6	0 2
192	1d. brown-red	1 3	0 3
193	1d. red	1 6	0 2
194	1d. scarlet	0 4	0 2
195	1d. rose-red	1 3	0 2
196	1d. crimson	60 0	7 6
	a. Imperf. between (pair)	£15	
197	1½d. brown-ochre (1919)	0 6	0 3
	a. Imperf. between (pair)	£20	
198	1½d. bistre-brown (1917)	0 9	0 4
	a. Imperf. between (pair)		
199	1½d. drab-brown	1 0	0 3
	a. Imperf between (pair)		
200	2½d. deep blue	2 6	2 6
201	2½d. bright blue	2 6	2 6

(*b*) *P* 15.

No.	Description	Unused	Used
202	½d. blue-green	2 3	1 3
203	½d. green	2 0	1 3
204	1d. carmine	£7	2 6
	a. Imperf. between (pair)	£30	
205	1d. brown-red	2 0	1 6
206	1½d. bistre-brown (1919)	4 6	2 0
206*a*	1½d. drab-brown	4 0	2 0
207	2½d. deep blue	5 0	6 0
208	2½d. bright blue	2 0	2 6

(*c*) *P* 14×15.

No.	Description	Unused	Used
208*a*	½d. green	—	£5

(*d*) *P* 15×14.

No.	Description	Unused	Used
208*b*	½d. green	—	£5
208*c*	1½d. drab brown		

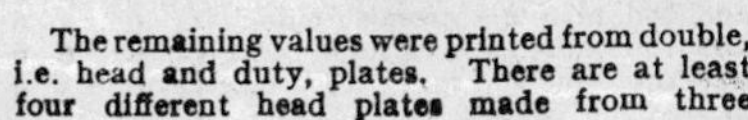

Die I Die II Die III

The remaining values were printed from double, i.e. head and duty, plates. There are at least four different head plates made from three different dies, which may be distinguished as follows :—

Die I. The King's left ear is neither shaded nor outlined ; no outline to cap.

Die II. The ear is shaded all over, but has no outline. The top of the cap has a faint outline.

Die III. The ear is shaded and outlined ; a heavy continuous outline round the cap.

(ii.) *Printed from double plates, head Die* I.

(*a*) *P* 14.

No.		Unused	Used
209	2d. black and grey	7 6	3 0
210	3d. black and yellow ..	20 0	3 6
211	4d. black and orange-red ..	6 0	3 6
212	5d. black and green ..	5 0	3 6
213	6d. black and mauve ..	£6	8 6
214	2s. black and brown ..	22 6	10 0

(*b*) *P* 15.

No.		Unused	Used
215	3d. black and yellow ..	6 6	3 6
216	4d. black and orange-red ..	£10	7 6
217	6d. black and mauve ..	4 0	4 6
218	2s. black and brown.. ..	8 6	8 6

(iii.) *Head Die* II. (*a*) *P* 14.

No.		Unused	Used
219	2d. black and grey	2 6	1 6
220	2d. black and brownish grey	10 0	2 0
221	3d. black and deep yellow	7 6	1 3
222	3d. black and yellow ..	10 0	1 6
223	3d. black and buff	2 0	1 0
224	4d. black and orange-red ..	5 0	1 9
225	4d. black and deep orge.-red	2 6	1 3
226	5d. black and grey-green ..	8 6	2 6
227	5d. black and bright green ..	3 0	3 6
228	6d. black and mauve ..	6 0	1 3
229	6d. black and purple ..	6 0	1 0
230	8d. violet and green ..	6 0	4 0
231	10d. blue and carmine-red ..	10 0	10 0
232	1s. black and greenish blue..	7 0	3 0
233	1s. black and turquoise-blue	4 0	2 0
234	2s. black and brown.. ..	15 0	4 0
235	2s. black and yellow-brown	30 0	4 6
236	2s. 6d. indigo & grey-brown	17 6	6 0
236*a*	3s. brown and blue ..	22 6	7 6
237	3s. chestnut and bright blue	17 6	7 6
238	5s. blue and yellow-green ..	42 6	17 6
239	5s. blue and blue-green ..	17 6	12 6
240	7s. 6d. mauve & grey-black	32 6	35 0
241	10s. crimson & yellow-green	30 0	32 6
242	£1 black and purple ..	£8	£8
243	£1 black and violet ..	£12	£12

(*b*) *P* 15.

No.		Unused	Used
244	2d. black and grey	3 0	2 0
245	4d. black and deep oran-ver.	£10	65 0
246	8d. violet and green ..	£7	60 0
247	10d. blue and red	5 0	5 6
248	1s. black and greenish blue..	5 0	2 6
249	2s. 6d. indigo & grey-brown	17 6	10 0
250	3s. chocolate and blue ..	£22	£6
251	5s. blue and yellow-green ..	40 0	27 6
251*a*	5s. blue and blue-green ..	£16	
252	7s. 6d. mauve & grey-black	30 0	30 0
253	10s. red and green	£16	
254	£1 black and purple ..	£15	

(iv.) *Head Die* III. *Toned paper, yellowish gum.*

(*a*) *P* 14.

No.		Unused	Used
255	2d. black & brownish grey ..	7 6	1 6
256	2d. black and grey-black ..	1 6	0 6
	a. Imperf. between (pair) ..		
257	2d. black and grey	2 6	0 8
258	2d. black and sepia ..	2 0	0 6
259	3d. black and yellow ..	2 6	0 6
260	3d. black and ochre ..	2 6	0 6
261	4d. black and orange-red ..	2 6	0 6
262	4d. black and dull red ..	3 6	0 10
263	5d. black and pale green ..	4 6	2 0
	a. Imperf. between (pair) ..		
264	5d. black and green ..	4 6	2 0
265	6d. black and reddish mauve	4 0	1 3
266	6d. black & dull mauve ..	1 6	1 0
	a. Imperf. between (pair) ..		
267	8d. mauve & dull blue-green	10 0	6 0
268	8d. mauve & greenish blue ..	14 0	4 6
269	10d. indigo and carmine ..	14 0	6 0
270	10d. blue and red	12 6	5 0
271	1s. black and greenish blue	9 6	1 9
272	1s. black & pale blue-green	2 6	1 6
272*a*	1s. black and light blue ..	15 0	3 6
272*b*	1s. black and green	60 0	16 0
273	2s. black and brown ..	10 0	4 0
273*a*	2s. black and yellow-brown	30 0	
274	2s. 6d. deep ult. & grey-brn.	20 0	5 0
274*a*	2s. 6d. pale blue and pale bistre-brown	£5	30 0
274*b*	3s. chestnut and light blue..	32 6	13 6
275	5s. deep blue and blue-green	22 6	12 6
276	5s. blue & pale yellow-green	20 0	12 6
276*a*	7s. 6d. mauve and grey-black	£10	
277	10s. carm.-lake & yell.-green	£10	£5
278	£1 black and bright purple	£7	£7
279	£1 black and deep purple ..	£7	£7
279*a*	£1 black and violet-indigo	£10	£10
279*b*	£1 black and deep violet ..	£10	£8

(*b*) *P* 15.

No.		Unused	Used
279*c*	2d. black and brownish grey	£15	£5

Half Penny (19)

Half- Penny. (20)

1917 (15 Aug.). *No.* 190, *surch. at the Northern Rhodesian Administrative Press, Livingstone with T* 19, *in violet or violet-black.*

No.		Unused	Used
280	½d. on 1d. rose-carmine ..	1 0	1 6
	a. Surcharge inverted ..	£10	
	b. Letters "n n" spaced wider	3 6	
	c. Letters "n y" spaced wider	2 6	2 6

The setting was two rows of 10 three times on the sheet.

Of Variety *a* only two sheets were found.

The two colours of the surcharge occur on the same sheet.

1917 (22 Sept.). *No.* 190 *surch. as T* 20 (*new setting with hyphen, and full stop after* "Penny"), *in deep violet.*

No.		Unused	Used
281	½d. on 1d. rose-carmine ..	1 0	1 6

1922–25. *New printings on white paper, with clear white gum.*

2 (i) *Single working plates.*

(*a*) *P* 14.

No.		Unused	Used
82	½d. dull green (1922) ..	0 4	0 3
	a. Imperf. between (pair) ..		
283	½d. deep blue-green (1923) ..	2 0	0 6
284	1d. bright rose (1922) ..	1 0	0 4
285	1d. bright rose-scarlet (1923)	1 0	0 4
286	1d. aniline red (Oct., 1924) ..	£6	2 6
286*a*	1d. carmine-red (4.25) ..	40 0	5 0
287	1½d. brown-ochre (1923) ..	2 6	0 3
	a. Imperf. between (pair) ..	£20	

(*b*) *P* 15.

No.		Unused	Used
288	½d. dull green (1923) ..	8 6	
289	1d. bright rose-scarlet (1923)	12 6	
290	1½d. brown-ochre (1923) ..	15 0	

(ii.) *Double plates.* Die III.

(*a*) *P* 14.

No.		Unused	Used
291	2d. black & grey-pur. (1922)	1 0	0 4
292	2d. black & slate-pur. (1923)	2 6	1 3
293	3d. black & yellow (1922) ..	8 6	2 6
294	4d. blk. & oran.-ver. (1922–3)	3 0	0 6
295	6d. jet-black & lilac (1922–3)	2 0	0 6
296	8d. mve. & pale bl.-grn. (1922)	10 0	7 6
297	8d. violet & grey-grn. (1923)	12 6	8 6
298	10d. brt. ultram. & red (1922)	7 0	7 0
299	10d. brt. ult. & carm.-red (1923)	8 6	8 6
300	1s. blk. & dull blue (1922-3)	3 0	1 6
	a. Imperf. between (pair) .		
301	2s. black & brown (1922-23)	10 0	2 6
302	2s. 6d. ultram. & sepia (1922)	20 0	5 0

303 2s. 6d. violet-blue & grey-brown (1923) 20 0 4 6
304 3s. red-brown & turquoise-blue (1922) 17 0 3 6
305 3s. red-brown & grey-blue (1923) 30 0 6 6
306 5s. bright ultram. & emerald (1922) 40 0 25 0
307 5s. dp. blue & brt. grn. (1923) 40 0 32 6
308 7s. 6d. plum & slate (1922) .. 50 0 60 0
309 10s. crimson & bright yellow-green (1922) 75 0 75 0
310 10s. carm. & yell.-grn. (1923) 80 0 80 0
311 £1 blk. & dp. magenta (1922) £10
311*a* £1 black & magenta (1923) .. £9 £6

(*b*) *P* 15 (1923).

312 2d. black & slate-purple .. 5 0 6 0
313 4d. black & orange-verm. .. 8 6 10 0
314 6d. jet-black and lilac .. 12 0 12 6
315 8d. violet and grey-green .. 16 0 17 6
316 10d. brt. ultram. & carm.-red 22 6 25 0
317 1s. black and dull blue .. 25 0 27 6
318 2s. black and brown .. 42 6 47 6
319 2s. 6d. vio.-blue & grey-brn. 55 0 60 0
320 3s. red-brn. & grey-blue .. 60 0 70 0
321 5s. deep blue & brt. green .. 80 0 £5
322 £1 black and magenta .. £12 £15

The 1922 printing shows the mesh of the paper very clearly through the gum. In the 1923 printing the gum is very smooth and the mesh of the paper is not so clearly seen. Where date is given as "(1922–23)" two printings were made, which do not differ sufficiently in colour to be listed separately.

For later issues see NORTHERN RHODESIA and SOUTHERN RHODESIA.

ST. CHRISTOPHER.

1

(Typo. De La Rue & Co.)

T 1.

1870 (1 April). *Wmk. Crown CC.* (*a*) *P* 12½.

1 1d. dull rose 22 6 25 0
2 1d. magenta 25 0 20 0
3 1d. pale magenta 30 0 25 0
4 6d. green 60 0 8 0
5 6d. yellow-green 65 0 7 6

(*b*) *P* 14 (1875–76).

6 1d. magenta (*pen-canc.* 2s.) .. 45 0 15 0
a. Bisected diagonally or vert. (½d.) — £5
7 1d. pale magenta 40 0 15 0
8 6d. green 20 0 8 0
a. Imperf. between (pair) ..

No. 1 exists with wmk. sideways.

1879 (Nov.). *Wmk. Crown CC. P* 14.

9 2½d. red-brown 90 0 95 0
10 4d. blue 90 0 17 6

1882–90. *Wmk. Crown CA. P* 14.

11 ½d. dull green 3 0 3 0
12 1d. dull magenta £18 75 0
a. Bisected diagonally (½d.) ..
13 1d. carmine-rose 2 6 3 0
a. Bisected (½d.) .. ..
14 2½d. pale red-brown £6 42 6
15 2½d. deep red-brown £10 42 6
16 2½d. ultramarine (1884) .. 5 0 6 0
17 4d. blue £25 35 0
18 4d. grey (1884) 4 6 5 0
19 6d. olive-brown (1890) .. 50 0 75 0
20 1s. mauve (1887) 60 0 60 0
21 1s. bright mauve 57 6 75 0

Halfpenny (2) FOUR PENCE (3)

1885 (March). *No.* 13 *bisected and No.* 8 *surcharged with T* 2 (*diag.*) *and T* 3 *respectively.*

22 ½d. on half of 1d. carm.-rose .. 35 0 35 0
a. Unsevered pair 75 0 75 0
b. Surcharge inverted £15 £15
23 4d. on 6d. green 45 0 47 6

Varieties.

(i.) *With full stop after* "PENCE."

24 4d. on 6d. green 75 0 75 0

(ii.) *Surcharge double.*

24*a* 4d. on 6d. green .. ..

ONE PENNY. (4) 4d. (5)

1886 (June). *No.* 8 *surcharged with T* 4 *or* 5.

25 1d. on 6d. green 17 6 20 0
26 4d. on 6d. green 60 0 55 0

Varieties.

(i.) *No stop after* "d".

27 4d. on 6d. green £15

(ii.) *Surcharge inverted.*

28 1d. on 6d. green £45

(iii.) *Surcharge double.*

28*a* 1d. on 6d. green .. .. — £75
28*b* 4d. on 6d. green .. .. — £50

No. 28*a* is only known penmarked or with violet handstamp.

ONE PENNY. (6) ONE PENNY. (7)

1887 (May). *No.* 11 *surcharged with T* 6.

29 1d. on ½d. dull green 30 0 30 0

1888 (May). *No.* 16 *surcharged in black.*

I. *Small surcharge, similar to T* 6, *but letters* 2 *mm. high, and* "PENNY" 12 *mm. long. No bar through old value.*

33 1d. on 2½d. ultramarine .. — £500

II. *With T* 7.

35 1d. on 2½d. ultramarine .. 55 0 55 0

Variety. Surcharge inverted.

36 1d. on 2½d. ultramarine .. — £150

The 1d. of Antigua was used provisionally in St. Christopher in 1890, but can only be distinguished by the postmark, which is "A 12" in place of "A 02."

REVENUE STAMPS USED FOR POSTAGE.

SAINT KITTS
NEVIS

REVENUE (8)

REVENUE (9)

Wmk. Crown C 4. P 14.

1883. *Nevis stamps, T* **5**, *overprinted* " REVENUE " *in black, and* " Saint Christopher " *in violet, as T* **8**.

51	1d. lilac-mauve	65	0		
52	6d. green	35	0	55	0

1885. *T* **1** *overprinted with T* **9**, *in black.*

53	1d. rose	2	6	3	6
54	3d. mauve	5	0	6	6
55	6d. orange-brown	5	0	6	6
56	1s. olive	4	0	8	0

Other fiscal stamps with overprints as above also exist, but none of these was ever available for postal purposes.

The stamps for St. Christopher were superseded by the general issue for Leeward Islands on 31st October, 1890.

For later issues see also " St. Kitts-Nevis."

ST. CHRISTOPHER AND NEVIS.

See **ST. KITTS-NEVIS.**

ST. HELENA.

SIMPLIFICATION (see p. xii)

Nos. 1 to 45.

1, 2a. 3, 5. 7, 8, 9, 10.
23, 24, 14, 22, 25, 18a. 26, 27, 28. 31, 32.
35, 36, 38, 39, 40, 41, 42, 43a, 44, 45.

1

(Recess. Perkins, Bacon & Co.)

T **1**. *Wmk. Large Star, Type* w. 1.

1856 (Jan.). *Imperf.*

1	6d. blue	£12	£10

1861 (April (?)). *Clean-cut perf.* 14 *to* 16.

2	6d. blue	£30	£10

1863 (Jan.). *Rough perf.* 14 *to* 16.

2a	6d. blue	£10	£8

ONE PENNY (2)

FOUR PENCE (3)

ONE SHILLING (4)

ONE SHILLING (5)

ONE PENNY (6)

ONE SHILLING (7)

(Printed by Messrs. De La Rue & Co.)

> **NOTE.**—The issues which follow consist of 6d. stamps, T **1**, printed in various colours and (except in the case of the 6d. values) surcharged with a new value, as T **2** to **7**, *e.g.* stamps described as " 1d." are, in fact, 1d. on 6d. stamps, and so on.
>
> The numbers in the Type column below refer to the *types of the lettering* of the surcharge.

The supply of 6d. stamps printed by Messrs. Perkins Bacon & Co. lasted till the year 1873.

Wmk. Crown CC.

1863 (July). *Thin bar approximately the same length as the words. Two varieties of the* 1d. *Imperf.*

3	**2**	1d. lake (bar 16–17 mm.) ..	90	0	95	0
		a. Surcharge double	£75			
4	**2**	1d. lake (bar 18½–19 mm.)	75	0	80	0
4a	,,	1d. brown-red	£15			
5	**3**	4d. carm. (bar 15½–16½ mm.)	£12		£12	
		a. Surcharge double				

Error. Surcharge omitted.

6	6d. lake	£250	

1864–83.

(A) *Thin bar* (16½ *to* 17 *mm.*) *nearly the same length as the words. P* 12½ (1864–67).

7	**2**	1d. lake	22	6	22	6
8	**3**	3d. purple	75	0	50	0
9	,,	4d. carmine	55	0	45	0
		a. Surcharge double	£100		£125	
10	**4**	1s. deep yellow-green ..	45	0	27	6
		a. Surcharge double				

(B) *Thick bar* (14 *to* 14½ *mm.*) *much shorter than words* (*except in the* 2d., *where it is nearly the same length*). (*a*) *P* 12½ (1865–68).

12	**2**	1d. lake	65	0	55	0
13	**3**	2d. yellow (1868)	50	0	45	0
14	,,	3d. purple (1868)	35	0	30	0
14a	,,	3d. light purple	£25		£30	
15	,,	4d. carmine (words 18 mm.)	65	0	45	0
16	,,	4d. carmine-rose (words 19 mm.)	95	0	55	0
17	**5**	1s. deep yellow-green ..	£10		60	0
18	,,	5s. yellow (1868)	80	0	80	0
18a	,,	5s. orange (1868)	42	6	45	0

Varieties. (i) *Surcharge double.*

18b	**2**	1d. lake		
18c	**3**	3d. purple	—	£100
18d	,,	4d. carmine	£90	£90
18e	**5**	1s. deep yellow-green ..	£250	

(ii) *Surcharged with the long and short surcharges on same stamp.*

18f	**3**	4d. carmine	

(iii) *Imperf.*

18g	**2**	1d. lake	£40
18h	**3**	2d. yellow	£75
18i	,,	3d. purple	£55
18j	,,	4d. carmine	£100

(iv) *Surcharge omitted.*

18k	6d. carmine	
18l	6d. deep yellow-green ..	£200

A sheet of 1s., deep yellow-green, was found some years ago on which the surcharge had shifted, causing the fifth row of 12 stamps to be doubly surcharged, and the tenth row of 12 stamps to be without surcharge.

(*b*) *P* 14×12½ (1882).

No.	Type	Description	Unused	Used
19	2	1d. lake	20 0	20 0
20	3	2d. yellow	52 6	35 0
21	,,	3d. purple	£8	60 0
22	,,	4d. carm. (words 16½ mm.)	45 0	32 6

(*c*) *P* 14 (1883).

No.	Type	Description	Unused	Used
23	2	1d. lake	17 6	17 6
24	3	2d. yellow	25 0	17 6
25	5	1s. yellow-green	15 0	12 6

(C) *Words of surcharge same length as bar* (17 *to* 18 *mm.*), *the* 1*d. in thin, taller type.*

(*a*) *P* 12½ (1871–73).

No.	Type	Description	Unused	Used
26	6	1d. lake	12 6	12 6
		a. Surcharge in blue-black ..	£15	£10
27	6	2d. yellow	75 0	27 6
		a. Surcharge in blue-black ..	£175	£40
28	7	1s. deep green	£8	15 0
		a. Surcharge in blue-black ..		

(*b*) *P* 14×12½ (1882).

No.	Type	Description	Unused	Used
29	7	1s. deep green	90 0	20 0

1873–89. *T* **1.** *No surcharge. Wmk. Crown CC.*

(*a*) *P* 12½.

No.	Description	Unused	Used
30	6d. dull blue (1873)	£17	95 0
31	6d. ultramarine (1874) ..	£10	65 0

(*b*) *P* 14×12½ (1882).

No.	Description	Unused	Used
32	6d. milky blue..	75 0	30 0

(*c*) *P* 14 (1889).

No.	Description	Unused	Used
33	6d. milky blue..	60 0	25 0

2½d

(8)

1884–94. *Sixpenny stamps printed as before and surcharged similarly to* (B) *above* (*except the* 2½*d., which is surcharged with T* **8**, *and the* 1*s., in which the bar is nearly the same length as the words*). *Two varieties of the* ½*d.*—(*a*) *words* 17 *mm.* (*b*) *words* 14½ *mm. The* 6*d. as before without surcharge.*

Wmk. Crown CA. P 14.

No.	Type	Description	Unused	Used
34	3	½d. green (*a*)	1 9	2 6
35	,,	½d. emerald (*a*)	5 0	5 6
		a. Surcharge double	£25	
36	3	½d. deep green (*b*) (1894) ..	0 9	1 6
37	2	1d. red (1887)	3 0	2 6
38	,,	1d. pale red (1887) ..	1 6	1 6
39	3	2d. yellow (1894)	1 9	2 6
40	8	2½d. ultramarine (1893) ..	2 0	2 6
		a. Surcharge double	£175	
		b. Stamp printed double ..	£100	
41	3	3d. mauve (1887)	2 6	3 6
42	,,	3d. deep violet (1887) ..	2 0	3 6
		a. Surcharge double	£100	
43	3	4d. p. brown (words 16½ mm.) (1890)	5 0	5 0
43*a*	,,	4d. sepia (words 17 mm.) ..	4 0	4 6
44	–	6d. grey (1889)	4 0	4 6
45	7	1s. yellow-green (1894) ..	10 0	12 6
		a. Surcharge double		

Specimens of the above are sometimes found showing no watermark; these are from the bottom row of the sheet, which has escaped the watermark.

Some are found without bar and others with bar at top of stamp, but this is due to careless overprinting.

Of the 2½d. with double surcharge only six copies exist, and of the 2½d. with the stamp double printed, one row of 12 stamps existed on one sheet only.

9

10

(Typo. De La Rue & Co.)

1890–97. *T* 9. *Wmk. Crown CA. P* 14.

Plate I for the 1½*d. Plate II for the other values* (*for difference see Seychelles*).

No.	Description	Unused	Used
46	½d. green (1897)	1 3	1 6
47	1d. carmine (1896)	2 6	3 0
48	1½d. red-brown & green (1890)	3 6	4 6
49	2d. orange-yellow (1896) ..	5 0	5 0
50	2½d. ultramarine (1896) ..	5 0	5 0
51	5d. violet (1896)	8 6	10 0
52	10d. brown (1896)	12 6	12 6

NOTE.—Nos. 36–52, both inclusive, and No. 18*a*, have been sold cancelled with a violet diamond-shaped grille with four interior bars extending over two stamps. These cannot be considered as *used* stamps, and they are consequently not priced in the list.

This violet obliteration is easily removed and many of these remainders were cleaned in Paris and offered as unused; some were re-postmarked with a date and name in thin type rather larger than the original, a usual date being "Ap. 4.01."

1902 (Mar.). *T* **10.** *Wmk. Crown CA. P* 14.

No.	Description	Unused	Used
53	½d. green	1 0	1 3
54	1d. carmine	5 0	6 0

11. Government House. **12.** The Wharf.

(Typo. De La Rue & Co.)

1903 (June). *T* **11** (½*d.*, 2*d.*, *and* 1*s.*) *and* **12.** *Picture in second colour. Wmk. Crown CC. P* 14.

No.	Description	Unused	Used
55	½d. grey-green and brown ..	1 3	1 6
56	1d. carmine and black ..	2 6	2 6
	a. Bluish paper	40 0	35 0
57	2d. sage-green and black ..	15 0	15 0
58	8d. brown and black	20 0	20 0
59	1s. brown-orange and brown	25 0	25 0
60	2s. violet and black	37 6	37 6

13

(Typo. De La Rue & Co.)

1908 (May). *T* **13.** *Wmk. Mult. Crown CA. P* 14.

No.	Description				
64	2½d. blue, O	4	0	4	6
66	4d. black and red/*yellow*, OC	4	6	6	0
67	6d. dull and deep purple, OC	4	6	6	6

Wmk. Crown CA.

No.	Description		
71	10s. green and red/*green*, C ..	£12	£14

14 15

(Typo. De La Rue & Co.)

1912–16. *T* 14 (½*d.*, 2*d.*, 3*d.*, *and* 1*s.*) *and* **15.** *Picture in black. Wmk. Mult. Crown CA. P* 14.

No.	Description				
72	½d. green	0	9	0	10
73	1d. carmine-red	1	3	1	3
73*a*	1d. scarlet (1916)	1	3	1	3
74	1½d. orange	2	6	3	0
75	2d. greyish slate	4	0	4	6
76	2½d. bright blue	5	0	6	0
77	3d. purple/*yellow*	5	0	6	0
78	8d. dull purple	8	0	10	0
79	1s. black/*green*	15	0	17	6
80	2s. blue/*blue*	20	0	22	6
81	3s. violet	30	0	32	6

No. 73*a* is on thicker paper than 73.

16 17

(Typo. De La Rue & Co.)

1912. *T* **16.** *Wmk. Mult. Crown CA. P* 14.

No.	Description				
83	4d. black and red/*yellow*, C ..	10	0	12	6
84	6d. dull and deep purple, C ..	4	0	4	6

1913. *T* **17.** *Wmk. Mult. Crown CA. P* 14.

No.	Description				
85	4d. black and red/*yellow*, O ..	4	0	4	6
86	6d. dull and deep purple, O ..	4	6	5	0

WAR TAX
ONE PENNY
(18)

WAR TAX
1d.
(19)

1916 (Sept.). *T* 15, *thin paper, surcharged with T* 18, *in black.*

No.	Description				
87	1d.+1d. black and scarlet ..	0	8	0	10
	a. Surcharge double				

1919. *T* 15, *thicker paper, surcharged with T* 19, *in black.*

No.	Description				
88	1d.+1d. black & carmine-red	0	6	0	8

1922 (Jan.). *T* 14 (3*d.*) *and* **15** *printed in one colour. Wmk. Mult. Script CA. P* 14.

No.	Description				
89	1d. green	2	0	2	6
90	1½d. rose-scarlet	3	6	4	0
91	3d. bright blue	6	0	7	6

20. Badge of St. Helena.

(Des. T. Bruce. Typo. De La Rue & Co.)

1922–27. *T* **20.** *P* 14. (*a*) *Wmk. Mult. Crown CA.*

No.	Description				
92	4d. grey and black/*yellow*, C ..	6	6	7	6
93	1s. 6d. grey & grn./*bl.-grn.*, C	22	6	25	0
94	2s. 6d. grey & red/*yellow*, C ..	22	6	25	0
95	5s. grey and green/*yellow*, C ..	45	0	50	0
96	£1 grey and purple/*red*, C ..	£9		£10	

The paper of No. 93 is bluish on the surface with a full green back.

(*b*) *Wmk. Mult. Script CA.*

No.	Description				
97	½d. grey and black, C ..	0	6	0	6
98	1d. grey and green, C ..	0	8	0	8
99	1½d. rose-red, C	1	9	2	0
	a. Carmine-rose	5	0	6	0
	b. Deep carmine-red ..	25	0	25	0
100	2d. grey and slate, C ..	2	0	2	6
101	3d. bright blue, C	2	0	2	6
103	5d. grn. & car./*green*, C ('27)	6	0	7	0
104	6d. grey & bright purple, C	4	6	5	0
105	8d. grey and bright violet, C	6	0	7	0
106	1s. grey and brown, C ..	10	0	11	6
107	1s. 6d. grey & green/*green* ..	12	6	15	0
108	2s. purple & blue/*blue*, C ('27)	15	0	17	6
109	2s. 6d. grey & red/*yellow* ..	20	0	22	6
110	5s. grey and green/*yellow* ..	40	0	45	0
111	7s. 6d. grey and yell.-orge., C	55	0	60	0
112	10s. grey and olive-green, C	75	0	85	0
113	15s. grey and purple/*blue*, C	£50		£55	

21. Lot and Lot's wife.

22. The "Plantation."
23. Map of St. Helena.
24. Quay at Jamestown.
25. James Valley.
26. Jamestown.
27. Mundens Promontory.

28. St. Helena.

29. High Knoll. **30.** Badge of St. Helena.

Types **21** to **30** are horizontal except T **28.**

(Recess. Bradbury, Wilkinson & Co., Ltd.)

1934 (23 April). *Centenary of British Colonization. T* **21** *to* **30.** *Wmk. Mult. Script CA. P* 12.

114	½d. black and purple ..	1	0	1	6
115	1d. black and green ..	1	6	1	9
116	1½d. black and scarlet ..	3	6	4	0
117	2d. black and orange ..	5	0	5	6
118	3d. black and blue ..	7	0	8	0
119	6d. black and light blue ..	14	0	16	6
120	1s. black and chocolate ..	35	0	40	0
121	2s. 6d. black and lake ..	65	0	70	0
122	5s. black and chocolate ..	£7		£8	
123	10s. black and purple ..	£16		£18	

1935 (6 May). *Silver Jubilee. As T* **13** *of Antigua, inscr.* "ST. HELENA". *Recess. D.L.R. & Co. Wmk. Mult. Script CA. P* 13½ × 14.

124	1½d. deep blue and carmine ..	1	9	2	6
125	2d. ultramarine and grey ..	4	0	5	0
126	6d. green and indigo ..	12	6	15	0
127	1s. slate and purple ..	30	0	35	0

ST. KITTS-NEVIS.

Christopher Columbus.
1

Medicinal spring.
2

(Typo. De La Rue & Co.)

1903. *T* **1** (*½d., 2d., 2½d., 6d., 1s., 2s. 6d.*) *and* **2** (*other values*). *Wmk. Crown CA. P* 14.

1	½d. dull purple and deep green	1	3	1	6
2	1d. grey-black and carmine ..	1	9	1	0
3	2d. dull purple and brown ..	10	0	10	0
4	2½d. grey-black and blue ..	12	6	12	6
5	3d. deep green and orange ..	12	6	12	6
6	6d. grey-black & bright purple	12	6	12	6
7	1s. grey-green and orange ..	12	6	15	0
8	2s. deep green and grey-black	15	0	17	6
9	2s. 6d. grey-black and violet	20	0	20	0
10	5s. dull purple and sage-green	40	0	42	6

1905–9. *T* **1** *and* **2.** *Wmk. Mult. Crown CA. P* 14.

11	½d. dull pur. & deep grn., O	17	6	15	0
12	1d. grey-black & carmine, C	3	0	3	0
13	2d. dull purple & brown, OC	3	6	4	0
14	2½d. grey-black and blue, O ..	20	0	20	0
15	3d. deep green & orange, OC	4	0	4	6
16	6d. grey-black & deep vio., O	17	6	20	0
16*a*	6d. grey-black and deep pur., C (1908)	10	0	12	6
17	1s. grey-grn. & orge., OC ('09)	7	6	8	6

1907–18. *T* **1** *and* **2.** *Wmk. Mult. Crown CA. P* 14.

19	½d. grey-green, O	1	0	1	0
19*a*	½d. dull blue-green, O ..	1	0	1	0
20	1d. carmine, O	1	3	1	0
20*a*	1d. scarlet, O	1	3	1	0
21	2½d. bright blue, O	2	6	3	6
22	6d. grey-black and bright pur., C ('16)	7	6	7	6
23	5s. dull purple & sage-green, C (Nov. 1918)	40	0	65	0

WAR TAX (3) **WAR STAMP** (3*a*)

1916 (Oct.). *T* **1** *optd. with T* **3.** *Wmk. Mult. Crown CA. P* 14.

24	½d. green	0	2	0	3
25	½d. grey-green	0	3	0	4

1918 (Aug.). *T* **1,** *Special printing, optd. with T* **3a,** *in black.*

26	1½d. orange	0	6	0	8

4

5

(Typo. De La Rue & Co.)

1920–22. *T* **4** *and* **5.** *Wmk. Mult. Crown CA. P* 14.

27	**4**	½d. blue-green, O	0	9	1	0
28	**5**	1d. carmine, O	1	3	1	6
29	**4**	1½d. orange-yellow, O ..	2	0	2	0
30	**5**	2d. slate-grey, O	5	0	6	0
31	**4**	2½d. ultramarine, O ..	4	6	4	6
32	**5**	3d. purple/*yellow*, C ..	4	0	4	6
33	**4**	6d. dull pur. & brt. mve., C	5	0	6	0
34	**5**	1s. grey & black/*green*, C ..	8	6	10	0
35	**4**	2s. dull pur. & blue/*blue*, C	12	6	12	6
36	**5**	2s. 6d. grey & red/*blue*, C ..	22	6	25	0
37	**4**	5s. grn. & red/*pale yellow*, C	22	6	30	0
38	**5**	10s. green and red/*green*, C	40	0	47	6
39	**4**	£1 pur. & blk./*red*, C (1922)	£14		£15	

1921–27. *T* **4** *and* **5.** *Wmk. Mult. Script CA. P* 14.

No.	Description	Unused	Used
40	½d. blue-green, O	0 4	0 6
40*a*	½d. yellow-green, O	0 6	0 8
41	1d. rose-carmine, O	0 9	0 10
42	2d. slate-grey, O	1 6	1 9
43	2½d. pale bright blue, O	5 0	6 0
43*a*	2½d. ultramarine, C (1927)	3 0	3 6
43*b*	2½d. ultramarine, O (1927)	2 6	3 0
43*c*	6d. dull & bright purple, C	4 6	5 0
44	2s. purple and blue/*blue*, C	17 6	20 0
44*a*	2s. 6d. black & red/*blue*, C ('27)	22 6	25 0

1922–29. *T* **4** *and* **5.** *Colours changed. Wmk. Mult. Script CA. P* 14.

No.	Description	Unused	Used
45	1d. deep violet, O	1 0	1 0
45*a*	1d. pale violet, O ('29)	1 0	1 0
45*b*	1½d. red, O (1925)	2 0	2 0
45*c*	1½d. red-brown, O ('29)	1 6	1 6
46	2½d. brown, O	3 0	3 6
47	3d. dull ultramarine, O	3 6	4 0
47*a*	3d. purple/*yellow*, C	3 0	4 6
47*b*	1s. black/*green*, C ('29)	10 0	10 6
47*c*	5s. green & red/*yell.*, C ('29)	30 0	35 0

6. Old Road Bay and Mount Misery.

(Typo. De La Rue & Co.)

1923. *Tercentenary Commemorative series. T* **6.** *Centres in black. Chalk-surfaced paper. P* 14.

(*a*) *Wmk. Mult. Script CA.*

No.	Description	Unused	Used
48	½d. green	2 6	2 6
49	1d. bright violet	2 6	2 6
50	1½d. scarlet	8 6	8 6
51	2d. slate-grey	6 0	7 0
52	2½d. brown	10 0	12 6
53	3d. ultramarine	10 6	12 6
54	6d. bright purple	22 6	25 0
55	1s. sage-green	30 0	32 6
56	2s. blue/*blue*	47 6	60 0
57	2s. 6d. red/*blue*	70 0	80 0
58	10s. red/*emerald*	£20	£22

(*b*) *Wmk. Mult. Crown CA.*

No.	Description	Unused	Used
59	5s. red/*pale yellow*	£7	£8
60	£1 purple/*red*	£35	£40

The remainders of this issue were destroyed on 7th March, 1924.

1935 (6 May). *Silver Jubilee. As T* **13** *of Antigua, inscr.* "ST. CHRISTOPHER AND NEVIS". *Recess. W'low. & Sons. Wmk. Mult. Script CA. P* 11×12.

No.	Description	Unused	Used
61	1d. deep blue and scarlet	0 8	1 3
62	1½d. ultramarine and grey	1 6	2 6
63	2½d. brown and deep blue	5 0	7 6
64	1s. slate and purple	17 6	22 6

ST. LUCIA.

1

(Recess. Perkins Bacon & Co.)

1860 (18 Dec.). *T* **1.** *Wmk. Small Star, T* w. **2.** *P* 14 *to* 16.

No.	Description	Unused	Used
1	(1d.) rose-red	65 0	67 6
	a. Imperf. between (horiz. pair)		
	b. Double impression		
2	(4d.) blue	£20	£20
2*a*	(4d.) deep blue	£18	£18
	b. Imperf. between (horiz. pair)		
3	(6d.) green	£20	£20
	a. Imperf. between (horiz. pair)		
4	(6d.) deep green	£18	£18

(Printed by Messrs. De La Rue & Co.)

1863. *Wmk. Crown CC. P* 12½.

No.	Description	Unused	Used
5	(1d.) lake	60 0	65 0
	a. Imperf.	£15	
6	(1d.) brownish lake	85 0	95 0
7	(4d.) indigo	£5	£6
	a. Imperf.	£25	
8	(6d.) emerald green	£12	£10

Half penny

(2)

Prepared for use, but not issued.

T **1** *surch. as T* **2.** *Wmk. Crown CC. P* 12½

No.	Description	Unused	Used
8*a*	½d. on (6d.) emerald-green	50 0	
8*b*	6d. on (4d.) indigo	£40	

1864 (19 Nov.). *Wmk. Crown CC.* (*a*) *P* 12½.

No.	Description	Unused	Used
9	(1d.) black	17 6	17 6
10	(1d.) intense black	20 0	18 0
	a. Imperf	95 0	
11	(4d.) yellow	£12	60 0
12	(4d.) chrome-yellow	£12	45 0
13	(6d.) violet	70 0	40 0
14	(6d.) mauve	£12	55 0
	a. Imperf.	£25	
14*b*	(6d.) deep lilac	£10	45 0
	c. Imperf.	£20	
15	(1s.) brown-orange	£12	40 0
	a. Imperf.	£30	
16	(1s.) orange	£10	35 0

(*b*) *P* 14.

No.	Description	Unused	Used
17	(1d.) black	20 0	20 0
18	(4d.) yellow	70 0	32 6
19	(6d.) mauve	£5	37 6
20	(6d.) pale lilac	£5	40 0
21	(1s.) orange	£15	35 0
22	(1s.) deep orange	£12	40 0

HALFPENNY (3) 2½ PENCE (4)

T **1** *surcharged with value in black or carmine* (C.).

A. **1881** (Sept.). *Wmk. Crown CC. P* 14. *With T* **3** *or* **4.**

No.	Description	Unused	Used
23	½d. green	40 0	40 0
24	2½d. brown-red	30 0	27 6

The 1d. black is known surcharged "1d." in violet ink by hand, but as there is no evidence that this was done officially, this variety is now omitted.

B. **1882–84.** *Wmk. Crown CA. As T* **3.**

(*a*) *P* 14.

No.	Description	Unused	Used
25	½d. green (1882)	22 6	25 0
26	1d. black (C.)	22 6	25 0
	a. Bisected		
27	4d. yellow	£10	45 0
28	6d. violet	30 0	37 6
29	1s. orange	£20	£20

(b) P 12.

No.	Description	Unused	Used
30	4d. yellow	£20	47 6

The *deep blue* stamps, wmk. Crown CA, perf. 14 or 12, are fiscals from which the overprints "THREE PENCE—REVENUE", or "REVENUE", have been fraudulently removed.

5

(Typo. De La Rue & Co.)

1882–86. *T* **5**. *Wmk. Crown CA. P* 14. Die I.

No.	Description	Unused	Used
31	½d. dull green	6 6	7 6
32	1d. carmine-rose	25 0	25 0
33	2½d. blue	17 6	6 0
34	4d. brown (1885)	17 6	8 0
	a. Imperf.	£12	
35	6d. lilac (1886)	£12	£15
	a. Imperf.	£20	
36	1s. orange-brown (1885) ..	£20	£12

T **5**. *Wmk. Crown CA. P* 14.

1886–87. Die I.

No.	Description	Unused	Used
39	1d. dull mauve	5 0	5 0
	a. Imperf.	£20	
40	3d. dull mauve and green ..	35 0	22 6
41	6d. dull mauve & blue (1887)	7 6	8 0
42	1s. dull mauve & red (1887)..	40 0	27 6

1891–98. Die II.

No.	Description	Unused	Used
43	½d. dull green	0 10	0 10
44	1d. dull mauve	1 6	1 6
45	2d. ultramarine & orange ('98)	5 0	6 0
46	2½d. ultramarine	4 6	2 6
47	3d. dull mauve and green ..	7 6	8 0
48	4d. brown	7 0	7 6
49	6d. dull mauve and blue ..	10 6	10 6
50	1s. dull mauve and red ..	12 0	12 0
51	5s. dull mauve and orange ..	37 6	37 6
52	10s. dull mauve and black ..	55 0	55 0

For description and illustration of differences between Die I *and* Die II *see* Introduction.

ONE HALF PENNY (6) $\frac{1}{2}d$ (7) ONE PENNY (8)

1891–92. *Stamps of Die I surch. in black.*

No.	Description	Unused	Used
53	**6** ½d. on 3d. dull mve. & grn.	£5	70 0
54	**7** ½d. on half 6d. dull mauve and blue	40 0	37 6
	a. No fraction bar	£10	75 0
	b. Surcharge sideways ..	£50	
	c. Surcharge double ..		
	d. "2" in fraction omitted ..		
	e. Thick "1" with sloping serif	95 0	
55	**8** 1d. on 4d. brown (Dec. '91)	10 0	12 0
	a. Surcharge double	£12	
	b. Surcharge inverted ..	—	£45

Stamp of Die II surcharged in black.

No.	Description	Unused	Used
56	**6** ½d. on 3d. dull mve. & grn.	55 0	50 0
	a. Surcharge double		
	b. Surcharge inverted .. .	£95	£45

There is a variety of T **6** with narrow "O" in "ONE", and two varieties of the "*d*" in T **7**.

9 10

(Typo. De La Rue & Co.)

1902–3. *T* **9** *and* **10** (3*d. and* 1*s.*). *Wmk. Crown CA. P* 14.

No.	Description	Unused	Used
58	½d. dull purple and green ..	1 9	1 6
59	1d. dull purple and carmine ..	1 9	1 9
60	2½d. dull purple & ultramarine	17 6	17 6
61	3d. dull purple and yellow ..	10 0	10 0
62	1s. green and black	17 6	15 0

11. The Pitons.

(Recess. De La Rue & Co.)

1902. *T* **11**. *Centre in first colour. Wmk. Crown CC, sideways. P* 14.

No.	Description	Unused	Used
63	2d. green and brown	7 6	8 6

1904–10. *T* **9** (½*d.*, 1*d.*, *and* 2½*d.*) *and* **10**. *Wmk. Mult. Crown CA. P* 14.

No.	Description	Unused	Used
64	½d. dull pur. & green, C ..	1 9	1 0
	a. Ordinary paper	1 9	1 0
65	1d. dull purple & carmine, C	3 0	1 3
	a. Ordinary paper	2 6	1 0
66	2½d. dull pur. & ultramarine, C	10 0	10 0
	a. Ordinary paper	10 6	10 6
67	3d. dull purple and yellow, O	10 0	10 0
68	6d. dull pur. & violet, C ('05)	17 6	20 0
	a. Ordinary paper	12 6	15 0
68*b*	6d. dull purple, C (1910) ..	20 0	22 6
69	1s. green and black, C (1905)	25 0	30 0
71	5s. green & carm., O (1905) ..	55 0	57 6

1907–9 *T* **9** *and* **10** *Wmk. Mult. Crown CA. P* 14.

No.	Description	Unused	Used
72	½d. green, O	1 6	0 10
73	1d. carmine, O	1 9	0 10
74	2½d. blue, O	4 6	5 0
75	3d. purple/*yellow*, C (1909) ..	5 0	6 0
76	6d. dull and bright purple, C	20 0	22 6
77	1s. black/*green*, C (1909) ..	20 0	22 6
78	5s. green and red/*yellow*, C ..	50 0	60 0

12 13

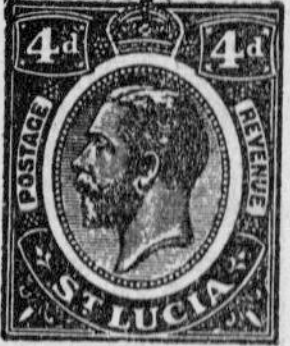

14

15

16

(Typo. De La Rue & Co.)

1912–19 *T* 12 *to* 16 *Wmk. Mult. Crown CA. P* 14.

No.	Type	Description				
79	12	½d. deep green, O ..	0	6	0	4
80	,,	½d. yellow-green, O (1916)	0	8	0	4
81	,,	1d. carmine-red, O ..	3	6	1	6
82	,,	1d. scarlet, O (1916) ..	2	6	1	6
82a	,,	1d. rose-red, O	0	9	0	8
83	13	2d. grey, O	4	6	4	6
83a	,,	2d. slate-grey, O (1916) ..	4	6	4	0
84	12	2½d. ultramarine, O ..	6	0	6	6
84a	,,	2½d. bright blue, O (1918)	3	0	3	6
84b	,,	2½d. deep bright blue, O ..	5	0	6	0
85	15	3d. purple/*yellow*, C ..	3	0	3	0
		a. *On pale yellow* (Die I) ..	7	6	6	6
		b. *On pale yellow* (Die II) ..	12	0	12	6
86	14	4d. black & red/*yellow*, C	4	6	5	0
		a. *White back*	3	6	4	0
88	15	6d. dull & bright pur., C	6	0	6	0
88a	,,	6d. grey-pur. & pur., C ('18)	7	0	8	0
89	,,	1s. black/*green*, C ..	12	0	12	6
		a. *On blue-green, olive back* ..	10	6	12	0
90	16	2s. 6d. blk. & red/*blue*, C	17	6	20	0
91	15	5s. green & red/*yellow*, C	22	6	25	0

WAR TAX (17) WAR TAX (18)

1916 (June). *T* 12 *optd. locally with T* 17.

No.	Description				
92	1d. scarlet	7	6	8	0
	a. Overprint double	£15		£15	
92b	1d. carmine	45	0	45	0

1916 (Sept.). *T* 12 *optd. in London with T* 18.

No.	Description				
93	1d. scarlet	0	3	0	4

1920. *T* 15. *Colour changed. Wmk. Mult. Crown CA. P* 14.

No.	Description				
94	1s. orange-brown, C	6	6	7	6

1921–26 *T* 12 *to* 16 *Wmk. Mult. Script CA. P* 14.

No.	Description				
95	½d. green, O	0	4	0	4
96	1d. rose-carmine, O ..	6	0	6	6
97	2d. slate-grey, O ..	1	3	0	9
98	2½d. bright blue, O	2	0	2	6
98a	2½d. dull blue, O (1926) ..	5	0	6	0
98b	3d. purple/*yellow*, C (1926)	3	0	3	0
98c	3d. deep purple/*yellow*, C ..	4	0	4	6
99	4d. black and red/*yellow*, C	3	6	4	0
100	6d. grey-purple & purple, C	4	0	4	6
101	1s. orange-brown, C ..	10	0	10	6
102	2s. 6d. black & red/*blue*, C	17	6	20	0
103	5s. green & red/*pale yell.*, C	30	0	30	0

1922–26 *Colours changed and new value. Wmk. Mult. Script CA. P* 14.

No.	Type	Description				
104	12	1d. deep brown, O ..	0	8	0	8
105	14	1½d. dull carmine, O ..	1	0	1	6
106	12	2½d. orange, O	10	0	10	6
107	15	3d. bright blue, O ..	12	6	15	0
108	,,	3d. dull blue, O (1926) ..	4	6	5	0

1935 (6 May). *Silver Jubilee. As T* 13 *of Antigua, inscr.* "ST. LUCIA". *Recess. D.L.R. & Co. Wmk. Mult. Script CA. P* 13½×14.

No.	Description				
109	½d. black and green	0	8	1	9
110	2d. ultramarine and grey ..	4	6	5	0
111	2½d. brown and deep blue ..	7	6	8	0
112	1s. slate and purple ..	22	6	25	0

19. Port Castries.

20. Columbus Square, Castries (*horiz.*).

21. Ventine Falls.

22. Fort Rodney, Pigeon Island (*horiz.*).

23. Inniskilling Monument (*vert.*).

24. Government House (*horiz.*).

25. The Badge of the Colony (*horiz.*).

(Recess. De La Rue & Co., Ltd.)

1936 (Mar.–Apr.). *Various designs. Wmk. Mult. Script CA. P* 14 *or* 13×12 (1s. *and* 10s.).

No.	Type	Description				
113	19	½d. black & bright green	0	3	0	4
		a. P 13×12 (8.4.36) ..	1	6	2	0
114	20	1d. black and brown ..	0	6	0	9
		a. P 13×12 (8.4.36) ..	1	6	2	0
115	21	1½d. black and scarlet ..	1	0	1	3
		a. P 12×13	45	0	15	0
116	19	2d. black and grey ..	1	3	1	6
117	20	2½d. black and blue ..	1	6	2	0
118	21	3d. black and dull green	2	0	2	6
119	19	4d. black and red-brown	2	6	3	0
120	20	6d. black and orange ..	3	6	4	6
121	22	1s. black and light blue	6	6	8	0
122	23	2s. 6d. black and ultram.	18	0	20	0
123	24	5s. black and violet ..	40	0	45	0
124	25	10s. black and carmine ..	60	0	65	0

POSTAGE DUE STAMPS.

No. ..4545
ST. LUCIA.
1d.
POSTAGE DUE

D 1

1931. *Type* D 1. *No wmk. or gum. Rough perf.* 12. (*a*) *Horizontally laid paper.*

D1	1d. black/*blue*	1	9	1	9
	a. Wide, wrong fount "No." ..	8	6	10	0

(*b*) *Wove paper.*

D2	2d. black/*yellow*	2	0	2	0
	a. Wide, wrong fount "No." ..	14	0	15	0

D 2

(Typo. De La Rue & Co.)

1933. *Wmk. Mult. Script CA.* P 14.

D3	D 2 1d. black	0	2	0	3
D4	,, 2d. black	0	3	0	5

FISCAL STAMPS.

Allowed to be used for Postage.

SHILLING
STAMP
(F 1)

1881. T 1. *Wmk. Crown CC.* P 14.

(1) *Overprinted as Type* F 1.

F1	ONE PENNY STAMP, black (C.)	20	0	17	6
F2	FOUR PENNY STAMP, yellow	55	0	60	0
F3	SIX PENCE STAMP, mauve ..	70	0	75	0
F4	SHILLING STAMP, orange ..	50	0	55	0

Errors.

F4*a*	ONE PENNY STAMP, inverted				
F5	SHILEING STAMP, orange ..	£35			
F6	SHILDING STAMP, orange ..	£35			

One Penny
Stamp
(F 2)

(2) *Overprinted as Type* F 2, *in black.*

F 7	One Penny Stamp, black (R.)	20	0	20	0
F 8	Four Pence Stamp, yellow	35	0	35	0
F 9	Six Pence Stamp, mauve ..	35	0	35	0
F10	Shilling Stamp, orange ..	45	0	45	0

HALFPENNY
Stamp
(F 3)

(3) *Overprinted as Type* F 3, *in black.*

F11	Halfpenny Stamp, green ..	20	0	15	0
F12	One Shilling Stamp, orange (*wmk. Crown CA*)	40	0	40	0

FOUR PENCE
REVENUE
(F 4)

1882. T 1. *Wmk. Crown CA. Overprinted as Type* F 4, *in first colour given.*

(*a*) P 14.

F13	1d. carmine and black ..	15	0	15	0
	a. Imperf.	60	0		
F14	2d. black and pale blue ..	7	6	6	6
F15	3d. carmine and deep blue ..	25	0	15	0
F16	4d. black and yellow ..	10	0	6	6
F17	6d. black and mauve ..	17	6	15	0

(*b*) P 12.

F18	1d. carmine and black ..	15	0	15	0
F19	3d. carmine and deep blue	17	6	8	6
F20	1s. black and orange ..	17	6	15	0

Revenue
(F 5)

1883. *Nos.* 25 *and* 26 *overprinted at foot with Type* F 5 *locally, in carmine* (*C.*) *or black* (*Bk.*).

(1) *Word* 11 *mm. long.*

F21	1d. black (C.)	7	6		

(2) *Word* 13 *mm.*

F22	1d. black (C.)	—		35	0

(3) *Word* 15½ *mm.*

F23	½d. green (Bk.)	—		40	0
	a. "Revenue" double ..	—		£17	
F24	1d. black (C.)	10	0	6	6
	a. "Revenue" double ..				

As last, but a second overprint at top inverted.

F25	1d. black (C.)	30	0		

Nos. 30 *and* 32 *overprinted as* (3) *above, in black.*

F26	1d. rose	—		17	6
F27	4d. yellow	—		32	6

REVENUE
(F 6)

1884. T 5. *Wmk. Crown CA. Overprinted with Type* F 6. P 14.

F28	1d. slate (C.)	7	0	6	0
F29	1d. dull mauve (Bk.) (Die I)	6	0	3	0

ST. VINCENT.

SIMPLIFICATION (see p. xii)

Nos. 1 to 66a.

5, 8, 12, 4, 11, 13, 14.
33, 15, 25, 34, 24, 35, 16, 23, 26, 19, 20, 22, 28.
29, 30, 31, 32.
40, 36, 41, 44, 64, 51, 42, 47, 60, 65, 48, 53, 57, 48a, 58, 49.
37, 39, 45, 56, 55, 66, 59, 62.

The above arrangement is purely arbitrary and collectors may prefer to arrange the stamps more nearly in order of date.

(Recess. Perkins Bacon & Co.)

1

T 1. *No wmk.*

1861 (May). *Intermediate perf.* 14 *to* 16.

1 1d. rose-red £60 £15
 a. Imperf. between (horiz. pair) .. £50
2 6d. deep yellow-green .. £140 80 0

1862 (Sept.). *Rough perf.* 14 *to* 16.

3 1d. rose-red 40 0 27 6
 a. Imperf. between (horiz. pair) .. £40
4 6d. deep green.. .. .. 60 0 30 0
 a. Imperf. between (horiz. pair) .. £80

1863–66. *P* 11 *to* 12½.

5 1d. rose-red 27 6 25 0
6 6d. deep green.. .. .. £15 80 0

P 11 *to* 12½ × 14 *to* 16.

7 1d. rose-red £250 £50

Varieties. Imperf.

7*a* 1d. rose-red 95 0
7*b* 6d. deep green.. .. .. £15

The imperf. stamps are not known used.

1866. *P* 11 *to* 12½.

8 4d. deep blue £15 95 0
 a. Imperf. between (pair) ..
9 1s. slate-grey £75

P 14 *to* 16.

10 1s. slate-grey £18 £5

P 11 *to* 12½ × 14 *to* 16.

11 1s. slate-grey £18 80 0

1868. *P* 11 *to* 12½.

12 4d. yellow £10 90 0
13 1s. indigo £22 90 0
14 1s. brown £35 £10

T 1. *Wmk. Small Star, T* w. 2.

1871. *Rough perf.* 14 *to* 16.

15 1d. black 30 0 20 0
 a. Imperf. between (vert. pair) .. £90
16 6d. blue-green £20 50 0

1872. *P* 11 *to* 12½.

17 1s. lilac-red £70 £5

1872–73. *Clean-cut perf. about* 15.

17*b* 1d. black 55 0 25 0
17*c* 6d. blue-green £20 60 0
17*d* 6d. dull blue-green £25 65 0

1873–74. *P* 11 *to* 12½ × 15.

18 1d. black 45 0 17 6
 a. Imperf. between (pair) ..
19 1s. lilac-rose £150 £15

1875. *P* 11 *to* 12½.

20 1s. claret £45 £10

1877 (Feb.). *P* 11 *to* 12½ × 15.

21 6d. pale yellow-green .. £22 55 0
 a. Imperf. .. .. ..
22 1s. vermilion £30 45 0
 a. Imperf. between (pair) ..

1877 (Apr.). *Clean-cut perf. about* 15.

23 6d. pale yellow-green .. £22 50 0

1877 (July). *P* 11 *to* 12½.

24 4d. deep blue £22 95 0

2

1880 (June). *T* 1 *and* 2 (5s.). *Wmk. Small Star, T* w. 2. *P* 11 *to* 12½.

25 1d. olive-green 70 0 15 0
 a. Imperf. .. .. ..
26 6d. bright green £22 75 0
27 1s. bright vermilion £25 70 0
 a. Imperf. between (pair) ..
28 5s. rose-red £70 £75
 a. Imperf. .. .. ..

d.
1

(3)

1880. *No.* 17*c divided vertically by a line of perforation, gauging* 12, *and surcharged as T* 3, *in red.*

29 1d. on half 6d. blue-green .. £40 £35
 a. Unsevered pair £125 £90

d
1
2

(4)

ONE PENNY

(5)

4d

(6)

1881. *Stamps of June,* 1880, *surcharged* ½d. *in red,* 1d. *or* 4d. *in black. No* 30 *is divided similarly to No.* 29.

30 **4** ½d. on half 6d. bright green £12 £15
 a. Unsevered pair £30 £35
 b. Fraction bar omitted (pair with and without bar) .. £140 £140
31 **5** 1d. on 6d. bright green .. £25 £22
32 **6** 4d. on 1s. vermilion .. £125 £75

T **3**, **4** and **6** are not exactly like the genuine surcharges.

7

1881 (Dec.). *T* 7 (½*d.*) *and* 1. *Wmk. Small Star T* w. 2. *P* 11 *to* 12½.

33 ½d. orange 12 0 8 6
34 1d. drab 75 0 15 0
35 4d. bright blue £20 65 0
 a. Imperf. between (pair) ..

(Printed by Messrs. De La Rue & Co.)

2½ PENCE

(8)

1882–84. *T* 1 (*the* 1d. *surcharged as T* 8, *in black, to form the* 2½*d.*). *Wmk. Crown CA. P* 14.

36 1d. drab 12 6 8 6
37 2½d. on 1d. lake 10 6 8 0
38 4d. bright blue £20 55 0
38*a* 4d. dull blue £35 £12

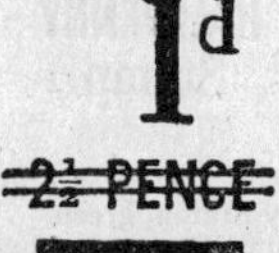

9)

1885. *No. 37 surcharged as in T 9, in black.*

39 1d. on 2½d. on 1d. lake .. 17 6 17 6

T 7 and 1. Wmk. Crown CA. P 14.

40 ½d. green 1 0 0 8
40*a* ½d. deep green.. .. .. 3 0 2 0
41 1d. rose-red 3 0 2 6
42 4d. red-brown £30 37 6

1886–89. *T 7, 1, and 2. Wmk. Crown CA.*

(*a*) *P 14.*

43 1d. rose 10 0 5 0
44 1d. red 1 3 1 3
45 2½d. in black, on 1d. milky blue 25 0 12 6
46 4d. purple-brown 25 0 15 0
47 4d. lake-brown 17 6 15 0
48 6d. violet £6 £7
48*a* 1s. deep orange 25 0 22 6
49 5s. carmine-lake 35 0 40 0
49*a* 5s. brown-lake 35 0 40 0

(*b*) *P 12.*

50 ½d. green 22 6 15 0
50*a* ½d. orange £60
50*b* 1d. rose-red .. .. ..
50*c* 1d. milky blue (without surch.)
51 4d. bright blue £15 40 0
52 4d. dull blue £60 £10
53 6d. bright green £12 £12
54 1s. orange-vermilion 70 0 70 0
54*a* 5s. carmine-lake £175

(*c*) *Imperf.*

54*b* 1s. orange-vermilion .. ..

The ½d. *orange*, 1d. *rose-red*, and 5s., *perf.* 12, are only known unused.

2½d. (10)

5 PENCE (11)

Wmk. Crown CA. P 14.

1890. *T 1 surcharged with T 10, in black.*

55 2½d. on 4d. lake-brown .. 85 0 90 0
a. No bar in fraction £12 £15

1890–91. *T 1 (the 1d. surcharged with T 8, in black, to form the 2½d., as before).*

55*b* 2½d. on 1d. grey-blue .. 22 6 6 6
56 2½d. on 1d. blue 2 6 1 6
57 6d. dull purple 5 0 6 0
58 1s. orange-vermilion .. 10 0 12 6

1892. *T 1 surcharged with T 11, in purple.*

59 5d. on 4d. lake-brown .. 12 6 16 6

T 11 is found with the first "E" double, once on some sheets.

1893. *T 1.*

60 4d. yellow 4 0 5 0
60*a* 4d. olive-yellow £15

FIVE PENCE
(12)

T 1 surcharged with T 12 in black.

61 5d. on 6d. carmine-lake .. 17 6 20 0
62 5d. on 6d. deep lake 2 6 4 0
63 5d, on 6d. lake 4 0 6 0

1897. *T 1. Wmk. Crown CA. P 14.*

64 2½d. blue 8 6 10 0
65 5d. sepia 12 6 15 0

T 1 surcharged as T 12, in black.

66 3d. on 1d. mauve 5 0 6 0
66*a* 3d. on 1d. red-mauve .. 8 0 8 6

13 14

(Typo. De La Rue & Co.)

1899. *T 13 and 14 (1s. and 5s.). Wmk. Crown CA. P 14.*

67 ½d. dull mauve and green .. 1 6 1 9
68 1d. dull mauve and carmine 4 0 1 6
69 2½d. dull mauve and blue .. 10 0 10 6
70 3d. dull mauve and olive .. 10 0 10 0
71 4d. dull mauve and orange .. 8 6 10 0
72 5d. dull mauve and black .. 10 0 10 0
73 6d. dull mauve and brown .. 17 6 20 0
74 1s. green and carmine .. 20 0 22 6
75 5s. green and blue 60 0 70 0

15 16

(Typo. De La Rue & Co.)

1902. *T 15 and 16 (2d., 1s., and 5s.). Wmk. Crown CA. P 14.*

76 ½d. dull purple and green .. 1 9 1 9
77 1d. dull purple and carmine 1 9 1 3
78 2d. dull purple and black .. 6 0 6 6
79 2½d. dull purple and blue .. 10 0 10 6
80 3d. dull purple and olive .. 8 0 8 6
81 6d. dull purple and brown .. 17 6 17 6
82 1s. green and carmine .. 35 0 37 6
83 2s. green and violet 30 0 35 0
84 5s. green and blue 50 0 52 6

1904–11. *T 15 and 16 (£1 as T 16), but wmk. Multiple Crown CA. P 14*

85 ½d. dull pur. & grn., OC ('05) 1 6 1 6
86 1d. dull pur. & carmine, OC.. 6 0 1 9
88 2½d. dull pur. & blue, C (1906) 8 6 10 0
90 6d. dull pur. & brn., C (1905) 17 6 17 6
91 1s. green & carm., OC (1908) 17 6 17 6
92 2s. pur. & brt. blue/*bl.*, C ('09) 25 0 25 0
93 5s. green & red/*yell.*, C (1909) 50 0 50 0
93*a* £1 pur. & black/*red*, C (1911) £17 £17

17 18

(Recess. De La Rue & Co.)

1907. *T 17. Wmk. Mult. Crown CA. P 14.*

94 ½d. green 1 6 1 6
95 1d. carmine 4 0 2 0
96 2d. orange 8 6 10 0
97 2½d. blue 20 0 20 0
98 3d. violet 20 0 20 0

1909. *T* **18.** *Wmk. Mult. Crown CA. P* 14.

No.	Description	Unused	Used
99	1d. carmine	4 0	2 0
100	6d. dull purple	17 6	17 6
101	1s. black/*green*	15 0	15 0

1909–11. *T* **18,** *redrawn* (*dot below* "d," *as in T* **17**). *Wmk. Mult. Crown CA. P* 14.

No.	Description	Unused	Used
102	½d. green (1910)	1 3	0 8
103	1d. carmine	1 6	0 8
104	2d. grey (1911)	5 0	6 0
105	2½d. ultramarine	6 0	6 6
106	3d. purple/*yellow*	7 6	8 0
107	6d. dull purple	10 0	10 6

19

(Recess. De La Rue & Co.)

1913. *Wmk. Mult. Crown CA. P* 14.

No.	Type	Description	Unused	Used
108	**19**	½d. green	0 6	0 6
109	,,	1d. red	0 6	0 4
109*a*	,,	1d. rose-red	2 6	0 4
110	,,	2d. grey	4 0	5 0
110*a*	,,	2d. slate	4 0	4 6
111	,,	2½d. ultramarine	2 6	3 0
112	,,	3d. purple/*yellow*	5 0	5 0
		a. On lemon	6 0	6 0
		b. On pale yellow	4 6	5 0
113	,,	4d. red/*yellow*	3 0	3 6
113*a*	,,	5d. olive-green	5 0	6 0
114	,,	6d. claret	4 0	4 6
115	,,	1s. black/*green*	8 6	10 0
116	**18**	2s. blue and purple ..	15 0	17 6
117	,,	5s. carmine and myrtle ..	30 0	35 0
118	,,	£1 mauve and black ..	£7	£8

1914. *T* **19.** *Colour changed. Wmk. Mult. Crown CA. P* 14.

No.	Description	Unused	Used
119	1s. bistre	8 6	10 0

ONE

PENNY.

(20)

1915. *Provisional. T* **19** *surch. with T* **20.**

No.	Description	Unused	Used
120	1d. on 1s. black/*green* (R.) ..	10 0	12 6
	a. "ONE" omitted	£50	

The spacing between the two words varies from 7¾ mm. to 10 mm.

WAR STAMP.

(21)

WAR STAMP.

(23)

1916 (June). *T* **19** *overprinted locally with T* **21,** *in black.* (*First and second settings; words 2 to 2½ mm. apart.*)

No.	Description	Unused	Used
122	1d. red	2 6	3 6
	a. Double overprint	£5	£5
	b. Comma for stop	8 6	12 6

In the first printing every second stamp has the comma for stop. The second printing of this setting has full stops only. These two printings can therefore only be distinguished in blocks or pairs.

Third setting; words only 1½ mm. apart.

No.	Description	Unused	Used
123	1d. red	70 0	

Stamps of the first setting are offered as this rare one. Care must be taken to see that the width between the lines is not over 1½ mm.

Fourth setting; overprinted with T **23.** *Words 3½ mm. apart.*

No.	Description	Unused	Used
124	1d. carmine-red	2 0	3 0
	a. Double overprint		

WAR STAMP

(24)

1916 (Aug.)–**1918.** *T* **19,** *new printing, overprinted with T* **24,** *in black.*

No.	Description	Unused	Used
126	1d. carmine-red	1 3	1 3
127	1d. pale rose-red	0 6	0 6
128	1d. deep rose-red	0 4	0 4
129	1d. pale scarlet (1918) ..	0 5	0 5

1917 (Jan.). *T* **19.** *Colour changed. Wmk. Mult. Crown CA. P* 14.

No.	Description	Unused	Used
130	1d. scarlet	1 6	2 0

1921–32. *T* **19** (*to* 1s.) *and* **18.** *Wmk. Mult. Script CA. P* 14.

No.	Description	Unused	Used
131	½d. green	0 6	0 6
132	1d. carmine	1 6	0 8
132*a*	1d. red	0 10	0 8
132*b*	1½d. brown ('32)	1 6	1 6
133	2d. grey	1 6	1 6
133*a*	2½d. bright blue (1926) ..	2 6	2 9
134	3d. bright blue	5 0	6 0
135	3d. purple/*yellow* (1926) ..	3 0	3 6
135*a*	4d. red/*yellow* ('30) ..	4 0	4 6
136	5d. sage-green	6 0	6 6
137	6d. claret (1.11.27) ..	6 0	6 6
138	1s. bistre-brown	7 6	8 0
139	2s. blue and purple ..	20 0	22 6
140	5s. carmine and myrtle ..	50 0	55 0
141	£1 mauve and black ('28)	£6	£7

1935 (6 May). *Silver Jubilee. As T* **13** *of Antigua. Inscr.* "St. Vincent". *Recess. W'low & Sons. Wmk. Mult. Script CA. P* 11×12.

No.	Description	Unused	Used
142	1d. deep blue and scarlet	0 6	1 0
143	1½d. ultramarine and grey	0 8	1 9
144	2½d. brown and deep blue ..	5 0	6 0
145	1s. slate and purple ..	20 0	22 6

SAMOA.

(Issues prior to the Anglo-German-American agreement of 1899.)

1

(Designed by H. H. Glover; lithographed by S. T. Leigh & Co., Sydney, N.S.W.)

1877. *T* 1. *P* 12½.

A. 1st state; *line above* " x " *in* " EXPRESS " *not broken.*

1	1d. ultramarine	25	0	35	0
2	3d. deep scarlet.. ..	30	0	35	0
3	6d. bright violet	30	0	30	0
4	6d. pale violet	35	0	35	0

B. *2nd state; line above* " x " *broken, and an extra dot to the left of* " o," *in the row of small pearls over* " SAMOA."

5	1d. ultramarine	25	0	35	0
6	3d. bright scarlet	25	0	35	0
7	6d. bright violet	30	0	35	0
8	1s. dull yellow	40	0	57	6
	a. Line above " X " not broken ..	57	6	57	6
9	1s. orange-yellow	57	6	57	6
10	2s. red-brown	70	0	70	0
11	2s. chocolate	£6		£6	
12	5s. green	£8		£14	

C. *3rd state; line above* " x " *repaired.*

(*a*) *P* 12½.

13	1d. ultramarine	30	0	30	0
14	3d. vermilion	30	0	35	0
15	6d. violet	30	0	30	0
16	2s. brown	80	0	92	6
17	2s. deep brown	80	0	92	6
18	5s. green	£8		£10	

(*b*) *P* 12.

19	1d. blue	15	0	16	6
20	1d. deep blue	16	6	24	0
21	1d. ultramarine	22	6	30	0
22	3d. vermilion	20	0	30	0
23	3d. carmine-vermilion ..	22	6	35	0
24	6d. bright violet	22	6	30	0
25	6d. deep violet	20	0	30	0
26	9d. orange-brown	30	0	35	0
28	2s. deep brown	70	0	85	0
29	5s. yellow-green	£8		£10	
30	5s. deep green	£8		£10	

Originals are known imperf., but are believed not to have been used in this state.

In all printings of the 1d. some stamps on the sheet have a stop after the word " PENNY."

Originals of the 1d., 3d., and 6d. were in sheets of 20 stamps, and of all values in sheets of 10, and all sheets of all printings were imperf. at the outer edges; therefore originals of the 9d., 1s., 2s., and 5s. must always have at least one imperf. edge. Only the 1d., 3d., and 6d. exist perforated all round, and that only in the first printing.

Reprints were made of all values in sheets of 40, and there are " remainders " of stamps prepared for use but not issued, in sheets of 21 for some values and of 12 for others. In all of them (reprints and " remainders ") there is a spot of colour immediately below the middle strokes of the " M " of " SAMOA ", which is never found in the originals except in the 9d. A new value, 2d., exists in the " remainders " (in sheets of 21) and also in the reprints.

Collectors should be on their guard against buying either reprints or " remainders " in mistake for the genuine originals, as they are practically worthless.

2. Palm Trees.

3. King Malietoa.

4

5

(Engraved by Messrs. Bock & Cousins. Printed at the New Zealand Government Printing Office.)

1887–95. *T* 2, 3 (2½*d.*), *and* 4 (5*d.*). *Wmk.* N Z *and Star, T* 5. (*a*) *P* 12½.

31	½d. purple-brown	1	3	1	3
32	1d. yellow-green	1	3	1	3
33	2d. orange	1	3	1	3
34	2½d. rose (1892)	1	3	1	3
35	4d. blue	2	6	2	6
35*a*	6d. brown-lake	£35			
36	1s. rose	8	6	6	0
37	2s. 6d. violet	17	6	12	6

The 1s. rose was bisected, and each half used as a 6d. stamp. These were used from April to June, 1895. Price 10s. on piece of original.

(*b*) *P* 12 × 11½ (1893).

38	½d. purple-brown	0	6	0	5
39	1d. yellow-green	1	6	1	0
40	1d. blue-green	1	0	0	8
41	2d. dull orange .. .	2	0	0	10
42	2½d. rose	1	6	0	10
43	4d. blue	3	6	1	0
44	5d. red (1894)	1	6	1	6
45	6d. brown-lake ..	3	0	1	6
46	6d. marone	5	0	1	9
47	1s. rose	4	0	1	6
48	2s. 6d. bright violet .	20	0	2	9

(*c*) *P* 11 (1895).*

49	½d. purple-brown	0	5	0	6
50	½d. deep brown	0	4	0	5
51	1d. deep blue-green	0	9	0	5
52	1d. blue-green .. .	0	9	0	3
53	2d. orange-yellow	1	3	1	6
54	2d. ochre	1	3	1	6
55	2d. orange	1	6	1	9
55*a*	2d. bright orange	1	0	0	8
56	2½d. rose	1	0	0	8
57	4d. blue	1	6	0	10
58	4d. deep blue	2	0	1	6
59	5d. red	1	9	1	0
60	6d. brown-lake	2	6	1	9
61	6d. marone	2	0	1	6
62	1s. rose	2	6	1	6
63	2s. 6d. deep purple	4	0	5	0
63*a*	2s. 6d. mauve	7	6	2	0
	b Imperf. between (pair) ..	£10			

* These stamps and Nos. 72–74, 77–81 and 84–95 all perf. 11, are usually very unevenly perforated, owing to the large size of the pins. Evenly centred copies are extremely hard to find.

FIVE PENCE	FIVE PENCE	5d
(6)	(7)	(8)

1893 (Nov.). *No.* 43 *surcharged in black.*

64	6	5d. on 4d. blue	30	0	30	0
		a. " FI PENCE "	90	0		
		b. " FIVE PENOE " ..	—		90	0
65	7	5d. on 4d. blue	50	0	50	0

No. 43 *surcharged in red* (*a*) *as T* 8, *but* "d" *raised,* (*b*) *with the* "d" *on a line with the* "5" *as illustrated.*

No.		Unused	Used
66	5d. on 4d. (*a*)	15 0	8 6
67	5d. on 4d. (*b*)	10 0	10 0
	a. Stop after "d"	62 6	

Varieties. (i.) *Surcharge inverted.*

No.		Unused	Used
68	5d. on 4d. (*a*)	£15	

(ii.) *Surcharge double.*

No.		Unused	Used
68*a*	5d. on 4d. (*a*)	£10	

Surcharged 1½d. (9)

R 3d. (10)

1895 (28 Jan.). *T* 2 *surcharged with T* 9 *in blue, or* 10 *in black.* (*a*) *P* 12×11½.

No.		Unused	Used
69	1½d. on 2d. dull orange ..	2 0	1 3
70	3d. on 2d. dull orange ..	3 0	2 0

Variety. Surcharge double.

No.		Unused	Used
71	3d. on 2d. dull orange ..	87 6	

(*b*) *P* 11.*

No.		Unused	Used
72	1½d. on 2d. orange	1 3	1 3
73	3d. on 2d. orange	2 0	2 0
74	3d. on 2d. yellow	1 9	2 0
	a. Imperf. between (pair) ..	85 0	

Variety. Surcharge double.

No.		Unused	Used
75	3d. on 2d. orange	55 0	

* See note below No. 63b.

Both the above were reprinted in 1900 on stamps perf. 11. The 1½d. surcharge is in *ultramarine* and the 3d. in *green*. Some people say that these have been found genuinely used.

1896. *T* 3. *Error of colour. P* 10×11.

No.		Unused	Used
76	2½d. black	1 0	1 3
	a. Perf. 11		

Surcharged 2½d. (11)

PROVISIONAL GOVT. (12)

1898–99. *T* 2 *surcharged with T* 11. *P* 11.*

No.		Unused	Used
77	2½d. in *black*, on 1s. rose ..	1 3	1 3
78	2½d. in *black*, on 1s. carmine	1 6	1 6
79	2½d. in *red*, on 1d. blue-green	0 8	0 8
80	2½d. in *red*, on 1s. carmine ..	1 6	1 9
81	2½d. in *black*, on 2s. 6d. violet	1 6	2 0

Varieties. (i.) *Surcharge inverted.*

No.		Unused	Used
82	2½d. in *red*, on 1d. green ..	—	£9

(ii.) *Surcharge double.*

No.		Unused	Used
83	2½d. *in black*, on 1s. carmine	80 0	

* See note below No. 63b.

There are two types of the 2½d. surcharge. In the second type the fractional line is more upright and the tail of the large numeral "2" is further from the line.

1899. *T* 2. *W* 5. *Colours changed. P* 11.*

No.		Unused	Used
84	½d. green	0 8	0 10
85	1d. red-brown	0 8	0 10

* See note below No. 63b.

T 2 *and* 4 *overprinted with T* 12 (*words longer and letters shorter on* 5d.), *in red* (R.) *or blue* (B.). *P* 11.*

No.		Unused	Used
86	½d. blue-green (R.)	0 4	0 6
87	½d. deep yellow-green (R.) ..	0 3	0 6
88	1d. red-brown (B.)	0 3	0 6
88*a*	2d. orange-yellow (R.) ..	0 6	0 9
89	2d. orange (R.)	0 6	0 9
90	4d. blue (R.)	0 8	1 0
91	5d. red (B.)	1 0	1 6
92	5d. deep red (B.)	1 3	1 6
93	6d. lake (B.)	1 0	1 6
94	1s. rose (B.)	1 9	2 3
95	2s. 6d. violet (R.)	4 0	5 0

* See note below No. 63b.

The Samoan group of islands was in 1900 partitioned between the German Empire (*see* German Colonies) and the United States of America. No separate stamps are issued by the latter for this territory.

The German Islands of Samoa surrendered to the New Zealand Expeditionary Force on August 29, 1914. They are now administered by New Zealand.

G.R.I. 1d. (13)

G.R.I. 1 Shillings. (14)

1914 (3 Sept.). *Stamps of German Colonial issue* (*see* Cameroons), *surcharged as T* 13 *and* 14 (mark *values*), *in black, at the office of the Samoanische Zeitung at Apia. No wmk.*

No.		Unused	Used
101	½d. on 3 pf. brown ..	3 6	5 0
	a. Surcharge double	£40	
	b. No fraction bar	20 0	20 0
	c. Comma after "I"	£8	£6
	d. "1" to left of "2" in "½"	20 0	25 0
102	½d. on 5 pf. green	10 0	10 0
	a. No fraction bar	25 0	15 0
	c. Comma after "I"	60 0	60 0
	d. Surcharge double ..	£20	
	e. "1" to left of "2" in "½"	35 0	35 0
103	1d. on 10 pf. carmine ..	12 6	12 6
	a. Surcharge double	£25	£25
104	2½d. on 20 pf. ultram. ..	5 0	5 0
	a. No fraction bar	12 6	15 0
	b. "1" to left of "2" in "½"	15 0	20 0
	c. Surcharge inverted	£25	£25
	d. Comma after "I"	£10	£10
	e. Surcharge double	£25	£25
105	3d. on 25 pf. blk. & red/*yell.*	30 0	30 0
	a. Surcharge double	£15	£10
	b. Comma after "I"		
106	4d. on 30 pf. blk. & orge./*buff*	50 0	50 0
	a. Error. 3d. on 30 pf. ..	£150	£175
107	5d. on 40 pf. blk. & carm. ..	60 0	70 0
	a. Error. 4d. on 40 pf. ..	£100	£125
108	6d. on 50 pf., blk. & pur./*buff*	10 0	10 0
	a. Surcharge double	£25	£30
	b. Inverted "9" for "6" ..	35 0	35 0
109	9d. on 80 pf., blk. & car./*rose*	80 0	50 0
110	"1 shillings" on 1 m. carm.	£80	£60
111	"1 shilling" on 1 m. carm.	£200	£120
112	2s. on 2 m. blue	£60	£45
113	3s. on 3 m. violet-black ..	£20	£18
	a. Surcharge double	£250	£300
114	5s. on 5 m. carmine & blk. ..	£18	£12

The ½d. to 9d. values were surcharged in vertical rows of ten, repeated ten times on each sheet, and this caused many errors to be made.

No. 108*b* is easily distinguished from 108, as the "d" and the "9" are not in a line, and the upper loop of the "9" turns downwards to the left.

SAMOA.

(15)

1914 (29 Sept.). *Stamps of New Zealand, T* **50, 51, 52,** *and* **27,** *overprinted as T* **15,** *but opt. only* 14 *mm. long on all except* 2½*d. Wmk.* "N Z" *and Star, T* **41.**

No.		s.	d.	s.	d.
115	½d. yell.-grn. (R.) (*p.* 14×15)	0	4	0	5
116	1d. carm. (B.) (*p.* 14×15) ..	0	5	0	6
118	2d. mauve (R.) (*p.* 14×14½)	1	6	2	0
119	2½d. deep blue (R.) (*p.* 14) ..	2	6	3	0
121	6d. carm. (B.) (*p.* 14×14½) ..	4	6	5	0
	a. Perf. 14×13½	6	0	7	6
	b. Vert. pair, 121/21a	25	0	35	0
122	6d. pale car. (B.) (*p.* 14×14½)	5	6	6	0
124	1s. verm. (B.) (*p.* 14×14½) ..	6	0	7	0

1914 (Dec.)–**1931.** *T* **154** *of New Zealand overprinted with T* **15.**

(*a*) *Rough perf.* 14, 14½ (*small holes*).

No.		s.	d.	s.	d.
125	2s. blue (R.)	15	0	17	6
126	2s. 6d. brown (B.)	6	0	7	6
127	5s. yellow-green (R.) ..	20	0	22	6
128	10s. purple-brown (B.) ..	40	0	50	0
129	£1 rose (B.)	77	6	82	6

(*b*) *Clean cut perf.* 14½×14.

No.		s.	d.	s.	d.
130	2s. blue (R.)	6	0	7	0
130*a*	2s. 6d. brown (B.) ('31) ..	6	0	7	6
131	5s. yellow-green (R.) ..	10	0	12	6
132	10s. purple-brown (B.) ..	27	6	30	0
133	£1 rose (B.)	40	0	50	0

1916–19. *Head of King George V overprinted as T* **15,** *but* 14 *mm. long.*

(*a*) *Surface-printed. P* 14×15.

No.		s.	d.	s.	d.
134	½d. yellow-green (R.) ..	0	2	0	3
135	1½d. slate (R.) (1917) ..	0	10	1	0
136	1½d. orange-brown (R.) (1919)	0	8	1	0
137	2d. yellow (R.) (1918) ..	0	8	0	8
138	3d. chocolate (B.)	1	3	1	6

(*b*) *Line-engraved. P* 14×14½, *etc.*

No.		s.	d.	s.	d.
139	2½d. blue (R.)	0	10	1	0
	a. Perf. 14×13½	0	9	1	0
	b. Vert. pair, 139/9a	5	0	5	6
140	3d. chocolate (B.)	2	0	3	0
	a. Perf. 14×13½	2	6	3	6
	b. Vert. pair, 140/40a	12	6	13	6
141	6d. carmine (B.)	2	6	3	0
	a. Perf. 14×13½	2	9	3	3
	b. Vert. pair, 141/1a	8	6	9	6
142	1s. vermilion (B.)	3	6	4	0
	a. Perf. 14×13½	3	6	4	0
	b. Vert. pair, 142/2a	12	6	13	6

1920. *Victory series, T* **62** *to* **67** *of New Zealand, overprinted as T* **15,** *but* 14 *mm. long.*

No.		s.	d.	s.	d.
143	½d. green (R.)	0	6	0	10
144	1d. carmine (B.)	0	8	0	9
145	1½d. brown-orange (R.) ..	1	3	1	3
146	3d. chocolate (B.)	1	9	2	6
147	6d. violet (R.)	4	6	5	0
148	1s. orange-red (B.)	6	6	7	6

16. Native hut.

(Plates engraved by Bradbury, Wilkinson & Co. Recess-printed at Wellington, N.Z.)

1921 (23 Dec.). *T* **16.** *W* **41** *of New Zealand* ("N Z" *and Star*). (*a*) *P* 14×14½.

No.		s.	d.	s.	d.
149	½d. green	1	3	1	6
150	1d. lake	0	9	1	0
151	1½d. chestnut	1	0	1	3
152	2d. yellow	1	3	1	6

(*b*) *P* 14×13½.

No.		s.	d.	s.	d.
153	½d. green	0	7	0	9
154	1d. lake	0	9	0	8
155	1½d. chestnut	2	6	3	0
156	2d. yellow	1	3	1	0
157	2½d. grey-blue	1	3	1	6
158	3d. sepia	1	6	1	9
159	4d. violet	1	9	2	0
160	5d. light blue	2	0	2	6
161	6d. bright carmine ..	2	3	2	6
162	8d. red-brown	4	0	4	6
163	9d. olive-green	4	0	4	6
164	1s. vermilion	5	0	5	0

1922–24. *As T* **154** *of New Zealand overprinted with T* **15,** *in red.*

No.		s.	d.	s.	d.
165	3s. mauve	12	6	15	0
166	£2 mauve	90	0	£5	

1926–28. *T* **72** *of New Zealand, overprinted with T* **15,** *in red.* (*a*) "*Jones*" *paper.*

No.		s.	d.	s.	d.
167	2s. deep blue	8	6	10	0
168	3s. mauve	12	6	15	0

(*b*) "*Cowan*" *paper.*

No.		s.	d.	s.	d.
169	2s. light blue (1928) ..	4	6	5	6
170	3s. pale mauve (1928) ..	6	6	7	6

1932. *Types as* **73a** *of New Zealand (various frames) overprinted with T* **15.** *P* 14.

No.		s.	d.	s.	d.
171	2s. 6d. brown (B.)	7	6	8	6
172	5s. green (R.)	15	0	17	6
173	10s. carmine (B.)	32	6	37	6
174	£1 pink (B.)	65	0	70	0
175	£2 violet (R.)	£6			
176	£5 blue (R.)	£22			

SILVER JUBILEE
OF
KING GEORGE V
1910 - 1935.

(17)

1935 (7 May). *Silver Jubilee. Optd. with T* **17.** *P* 14×13½.

No.		s.	d.	s.	d.
177	**16** 1d. lake	0	10	3	0
	a. Perf. 14×14½	£15			
178	" 2½d. grey-blue	4	0	10	0
179	" 6d. bright carmine	17	0	27	6

18. Samoan Girl.

19. Apia.

20. River Scene (*horiz.*).

21. Chief and Wife (*vert.*).

22. Canoe and House (*horiz.*).

23. R. L. Stevenson's home "Vailima" (*horiz.*).

24. Stevenson's Tomb (*horiz.*).

25. Lake Lanuto'o (*vert.*).

26. Falefa Falls (*vert.*)

(Recess. De La Rue & Co.)

1935 (7 Aug.). *T* **18** *to* **26**. *W* **41** *of New Zealand* ("N Z" *and Star*). (*a*) *P* 14×13½, (*b*) 13½×14 *or* (*c*) 14.

180	**18**	½d. green (*a*)	0	2	0	2
181	**19**	1d. black and carmine (*b*)	0	2	0	3
182	**20**	2d. black and orange (*c*)	0	5	0	6
		a. Perf. 13½×14	3	6	1	0
183	**21**	2½d. black and blue (*a*)	0	3	0	4
184	**22**	4d. slate and sepia (*b*)	0	5	0	7
185	**23**	6d. bright magenta (*b*)	0	7	0	10
186	**24**	1s. violet and brown (*b*)	1	1	2	0
187	**25**	2s. green & pur.-brn. (*a*)	2	2	4	0
188	**26**	3s. blue & brown-orge. (*a*)	3	3	6	0

WESTERN SAMOA.

(27)

1935. *As T* **73a** *of New Zealand optd. with T* **27**. *W* **41**.

189	2s. 6d. brown (B.)	2	8	5	0
190	5s. green (B.)	10	0	15	0
191	10s. carmine-lake (B.)	15	0	20	0
192	£1 pink (B.)	30	0	40	0
193	£2 violet (R.)	70	0	60	0
194	£5 blue (R.)	£8		£8	

For T **18** to **26** and Arms types as **73a** of New Zealand with Multiple wmk., see Nos. 202 onwards in King George VI Catalogue.

SARAWAK.

(Sarawak was placed under British protection in 1888.)

Sir James Brooke. 1842–11 June, 1868.
Sir Charles Brooke. 11 June, 1868–17 May, 1917.

1. Sir James Brooke. 2. Sir Charles Brooke.

The initials in the corners of T **1** and **2** stand for "James (Charles) Brooke, Rajah (of) Sarawak."

(T **1** and **2**. Die eng. Wm. Ridgway. Litho. Maclure, Macdonald & Co., Glasgow.)

1869 (1 Mar.). *P* 11.

1	**1**	3 c. brown/*yellow*	8	6	12	6

Specimens are known printed from the engraved die in orange-brown on orange surface-coloured paper, and perf. 12. These were submitted to the Sarawak authorities as examples of the stamps and exist both with and without obliterations.

1871 (1 Jan.). *P* 11 (*irregular*).

2	**2**	3 c. brown/*yellow*	1	6	1	9
		a. Stop after "THREE"	17	0		
		b. Imperf. between (vert. pair)	£8			
		c. Imperf. between (horiz. pair)	£8			

The "stop" variety, No. 2a, which occurs on stamp No. 97 in the sheet, is of no more philatelic importance than any of the numerous other variations, such as narrow first "A" in "SARAWAK" (No. 17) and "R" with long tail in left lower corner (No. 90), but it has been accepted by collectors for many years and we therefore retain it. The papermaker's wmk. "LNL" appears once or twice in sheets of No. 2.

Specimens are known, recess-printed, similar to those mentioned in note after No. 1.

1875 (1 Jan.). *P* 11½×12.

3	**2**	2 c. mauve/*lilac* (*shades*)	3	6	4	0
4	„	4 c. red-brown/*yellow*	5	0	6	0
		a. Imperf. between (vert. pair)	£7			
5	„	6 c. green/*green*	3	6	4	6
6	„	8 c. bright blue/*blue*	3	6	4	6
7	„	12 c. red/*pale rose*	5	0	6	0

Nos. 3, 4, 6 and 7 have the wmk. "LNL" in the sheet, as No. 2. No. 5 is wmkd. "LNT".

All values exist imperf. and can be distinguished from the proofs by shade and impression. Stamps rouletted, pin-perf., or roughly perf. 6½ to 7 are proofs clandestinely perforated.

The 12 c. "laid" paper, formerly listed, is not on a true laid paper, the "laid" effect being accidental and not consistent.

The lithographic stones for Nos. 3 to 7 were made up from strips of five distinct impressions, hence there are five types of each value differing mainly in the lettering of the tablets of value. There are flaws on nearly every individual stamp, from which they can be plated.

TWO CENTS

(3)

The 3 c. brown/*yellow* (No. 2), surcharged with T **3**, in black, appeared about 1876, but the surcharge is generally considered bogus.

4. Sir Charles Brooke.

(Die eng. and typo. De La Rue & Co.)

1888 (10 Nov.)–**1897**. *No wmk.* *P* 14.

8	**4**	1 c. purple & blk. (6.6.92)	1	6	1	6
9	„	2 c. purple and carmine	3	0	2	0
		a. Purple and rosine (1897)	3	6	1	9
10	„	3 c. purple & blue (11.88)	2	6	1	9
11	„	4 c. pur. & yell. (10.11.88)	5	0	6	0
12	„	5 c. purple & grn. (12.6.91)	3	6	4	0
13	„	6 c. pur. & brn. (11.11.88)	7	6	8	0
14	„	8 c. green and carmine	5	0	4	0
		a. Green and rosine (1897)	5	0	6	0
15	„	10 c. green & pur. (12.6.93)	5	0	4	6
16	„	12 c. green & blue (11.11.88)	4	0	4	0
17	„	25 c. green & brn. (19.11.88)	15	0	16	6

The tablet of value in this and later similar issues is in the second colour given.

The purple and green of the main design vary considerably in shade and there are minor variations in the tablets of some values. Some of these variations were due to printing, but in others the climate of Sarawak played a part.

One Cent. (5)

one cent. (6)

2c. (7) **5c.** (8) **5c.** (9)

1889 (3 Aug.)–**1892.** *T* **4** *surcharged.* *P* 14.

No.	Type	Description	Unused	Used
18	**5**	1 c. on 3 c. (12.1.92)	15 0	15 0
		a. Surch. double	£12	£10
19	**6**	1 c. on 3 c. (Feb., 1892) ..	6 0	6 0
		a. No stop after "cent" ..	85 0	
20	**7**	2 c. on 8 c. (3.8.89) ..	5 0	5 6
		a. Surch. double	£7	
		b. Surch. inverted	£42	
		c. Surch. omitted (in pair with normal) ..	£22	
21	**8**	5 c. on 12 c. (17.2.91) ..	10 0	12 6
		a. No stop after "C" ..	65 0	65 0
		b. "C" omitted	£6	
		c. Surch. double	£22	
		d. Surch. double, one vertical ..	£42	
		e. Surch. omitted (in pair with normal) ..		
22	**9**	5 c. on 12 c. (17.2.91) ..	45 0	50 0
		a. No stop after "C" ..	£9	£9
		b. "C" omitted	£12	
		c. Surch. double	£20	

ONE
CENT

(10)

1892 (23 May). *No.* 2 *surcharged with T* **10.**

No.	Type	Description	Unused	Used
23	**2**	1 c. on 3 c. brown/*yellow* ..	0 9	0 9
		a. Stop after "THREE" ..	17 6	17 6
		b. Imperf. between (vert. pair)	£8	
		c. Surch. double	95 0	

Varieties with part of the surcharge missing are due to gum on the face of the unsurcharged stamps receiving part of the surcharge, which was afterwards washed off.

11

12

13. Sir Charles Brooke. **14**

(Die eng. Wm. Ridgway. Recess. Perkins, Bacon & Co.)

1895 (1 Jan.–Sept.). *No wmk.* *P* 11½–12.

No.	Type	Description	Unused	Used
24	**11**	2 c. brown-red	2 0	2 6
		a. Imperf. between (vert. pair)	35 0	
		b. Imperf. between (horiz. pair)	35 0	
		c. Second printing. Perf. 12½ (Sept., '95)	2 6	3 6
		ca. Perf. 12½. Imperf. between (horiz. pair)	55 0	
25	**12**	4 c. black	4 0	4 6
		a. Imperf. between (horiz. pair)	£7	
26	**13**	6 c. violet	3 0	4 0
27	**14**	8 c. green	4 0	4 6

Stamps of these types, printed in wrong colours and also any impressions surcharged with values in "pence," are from waste sheets that were used by Perkins Bacon & Co. as trial paper when preparing an issue of stamps for British South Africa.

The 2 c. in green, perf. 12½, is a colour trial.

(Typo. De La Rue & Co.)

1897. *No wmk.* *P* 14.

No.	Type	Description	Unused	Used
28	**4**	16 c. green & orge. (28 Dec.)	7 6	8 6
29	,,	32 c. green & black (28 Dec.)	7 6	8 6
30	,,	50 c. green (26 July) ..	7 0	8 6
31	,,	$1 green & black (2 Nov.)	17 6	18 0

On No. 31 the value is in black on an uncoloured ground.

4
CENTS.

(15)

1899. *Surch. as T* **15.**

No.	Type	Description	Unused	Used
32	**2**	2 c. on 3 c. brn./*yell.* (19.9.99)	2 0	2 6
		a. Stop after "THREE" ..	40 0	
		b. Imperf. between (vert. pair)	£6	
33	,,	2 c. on 12 c. red/*pale rose* (29.6.99)	2 6	3 6
		a. Surch. inverted	£20	
34	,,	4 c. on 6 c. grn./*grn.* (R.) (16.11.99)	10 6	12 0
35	,,	4 c. on 8 c. bt. blue/*blue* (R.) (29.6.99)	5 0	6 0

Re "laid paper" varieties, previously listed, see note after No. 7.

A variety of surcharge with small "S" in "CENTS" may be found in the 2 c. on 12 c. and 4 c. on 8 c. and a raised stop after "CENTS" on the 4 c. on 6 c.

The omission of parts of the surcharge is due to gum on the surface of the stamps (see note after No. 23).

(Typo. De La Rue & Co.)

1899 (10 Nov.)–**1908.** *Inscribed* "POSTAGE POSTAGE." *No wmk.* *P* 14.

No.	Type	Description	Unused	Used
36	**4**	1 c. grey-blue & rosine (1.01)	0 9	0 9
		a. Grey-blue and red	1 0	0 6
		b. Ultramarine and rosine ..	5 0	5 0
		c. Dull blue and carmine ..	3 6	5 0
37	,,	2 c. green (16.12.99) ..	1 6	0 9
38	,,	3 c. dull purple (1908) ..	0 9	0 6
39	,,	4 c. bright rose (10.11.99)	3 0	1 0
		a. Aniline-carmine	2 0	1 0
40	,,	8 c. yellow & blk. (6.12.99)	3 6	2 0
41	,,	10 c. ultramarine (10.11.99)	4 0	3 0
42	,,	12 c. mauve (16.12.99) ..	4 6	4 0
		a. Bright mauve ('05)	8 6	8 6
43	,,	16 c. chest. & grn. (16.12.99)	5 0	6 0
44	,,	20 c. bistre & bt. mauve (5.00)	5 0	6 0
45	,,	25 c. brown & blue (16.12.99)	6 6	7 6
46	,,	50 c. sage-green and carmine (16.12.99)	12 0	12 6
47	,,	$1 rose-carm. and dp. grn. (16.12.99)	17 6	17 6
		a. Rosine and pale green ..	20 0	20 0

The figures of value in the $1 are in colour on an uncoloured ground.

Prepared for use but not issued.

No.	Type	Description	Unused	Used
48	**4**	5 c. olive-grey and green ..	70 0	

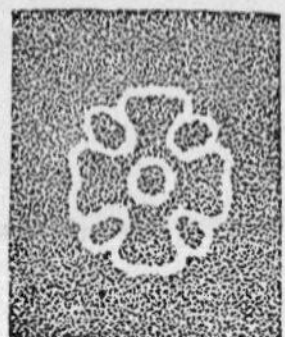

16

1901. *Inscribed* "POSTAGE POSTAGE." *Wmk. T* **16.** *P* 14.

No.	Type	Description				
49	4	2 c. green	8	6	10	0

Sir Charles Vyner Brooke. 17 May, 1917.

17. Sir Charles Vyner Brooke.

(Typo. De La Rue & Co.)

1918. *No wmk. Chalky paper. P* 14.

No.	Type	Description				
50	17	1 c. slate-blue and red ..	0	4	0	4
		a. Dull blue and carmine ..	0	8	0	4
51	,,	2 c. green	1	0	0	9
52	,,	3 c. brown-purple ..	1	0	1	0
53	,,	4 c. rose-carmine ..	1	3	0	9
		a. Rose-red	1	0	0	10
54	,,	8 c. yellow and black ..	3	6	4	0
55	,,	10 c. ultramarine	4	0	4	6
		a. Bright blue	3	6	4	0
56	,,	12 c. purple	4	0	4	6
57	,,	16 c. chestnut and green ..	2	0	1	6
58	,,	20 c. olive-bistre and violet	2	0	1	6
59	,,	25 c. brown & bright blue ..	4	0	1	6
60	,,	50 c. olive-green & carmine	4	6	1	9
61	,,	$1 bright rose and green	8	6	5	6

On the $1 the figures of value are in colour on an uncoloured ground.

The 20 c. in olive-green is believed to be a changeling due to climatic influences.

Prepared for use but not issued.

No.	Type	Description		
62	17	1 c. slate-blue and slate ..	35	0

1922–23. *New colours and values. No wmk. P* 14.

No.	Type	Description				
63	17	2 c. purple (1923)	0	6	0	6
64	,,	3 c. dull green	0	6	0	6
65	,,	4 c. brown-purple (1923) ..	0	8	0	4
66	,,	5 c. yellow-orange (1923)	1	0	0	6
67	,,	6 c. claret	1	0	1	0
68	,,	8 c. bright rose-red ..	2	0	2	0
69	,,	10 c. black (1923) ..	2	0	1	9
70	,,	12 c. bright blue ..	3	6	4	0
		a. Pale dull blue	2	6	2	6
71	,,	30 c. ochre-brown and slate	7	6	2	6

ONE
cent

(18)

1923 (Nov.). *Surcharged as T* **18.**

(*a*) *First printing. Bars* 1½ *mm. apart.*

No.	Type	Description				
72	17	1 c. on 10 c. dull blue ..	7	6	8	6
		a. "cnet" for "cent" ..	£16			
		b. Pale ultramarine	40	0	30	0
		ba. Do. "cnet" for "cent" ..				
73	,,	2 c. on 12 c. purple ..	5	0	6	0
		a. Thick, narrow "W" in "TWO"	10	0	10	0

(*b*) *Second printing. Bars* ¾ *mm. apart.*

No.	Type	Description		
74	17	1 c. on 10 c. bright blue ..	75	0
		a. "en" of "cent" scratched out and "ne" overprinted		
75	,,	2 c. on 12 c. purple ..	60	0
		a. Thick, narrower "W" in "TWO"	£5	

In the 2 c. on 12 c. the words of the surcharge are about 7½ mm. from the bars.

Variety 74*a* arose through a native printer "correcting" an already correct surcharge in the second printing in the endeavour exactly to reproduce the "cnet" error of the first printing.

The thick "W" variety occurs on all stamps of the last two horizontal rows of the first printing (12 stamps per sheet), and in the last two vertical rows of the second (20 stamps per sheet).

1928–29. *Wmk. Multiple Rosettes* (*T* **16,** *Mult.*). *Chalk-surfaced paper. P* 14.

No.	Type	Description				
76	17	1 c. slate-blue and carmine	0	6	0	4
77	,,	2 c. bright purple ..	0	9	0	4
78	,,	3 c. green	0	8	0	9
79	,,	4 c. brown-purple ..	0	8	0	4
80	,,	5 c. yellow-orange (12.29)	1	0	1	0
81	,,	6 c. claret	1	0	1	0
82	,,	8 c. bright rose-red ..	1	6	1	9
83	,,	10 c. black	1	3	1	0
84	,,	12 c. bright blue	1	9	1	6
85	,,	16 c. chestnut and green ..	2	0	2	0
86	,,	20 c. olive-bistre & violet ..	2	0	2	0
87	,,	25 c. brown & bright blue	2	6	1	6
88	,,	30 c. bistre-brown & slate	2	6	1	6
89	,,	50 c. olive-green & carmine	5	0	5	0
90	,,	$1 bright rose and green	10	0	10	6

In the $1 the value is as before.

19. Sir Chas. Vyner Brooke. **20**

(Recess. Waterlow & Sons, Ltd.)

1932 (1 Jan.). *W* **20.** *P* 12½.

No.	Type	Description				
91	19	1 c. indigo	1	3	0	10
92	,,	2 c. green	1	3	0	10
93	,,	3 c. violet..	1	6	1	6
94	,,	4 c. red-orange	1	6	1	0
95	,,	5 c. deep lake	1	6	1	0
96	,,	6 c. scarlet	2	0	2	0
97	,,	8 c. orange-yellow ..	2	0	2	0
98	,,	10 c. black	2	9	2	9
99	,,	12 c. deep ultramarine ..	3	6	3	6
100	,,	15 c. chestnut	3	6	3	6
101	,,	20 c. red-orange & violet..	4	0	3	0
102	,,	25 c. oran.-yell. & chestnut	5	0	5	0
103	,,	30 c. sepia and vermilion	6	6	6	6
104	,,	50 c. carm.-red & olive-grn.	10	0	6	0
105	,,	$1 green and carmine ..	20	0	20	0

21. Sir Charles Vyner Brooke.

(Recess. Bradbury, Wilkinson & Co., Ltd.)

1934 (1 May). *No wmk.* *P* 12.

No.	Type	Description	Unused	Used
106	21	1 c. purple	0 5	0 3
107	„	2 c. green	0 4	0 4
108	„	3 c. black	0 4	0 4
109	„	4 c. bright purple ..	0 5	0 5
110	„	5 c. violet	1 3	0 9
111	„	6 c. carmine	0 8	0 6
112	„	8 c. red-brown	0 8	0 9
113	„	10 c. scarlet	2 0	1 0
114	„	12 c. blue	1 0	1 0
115	„	15 c. orange	1 3	1 6
116	„	20 c. olive-grn. & carm...	1 6	1 6
117	„	25 c. violet and orange ..	1 6	1 9
118	„	30 c. red-brown and violet	2 6	2 0
119	„	50 c. violet and scarlet ..	3 6	3 0
120	„	$1 scarlet and sepia ..	7 6	5 0
121	„	$2 bright pur. & violet	12 6	10 6
122	„	$3 carmine and green	20 0	20 0
123	„	$4 blue and scarlet ..	25 0	27 6
124	„	$5 scarlet & red-brown	32 6	32 6
125	„	$10 black and yellow ..	65 0	65 0

For other colours, see Nos. 107*a* onwards in King George VI Catalogue.

SEYCHELLES.

PRINTERS. All the stamps of Seychelles were typographed by De La Rue & Co., unless otherwise stated.

1

Plate I.

Plate II.

In Plate I there are lines of shading in the middle compartment of the diadem, which contains the diamond-shaped jewel, which are absent from impressions from Plates II and III.

1890 (5 April). *T* **1**. *Wmk. Crown CA.* *P* 14.

(i.) Plate I.

No.	Description	Unused	Used
1	2 c. green and carmine ..	3 6	4 0
2	4 c. carmine and green ..	15 0	17 6
3	8 c. brown-purple and blue ..	6 6	7 6
4	10 c. ultramarine & brown ..	10 0	10 6
5	13 c. grey and black	6 0	6 6
6	16 c. chestnut and blue ..	10 0	10 0
7	48 c. ochre and green	17 6	17 6
8	96 c. mauve and carmine ..	37 6	40 0

(ii.) Plate II.

No.	Description	Unused	Used
9	2 c. green and rosine	2 6	3 0
10	4 c. carmine and green ..	2 6	3 0
11	8 c. brn.-pur. & ultramarine	4 6	4 6
12	10 c. bright ultramarine & brn.	7 6	7 6
13	13 c. grey and black	5 0	6 0
14	16 c. chestnut and ultramarine	5 0	6 0

3
cents
(2)

1893 (Jan.). *Surcharged as T* **2** *in black.*

No.	Description	Unused	Used
15	3 c. on 4 c. (No. 10) ..	1 9	1 9
	a. Surcharge omitted (in pair with normal)		
16	12 c. on 16 c. (No. 6)	4 0	5 0
17	12 c. on 16 c. (No. 14) ..	5 0	5 0
18	15 c. on 16 c. (No. 6) ..	7 6	7 6
19	15 c. on 16 c. (No. 14) ..	5 0	5 0
20	45 c. on 48 c. (No. 7) ..	17 0	15 0
21	90 c. on 96 c. (No. 8) ..	30 0	32 6

Varieties. (i.) *Surcharge inverted.*

No.	Description	Unused	Used
22	3 c. on 4 c. (No. 10) ..	£6	£7
23	12 c. on 16 c. (No. 6)	£12	
24	15 c. on 16 c. (No. 6) ..	£10	£10
24*aa*	15 c. on 16 c. (No. 14) ..	£15	£16

(ii.) *Surcharge double.*

No.	Description	Unused	Used
24*a*	3 c. on 4 c. (No. 10) ..	£15	
24*b*	12 c. on 16 c. (No. 6) ..		
24*c*	15 c. on 16 c. (No. 6) ..	£10	
24*d*	15 c. on 16 c. (No. 14) ..		

1893 (Nov.). *T* **1** (*Plates II and III*). *Wmk. Crown CA.* *P* 14.

No.	Description	Unused	Used
25	3 c. dull purple and orange	1 3	1 3
26	12 c. sepia and green ..	3 0	3 6
27	15 c. sage-green and lilac .	7 6	7 6
28	45 c. brown and carmine ..	27 6	27 6

18 CENTS
(3)

1896 (1 Aug.). *No.* 28 *surcharged as T* **3**.

No.	Description	Unused	Used
29	18 c. on 45 c. brown & carm.	10 6	10 0
	a. Surcharge double	£30	£30
	b. Surcharge treble	£35	
30	36 c. on 45 c. brown & carm.	12 6	15 0
	a. Surcharge double		

4

1897–1900. *T* **1** (*Plates II and III*) *and* **4** (75 *c. and higher values*). *Wmk. Crown CA.* *P* 14.

No.	Description	Unused	Used
32	2 c. orange-brn. & grn. (1900)	1 6	1 6
33	6 c. carmine (1900)	2 0	2 6
34	15 c. ultramarine (1900) ..	10 0	10 6
35	18 c. ultramarine	8 6	8 6
36	36 c. brown and carmine ..	12 6	15 0
37	75 c. yellow & violet (1900) ..	30 0	32 6
38	1 r. bright mauve & deep red	17 6	17 6
39	1 r. 50 c. grey & carm. (1900)	32 6	32 6
40	2 r. 25 c. brt. mve. & grn (1900)	60 0	50 0

3 cents

6 cents

(5) (5*a*)

1901. *Surcharged with T* **5** *or* **5*a***.

No.	Description	Unused	Used
41	3 c. on 10 c. (No. 12) ..	3 0	4 0
42	3 c. on 16 c. (No. 14) ..	3 6	4 6
43	3 c. on 36 c. (No. 36) ..	3 0	3 6
44	6 c. on 8 c. (No. 11)	3 0	3 6

Varieties. (i.) *Surcharge inverted.*

No.	Description	Unused	Used
44*a*	3 c. on 16 c.	£22	£22
44*b*	6 c. on 8 c.	£22	£22

(ii.) *Surcharge double.*

No.	Description	Unused	Used
44*c*	3 c. on 10 c.	£28	
44*d*	3 c. on 16 c.	£18	
44*e*	3 c. on 36 c.	£30	

(iii.) "3 cents" *omitted.*

No.	Description	Unused	Used
44*f*	= on 16 c.	£15	
44*g*	= on 36 c.		

1902 (June). *Surcharged as T* **5**.

No.	Description	Unused	Used
45	2 c. on 4 c. (No. 10)	8 0	8 6
46	30 c. on 75 c. (No. 37)	8 0	10 0
47	30 c. on 1 r. (No. 38)	20 0	20 0
48	45 c. on 1 r. (No. 38)	17 6	17 6
49	45 c. on 2 r. 25 c. (No. 40)	27 6	27 6

Varieties. (i.) *Narrow* "o" *in* "30."

No.	Description	Unused	Used
50	30 c. on 75 c.	22 6	27 6
51	30 c. on 1 r.	70 0	70 0

(ii.) *Narrow* "5" *in* "45."

No.	Description	Unused	Used
52	45 c. on 2 r. 25 c.	£12	

(iii.) *Double surcharge.*

No.	Description	Unused	Used
52*a*	30 c. on 1 r.	£18	

6

7

1903 (June)–**1904**. *T* **6** (2 *c. to* 45 *c.*) *and* **7** (*higher values*). *Wmk. Crown CA. P* 14.

No.	Description	Unused	Used
53	2 c. chestnut and green	0 8	0 8
54	3 c. dull green	1 3	1 6
55	6 c. carmine	1 9	1 6
56	12 c. olive-sepia & dull green	5 0	4 0
57	15 c. ultramarine	5 0	6 0
58	18 c. sage-green and carmine	10 0	10 0
59	30 c. violet and dull green	10 6	10 6
60	45 c. brown and carmine	10 6	10 6
61	75 c. yellow and violet	12 6	12 6
62	1 r. 50 c. black & carmine	22 6	22 6
63	2 r. 25 c. purple and green	27 6	27 6

3 cents

(8)

T **6** *surcharged with T* **8**, *in black.*

No.	Description	Unused	Used
64	3 c. on 15 c. ultramarine	7 6	8 0
65	3 c. on 18 c. sage-green & car.	20 0	22 6
66	3 c. on 45 c. brown & carmine	10 0	10 6

1906. *T* **6** *and* **7**. *Wmk. Mult. Crown CA. P* 14.

No.	Description	Unused	Used
67	2 c. chestnut and green	1 3	1 6
68	3 c. dull green	1 6	1 3
69	6 c. carmine	1 6	1 6
70	12 c. olive-sepia and dull grn.	4 0	3 6
71	15 c. ultramarine	5 0	5 0
72	18 c. sage-green & carmine	6 0	6 0
73	30 c. violet and dull green	6 0	7 6
74	45 c. brown and carmine	10 0	10 6
75	75 c. yellow and violet	10 6	12 0
76	1 r. 50 c. black and carmine	22 6	22 6
77	2 r. 25 c. purple and green	35 0	35 0

9

10

1912. *T* **9** *and* **10** (75 *c. to* 2 *r.* 25 *c.*). *Wmk. Mult. Crown CA. P* 14.

No.	Description	Unused	Used
78	2 c. chestnut and green	1 6	1 6
79	3 c. green	1 6	1 3
80	6 c. aniline carmine	5 0	5 0
80*a*	6 c. carmine-red	2 0	2 0
81	12 c. olive-sepia & dull green	3 0	3 6
82	15 c. ultramarine	5 0	5 0
83	18 c. sage-green & carmine	4 0	5 0
84	30 c. violet and green	7 6	8 6
85	45 c. brown and carmine	7 6	8 6
86	75 c. yellow and violet	10 0	12 6
87	1 r. 50 c. black & carmine	12 0	10 0
88	2 r. 25 c. rose-purple & green	35 0	22 6
88*a*	2 r. 25 c. bright purple & grn.	25 0	20 0

11

12

13

1917–20. *T* **11**, **12** *and* **13** *inscr.* "Postage and Revenue." *Wmk. Mult. Crown CA. P* 14.

No.	Type	Description	Unused	Used
89	**11**	2 c. chestnut & grn., O	0 4	0 6
90	,,	3 c. green, O (1917)	0 8	0 8
91	**12**	5 c. deep brown, O	1 3	1 3
92	**11**	6 c. carmine, O (1917)	2 0	0 10
92*a*	,,	6 c. rose, O	2 6	1 3
93	,,	12 c. grey, O	2 0	1 9
94	,,	15 c. ultramarine, O ('17)	2 0	2 6
95	,,	18 c. purple/*yellow*, C	3 6	4 0
		a. On orange-buff	12 6	17 6
		b. On paleyellow (Die II)	2 0	2 6
96	**13**	25 c. blk. & red/*yellow*, C	5 0	6 0
		b. On paleyellow (Die II)	3 6	3 6
97	**11**	30 c. dull pur. & olive, C	4 6	5 0
98	,,	45 c. dull pur. & orange, C	6 0	6 6
99	**13**	50 c. dull pur. & black, C	6 0	6 6
100	,,	75 c. black/*blue-green*, C (*olive back*)	6 6	7 6
		a. On emerald back (Die II)	6 0	7 6
101	,,	1 r. dull purple & red, C	10 0	10 6
102	,,	1 r. 50 c. reddish purple and blue/*blue*, C	12 6	15 0
102*a*	,,	1 r. 50 c. blue-purple & blue/*blue*, C (Die II)	10 0	12 6
103	,,	2 r. 25 c. yellow-green & violet, C	20 0	22 6
104	,,	5 r. green and blue, C	50 0	55 0

1921–32. *Wmk. Mult. Script CA. P* 14.

No.	Type	Description	Unused	Used
105	**11**	2 c. chestnut & green, O	0 4	0 6
106	,,	3 c. green, O	0 6	0 8
107	**12**	5 c. deep brown, O	1 0	1 3
108	**11**	6 c. carmine, O	1 0	1 3
109	,,	12 c. grey, O (Die II)	2 0	2 6
		a. Die I ('32)	1 6	1 9
110	,,	15 c. bright blue, O	2 6	3 6
111	,,	18 c. purple/*pale yellow*, C	2 6	2 9
112	**13**	25 c. blk. & red/*pale yell.*, C	2 0	2 6
113	**11**	30 c. dull purple & olive, C	4 0	4 6
114	,,	45 c. dull pur. & orange, C	3 6	4 6

No.	Type	Description	s.	d.	s.	d.
115	13	50 c. dull purple & black, C	3	6	4	6
116	,,	75 c. black/*emerald*, C	6	6	7	0
117	,,	1 r. dull purple and red, C (Die II)	12	6	15	0
		a. Die I ('32)	7	6	10	0
118	,,	1 r. 50 c. pur. & blue/*blue*, C	15	0	17	6
119	,,	2 r. 25 c. yell.-grn. and violet, C	15	0	17	6
120	,,	5 r. yellow-grn. & blue, C	35	0	37	6

1922–28. *Colours changed and new values. Wmk. Mult. Script CA. P* 14.

No.	Type	Description	s.	d.	s.	d.
121	11	3 c. black, O	0	4	0	4
122	,,	4 c. green, O	0	8	0	8
122*a*	,,	4 c. sage-green and carmine, O ('28)	6	6	7	6
123	,,	6 c. deep mauve, O	0	8	0	8
123*a*	13	9 c. red, O	2	0	2	6
124	11	12 c. carmine-red, O	2	0	2	6
125	,,	15 c. yellow, O	2	6	3	0
126	13	20 c. bright blue, O	2	0	2	6
127	,,	20 c. dull blue, O	3	6	4	0

1935 (6 May). *Silver Jubilee. As T* **13** *of Antigua, inscr.* "SEYCHELLES". *Recess. B.W. & Co. Wmk. Mult. Script CA. P* 11×12.

No.	Description	s.	d.	s.	d.
128	6 c. ultramarine & grey-black	0	8	1	0
129	12 c. green and indigo	2	6	3	0
130	20 c. brown and deep blue	4	0	5	0
131	1 r. slate and purple	15	0	20	0

All values exist with double "flagstaff" variety.

SIERRA LEONE.

PRINTERS. All issues of Sierra Leone were typographed by De La Rue & Co. unless otherwise stated.

1

The 6d. on *blue* paper, *imperf.*, is believed to be only a proof, and is therefore omitted. (*Price*, 150s.)

1860. *T* **1.** *No wmk. P* 14.

(a) Bluish paper.

No.	Description	Unused		Used	
2	6d. dull purple	75	0	55	0

(b) White paper.

No.	Description	Unused		Used	
3	6d. grey-lilac	£6		45	0
4	6d. dull violet	£5		30	0

1872. *T* **1.** *No wmk. P* 12½.

(a) Bluish paper.

No.	Description	Unused		Used	
5	6d. dull violet	£5		35	0

(b) White paper.

No.	Description	Unused		Used	
6	6d. dull violet	£15		£8	

2

HALF
PENNY

(3)

1872–73. *T* **2.** *Wmk. Crown CC. P* 12½.

1872 (Apr.). *(a) Wmk. sideways.*

No.	Description	Unused		Used	
7	1d. rose-red	25	0	20	0
8	3d. buff	50	0	35	0
9	4d. blue	65	0	45	0
10	1s. green	90	0	45	0

1873 (Sept.). *(b) Wmk. upright.*

No.	Description	Unused		Used	
11	1d. rose-red	22	6	20	0
11*a*	2d. magenta	55	0	45	0
12	3d. saffron-yellow	£20		55	0
12*a*	4d. blue	85	0	55	0
12*b*	1s. green	£12		85	0

1876–77. *T* **2.** *Wmk. Crown CC. P* 14.

No.	Description	Unused		Used	
13	½d. brown	6	6	7	6
14	1d. rose	20	0	12	6
15	1½d. lilac (1877)	10	6	10	0
16	2d. magenta	27	6	12	0
17	3d. buff	20	0	10	6
18	4d. blue	60	0	10	6
20	1s. green	40	0	30	0

1883 (June)–**1884.** *T* **2.** *Wmk. Crown CA P* 14.

No.	Description	Unused		Used	
21	½d. brown	20	0	20	0
21*a*	1d. rose-carmine	70	0	12	6
21*b*	1d. rose-red	£10		15	0
22	2d. magenta	45	0	12	6
23	4d. blue	£30		45	0

1884–93. *T* **2.** *Wmk. Crown CA. P* 14.

No.	Description	Unused		Used	
24	½d. dull green	1	3	1	0
25	1d. carmine	3	6	1	3
26	1½d. pale violet (1893)	4	0	5	0
27	2d. grey	10	6	7	6
28	2½d. ultramarine (1891)	6	6	2	0
29	3d. yellow (1892)	6	0	6	0
30	4d. brown	4	6	4	6
31	1s. red-brown (1888)	12	6	15	0

1885–96. *T* **1.** *Wmk. Crown CC. P* 14.

No.	Description	Unused		Used	
32	6d. dull violet (1885)	75	0	30	0
	a. Bisected (3d.)				
33	6d. brown-purple (1890)	27	6	17	6
33*a*	6d. purple-lake (1896)	7	6	8	0

Variety. Paper slightly blued.

No.	Description	Unused		Used	
34	6d. brown-purple	70	0	50	0

1893. *T* **2** *surcharged with T* **3.** *P* 14.

(a) Wmk. Crown CC.

No.	Description	Unused		Used	
35	½d. on 1½d. pale violet	£20		£20	
36	½d. on 1½d. (PFNNY)	£100			

(b) Wmk. Crown CA.

No.	Description	Unused		Used	
37	½d. on 1½d. pale violet	8	6	10	6
38	½d. on 1½d. (PFNNY)	90	0	90	0

Varieties. (i.) *Surcharge inverted.*

No.	Description	Unused		Used	
39	½d. on 1½d. pale violet	90	0	90	0
40	½d. on 1½d. (EFNNY)	£60			

(ii.) *Double surcharge.*

No.	Description	Unused		Used	
40*a*	½d. on 1½d. pale violet	£25			

4

5

1896–97. *T* **4** (*½d. to 2½d.*) *and* **5** (*other values*). *Wmk. Crown CA. P* 14.

41	½d. dull mauve & grn. (1897) ..	0 8	0 8
42	1d. dull mauve & carmine ..	0 10	0 6
43	1½d. dull mauve & black (1897)	5 0	4 0
44	2d. dull mauve & orange ..	5 0	4 0
45	2½d. dull mauve & ultramarine	4 0	2 0
46	3d. dull mauve & slate ..	7 6	7 6
47	4d. dull mauve & carm. (1897)	12 6	10 6
48	5d. dull mauve & black (1897)	10 6	10 6
49	6d. dull mauve (1897) ..	10 6	10 0
50	1s. green and black	12 6	12 6
51	2s. green & ultramarine ..	30 0	32 6
52	5s. green and carmine ..	50 0	50 0
53	£1 purple/*red*	£8	£9

6

POSTAGE
AND
REVENUE
(7)

1897 (March). *T* **6**. *Value in second colour. Wmk. CA over Crown, T* w. 7. *Overprinted with T* 7, *in black. P* 14.

54	1d. dull purple and green ..	3 0	2 6

Variety. Overprint double.

54*a*	1d. dull purple and green ..	£20	£20

2½d.

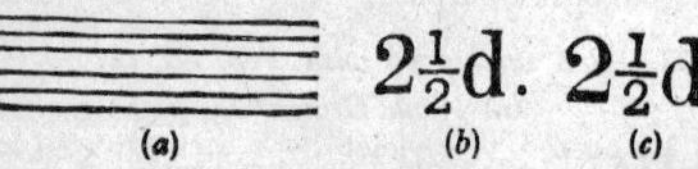

(*a*) (*b*) (*c*)

2½d. 2½d. 2½d.
(*d*) (*e*) (*f*)

T **6** *surcharged in addition with* "2½d." *below T* 7, *in black. Original value cancelled by* 6 *bars in black.*

55	2½d. on 3d. dull pur. & grn. (*a*)	5 0	6 0
56	2½d. on 3d. dull pur. & grn. (*c*)	32 6	32 6
57	2½d. on 3d. dull pur. & grn. (*d*)	52 6	65 0
58	2½d. on 3d. dull pur. & grn. (*e*)	85 0	85 0
59	2½d. on 6d. dull pur. & grn. (*a*)	5 0	5 6
60	2½d. on 6d. dull pur. & grn. (*c*)	12 6	15 0
61	2½d. on 6d. dull pur. & grn. (*d*)	22 6	22 6
62	2½d. on 6d. dull pur. & grn. (*e*)	75 0	75 0

Variety. Surcharge double.

62*b*	2½d. (*c*) and 2½d. (*f*) on 3d. dull purple and green ..	£20	

The 2½d. on 3d. and 2½d. on 6d. are printed in sheets of thirty, of which there are twenty-two of (*a*), five of (*c*), two of (*d*), and one of (*e*).

POSTAGE AND
REVENUE
(8)

Similar to last, but overprinted with T **8**, *in black. The surcharge* "2½d." *is above T* **8**, *and there are only* 5 *bars cancelling original value instead of* 6.

63	2½d. on 1s. dull purple (*a*) ..	35 0	35 0
64	2½d. on 1s. dull purple (*b*)	£8	£8
65	2½d. on 1s. dull purple (*c*) ..	£7	£7
66	2½d. on 1s. dull purple (*d*) ..	80 0	80 0
66*a*	2½d. on 1s. dull purple (*f*) ..	£8	£8
67	2½d. on 2s. dull purple (*a*) ..	£8	£8
68	2½d. on 2s. dull purple (*b*) ..	£50	
69	2½d. on 2s. dull purple (*c*) ..	£25	
70	2½d. on 2s. dull purple (*d*) ..	£14	
71	2½d. on 2s. dull purple (*f*) ..	£50	

9

10

1903. *T* **9** (*½d. to 2½d.*) *amd* **10** (*other values*). *Wmk. Crown CA. P* 14.

72	½d. dull purple & green ..	4 0	3 6
73	1d. dull purple & rosine ..	1 6	0 8
74	1½d. dull purple & black ..	8 0	8 6
75	2d. dull pur. & brown-orange	8 0	8 6
76	2½d. dull purple & ultram. ..	10 0	10 0
77	3d. dull purple and grey ..	10 0	10 0
78	4d. dull purple and rosine ..	17 6	20 0
79	5d. dull purple and black ..	12 6	15 0
80	6d. dull purple	15 0	15 0
81	1s. green and black	35 0	35 0
82	2s. green and ultramarine ..	50 0	55 0
83	5s. green and carmine ..	85 0	90 0
84	£1 purple/*red*	£10	£12

1904–5. *T* **9** *and* **10**. *Wmk. Mult. Crown CA P* 14.

85	½d. dull pur. & green, C ('04)	3 6	2 0
86	1d. dull pur. & rosine, OC ('04)	2 0	0 9
86*a*	1½d. dull pur. and black, C ..	4 0	4 6
87	2d. dull pur. & brn.-orge., C	5 0	5 6
88	2½d. dull pur. & ultram., C ..	8 0	7 6
89	3d. dull purple and grey, C	10 6	10 0
90	4d. dull purple and rosine, C	6 6	7 6
91	5d. dull purple and black, C	7 6	8 0
92	6d. dull purple, C ..	10 0	10 6
93	1s. green and black, C ..	12 0	12 0
94	2s. green and ultramarine, C	17 6	20 0
95	5s. green and carmine, C ..	50 0	40 0
96	£1 purple/*red*, C	£18	£18

1907–10. *T* **9** *and* **10**. *Wmk. Mult. Crown CA. P* 14.

97	½d. green, O (1907)	0 8	0 4
98	1d. carmine, O	3 0	0 3
99	1d. red, O (1907)	2 0	0 3
100	1½d. orange, O (1910) ..	4 6	5 0
101	2d. greyish slate, O	4 6	5 0
102	2½d. blue, O (1907)	4 6	3 0
103	3d. purple/*yellow*, OC ..	5 0	5 0
104	4d. black and red/*yellow*, C..	7 6	8 0
105	5d. purple & olive-green, C..	8 6	10 0
106	6d. dull and bright purple, C	10 0	10 6
107	1s. black/*green*, C	8 6	8 6
108	2s. pur. & bright blue/*blue*, C	27 6	30 0
109	5s. green and red/*yellow*, C..	50 0	42 6
111	£1 purple and black *red*, C	£12	£12

11

12

13

14

1912–16. *T* **11** (½d. *to* 2½d.) **12** *and* **13** (7d. *and* 9d.). *Wmk. Mult. Crown CA.* *P* 14.

No.	Description	Unused	Used
112	½d. blue-green, O	0 8	0 4
113	½d. yellow-green, O	1 3	0 3
114	½d. deep green, O	1 6	0 8
115	1d. carmine-red, O	1 0	0 1
116	1d. scarlet, O (1916)	1 0	0 1
116a	1d. rose-red, O	0 6	0 1
117	1½d. orange, O	2 6	2 6
118	1½d. orange-yellow, O	3 0	3 0
119	2d. greyish slate, O	2 0	0 9
120	2½d. deep blue, O	4 0	4 0
121	2½d. ultramarine, O	2 6	2 6
122	4d. black & red/*yellow*, O	3 6	2 0
	a. On lemon	15 0	10 0
	b. On pale yellow (Die II)	4 6	5 0
123	5d. purple & olive-green, O	4 0	4 6
124	6d. dull and bright purple, C	5 0	5 0
125	7d. purple and orange, C	5 0	6 0
126	9d. purple and black, C	6 6	7 0
127	10d. purple and red, C	7 6	8 0

T **14.** *Wmk. Mult. Crown CA.* *P* 14.

No.	Description	Unused	Used
128	3d. purple/*yellow*, C	2 6	2 0
	a. On pale yellow	5 0	2 0
129	1s. black/*green*, C	7 6	4 0
	a. On blue-green, green back	6 6	4 0
130	2s. blue & purple/*blue*, C	10 6	10 6
131	5s. red and green/*yellow*, C	20 0	22 6
132	10s. red & green/*green*, C	52 6	45 0
133	10s. carm. & bl.-grn./*grn.*, C	65 0	70 0
133a	10s. carm. & yell.-grn./*grn.*, C	55 0	60 0
134	£1 black and purple/*red*, C	75 0	85 0
135	£2 blue and dull purple, C	£20	£20
136	£5 orange and green, C	£40	

1921–28. *Wmk. Mult. Script CA.* *P* 14.

No.	Type	Description	Unused	Used
137	**11**	½d. dull green, O	0 6	0 4
138	,,	½d. bright green, O	0 6	0 4
139	,,	1d. bright violet O (Die I) ('24)	0 10	0 4
139a	,,	1d. bright violet, O (Die II) ('26)	0 6	0 2
140	,,	1½d. scarlet, O	1 0	1 0
141	,,	2d. grey, O	1 3	0 9
142	,,	2½d. ultramarine, O	2 0	2 6
143	**12**	3d. bright blue, O	2 0	0 8
144	,,	4d. blk. & red/*pale yell.*, O	2 0	2 0
145	,,	5d. pur. & olive-green, O	2 0	2 0
146	,,	6d. grey-purple & bright purple, C	2 6	3 0
146a	**13**	7d. purple & orange, C	5 0	6 0
147	,,	9d. purple and black, C	5 0	6 0
147a	**12**	10d. purple and red, C	6 0	6 6
148	**14**	1s. black/*emerald*, C	8 6	6 6
149	,,	2s. blue & dull purple/*blue*, C	10 0	10 0
150	,,	5s. red & grn./*yellow*, C	17 6	20 0
151	,,	10s. red & grn./*green*, C	35 0	40 0
153	,,	£2 blue & dull purple, C	£18	£25
154	,,	£5 orange and green, C	£40	

15. Rice Field.

16. Palms and Kola Tree.

1932 (1 Mar.). *Wmk. Mult. Script CA.*

(*a*) *T* **15.** *Recess. Waterlow.* *P* 12½.

No.	Description	Unused	Used
155	½d. green	0 4	0 3
156	1d. violet	0 6	0 4
157	1½d. carmine	1 6	0 8
158	2d. brown	1 9	0 9
159	3d. blue	2 6	3 0
160	4d. orange	4 0	5 0
161	5d. bronze-green	4 6	6 0
162	6d. light blue	5 0	6 0
163	1s. lake	15 0	15 0

(*b*) *T* **16.** *Recess. Bradbury, Wilkinson.* *P* 12.

No.	Description	Unused	Used
164	2s. chocolate	25 0	27 6
165	5s. deep blue	50 0	55 0
166	10s. green	90 0	95 0
167	£1 purple	£10	£10

17. Arms of Sierra Leone (*vert.*).

18. Slave throwing off shackles (*vert.*).

19. Map of Sierra Leone.

20. Old Slave Market, Freetown.
21. Native fruit seller (*horiz.*).
22. Government Sanatorium (*vert.*).
23. Bullam Canoe (*horiz.*).
24. Punting near Banana Islands (*horiz.*).
25. Government Buildings, Freetown (*horiz.*)
26. Bunce Island (*horiz.*).
27. African Elephant (*vert.*).
28. King George V (*horiz.*).
29. Freetown Harbour (*horiz.*).

(Des. Father F. Welch. Recess-printed by Bradbury, Wilkinson & Co., Ltd.)

1933 (2 Oct.). *Centenary of the Abolition of Slavery and of the Death of William Wilberforce.* ***T 17 to 29*** *(various designs dated* " 1833–1933 ". *Wmk. Mult. Script CA. P* 12.

No.	Description				
168	½d. green	1	3	1	3
169	1d. black and brown ..	1	3	0	9
170	1½d. chestnut	3	6	3	0
171	2d. purple	4	0	2	3
172	3d. blue	6	6	5	6
173	4d. brown	8	6	8	0
174	5d. green & chestnut ..	16	6	15	0
175	6d. black & brown-orange ..	20	0	22	6
176	1s. violet	30	0	32	6
177	2s. brown and light blue ..	110	0	£6	
178	5s. black and purple ..	£12		£12	
179	10s. black & sage-green ..	£14		£15	
180	£1 violet and orange ..	£35		£38	

1935 (6 May). *Silver Jubilee. As* ***T 13*** *of Antigua, inscr.* " SIERRA LEONE ". *Recess. B.W. & Co. Wmk. Mult. Script CA. P* 11 × 12.

No.	Description				
181	1d. ultramarine & grey-blk. ..	0	6	0	8
182	3d. brown and deep blue ..	5	0	6	0
183	5d. green and indigo	6	6	6	6
184	1s. slate and purple	10	6	12	6

All values exist with " double flagstaff " variety.

Various fiscal stamps used postally have been chronicled, but these were never authorized or issued for postal use.

SOMALILAND PROTECTORATE.

See **BRITISH SOMALILAND.**

SOUTH AFRICA.

1

(Des. H. S. Wilkinson. Recess. De La Rue & Co.)

1910 (4 Nov.). ***T 1.*** *Wmk. Multiple Rosettes. P* 14.

No.	Description				
1	2½d. deep blue	4	6	4	0
2	2½d. blue	4	6	4	0

The deep blue shade is generally accompanied by a blueing of the paper.

2

3

4

(Typo. De La Rue & Co.)

1913 (1 Sept.)–**1921.** ***T 2*** *(½d., 1d. and 1½d.* ***and 3.*** *Wmk. Springbok's Head.* ***T 4.*** *P* 14.

No.	Description				
3	½d. green	0	6	0	1
	a. Perf. 14× Imperf.	1	3	0	6
	b. Stamp doubly printed ..	£80			
4	½d. blue-green	0	9	0	1
5	½d. yellow-green	0	6	0	1
6	1d. rose-red (*shades*)	0	7	0	1
	a. Perf. 14× Imperf. (13.2.14) ..	3	6	1	0
7	1d. carmine-red	0	8	0	1
8	1d. scarlet (*shades*)	0	6	0	1
	a. Perf. 14× Imperf.	3	6	1	0
9	1½d. chestnut (*shades*) (23.8.20)	0	4	0	1
	a. Tête-bêche, pair	3	6	4	0
	b. Perf. 14× Imperf. (15.11.20) ..	3	6	1	9
10	2d. dull purple	1	0	0	1
	a. Perf. 14× Imperf. (7.10.21) ..	4	0	1	9
11	2d. deep purple	1	6	0	1
12	2½d. bright blue	3	6	1	6
13	2½d. deep blue	4	0	2	0
14	3d. blk. & orange-red	5	0	0	6
15	3d. blk. & dull orange-red ..	5	0	0	6
16	4d. orange-yell. & olive-grn.	4	6	0	8
17	4d. orange-yell. & sage-grn. ..	5	0	0	8
18	6d. black and violet	4	6	0	6
18*a*	6d. black & bright violet ..	5	0	0	6
19	1s. orange	8	6	1	0
19*a*	1s. orange-yellow	8	6	1	0
20	1s. 3d. vio. (*shades*) (1.10.20)	7	6	4	0
21	2s. 6d. purple and green ..	17	6	4	6
22	5s. purple and blue	40	0	8	0
22*a*	5s. reddish pur. & light blue ..	45	0	8	6
23	10s. deep blue & olive-green ..	65	0	10	6
24	£1 green and red (July, '16) ..	£7		60	0
24*a*	£1 pale olive-grn. and red ..	£8		60	0

The 6d. of this series exists with " z " of " ZUID " wholly or partly missing, due to the wear of the plate. (*Wholly missing,* 20/– *un.* 10/– *us.*)

1922 (Oct.). ***T 3.*** *Colour changed.* ***W 4.*** *P* 14.

25 3d. ultramarine (*shades*)

5

(Original engraved by A. J. Cooper. Printed by the *Cape Times, Ltd.*, by photo-litho. offset process.)

1925 (25 Feb.). *Air stamps. T* **5**. *P* 12.

26	1d. carmine	7	6	8	6
27	3d. ultramarine	12	0	15	0
28	6d. magenta	22	6	27	6
29	9d. green	45	0	50	0

The following issues, unless otherwise stated, have English and Afrikaans inscriptions on alternate stamps throughout the sheet and are therefore best collected in pairs.

6 7

8 9

(Typo. first by Messrs. Waterlow & Sons, and later by the Government Printer, Pretoria.)

1926. *T* **6** *to* **8**. *W* **9**. *P* 14½×14.

		Un. pair		*Us. pair*		*Us. single*	
30	½d. blk. & green ..	1	0	0	3	0	1
	a. Missing "1" in fraction ..						
	b. Perf. 14.	2	0	2	6	0	9
	ba. Tête-bêche (pair)	£60					
31	1d. black & car. ..	0	8	0	3	0	1
	a. Perf. 14.	2	6	2	6	0	9
	aa. Tête-bêche (pair)	£60					
32	6d. grn. & orge. ..	6	0	2	0	0	8

No. 30a exists in Afrikaans only. Nos. 30b and 31a are from booklets of Pretoria printed stamps.

For rotogravure printing see Nos. 42, etc.

10

(Recess. Bradbury, Wilkinson & Co.)

1926. *T* **10**. *Inscribed in English* E.) *or Afrikaans* (A.). *Wmk. T* **9**. *Imperf.*

		Single stamps E.		A.	
33	4d. grey-bl. (*shades*)	3 0	2 6	3 0	2 6

In this value the English and Afrikaans inscriptions are on separate sheets.

This stamp is known with private perforation or roulette.

11. Union Buildings, Pretoria.

12. Groote Schuur.

12a. A Kaffir kraal.

13. Gnus.

14. Ox-wagon inspanned.

15. Ox-wagon outspanned.

16. Cape Town and Table Bay.

(Recess. Bradbury, Wilkinson & Co., Ltd.)

1927–28. *T* **11** *to* **16.** *W* 9 *P* 14.

No.		Un. pair	Us. pair	Us. single
34	2d. grey & pur. ..	4 0	0 9	0 3
35	3d. black & red ..	7 0	0 9	0 3
35*a*	4d. brown ..	10 0	2 6	0 10
36	1s. brn. & dp. blue	20 0	2 6	0 9
37	2s. 6d. grn. & brn.	32 0	12 0	4 0
38	5s. blk. & green ..	55 0	25 0	8 6
39	10s. brt. blue & brn.	70 0	37 6	12 6

17

(Typo. Govt. Printing Works, Pretoria.)

1929 (16 Aug.). *Air.* *T* **17** *inscribed bilingually No wmk.* *P* 14 × 13½.

No.		Un. pair	Us. pair	Us. single
40	4d. green		6 6	6 6
41	1s. orange		15 0	15 0

(Printed by rotogravure at Pretoria.)

1930–45. *T* **6** *to* **8** *and* **11** *to* **14** *redrawn.* *W* **9.** *P* 15 × 14 (½d., 1d., *and* 6d.) *or* 14.

No.		Un. pair	Us. pair	Us. single
42	½d. blk & green ..	1 4	0 3	0 1
	a. Two English or two Afrikaans stamps *se tenant* (vert. pair) ..	12 6	—	—
43	1d. blk. & car. (I)	1 6	0 3	0 1
	a. Error. No wmk.	47 6	—	—
43*c*	1d. blk. & car. (II)	2 0	0 6	0 2
44	2d. slate-grey & lil.	3 0	0 3	0 1
44*b*	2d. blue & viol ('38)	5 0	1 0	0 4
45	3d. blk. & red ..	12 0	3 0	1 0
45*a*	3d. blue	4 0	1 0	0 3
46	4d. brown ..	7 0	2 0	0 8
46*a*	4d. brn. ('36) (*again redrawn*) ..	2 0	1 0	0 4
47	6d. grn. & orange	10 0	0 9	0 3
48	1s. brn. & dp. blue	10 6	2 0	[illegible]
49	2s. 6d. grn. & brn.	10 0	3 0	1 0
	a. *Blue and brn.* ('45)	8 0	5 0	1 6 [illegible]

Variety: Frame omitted.

No.		Un. single
43*b*	1d. black and carmine	£18 10s.
44*a*	2d. slate-grey and lilac	£40

For similar designs with "SUID-AFRIKA" hyphenated, see King George VI Catalogue.

The two types of the 1d. differ by the spacing of the horizontal lines in the side panels:—Type I, close spacing; Type II, wide spacing. The Afrikaans stamp may be further distinguished by the spacing of the words POSSEEL-INKOMSTE which are close in Type I and more widely spaced in Type II.

The Rotogravure printings may be distinguished from the preceding Typographed and Recess-printed issues by the following tests:—

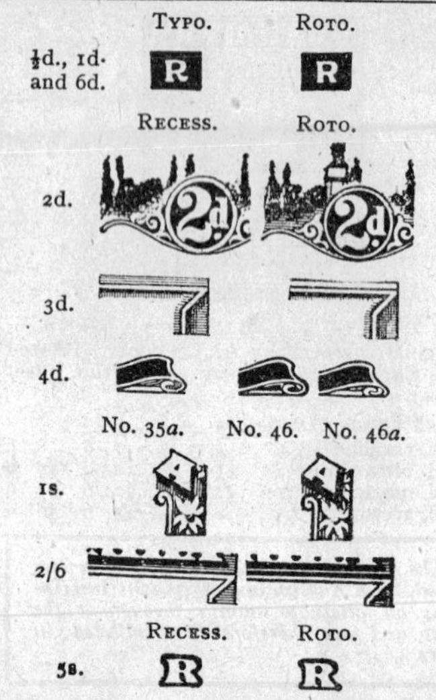

Rotogravure:

½d., 1d. & 6d. Leg of "R" in "AFR" ends squarely on the bottom line.

2d. The newly built War Memorial appears to the left of the value.

3d. Two fine lines have been removed from the top part of the frame.

4d. No. 46. The scroll is in solid colour.
No. 46*a*. The scroll is white with a crooked line running through it. (No. 35*a*. The scroll is shaded by diagonal lines.)

1s. The shading of the last "A" partly covers the flower beneath.

2s. 6d. The top line of the centre frame is thick and leaves only one white line between it and the name.

5s. The leg of the R is straight.

The Rotogravure impressions are generally coarser.

17*a*. Church of the Vow.

18. The "Great Trek."

19. A Voortrekker.

20. Voortrekker woman.

SOUTH AFRICA.

Add:—As T **14**, *but* " SUID-AFRIKA " *hyphenated on Afrikaans stamp.*

			Un. pair
63	**14**	2s. 6d. grn. & brown ('49)	6 6

A single stamp of No. 63 inscribed in English may be distinguished from No. 49 as follows:—In No. 49 the frame is composed of solid lines and the design measures 27×21½ *mm.* In No. 63 the frame appears as dotted lines due to the use of a photogravure screen and the design measures 26½×21¼ *mm.*

OFFICIAL STAMPS

Add:—No, 55*b optd. as Type* O **2**. *Un. pair*

O24*b*	**21**	½d. grey & green (11) ('49)	0 2

CORRECTIONS. *Cancel Nos.* O8*a*, O10*a*, O11*a*, O13*a*, O16*a*, O21*a and* O22*a*, *and substitute the following list of alterations. These are not revised prices but corrections of mistakes made when the 3-column method of pricing was introduced. The pairs include one stamp with variety and the other normal.*

		Un. pair	*Us. pair*	*Us. single*
O 8*a*.	**Stop after " OFFISIEEL " on English stamp ..**	7 0	7 0	6 0
O 8*b*.	**Ditto on Afrikaans stamp**	10 0	10 0	8 6
O10*a*.	**Stop after " OFFISIEEL " on English stamp ..**	30 0	30 0	27 6
O10*b*.	**Ditto on Afrikaans stamp**	32 6	32 6	30 0
O11*a*.	**Stop after " OFFISIEEL " on English stamp ..**	6 0	6 0	5 0
O11*b*.	**Ditto on Afrikaans stamp**	5 0	5 0	4 6
O13*a*.	**Stop after " OFFISIEEL " on English stamp ..**	12 6	12 6	10 0
O13*b*.	**Ditto on Afrikaans stamp**	9 0	10 0	8 0
O16*a*.	**Stop after " OFFISIEEL " on English stamp ..**	20 0	22 6	17 6
O16*b*.	**Ditto on Afrikaans stamp**	17 6	18 6	16 0
O21*a*.	**Stop after " OFFICIAL " on Afrikaans stamp ..**	£5	£7	£5
O22*a*.	**Stop after " OFFICIAL " on Afrikaans stamp ..**	£9	£10	£9

…d., anywhere. For postage on individual sets reckon 3d. per twenty sets.

● Registration is a further 4d. extra. (Registration fee *must* be enclosed for all orders over £2 in U.K., and for *all* orders going abroad).

Set No.		*No. of stamps*	*Price s.*	*d.*
	GERMANY			
	Goethe Bicentenary.			
Z 1397	ANGLO-AMERICAN ZONE. 10 pf.+5 pf., 20 pf.+10 pf. and 30 pf.+15 pf.	3	2	6
Z 1396	FRENCH ZONE. Baden, Rhineland and Wurtemberg. 10 pf.+5 pf. (3), 20 pf.+10 pf. (3), and 30 pf.+15 pf. (3). Portraits. Complete ...	9	7	0
Z 1400	RUSSIAN ZONE. 6 pf.+4 pf. to 84 pf.+36 pf. ...	5	1	4
Z 1398	BERLIN (Western Sector). 10 pf., 20 pf. and 30 pf. ...	3	1	9
	New Pictorials.			
Z 1407	BERLIN (Western Sector). Various Berlin buildings. 1 pf. to 1 Dm.	16	17	6
Z 1417	Ditto. 2 Dm. "Gendarmarkt."	1	4	6
S 5912	**NETHERLANDS.** Charity. Sunflower. 2 c.+3 c. to 30 c.+10 c.	4	2	0
Z 1391	**POLAND.** 5th Anniv. of Government—Portrait and Pictorials.	3	1	6
	SWITZERLAND			
	New Pictorial Definitives.			
Z 1389	3 c. to 40 c.	9	5	0
Z 1390	50 c., 60 c. and 70 c. ...	3	5	0

TRIESTE

(Printed by rotogravure at Pretoria.)

1933–36. *Voortrekker Memorial Fund.* *W* **9.** *P* 14.

			Un. pair	*Us. pair*	*Us. single*
50	**17a**	½d.+½d. blk. & grn. (15.1.36)	2 0	3 9	1 3
51	**18**	1d.+½d. grey-blk. & pink	2 6	4 6	1 6
52	**19**	2d.+1d. grey-grn. & pur.	8 0	12 6	4 6
53	**20**	3d.+1½d. grey-grn. & blue	13 0	21 0	7 0

23a

1935 (1 May). *Silver Jubilee. Inscriptions* "SOUTH AFRICA" *and* "SUID-AFRIKA" *at top and bottom, reverse positions on alternate stamps. Roto.* *W* **9.** *P* 15×14.

65	**23a**	½d. black & blue-green ..	2 6	1 6	0 6
66	,,	1d. blk. & carm.	3 6	1 0	0 4
67	,,	3d. blue ..	40 0	60 0	22 6
68	,,	6d. grn. & orge.	40 0	60 0	22 6

In the ½d., 3d. and 6d., Type E, "SILWER JUBILEUM" is to left of portrait and "POSTAGE REVENUE" or "POSTAGE" (3d. and 6d.) in left value tablet. In Type A the positions of English and Afrikaans inscriptions are reversed. In the 1d., "SILVER JUBILEE" is to left of portrait in Type E and vice-versa.

JIPEX

1936

(24)

1936 (2 Nov.). *Johannesburg International Philatelic Exhibition. Optd. with T* **24.**

			Un. sheet	*Us. sheet*
69	**6**	½d. grey & green (No. 54) ..	10 0	
70	**7**	1d. grey & carm. (No. 56) ..	8 6	

Issued each in miniature sheet of six stamps with marginal advertisements.

POSTAGE DUE STAMPS.

D 1

UNION OF SOUTH AFRICA

(A.)

UNION OF SOUTH AFRICA

(B.)

(Typographed by Messrs. De La Rue & Co.)

1914–22. *Type* D **1.** *Lettering as A.* *W* **4.** *P* 14.

D1	½d. black & green (19.3.15) ..	1 9	2 0
D2	1d. blk. & scarlet (19.3.15) ..	1 3	0 10
D3	2d. blk. & reddish vio. (12.12.14)	2 3	0 8
D3a	2d. blk. & brt. violet (1922)	2 3	0 10
D4	3d. blk. & bright blue (2.2.15)	1 6	1 6
D5	5d. blk. & sepia (19.3.15) ..	2 6	2 9
D6	6d. blk. & slate (19.3.15) ..	6 6	8 6
D7	1s. red and black (19.3.15) ..	75 0	85 0

There are interesting minor varieties in some of the above values, e.g. ½d. to 3d., thick downstroke to "d"; 1d., short serif to "1"; raised "d": 2d., forward point of "2" blunted: 3d., raised "d"; very thick "d".

(Litho. by the Government Printer, Pretoria.)

1922. *Type* D **1.** *Lettering as* A. *No wmk. Rouletted.*

D 8	½d. black & brt. grn. (6.6.22)	1 3	1 9
D 9	1d. black & rose-red (3.10.22)	2 0	2 6
D10	1½d. black & yell.-brn. (3.6.22)	3 0	3 6

(Litho. by the Government Printer, Pretoria.)

1922–26. *Type* D **1** *redrawn. Lettering as* B. *P* 14.

D11	½d. black and green (1.11.22)	0 6	0 7
D12	1d. black and rose (16.5.23)	0 10	0 9
D13	1½d. black & yell.-brn. (12.1.24)	1 9	2 0
D14	2d. black & pale vio. (16.5.23)	1 3	0 10
	a. Imperf.	£10	
D14b	2d. black and deep violet ..	2 0	1 0
D15	3d. black and blue (3.7.26)	3 0	3 0
D16	6d. black & slate (Sept. '23)	3 6	2 0

The locally printed stamps, perf. 14, differ both in border design and in figures of value from the rouletted stamps. All values except the 3d. and 6d. are known with closed "G" in "POSTAGE" usually referred to as the "POSTADE" variety. This was corrected in later printings.

D 2

(Typographed at Pretoria.)

1927–28. *Type* D **2.** *No wmk.* *P* 14.

D17	½d. black and green ..	1 0	1 3
D18	1d. black and carmine ..	0 9	0 9
D19	2d. black and mauve ..	1 6	1 6
	a. Black and purple	10 0	5 0
D20	3d. black and blue	2 0	2 0
D21	6d. black and slate	3 6	2 6

1932–40. *Type* D **2** *redrawn.* *W* **9.** *P* 15×14.

(*a*) *Frame roto., value typo.*

D22	½d. blk. & blue-grn. (–.–.34)	0 2	0 2
D23	2d. blk. & dp. pur. (10.4.33)	0 6	0 6

(*b*) *Whole stamp roto.*

D25	1d. black & carm. (–.3.34) ..	0 3	0 3
D26	2d. blk. & dp. pur. ('40) ..	0 4	
D27	3d. blk. & Prussian blue (3.8.32)	1 3	1 6
D28	3d. deep blue & blue ('35) ..	0 6	0 7
D29	6d. grn. & brn.-ochre (7.6.33)	1 6	2 0
D30	6d. green & bright orge. ('38)	0 8	0 10

In No. D26 the value, when magnified, has the meshed appearance of a photogravure screen, whereas in No. D23 the black of the value is solid.

OFFICIAL STAMPS

OFFICIAL. OFFISIEEL.

(O 1)

(Approximate measurements between lines of opt. are shown in mm. in brackets.)

1926 (1 Dec.). *Optd. vertically upwards, with stops, as Type* O 1.

		Un. single	*Us. single*	
	(a) **1913** *issue*			
O1 **3**	2d. Nos. 10/11 (12½) ..	50 0	7 6	
	(b) **1926** *issue*	*Un. pair*	*Us. pair*	*Us. single*
O2 **6**	½d. No. 30 (12½)	6 0	9 0	3 0
O3 **7**	1d. No. 31 (12½)	3 0	4 6	1 6
O4 **8**	6d. No 32 (12½)	£5	15 0	5 6

This overprint is found on the ½d., 1d. and 6d. values of both the London and Pretoria printings. The London printings of the ½d. and 1d. stamps are considerably scarcer than the Pretoria, but the 6d. Pretoria printing is scarcer still.

1928–29. *Optd. vertically upwards, as Type* O 1, *but without stops.*

O5 **11**	2d. No. 34 (17½)	2 6	5 0	1 9
O6 ,,	2d. No. 34 (19) ('29) ..	1 4	1 6	0 6
O7 **8**	6d. No. 32 (11½)	20 0	22 6	7 6

Overprinted as Type O 1, *but vertically downwards with ut tops.*

(a) "OFFICIAL" *at right.*

I. **1929.** TYPOGRAPHED PRINTINGS.

O 8 **6**	½d. No. 30 (13½)	0 8	1 0	0 4
	a. Pair, one stamp with stop after "OFFISIEEL"	12 0	18 0	6 0
O 9 **7**	1d. No. 31 (13½)	2 0	1 6	0 6
O10 **8**	6d. No. 32 (13½)	6 6	4 6	1 6
	a. Pair, one stamp with stop after "OFFISIEEL"	55 0	80 0	27 6

II. **1930–46.** ROTOGRAVURE PRINTINGS.

O11 **6**	½d. No. 42 (9½ to 12) ..	1 0	0 9	0 3
	a. Pair, one stamp with stop after "OFFISIEEL"	10 0	12 0	4 0
O12 ,,	½d. No. 42 (12½)	1 4	0 9	0 3
O13 **7**	1d. No. 43 (12½ & 13½)	1 0	1 0	0 4
	a. Pair, one stamp with stop after "OFFISIEEL"	15 0	24 0	8 0
O14 ,,	1d. No. 43*a*(12½)	1 4	1 6	0 6
O15 **11**	2d. No. 44 (21)	2 0	1 0	0 4
O15*a* ,,	2d. No. 44*b*(20½)	2 0	1 0	0 4
O16 **8**	6d. No. 47 (12½)	4 0	7 6	2 6
	a. Pair, one stamp with stop after "OFFISIEEL"	30 0	50 0	16 0
O17 **13**	1s. No. 48 (19)	7 0	10 6	3 6
O18 ,,	1s. No. 48 (21)	4 0	4 6	1 6
O19 **14**	2s. 6d. No. 49 (18) ..	15 0	12 6	4 6
O20 ,,	2s. 6d. No. 49 (21) ..	6 6	7 6	2 6
O20*a* ,,	2s. 6d. No 49*a* (20) ..	6 6	—	—

Dates of issue:—1930, Nos. O11–O16. 1936, No. O20. 1937, No. O18. 1939, No. O15*a*. 1946, No. O20*a*.

Nos. O17 to O20 were actually issued after Nos. O21 and O22, but are placed before them, in this list, for convenience of reference.

III. **1932–33.** LONDON RECESS PRINTINGS.

O21 **13**	1s. No. 36 (17½, 18 & 20½) ..	13 0	30 0	10 0
	a. Pair, one stamp with stop after "OFFICIAL"	85 0	£6	†
O22 **14**	2s. 6d. No. 37 (17½ & 18)	18 0	37 6	12 6
	a. Pair, one stamp with stop after "OFFICIAL"	£16	£25	†

SOUTH AUSTRALIA.

SIMPLIFICATION (see p. xii)

Nos. 1 to 151.

1, 3, 4. 6, 9, 10, 12 : 13, 15, 17, 18.
21, 26, 27, 28, 31, 34, 35, 36, 37, 38, 41, 43 : 62, 64, 66, 68, 71, 73, 75, 76, 78, 107, 82, 87.
11. 112, 113, 138, 139, 141, 118, 121, 123, 125, 126, 128, 131, 132. 146, 147, 151.

Nos. 152 to 181.

153 : 158, 160 : 164 : 166 : 167, 169, 172, 173. 181.
Later issues. Omit perfs. and shades.

Official Stamps. Nos. 401 to 449.

406, 407, 408, 410, 411, 412, 413.
415, 417, 418, 419, 428, 421. 430, 433, 435. 436. 441, 438 : 443, 445.
Later issues. Omit perfs., shades and opt. varieties.

1

2

(Recess. Perkins, Bacon & Co.)

1855. *T* **1.** *Printed in London. Wmk. Large Star, T* **2.** *Imperf.*

		Un. sing.	*Used. sing.*
1	1d. dark green (26.10.55)	£65	80 0 to £15
2	2d. dull carmine (1.1.55)	£25	12 6 to 45 0
3	2d. carmine	£10	10 0 to 40 0
4	6d. dp. blue (26.10.55)	£48	15 0 to 70 0

Prepared and sent to the Colony, but not issued.

5	1s. violet	£110	

Note.—Proofs of the 1d. *and* 6d., *without wmk., exist, and these are found with forged star watermarks added, and are sometimes offered as originals.*

1856–59. *T* **1.** *Printed in the Colony from the Perkins, Bacon & Co's. plates. W* **2.** *Imperf.*

6	1d. deep yellow-grn.	£150	£8 to £20
7	1d. light yellow-green	—	£8 to £25
8	2d. blood-red (12.56)	£55	20 0 to 60 0
	a. Printed on both sides		..
9	2d. red	£28	10 0 to 40 0
	a. Printed on both sides	—	£30
10	6d. slate-blue ..	£90	40 0 to £10
11	1s. red-orange ..	—	£6 to £40
12	1s. orange	£130	£6 to £35

Note. Proofs of the 1d., *without wmk., are known.*

1859. *T* **1.** *W* **2.** *Rouletted.* (*This first rouletted issue has the same colours as the local imperf. issue.*)

13	1d. deep yell.-grn. (May, '59)	£18	35 0
14	1d. light yell.-grn. (18.7.59) ..	£18	40 0
	a. Imperf. between (pair)		..

15 2d. red (Feb., 1859) .. 70 0 7 6
17 6d. slate-blue (May, 1859) .. £12 20 0
18 1s. orange (Mar., 1859) .. £35 30 0
a. Printed on both sides .. — £30

The 2d. formerly listed as No. 16 will now be found under 24*a*.

3

4

TEN PENCE

(5)

1859–69. *Second rouletted issue, printed in colours only found rouletted or perforated. The 10d. is formed from the 9d. by a surcharge (T* **5***). T* **1**, **3** *(4d. and 2s.), and* **4** *(9d.). W* **2**.

19 1d. bright yell.-grn. (1863) .. 45 0 25 0
20 1d. dull blue-grn. (1864–67) .. 30 0 27 6
21 1d. sage-green (1865) .. 60 0 30 0
22 1d. pale sage-green (1866) .. 40 0
23 1d. deep green (1864).. .. £12 75 0
24 1d. deep yellow-green (1869) 90 0
24*a* 2d. pale red (Aug., 1860) .. 60 0 4 0
b. Printed on both sides .. — £18
25 2d. pale verm. (July, 1863) .. 50 0 4 6
26 2d. bright verm. (Aug., 1864) 35 0 4 0
a. Imperf. between (horiz. pair) .. — £18
27 4d. dull violet (Jan., 1867) .. 45 0 25 0
28 6d. violet-blue (1859) .. 85 0 5 6
29 6d. greenish blue (1863) .. 57 6 8 0
30 6d. dull ultramarine (1864) .. 57 6 6 0
31 6d. vio.-ultram. (1865 & 1868) £8 8 6
32 6d. dull blue (1865–68) .. 80 0 15 0
a. Imperf. between (pair) ..
33 6d. Prussian blue (1868–70) .. £35 80 0
33*a* 6d. indigo .. ..
34 9d. grey-lilac (Dec., 1860) .. 40 0 12 6
a. Imperf. between (horiz pair) ..
35 10d. in *blue*, on 9d., orange-red (Oct., 1865) .. 75 0 25 0
36 10d. in *blue*, on 9d. yell. (1867) £8 27 6
37 10d. in *black*, on 9d. yell. (1869) £75 50 0
a. Surch. inverted at the top .. — £150
b. Printed on both sides .. — £30
38 1s. yellow (Oct., 1861) .. £20 40 0
39 1s. grey-brown (March, 1863) £8 20 0
40 1s. dark grey-brown (1863) .. £6 20 0
41 1s. chestnut (1864) .. £6 12 6
42 1s. lake-brown (Aug., 1865) .. £5 17 6
a. Imperf. between (horiz. pair) .. — £20
43 2s. rose-carmine (April, 1867) £7 30 0

1868–72. *Remainders of old stock perforated by the 11½–12½ machine.*

(*a*) *Imperf. stamps. P* 11½–12½.

44 2d. pale vermilion (Feb., 1868) — £50
45 2d. vermilion .. .. .. — £55

(*b*) *Rouletted stamps. P* 11½–12½.

46 1d. bright green (Dec., 1869)
47 2d. pale vermilion .. .. — £45
48 6d. Prussian blue .. .. — £18
48*a* 6d. indigo .. .. ..
49 9d. grey-lilac (June, 1872) .. £80 £18
a. Variety. Perf. roulette ..
49*b* 1s. lake-brown .. ..

1867–70. *T* **1**, **3** *and* **4**. *W* **2**. *P* 11½–12½ × *roulette.*

50 1d. pale bright green (1867) £10 30 0
51 1d. bright green (1868) .. £8 25 0
52 1d. grey-green (Dec., 1867) .. £10 45 0
53 1d. blue-green (1870) .. £15 50 0
54 4d. dull violet (July, 1868) .. £95 £12
55 4d. dull purple (1869) .. — £8
56 6d. bright pale blue (Sept., '68) £30 35 0
57 6d. Prussian blue (1869) .. £25 35 0
a. Printed both sides .. ..
58 6d. indigo (1869) .. .. — 40 0
59 10d. in *blue*, on 9d., yell. (1869) £35 50 0
a. Printed both sides .. .. — £30
60 1s. chestnut (April, 1868) .. £16 27 6
61 1s. lake-brown (1869) .. £16 27 6

NOTE.—The stamps hitherto listed separately as perf. 11½, 12½, or compound of the two, have now been combined in one list, as both perforations are on the one machine, and all the varieties *may* be found in each sheet of stamps. This method of classing the perforations by the machines is that adopted some time ago for St. Vincent, Grenada, etc., and seems by far the most simple and convenient.

3-PENCE

(6)

1867–79. *T* **1**, **3** *and* **4**. *The 3d. is made from the 4d. by a surcharge (T* **6***). W* **2**. *P* 11½–12½.

62 1d. pale bright grn. (5.1868) £10 27 6
63 1d. grey-green (1868) .. £6 60 0
64 1d. dark green (1870).. .. 65 0 20 0
a. Printed both sides .. ..
65 1d. deep yellow-green (1874) 55 0 35 0
66 3d. in *black*, on 4d., Prussian blue (1871) .. .. — £30
67 3d. in *black*, on 4d. sky-blue (1871) £12 15 0
a. Imperf. .. .. ..
b. Rouletted .. .. ..
68 3d. in *black*, on 4d. deep ultramarine (Sept., 1870) .. 45 0 11 6
a. Double surcharge (1874) .. — £95
b. Additional surch. on back .. — £160
69 4d. deep ultram. (error) (1879) £400 £300
70 4d. dull purple (1868) .. 55 0 15 0
a. Imperf. vertically .. ..
71 4d. dull violet (1868) 45 0 12 6
72 6d. bright pale blue (1868) .. £20 20 0
73 6d. Prussian blue (1869) .. 80 0 7 6
74 6d. indigo (1869) £5 25 0
75 9d. claret (Aug., 1872) .. £5 12 6
76 9d. bright mauve (1873) .. £5 12 6
a. Printed on both sides.. .. — £15
77 9d. red-purple (1874) .. 35 0 10 0
78 10d. in *blue*, on 9d. yell. (1868) £60 40 0
a. Error. Wmk. Crown and S A (1868) .. .. — £55
79 10d. in *black*, on 9d. yell. (9.69) £12 42 6
80 1s. lake-brown (Sept., 1868) £10 22 6
81 1s. chestnut (1869) .. £5 22 6
82 1s. dark red-brown (1874) .. 70 0 17 6
83 1s. red-brown (1875) .. £5 20 0
84 2s. pale rose-pink (Mar., 1870) £50 £9
85 2s. deep rose-pink (Aug. 1869) — £5
86 2s. crimson-carm. (Nov., 1870) 65 0 17 6
87 2s. carmine (1869) 57 6 12 6
a. Printed on both sides.. .. — £10

1867–71. *T* **1** *and* **3**. *W* **2**. *P* 10.

88 1d. grey-green (June, 1870) .. £5 27 6
89 1d. pale bright grn. (Aug., '70) £5 27 6
90 1d. bright green (1871) .. 75 0 22 6
91 3d. in *red*, on 4d., dull ultramarine (Aug., 1870) .. £15 70 0
92 3d. in *black*, on 4d. pale ultramarine £8 17 6
93 3d. in *black*, on 4d., ultramarine (1870) 42 6 17 6
94 4d. dull lilac (1870) .. £5 18 6
95 4d. dull purple (1871) .. 85 0 18 6
96 6d. bright blue (1870) .. £10 30 0
97 6d. indigo (1870) .. .. — 25 0
98 1s. chestnut (1870) £8 30 0

1870–78. *T* **1, 3** *and* **4.** *W* **2.** *P* 10×11½–12½.

99 1d. pale bright green (1870) £9 30 0
100 1d. grey-green (1872) .. £8 32 6
101 1d. deep green (1874) .. 85 0 17 6
102 3d. in *black*, on 4d. pale ultramarine (1871) £10 65 0
103 4d. dull lilac (1870) .. — 15 0
104 4d. slate-lilac (1878) .. £6 15 0
105 6d. Prussian blue (2.3.70) .. 90 0 10 0
106 6d. bright Pruss. blue (2.3.70) £8 10 0
107 10d. in *black*, on 9d. yell. (1870) 80 0 22 6
108 1s. chestnut (1872) .. .. — 50 0
109 2s. rose-pink .. .. ..
110 2s. carmine (1870) £6 17 6

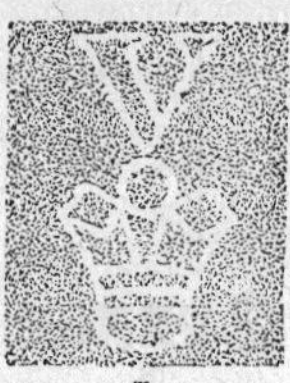

7

1871. *T* **3.** *W* **7.** *P* 10.

111 4d. dull lilac £85 £7
a. Printed both sides .. ..

8

8 PENCE

(9)

1876–1900. *T* **1, 3** *and* **4.** *Wmk. Broad Star, T* **8.** *The 8d. is made from the 9d. by a surcharge (T* **9**). (*a*) *P* 11½–12½.

112 3d. in *black*, on 4d. ultramarine (Oct., 1879) .. 40 0 18 6
a. Double surcharge .. .. — £40
113 4d. violet-slate (1879) .. £6 25 0
114 4d. plum (1880) 40 0 12 0
115 4d. deep mauve (1888) .. 35 0 6 6
116 6d. indigo (1876) 80 0 7 6
117 6d. Prussian blue (1877) .. 40 0 4 6
118 8d. in *black*, on 9d. brown-orange (1876) 30 0 4 0
119 8d., in *blk.*, on 9d. burnt umber (1880) 40 0 3 6
120 8d. in *blk.*, on 9d., brn. (1884) 35 0 4 6
a. Imperf. between (vert. pair) .. £20
121 8d. in *blk.*, on 9d., grey-brn. (1886) 30 0 8 6
a. Double surcharge .. ..
122 9d. purple (1881) 20 0 10 0
a. Printed on both sides .. — £12
123 9d. rose-lilac (1891) 5 0 4 0
124 9d. rose-lilac (*large holes*) (1900) 4 0 4 0
125 1s. red-brown (1877) .. 35 0 6 6
126 1s. reddish lake-brown (1880) 30 0 6 6
127 1s. lake-brown (1884) .. 35 0 6 0
128 1s. Vandyke brown (1891) .. 50 0 15 0
129 1s. dull brown 20 0 6 0
130 1s. choc. (*large holes*) (1900) 11 0 5 0
131 1s. sepia (*large holes*) (1900) 10 0 6 0
a. Imperf. between (vert. pair) .. £5
132 2s. carmine (1877) 12 0 6 0
133 2s. rose-carmine (1885) .. 16 6 8 0
134 2s. rose-car. (*large holes*)(1900) 12 0 7 6

In 1900 the perforating machine was fitted with new pins, which produced larger clean-cut holes, these may be found on the 9d. rose-lilac; 1s. chocolate and sepia; and 2s. rose-carmine.

(*b*) *P* 10.

135 6d. Prussian blue (1877) .. 90 0 25 0
136 6d. bright blue (1879) .. £8 15 0
136*a* 1s. reddish lake-brown ..

(*c*) *P* 10×11½–12½.

137 4d. violet-slate (1876) .. £6 15 0
138 4d. dull purple 20 0 5 0
139 6d. Prussian blue (1878) .. 30 0 4 0
140 6d. bright blue 50 0 10 0
141 6d. bright ultramarine .. 20 0 3 0
142 1s. reddish lake-brn. (5.85) 80 0 10 0
143 1s. dull brown £6 12 6
144 2s. carmine (1880) 25 0 5 6
145 2s. rose-carmine (1887) .. 17 6 4 0
a. Imperf. between (pair) .. — £22

10

1901–2. *T* **1, 3** *and* **4.** *Wmk. Crown SA (wide), T* **10.** *P* 11½–12½, *large holes.*

146 9d claret (1902) 10 0 10 6
147 1s. dull brown (Sept., 1901) 12 6 10 0
148 1s. dark reddish brown ('02) 12 6 12 6
149 1s. red-brown (aniline) .. 15 0 16 0
150 2s. crimson 17 6 15 0
151 2s. carmine (1902) 12 0 10 0

(Plates engraved and stamps typographed by De La Rue & Co.)

11

12

1868–76. *T* **11** *and* **12.** *Wmk. Crown SA (wide), T* **10.** (*a*) *Rouletted.*

152 2d. deep brick-red (Aug., '68) 50 0 6 6
153 2d. pale orange-red (Oct. '68) 45 0 5 0
a. Printed both sides .. — £12
b. Imperf. between (pair) .. — £10

(*b*) *P* 11½–12½.

154 1d. blue-green (Jan., 1875) .. 75 0 25 0
155 2d. pale orge.-red (June, 1875) £50 £20

(*c*) *P* 11½–12½ × *roulette.*

156 2d. pale orge.-red (Aug., '69) — £10

(*d*) *P* 10 × *roulette.*

157 2d. pale orge.-red (June, '70) £18. 30 0

(*e*) *P* 10.

158 1d. blue-green (April, 1870) 20 0 5 0
159 2d. brick-red (April, 1870) .. — 0 8
160 2d. orge-red (July, 1870) .. 10 0 0 6
a. Printed both sides .. .. — £10

(*f*) *P* 10×11½–12½.

161 1d. blue-green (Oct., 1875) .. 55 0 18 6
162 2d. brick-red (Jan., 1871) .. £25 12 6
163 2d. orge-red (March, 1873) .. — 15 0
a. Imperf. (Aug., 1876) ..

1869. *T* **12.** *Wmk. Large Star, T* **2.**

(*a*) *Rouletted.*

164 2d. orange-red (Mar., 1869) 40 0 10 0

(*b*) *P* 11½–12½ × *roulette.*

165 2d. orange-red (Aug., 1869) — £8

(*c*) *P* 11½, 12½.

165*a* 2d. orange-red .. ..

1871 (July). *T* **12.** *Wmk. V and Crown, T* **7.** *P* 10.

166 2d. brick-red 65 0 15 0

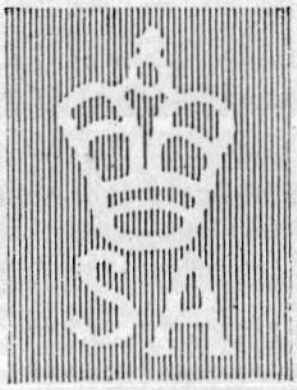

13

(14)

1876–90. *T* **11** *and* **12.** *Wmk. Crown SA* (*close*), *T* **13.** (*a*) *P* 10.

167 1d. blue-green (Sept., 1876) 2 0 0 2
168 1d. yellowish grn. (Nov. '78) 3 0 0 2
169 1d. deep green (Nov., 1879) 4 0 0 3
170 2d. orange-red (Aug., 1876) 2 6 0 2
171 2d. dull brick-red (Jan., 1878) 3 0 0 3
172 2d. blood-red (May, 1880) .. £8 5 0
173 2d. pale red (April, 1885) .. 3 0 0 1

(*b*) *P* 10 × 11½–12½.

174 1d. deep green (March, 1880) 20 0 3 6
175 1d. blue-green (Oct., 1890) 7 6 2 0
176 2d. orange-red (Oct., 1878) £10 6 0
177 2d. brick-red (June, 1880) .. £10 6 6

(*c*) *P* 11½–12½.

178 1d. blue-green (Feb., 1884) — £10
179 2d. orange-red (Nov., 1877) — £10
180 2d. blood-red (June, 1880) .. — £10

1882 (1 Jan.). *The* 1d. *green* (*W* **13**, *P* 10), *surcharged as T* **14**, *in black.*

181 ½d. on 1d., green 1 3 1 6

15

16

17

18

1883–95. *T* **15** *to* **18.** *Wmk. Crown SA* (*close*), *T* **13.** (*a*) *P* 10.

182 ½d. chocolate (March, 1883) 1 0 1 0
183 ½d. Venetian red (1891) .. 0 9 0 9
184 ½d. brown (1895) 1 0 0 9
185 3d. sage-green (Sept., 1891) 8 6 4 0
186 3d. olive-green (1893) .. 8 0 3 6
187 3d. deep green 3 6 1 3
188 4d. pale violet (1890) .. 6 0 2 0
189 4d. aniline violet 7 0 2 6
190 6d. pale blue 4 6 1 3
191 6d. blue 6 6 0 9

(*b*) *P* 10 × 11½–12½.

192 ½d. pale brown 15 0 2 6
193 ½d. dark brown 2 6 1 6
a. Imperf. between (horiz. pair)

(*c*) *P* 11½ × 12½.

194 ½d. Venetian red 6 0 1 3

19

(20)

(21)

1887–96. *T* **19.** *Wmk. Crown SA* (*close*), *T* **13,** (*inscribed* "POSTAGE & REVENUE"). *Portions of two or more wmks. show on each stamp, and sometimes the wmks. are sideways.* A. *Perf.* 10. B. *Perf.* 11½–12½ (*small or large holes*).

		A.		B.	
195	2s. 6d. mauve	10 0	4 0	†	
	a. *Dull violet*	†		6 0	4 0
	b. *Bright aniline-vio.*	†		7 6	4 6
196	5s. rose-pink ..	17 6	8 6	12 6	10 0
	a. *Rose-carmine*	†		18 6	13 6
197	10s. green ..	30 0	17 6	20 0	15 0
198	15s. brownish yellow	45 0	—	85 0	45 0
199	£1 blue ..	60 0	30 0	45 0	27 6
200	£2 Venetian red	£8	£6	£8	£6
201	50s. dull pink	£15	—	£15	—
202	£3 sage-green	£30	—	£30	—
203	£4 lemon ..	£50	—	£50	—
204	£5 grey ..	£65	—	£65	—
205	£5 brown (1896)	†		£65	—
206	£10 bronze ..	£65	—	£65	—
207	£15 silver ..	£200	—	£200	—
208	£20 claret ..	£300	—	£300	—

The 2s. 6d. dull violet, 5s. rose-pink, 10s., £1 and £5 brown exist perf. 11½–12½ with either large or small holes; the 2s. 6d. aniline, 5s. rose-carmine, 15s., £2, and 50s. with large holes only and the remainder only with small holes.

Stamps perforated 11½–12½ small holes, are, generally speaking, rather rarer than those with the 1895 (large holes) gauge.

1891. *T* **17** *and* **18** *in new colours surcharged as T* **20** *and* **21**, *in brown or carmine respectively. Wmk. Crown SA* (*close*), *T* **13.**

(*a*) *P* 10.

229 2½d. on 4d. pale green .. 1 9 1 0
230 2½d. on 4d. deep green .. 2 0 0 9
a. "2" and "½" closer together 15 0 15 0
231 5d. on 6d. pale brown .. 4 6 4 0
232 5d. on 6d. dark brown .. 4 6 3 6
a. No stop after "5D" .. £5

(*b*) *P* 10×11½–12½.

233 2½d. on 4d. pale green .. 1 6 1 6
234 2½d. on 4d. deep green .. 2 0 2 0

(*c*) *P* 11½–12½.

235 2½d. on 4d. green 20 0

1893. *T* **15, 11, 12, 20** *on* **17, 17** *and* **18.** *Wmk. Crown SA* (*close*), *T* **13.** *P* 15.

236 ½d. pale brown 0 8 0 5
237 ½d. dark brown 0 10 0 5
a. Perf. 12½ between, p. 15 all round, pair £6 60 0
b. Imperf. between (pair) .. 60 0
238 1d. green 0 9 0 3
239 2d. pale orange 3 0 0 1
240 2d. orange-red 3 6 0 1
a. Imperf. between (pair) .. £8
241 2½d. on 4d. green 3 6 2 0
a. "2" and "½" closer .. 25 0 25 0
b No bar in fraction .. ..
242 4d. purple 7 0 3 0
243 4d. slate-violet 6 0 2 6
244 6d. blue 16 0 3 0

22

23

(Designed by Tannenberg, Melbourne; plates by Sands and McDougall.)

1894. *T* **22** *and* **23.** *Wmk. Crown SA* (*close*), *T* **13.** *P* 15.

245 2½d. violet-blue 3 0 1 0
246 5d. brown-purple 5 0 2 6

1895. *Wmk. Crown SA* (*close*), *T* **13.** *P* 13.

247 **15** ½d. pale brown 0 6 0 4
248 „ ½d. deep brown 0 8 0 4
249 **11** 1d. pale green 1 3 0 1
250 „ 1d. green 1 6 0 1
251 **12** 2d. pale orange 0 9 0 2
252 „ 2d. orange-red 0 9 0 3
253 **22** 2½d. violet-blue 2 6 0 8
254 **16** 3d. pale olive-green .. 3 0 1 0
255 „ 3d. dark olive-green .. 2 6 0 9
256 **17** 4d. violet 1 3 0 4
257 **23** 5d. brown-purple 1 6 1 3
258 „ 5d. purple 1 3 1 0
259 **18** 6d. pale blue 1 9 0 8
260 „ 6d. blue 1 9 0 8

Varieties of the 1d. show lines and blotches of colour on the face and background. Price 2s. each, *unused*.

1897. *T* **11.** *Redrawn, lettering slightly thicker. W* **13.** *P* 13.

261 1d. pale green 0 9 0 3
a. Imperf. between (vert. pair) ..

All later 1d. postage stamps are in this redrawn type.

24. G.P.O., Adelaide.

1899–1906. *Wmk. Crown SA* (*close*). *T* **13.**
A. *Perf.* 13 (1899) *except* 264A/Aa.
B. *Perf.* 12×11½ (*comb*) (1904–6).

			A		B	
262	**24**	½d. yell.grn. ..	0 6	0 2	0 8	0 8
263	**11**	1d. rosine ..	0 8	0 2	5 6	1 0
264	„	1d. scarlet ('04)	2 6	1 0	2 3	0 9
		a. Deep red ..	2 3	0 9	†	
265	**12**	2d. brt. violet	0 6	0 1	2 6	0 4
266	**22**	2½d. indigo ..	0 9	0 3	0 6	0 6
267	**23**	5d. dull pur.	†		1 3	1 0

25

1902–4. *As T* **19,** *but top tablet as T* **25** (*thin* "POSTAGE"). *Wmk. Crown SA* (*close*), *T* **13.**

(*a*) *P* 11½–12½.

The measurements given indicate the length of the value inscription in the bottom label. The dates are those of the earliest postmarks known to us.

268 3d. olive-grn. (18½ mm.) (12.02) 1 3 0 6
269 4d. red-orge. (17 mm.) (12.02) 1 9 1 0
270 6d. blue-grn. (16–16½ mm.) (12.02) .. 1 9 1 3
271 8d. ultram. (19 mm.) (11.02) 2 6 2 0
272 8d. ultram. (16½ mm.) (5.04) 2 6 2 0
a. Error. "EIGNT" .. £50 £40
273 9d. rosy lake (9.02) .. 1 6 1 6
a. Imperf. between (vert. pair) ..
274 10d. dull yellow (12.02) .. 2 6 2 6
275 1s. brown (1.03) 3 0 2 6
a. Imperf. between (pair) ..
b. Value in red-brown .. 50 0 40 0
276 2s. 6d. pale violet (10.02) .. 20 0
a. Bright violet 6 0 6 0
277 5s. rose (10.02) 17 6 17 6
278 10s. green (4.03) 27 6 27 6
279 £1 blue (10.02) £5 75 0

(*b*) *P* 12.

280 3d. olive-grn. (20 mm.) (4.04) 2 6 1 6
281 4d. oran.-red. (17½–18 mm.) (1.04) 3 0 1 6
282 6d. blue-grn. (15 mm.) (11.03) 10 0 4 6
283 9d. rosy lake (11.03) .. 15 0 6 0

26

TWO SHILLINGS AND SIXPENCE
V

TWO SHILLINGS AND SIXPENCE
X

FIVE SHILLINGS
Y

FIVE SHILLINGS
Z

1904–11. *As T* **19,** *but top tablet as T* **26** (*thick* "POSTAGE"). *Wmk. Crown SA* (*close*), *T* **13.** *P* 12.

284 6d. blue-green (5.04) .. 1 0 1 0
285 8d. bright ultramarine (3.06) 2 6 1 6
a. Value closer .. 10 0
b. Dull ultramarine (2.08) .. 5 0 4 0
ba. Do. Value closer .. 20 0
86 9d. rosy lake (17–17½ mm.) (8.04) .. 2 0 1 6
a. Value 16¼–16½ mm. (2.06) .. 6 0 4 6
b. Brown-lake. Perf. 12½ (small holes) (3.11) 3 6

287 10d. dull yellow (8.07) .. 7 6 5 0
a. Imperf. between (horiz. pair)
288 1s. brown (4.04) 2 6 1 6
a. Imperf. between (vert. pair) .. £5
289 2s. 6d. bright violet (V) (9.05) 18 6 7 6
a. Dull violet (X) (8.06) .. 18 6 7 6
290 5s. rose-scarlet (Y) (6.04) .. 15 0 15 0
a Scarlet (Z) (8.06) 15 0 15 0
b. Pale rose. Perf. 12½ (small holes) (Z) (6.10) .. 25 0 20 0
291 10s. green (7.08) 22 6
292 £1 blue (11.04) 57 6
a. Perf. 12½ (small holes) (6.10) .. 52 6

Types V and X of the 2s. 6d. may be distinguished by variations in the lettering, *e.g.* in Type V the "A" of "AND" and the "S" of "SIXPENCE" appear much smaller than in Type X.

In the 5s. the letters "S" of "SHILLINGS" are more closed in Type Y than in Type Z, and in Z the "G" of "SHILLINGS" is taller and the lower curve does not extend to the right of the upper curve as it does in Y.

The "value closer" variety on the 8d. occurs six times in the sheet of 60. The value normally measures 16½ mm. but in the variety it is 15¼ mm.

The 9d., 5s. and £1, perf. 12½ (small holes), are late printings made in 1910–11 to use up the Crown SA paper.

No. 286b has the value as Type C of the 9d. on Crown A paper.

27

1906–11. *Wmk. Crown over* A, *T* 27. *P* 12 × 11½ (*new comb machine*).

293 **24** ½d. pale green (1907) .. 0 4 0 3
a. Yellow-green 1 6 0 4
294 **11** 1d. rosine 1 0 0 4
a. Scarlet 0 4 0 2
295 **12** 2d. bright violet .. 1 6 0 4
a. Mauve 0 6 0 3
296 **22** 2½d. indigo-blue (1911) .. 6 0 2 0
297 **23** 5d. brown-purple (1908) 2 9 3 3

1906–12. *T* **19** ("POSTAGE" *thick as T* **26**). *Wmk. Crown over* A, *T* **27**. *P* 12 *or* 12½ (*small holes*).

Three types of the 9d., perf. 12½, distinguishable by the distance between "NINE" and "PENCE".

A. Distance 1⅝ mm. B. Distance 2¼ mm.
C. Distance 2½ mm.

298 3d. sage-green (19 mm.) (7.06) 4 0 2 0
a. Imperf. between (horiz. pair))
b. Perf. 12½. Sage-green (17 mm.) (12.09) 5 0 2 0
c. Perf. 12½. Deep olive (20 mm.) (7.10) 10 0 4 0
d. Perf. 12½. Yellow-olive (9.11) 5 0 2 0
da. Perf. 12½. Bright olive-green (19–19½ mm.) (5.12) .. 5 0 1 6
e. Perf. 11 (17 mm.) £10
299 4d. orange-red (9.06) .. 5 0 3 0
a. Orange (9.08) 6 0 2 0
b. Perf. 12½. Orange (10.09) .. 5 0 1 6
300 6d. blue-green (6.07) .. 3 0 2 0
a. Perf. 12½ (3.10) 1 9 0 8
ab. Perf. 12½. Imp. between (vert. pair) .. .. ..

301 8d. bright ultram. (P 12½) (8.09) 6 0 4 0
a. Value closer (1.11) 25 0 20 0
302 9d. brown-lake (10.06) .. 4 6 2 0
a. Imperf. between (vert. pair) .. £6
aa. Imperf. between (horiz. pair) £10
b. Deep lake (6.08) 20 0 2 6
c. Perf. 12½. Lake (A) (8.09) .. 6 0 4 0
d. Perf. 12½. Lake (B) (3.10) .. 7 6 5 0
e. P 12½. Brown-lake (C) (4.11) 15 0 6 0
ea. Perf. 12½. Deep lake. Thin pp. (C) (2.12) 6 0 4 0
303 1s. brown (6.06) .. 4 6 2 6
a. Imperf. between (horiz. pair) £6
b. Perf. 12½ 2 6 0 10
304 2s. 6d. bright violet (6.09) .. 10 0 6 0
a. Perf. 12½. Pale violet (9.10) .. 16 0 8 6
ab. Perf. 12½. Deep purple (9.12) 25 0 10 0
305 5s. bright rose (P 12½) (12.12) 18 6

The "value closer" variety of the 8d. occurred 11 times in the sheet of 60 in the later printing only. On No. 301 the value measures 16½ mm. while on No. 301a it is 15¼ mm.

The 1s. brown, perf. compound of 11½ and 12½, formerly listed, is now omitted, as it must have been perforated by the 12 machine, which in places varied from 11½ to 13.

OFFICIAL STAMPS.

A. *Departmental.*

1868–74.

The following is a list of initials which are found on the stamps of the above period, in *red*, *blue*, and *black*. Selections can be submitted on approval on request.

A. Architect; A.G. Attorney-General; A.O. Audit Office; B.D. Barracks Department; B.G. Botanic Garden; B.M. Bench of Magistrates (Licensing Bench); C. Customs; C.D. Convict Department; C.L. Crown Lands; C.O. Commissariat Officer; C.P. Commissioner of Police; C.S. Chief Secretary; C.Sgn. Colonial Surgeon; D.B. Destitute Board; D.R. Deeds Registration; E. Engineer; E.B. Education Board; G.F. Gold Fields; G.P. Government Printer; G.S. Government Storekeeper; G.T. Goolwa Tramway; H. Hospital; H.A. House of Assembly; I.A. Immigration Agent; I.E. Intestate Estates; I.S. Inspector of Sheep; L.A. Lunatic Asylum; L.C. Legislative Council; L.L. Legislative Librarian; L.T. Lands Titles; M. Military; M.B. Marine Board; M.R. Manager of Railways; M.R.G. Main Roads, Gambierton; N.T. Northern Territory; O.A. Official Assignee; P. Police; P.A. Protector of Aborigines; P.O. Post Office; P.S. Private Secretary; P.W. Public Works; R.B. Road Board; R.G. Registrar-General; S. Sheriff; S.C. Supreme Court; S.G. Surveyor-General; S.M. Stipendiary Magistrates; S.T. Superintendent of Telegraphs; T. Treasurer; T.R. Titles Registration; V. Volunteers; V.A. Valuator; V.N. Vaccination; W. Waterworks.

B. *General.*

O.S.

(51)

Contemporary stamps overprinted with T **51**, *in black.*

1874. *Wmk. Large Star, T* **2**. (*a*) *P* 10.

401 4d. dull purple £60 £15

(*b*) *P* 10 × 11½–12½.

402 1d. green (Dec., 1874) .. — 150 0
403 4d. dull violet 50 0 10 0
404 6d. Prussian blue .. — 20 0
404*a* 2s. rose-pink .. ..
405 2s. carmine .. .. .. — 150 0

(*c*) *P* 11½, 12½.

406 1d. deep yellow-green (Feb., 1874) .. .. .. — 40 0
  a. Printed both sides .. ..
407 3d. in *black* on 4d. ultram. .. — £15
408 4d. dull violet 20 0 10 0
  a. No stop after "S" .. .. — 30 0
409 6d. bright blue 50 0 30 0
  a. "O.S." double .. .. — 60 0
410 6d. Prussian blue 30 0 10 0
  a. No stop after "S" .. .. — 30 0
411 9d. red-purple 80 0 50 0
  a. No stop after "S" £6
412 1s. red-brown 50 0 10 0
  a. "O.S." double .. .. — 35 0
  b. No stop after "S" 50 0 30 0
413 2s. crimson-carmine .. 60 0 15 0
  a. No stop after "S" .. ..
  b. No stops .. .. — 40 0
  c. Stops at top of letters

1876–77. *Wmk. Broad Star, T* **8.** (*a*) *P* 10.

414 6d. bright blue .. 60 0 15 0

(*b*) *P* 10×11½–12½.

415 4d. violet-slate 75 0 15 0
416 4d. plum 20 0 4 0
417 4d. deep mauve 6 0 2 0
  a. No stop after "S" .. — 20 0
  b. "O.S." double .. ..
  c. "O.S." inverted .. ..
418 6d. bright blue 12 6 1 6
  a. "O.S." inverted .. ..
419 6d. bright ultramarine .. 10 0 1 3
  a. "O.S." inverted .. ..
  b. "O.S." double .. ..
  c. "O.S." double, one inverted
  d. No stop after "S" .. ..
  e. No stops after "O" and "S"
420 1s. red-brown 30 0 7 6
  a. "O.S." inverted .. ..
421 2s. carmine 15 0 5 0
  a. "O.S." inverted .. ..
  b. No stop after "S" .. ..

(*c*) *P* 11½–12½.

422 3d. in *black* on 4d. ultram. ..
423 4d. violet-slate £6 12 6
424 4d. deep mauve 40 0 3 6
  a. "O.S." inverted .. ..
  b. "O.S." double, one inverted
  c. No stop after "S" .. ..
425 6d. Prussian blue 15 0 4 0
  a. "O.S." double .. .. — 40 0
426 8d. in *black* on 9d. brown £15 £5
  a. "O.S." double .. ..
  b. "O" only .. .. — £8
426*c* 9d. purple .. ..
427 1s. red-brown 15 0 4 0
  a. "O.S." inverted £6
  b. No stop after "S" .. ..
428 1s. lake-brown 12 6 3 0
429 2s. rose-carmine 20 0 6 0
  a. "O.S." double .. .. — 80 0
  b. "O.S." inverted .. ..
  c. No stop after "S" .. ..

O.S.

(52)

1891–1903. *Contemporary stamps overprinted with T* **52**, *in black.*

Wmk. Broad Star, T 8. (April, 1891.)

(*a*) *P* 11½–12½.

430 1s. lake-brown 15 0 4 0
431 1s. Vandyke brown .. 25 0 10 0
432 1s. dull brown 15 0 4 0
  a. No stop after "S" .. ..
433 1s. sepia (*large holes*) .. 7 6 2 6
  a. "O.S." double .. ..
  b. No stop after "S" .. ..
434 2s. carmine 30 0 10 0

(*b*) *P* 10×11½–12½.

435 2s. rose-carmine 7 6 3 0
  a. No stop after "S" 35 0
  b. "O.S." double .. ..

Wmk. Crown SA (wide), T **10.** *P* 11½, 12½ (1903).

436 1s. dull brown 10 0 3 0

1874–76. *T* **11** *and* **12.** *Wmk. Crown SA (wide), T* **10.** "O.S." *T* **51.** (*a*) *P* 10.

437 1d. blue-green 75 0 30 0
  a. "O.S." inverted .. ..
438 2d. orange-red 10 0 0 9
  a. No stop after "S" .. ..

(*b*) *P* 10×11½–12½.

439 1d. blue-green (Feb., 1876) ..
440 2d. orange-red .. .. — 10 0

(*c*) *P* 11½–12½.

441 1d. blue-green .. .. — 25 0
442 2d. orange-red .. .. — £6

1876–77. *T* **11** *and* **12.** *Wmk. Crown SA (close), T* **13.** "O.S." *T* **51.** (*a*) *P* 10.

443 1d. blue-green 2 0 0 3
  a. "O.S." inverted .. .. — 50 0
  b. "O.S." double 30 0 30 0
  c. "O.S." double, one inverted
  d. No stops .. .. — 20 0
  e. No stop after "S" .. .. — 10 0
  f. No stop after "O" .. ..
444 1d. deep green 5 0 0 6
  a. "O.S." double .. .. — 40 0
445 2d. orange-red 2 6 0 2
  a. "O.S." double 40 0 20 0
  b. "O.S." inverted .. .. — 17 6
  c. "O.S." double, both inverted — 100 0
  d. "O.S." double, one inverted
  e. No stop after "O" .. — 15 0
  f. No stop after "S" .. ..
  g. No stops after "O" and "S"
446 2d. brick-red 40 0 2 0

(*b*) *P* 10×11½–12½.

447 1d. deep green .. .. — 50 0
  a. "O.S." double .. ..
448 2d. orange-red 70 0 20 0
  a. "O.S." inverted .. ..

(*c*) *P* 11½–12½.

449 2d. orange-red .. .. — £6

1882. *T* **11** *surch. with T* **14.** *W* **13.** "O.S." *T* **51.** *P* 10.

450 ½d. on 1d. blue-green .. 4 0 1 6
  a. "O.S." inverted .. ..

1887–90. *T* **17** *and* **18.** *W* **13.** "O.S." *T* **51.** *P* 10.

451 4d. violet 7 6 2 6
452 6d. blue 4 0 0 9
  a. "O.S." double ..
  b. No stop after "S" ..

1891. *T* **17** *surch. with T* **20.** *W* **13.** "O.S." *T* **51.** (*a*) *P* 10.

453 2½d. on 4d. green 10 0 7 6
  a. "2" and "½" closer .. — 60 0
  b. No stop after "S" .. ..

(*b*) *P* 10×11½–12½.

454 2½d. on 4d. green 20 0 10 0

1891–95. "O.S." *T* **52.** (*a*) *P* 10.

455 **15** ½d. brown 6 0 2 0
  a. No stop after "S" ..
456 **11** 1d. green 5 0 0 5
  a. "O.S." double 60 0
  b. No stop after "S" .. — 10 0
  c. "O.S." in blackish blue .. £6 7 6
  d. "O.S." double, one inverted 7 6

No.	Type	Description	Unused	Used
457	12	2d. orange-red	4 0	0 2
		a. No stop after "S"	—	5 0
458	17	2½d. on 4d. green	3 6	1 6
		a. No stop after "S"	—	15 0
		b. "O.S." inverted	100 0	
		c. "2" and "½" closer ..	30 0	20 0
459	17	4d. pale violet	6 0	1 6
		a. "O" only	—	80 0
		b. "O.S." double		
		c. No stop after "S" ..		
460	17	4d. aniline violet ..	7 6	0 9
461	18	5d. on 6d. brown ..	4 0	2 6
		a. No stop after "S" ..	40 0	20 0
		b. No stop after "5D" ..		
462	18	6d. blue	5 0	1 0
		a. No stop after "S" ..		
		b. "O.S." in blackish blue ..		

(*b*) *P* 10×11½–12½.

No.	Type	Description	Unused	Used
463	15	½d. pale brown	4 0	2 0
464	17	2½d. on 4d. green	—	60 0

(*c*) *P* 11½–12½.

No.	Type	Description	Unused	Used
465	15	½d. Venetian red ..	12 6	3 0

1893. "O.S." *T* **52.** *P* 15.

No.	Type	Description	Unused	Used
466	15	½d. pale brown	2 6	1 6
467	11	1d. green	1 0	0 2
		a. No stop after "S" ..		
468	12	2d. orange-red	4 0	0 3
		a. "O.S." double	—	20 0
		b. "O.S." inverted	—	10 0
468*c*	22	2½d. violet-blue		
469	17	4d. slate-violet	12 0	2 0
		a. "O.S." double	—	20 0
470	23	5d. purple	10 0	4 0
471	18	6d. blue	2 6	0 6

1895. "O.S." *T* **52.** *P* 13.

No.	Type	Description	Unused	Used
472	15	½d. brown	3 0	1 0
		a. Opt. triple, twice sideways		
473	11	1d. green	3 0	0 4
		a. No stop after "S" ..	15 0	10 0
474	12	2d. orange	2 0	0 3
		a. No stop after "S" ..	—	10 0
		b. "O.S." double		
475	22	2½d. violet-blue	10 0	1 6
		a. No stop after "S" ..		
476	17	4d. violet	3 6	0 9
		a. No stop after "S" ..	15 0	10 0
		b. "O.S." double	12 6	17 6
477	23	5d. purple	5 0	4 0
		a. No stop after "S" ..		
478	18	6d. blue	5 0	1 6
		a. No stop after "S" ..	15 0	

1897. "O.S." *T* **52.** *On the redrawn design. P* 13.

No.	Type	Description	Unused	Used
479	11	1d. green	2 6	0 6
		a. No stop after "S" ..	7 6	

O. S.

(53)

1900. *Contemporary stamps (wmk. Crown SA (close), T* **13**), *overprinted with T* **53**, *in black. P* 13.

No.	Type	Description	Unused	Used
480	24	½d. yellow-green	1 0	0 6
		a. No stop after "S" ..		
481	11	1d. rosine	1 0	0 2
		a. "O.S." inverted		
		b. "O.S." double		
		c. No stop after "S" ..	—	15 0
482	12	2d. bright violet	1 0	0 4
		a. "O.S." inverted ..	15 0	
		b. No stop after "S" ..		
483	22	2½d. indigo	1 6	0 8
		a. "O.S." inverted ..	—	15 0
		b. No stop after "S" ..	22 0	
484	17	4d. violet	3 0	0 9
		a. "O.S." inverted ..	80 0	
		b. No stop after "S" ..	20 0	
485	18	6d. blue	2 6	0 9
		a. No stop after "S" ..	20 0	

1900. *T* **19.** *Wmk. Crown SA (close), T* **13.** *P* 10. *Optd. with T* **53.**

No.	Description	Unused	Used
486	2s. 6d. pale violet	£30	£30
487	5s. pale rose	£30	£30

Only one small sheet (20 ?) of each of these stamps was printed.

South Australia now uses the stamps of AUSTRALIA.

SOUTHERN NIGERIA.

PRINTERS. All issues of Southern Nigeria were typographed by De La Rue & Co.

1

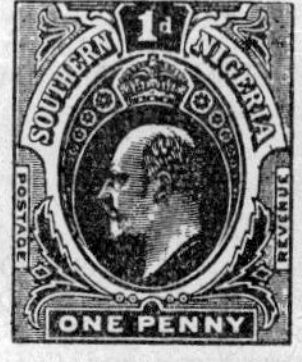

2

1901 (MAR.). *T* **1.** *Wmk. Crown CA. P* 14.

No.	Description	Unused	Used
1	½d. black and pale green ..	0 10	1 0
1*a*	½d. black and green (1902) ..	0 10	1 0
2	1d. black and carmine ..	1 0	0 10
3	2d. black and red-brown ..	5 0	5 0
4	4d. black and sage-green ..	7 0	7 0
5	6d. black and purple ..	10 0	10 0
6	1s. green and black ..	20 0	18 6
7	2s. 6d. black and brown ..	35 0	37 6
8	5s. black & orange-yellow ..	50 0	40 0
9	10s. black and purple/*yellow* ..	75 0	60 0

1903 (MAR.)–**1904.** *T* **2.** *Wmk. Crown CA. P* 14.

No.	Description	Unused	Used
10	½d. grey-black & pale green ..	1 9	1 3
11	1d. grey-black & carmine ..	2 0	1 6
12	2d. grey-black & chestnut ..	5 0	6 0
12*a*	2½d. grey-black & blue (1904)	6 0	6 6
13	4d. grey-black & olive-grn. ..	6 0	6 6
14	6d. grey-black & purple ..	12 0	12 0
15	1s. green and black ..	15 0	16 0
16	2s. 6d. grey-black & brown ..	17 6	17 6
16*a*	2s. 6d. grey & yellow-brn. ..	32 6	
17	5s. grey-black & yellow ..	35 0	37 6
18	10s. grey-blk. & pur./*yellow* ..	45 0	45 0
19	£1 green and violet	£20	£20

1904 (JUNE)–**1908.** *T* **2.** *Wmk. Mult. Crown CA. P* 14.

No.	Description	Unused	Used
20	½d. grey-blk. & pale grn., OC	0 8	0 9
21	1d. grey-black & carm., OC ..	1 9	1 3
22	2d. grey-black & chestnut, O	4 0	4 0
22*a*	2d. pale grey & chest. O ('07)	4 0	4 0
23	2½d. grey-blk. & brt. blue, O ('05)	4 6	5 6
23*a*	3d. orange-brown and bright purple, C (1907)	6 6	6 0
24	4d. grey-black & olive-green, OC ('05)	10 0	8 0
24*a*	4d. grey-black and pale olive-green, C (1907)	12 6	10 0
25	6d. grey-blk. & brt. pur., OC	7 6	5 0
26	1s. grey-green & black, OC ..	5 0	3 6

27	2s. 6d. grey-black and brown, OC (1905)	12	6	15	0
28	5s. grey-blk. & yell, OC ('05)	35	0	37	6
29	10s. grey-blk & purple/*yell*, C ('08)	£8		£9	
30	£1 green & violet, OC ('05) ..	£12		£15	

The plate for printing the central portrait was retouched early in 1907, the lines of shading on the King's cheek, and particularly the fifth line counting upward from the base of the throat, which were broken in the original die, now being filled in.

All despatches from London after 7 June, 1907, were from the retouched plate. No stamps were printed on "ordinary" paper from the retouched plate. Of the stamps on chalk-surfaced paper, the ½d. and 1d. are always unretouched, the 3d., 1s., 5s. and 10s. are always retouched, while the 4d., 6d., 2s. 6d. and £1 exist both unretouched and retouched.

(Die I)

(Die II)

In Die II of the 1d. the "1" of "1d." is not so thick as in Die I, while the "d" is larger and broader.

1907 (Aug.)–**1910.** *T* **2** *Wmk. Mult. Crown CA. P* 14.

31	½d. pale green, O (1907) ..	0	6	0	3
31*a*	½d. blue-green, O (1910) ..	1	6	0	3
32	1d. carm., O (Die I) (1907) ..	1	3	0	8
32*a*	1d. car.-red, O (Die II) ('10) ..	1	0	0	3
33	2d. greyish slate, O (1909) ..	2	6	2	9
34	2½d. blue, O (1909)	6	0	6	6
35	3d. pur./*yellow*, C (1909) ..	6	0	2	6
36	4d. blk. & red/*yell.*, C ('09) ..	6	0	4	0
37	6d. dull pur. & pur., C (09) ..	6	0	4	0
37*a*	6d. dull & brt. pur., C ('11) ..	8	6	5	0
38	1s. black/*green*, C (1909) ..	6	0	3	0
39	2s. 6d. blk. & red/*blue*, C ('09)	9	6	7	6
40	5s. grn. & red/*yell.*, C ('09) ..	35	0	40	0
41	10s. grn. & red/*grn.*, C ('09) ..	80	0	85	0
42	£1 pur. & black/*red*, C ('09) ..	£10		£12	

All values of this issue were printed from the retouched head-plate.

3

1912. *T* **3.** *Wmk. Mult. Crown CA. P* 14.

43	½d. green	0	8	0	4
44	1d. red	1	6	0	4
45	2d. grey	2	6	2	0
46	2½d. bright blue	6	0	6	0
47	3d. purple/*yellow*	3	6	2	0
48	4d. black and red/*yellow* ..	6	0	6	0
49	6d. dull and bright purple ..	4	0	3	0
50	1s. black/*green*	4	6	3	0
51	2s. 6d. black and red/*blue* ..	15	0	15	0
52	5s. green and red/*yellow* ..	37	6	37	6
53	10s. green and red/*green* ..	55	0	55	0
54	£1 purple and black/*red* ..	£8		£9	

Since 1914 Southern Nigeria has used the stamps of Nigeria.

SOUTHERN RHODESIA.

1

(Recess. Waterlow & Sons, Ltd.)

1924–29. *T* **1.** *P* 14.

1	½d. blue-green	0	4	0	1
	a. Imperf. between (horiz. pair) ..	£8			
	b. Imperf. between (vert. pair) ..	£12			
2	1d. bright rose	0	5	0	1
	a. Imperf. between (horiz. pair) ..	£9			
	b. Imperf. between (vert. pair) ..	£9			
	c. Perf. 12½ ('29)	2	0	2	6
3	1½d. bistre-brown	0	9	0	1
	a. Imperf. between (horiz. pair) ..	£12			
4	2d. black and purple-grey ..	1	6	0	9
	a. Imperf. between (horiz. pair) ..	£25			
5	3d. blue	2	0	1	9
6	4d. black and orange-red ..	4	0	3	6
7	6d. black and mauve ..	5	0	3	6
	a. Imperf. between (pair) ..				
8	8d. purple and pale green	7	6	5	0
9	10d. blue and rose ..	7	0	7	0
10	1s. black and light blue	5	0	3	0
11	1s. 6d. black and yellow ..	12	6	7	6
	a. Imperf. between (pair) ..				
12	2s. black and brown	12	6	7	6
13	2s. 6d. blue and sepia ..	22	6	15	0
	a. Imperf. between (pair) ..				
14	5s. blue and blue-green ..	37	6	27	6
	a. Error. Blue and light blue ..	£20			

Prices for "imperf. between" varieties are for adjacent stamps from the same pane and not for those separated by wide gutter margins between vertical pairs, which come from the junction of two panes.

Collectors are warned against dangerous fakes of No. 14a. chemically produced.

2. King George V.

3. Victoria Falls.

(T **2** recess. by Bradbury, Wilkinson & Co.; T **3** typo. by Waterlow & Sons.)

1931 (7 April)–**1938.** *T* **2** (*line perf.* 12 *unless otherwise stated) and* **3** (*comb. perf.* 15×14). (*The* 11½ *perf. is comb*).

15	**2**	½d. green	0	2	0	3
		a. Perf. 11½ ('33)	0	3	0	4
		b. Perf. 14 ('35)	0	9	0	9
16	„	1d. scarlet	0	6	0	1
		a. Perf. 11½ ('33)	1	0	0	2
		b. Perf. 14 ('35)	0	6	0	3
16*c*	„	1½d. chocolate ('38)	60	0	60	0
		d. Perf. 11½ ('32)	0	10	0	4

No.	Type	Description		Un.		Us.	
17	3	2d. black and sepia	..	10	0	10	0
18	,,	3d. deep ultramarine	..	20	0	22	6
19	2	4d. black and vermilion	..	1	9	0	8
		a. Perf. 11½ ('35)	..	2	0	0	8
		b. Perf. 14 ('37)	..	60	0	20	0
20	,,	6d. black and magenta	..	3	0	0	8
		a. Perf. 11½ ('33)	..	2	9	0	8
		b. Perf. 14 ('36)	..	4	0	1	3
21	,,	8d. violet and olive-green	..	4	0	3	0
		a. Perf. 11½ ('34)	..	5	0	5	0
21*b*	,,	9d. verm. & olive-grn. ('34)		5	0	3	6
22	,,	10d. blue and scarlet	..	10	0	6	0
		a. Perf. 11½ ('33)	..	5	0	5	0
23	,,	1s. black & greenish blue	..	5	0	1	6
		a. Perf. 11½ ('36)	..	5	0	2	6
		b. Perf. 14 ('37)	..	—		80	0
24	,,	1s. 6d. blk. & orange-yell.	..	8	6	6	0
		a. Perf. 11½ ('36)	..	12	6	8	6
25	,,	2s. black and brown	..	12	6	5	0
		a. Perf. 11½ ('33)	..	12	6	6	0
26	,,	2s. 6d. blue and drab	..	15	0	10	0
		a. Perf. 11½ ('33)	..	12	6	8	6
27	,,	5s. blue and blue-green	..	22	6	15	0
		a. Printed on gummed side	..	£20			

4

(Recess. Waterlow & Sons.)

1932 (May). *T* **4**. *P* 12½.

No.	Description		Un.		Us.	
29	2d. green and chocolate	..	0	10	0	10
30	3d. deep ultramarine ..	..	2	0	1	6
	a. Imperf. between (vert. pair)	..	£30			

5. Victoria Falls.

(Recess. Waterlow & Sons.)

1935 (6 May). *Silver Jubilee*. *P* 11 × 12.

No.	Type	Description		Un.		Us.	
31	5	1d. olive and rose-carmine		0	6	0	6
32	,,	2d. emerald and sepia	..	1	6	2	0
33	,,	3d. violet & deep blue	..	4	0	5	0
34	,,	6d. black and purple	..	4	6	5	0

1935 *Inscr.* "POSTAGE AND REVENUE". *P* 12½.

No.	Type	Description		Un.		Us.	
35	4	2d. green & chocolate	..	0	3	0	3

For 2d. and 3d. perf. 14, see King George VI Catalogue.

SOUTH WEST AFRICA.

(Formerly German S.W. Africa.)

> *The following issues, unless otherwise stated, have English or Afrikaans overprints or inscriptions on alternate stamps throughout the sheet and are therefore best collected in pairs.*

South West | **Zuid-West**

Africa. (1) | **Afrika.** (2)

1923. *Stamps of South Africa, T* **2** *and* **3**, *overprinted typographically as T* **1** *and* **2** *alternately in black.*

I. 14 *mm. between lines of overprint.* (2 Jan.)

No.	Description		*Un. pair*		*Us. pair*		*Us. single*	
1	½d. green	..	0	6	0	9	0	3
	a. "Wes" for "West"		20	0				
2	1d. rose-red	..	0	8	1	0	0	4
	a. Overprint inverted		£10					
	b. "Wes" for "West"		17	6				
	c. "Af.rica" for "Africa."		22	6				
3	2d. dull purple	..	1	0	1	0	0	4
	a. Overprint inverted		£6					
4	3d. ultramarine	..	2	6	3	0	1	0
5	4d. orge.-yell. & sage grn.		4	6	3	9	1	3
6	6d. black and violet	..	5	0	7	6	2	6
7	1s. orange-yellow	..	8	0	10	6	3	6
8	1s. 3d. pale violet	..	9	0	16	0	5	6
	a. Overprint inverted	..	£15					
9	2s. 6d. purple & green		22	0	37	6	12	6
10	5s. purple and blue	..	75	0	£6		40	0
11	10s. blue and olive-grn.		£25					
12	£1 green and red	..	£15					

Minor varieties, due to wear of type, including broken "t" in "West," may be found. Varieties showing one line of overprint only, or lower line above upper line, due to misplacement, may also be found. All values may be found with faint stop after "Afrika," and the ½d., 1d., 2d., and 3d. occasionally without stop.

Ia. 14 *mm. between lines, but opt. lithographed in shiny black ink.*

No.	Description		*Un. pair*		*Us. pair*		*Us. single*	
12*a*	½d. green	..	0	10	0	9	0	3
12*b*	4d. orge-yell & sage-grn		10	0	16	0	5	6
12*c*	6d black and violet	..	7	6	12	0	4	0
12*d*	1s. orange-yellow	..	15	0	18	6	6	6
12*e*	1s. 3d. pale violet	..	17	6	25	0	8	6
12*f*	2s. 6d. purple & green		20	0	30	0	10	0

II. 10 *mm. between lines of overprint.* (May, 1923.)

No.	Description	Un. pair
13	5s. purple and blue	£5
	a. "Afrika" without stop	£20
14	10s. blue and olive-green	£10
	a. "Afrika" without stop	
15	£1 green and red	£20
	a. "Afrika" without stop	

Zuidwest | **South West**

Afrika. (3) | **Africa.** (4)

1923–24. *Stamps of South Africa, T* **2** *and* **3**, *overprinted as T* **3** ("Zuidwest" *in one word, without hyphen*) *and* **4** *alternately, in black.*

III. "South West" 14 *mm. long;* "Zuidwest" 11 *mm. long;* 14 *mm. between lines of overprint.* (Aug.-Sept., 1923)

No.		Un. pair	Us. pair	Us. single
16	½d. green (Sept. 1924)	0 6	0 9	0 3
	a. "outh" for "South"			
17	1d. rose-red	1 0	0 9	0 3
18	2d. dull purple ..	1 8	2 0	0 8
	a. Overprint double ..			
19	3d. ultramarine ..	2 6	5 6	1 9
20	4d. orge.-yell. & sage-grn.	3 0	3 9	1 3
21	6d. black and violet ..	4 0	7 6	2 6
22	1s. orange-yellow ..	6 6	12 0	4 0
23	1s. 3d. pale violet ..	8 6	20 0	6 6
24	2s. 6d. purple & green	35 0	60 0	18 6
25	5s. purple and blue ..	30 0	52 6	17 6
26	10s. blue & olive-green	50 0	90 0	30 0
27	£1 green and red ..	£10		

Two sets may be made with this overprint, one with bold lettering, and the other with thinner lettering and smaller stops.

IV. "South West" 16 *mm. long;* "Zuidwest" 12 *mm. long;* 14 *mm. between lines of overprint.* (July, 1924.)

No.		Un. pair	Us. pair	Us. single
28	2s. 6d. purple & green	32 6	60 0	20 0

VI. "South West" 16 *mm. long;* *"Zuidwest" 12 *mm. long;* 9½ *mm. between lines of overprint* (Dec., 1924.)

No.		Un. pair	Us. pair	Us. single
29	½d. green	1 4	2 3	0 9
30	1d. rose-red	0 8	1 6	0 6
31	2d. dull purple ..	1 4	1 0	0 4
32	3d. ultramarine ..	4 0	6 0	2 0
32a	3d. deep bright blue ..	25 0		
33	4d. orge.-yell. & sage-grn.	3 6	3 0	1 0
34	6d. black and violet ..	5 0	9 0	3 0
35	1s. orange-yellow ..	6 0	10 6	3 6
36	1s. 3d. pale violet ..	8 0	15 0	5 0
37	2s. 6d. purple & green	17 6	30 0	10 0
38	5s. purple and blue ..	40 0	75 0	25 0
39	10s. blue & olive-green	60 0	£6	40 0
40	£1 green and red ..	£9		
40a	£1 pale olive-grn. & red	£7		

* Two sets with this overprint may be made one with "South West" 16 mm. long, and the other 16½ mm., the difference occurring in the spacing between the words. No. 40*a* only exists with the latter spacing.

Suidwes Afrika.
(5)

South West Africa.
(6)

1926. *Pictorial types of S. Africa overprinted with T* **5** (*on stamps inscribed in Afrikaans*) *and* **6** (*on stamps inscribed in English*) *sideways, alternately, in black.*

41	½d. black and green ..	0 6	0 9	0 3
42	1d. black and carmine	0 8	1 0	0 4
43	6d. green and orange ..	4 6	9 0	3 0

SOUTH WEST AFRICA
(7)

SUIDWES-AFRIKA
(8)

Triangular stamps of S. Africa, overprinted.
E. *Type* **7**. A. *Type* **8**.

No.		Single stamps. E.		A.	
44	4d. grey-blue ..	1 6	1 9	1 6	1 9

1927. *As Nos.* 41 *to* 43, *but Afrikaans overprint on stamp inscribed in English and vice versa.*

No.		Un. pair	Us. pair.	Us. single
45	½d. black and green ..	0 6	0 9	0 3
	a. "Africa" without stop			
46	1d. black and carmine	0 8	1 3	0 5
	a. "Africa" without stop			
47	6d. green and orange ..	3 0	7 6	2 6
	a. "Africa" without stop ..			

SOUTH WEST AFRICA
(9)

1927. *As No.* 44E, *but overprint T* **9**.

No.		Single stamps.	
48	4d. grey-blue	2 6	3 0

1927. *Pictorial stamps of South Africa overprinted alternately as T* **5** *and* **6**, *in blue, but with lines of overprint spaced* 16 *mm.*

No.		Un. pair	Us. pair	Us. single
49	2d. grey and purple ..	1 4	2 0	0 8
50	3d. black and red ..	2 0	3 9	1 3
51	1s. brown and blue ..	7 0	12 6	4 6
52	2s. 6d. green & brown	40 0	75 0	25 0
53	5s. black and green ..	50 0	90 0	40 0
54	10s. blue & bistre-brn.	60 0	90 0	40 0

A variety of Nos. 49, 50, 51 and 54, with spacing 16½ mm. between lines of overprint, occurs in one vertical row of each sheet.

1927. *As No.* 44, *but perf.* 11½ *by John Meinert, Ltd., Windhoek.*

No.		Single stamps. E.		A.	
55	4d. grey-blue ..	1 6	1 9	1 6	1 9
	a. Imp. between (pair)	50 0	—	—	—

S.W.A.
(10)

1927–30. *Overprinted with T* **10**, *in black.*

(*a*) *T* **3** *of South Africa.*

No.		Single stamps.	
56	1s. 3d. pale violet	3 0	3 6
	a. Without stop after "A" ..	40 0	
57	£1 pale olive-green and red ..	42 6	50 0
	a. Without stop after "A" ..		

(*b*) *Pictorial stamps of South Africa.*

No.		Un. pair	Us. pair	Us. single
58	½d. black and green ..	0 4	0 6	0 2
	a. Without stop after "A"	10 0		
	b. "S.W.A." opt. above value	2 0		
59	1d. black & carmine ..	0 6	0 3	0 1
	a. Without stop after "A"	10 0		
	b. "S.W.A." opt. at top (30.4.30)	1 0		
60	2d. grey and purple ..	0 10	0 9	0 3
	a. Without stop after "A"	12 6		
	b. Opt. double, one invert.			
61	3d. black and red ..	1 4	1 3	0 5
	a. Without stop after "A"	15 0		
62	4d. brown (1928) ..	1 8	1 6	0 6
	a. Without stop after "A"	17 6		
63	6d. green and orange ..	2 6	2 0	0 8
	a. Without stop after "A"	20 0		

		Un. pair	Us. pair	Us. single
64	1s. brown and blue ..	5 0	3 9	1 3
	a. Without stop after "A"			
65	2s. 6d. green & brown	11 0	18 0	6 0
	a. Without stop after "A"	40 0		
66	5s. black and green ..	20 0	35 0	12 6
	a. Without stop after "A"	60 0		
67	10s. blue and bistre-brn.	40 0	75 0	25 0
	a. Without stop after "A"	80 0		

The overprint is normally found at the base of the ½d., 1d., 6d., 1s. 3d. and £1 values and at the top of the remainder.

1930. *Nos. 42 and 43 of South Africa (rotogravure printing), overprinted with T* **10**.

68	½d. black and green ..	0 6	0 9	0 3
69	1d. black and carmine	0 6	0 6	0 2

1930. *Air stamps. T* **17** *of South Africa. Overprinted (a) As T* **10**.

		Un. single	Us. single
70	4d. green (first printing) ..	5 0	6 0
	a. No stop after "A" of "S.W.A"	£5	£5
	b. Later printings	3 0	3 6
71	1s. orange (first printing) ..	25 0	27 6
	a. No stop after "A" of "S.W.A"	£15	£15
	b. Later printings	6 0	7 0

First printing: Thick letters, blurred impression. Stops with rounded corners.

Later printings: Thinner letters, clear impression. Clean cut, square stops.

S.W.A.

(11)

(*b*) *As T* **11**.

72	4d. green	1 6	2 0
73	1s. orange	4 6	5 0

12. Gom-pauw.

13. Cape Cross. **14.** Bogenfels.
15. Windhoek. **16.** Waterberg.
17. Luderitz Bay. **18.** Bush scene.
19. Elands. **20.** Zebra and Wildebeeste.
21. Kaffir huts. **22.** The Welwitschia plant.
23. Okuwahaken Falls.

24. Monoplane over Windhoek.

25. Biplane over Windhoek.

(Recess. Bradbury, Wilkinson & Co., Ltd.)

1931 (5 Mar.). *T* **12** *to* **25** (*various horizontal pictorial designs inscribed alternately in English and Afrikaans*). *W* **9** *of South Africa. P* 14 × 13½. (*a*) *Postage stamps.*

		Un. pair	Us. pair	Us. single
74	½d black and emerald	0 2	0 3	0 1
75	1d. indigo and scarlet	0 4	0 3	0 1
76	2d. blue and brown ..	0 6	0 6	0 2
77	3d. grey-blue & blue ..	0 10	1 0	0 4
78	4d. green and purple ..	1 0	1 6	0 6
79	6d. blue and brown ..	1 4	1 6	0 6
80	1s. chocolate and blue	2 8	2 0	0 8
81	1s. 3d. violet and yell.	3 4	3 0	1 0
82	2s. 6d. carmine & grey	6 6	7 6	2 6
83	5s. sage-grn. & red-brn.	13 0	12 0	4 0
84	10s. red-brn. & emerald	25 0	22 6	7 6
85	20s. lake & blue-green..	50 0	90 0	35 0

(*b*) *Air stamps.*

86	3d. brown and blue ..	12 6	37 6	12 6
87	10d. black & purple-brn.	35 0	90 0	40 0

26

(Recess. Bradbury, Wilkinson.)

1935 (6 May). *Silver Jubilee. Inscr. bilingually. W* **9** *of South Africa. P* 14 × 13½.

			Un. single	Us. single
88	**26**	1d. black and scarlet ..	0 10	2 6
89	,,	2d. black and sepia ..	1 6	4 0
90	,,	3d. black and blue ..	40 0	45 0
91	,,	6d. black and purple ..	15 0	17 6

1935–36. *Voortrekker Memorial Fund. T* **17a** *to* **20** *of South Africa optd. with T* **10**.

		Un. pair	Us. pair	Us. single
92	½d. + ½d. olive-green & green ..	2 6	4 6	1 6
93	1d. + ½d. grey-black & pink ..	3 6	7 6	2 6
94	2d. + 1d. grey-grn. & purple ..	7 0	12 0	4 0
	a. Without stop after "A"			
95	3d. + 1½d. grey-green & blue	12 6	22 6	7 6
	a. Without stop after "A" ..			

POSTAGE DUE STAMPS.

1923. *Postage Due stamps of Transvaal or South Africa overprinted as T* **1** *and* **2**, *in black.*

I. 14 *mm. between lines of overprint.*

(*a*) *On stamps of Transvaal.*

D1	5d. black and violet ..	4 0	9 0	3 0
	a. "Wes" for "West"	£7		
	b. 'Afrika" without stop	90 0		
D2	6d. black & red-brown	6 0		
	a. "Wes" for "West"			
	b. "Afrika" without stop	£6		

(*b*) *On S. African stamps (De La Rue printing).*

D3	2d. black and violet ..	7 6	18 0	6 0
	a. "Wes" for "West"	£8		
	b. "Afrika" without stop	£7		
D4	3d. black and blue ..	3 6	15 0	5 0
	a. "Wes" for "West"	50 0		
D5	6d. black and slate ..	4 6		
	a. "Wes" for "West"	80 0		

(*c*) *On S. African stamps* (*Pretoria printing, Type* D 1 *redrawn*). (i) *Rouletted.*

		Un. pair	*Us. pair*	*Us. single*
D6	1d. black and rose ..	0 10		
	a. "Wes" for "West"	22 6		
	b. "Afrika" without stop	55 0		
	c. Unrouletted between (pair)			
D7	1½d. blk. & yell.-brown	1 0		
	a. "Wes" for "West"	20 0		
	b. "Afrika" without stop	20 0		

(ii) *P* 14.

D8	½d. black and green ..	0 6	1 6	0 6
	a. Overprint inverted ..	£15		
	b. Overprint double ..			
	c. "Wes" for "West"	15 0		
	d. "Afrika" without stop	10 0		
D9	2d. black and violet ..	2 0	3 6	1 3
	a. "Wes" for "West"	35 0		
	b. "Afrika" without stop	17 6		

The "Wes" variety occurs in the English overprint only, in some printings.

A variety of Nos D1, D4, D5 and D9 with spacing 15 mm. between lines of overprint occurs on four stamps in each pane of certain printings of this setting.

Nos. D1, D4, D6, D7 and D9 exist with 2 mm. spacing between "South" and "West," and also with 2½ mm.; Nos. D2, D3 and D8 only with 2 mm. spacing; and No. D5 only with 2½ mm.

II. 10 mm *between lines of overprint.*

(*a*) *On stamp of Transvaal.*

D10	5d. black and violet	£6		

(*b*) *On S. African stamps* (*De La Rue printing*).

D11	2d. black and violet	3 0	9 0	3 0
	a. "Afrika" without stop	65 0		
D12	3d. black and blue ..	3 0		
	a. "Afrika" without stop	40 0		

(*c*) *On S. African stamp* (*Pretoria printing, Type* D 1 *redrawn, rouletted*).

D13	1d. black and rose ..			

1923-27. *Overprinted as T* **3** ("*Zuidwest*" *in one word without hyphen*) *and* **4.**

III. "South West" 14 *mm. long*; "Zuidwest" 11 *mm. long*; 14 *mm. between lines of overprint.* (SEPT., 1923)

(*a*) *On stamp of Transvaal.*

D14	6d. black and red-brn.	6 0		

(*b*) *On S. African stamps* (*Pretoria printing, Type* D 1 *redrawn*). (i.) *Rouletted.*

D15	1d. black and rose ..	1 6		

(ii.) *P* 14.

D16	½d. black and green	3 0		
D17	1d. black and rose ..	4 0	7 6	2 6

IV. "South West" 16 *mm. long*; "Zuidwest" 12 *mm. long*; 14 *mm. between lines of overprint.*

(*a*) *On stamp of Transvaal.*

D17*a*	5d. black & violet ..	£25		

(*b*) *On S. African stamps* (*Pretoria printing, Type* D 1 *redrawn. P* 14).

D18	½d. black and green ..	0 8		
D19	1d. black and rose ..	5 0	9 0	3 0
D20	6d. black and slate ..	3 6	5 0	1 9
	a. "Africa" without stop			

V. *As* IV, *but* 12 *mm. between lines of overprint.*

(*a*) *On stamp of Transvaal.*

D21	5d. black and violet	5 0		

(*b*) *On S. African stamp* (*De La Rue printing*).

		Un. pair	*Us. pair*	*Us. single*
D22	3d. black and blue ..	6 6		

(*c*) *On S. African stamps* (*Pretoria printing, Type* D 1, *redrawn. P* 14).

D23	½d. black and green	1 6		
D24	1½d. blk. & yell.-brn.	1 6		

VI. *As* IV, *but* 9½ *mm. between lines of overprint.*

(*a*) *On stamp of Transvaal.*

D25	5d. black and violet	2 0	4 6	1 6
	a. " Africa" without stop	40 0		

(*b*) *On S. African stamp* (*De La Rue printing*).

D26	3d. black and blue	10 0		

(*c*) *On S. African stamps* (*Pretoria printing, Type* D 1, *redrawn. P* 14).

D27	½d. black and green	3 6		
D28	1d. black and rose ..	0 8		
	a. "Africa" without stop			
D29	1½d. black & yell.-brn.	0 10		
	a. "Africa" without stop	12 6		
D30	2d. black and violet	1 0		
	a. "Africa" without stop	12 6		
D31	3d. black and blue ..	1 0		
	a. "Africa" without stop	20 0		
D32	6d. black and slate ..	10 0		
	a. "Africa" without stop	£5		

In Nos. D18 to D25, D29, D31 and D32, "South West" is 16 mm. long, and in Nos. D26 and D27, 16½ mm. long. Nos. D28 and D30 exist in both 16 mm. and 16½ mm. varieties. (*See note after* No. 40*a*.) In Nos. D20, D29, D31 and D32 a variety with "South West" 16½ mm. long occurs once only in each sheet of 120 stamps (in certain printings only, in the case of D20), and similarly Nos. D28 and D30 occur with the two measurements on the same sheet of certain printings.

Suidwes	**South West**
Afrika.	**Africa.**
(D 1)	(D 2)

1927. *Overprinted as Types* D 1 *and* D 2, *alternately.* 12 *mm. between lines of overprint.*

(*a*) *On stamp of Transvaal.*

D33	5d. black and violet	12 0		

(*b*) *On S. African stamps* (*Pretoria printing, Type* D 1, *redrawn. P* 14).

D34	1½d. black & yell.-brn.	2 0	4 6	1 6
	a. "Africa" without stop	20 0		
D35	2d. blk. & pale vio..	2 0	4 6	1 6
	a. "Africa" without stop	30 0		
D36	2d. black & deep vio.	3 0	4 6	1 6
	a. "Africa" without stop	30 0		
D37	3d. black and blue ..	10 0	15 0	5 0
	a. "Africa" without stop	70 0		
D38	6d. black and slate ..	10 0		
	a. "Africa" without stop	£5		

(*c*) *On S. African stamp* (*Pretoria printing, Type* D 2. *P* 14.)

D39	1d. black and carmine	1 4	2 0	0 8
	a. "Africa" without stop	10 0		

1928–29. *Overprinted with* T **10** ("S.W.A."), *in black. On S. African stamps, Pretoria printing.* P 14. (a) *Type* D **1**, *redrawn.*

		Un. single	Us. single
D40	3d. black and blue	2 0	2 6
	a. Without stop after "A" ..	40 0	
D41	6d. black and slate	8 6	10 0

(b) *Type* D **2.**

		Un. single	Us. single
D42	½d. black and green ..	0 3	0 4
D43	1d. black and carmine ..	0 2	0 3
	a. Without stop after "A" ..		
D44	2d. black and mauve ..	0 4	0 6
D45	3d. black and blue	0 9	1 0
D46	6d. black and slate	1 6	2 0
	a. Without stop after "A"	60 0	

D 3

(Litho. Bradbury, Wilkinson & Co., Ltd.)

1931 (23 Feb.). *Type* D **3.** W **9** *of South Africa.* P 12.

D47	½d. black and green ..	0 1	0 2
D48	1d. black and scarlet ..	0 2	0 3
D49	2d. black and violet ..	0 3	0 4
D50	3d. black and blue	0 5	0 7
D51	6d. black and slate	0 8	1 0

OFFICIAL STAMPS.

OFFICIAL South West Africa. OFFISIEEL Suidwes Afrika.

(O 1) (O 2)

1927. *Pictorial and portrait (2d.) types of S Africa alternately overprinted with Types* O **1** *and* O **2.**

		Un. pair	Us. pair	Us. single
O1	½d. black and green ..	70 0		
O2	1d. black & carmine ..	80 0		
O3	2d. dull purple ..	£10		
O4	6d. green and orange	60 0		

OFFICIAL S.W.A. OFFISIEEL S.W.A.

(O 3) (O 4)

1929. *Stamps of 1927–30 alternately overprinted with Types* O **3** *and* O **4.**

		Un. pair	Us. pair	Us. single
O5	½d. black and green ..	1 0	2 3	0 9
O6	1d. black & carmine ..	1 6	3 0	1 0
O7	2d. grey and purple ..	2 6	4 6	1 6
	a. Pair, one stamp without stop after "OFFICIAL" ..	5 0	15 0	5 0
	b. Pair, one stamp without stop after "OFFISIEEL" ..	5 0	15 0	5 0
	c. Pair consisting of a. and b. ..	12 6	22 0	7 6
O8	6d. green and orange	5 0	15 0	5 0

Types O 3 and O 4 are normally spaced 17 mm. between lines on all except the 2d. value, which is spaced 13 mm.

Except on No. O7, the words "OFFICIAL" or "OFFISIEEL" normally have no stops after them.

OFFICIAL S.W.A. OFFISIEEL S.W.A.

(O 5) (O 6)

OFFICIAL. S.W.A. OFFISIEEL. S.W.A.

(O 7) (O 8)

1929. *Pictorial types of South Africa alternately overprinted.* T **6** *to* **8** *with Types* O **5** *and* O **6**; T **11** *with Types* O **7** *and* O **8.**

		Un. pair	Us. pair	Us. single
O 9	½d. black & green ..	0 4	0 9	0 3
O10	1d. black and carm.	0 6	1 0	0 4
O11	2d. grey and purple ..	1 6	2 3	0 9
	a. Pair, one stamp without stop after "OFFICIAL" ..	3 6		
	b. Pair, one stamp without stop after "OFFISIEEL" ..	3 6		
	c. Pair consisting of a. and b.	7 6		
O12	6d. green and orange	1 6	3 0	1 0

OFFICIAL OFFISIEEL

(O 9) (O 10)

1931. T **12** *to* **14** *and* **17** *alternately overprinted with Types* O **9** *and* O **10.**

		Un. pair	Us. pair	Us. single
O13	½d. black & emer. (R.)	0 4	1 0	0 4
O14	1d. indigo & scar. (R)	0 4	0 9	0 3
O15	2d. blue & brn. (R) ..	0 6	1 0	0 4
O16	6d. blue & brn. (R) ..	3 0	4 6	1 6

STELLALAND.

1. (Arms of the Republic.)

(Printed by Van der Sandt, de Villiers & Co., Cape Town.)

1884 (1 Feb.). T **1.** P 12.

1	1d. red	7 6
	a. Imperf. between (pair) ..	25 0

2	3d. orange	12	6
	a. Imperf. between (pair) ..	35	0
3	4d. blue	12	6
	a. Imperf. between (pair) ..	35	0
4	6d. lilac-mauve	12	6
5	1s. green	22	6

Surcharged "Twee" in violet lake.

6	2d. on 4d. blue	£10

STRAITS SETTLEMENTS.

(Comprising SINGAPORE, PENANG (with PROVINCE WELLESLEY and (until 1934) THE DINDINGS), MALACCA, LABUAN, COCOS or KEELING ISLANDS and CHRISTMAS ISLAND.)

PRINTERS. All stamps of the Straits Settlements were typographed by De La Rue & Co. unless otherwise stated.

THREE-HALF-CENTS
(1)

32 CENTS
(2)

1867 (1 SEPT.). *Types* **11** *and* **17** *of India* (8 a., Die II, *others,* Die I), *wmk. Elephant's Head, surch. as T* **1** *and* **2** (24 c. *and* 32 c.) *in red* (R.), *blue* (B.), *black* (Bk.). *purple* (P.) *or green* (G.). *P* 14.

1	1½ c. on ½ a. blue (R.)	25	0	22	6
2	2 c. on 1 a. brown (R.) ..	40	0	35	0
3	3 c. on 1 a. brown (B.) ..	40	0	25	0
4	4 c. on 1 a. brown (Bk.) ..	55	0	47	6
5	6 c. on 2 a. yellow (P.) ..	£8		75	0
6	8 c. on 2 a. yellow (G.) ..	67	6	22	6
7	12 c. on 4 a. green (R.) ..	£10		60	0
8	24 c. on 8 a. rose (B.)	95	0	37	6
9	32 c. on 2 a. yellow (Bk.) ..	70	0	40	

The 32 c. was re-issued for postal use in 1884

Varieties. (i.) *Surcharge double.*

10	12 c. on 4 a. green (R.) ..	£15

This variety is only known unused.

(ii.) "THREE HALF" *deleted in black and figure* "2" *written above, in black.*

11	2 on 1½ c. on ½ a. blue (No. 1)	—	£15

This variety has been known from very early days and was apparently used in the Straits Settlements, but nothing is known of its history.

5

6

7

8

1867 (DEC.).–**1868.** *T* **5** *to* **8**. *Wmk. Crown CC. P* 14. (*The ornaments in the corners of the frames differ for each value.*)

12	**5**	2 c. brown (June, 1868)	3	6	3	0
13	,,	2 c. yellow-brown ..	3	6	3	0
14	,,	2 c. deep brown	6	0	3	6
15	,,	4 c. rose (July, 1868) ..	4	0	3	0
15*a*	,,	4 c. deep rose	4	6	3	6
16	,,	6 c. dull lilac (Jan., 1868)	17	6	9	0
17	,,	6 c. bright lilac	22	6	8	0
18	**6**	8 c. orange-yellow ..	20	0	6	0
19	,,	8 c. orange	22	6	8	6
20	,,	12 c. blue	22	6	6	6
21	,,	12 c. ultramarine	25	0	6	6
22	**7**	24 c. blue-green	25	0	7	6
23	,,	24 c. yellow-green ..	30	0	8	6
24	**8**	32 c. pale red	55	0	25	0
25	,,	96 c. grey	40	0	22	6

Variety. P 12½.

26	**8**	96 c. grey (1872)	£16	50	0

9

1872. *T* **9**. *Wmk. Crown CC. P* 14.

27	30 c. claret	40	0	6	6

All the surcharges in the following issues are in *black*, except when otherwise described.

Stamps of 1867–72, *surcharged.*

Five Cents.
(10)

Seven Cents.
(11)

1879 (MAY). *With T* **10** *and* **11**.

28	5 c. on 8 c. orange	45	0	45	0
	a. No stop after "Cents" ..	£15		£15	
	b. "F i" spaced	£14		£14	
	c. Comma between "F" and "i"				
29	7 c. on 32 c. pale red ..	40	0	40	0
	a. No stop after "Cents" ..	£14		£14	

10
cents.
(12)

10 (*a*)	10 (*b*)	10 (*c*)	10 (*d*)
10 (*e*)	10 (*f*)	10 (*g*)	10 (*h*)
10 (*i*)	10 (*j*)	10 (*k*)	10 (*l*)

1880 (Mar.). *With T* **12** *(ten varieties of figures "10").*

(*a*) "1" thin curved serif and thin foot; "0" narrow. (*b*) "1" thick curved serif and thick foot; "0" broad. Both numerals heavy. (*c*) "1" as (*a*); "0" as (*b*). (*d*) "1" as (*a*) but thicker; "0" as (*a*). (*e*) As (*a*) but sides of "0" thicker. (*f*) "1" as (*d*); "0" as (*e*). (*g*) As (*a*) but "0" narrower. (*h*) "1" thin, curved serif and thick foot; "0" as (*g*). (*i*) "1" as (*b*); "0" as (*a*). (*j*) "1" as (*d*); "0" as (*g*). Numerals much closer than (*g*). (*k*) "1" as (*a*) but shorter, and with shorter serif and thicker foot; "0" as (*d*). (*l*) "1" straight serif; "0" as (*d*).

No.	Description	Unused	Used
30	10 c. on 30 c. claret (*a*)	70 0	42 6
31	10 c. on 30 c. claret (*b*)	82 6	42 6
32	10 c. on 30 c. claret (*c*)		
33	10 c. on 30 c. claret (*d*)	£15	£7
34	10 c. on 30 c. claret (*e*)		
35	10 c. on 30 c. claret (*f*)		
36	10 c. on 30 c. claret (*g*)	£22	£22
37	10 c. on 30 c. claret (*h*)		
38	10 c. on 30 c. claret (*i*)		
39	10 c. on 30 c. claret (*j*)		

No. 31 is known with large stop after "cents" and also with stop low.

1880 (April). *As T* **12**, *but without "cents." (eight varieties of figures "10").*

No.	Description	Unused	Used
40	10 on 30 c. claret (*a*)	40 0	32 6
41	10 on 30 c. claret (*b*)	40 0	32 6
42	10 on 30 c. claret (*c*)	£6	47 6
43	10 on 30 c. claret (*g*)	£12	£10
44	10 on 30 c. claret (*i*)		
45	10 on 30 c. claret (*k*)		
46	10 on 30 c. claret (*l*)		
46*a*	10 on 30 c. claret (*m*)		

Variety (*m*) has the "1" as (*b*) and the "0" as (*g*).

5 cents (13) 5 cents. (14) 5 cents. (15)

1880 (Aug.). *With T* **13** *to* **15**.

No.	Type	Description	Unused	Used
47	**13**	5 c. on 8 c. orange	50 0	57 6
48	**14**	5 c. on 8 c. orange	40 0	47 6
49	**15**	5 c. on 8 c. orange	£8	£9

In this setting, the first four rows of the pane have surcharge T **13**; the next five, T **14**; and the last, T **15**.

10 cents. (16) 5 cents. (17)

1880–81. *With T* **16**.

No.	Description	Unused	Used
50	10 c. on 6 c. lilac (11.81)	17 6	8 0
51	10 c. on 12 c. ultram. (1.81)	15 0	10 6
52	10 c. on 12 c. blue	16 0	10 6
53	10 c. on 30 c. claret (12.80)	90 0	25 0

A second printing of the 10 c. on 6 c. has the surcharge heavier and the "10" usually more to the left or right of "cents."

1882 (Jan.). *With T* **17**.

No.	Description	Unused	Used
54	5 c. on 4 c. rose	£6	90 0

18

19

1882 (Jan.). *T* **18** *and* **19**. *Wmk. Crown CC. P 14.*

No.	Type	Description	Unused	Used
55	**18**	5 c. purple-brown	17 6	15 0
56	**19**	10 c. slate	22 6	10 0

1882. *Wmk. Crown CA. P 14.*

No.	Type	Description	Unused	Used
57	**5**	2 c. brown (Aug.)	25 0	8 6
58	,,	4 c. rose (April)	35 0	7 6
59	**6**	8 c. orange (Sept.)	4 0	1 0
60	**19**	10 c. slate (Oct.)	2 6	0 8

TWO CENTS

(20)

1883 (April). *Nos.* 59 *and* 24 *surcharged with T* **20** *vertically upwards.*

(*a*) "CENTS" in narrow letters. (*b*) With wide "E." (*c*) Wide "EN" and "S." (*d*) Wide "N." (*e*) Wide "S." (*f*) Wide "E" and "S."

No.	Type	Description	Unused	Used
61	**6**	2 c. on 8 c. orange (*a*)	55 0	50 0
		a. Surcharge double		
62	**6**	2 c. on 8 c. orange (*c*)	£5	90 0
63	,,	2 c. on 8 c. orange (*d*)	37 6	32 6
64	,,	2 c. on 8 c. orange (*e*)	37 6	32 6
65	,,	2 c. on 8 c. orange (*f*)	36 0	32 6
66	**8**	2 c. on 32 c. pale red (*b*)	£5	65 0
		a. Surcharge double		
67	**8**	2 c. on 32 c. pale red (*e*)	£5	65 0

2 Cents.

(21)

1883 (July). *Nos.* 58 *and* 20 *surch. with T* **21**.

No.	Description	Unused	Used
68	2 c. on 4 c. rose (CA)	16 0	20 0
	a. "s" of "Cents" inverted	£16	£14
69	2 c. on 12 c. blue (CC)	£6	65 0
	a. "s" of "Cents" inverted	£55	

1883 (July)–1891. *Wmk. Crown CA. P 14.*

No.	Type	Description	Unused	Used
70	**5**	2 c. pale rose	3 0	0 6
71	,,	2 c. bright rose	0 8	0 3
72	,,	4 c. pale brown	4 6	3 0
73	,,	4 c. deep brown	7 6	4 0
74	**18**	5 c. blue (8.83)	1 9	0 10
75	**5**	6 c. lilac (11.84)	12 6	6 6
76	,,	6 c. violet	4 6	3 6
77	**6**	12 c. dull purple	16 0	8 0
78	**7**	24 c. yellow-green (2.84)	18 6	5 0
79	,,	24 c. blue-green	8 0	4 6
80	**9**	30 c. claret (9.91)	6 0	4 0
81	**8**	32 c. orange-verm. (1.87)	7 0	4 0
82	,,	96 c. olive-grey (8.88)	22 6	15 0

4 Cents (22) 8 Cents (23)

1884 (Feb.–Aug.). *Surcharged with T* **22** *or* **23**, *in black or red* (*R.*). *(The* 12 *c. blue, wmk. Crown CC.)*

No.	Type	Description	Unused	Used
83	**18**	4 c. on 5 c. blue (Aug.)	£35	
84	,,	4 c. on 5 c. blue (R.) (Aug.)	57 6	52 6
85	**6**	8 c. on 12 c. blue (Feb.)	£7	55 0
86	,,	8 c. on 12 c. dl. pur. (Aug.)	£6	75 0

1884 (Aug.). *Surcharged with T* **20** *vertically upwards.*

No.	Type	Description	Unused	Used
87	**18**	2 c. on 5 c. blue (*a*)	27 6	32 6
88	,,	2 c. on 5 c. blue (*b*)	27 6	32 6
89	,,	2 c. on 5 c. blue (*c*)	27 6	32 6
		a. Surcharge omitted, pair		
		b. Surcharge double		

In Type (*a*) the letters "TS" are below the line of the word.

8

(24)

1884 (Sept.). *Nos.* 84 *and* 86 *surcharged with large numeral, as* **T 24**, *in addition, in red.*

90 "4" on 4 c. in *red* on 5 c. blue — £170

91 "8" on 8 c. in *black* on 12 c. dull purple £5 £5

92 "8" on 8 c. in *blue* on 12 c. dull purple £85

Nos. 86 and 91 are known with "s" of "Cents" low.

3 CENTS (25) THREE CENTS (26)

1885. *No.* 74 *and* **T 8** *in new colour, wmk. Crown CA, surcharged with* **T 25** *and* **26.**

93 **25** 3 c. on 5 c. blue (Sept.) .. 70 0 72 6

94 **26** 3 c. on 32 c. pale magenta (Dec.) 2 6 2 6

95 „ 3 c. on 32 c. deep magenta .. 2 6 2 0

3 cents (27) 2 Cents. (28)

1886 (June). *No.* 55 *surcharged with* **T 27.**

96 **18** 3 c. on 5 c. purple-brown .. £6 £6

1887 (July). *No.* 74 *surcharged with* **T 28.**

97 **18** 2 c. on 5 c. blue .. 10 0 12 6

a. "C" of "Cents" omitted ..

b. Surcharge double £14

10 CENTS (29) THIRTY CENTS (30)

1891 (Nov.). *Nos.* 78 *and* 81 *surcharged with* **T 29** *and* **30.**

98 **7** 10 c. on 24 c. yellow-green 2 6 2 0

a. Narrow "0" in "10" .. 20 0 20 0

99 **8** 30 c. on 32 c. orange-verm. 7 6 7 6

The "R" of "THIRTY" and "N" of "CENTS" are found wide or narrow and in all possible combinations.

ONE CENT (31)

1892. *Stamps of* 1882–91 (*wmk. Crown* CA) *surcharged with* **T 31.**

100 1 c. on 2 c. rose (March) .. 0 10 0 10

101 1 c. on 4 c. brown (May) .. 2 6 2 6

a. Surcharge double £15

102 1 c. on 6 c. lilac (Feb.) .. 2 6 2 0

a. Surcharge double, one inverted — 150 0

103 1 c. on 8 c. orange (Jan.) .. 1 0 1 0

104 1 c. on 12 c. dull purple (Mar.) 1 3 8 0

The following varieties may be found in **T 31**:—(1) narrow "N" in "ONE" and "CENT"; (2) wide "N" in "ONE" and "CENT"; (3) narrow "N" in "ONE", wide "N" in "CENT"; (4) wide "N" in "ONE," narrow "N" in "CENT"; (5) narrow "O" in "ONE"; (6) antique "E" in "CENT".

ONE CENT (32)

1892–94. *Colours changed. Wmk. Crown CA P* 14. *Surcharged with* **T 32** *and* **26.**

105 **6** 1 c. on 8 c. green (Mar.,'92) 0 4 0 4

106 **8** 3 c. on 32 c. carmine-rose (June, 1894) 0 10 0 6

a. Error. Surcharge omitted £65

33

34

1892 (Mar.)–**1898.** *Wmk. Crown* CA. *P* 14.

107 **33** 1 c. green (Sept., 1892) .. 0 6 0 1

108 „ 3 c. carmine-rose (2.95) .. 0 8 0 2

109 „ 25 c. purple-brown & grn. 8 0 4 6

110 „ 25 c. dull purple & green 10 0 5 0

111 „ 50 c. olive-grn. & carmine 7 6 5 0

112 **34** $5 oran. & carm. (10.98) 85 0 60 0

1894. *New colours. Wmk. Crown CA. P* 14.

113 **18** 5 c. brown (July) .. 3 6 2 6

114 **6** 8 c. ultramarine (July) 3 6 0 6

115 „ 8 c. bright blue .. 4 0 0 6

116 „ 12 c. brown-purple (Mar.) 7 6 8 0

4 cents. (35) FOUR CENTS (36)

1899. *T* **18** *and* **6,** *surcharged with* **T 35.**

117 4 c. on 5 c. brn. (No. 113)(Jan.) 2 0 2 6

118 4 c. on 5 c. blue (No. 74) (Feb.) 2 0 2 6

119 4 c. on 8 c. ultram (No. 114) (Feb.) 2 6 2 6

a. Surcharge double .. .. — £28

120 4 c. on 8 c. brt. blue (No. 115) 1 6 1 6

Nos. 118 and 119 exist with stop spaced 1½ mm. from the "s."

1899 (March). **T 18** (*wmk. Crown CA. P* 14), *surcharged with* **T 36.**

121 4 c. on 5 c. carmine .. 0 9 0 6

Error. Surcharge omitted.

122 5 c. carmine £190

This stamp is only known unused.

1899. *Colours changed. Wmk. Crown* CA. *P* 14.

123 **33** 3 c. brown (March) .. 1 6 0 4

124 „ 3 c. yellow-brown .. 0 8 0 4

125 **5** 4 c. deep carmine (July) .. 1 9 1 0

126 **18** 5 c. magenta (July) .. 5 0 3 6

37

38

1902. *Wmk. Crown* CA. *P* 14.

127	**37**	1 c. grey-green	0	6	0	4
128	,,	1 c. pale green	0	9	0	5
129	,,	3 c. dull purple & orange	0	9	0	6
130	,,	4 c. purple/*red*	1	0	0	9
131	**38**	5 c. dull purple	1	0	0	8
132	,,	8 c. purple/*blue*	1	6	0	6
133	,,	10 c. purple & black/*yell.*	3	0	0	9
134	**37**	25 c. dull purple & green	3	6	4	0
135	**38**	30 c. grey and carmine ..	10	0	8	6
136	**37**	50 c. deep green & carmine	12	6	10	0
137	,,	50 c. dull green & carmine	10	6	8	6
138	**38**	$1 dull green and black	17	6	15	0
139	**37**	$2 dull purple & black ..	30	0	22	6
140	**38**	$5 dull grn. & brn.-orge.	£5		40	0
141	**37**	$100 purple & green/*yellow*	£180			

39

40

41

42

1903–4. *T* **39** *to* **42**. *Wmk. Crown CA. P* 14.

142	1 c. grey-green	1	3	1	0
143	3 c. dull purple	2	9	1	6
144	4 c. purple/*red*	2	3	0	3
145	8 c. purple/*blue*	5	0	1	0

1904–6. *Wmk. Multiple Crown CA. P* 14.

146	**39**	1 c. deep green, OC ..	0	4	0	1
147	**40**	3 c. dull purple, OC ..	0	9	0	2
148	,,	3 c. plum, O	1	0	0	3
149	**41**	4 c. purple/*red*, OC ..	1	3	0	2
150	**38**	5 c. dull purple, OC ('06)	3	0	2	0
151	**42**	8 c. purple/*blue*, OC ..	4	6	0	8
152	**38**	10 c. pur. & blk./*yell*, OC	3	0	0	10
153	**37**	25 c. dull pur. & grn., OC	5	0	3	6
154	**38**	30 c. grey & carmine, OC	6	0	3	0
155	**37**	50 c. dull grn. & car., OC	15	0	5	0
156	**38**	$1 dull grn. & black OC	17	6	7	6
157	**37**	$2 dull pur. & blk., C ..	40	0	20	0
158	**38**	$5 dull grn. and brown-orange, OC	85	0	35	0
159	,,	$25 grey-grn. & black, C	£35			
160	**37**	$100 pur. & grn./*yell*, C ..	£190			

STRAITS
SETTLEMENTS.
(43)

Straits Settlements.
(44)

STRAITS
SETTLEMENTS.

FOUR CENTS.
(45)

1907. *T* **42** *of Labuan* (*Nos.* 116*a, etc.*) *overprinted with T* **43** (*the* 10 *c. with T* **44**), *or surcharged with T* **45**, *in brownish red or black* (*Bk.*).

161	1 c. black and purple ..	15	0	15	0
162	2 c. black and green.. ..	30	0	30	0
163	3 c. black and sepia ..	10	0	11	0
164	4 c. on 12 c. black & yellow	2	6	2	6
	a. No stop after "CENTS" ..	70	0		
165	4 c. on 16 c. grn. & brn. (Bk.)	2	0	2	0
166	4 c. on 18 c. blk. & pale brown	2	0	2	0
	a. No stop after "CENTS" ..	70	0		
167	8 c. black and vermilion ..	3	0	3	0
168	10 c. brown and slate ..	2	6	2	6
	a. No stop after "SETTLEMENTS"	47	6		
169	25 c. green & greenish blue ..	5	0	6	0
170	50 c. dull purple & lilac ..	7	6	8	0
171	$1 claret and orange ..	12	6	12	6

Varieties. (i.) "STRAITS SETTLEMENTS" *in both black and red.*

172 4 c. on 16 c. green & brown £9

(ii.) 14 *mm. between name and value in surcharge, instead of* 12½ *mm.*

173 4 c. on 18 c. black & pale brn. 62 6

This variety only occurs in a few sheets of the first printing; it was corrected in the bulk of the issue.

(iii.) "FOUR CENTS" *double.*

174 4 c. on 18 c. black & pale brn. £70

46

1906–11. *Wmk. Mult. Crown CA. P* 14.

175	**39**	1 c. blue-green, O (1910)	0	4	0	2
176	**40**	3 c. red, O (1908) ..	0	6	0	1
177	**41**	4 c. red, O (1907) ..	1	3	0	9
178	,,	4 c. dull purple, OC ('08)	0	8	0	3
179	,,	4 c. claret, O (1911) ..	3	6	2	0
180	**38**	5 c. orange, O (1909) ..	1	9	0	6
181	**42**	8 c. blue, O (1906) ..	1	0	0	4
182	**38**	10 c. purple/*yell*, OC ('08)	1	9	0	6
183	**37**	25 c. dull & brt. pur., C ('09)	2	6	2	0
184	**38**	30 c. pur. and orange-yell., C ('09)	3	6	2	0
185	**37**	50 c. black/*green*, C ('10)..	5	0	3	6
186	**38**	$1 blk. & red/*bl.*, C ('11)	10	0	7	6
187	**37**	$2 grn. & red/*yell.*, C ('09)	17	6	16	0
188	**38**	$5 green and red/*green*, C ('10)	50	0	25	0
189	**46**	$25 pur. & blue/*bl.*, C ('11)	£38		£6	
189*a*	,,	$500 purple & orange, C..	£750			

Beware of dangerous forgeries of No. 189*a*.

47

1911. *T* **47.** *Wmk. Mult. Crown CA.* *P* 14.

190 21 c. dull purple & claret, C 10 6 12 6
191 45 c. black/*green*, C 7 6 7 6

48  49

50  51

52  53

54

RED CROSS

2c.
(55)

1912–22. *T* **48** *to* **54.** *$25, $100 and $500 as T* **46**, *but with head of King George V. Wmk. Mult. Crown CA. P* 14.

192 **48** 1 c. green, O 0 6 0 2
193 ,, 1 c. blue-green, O (1917) 0 5 0 2
194 **49** 3 c. red, O 0 5 0 1
195 ,, 3 c. scarlet, O (1917) 0 5 0 1
196 **50** 4 c. dull purple, C .. 0 7 0 3
197 **51** 5 c. orange, O 0 10 0 1
198 ,, 5 c. yellow-orange, O .. 0 9 0 1
199 **52** 8 c. ultramarine, O .. 1 6 0 2
200 **51** 10 c. pur./*yellow*, C (1913) 2 0 0 4
a. White back 2 3 0 6
b. On lemon 15 0 1 9
201 **53** 21 c. dull & brt. purple, C 5 0 2 6
202 **54** 25 c. dull purple & mauve, C ('14) 5 0 1 6
203 ,, 25 c. dull purple & vio., C 6 0 2 0
204 **51** 30 c. dull pur. & orge., C (1914) 4 0 1 6
205 **53** 45 c. black/*green*, C (white back) (1914) .. 5 0 5 0
a. On blue-green, olive back .. 5 0 5 0
b. On emerald back .. 6 0 3 6
206 **54** 50 c. black/*green*, C (1914) 6 0 3 6
a. On blue-green, olive back .. 12 6 3 0
b. On emerald back .. 8 6 2 6
c. On emerald back (Die II) 7 6 2 6
207 **51** $1 blk. & red/*blue*, C ('14) 12 6 4 0
208 **54** $2 green & red/*yellow*, C ('15) 25 0 8 0
a. White back (1914) .. 15 0 6 6
b. On orange-buff .. 55 0 17 6
c. On pale yellow 40 0
209 **51** $5 grn & red/*grn.*, C ('14) 45 0 8 0
a. White back (1913) .. 35 0 10 0
b. On blue-green, olive back 75 0 8 6
c. On emerald back .. 80 0
d. Die II 35 0 8 6
210 – $25 pur. & blue/*blue*, C .. £20 £12
211 – $100 carm. & blk./*blue*, C £60
212 – $500 pur. & orge.-brn., C £220

1917. *Surcharged with T* **55** *in black.*

213 **49** 2 c. on 3 c. scarlet .. 1 0 1 6
a. No stop £5
214 **50** 2 c. on 4 c. dull purple .. 1 6 2 0
a No stop £7

1919–20. *Colours changed. Wmk. Mult. Crown CA. P* 14.

215 **48** 1 c. black, O 0 6 0 3
216 **52** 2 c. green, O 0 6 0 6
217 **50** 4 c. rose-scarlet, O .. 0 9 0 2
218 ,, 4 c. carmine, O 0 10 0 2
219 **52** 6 c. dull claret, O .. 1 6 0 6
220 ,, 6 c. deep claret, O .. 2 0 0 4
221 **51** 10 c. bright blue, O .. 3 6 0 6
222 ,, 10 c. deep bright blue, O 3 6 0 6

The 6 c. is similar to T **52**, but the head is in a beaded oval as in T **53**. The 2 c., 6 c. (and 12 c. below) have figures of value on a circular ground while in the 8 c. this is of oval shape.

Type I.  Type II.

Two types of duty plate in the 25 c. In Type II the solid shading forming the back of the figure 2 extends to the top of the curve; the upturned end of the foot of the 2 is short; two background lines above figure 5; c close to 5; STRAITS SETTLEMENTS in taller letters.

1921–33. *Wmk. Mult. Script CA. P* 14.

223 **48** 1 c. black, O 0 4 0 1
224 **52** 2 c. green, O 0 4 0 1
224*a* ,, 2 c. brown, O 1 0 0 4
225 **49** 3 c. green, O 0 6 0 3
226 **50** 4 c. carmine-red, O .. 1 6 0 2
226*a* ,, 4 c. brt. vio., O (1925) .. 0 9 0 1
226*b* ,, 4 c. orange, O (1929) .. 0 8 0 2
227 **51** 5 c. orange, O (Die I) ('21) 2 0 0 3
a. Die II ('23) .. 1 3 0 1
227*b* ,, 5 c. brn., O (Die II) ('32) 2 0 0 3
227*c* ,, 5 c. brn., O (Die I) ('33) 0 10 0 2
228 **52** 6 c. dull claret, O .. 2 0 0 3
228*a* ,, 6 c. rose-pink, O (1925) 6 0 2 0
228*b* ,, 6 c. scarlet, O (1927) .. 1 3 0 4
229 **51** 10 c. bright blue, O (Die I) 5 0 0 4
229*a* ,, 10 c. purple/*yellow*, C (Die I) ('25) 6 0 0 8
b. Die II *pale yellow* ('27) .. 3 6 0 2
229*c* ,, 10 c. purple/*pale yellow*, C (Die I) ('33) .. 2 0 0 6
230 **52** 12 c. bright blue, O .. 2 6 0 4
231 **53** 21 c. dull & bright pur., C 17 6 12 6
232 **54** 25 c. dull purple & mauve, C (Die I. Type I) .. 10 0 6 6
a. Die II. Type I .. 35 0 6 0
b. Die II. Type II .. 17 6 0 10
233 **51** 30 c. dull pur. & orge., C (Die. I) 35 0 12 6
a. Die II 7 6 0 6
234 **53** 35 c. dull purple & orange-yellow, C 12 6 4 0
235 ,, 35 c. dull pur. & orge., C 6 0 1 6
235*a* ,, 35 c. scar. & pur., C ('31) 4 0 1 0

235*b*	**54**	50 c. black/*emerald*, C ..	6 0	0 8
236	**51**	$1 black & red/*blue*, C	15 0	1 9
237	**54**	$2 grn and red/*pale yellow*, C ..	25 0	4 0
238	**51**	$5 grn. & red/*green*, C	55 0	5 0
239	–	$25 pur. & blue/*blue*, C	£12	50 0
240	–	$100 carm. & blk./*blue*, C	£45	
240*a*	–	$500 pur. & orge.-brn., C	£140	

An 8 c. in carmine, was prepared but not issued.

The paper of No. 229*c* is the normal *pale yellow* at the back, but with a bright yellow surface. No. 229*a* is on paper of a *pale lemon* tint and the impression is smudgy.

MALAYA-

BORNEO

EXHIBITION.

(56)

1922. *T* **48** *and* **50** *to* **54**, *overprinted with T* **56.**

(*a*) *Wmk. Mult. Crown CA.*

241	2 c. green	10 0	12 6
242	4 c. scarlet	8 6	7 0
243	5 c. orange	10 6	7 6
244	8 c. ultramarine ..	2 6	2 6
245	25 c. dull pur. & mve. (No. 232)	4 0	5 0
246	45 c. black/*blue-grn., olive back*	5 0	6 0
247	$1 black and red/*blue* ..	95 0	110 0
248	$2 green & red/*orange-buff*	20 0	20 0
	a. On pale yellow ..	65 0	70 0
249	$5 green and red/*blue green, olive back*	£9	£10

(*b*) *Wmk. Mult. Script CA.*

250	1 c. black	0 9	0 9
251	2 c. green	0 9	0 9
252	4 c. carmine-red	1 0	1 3
253	5 c. orange (Die II)	1 9	2 0
254	10 c. bright blue (Die I) ..	2 0	2 6
255	$1 black & red/*blue* (Die II)	10 0	10 6

The following varieties may be found in most values: (a) Small second "A" in "MALAYA." (b) No stop. (c) No hyphen. (d) Oval last "O" in "BORNEO." (e) "EXH.BITION." Selections can be sent to collectors interested.

1935 (6 MAY). *Silver Jubilee. As T* **13** *of Antigua inscr.* "STRAITS SETTLEMENTS". *Recess. W'low & Sons. Wmk. Mult. Script CA. P* 11×12.

256	5 c. ultramarine and grey ..	0 8	0 6
257	8 c. green and indigo ..	2 6	3 0
258	12 c. brown and deep blue ..	3 0	3 6
259	25 c. slate and purple ..	6 0	6 0

57

1936–37. *Chalk-surfaced paper. Wmk. Mult. Script CA. P* 14.

260	**57**	1 c. black (1.1.37) ..	0 4	0 3
261	,,	2 c. green	0 6	0 3
262	,,	4 c. orange	0 8	0 3
263	,,	5 c. brown	0 9	0 3
264	,,	6 c. scarlet	0 9	0 6
265	,,	8 c. grey	1 0	0 6
266	,,	10 c. dull purple	1 9	0 4
267	,,	12 c. bright ultramarine ..	2 0	0 9
268	,,	25 c. dull purple & scarlet	3 6	0 9
269	**57**	30 c. dull purple & orange	5 0	1 3
270	,,	40 c. scarlet & dull purple	5 0	2 0
271	,,	50 c. black/*emerald* ..	6 0	3 0
272	,,	$1 black and red/*blue* ..	10 0	5 0
273	,,	$2 green and scarlet ..	20 0	15 0
274	,,	$5 green & red/*emerald* (1.1.37)	60 0	37 6

POSTAGE DUE STAMPS.

D 1

1924–6. *Type* D **1.** *Wmk. Mult. Script CA. P* 14.

D1	1 c. violet	0 2	0 3
D2	2 c. black	0 3	0 2
D2*a*	4 c. green (1926)	0 4	0 4
D3	8 c. scarlet	0 8	0 5
D4	10 c. orange	0 10	0 6
D5	12 c. bright blue	1 0	0 4

BRITISH POST OFFICES IN SIAM.

BANGKOK.

1882–85. *Various issues of the stamps of* STRAITS SETTLEMENTS *overprinted in black, with a large capital* "B" (T 1).

B

(1)

On issue of **1867.**

1	32 c. in black, on 2 a. yellow ..	£50	£50

On issues of **1868–82.**

Wmk. Crown CC.

2	2 cents brown	£14	£14
3	4 cents rose	£12	£9
	a. Overprint double		
4	5 cents purple-brown ..	52 6	52 6
5	6 cents lilac	32 6	27 6
6	8 cents orange	£14	45 0
7	10 cents slate	55 0	32 6
8	12 cents blue	£7	85 0
9	24 cents green	70 0	32 6
10	30 cents claret	£55	£40
11	96 cents grey	£16	£12

On issue of **1883.**

Wide "E" (No. 66).

12	2 c. on 32 c. pale red ..	£15	

Wide "S" (No. 67).

13	2 c. on 32 c. pale red ..	£15	

Wmk. Crown CA.

14	2 cents, brown	57 6	47 6
15	2 cents, rose	8 0	6 6
16	4 cents, rose	67 6	57 6
17	4 cents, brown	22 6	17 6
18	5 cents, blue	52 6	42 6
19	6 cents, lilac	32 6	32 6

20	8 cents, orange	25 0	17 6
21	10 cents, slate	30 0	25 0
22	12 cents, dull purple	55 0	50 0
23	24 cents, green	£15	£12

Variety. Overprinted inverted.

24	2 c. rose		
25	8 c. orange		

The use of these stamps ceased 1 July, 1885.

STRAITS SETTLEMENTS NATIVE STATES.

I. SEPARATE ISSUES.

There were no separate issues for Negri Sembilan, Pahang, Perak and Selangor between 1900 and 1935, during which time the general issues of the Federated Malay States (see later) were in use. In 1935 the formation of the Malayan Postal Union resulted in the reappearance of distinctive sets. Sungei Ujong ceased issuing stamps in 1895 when it was merged in Negri Sembilan.

PRINTERS. Stamps of these states were typographed by De La Rue & Co. unless otherwise stated.

Surcharges or overprints are in black unless stated otherwise.

Overprinted stamps are those of the Straits Settlements unless otherwise described.

JOHORE.

(UNFEDERATED STATE)

1876. *Overprinted with Crescent and Star.*

1	2 cents brown (*wmk.* Crown CC)	£120	£85

1884-86. *Wmk. Crown CA. Overprinted with name in various types.*

JOHORE.

2	2 c. rose	40 0	60 0

JOHORE

3	2 c. rose	£20	

JOHORE

(*a*) " H " *and* " E " *wide, as shown.*

(*b*) " H " *wide,* " E " *narrow.*

(*c*) *All letters narrow.*

4	2 c. rose (*a*)	£10	80 0
5	2 c. rose (*b*)	—	£5
6	2 c. rose (*c*)		

JOHORE

7	2 c. rose	27 6	

JOHORE

8	2 c. rose		

JOHOR *All letters narrow.*

9	2 c. rose	2 6	3 0
10	2 c. rose (" H " wide) ..	16 6	16 6

There were several settings similar in type to No. 10, the word varying in length from 12 to 15 mm. The wide " H " occurs on every third stamp of one setting.

JOHOR

11	2 c. brown		
12	2 c. rose	10 0	7 6

JOHOR

13	2 c. rose	10 0	12 6

JOHOR

14	2 c. rose	5 0	4 0
15	2 c. rose (thin narrow " J ")	8 0	8 6

Type similar to No. 14, but with stop.

16	2 c. rose	25 0	27 6

JOHOR

17	2 c. rose	4 6	5 0

JOHOR

17*a*	2 c. rose	£20	

Only 4 specimens of No. 17*a* are known. The overprint is in much heavier type than that of No. 17, which is in thin letters.

JOHOR Two CENTS (*a*)

JOHOR Two CENTS (*b*)

JOHOR *Two* CENTS (*c*)

JOHOR *Two* CENTS (*d*)

1891. *Overprinted with name as on No. 14, and surcharged as Types (a) to (d).*

18	2 c. on 24 c. green (*a*) ..	20 0	20 0
19	2 c. on 24 c. green (*b*) ..	8 6	8 6
20	2 c. on 24 c. green (*c*) ..	30 0	30 0
21	2 c. on 24 c. green (*d*) ..	7 6	7 6

Error. " CENST."

22	2 c. on 24 c. green (*d*) ..	£12	£8

1. Sultan Aboubakar.

1891-94. *T* **1.** *No wmk. P* 14.

23	1 c. dull purple and mauve ..	0 10	0 10
24	2 c. dull purple and yellow ..	1 6	1 3
25	3 c. dull purple and carmine	1 9	1 6
26	4 c. dull purple and black ..	5 0	4 6
27	5 c. dull purple and green ..	6 6	6 6
28	6 c. dull purple and blue ..	10 0	8 6
29	$1 green and carmine ..	25 0	27 6

3 cents.

(2)

T **1** *surcharged with T* **2**, *in black.*

No.	Description	Unused	Used
30	3 c. on 4 c. dull pur. & black	1 6	1 0
31	3 c. on 5 c. dull pur. & green	2 6	1 9
32	3 c. on 6 c. dull pur. & blue ..	1 6	1 9
33	3 c. on $1 green & carmine ..	5 0	6 0

Varieties. No stop.

No.	Description	Unused	Used
33*a*	3 c. on 4 c. dull pur. & black	25 0	25 0
33*b*	3 c. on 5 c. dull pur. & green	25 0	25 0
33*c*	3 c. on $1 green & carmine ..	50 0	55 0

KEMAHKOTAAN

(2*a*)

1896. *Stamps of* 1891–4 *overprinted with Type* 2*a*, *in black, to commemorate the coronation of the new Sultan.*

No.	Description	Unused	Used
34	1 c. dull purple and mauve ..	1 6	1 6
35	2 c. dull purple and yellow ..	1 3	1 3
36	3 c. dull purple and carmine	3 0	3 0
37	4 c. dull purple and black ..	3 0	3 0
38	5 c. dull purple and green ..	3 6	3 0
39	6 c. dull purple and blue ..	3 0	3 0
40	$1 green and carmine ..	25 0	25 0

Errors. "KETAHKOTAAN."

No.	Description	Unused	Used
41	1 c. dull purple and mauve ..	5 6	5 6
42	2 c. dull purple and yellow ..	5 6	5 6
43	3 c. dull purple and carmine	8 6	7 6
44	4 c. dull purple and black ..	4 0	5 0
45	5 c. dull purple and green ..	4 6	4 6
46	6 c. dull purple and blue ..	5 0	5 6
47	$1 green and carmine ..	27 6	27 6

3. Sultan Ibrahim. **4**

5

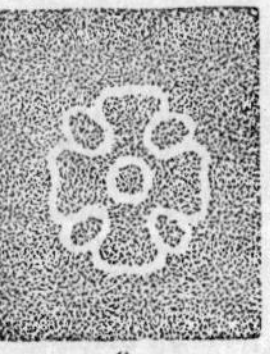

6

1896 (26 Aug.)–**1899.** *Wmk. T* **6.** P 14.

No.	Type	Description	Unused	Used
48	3	1 c. green	0 8	0 8
49	,,	2 c. green and blue ..	1 3	1 3
50	,,	3 c. green and purple ..	1 3	0 10
51	,,	4 c. green and carmine ..	1 9	1 3
52	,,	4 c. yellow and red ..	1 9	1 3
53	,,	5 c. green and brown ..	1 9	1 9
54	,,	6 c. green and yellow ..	3 6	3 0
55	4	10 c. green and black ..	6 0	6 6
56	,,	25 c. green and mauve ..	7 6	8 0
57	,,	50 c. green and carmine ..	10 0	10 0
58	3	$1 dull purple & green ..	17 6	15 0
59	5	$2 dull purple & carmine..	22 6	17 6
60	,,	$3 dull purple & blue ..	27 6	27 6
61	,,	$4 dull purple & brown ..	40 0	35 0
62	,,	$5 dull purple & yellow ..	70 0	40 0

3 cents. (7) **10 cents.** (8)

1903. *T* **3** *and* **5** *surcharged in black. With T* **7** *or* **8** (*with stop*).

No.	Description	Unused	Used
63	3 c. on 4 c. yellow and red ..	0 8	0 10
64	10 c. on 4 c. green & carmine	2 0	2 6

Varieties. (i.) *Original value uncancelled.*

No.	Description	Unused	Used
65	3 c. on 4 c. yellow & red ..	2 0	2 6
66	10 c. on 4 c. green & carmine	7 6	8 6

(ii.) *Tall* "1" *in* "10."

No.	Description	Unused	Used
67	10 c. on 4 c. (No. 64) ..	50 0	50 0
68	10 c. on 4 c. (No. 66) ..	..	

50 Cents. (9) **One Dollar** (10)

With T **9** *or* **10.**

No.	Description	Unused	Used
69	50 c. on $3 dull purple & blue	20 0	22 6
70	$1 on $2 dull pur. & carmine	30 0	32 6

Variety with "e" *of* "One" *inverted.*

No.	Description	Unused	Used
71	$1 on $2 dull pur. & carmine	£35	

10 CENTS.

(11)

1904. *T* **3** *and* **5** *surcharged as T* **11.**

No.	Description	Unused	Used
72	10 c. on 4 c. yellow and red ..	5 0	5 6
73	10 c. on 4 c. green & carmine	4 0	3 6
74	50 c. on $5 dull pur. & yellow	17 6	17 6

Variety. Surcharge double.

No.	Description	Unused	Used
74*a*	10 c. on 4 c. yellow and red		

12

13

14. Sultan Ibrahim.

1904. *W* **6.** *P* 14.

No.	Type	Description	Unused	Used
75	12	1 c. dull pur. & grn., OC..	0 3	0 3
76	,,	2 c. dull pur. & orge., OC	1 3	0 5
77	,,	3 c. dull pur. & olive-blk., O	1 6	0 9
78	,,	4 c. dull pur. & carmine, O	4 0	2 0
79	,,	5 c. dull pur. & sage-grn., O	4 0	4 0
80	14	8 c. dull purple & blue, O	4 6	4 6

81	13	10 c. dull pur. & black, OC	4 6	4 6
82	,,	25 c. dull pur. & grn., O ..	6 6	6 6
83	,,	50 c. dull purple and red, O	7 0	7 0
84	12	$1 green & mauve, O ..	12 6	9 6
85	14	$2 green and carmine, O	17 6	15 0
86	,,	$3 green and blue, O ..	27 6	25 0
87	,,	$4 green and brown ..	35 0	30 0
88	,,	$5 green and orange, O	40 0	35 0
89	13	$10 green and black, O ..	80 0	50 0
89*a*	,,	$50 green and ultram., O ..	£38	£16
89*b*	,,	$100 green and scarlet, O ..	£85	£8

1910–12. *Wmk. Mult. Rosettes.* P 14.

90	12	1 c. dull purple & green, C	0 4	0 4
91	,,	2 c. dull pur. & orange, C	0 6	0 6
92	,,	3 c. dull pur. & olive-blk., C	0 4	0 1
93	,,	4 c. dull pur. & carmine, C	0 6	0 4
94	,,	5 c. dull pur. & sage-grn., C	0 8	0 8
95	14	8 c. dull purple & blue, C..	1 6	1 3
96	13	10 c. dull purple & black, C	3 0	1 0
97	,,	25 c. dull purple & green, C	5 0	5 0
98	,,	50 c. dull purple & red, C	12 6	8 6
99	12	$1 green and mauve, C ..	17 6	12 6

3 CENTS.

(15)

1912. *No.* 80 *surch. with T* **15**, *in black.*

100	3 c. on 8 c. dull pur. & blue, O	5 0	4 0
	a. "T" of "CENTS" omitted		

1919. *Chalk-surfaced paper. Wmk. Mult. Crown CA.* P 14.

102	12	2 c. dull purple & green	0 6	0 4
103	,,	2 c. purple and orange ..	0 6	0 4
104	,,	4 c. dull purple & red ..	0 4	0 4
105	,,	5 c. dull pur. & sage-grn.	0 8	0 8
107	13	10 c. dull purple & blue ..	1 3	0 8
108	,,	21 c. dull purple & orange	1 9	1 0
109	,,	25 c. dull purple & green	3 0	3 0
110	,,	50 c. dull purple & red ..	5 0	5 0
111	12	$1 green and mauve ..	7 0	7 0
112	14	$2 green and carmine ..	17 6	12 6
113	,,	$3 green and blue ..	16 0	15 0
114	,,	$4 green and brown ..	20 0	17 6
115	,,	$5 green and orange ..	40 0	27 6
116	13	$10 green and black ..	70 0	55 0

1921–36. *Chalk-surfaced paper. Wmk. Mult Script CA.* P 14.

117	12	1 c. dull purple & black	0 1	0 1
118	,,	2 c. purple and sepia ..	0 4	0 4
118*a*	,,	4 c. purple and carmine	0 3	0 2
119	,,	5 c. dull pur. & sage-grn.	0 4	0 2
120	,,	6 c. dull purple & claret	0 4	0 3
121	13	10 c. dull purple and blue	2 3	1 9
122	,,	10 c. dull purple & yellow	0 8	0 4
123	12	12 c. dull purple & blue	1 0	0 6
123*a*	13	21 c. dull pur. & orge. ('28)	1 0	0 8
124	,,	25 c. dull pur. & myrtle	1 6	0 8
124*a*	14	30 c. dull pur. & orge. ('36)	1 10	1 6
124*b*	,,	40 c. dull pur. & brn. ('36)	2 3	1 6
125	13	50 c. dull purple & red ..	2 6	1 0
126	12	$1 green and mauve ..	4 0	3 0
127	14	$2 green and carmine ..	10 0	6 0
128	,,	$3 green and blue ..	17 6	17 6
129	,,	$4 green and brown ..	22 6	22 6
130	,,	$5 green and orange ..	22 6	20 0
131	13	$10 green and black ..	50 0	50 0
132	,,	$50 green and ultram.	£16	
133	,,	$100 green and scarlet	£35	
134	,,	$500 blue and red ..	£120	

1925–28. *New colours. Chalk-surfaced paper. Wmk. Mult. Script CA.* P 14.

135	12	2 c. green ('28)	0 4	0 3
136	,,	3 c. green	0 6	0 5
137	,,	3 c. purple and sepia ('28)	0 4	0 3

For 12 c. ultramarine, see King George VI Catalogue.

16. Sultan Sir Ibrahim and Sultana.

(Recess. Waterlow & Sons.)

1935 (15 May). *Wmk. Mult. Script CA.* P 12½.

138	16	8 c. bright violet & slate ..	3 0	3 0

KEDAH.

(UNFEDERATED STATE)

(Sultan Abdul Hamid Halimshah.)

1. Sheaf of rice.

2. Malay ploughing.

3. Council Chamber.

(Recess. De La Rue & Co.)

1912 (July). *Wmk. Mult. Crown CA.* P 14.

1	1	1 c. black and green ..	0 6	0 4
2	,,	3 c. black and red ..	1 0	0 6
3	,,	4 c. rose and grey	2 0	1 0
4	,,	5 c. green and chestnut ..	2 0	1 6
5	,,	8 c. black and ultramarine	1 9	1 9
6	2	10 c. blue and sepia ..	2 6	1 0
7	,,	20 c. black and green ..	4 0	3 0
8	,,	30 c. black and rose ..	6 0	5 0
9	,,	40 c. black and purple ..	9 0	9 0
10	,,	50 c. brown and blue ..	10 0	10 0
11	3	$1 black and red/*yellow* ..	12 6	12 6
12	,,	$2 green and brown.. ..	20 0	22 6
13	,,	$3 black and blue/*blue* ..	32 6	35 0
14	,,	$5 black and red	55 0	55 0

1919–21. *New colours and values. Wmk. Mult. Crown CA.* P 14.

(i.) Printed from key and duty plates, with dotted shading extending close to the central sheaf.

(ii) Printed from single plate, with white space around sheaf (as shown in T 1).

15	1	1 c. brown (i)	0 4	0 4
18	,,	2 c. green (ii)	0 6	0 4
19	,,	3 c. deep purple (i)	0 10	0 9
20	,,	4 c. rose (i)	0 8	0 9
21	,,	4 c. red (ii)	1 0	0 8

22	2	21 c. purple	3	6	4	0
23	„	25 c. blue & purple (1921) ..	7	6	8	0

ONE

DOLLAR

(4)

(Surcharged by Ribeiro & Co., Penang.)

1919. *T* **3** *surcharged as T* **4**, *in black.*

24	50 c. on $2 green and brown	45	0	45	0
25	$1 on $3 black & blue/*blue* ..	30	0	30	0

In 1919 1 c., 3 c., and 4 c. (both purple and scarlet) stamps of Straits Settlements were authorized for use in Kedah during a temporary shortage of Kedah stamps. Stamps so used can be identified by the postmark.

1921–24. *Wmk. Mult. Script CA. P* 14.

26	1	1 c. brown (ii)	0	4	0	3
27	„	2 c. dull green (ii)	0	3	0	2
28	„	3 c. deep purple (ii) ..	1	3	0	8
29	„	4 c. deep carmine (ii) ..	1	0	0	3
30	2	10 c. blue and sepia ..	1	0	0	10
31	„	20 c. black & yellow-green ..	2	0	1	0
32	„	21 c. mauve and purple ..	2	0	1	9
33	„	25 c. blue and purple ..	3	0	2	0
34	„	30 c. black and rose ..	3	0	1	6
35	„	40 c. black and purple ..	3	0	2	6
36	„	50 c. brown and grey-blue ..	4	0	3	0
37	3	$1 black & red/*yellow* ..	10	0	7	6
38	„	$2 myrtle and brown ..	16	0	17	6
39	„	$3 black & blue/*blue* ..	20	0	20	0
40	„	$5 black & deep carmine ..	32	6	35	0

The 1 c. and 3 c. in this issue are from new combined plates.

For 2 c. with redrawn figures, see 1940 issue in King George VI Catalogue.

MALAYA-

BORNEO

EXHIBITION.

(5)

1922. *T* 1 *and* 2 *overprinted as T* 5, *in black.*

I. "BORNEO" 14 *mm. long.*

(*a*) *Wmk. Mult. Crown CA.*

41	2 c. green (ii)	1	9	1	9
42	21 c. mauve and purple ..	22	6	25	0
43	25 c. blue and purple	27	6	32	6
	a. Overprint inverted		£20		
44	50 c. brown and grey-blue ..	40	0	42	6

(*b*) *Wmk. Mult. Script CA.*

45	1 c. brown (ii)	1	6	1	6
46	3 c. purple (ii)	3	0	3	0
47	4 c. deep carmine (ii) ..	3	6	3	6
48	10 c. blue and sepia	6	0	6	0

There are numerous minor varieties in this setting, consisting of variations in the size and shape of the letters, stop raised, stop omitted, etc., etc.

II. "BORNEO" 15–15½ *mm. long.*

Wmk. Mult. Crown CA.

49	21 c. mauve and purple ..	7	6		
50	25 c. blue and purple ..	12	6		
51	50 c. brown and grey-blue ..	17	6		

1922–36. *New colours, etc. Wmk. Mult. Script CA. P* 14.

52	1	1 c. black (ii)	0	3	0	3
53	„	3 c. green (ii)	0	6	0	6
54	„	4 c. violet (ii) (1926) ..	0	7	0	4
55	„	5 c. yellow (ii)	0	7	0	4
56	„	6 c. carmine (ii) (1926) ..	0	8	0	8
57	„	8 c. grey-black (Oct. '36) ..	1	3	1	3
58	2	12 c. black & indigo (1926) ..	2	6	2	0
59	„	35 c. purple (1926)	6	6	6	6

KELANTAN.

(UNFEDERATED STATE)

1

1911. *T* 1. *Wmk. Mult. Crown CA. P* 14.

1	1 c. yellow-green, O	0	6	0	2
1*a*	1 c. blue-green, O	0	4	0	2
2	3 c. red, O	0	4	0	2
3	4 c. black and red, O ..	0	8	0	6
4	5 c. green & red/*yellow*, O ..	1	3	0	8
5	8 c. ultramarine, O ..	1	6	0	10
6	10 c. black and mauve, O ..	2	0	0	10
7	30 c. dull purple and red, C ..	3	0	0	10
7*a*	30 c. purple and carmine, C ..	4	6	3	6
8	50 c. black and orange, C ..	4	0	3	0
9	$1 green and emerald, C ..	20	0	18	6
10	$2 green and carmine, C ..	15	0	17	6
11	$5 green and blue, C ..	22	6	27	6
12	$25 green and orange, C ..		£5		£7

1915. *T* 1, *colour changed. Wmk. Mult. Crown CA. P* 14.

13	$1 green and brown, C ..	8	6	6	6

1921–28. *T* 1. *Wmk. Mult. Script CA. P* 14.

14	1 c. dull green, O	0	8	0	4
15	1 c. black, O	0	3	0	3
16	2 c. brown, O	0	8	0	8
16*a*	2 c. green O (1926)	0	3	0	3
16*b*	3 c. brown, O (1927) ..	0	4	0	4
17	4 c. black and red, O ..	0	6	0	4
18	5 c. green & red/*pale yell*, O	0	8	0	4
19	6 c. claret, O	1	0	0	10
19*a*	6 c. scarlet, O (1928) ..	0	9	0	6
20	10 c. black and mauve, O ..	1	6	0	8
21	30 c. purple & carm., C (1926)	2	6	1	6
22	50 c. black and orange, C ..	3	6	3	6
23	$1 green and brown, C ..	10	0	10	6

MALAYA

BORNEO

EXHIBITION

(2)

1922. *T* 1, *overprinted with T* 2, *in black.*

(*a*) *Wmk. Mult. Crown CA.*

30	4 c. black and red	1	9	1	9
31	5 c. green & red/*pale yellow* ..	2	6	2	6
32	30 c. dull purple and red ..	3	0	3	6
33	50 c. black and orange ..	3	0	4	0
34	$1 green and brown ..	12	6	12	6
35	$2 green and carmine ..	20	0	22	6
36	$5 green and blue	75	0	80	0

(*b*) *Wmk. Mult. Script CA.*

37	1 c. green	1	3	1	6
38	10 c. black and mauve ..	2	0	2	6

3. Sultan Ismail.

(Recess. De La Rue & Co.)

1928–36. *T* **3.** *Wmk. Mult. Script CA.*

39 $1 blue (*perf.* 12) 7 6 8 0
39*a* $1 blue (*perf.* 14) ('36) .. 10 0 12 6

NEGRI SEMBILAN.

(FEDERATED STATE.)

Negri
Sembilan
(1)

1891. *Wmk. Crown CA. Optd. with T* **1.**

1 2 cents, rose 4 6 4 6

Varieties. (i.) *Space between* " i " *and* " l," *or* (ii.) " m " *and* " b," *of* " Sembilan."

2

3

1892. *T* **2.** *Wmk. Crown CA. P* 14.

2 1 c. green 1 0 1 0
3 2 c. rose 2 0 2 6
4 5 c. blue 3 6 3 0

1896–99. *T* **3.** *Wmk. Crown CA. P* 14.

5 1 c. dull purple & green (1899) 4 6 5 0
6 2 c. dull purple & brown .. 12 6 12 6
7 3 c. dull purple & carmine .. 2 6 2 0
8 5 c. dull purple & olive-yellow 5 0 6 0
9 8 c. dull purple & ultramarine 4 0 4 6
10 10 c. dull purple & orange .. 5 0 5 0
11 15 c. green and violet .. 12 6 10 6
12 20 c. green and ochre 15 0 15 0
13 25 c. green and carmine .. 15 0 15 0
14 50 c. green and black 25 0 20 0

Four cents.

(4)

Four cents.

(5)

1899. *Surcharged as T* **4** *or* **5** *in black or green* (G.). (*a*) *T* **4.**

15 **2** 4 c. on 1 c. green 1 9 2 6
16 „ 4 c. on 5 c. blue 1 6 2 6
17 **3** 1 c. on 15 c. green & violet 40 0
a. Inverted stop £18
18 „ 4 c. on 3 c. dull pur. & carm. 3 6 4 0
a. Surcharge omitted (in pair with normal) .. £30
b. Surcharge double .. .. — £10
c. " cents " repeated at left .. £6 £6
d. " Four " repeated at right .
e. Without bar .. ..

On Nos. 17 and 18 the bar is at the top of the stamp.

(*b*) *T* **5.**

19 **3** 4 c. on 8 c. dull purple and ultramarine (G) .. 3 0 3 0
a. Surcharge omitted (in pair with normal) .. £45
b. Surcharge double in green .. £25
c. Surcharge double, one red, one green .. £25 £20
20 „ 4 c. on 8 c. dull purple and ultramarine (Bk.) £25 £20

From 1895 the stamps of Negri Sembilan were also used in Sungei Ujong.

MALAYA
1c 1c
NEGRI SEMBILAN

6

1935–41. *Chalk-surfaced paper. Wmk. Mult. Script CA. P* 14.

21 **6** 1 c. black 0 3 0 2
22 „ 2 c. green 1 0 0 2
23 „ 4 c. orange 0 9 0 2
24 „ 5 c. brown 0 9 0 2
24*a* „ 6 c. scarlet 1 3 0 5
25 „ 8 c. grey 1 3 0 6
26 „ 10 c. dull purple 1 3 0 5
27 „ 12 c. bright ultramarine .. 1 3 2 0
28 „ 25 c. dull purple & scarlet 2 0 3 0
29 „ 30 c. dull purple & orange 2 6 3 0
30 „ 40 c. scarlet and dull purple 3 0 3 6
31 „ 50 c. black/*emerald* .. 4 6 3 6
32 „ $1 black and red/*blue* .. 7 6 6 0
33 „ $2 green and scarlet .. 12 6 10 0
34 „ $5 green & red/*emerald* .. 35 0 25 0

The 8 c. scarlet, T **6**, was only issued overprinted during the Japanese occupation of Malaya.

For other values and colours in this design, see King George VI Catalogue.

Dates of issue :—2.12.35, 4 c., 8 c. and 40 c. 5.12.35, 5 c. 1.1.36, 1 c., 2 c. (grn.), 10 c., 12 c. and 30 c. 1.2.36, 50 c. 1.4.36, 25 c. and $1. 16.5.36, $2 and $5. 1.1.37, 6 c. (scar.). –.8.41.

PAHANG.

(FEDERATED STATE.)

1889. *Stamps wmkd. Crown CA, overprinted with name in various types.*

PAHANG

1 2 c. rose 17 6 12 6
2 8 c. orange £14 £12
3 10 c. slate 52 6 37 6

PAHANG

4	2 c. rose	6 0	6 0

As No. 4, but in antique letters.

4*a*	2 c. rose	£20	

The letters of the overprint on No. 4*a* are thinner and appear broader than those on No. 4

PAHANG

5	2 c. rose	£30	£15

PAHANG

6	2 c. rose	40 0	20 0

1891. *Overprinted as No. 6 and surcharged with new value with bar through old value.*

7	Two CENTS on 24 c. green ..	65 0	

No. 7 has the word "TWO" as in No. 8 and "CENTS" as in No. 10.

PAHANG
Two
CENTS

8	2 c. on 24 c. green	35 0	35 0

PAHANG
Two
CENTS

9	2 c. on 24 c. green	45 0	45 0

PAHANG
Two
CENTS

10	2 c. on 24 c. green	30 0	27 6

1

2

1891-94. *T* **1.** *Wmk. Crown CA. P* 14.

11	1 c. green	4 0	2 6
12	2 c. rose	1 6	1 9
13	5 c. blue	6 6	6 6

1895-99. *T* **2.** *Wmk. Crown CA. P* 14.

14	3 c. dull purple & carmine ..	2 6	1 9
14*a*	4 c. dull purple & carm. (1899)	3 0	3 6
15	5 c. dull purple & olive-yellow	4 0	4 6

1897. *No.* 13 *divided, and each half surcharged* "2 c." *or* "3 c." *in MS., with initials.*

(i.) *Diagonally.*

(*a*) *In red.* (13 *Jan.*)

16	2 c. on half of 5 c. blue ..	82 6	52 6
17	3 c. on half of 5 c. blue ..	82 6	52 6

(*b*) *In black.* (20 *Aug.*)

17*a*	2 c. on half of 5 c. blue ..	—	£6
17*b*	3 c. on half of 5 c. blue ..	£22	90 0

(ii.) *Horizontally or vertically, in red.*

17*c*	2 c. on half of 5 c. blue ..	—	65 0
17*d*	3 c. on half of 5 c. blue ..	—	65 0

The initials are "J. F. O.", standing for John Fortescue Owen, District Treasurer at Kuala Lipis, where the provisionals were made.

Pahang. (3)   **Pahang.** (4)

1898. *Stamps of Perak, T* **2** (*wmk. Crown CA*) *overprinted with T* **3**, *in black. P* 14.

18	10 c. dull purple and orange..	6 0	5 0
19	25 c. green and carmine ..	20 0	20 0
20	50 c. green and black.. ..	57 6	50 0
21	50 c. dull pur. & greenish blk.	57 6	55 0

Nos. 72 *and* 75 *of Perak, overprinted with T* **4.**

22	$1 green and pale green ..	60 0	60 0
23	$5 green and ultramarine ..	£7	£7

Pahang
Four cents
(5)

Four cents.
(6)

1898. *Stamp of Perak, T* **2** (*wmk. Crown CA, P* 14), *surcharged with T* **5**, *in black.*

24	4 c. on 8 c. dull pur. & ultram.	4 0	4 6

Varieties. (i.) *Surcharge inverted.*

25	4 c. on 8 c. dull pur. & ultram.	—	£30

(ii.) *Surcharge double.*

25*a*	4 c. on 8 c. dull pur. & ultram.	£10	

T **5** *on plain paper* (*no stamp*), *but issued for postage.*

26	4 c. black	—	£8
26*a*	5 c. black	£5	

1899. *No.* 15 *surcharged with T* **6**, *in black.*

27	4 c. on 5 c. dull pur. & olive-yellow	8 0	8 6

7. Sultan Abu Bakar.

1935-41. *Chalk-surfaced paper. Wmk. Mult. Script CA. P* 14.

28	**7**	1 c. black	0 3	0 3
29	"	2 c. green	0 9	0 3
30	"	4 c. orange	0 9	0 3
31	"	5 c. brown	0 9	0 3
32	"	6 c. scarlet	0 10	1 0
33	"	8 c. grey	1 6	0 9
34	"	10 c. dull purple	1 3	0 7
35	"	12 c. bright ultramarine ..	1 3	2 0
36	"	25 c. dull purple & scarlet ..	2 0	3 0
37	"	30 c. dull purple & orange ..	2 6	2 0
38	"	40 c. scarlet & dull purple ..	3 0	3 6
39	"	50 c. black/*emerald* ..	4 6	3 6
40	"	$1 black and red/*blue* ..	7 6	6 0
41	"	$2 green and scarlet ..	12 6	10 0
42	"	$5 green & red/*emerald* ..	25 0	25 0

For other values and colours in this design, see King George VI Catalogue.
Dates of issue as for Negri Sembilan.

PERAK.

(FEDERATED STATE)

1878. *Wmk. Crown CC. Overprinted with Crescent, Star, and* "P" *in an oval.*

1	2 cents brown	£16	£14

880-82. *Overprinted with name in various types.*

PERAK

2 c. brown 7 6 15 0

PERAK

(This illustration shows all letters narrow.)

(*a*) *All letters wide.* (*b*) *All letters wide, but close together.* (*c*) *"* R *" narrow.* (*d*) *"* R *" and "* A *" narrow.* (*e*) *"* P *" and "* K *" wide.* (*f*) *All letters narrow.* (*g*) *All letters narrow, but close together.*

3 2 c. brown (*a*) .. .. .. — £5

4 2 c. brown (*b*) .. .. .. — 80 0

5 2 c. brown (*c*) 35 0 35 0

6 2 c. brown (*d*) 35 0 35 0

7 2 c. brown (*e*) 75 0 55 0

8 2 c. brown (*f*) 25 0 25 0

9 2 c. brown (*g*) £5 80 0

1883. *Wmk. Crown CA.*

10 2 c. brown (*f*) 7 6 8 6

11 2 c. rose (*a*) .. .. ..

12 2 c. rose (*f*) 6 6 7 6

13 2 c. rose ("E" *wide*) 6 6 7 6

14 2 c. rose ("A" *wide*) 6 6 7 6

PERAK

15 2 c. rose ("E" *wide*) 1 6 1 0

16 2 c. rose ("E" *narrow*) .. 8 6 8 6

Variety. "PERAK" *inverted.*

17 2 c. rose £10 £8

1886-1890. *Wmk. Crown CA.*

PERAK

18 2 c. rose 0 6 0 8

19 2 c. rose (*error* "FERAK") £6 75 0

This error is usually found with the " F *" altered in ink to "* P.*"*

PERAK

20 2 c. rose 8 0 8 6

PERAK

21 2 c. rose 2 0 2 6

PERAK

22 2 c. rose 25 0 18 6

"PERAK" *in bold Roman letters,* $2\frac{3}{4}$ *mm. high and* 13 *mm. long.*

22*a* 2 c. rose £20

Only 4 specimens are known with this overprint.

Surcharged vertically.

2 CENTS

PERAK

"E" *of* "PERAK" *wide* ($1\frac{3}{4}$ *mm.*).

23 2 c. on 4 c. rose £8 130 0

All letters narrow ("E" $1\frac{1}{2}$ *mm. wide.*)

24 2 c. on 4 c. rose £6 £5

Surcharged PERAK ONE CENT.

25 1 c. on 2 c. rose 42 6 30 0

Variety. No stop after " CENT.*"*

25*a* 1 c. on 2 c. rose .. .. — £5

Surcharged vertically ONE CENT PERAK

26 1 c. on 2 c. rose £25

Stop after " PERAK.*"*

27 1 c. on 2 c. rose 10 0 11 0

Wide " N *" in "* ONE *" and "* CENT.*"*

28 1 c. on 2 c. rose 10 0 11 0

Surcharged vertically ONE CENT PERAK *in blue.*

29 1 c. on 2 c. rose 13 6 13 6

Same surcharge in black.

29*a* 1 c. on 2 c. rose £30 £30

Surcharged 1 CENT PERAK *black.*

30 1 c. on 2 c. rose 12 6 10 0

1 CENT PERAK

31 1 c. on 2 c. rose £10 £10

The figure "1" in the above surcharge is a small Roman character, sometimes with a slanting top.

Surcharged 1 CENT PERAK

32 1 c on 2 c. rose £30

Surcharged One CENT PERAK

33 1 c. on 2 c. rose 1 6 1 6

Variety. "One" inverted.

33*a* 1 c. on 2 c. rose £15

Surcharged One CENT PERAK

34 1 c. on 2 c. rose 1 0 1 0

Same with ordinary italic "K."

35 1 c. on 2 c. rose 30 0

As No. 34, *but "* CENT *" in Roman (upright) letters as* No. 37.

36 1 c. on 2 c. rose £20 £20

Surcharged One CENT PERAK

37 1 c. on 2 c. rose 7 6 7 6

Error. " PREAK.*"*

38 1 c. on 2 c. rose £7 £6

"One CENT" italic, " PERAK *" upright as* No. 37.

39 1 c. on 2 c. rose 20 0 20 0

Surcharged One CENT PERAK

40 1 c. on 2 c. rose 6 0 6 0

Surcharged One CENT PERAK.

41 1 c. on 2 c. rose 3 0 3 0

Surcharged One CENT PERAK

42 1 c. on 2 c. rose 4 6 3 6

1891. *Surcharged in three lines with bar obliterating old value (Nos. 43 to 56).*

PERAK One CENT

43 1 c. on 2 c. rose 1 0 1 3
44 1 c. on 6 c. lilac 10 0 10 0

PERAK Two CENTS

45 2 c. on 24 c. green 4 0 4 6

PERAK One CENT

46 1 c. on 2 c. rose 3 6 4 0

PERAK One CENT

47 1 c. on 2 c. rose 1 3 1 6
48 1 c. on 6 c. lilac 18 6 15 0
49 2 c. on 24 c. green 6 6 6 6

PERAK One CENT

50 1 c. on 2 c. rose 2 6 2 6
51 1 c. on 6 c. lilac 18 6 18 6
52 2 c. on 24 c. green 10 0 10 0

PERAK One CENT

53 1 c. on 6 c. lilac 15 0 15 0
54 2 c. on 24 c. green 12 6 12 6

PERAK One CENT

55 1 c. on 6 c. lilac 25 0 25 0
56 2 c. on 24 c. green 12 6 10 0

Nos. 55 and 56 also have the bar through value at foot.

1

1891-95. *T 1. Wmk. Crown CA. P 14.*

57 1 c. green 0 6 0 6
58 2 c. rose 0 9 0 6
59 2 c. orange (1895) 0 8 0 10
60 5 c. blue 3 0 3 6

1895. *T 1, surcharged* **3 CENTS** *in black.*

61 3 c. on 5 c. rose 1 9 2 0

2

3

1895-99. *P 14. T 2. Wmk. Crown CA.*

62 1 c. dull purple and green .. 0 10 0 4
a. "1 G" for "1 C" at left .. 10 0
63 2 c. dull purple and brown .. 0 8 0 5
64 3 c. dull purple & carmine .. 0 6 0 3
65 4 c. dull purple & carm (1899) 2 6 2 6
66 5 c dull purple & olive-yellow 2 0 2 0
67 8 c. dull purple & ultram. .. 3 6 1 6
68 10 c. dull purple and orange .. 3 6 1 0
69 25 c. green and carmine .. 18 0 14 6
70 50 c. dull pur & greenish black 17 6 15 0
71 50 c. green & black (1899) .. 30 0 30 0

T 3. Wmk. Crown CC.

72 $1 green and pale green .. 37 6 27 6
73 $2 green and carmine .. 90 0 70 0
74 $3 green and ochre 45 0 35 0
75 $5 green and ultramarine .. £6 85 0
75a $25 green and orange .. £20 £10

One Cent.
(5)

ONE CENT.
(6)

Three Cent.
(7)

Three Cent.
(8)

1900. *Stamps of 1895–99 surcharged, in black.*

No.	Type	Description	Unused	Used
77	5	1 c. on 2 c. dull pur. & brn.	1 0	1 0
		a. Antique "e" in "One"	25 0	
		b. Antique "e" in "Cent" ..	15 0	
78	6	1 c. on 4 c. dull pur. & carm.	0 4	1 0
79	5	1 c. on 5 c. dull purple and olive-yellow ..	0 8	1 0
		a. Antique "e" in "One" ..	25 0	
		b. Antique "e" in "Cent" ..	15 0	15 0
81	7	3 c. on 8 c. dull pur. & ult. ..	2 0	2 0
		a. Antique "e" in "Cent" ..	45 0	
		b. Antique "e" in "Three" ..		
		c. No stop after "Cent" ..	70 0	
		d. Surcharge double	£7	
82	7	3 c. on 50 c. green & black ..	2 0	2 6
		a. Antique "e" in "Cent" ..	55 0	
		b. Antique "e" in "Three"		
		c. No stop after "Cent" ..	42 6	
83	8	3 c. on $1 grn. & pale grn. ..	7 0	7 6
		a. Small "t" in "Cent" ..	85 0	85 0
84	8	3 c. on $2 green & carmine	4 6	5 0

9. Sultan Iskandar.

1935–37. *Chalk-surfaced paper. Wmk. Mult. Script CA. P 14.*

No.	Type	Description	Unused	Used
95	9	1 c. black	0 3	0 2
96	,,	2 c. green	0 3	0 3
97	,,	4 c. orange	0 4	0 2
98	,,	5 c. brown	0 4	0 1
99	,,	6 c. scarlet (1.1.37) ..	0 6	0 4
100	,,	8 c. grey	0 9	0 6
101	,,	10 c. dull purple	0 10	0 3
102	,,	12 c. bright ultramarine ..	0 10	0 6
103	,,	25 c. dull pur. & scarlet ..	1 6	0 9
104	,,	30 c. dull pur. & orange ..	1 9	0 9
105	,,	40 c. scarlet & dull pur. ..	2 6	1 3
106	,,	50 c. black/*emerald* ..	3 0	1 0
107	,,	$1 black and red/*blue* ..	6 6	2 6
108	,,	$2 green and scarlet ..	12 6	3 0
109	,,	$5 green and red/*emerald*	25 0	12 6

Dates of issue as for Negri Sembilan.

OFFICIAL STAMPS.

P.G.S. (O 1) Service. (O 2)

1890. *Stamps of Straits Settlements optd. with Type O 1 in black.*

No.	Description	Unused	Used
O1	2 cents, CA, rose	5 0	5 0
	a. Overprint double	£25	£25
	b. No stop after "S" ..	55 0	
	c. Wide space between "G" & "S"	65 0	
O2	4 cents, CA, brown	15 0	15 0
	a. No stop after "S" ..	£6	
	b. Wide space between "G" & "S"	85 0	
O3	6 cents, CA, lilac	27 6	27 6
	a. Wide space between "G" & "S"	£9	
O4	8 cents, CA, orange	27 6	27 6
	a. Wide space between "G" & "S"	£9	
O5	10 cents. CA, slate	50 0	50 0
	a. Wide space between "G" & "S"	£18	£18
O6	12 cents, CC, blue ..	110 0	
	a. Wide space between "G" & "S"	£35	
O7	12 cents, CA, brown-purple ..	95 0	
	a. Wide space between "G" & "S"	£28	
O8	24 cents, CC, green	£12	
	a. Wide space between "G" & "S"	£50	
O9	24 cents. CA, green	75 0	
	a. Wide space between "G" & "S"	£25	

1894. *No. 60 optd. with Type* O 2.

No.	Description	Unused	Used
O10	5 c. blue	5 0	1 6
	a. Overprint inverted	£15	£10

1897. *No. 66 optd. with Type* O 2.

No.	Description	Unused	Used
O11	5 c. dull purple & olive-yell.	3 0	1 0
	a. Overprint double ..	£6	

SELANGOR.

(FEDERATED STATE.)

1878–82. *Overprinted with Crescent, Star, and "S" in an oval.*

Wmk. Crown CA.

No.	Description	Unused	Used
3	2 c. brown (R.)	£15	

Overprinted with capital "S" in black. Wmk. Crown CA.

No.	Description	Unused	Used
4	2 c. brown	—	£22
5	2 c. rose		

Overprinted SELANGOR

1881. *Wmk. Crown CC.*

Varieties. (a) All letters narrow. (b) "S" wide. (c) "S," "E," "A," and "N" wide. (d) "SELAN" wide. (e) "SEL" and "N" wide. (f) "EL" wide. (g) "E" wide. (h) "E," "N," and "G" wide. (s) "N" wide.

No.	Description	Unused	Used
6	2 c. brown (*a*)	15 0	16 6
7	2 c. brown (*b*)	17 6	20 0
8	2 c. brown (*c*)	50 0	
9	2 c. brown (*d*)	60 0	
10	2 c. brown (*e*)	35 0	
11	2 c. brown (*f*)		
12	2 c. brown (*g*)		
13	2 c. brown (*h*)		
13*a*	2 c. brown (*s*)	—	£20

1882. *Wmk. Crown CA.*

Varieties. (i) "SEL," "N," and "G" wide. (j) "E" and "ANG" wide. (k) "ELANG" wide. (l) "SE," and "N" wide. (m) "S" and "N" wide. (n) "S" and "A" wide.

No.	Description	Unused	Used
14	2 c. brown (*a*)	—	35 0
15	2 c. brown (*b*)	50 0	40 0
16	2 c. brown (*c*)		
17	2 c. brown (*d*)		
18	2 c. brown (*e*)	60 0	
19	2 c. brown (*f*)	—	75 0
20	2 c. brown (*g*)	60 0	60 0
21	2 c. brown (*i*)	35 0	
22	2 c. brown (*j*)	50 0	50 0
23	2 c. brown (*k*)	60 0	60 0
24	2 c. brown (*l*)	30 0	30 0
25	2 c. brown (*m*)	30 0	30 0
26	2 c. brown (*n*)	—	80 0

Varieties. (o) "E" and "A" wide. (p) "S" and "L" wide. (q) "A" wide. (r) "L" wide. (s) "N" wide. (t) All letters wide. (u) "A" narrow. (v) "L" narrow.

No.	Description	Unused	Used
27	2 c. rose (*a*)	50 0	35 0
28	2 c. rose (*b*)	15 0	15 0
29	2 c. rose (*f*)	7 6	7 6
30	2 c. rose (*g*)	10 0	10 0
31	2 c. rose (*o*)	15 0	15 0
32	2 c. rose (*p*)	25 0	
33	2 c. rose (*q*)	32 6	20 0
34	2 c. rose (*r*)	37 6	37 6
35	2 c. rose (*s*)	12 6	12 6
36	2 c. rose (*t*)	35 0	25 0
37	2 c. rose (*u*)	17 6	17 6
38	2 c. rose (*v*)	10 0	10 0

1883–89. *Overprinted with name in various types. Wmk. Crown CA.*

SELANGOR

No.	Description	Unused	Used
39	2 c. rose	2 0	2 0

SELANGOR

40 2 c. rose 5 0 5 0

SELANGOR

41 2 c. rose 7 6 8 6

SELANGOR. *With stop.*

42 2 c. rose 6 0 5 6

Without stop.

43 2 c. rose 1 0 0 6

Same overprint, but vertical. No stop.

44 2 c. rose 10 0

SELANGOR

45 2 c. rose 40 0 2 6
45a 5 c. blue .. .. ..

Selangor

46 2 c. rose £25

SELANGOR

47 2 c. rose £6 75 0

Overprinted vertically.

SELANGOR

48 2 c rose £6 17 6

Overprinted vertically.

SELANGOR

49 2 c. rose 40 0 10 0

Similar overprint, but diagonal.

50 2 c. rose . . .

Overprinted vertically SELANGOR

51 2 c. rose 8 0 1 9

As last, but horizontal.

51a 2 c. rose .. .. ..

1891. *Surcharged horizontally, with bar obliterating the value.*

SELANGOR
Two
CENTS

52 2 c. on 24 c. green 20 0

SELANGOR
Two
CENTS

53 2 c. on 24 c. green 10 0
a. Error "SELANGCR" ..

This error occurs in the first printing only and is No. 45 on the pane.

SELANGOR
Two
CENTS

54 2 c. on 24 c. green 18 6

SELANGOR
Two
CENTS

55 2 c. on 24 c. green 17 6

SELANGOR
Two
CENTS

56 2 c. on 24 c. green 4 0

1

1891–95. *T* **1.** *Wmk. Crown CA. P* 14.

57 1 c. green 0 8 0 6
58 2 c. rose 1 9 1 0
59 2 c. orange (1895) 1 0 1 3
60 5 c. blue 3 6 3 6

1894. *T* **1**, *surcharged* **3 CENTS** *in black.*

61 3 c. on 5 c. rose 1 3 1 3

2  3

1895–98. *P* 14. *T* **2.** *Wmk. Crown CA.*

62 3 c. dull pur. & carmine .. 0 6 0 4
63 5 c. dull pur. & olive-yellow 0 10 0 10
64 8 c. dull pur. & ultram. .. 4 0 4 0
65 10 c. dull pur. & orange .. 1 6 1 6
66 25 c. green and carmine .. 15 0 15 0
67 50 c. green and black .. 60 0 47 6
67a 50 c. dull pur. & greenish blk. 15 0 15 0

T **3.** *Wmk. Crown CC.*

68 $1 green & yellow-green .. 9 0 10 0
69 $2 green and carmine .. 47 6 42 6
70 $3 green and ochre 60 0 60 0
71 $5 green and blue 45 0 45 0
72 $10 green and purple £6 £6
73 $25 green and orange £14

One cent. (4) Three cents. (5)

1900. *Nos.* 63 *and* 67 *surcharged with T* **4** *or* **5.**

74 1 c. on 5 c. dull purple and olive-yellow .. 15 0 15 0
75 1 c. on 50 c. green & black .. 2 6 2 6
76 3 c. on 50 c. green & black .. 3 0 3 0

Varieties. (i.) *Word* " cent " *repeated at left.*

77 1 c. on 50 c. green & black .. £12

(ii.) *Surcharge double.*

78 1 c. on 50 c. green and black ..

(iii.) *Antique* " t " *in* " cents."

79 3 c. on 50 c. green & black .. 40 0 40 0

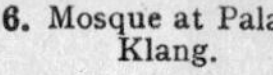

6. Mosque at Palace, Klang.

7. Sultan Suleiman.

1935–41. *Chalk-surfaced paper. Wmk. Mult. Script CA. P* 14.

No.	Type	Description	Unused	Used
80	6	1 c. black	0 3	0 2
81	„	2 c. green	0 9	0 2
82	„	4 c. orange	0 9	0 2
83	„	5 c. brown	0 9	0 2
84	„	6 c. scarlet	0 10	1 0
85	„	8 c. grey	1 3	0 8
86	„	10 c. dull purple	1 3	0 7
87	„	12 c. bright ultramarine ..	1 3	1 0
88	„	25 c. dull purple & scarlet ..	2 0	2 6
89	„	30 c. dull purple & orange ..	2 6	3 0
90	„	40 c. scarlet and dull pur. ..	3 0	3 6
91	„	50 c. black/*emerald*	4 6	2 6
92	7	$1 black and red/*blue* ..	6 0	3 0
93	„	$2 green and scarlet ..	12 6	3 6
94	„	$5 green & red/*emerald* ..	35 0	17 6

For other values and colours in this design see King George VI Catalogue.
Dates of issue as for Negri Sembilan.

SUNGEI UJONG.

(FEDERATED STATE.)

(1)

SUNGEI
UJONG
(2)

SUNGEI
UJONG
(3)

The ½ anna blue, India, with overprint T 1 is now believed not to have existed as an officially issued stamp.

Stamps of Straits Settlements.
Wmk. Crown CC.

1878. *Overprinted with T* **1**, *in black.*

No.	Description	Unused	Used
2	2 c. brown	£45	£40

1881–83. *Overprinted with letters* "S.U.", *in black.*

No.	Description	Unused	Used
3	2 c. brown		

1881–84. *Overprinted as T* **2**.

Varieties. (*a*) "S" *wide.* (*b*) *All letters narrow.* (*c*) *Letters* "N" *wide.* (*d*) "N," "E" *of* "SUNGEI," *and* "U," "NG" *of* "UJONG" *wide.* (*e*) "G," "J," *and* "O" *narrow.* (*f*) "GE" *and* "JO" *narrow.* (*g*) "S" *and* "JO" *narrow.* (*h*) "S" *and* "E" *wide.*

No.	Description	Unused	Used
4	2 c. brown (*a*)	30 0	
5	2 c. brown (*b*)	30 0	
6	2 c. brown (*c*)		
7	2 c. brown (*d*)	30 0	
8	2 c. brown (*e*)	30 0	
9	2 c. brown (*f*)	30 0	
9*a*	2 c. brown (*g*)		
10	4 c. rose (*a*)	£26	
11	4 c. rose (*b*)	£14	
2	4 c. rose (*h*)		

Overprinted as T **3**.

No.	Description	Unused	Used
13	2 c. brown (*a*)	£7	
14	2 c. brown (*b*)	20 0	
14*a*	2 c. brown (*c*)	£14	£14

Wmk. Crown CA.
Overprinted with letters "S.U."

No.	Description	Unused	Used
15	2 c. brown	55 0	
15*a*	4 c. rose	£35	

"S U" *without stops.*

No.	Description	Unused	Used
20	2 c. brown	42 6	

Overprinted with T **2**. *Varieties.* (*i*) "E" *wide.* (*k*) "N" *of* "UJONG" *wide.*

No.	Description	Unused	Used
23	2 c. brown (*a*)	£8	£6
24	2 c. brown (*b*)	£10	£6
25	2 c. rose (*a*)	17 6	15 0
26	2 c. rose (*b*)	20 0	20 0
27	2 c. rose (*h*)	10 0	10 0
28	2 c. rose (*i*)	10 0	10 0
29	2 c. rose (*k*)	10 0	10 0
30	8 c. orange (*a*)	£20	£18
31	8 c. orange (*b*)	£20	£18
32	10 c. slate (*a*)	£9	£6
33	10 c. slate (*b*)	£8	£8

Overprinted with T **3**.

No.	Description	Unused	Used
34	10 c. slate (*a*)		
35	10 c. slate (*b*)	—	£9

SUNGEI
UJONG
(4)

Overprinted with T **4**.

No.	Description	Unused	Used
36	2 c. rose (*b*)	12 6	12 6
37	2 c. rose (*h*)	12 6	12 6
38	2 c. rose (*i*)	12 6	12 6
39	4 c. brown (*b*)	70 0	70 0
40	4 c. brown (*h*)	60 0	
41	4 c. brown (*i*)	60 0	

With stop after "UJONG."

No.	Description	Unused	Used
42	2 c. brown (*b*)	12 6	
43	2 c. brown (*h*)	12 6	
44	2 c. brown (*k*)	12 6	

1885–90. *Overprinted with name in various types.*

SUNGEI
UJONG

Without stop.

No.	Description	Unused	Used
45	2 c. rose	7 6	

With stop.

No.	Description	Unused	Used
46	2 c. rose	10 0	
47	2 c. rose (error "UNJOG") ..	£40	£35

Sungei
Ujong

No.	Description	Unused	Used
48	2 c. rose	10 0	15 0

Variety. Overprint double.

No.	Description	Unused	Used
48*a*	2 c. rose	£8	£6

SUNGEI
UJONG

No.	Description	Unused	Used
49	2 c. rose	20 0	25 0

SUNGEI
UJONG

No.	Description	Unused	Used
50	2 c. rose	2 6	3 0

SUNGEI
UJONG

51 2 c. rose 7 6 8 6
a. Overprint double .. ..

SUNGEI
UJONG

52 2 c. rose (*long* " J ") 15 0 16 6

SUNGEI
UJONG

53 2 c. rose 2 6 2 6

SUNGEI
UJONG

54 2 c. rose 6 0 5 6

1891. *Name and value in four lines.* (*Name as on No.* 54.) *Line obliterating old value.*

55 **Two CENTS** on 24 c. green .. £6

No. 55 has the word " Two " as No. 56 and the word " cents " as No. 58.

SUNGEI
UJONG
Two
CENTS

56 2 c. on 24 c. green 60 0 60 0

SUNGEI
UJONG
Two
CENTS

57 2 c. on 24 c. green 70 0 70 0

SUNGEI
UJONG
Two
CENTS

58 2 c. on 24 c. green 35 0 35 0

5

6

1891–94. *T* 5. *Wmk. Crown CA.* *P* 14.

59 2 cents, rose 4 0 4 0
60 2 cents, orange (1894) .. 1 6 1 9
61 5 cents, blue 1 9 2 0

1894. *T* 5, *surcharged in black.* **1 (or 3) CENTS**

62 1 c. on 5 c. green 2 0 1 9
63 3 c. on 5 c. rose 1 9 2 6

1895. *T* 6. *Wmk. Crown CA.* *P* 14.

64 3 c. dull purple & carmine .. 1 6 1 6

Sungei Ujong was merged in Negri Sembilan in 1895.

TRENGGANU.

(UNFEDERATED STATE)

1. Sultan Zain ul ab din.

2. Sultan Zain ul ab din.

1910–19. *T* 1 *and* 2 ($5 *and* $25). *Wmk. Mult. Crown CA.* *P* 14.

1	1 c. blue-green, O	0 4	0 4
1*a*	1 c. green, O	0 4	0 3
2	2 c. brown & purple, C ('15)	0 6	0 8
3	3 c. carmine-red, O	1 3	1 3
4	4 c. orange, O	1 3	1 6
5	4 c. red-brn. & green, C ('15)	1 6	1 6
5*a*	4 c. carmine-red, O ('19) ..	1 0	1 0
6	5 c. grey, O	1 3	1 6
7	5 c. grey and brown, C ('15)	2 0	1 0
8	8 c. ultramarine, O	1 9	2 0
9	10 c. purple/*yellow*	1 9	2 0
	a. On pale yellow	2 0	2 6
10	10 c. green & red/*yell.*, O ('15)	2 6	2 6
11	20 c. dull & bright purple, C	1 9	2 0
12	25 c. green & dull pur., C ('15)	5 0	5 6
13	30 c. dull pur. & blk., C ('15)	5 6	6 0
14	50 c. black/*green*, C ..	5 6	6 6
15	$1 black & carmine/*blue*, C	12 0	12 6
16	$3 green & red/*green*, C ('15)	42 6	45 0
17	$5 green and dull purple, C	95 0	£6
18	$25 rose-carm. and green, C	£26	

RED CROSS

2c.
(3)

1917 (Oct.). *T* **1** *surcharged with T* **3**.

19	2 c. on 3 c. carmine-red ..	0	6	0	8
	a. Variety, "RED OROSS" ..				
	b. Variety "SS" in "CROSS" inverted	£4			
	c. Surcharge omitted (pair) ..	£18			
20	2 c. on 4 c. orange	0	9	1	6
	a. "SS" in "CROSS" inverted				
21	2 c. on 8 c. ultramarine ..	1	0	1	6

Errors. (i.) "csoss."

22	2 c. on 3 c. carmine-red ..	12	6		
23	2 c. on 4 c. orange ..	60	0		
24	2 c. on 8 c. ultramarine ..	40	0		

(ii.) *Comma after* "2 c,".

25	2 c. on 3 c. carmine-red ..	3	6		
26	2 c. on 4 c. orange	7	6		
27	2 c. on 8 c. ultramarine ..	7	6		

(iii.) "2" *in thick block type.*

27*a*	2 c. on 3 c. carmine-red ..	2	6	3	6

1918. *Colour changed.*

28	2 c. on 4 c. brown & green ..	1	6	2	0
	a. Variety, "RED IROSS" ..				
	b. Surcharge omitted (in pair) ..	£12			

In the first setting the error "csoss" for "cross" is on the first stamp on the second, fifth, and eighth rows, and on the bottom margin. The surcharge was set up in three rows—eighteen in all—repeated three times down the pane and then the bottom row of stamps overprinted from the top portion of this setting, one row of surcharges being on the stamps and the top portion of the second row being on the lower margins of the pane. Nos. 15 and 17 in each group have a comma after the "2 c,", and No. 7 in each group has a square stop after the "2 c."

The second setting has the "csoss" error corrected, but still shows six stamps on each pane with comma after "2 c,".

The third setting has all the comma errors corrected.

Variety No. 19*b* occurs on the margin below the 59th stamp on each pane.

During a temporary shortage in 1921, 2 c., 4 c. and 6 c. stamps of the Straits Settlements were authorised for use in Trengganu.

4. Sultan Suleiman. 5.

1921. *T* **4** *and* **5** ($5 *to* $100). *Chalk-surfaced paper. P* 14.

(*a*) *Wmk. Mult. Crown CA.*

29	$1 purple and blue/*blue* ..	8	6	8	6
30	$3 green and red/*emerald* ..	27	6	30	0
31	$5 green and red/*pale yellow* ..	25	0	32	6

(*b*) *Wmk. Mult. Script CA.*

32	2 c. green	0	4	0	4
33	4 c. carmine-red	0	6	0	6
34	5 c. grey and deep brown ..	1	9	0	10
35	10 c. bright blue			0	8
36	20 c. dull purple and orange ..	1	6	0	10
37	25 c. green and deep purple ..	1	9	1	9
38	30 c. dull purple and black ..	2	6	2	6
39	50 c. green & bright carmine ..	3	6	3	6
40	$25 purple and blue	£12		£14	
41	$50 green and yellow.. ..	£20			
42	$100 green and scarlet ..	£35			

1922. *Stamps of previous issues overprinted* "Malaya-Borneo Exhibition" *as T* **56** *of Straits Settlements, in black*

(*a*) *T* **1** *and* **2**.

43	5 c. grey and brown ..	1	0	1	6
44	10 c. green and red/*yellow* ..	2	0	2	6
45	20 c. dull and bright purple ..	3	6	4	6
46	25 c. green and dull purple ..	4	0	5	0
47	30 c. dull purple and black ..	5	0	6	0
48	50 c. black/*green*	6	0	7	6
49	$1 black and carmine/*blue*	17	6	18	0
50	$3 green and red/*green* ..	£5		£6	
51	$5 green and dull purple ..	£12		£15	

(*b*) *T* **4**.

52	2 c. green	0	10	1	0
53	4 c. carmine-red	1	0	1	3

Minor varieties of this overprint exist as in Straits Settlements (*q.v.*).

924–29. *Chalk-surfaced paper. Wmk. Mult. Script CA. P* 14.

54	**4**	1 c. black ('26)	0	2	0	2
55	,,	3 c. green ('26) ..	0	6	0	6
57	,,	5 c. purple/*yellow* ('26) ..	0	6	0	4
58	,,	6 c. orange (1924)	0	6	0	7
60	,,	12 c. bright ultramarine ('26)	1	3	1	3
61	,,	35 c. carmine/*yellow* ('26) ..	3	0	3	6
62	,,	$1 pur. & blue/*blue* ('29) ..	7	6	7	6
63	,,	$3 green and red/*green* ('26)	22	6	25	0

For other colours and values in T **4** and **5**, see King George VI Catalogue.

II. COMBINED ISSUES.

FEDERATED MALAY STATES.

PRINTERS. All the stamps of the Federated Malay States were typographed by De La Rue & Co.

FEDERATED MALAY STATES (1)   FEDERATED MALAY STATES (2)

1900. *Stamps of the Protected States overprinted with T* **1** (*cent values*) *or* **2** (*dollar values*), *in black.*

(*a*) *Stamps of* Negri Sembilan.

1	1 c. dull purple & green ..	1	9	2	0
2	2 c. dull purple & brown ..	4	0	4	6
3	3 c. dull purple & black ..	2	0	2	6
4	5 c. dull pur. & olive-yellow ..	27	6	30	0
5	10 c. dull purple & orange ..	5	0	6	0
6	20 c. green and olive	25	0	25	0
7	25 c. green and carmine ..	40	0	40	0
8	50 c. green and black	35	0	35	0

(*b*) *Stamps of* Perak.

9	5 c. dull purple & olive-yellow	10	6	10	6
10	10 c. dull purple and orange ..	25	0	25	0
	a. Bar omitted				
11	$1 green and pale green ..	17	6	17	6
12	$2 green and carmine ..	32	6	32	6
12*a*	$5 green and ultramarine ..	£7		£7	
12*b*	$25 green and orange ..	£70			

3

4

1900–1. *Perf.* 14. *T* **3.** *Wmk. Crown CA, sideways* (1901).

No.	Description				
13	1 c. black and green	0	8	0	3
13a	1 c. grey and green	0	10	0	2
14	3 c. black and brown	1	0	0	4
14a	3 c. grey and brown	1	0	0	4
15	4 c. black and carmine ..	2	0	0	6
15a	4 c. grey and carmine ..	2	6	0	6
16	5 c. green & carm./*yellow* ..	2	6	0	10
17	8 c. black & ultramarine ..	5	0	3	0
17a	8 c. grey-brn. and ultram. ..	5	0	4	0
18	10 c. black and claret.. ..	4	6	2	6
18a	10 c. black and purple ..	6	0	2	6
19	20 c. mauve and black ..	8	6	4	6
20	50 c. black & orange-brown ..	22	6	10	0
20a	50 c. grey-brn. & oran.-brn. ..	27	6	10	6

Later printings in 1903–4 show the two upper lines of shading in the background at the corner nearest to the "S" of "STATE" blurred and running into one another, whereas in earlier printings these lines are distinct. Two plates were used for printing the central design of T 3. In Plate 1 the lines of background are regular throughout, but in Plate 2 they are lighter around the head and back of the tiger. The 5 c. was the only value with single wmk. to be printed from Plate 2. Stamps with multiple wmk. were printed for a short time from Plate 1, and show the two blurred lines of background near "S" of "STATE," but the majority of these stamps were printed from Plate 2 and later plates.

T **4.** *Wmk. Crown CC* (1900).

No.	Description				
21	$1 green and pale green ..	20	0	12	6
22	$2 green and carmine ..	32	6	17	6
23	$5 green & bright ultram. ..	75	0	30	0
23a	$5 green & pale ultramarine ..	75	0	30	0
24	$25 green and orange ..	£18		£10	

1904–10. *T* **3** *and* **4.** *Wmk. Multiple Crown CA* (*sideways in T* **3.**) *P* 14.

No.	Description				
25	1 c. black & grn., O (10.04)	3	6	0	6
25a	1 c. grey-brown & green, O	3	0	0	6
26	3 c. grey & brown, OC (1.05)	3	6	0	4
26a	3 c. grey-brown & brown, C	5	0	0	3
27	4 c. black & scarlet, O (10.04)	2	0	0	3
27a	4 c. black and rose, O ..	1	9	0	3
27b	4 c. black and deep rose, O (*aniline*) (1909)	—		0	3
28	5 c. green & carmine/*yellow*, OC (June '05)	3	6	1	3
28a	5 c. dp. grn. & carm./*yell.*, O	2	6	0	8
	b. On pale yellow	8	6	0	10
29	8 c. grey & ultram., OC (Mar. '05)	4	6	3	0
	a. Wmk. upright	16	0	12	6
30	10 c. black & claret, OC (10.04)	2	6	0	4
31	10 c. grey and purple, OC ..	3	6	0	4
31a	10 c. jet-black & brt. pur., O	3	0	0	6
32	20 c. mauve & black, OC (3.05)	3	0	0	6
33	50 c. blk. & orange-brown, OC (Mar. '05)	6	0	2	6
34	$1 green & pale grn., C ('07)	12	6	7	6
35	$2 green and carmine, C ..	25	0	12	6
36	$5 green and blue, C ..	45	0	20	0
37	$25 green & orge., C (1910)	£15		£9	

1906–18. *T* **3.** *Wmk. Mult. Crown CA.* *P* 14.

No.	Description				
38	1 c. green, O (Die I) (1906)	1	9	0	3
38a	1 c. green, O (Die II) ..	1	0	0	2
38b	1 c. yellow-green, O (Die II)	1	3	0	2
38c	1 c. blue-green, O (Die II) ..	1	3	0	2
39	3 c. brown, O (July '06) ..	2	0	0	2
40	3 c. carmine, O (Feb. '09) ..	2	0	0	1
40a	3 c. scarlet, O (1918) ..	2	6	0	1
41	8 c. ultramarine, O (Mar. '10)	5	6	1	3
41a	8 c. deep blue, O	6	6	1	6

Die I of the 1 c. was printed at two operations from the old "head" and duty plates; Die II from a new combined plate, in one operation. They can be distinguished as follows: Die I, thick line under "MALAY"; serifs distinct. The "1c" has short serifs to "1," and the "c" is thinner than in Die II. Die II has thin line under "MALAY"; serifs are not distinct, and "1c" has longer serifs and a thicker "c." Other values from this date are all from double plates, except 2 c., 3 c. and 4 c.

1919. *T* **3.** *Colours changed and new values.*

No.	Description				
42	1 c. deep brown, O	0	4	0	3
43	2 c. green, O (July 1919) ..	0	6	0	3
43a	2 c. deep yellow-green, O ..	0	6	0	3
44	3 c. grey, O (18.12.19) ..	0	9	0	4
45	4 c. scar., O (Die I) (12.2.19)	1	3	0	3
45a	4 c. scarlet, O (Die II) ..	0	9	0	1
46	6 c. orange, O (12.2.19) ..	1	6	0	6
47	10 c. deep blue, O	2	0	0	5
48	10 c. bright blue, O	1	9	0	5

1922–28. *T* **3** *and* **4.** (*a*) *Wmk. Mult. Script CA.*

No.	Description				
49	1 c. deep brown, O (Sept. '22)	0	5	0	2
50	3 c. grey, O (Feb. '23) ..	1	0	0	9
51	4 c. car.-red, O (Die II)(2.24)	0	9	0	2
52	5 c. mauve/*pale yell.*, O (3.22)	0	8	0	2
53	6 c. orange, O (Aug. 1922) ..	1	6	0	4
54	10 c. bright blue, O (Mar. '23)	1	9	0	3
55	12 c. ultram., O (Sept. 1922)	1	9	0	3
56	20 c. dull purple and black, OC (Mar. '23)	3	0	0	5
57	50 c. black & orge., C (Apr. '24)	5	0	1	9
58	$1 pale green & grn., C ('26)	15	0	6	0
58a	$1 grey-grn. & emer., C ('27)	8	6	2	6
58b	$2 green & carm., C (1926)	15	0	6	0
59	$5 green & blue, C (1925) ..	35	0	15	0
59a	$25 green & orange, C (1928)	£9		£9	

(*b*) *Wmk. Mult. Crown CA.*

No.	Description				
60	35 c. scarlet/*pale yell.*, O (1922)	8	6	6	0

The 5 c. in mauve on white Script paper is the result of soaking early printings of No. 52 in water.

1923–34. *T* **3.** *New values, colours and type changed. Wmk. Mult. Script CA.*

No.	Description				
61	1 c. black, O (June 1923) ..	0	3	0	2
62	2 c. brown, O (1925) ..	0	7	0	5
63	2 c. green, O (1926)	0	3	0	1
64	3 c. green, O (March 1924)	1	3	0	4
65	3 c. brown, O (1927) ..	0	7	0	1
66	4 c. orange, O (1926) ..	0	5	0	2
66a	5 c. brown, O (1932) ..	0	6	0	2
67	6 c. scarlet, O (1926) ..	0	9	0	1
68	10 c. blk. & blue, O (Oct. '23)	1	6	0	4
69	10 c. purple/*pale yellow*, C ('31)	1	6	0	3
70	25 c. pur. & brt. mag., C ('29)	3	6	0	6
71	30 c. pur. & orge.-yell., C ('29)	4	0	1	3
72	35 c. scarlet/*pale yell.*, O ('28)	10	0	5	0
72a	35 c. scarlet & purple, C ('31)	12	6	6	6
73	50 c. black/*green*, C ('31) ..	4	6	0	10
74	$1 black & red/*blue*, C ('31)	5	6	1	9
75	$2 green & red/*yell.*, C ('34)	12	6	5	6
76	$5 green & red/*grn.*, C ('34)	77	6	52	6

POSTAGE DUE STAMPS.

D 1

1924 (1 Jan.)–**1926.** *Type* D 1. *Wmk. Mult. Script CA (sideways).* P 15 × 14.

D1	1 c. violet	0 4	0 6
D2	2 c. black	0 4	0 6
D2a	4 c. green (1926)	0 5	0 7
D3	8 c. red	0 8	1 0
D4	10 c. orange	1 3	1 9
D5	12 c. blue	2 0	1 0

SUDAN.

(Anglo-Egyptian Condominium.)

السودان
SOUDAN
(1)

1897. (1 Mar.). *Contemporary stamps of Egypt overprinted as T* 1, *in black.*

1	1 mil. pale brown	2 0	2 0
	a. Inverted	£6	
2	1 mil. deep brown	2 0	2 0
3	2 mils. green	1 6	2 0
4	3 mils. orange-yellow	2 0	2 6
5	5 mils. rose-carmine	4 0	4 0
	a. Inverted	£8	
6	1 pias. ultramarine	6 0	7 0
7	2 pias. orange-brown	25 0	25 0
8	5 pias. slate	25 0	22 6
	a. "SOUDAN" only double ..		
9	10 pias. mauve	22 6	22 6

There are six varieties of the overprint on each value, most of which can be supplied in vertical strips at double the catalogue price.

In some printings the large dot is omitted from the left-hand Arabic character. This has been noted on Nos. 41, 47, and 50 on different sheets.

The overprint was frequently misplaced, and pairs may be found with and without it, and also with the overprint diagonal.

2. Arab Postman.

3

(Des. Col. E. A. Stanton, C.M.G. Typo. De La Rue.)

1898 (1 Mar.). *T* 2. *W* 3. *P* 14.

10	1 mil. brown and pink ..	1 3	0 6
11	2 mils. green and brown ..	2 6	3 0
12	3 mils. mauve and green ..	3 0	3 0
13	5 mils. carmine and black ..	1 3	0 6
14	1 pias. blue and brown ..	4 6	3 6
15	2 pias. black and blue ..	10 0	1 3
16	5 pias. brown and green ..	12 6	3 0
17	10 pias. black and mauve ..	20 0	5 0

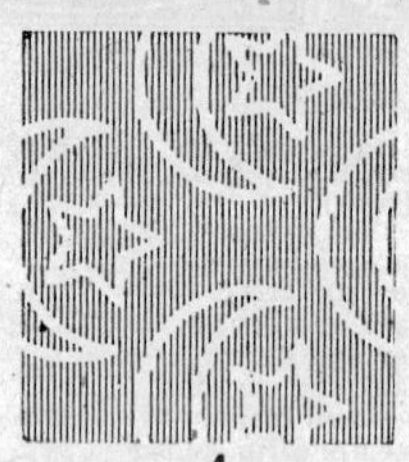

4

1902–11. *T* 2. *W* 4. *P* 14.

18	1 m. brown & carm. (5.05) ..	1 0	0 8
19	2 m. green & brown (11.02) ..	1 0	1 0
20	3 m. mauve & green (7.03) ..	1 3	1 3
21	4 m. blue & bistre (20.1.07) ..	1 6	1 6
22	4 m. verm. & brown (10.07) ..	6 0	5 0
23	5 m. scarlet & black (12.03) ..	2 0	0 4
24	1 pi. blue and brown (12.03)	5 0	0 6
25	2 pi. black and blue (2.08) ..	10 0	0 9
26	5 pi. brown & green, OC (2.08)	10 0	0 9
27	10 pi. blk. & mauve, OC (2.11)	15 0	2 6

5 Milliemes
(5)

1903 (Sept.). *No.* 16 *surcharged at Khartoum with T* 5, *in blocks of* 30, *in black.*

28	5 m. on 5 pi. brown & green	2 0	1 6
	a. Inverted	£8	£5

1921 (22 Dec.). *As* 1902–11. *Colours changed.*

29	2 pi. purple & orange-yell., C	5 0	1 6

6

7

(Typo. De La Rue & Co.)

1921–22. *T* 6. *Chalk-surfaced paper.* W 4. P 14.

30	1 m. black & orange (4.2.22)	0 8	0 8
31	2 m. yell.-orge. & choc. (1922)	2 6	1 0
31a	2 m. yellow and chocolate ..	1 3	1 3
32	3 m. mauve & grn. (25.1.22) ..	1 6	1 3
33	4 m. grn. & choc. (21.3.22) ..	1 9	2 6
34	5 m. olive-brn. & blk. (4.2.22)	2 6	0 4
35	10 m. carmine and blk. (1922)	5 0	0 10
36	15 m. bright blue and chestnut (14.12.21)	5 0	1 0

1927–40. *W* 7. *P* 14.

37	6	1 m. black & orange, CO	0 2	0 3
38	,,	2 m. orange & choc., CO	0 2	0 3
39	,,	3 m. mauve and green, CO	0 4	0 4
40	,,	4 m. green & chocolate, C	0 4	0 5

41	6	5 m. olive-brn. & blk., CO	0	6	0	3
42	,,	10 m. carmine and black, C	0	8	0	3
43	,,	15 m. brt. blue & chestnut, C	1	0	0	6
44	2	2 p. pur. & orange-yell., C	1	3	0	5
44a	,,	3 p. red-brown and blue	2	0	1	6
44b	,,	4 p. ultram. & black, C ..	2	6	1	6
45	,,	5 p. chestnut & green, C	3	0	1	0
45a	,,	6 p. grn'ish bl. & blk., CO	3	6	2	6
45b	,,	8 p. emerald & black, CO	4	6	3	0
46	,,	10 p. black & violet, CO ..	6	0	2	0
46a	,,	20 p. pale blue & blue, CO	12	0	10	0

The ordinary paper of Nos. 37–46a is thick, smooth and opaque and is a wartime substitute for chalky.

Dates of issue: 1927 (all except the following) —17.10.35, 20 p. 2.11.36, 4 p., 6 p. and 8 p. 1.1.40, 3 p.

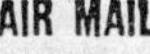

(8)

AIR MAIL

(9)

1931. *Air stamps. Stamps of 1927–28 overprinted with T* **8** *or* **9** (2 p.).

47	5 m. olive-brn. & blk. (1.3.31)	3	6	3	6
48	10 m. carmine & blk. (15.2.31)	4	6	5	0
49	p. pur. & orge.-yell. (15.2.31)	6	0	7	6

10. Statue of Gen. Gordon.

(Recess. De La Rue & Co., Ltd.)

1931 (22 Aug.)–**1935.** *Air. W* **7.** *P* 14.

49a	10	3 m. green & sepia (1.1.33)	12	0	12	0
50	,,	5 m. black and green ..	12	0	12	0
51	,,	10 m. black and carmine ..	15	0	15	0
52	,,	15 m. red-brown & sepia ..	6	6	7	6
53	,,	2 p. black and orange ..	2	6	2	6
53b	,,	2½ p. mag. & blue (1.1.33)	9	0	7	6
54	,,	3 p. black and grey ..	12	6	12	6
55	,,	3½ p. black and violet ..	17	6	18	6
56	,,	4½ p. red-brown and grey	60	0	65	0
57	,,	5 p. black & ultramarine	17	6	17	6
57b	,,	7½ p. green and emerald (17.10.35)	15	0	16	0
57d	,,	10 p. brown & greenish blue (17.10.35)	30	0	27	6

For similar stamps, perf. 11½×12½, see King George VI Catalogue.

2½ 2½

AIR MAIL

٢ ١/٢ ٢ ١/٢

(11)

1932 (18 July). *Air stamp. No. 44 surcharged with T* **11.**

58	2½ pi. on 2 pi. pur. & orge.-yell.	25	0	27	6

12. Gen. Gordon.

13. Gordon Memorial College, Khartoum.

14. Gordon Memorial Service, Khartoum.

(Recess. De La Rue.)

1935 (1 Jan.). *50th Anniv. of Death of Genera Gordon. W* **7.** *P* 14.

59	12	5 m. green	2	0	2	0
60	,,	10 m. yellow-brown ..	2	6	3	0
61	,,	13 m. ultramarine ..	15	0	12	6
62	,,	15 m. scarlet	6	0	7	6
63	13	2 p. blue	6	0	7	6
64	,,	5 p. orange-vermilion ..	8	6	12	6
65	,,	10 p. purple	17	6	22	6
66	14	20 p. black	85	0	95	0
67	,,	50 p. red-brown	£10		£12	

7½ PIASTRES

٧ ١/٢ قروش

(15)

1935. *Air. Surcharged as T* **15.**

68	10	15 m. on 10 m. black and carmine (Apr.) ..	1	3	1	9
		a. Surcharge double ..				
69	,,	2½ p. on 3 m. grn. and sepia (Apr.)	5	0	6	0
		a. Second Arabic letter from left missing	37	0	50	0
		b. Small "½"	8	6	10	0
70	,,	2½ p. on 5 m. blk. & grn. (Apr.)	2	0	2	6
		a. Second Arabic letter from left missing	30	0	35	0
		b. Small "½"	7	6	8	6
		c. Surcharge inverted ..				
		d. ditto, with variety a. ..				
		e. ditto, with variety b. ..				
71	,,	3 p. on 4½ p. red-brown and grey (Apr.) ..	4	0	6	6

72 10 7½ p. on 4½ p. red-brown and grey (Mar.) .. 10 0 12 6
73 „ 10 p. on 4½ p. red-brown and grey (Mar.) .. 6 6 8 6

POSTAGE DUE STAMPS.

1897 (1 Mar.). *Stamps of Egypt, Type* D 3. *Wmk. Star and Crescent, T* 12. *P* 14. *Overprinted with T* 1, *in black.*

D1 2 mils. green 2 6 1 9
D2 4 mils. marone 1 9 1 9
D3 1 pias. ultramarine 4 0 4 0
D4 2 pias. orange.. .. .. 6 0 6 0

Varieties are known with the large dot omitted in the first Arabic character on left.

The 4 mils. and the 2 pias. are known bisected and used for half their value.

D 1. Gunboat *Zafir.*

(Typo. De La Rue & Co.)

1901 (1 Jan.). *Type* D 1. *W* 4. *P* 14.

D5 2 m. black and brown, OC 0 3 0 4
D6 4 m. brown and green, OC 1 3 0 8
D7 10 m. green and mauve, OC 1 3 0 8
D8 20 m. ultramar. & carmine, O 1 6 1 3

1927-30. *Type* D 1. *W* 7. *P* 14.

D 9 2 m. black and brown ('30) 0 2 0 3
D10 4 m. brown and green .. 0 4 0 5
D11 10 m. green and mauve .. 0 8 0 10

OFFICIAL STAMPS.

1900 (8 Feb.). *The* 5 *mils. of* 1897 *punctured* "S G" *by hand. The* "S" *has* 14 *and the* "G" 12 *holes.*

O1 5 m. rose-carmine 20 0 0 8

1901 (Jan.). *The* 1 *m. wmk. Quatrefoil, punctured as No.* O1.

O2 1 m. brown and pink .. 4 6 2 6

O.S.G.S. (O 1) **O.S.G.S.** (O 2)

1902. *No.* 10 *overprinted in black at Khartoum as Type* O 1 (*on Sudan Government Service*) *in groups of* 30 *stamps.*

O3 1 m. brown and pink .. 7 6 6 0
a. Oval "O". No. 19 in setting of 30 .. .. .. £7
b. Round stops. Nos. 25 to 30 30 0 12 6
c. Inverted £7
d. Inverted and oval "O" ..
e. Inverted and round stops ..
f. Double £8
g. Double and round stops ..
h. Double and oval "O" ..

T 2 *overprinted as Type* O 2, *in black, by De La Rue & Co. in sheets of* 120 *stamps.*

1903-12. (i.) *Wmk. Quatrefoil.* (Mar., 1906)

O 4 10 pias. black and mauve .. 6 0 7 0

(ii.) *Wmk. Mult. Star and Crescent.*

O 5 1 m. brown & carm. (9.04) 0 6 0 4
a. Overprint double .. ..
O 6 3 m. mauve & grn. (Feb., '04) 0 8 0 9
a. Overprint double .. ..
O 7 5 m. scarlet & black (1.1.03) 0 9 0 3
O 8 1 pi. blue & brown (1.1.03) 2 0 0 3
O 9 2 pi. black & blue (1.1.03) .. 4 0 0 6
O10 5 pi. brown & green (1.1.03) 7 6 2 0
O11 10 pi. black & mauve (9.12) 4 6 5 0

ARMY SERVICE.

ARMY (A 1) — OFFICIAL ARMY (A 2) — Army OFFICIAL Service (A 3)

1905 (Jan.). *T* 2 *overprinted at Khartoum as Types A* 1 *and A* 2, *in black. Wmk. Mult. Star and Crescent.*

[In each setting of 30 stamps, No. 29 has a note of exclamation for first "I" in "OFFICIAL," and Nos. 6 and 12 are Type A 2.]

(i.) "ARMY" *reading up.*

A1 1 m. brown and carm. (A 1) 5 0 2 0
a. With "!" for "I" .. 50 0 37 6
b. Type A 2 .. .. .. 30 0 17 6

(ii.) *Overprint horizontal.*

A2 1 m. brown & carm. (A 1) £10
a. "!" for "I" .. ..
b. Type A 2 .. .. ..

(iii.) "ARMY" *reading down.*

A3 1 m. brown & carm. (A 1) .. 50 0 25 0
a. "!" for "I" .. ..
b. Type A 2 .. .. ..

1905 (Nov.). *As No.* A1, *but wmk. Quatrefoil.*

A4 1 m. brown & carm. (A 1) .. £5 70 0
a. "!" for "I" .. ..
b. Type A 2 .. ..

1906 (Jan.)-**1911.** *T* 2 *overprinted as Type* A 3, *in black.*

(i.) *Wmk. Multiple Star and Crescent.*

Two varieties of the 1 *mil.*

A. First printing "Army" and "Service" 14 mm. apart.
B. Later printings "Army" and "Service" 12 mm. apart.

All other values are Type B.

A 5 1 m. brown & carm. (Type A) £8 £6
A 6 1 m. brown & carm. (Type B) 3 0 0 10
a. Double .. .. ..
b. Inverted .. .. — £12
c. Pair, with and without overprint .. .. ..
d. "Service" omitted ..
A 7 2 m. green and brown .. 5 0 0 8
a. Pair, with and without overprint .. .. ..
b. "Army" omitted .. ..
A 8 3 m. mauve and green .. 5 0 1 3
a. Inverted .. ..
A 9 5 m. scarlet and black .. 3 0 0 4
a. Double £7 £5
b. Inverted .. .. .. — £20
c. Error. "Amry" ..
d. "A" for "A" in "Army" — £7
e. Double, one inverted .. £20 £12
A10 1 pi. blue and brown .. 4 6 0 8
a. "Army" omitted ..
A11 2 pi. black & blue (Jan., '09) 12 6 2 6
A12 5 pi. brown & grn. (May, '08) 50 0 15 0
A13 10 pi. black & mve. (May, '11) £18 £15

There are a number of printings of these Army Service stamps; the earlier are as Type A 3; the 1908 printing has a narrower "A" in "Army," and the 1910-11 printings have the tail of the "y" in "Army" much shorter.

(ii.) *Wmk. Quatrefoil,* T 3.

A14	2 pi. black and blue ..	20 0	3 0
A15	5 pi. brown and green ..	70 0	37 6
A16	10 pi. black and mauve	£8	£8

Since 1913 a number of stamps have been issued punctured "S G" (Sudan Government) or "A S" (Army Service), but we do not stock these varieties.

SWAZILAND.

I. Provisional Government under joint protection of Great Britain and the South African Republic (Transvaal).

1

1889 (18 Oct.). T **1**. *Stamps of the South African Republic (Transvaal) overprinted* **"Swazieland".**

(A) *Black overprint.* (*a*) P 12½ × 12.

1	1d. carmine	8 0	7 0
	a. Opt. inverted	60 0	60 0
2	2d. olive-bistre	50 0	7 6
	a. Opt. inverted		
	b. "Swazielan"	£6	80 0
3	1s. green	5 0	5 6
	a. Opt. inverted	30 0	30 0

(*b*) P 12½.

4	½d. grey	4 0	4 0
	a. Opt. inverted	60 0	60 0
	b. "Swazielan"	£7	£6
	c. "Swazielan" inverted ..	—	£10
5	2d. olive-bistre	5 0	5 0
	a. Opt. inverted	90 0	90 0
	b. "Swazielan"	£6	
	c. "Swazielan" inverted ..	—	£12
6	6d. blue	7 0	7 0
7	2s. 6d. buff	35 0	35 0
8	5s. slate-blue	35 0	40 0
	a. Opt. inverted	£12	
	b. "Swazielan"	£20	
	c. "Swazielan" inverted ..		
9	10s. fawn	£12	£12

The variety without "d" occurs on the stamp at the left-hand bottom corner of each sheet of certain printings.

1892 (Aug.). (B) *Carmine overprint.* P 12½.

10	½d. grey	4 0	4 6
	a. Opt. inverted	35 0	
	b. Opt. double	45 0	

In 1894–95 reprints of the above stamps were made in the Government Printing Works at Pretoria. These have a stop after the name.

In 1894 the South African Republic was, under a convention, given powers of protection and administration over Swaziland, but it was not incorporated. On 7 Nov. of that year the stamps were recalled from use. On 5 June, 1903, authority over Swaziland was conferred on the Governor of the Transvaal, and on 1 Dec., 1906, this authority was transferred to the High Commissioner for South Africa, Swaziland being considered as a British Protectorate. In 1933 stamps were again issued (*see below*).

II. British Protectorate.

2

(Des. Rev. C. C. Tugman. Recess. De La Rue.)

1933 (2 Jan.). T **2**. *Wmk. Mult. Script CA.* P 14.

11	½d. green	0 4	0 5
12	1d. carmine	0 5	0 6
13	2d. brown	1 2	1 6
14	3d. blue	1 8	1 8
15	4d. orange	2 6	3 0
16	6d. bright purple	5 0	5 0
17	1s. olive	8 0	5 0
18	2s. 6d. bright violet ..	20 0	22 6
19	5s. grey	30 0	32 6
20	10s. sepia	65 0	70 0

1935 (4 May). *Silver Jubilee. As* T **13** *of Antigua, inscribed* "SWAZILAND". *Recess. B.W.&.Co. Wmk. Mult. Script CA.* P 11 × 12.

21	1d. deep blue and scarlet ..	0 6	1 0
22	2d. ultram. and grey-black ..	2 6	3 0
23	3d. brown and deep blue ..	3 0	5 0
24	6d. slate and purple	5 0	8 0

All values exist with "double flagstaff" variety.

POSTAGE DUE STAMPS.

D 1

(Typo. De La Rue & Co.)

1933. *Type* D 1. *Wmk. Mult. Script CA.* P 14.

D1	1d. carmine	0 2	0 3
D2	2d. pale violet	0 3	0 5

TANGANYIKA.

(Formerly German East Africa.)

1915. *German East African fiscal stamps.* "Statistik des Waaren-Verkehrs" (*Trade Statistical Charge*) *overprinted in bluish green,* "O.H.B.M.S. Mafia" *in a circle.*

1	24 pesa, vermilion/*buff* ..	Set of 5, un., £75.
2	12½ heller, drab	
3	25 heller, dull green	
4	50 heller, slate	
5	1 rupee, lilac	

German East African "Ubersetzungs-Gebühren" (*Translation-fee*) *stamp, overprinted as before.*

6	25 heller, grey	£25

Stamps as above, but with further overprint of "G.R.—Post-Mafia," *in three lines, in green.*

No.	Description		
7	24 pesa, vermilion/*buff*	..	
8	12½ heller, drab	..	
9	25 heller, dull green	..	
10	50 heller, slate	..	
11	1 rupee, lilac	..	
12	25 heller, grey (No. 6)	..	

1915-16. *Stamps of India,* 1911-13, *overprinted* "I.E.F." *in black, with a further overprint of* "G.R.—Post—Mafia," *in three lines, in green.*

No.	Description		
13	3 pies, grey	7 6	10 0
	a. Inverted	50 0	
	b. Sideways	50 0	
	c. Pair, one stamp without opt.	£6	
14	½ a. green	8 6	10 0
	a. Inverted	40 0	
	b. Double	60 0	
	c. Sideways	40 0	
15	1 a. carmine	12 6	15 0
	a. Sideways	40 0	
	b. Double	50 0	
	c. Inverted	40 0	
16	2 a. mauve	20 0	25 0
	a. Inverted	£5	
17	2½ a. ultramarine	22 6	50 0
	a. Inverted	80 0	
18	3 a. orange-brown	20 0	20 0
	a. Sideways	£5	
	b. Double	£5	
	c. Inverted	£5	
19	4 a. olive	35 0	50 0
	a. Inverted	£10	
20	8 a. purple	60 0	75 0
	a. Inverted	£10	
21	12 a. dull claret	£8	£9
	a. Inverted	£12	
22	1 r. brown and green	£6	£7
	a. Inverted	£12	

The overprint, which is handstruck, appears in greenish black, dull blue, or almost black.

Stamps of India, 1911-13, *overprinted* "I.E.F." *in black, with further three-line overprint* "*G.R.—POST—MAFIA*" *in italics.*

No.	Description	
23	3 pies, grey	80 0
24	½ a. green	80 0
25	1 a. carmine	90 0
26	2 a. mauve	90 0
27	2½ a. ultramarine	£5
28	3 a. orange-brown	£5
29	4 a. olive	£6
30	8 a. purple	£6
31	12 a. dull claret	£8
32	1 r. brown and green	£10

Mafia Island was captured by the British from the Germans about January, 1915. Letters were first sent out unstamped, but the post office at Zanzibar objected to this, and sent the military various handstamps to overprint the German fiscal stamps that had been seized. The stamps were issued at Kilindini Harbour. When the German fiscals were exhausted, the "I.E.F." on India were used, and also ordinary Indian stamps.

Stamps of Nyasaland, **T 15**, *overprinted*

N. F. *in black.*

No.	Description		
33	½d. green	1 9	3 0
34	1d. scarlet	1 0	1 9
35	3d. purple/*yellow*	6 0	9 0
	a. Overprint double	£50	
36	4d. black and red/*yellow*	20 0	27 6
37	1s. black/*green*	47 6	45 0

This issue was sanctioned for use by the Nyasa-Rhodesian Force in conquered territory in German East Africa.

Of No. 35*a* only six copies were printed, these being the bottom row on one pane issued at M'bamba Bay F.P.O., German East Africa.

G.E.A. **G.E.A.** G.E.A.
(1) (2) (3)

1917-22. *Stamps of Kenya and Uganda,* **T 3** *and* **4** *optd. with* **T 1** *and* **2**, *in black, red* (R.) *or vermilion* (V.). *Wmk. Mult. Crown CA.*

No.	Description		
38	1 c. black, O (R.)	0 1	0 2
39	1 c. black, O (V.)	10 0	10 0
40	3 c. green, O	0 2	0 2
41	6 c. scarlet, O	0 4	0 3
42	10 c. orange, O	0 8	0 4
43	12 c. slate-grey, O	1 3	1 6
44	15 c. bright blue, O	1 0	1 6
45	25 c. blk. & red/*yellow*, C	1 3	1 9
	a. On pale yellow (1921)	1 9	1 9
46	50 c. black and lilac, C	3 0	3 0
47	75 c. black/*blue-green., olive back*, C (R.)	4 6	4 6
	a. On emerald back	6 0	8 6
48	1 r. black/*green*, C (R.)	5 0	6 0
	a. On emerald back	7 0	8 6
49	2 r. red and black/*blue*, C	9 0	12 0
50	3 r. violet and green, C	8 6	12 0
51	4 r. red & green/*yellow*, C	15 0	17 6
52	5 r. blue and dull purple, C	15 0	20 0
53	10 r. red & green/*green*, C	37 6	42 6
	a. On emerald back	52 6	62 6
54	20 r. black & purple/*red*, C	90 0	£5
55	50 r. carmine and green, C	£12	£16

The rupee values exist with very large stop after the "E" in "G.E.A.," and also with round, or very small stop in the same position.

The later printings of the "cent" values (except 6 c.) and of the 1 r., 3 r. and 10 r., have the overprint in heavier and more regular type.

1921. *As* 1917-22 *but wmk. Mult. Script CA.*

No.	Description		
60	12 c. slate-grey, O	1 0	1 6
61	15 c. bright blue, O	1 2	1 6
63	50 c. black & dull purple, C	4 0	4 6
66	2 r. red and black/*blue*, C	12 0	17 6
67	3 r. violet and green, C	15 0	18 6
68	5 r. blue and dull purple, C	35 0	40 0

1922. **T 3** *of Kenya and Uganda overprinted by the Government printer at Dar-es-Salaam with* **T 3**, *in black or red* (**R.**) *Wmk. Mult. Script CA.*

No.	Description		
72	1 c. black (R.)	0 6	0 6
73	10 c. orange-yellow	1 0	1 3

4

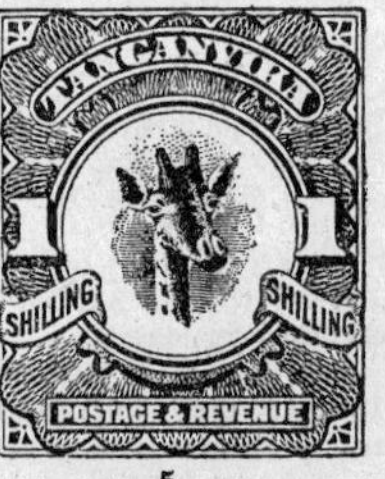

5

(Recess. Bradbury, Wilkinson & Co.)

1922. **T 4** ("cents" *values) and* **5**. *Head in black. Wmk. Mult. Script CA.* A. *Sideways.* B. *Upright.* (*a*) *P* 15 × 14.

No.	Description		B
74	5 c. slate-purple	0 8	0 4
75	10 c. green	0 10	0 4
76	15 c. carmine-red	1 0	0 4
77	20 c. orange	2 0	0 6
78	25 c. black	12 0	7 6
79	30 c. blue	2 6	2 6
80	40 c. yellow-brown	5 6	4 6
81	50 c. slate-grey	5 0	3 0
82	75 c. yellow-bistre	6 0	6 6

(*b*) *P* 14.

		A		B	
83	1s. green ..	12 0	12 0	10 0	10 0
84	2s. purple ..	15 0	15 0	12 6	12 6
85	3s. black ..	20 0	20 0	†	
86	5s. scarlet ..	47 6	50 0	25 0	25 0
87	10s. deep blue	75 0	77 6	55 0	57 6
88	£1 yell.-orge.	£8	£8	110 0	£6

In the £1 stamp the words of value are on a curved scroll running across the stamp above the words "POSTAGE AND REVENUE."

1925. *As* 1922. *Frame colours changed.*

89	5 c. green	0 8	0 7
90	10 c. orange	0 10	0 8
91	25 c. blue	1 10	2 2
92	30 c. purple	3 9	4 3

6

7

(Typo. De La Rue & Co.)

1927–31. *T* **6** *("* Cents *" values) and* **7.** *Head in black. Wmk. Mult. Script CA. P* 14.

93	5 c. green	0 3	0 2
94	10 c. yellow	0 4	0 2
95	15 c. carmine-red	0 6	0 2
96	20 c. orange-buff	0 8	0 2
97	25 c. bright blue	0 10	0 6
98	30 c. dull purple	1 6	0 10
98*a*	30 c. bright blue ('31)	7 6	5 0
99	40 c. yellow-brown ..	2 0	1 6
100	50 c. grey	2 0	0 8
101	75 c. olive-green	3 6	2 6
102	1s. green, O	4 0	2 0
103	2s. deep purple, O ..	7 6	4 0
104	3s. black O..	15 0	15 0
105	5s. carmine-red, C.. ..	17 6	10 6
106	10s. deep blue, C ..	45 0	45 0
107	£1 brown-orange, C ..	85 0	85 0

Postage Due stamps of Kenya and Uganda were issued for provisional use as such in Tanganyika on 1 July, 1933. The postmark is the only means of identification.

For later issues see "KENYA, UGANDA and TANGANYIKA."

TASMANIA.

SIMPLIFICATION (see p. xii)

Nos. 1 to 129.

3, 11. 14, 15, 17. 19, 20, 22.
28, 29, 31, 33, 34, 36, 37, 38, 45, 46, 47, 41.
84, 112, 99, 91, 102, 122, 124, 129, 127.

Type 11.

131, 139, 135, 136.
155, 156, 160, 161, 163, 165, 167, 168, 169, 171.
178, 179, 180, 182. 193, 186, 187, 194, 195, 188, 197, 198, 226, 228. 213, 210, 211, 212. 201, 207. 255. 258a, 259a.

Types 20 to 21a.

216 to 225. 256. 257. 260, 261.

Pictorials.

229 to 236. 237, 238, 240, 241, 239.
246, 247, 242, 248, 243, 249, 245, 250. 252.

1

2

1853 (1 Nov.). *Engraved by C. W. Coard and printed by H. and C. Best at the office of the "Courier" newspaper.* T1. *No wmk. Imperf.*

Twenty-four varieties in four rows of six each.

(*a*) *Medium soft yellowish paper with all lines clear and distinct.*

		Un.	*Used.*
1	1d. pale blue	£90	£8 *to* £35
2	1d. blue	£90	£8 *to* £35

(*b*) *Thin hard white paper with lines of the engraving blurred and worn.*

3	1d. pale blue	£85	£7 *to* £25
4	1d. blue	£85	£7 *to* £25

As last. T 2. *No wmk. Imperf. In each plate there are twenty-four varieties in four rows of six each.*

1853. *Plate I. Finely engraved. All lines in network and background thin, clear, and well defined.*

(*a*) *First state of the plate, brilliant colours.*

5	4d. bright red-orange ..	£45	80 0 *to* £14
6	4d. bright brownish oran.	—	£5 *to* £16

(*b*) *Second state of plate, with blurred lines and worn condition of the central background.*

7	4d. red-orange	£32	60 0 *to* £10
8	4d. orange	£32	60 0 *to* £9
9	4d. pale orange ..	—	60 0 *to* £8

1854. *Plate II. Coarse engraving, lines in network and background thicker and blurred.*

10	4d. orange	£30	40 0 *to* £9
11	4d. dull orange ..	£25	40 0 *to* £8
12	4d. yellowish orange ..	£25	40 0 *to* £8

Variety. Laid paper, with wide vertical lines.

13	4d. red-orange ..	£125	

In the 4d. Plate I., the outer frame-line is thin all round. In Plate II. it is, by comparison with other parts, thicker in the lower left angle.

In 1879 reprints were made of the 1d. in blue and the 4d., Plate I., in brownish yellow, on thin, tough, white wove paper, and perforated 11½. In 1887, a reprint from the other plate of the 4d. was made in reddish brown and in black, and in 1889 of the 1d. in blue and in black, and of the 4d. (both plates) in yellow and in black on white card, imperforate. The three plates having been defaced after the issue was superseded by new types, all these reprints show two thick strokes across the Queen's Head.

3

4

(Recess. Perkins, Bacon & Co.)

1855 (Aug.). *T* **3**. *Wmk. Large Star, Type* w. 1. *Imperf.*

14	1d. carmine	£120	£6 *to* £30
15	2d. deep green	£65	60 0 *to* £12
16	2d. green	£65	60 0 *to* £12
17	4d. deep blue	£50	20 0 *to* 60 0
18	4d. blue	£45	20 0 *to* 75 0

There is a proof of the 1d. on thick, no wmk. paper that is sometimes sold as the issued stamp.

(Printed by H. and C. Best, of Hobart.)

1856–57. *T* **3**. *No wmk. Imperf.*

19	1d. pale brk.-red (4.56)	£185	£8 *to* £30
20	2d. dull em.-grn. (1.57)	£275	£6 *to* £35
21	4d. deep blue	£33	35 0 *to* £5
22	4d. blue	£27	35 0 *to* £5
23	4d. pale blue	—	50 0 *to* £7

1856 (Nov.). *No wmk. Pelure paper. Imperf.*

24	1d. deep red-brown	£65	£5 *to* £20

1857–60. *T* **3**. *Wmk. double-lined numerals* "**1**," "**2**," *or* "**4**" *as T* **4**. *Imperf.*

25	1d. deep red-brown	£15	32 6
26	1d. pale red-brown	£10	25 0
27	1d. brick-red	£6	16 6
28	1d. dull vermilion	20 0	16 6
29	1d. carmine	35 0	16 6
	a. Double print	—	75 0
30	2d. dull emerald-green	—	55 0
31	2d. deep green	£6	42 6
32	2d. green	—	32 6
	a. Double print	—	£8
33	2d. yellow-green	£8	37 6
34	2d. sage-green	75 0	30 0
35	4d. blue	60 0	10 0
	a. Double print	—	£5
36	4d. pale blue	60 0	10 0
37	4d. bright blue	50 0	10 0
	a. Printed on both sides		
	b. Double print	—	60 0
38	4d. very deep blue	—	40 0
	a. Double print	—	100 0
39	4d. cobalt-blue	—	22 6

7

8

(Recess. Perkins, Bacon & Co.)

1858 (Jan.). *T* **7** *and* **8**. *Wmk. double-lined numerals* "**6**" *or* "**12**". *Imperf.*

40	6d. dull lilac	£22	20 0
41	1s. bright vermilion	£9	22 6
42	1s. dull vermilion	—	25 0

Prepared for use, but not issued. Wmk. Large Star. Imperf.

43	6d. lilac	£12	

1860–67. *T* **7**. *Wmk. double-lined* "**6**". *Printed in the Colony.*

44	6d. dull slate-grey (Mar., '60)	£10	18 6
45	6d. grey	—	25 0
46	6d. grey-violet (April, '63)	80 0	22 6
	a. Double print	—	70 0*
47	6d. dull bluish (Feb., '65)	£5	22 6
48	6d. bluish purple	£8	45 0
49	6d. reddish mauve (1867)	£30	85 0

In 1871 reprints were made of the 6d. (in mauve) and the 1s. on white wove paper, and perforated 11½. They are found with or without "REPRINT." In 1889 they were again reprinted on white card, imperforate and perforated 12. These later impressions are also found with or without "REPRINT."

1864–70. *T* **3**, **7** *and* **8** *(with double-line numeral watermarks), with various local roulettes and perforations.*

(*a*) **1864.** *Roughly punctured roulette about* 8, *by J. Walch, at Hobart.*

50	1d. brick-red	—	£10
51	1d. carmine	—	£5
52	4d. pale blue	—	£10
53	6d. dull lilac	—	£15
54	1s. vermilion	—	£25

(*b*) **1867** (March). *Pin-perf.* 5½ *to* 9½ *at Longford, near Launceston.*

55	1d. carmine	£8	60 0
56	4d. bright blue	—	£7
57	6d. grey-violet	—	£10
58	6d. reddish mauve	—	£20
59	1s. vermilion		

(*c*) **1867** (?). *Pin-perf.* 13½ *to* 14½.

60	1d. brick-red	—	£8
61	1d. dull vermilion	—	£8
62	1d. carmine		
63	2d. yellow-green	—	£12
64	4d. pale blue	—	£6
65	6d. grey-violet	—	£15
66	1s. vermilion		

(*d*) **1866** (?). *Oblique roulette* 10, 10½.

67	1d. brick-red	—	£8
68	1d. carmine	—	£6
69	2d. yellow-green	—	£12
70	4d. bright blue	—	£8
71	6d. grey-violet	—	£15

(*e*) **1867** (?) *Oblique roulette* 14 *to* 15, *used at Deloraine.*

72	1d. brick-red	—	£8
73	1d. dull vermilion	—	£8
74	1d. carmine	—	£6
75	2d. yellow-green	—	£12
76	4d. pale blue	—	£8
77	6d. grey-violet	—	£20
78	1s. vermilion	—	£25

(*f*) **1868–69.** *Serrated perf.* 19.

79	1d. carmine (*pen-canc.* 20s.)	£8	£4
80	2d. yellow-green	—	£12
81	4d. deep blue	£25	£5
82	4d. cobalt-blue	—	£6
83	6d. bluish purple	—	£30

1864–69. *T* **3**, **7** *and* **8** *with double-line numeral watermarks.*

I. *Perforated by J. Walch and Sons, Hobart.*

(*a*) *P* 10.

84	1d. brick-red	15 0	15 0
85	1d. vermilion	18 6	15 0
86	1d. deep carmine	15 0	15 0
87	1d. pale carmine	15 0	15 0
88	2d. sage-green	£7	£6
89	2d. yellow-green	£6	75 0
90	4d. blue	65 0	17 6
91	4d. pale blue	65 0	16 6
	a. Double print	—	50 0
92	6d. grey-violet	£6	16 6
93	6d. dull bluish	85 0	16 6
94	6d. bluish purple	—	25 0
95	6d. reddish mauve	£15	60 0
96	1s. vermilion	65 0	18 6

(*b*) *P* 11½ *to* 12.

No.	Stamp	Unused	Used
96*a*	1d. vermilion	27 6	
97	1d. deep carmine	15 0	10 0
98	1d. pale carmine	20 0	11 0
99	2d. pale yellow-green	£6	52 6
100	2d. deep yellow-green	£4	57 6
101	4d. blue	65 0	13 6
102	4d. deep blue	57 6	11 0
103	4d. cobalt-blue	—	27 6
104	6d. bluish purple	£6	22 6
105	6d. reddish mauve	75 0	17 6
106	1s. vermilion	85 0	16 0
	a. Double print	—	£5

(*c*) *Perf. compound* 10 × 11½, 12.

No.	Stamp	Unused	Used
107	1d. deep carmine		
108	4d. blue	—	£40

Error. Wmk. double-lined "2". *P* 11½–12. (Nov. 1869.)

No.	Stamp	Unused	Used
109	1d. carmine (*pen-canc.* £10)	—	£35

II. *Perforated by R. Harris, Launceston.*

P 12½, 13.

No.	Stamp	Unused	Used
110	1d. brick-red	25 0	25 0
111	1d. vermilion	18 6	18 6
112	1d. deep carmine	10 0	10 0
113	2d. sage-green	£8	£6
114	2d. yellow-green	£9	£6
115	4d. bright blue	£6	45 0
116	4d. blue	£6	45 0
117	6d. dull bluish	£8	50 0
118	6d. bluish purple	£10	50 0
119	6d. reddish mauve	£20	£6
120	1s. vermilion	£8	65 0

III. **1871–80.** *Perforated by the Government at Hobart.* (*a*) *P* 11, 11½.

No.	Stamp	Unused	Used
121	6d. dull mauve	55 0	17 6
122	6d. bright mauve	45 0	15 0
	a. Imperf. between (pair)	—	£15
123	6d. dull purple	30 0	12 6
	a. Imperf.	—	£10
124	6d. bright purple	37 6	12 6
	a. Double print	—	50 0
	b. Imperf. between (horiz. pair)	£18	
125	6d. lilac-purple	55 0	16 6
126	1s. dull vermilion	55 0	15 0
	a. Imperf. between (horiz. pair)		
127	1s. brownish vermilion	37 6	12 6

(*b*) *P* 12.

No.	Stamp	Unused	Used
128	6d. bright purple	65 0	25 0
129	6d. dull claret	8 6	10 0

The perforations of the "Walch" machine can be distinguished from those of the Government machine by noticing that all stamps gauging 11½ and under are made by the latter, and those gauging over 11½ and under 12 by the former machine.

11

12 13 14

(Plates made by De La Rue & Co.)

(Typographed in the Colony.)

1870–71. *T* **11.** *Wmk. single-lined numerals T* **12, 13,** *or* **14.** (*a*) *P* 12.

No.	Stamp	Unused	Used
130	1d. rose-red (10)	35 0	15 0
131	1d. deep rose (10)	52 6	10 0
132	1d. rose-red (4)	40 0	25 0
133	2d. yellow-green (2)	40 0	10 0
134	2d. blue-green (2)	47 6	10 0
135	4d. blue (4)	£10	£10
136	10d. black (10)	5 0	5 0

(*b*) *P* 11½.

No.	Stamp	Unused	Used
137	1d. rose-red (10)	£16	
138	2d. yellow-green (2)	£6	12 6
139	2d. blue-green (2)	42 6	5 0
140	10d. black (10)	12 6	12 6

(*c*) *Imperf.*

No.	Stamp	Unused	Used
141	1d. rose-red (4)	—	£5
142	1d. rose-red (10)	£7	£6
143	2d. green (2)		
144	10d. black (10)	50 0	

The above were printed on paper borrowed from New South Wales.

15

1871–79. *T* **11.** *W* **15.** (*a*) *P* 12.

No.	Stamp	Unused	Used
145	1d. rose	75 0	7 6
146	1d. carmine	£5	15 0
147	2d. green	£25	£10
148	3d. red-brown	65 0	32 6
149	3d. deep red-brown	65 0	32 6
150	4d. buff	£10	16 6
151	9d. pale blue	20 0	
152	5s. purple	£5	
153	5s. mauve	50 0	

(*b*) *P* 11½.

No.	Stamp	Unused	Used
154	1d. rose	3 0	0 8
155	1d. bright rose	2 6	0 8
156	1d. vermilion	£8	85 0
157	1d. carmine	6 6	1 6
158	1d. pink	6 6	1 3
159	2d. deep green	20 0	1 0
160	2d. yellow-green	£8	3 0
161	2d. blue-green	22 6	0 8
162	3d. pale red-brown	27 6	6 0
163	3d. deep red-brown	30 0	6 0
	a. Imperf. between (pair)		
164	3d. purple-brown	32 6	5 0
165	3d. brownish purple	30 0	5 0
166	4d. ochre	55 0	6 0
167	4d. buff	40 0	7 6
168	4d. pale yellow	35 0	6 6
169	9d. blue	8 0	6 6
170	5s. purple (*pen-canc.* 4s.)	50 0	25 0
171	5s. mauve	35 0	22 6

(*c*) *Imperf.*

No.	Stamp	Unused	Used
172	1d. rose (*pen-canc.* 40s.)		
173	2d. green	—	50 0
174	3d. pale red-brown	50 0	
175	3d. purple-brown	—	£10
176	9d. blue	27 6	
176*a*	5s. purple		

16

(Typo. De La Rue & Co.)

1878. *T* **11.** *W* **16.** *P* 14.

No.		Unused	Used
177	1d. carmine	1 6	0 3
178	1d. rose-carmine	1 6	0 3
179	1d. scarlet	1 6	0 3
180	2d. pale green	3 0	0 2
181	2d. green	3 0	0 2
182	8d. dull purple-brown	4 0	4 0

In 1871 the 1d., 2d., 3d., 4d. blue, 9d., 10d., and 5s., *T* **11**, were reprinted on soft white wove, and perforated 11½; and in 1879 the 4d. yellow and 8d. were reprinted on thin, tough, white wove. All nine varieties are found with and without "REPRINT." In 1889 the 4d. blue was also reprinted on white card, imperforate, and perforated 12. The 5s. has been reprinted in *mauve* on white card, perforated 12. These later impressions, like those of 1871 and 1879, are found with or without "REPRINT."

1880–91. *Colonial print. Wmk. T* **16.**

(*a*) *P* 12.

No.		Unused	Used
183	½d. orange	2 0	2 0
184	½d. deep orange	1 6	1 9
185	1d. pink	15 0	5 0
	a. Imperf.	12 6	12 6
186	1d. rosine	7 6	4 6
187	1d. dull rosine	9 6	5 0
188	3d. red-brown	3 0	2 6
	a. Imperf.	20 0	
	b. Imperf. between (pair)	£16	
189	4d. deep yellow	42 6	15 0
190	4d. chrome-yellow	65 0	15 0

Variety. Printed on both sides.

No.		Unused	Used
191	4d. lemon-yellow	40 0	

(*b*) *P* 11½.

No.		Unused	Used
192	½d. orange	2 6	1 3
193	½d. deep orange	1 6	1 0
194	1d. dull red	5 0	3 0
195	1d. vermilion-red	2 0	2 0
196	3d. red-brown	7 6	6 0
197	4d. deep yellow	30 0	6 0
198	4d. chrome-yellow	20 0	6 0
199	4d. olive-yellow	65 0	25 0
200	4d. buff	30 0	7 6

Halfpenny

(17)

1889–91. *T* **11** *surcharged with T* **17**, *in black.* *W* **16.** *P* 14.

No.		Unused	Used
201	½d. on 1d. scarlet	1 0	1 0

Varieties. (i) "p" *for* "p"; (ii) "p" *in* "Half."

No.		Unused	Used
202	½d. on 1d. scarlet (i)	5 0	
203	½d. on 1d. scarlet (ii)	£30	

d. 2½ **(18)** d. 2½ **(19)**

T **11.** *W* **16.** *Surcharged in black.* (*a*) *With T* **18** (2¼ *mm. between* "d" *and* "2"). *P* 11½.

No.		Unused	Used
204	2½d. on 9d. pale blue	3 6	3 6
	a. Imperf.	47 6	
205	2½d. on 9d. deep blue	7 0	6 6

Variety. Surcharge double, one inverted.

No.		Unused	Used
206	2½d. on 9d. pale blue	£5	£5

(*b*) *With T* **19** (3½ *mm. between* "d" *and* "2"). *P* 12.

No.		Unused	Used
207	2½d. on 9d. pale blue	3 0	1 9

Variety. Surcharged in blue.

No.		Unused	Used
208	2½d. on 9d. pale blue		

There is a reprint of the 2½d. on 9d. on stout white wove paper, perf. 12, overprinted "REPRINT."

1891. *Colonial print.* *T* **11.** *Reissue with wmk. T* **15.** (*a*) *P* 12.

No.		Unused	Used
209	½d. orange	13 6	13 6
	a. Imperf.	8 6	
210	1d. dull rosine	12 0	12 0
211	1d. rosine	12 0	11 0
212	4d. bistre	2 0	2 0

(*b*) *P* 11½.

No.		Unused	Used
213	½d. orange	15 0	7 6
214	½d. brown-orange	15 0	7 6
215	1d. rosine	12 6	7 6

20

21

21*a*

(Typo. De La Rue & Co.)

1892–99. *T* **20, 21** (2½*d.*) *and* **21*a*** (10*d.*). *W* **16.** *P* 14.

No.		Unused	Used
216	½d. orange and mauve	0 6	0 3
217	2½d. purple	1 9	0 9
218	5d. pale blue and brown	3 0	1 9
219	6d. violet and black	4 6	3 0
220	10d. purple-lake & deep green	5 6	4 6
221	1s. rose and green	3 6	1 6
222	2s. 6d. brown and blue	10 0	9 0
223	5s. lilac and red	12 6	12 6
224	10s. mauve and brown	30 0	20 0
225	£1 green and yellow	£10	110 0

1896. *Colonial print.* *T* **11.** *W* **16.** *P* 12

No.		Unused	Used
226	4d. pale bistre	6 0	3 6
227	9d. pale blue	3 0	2 6
228	9d. blue	5 0	5 0

22. Lake Marion.

23. Mount Wellington.

24. View of Hobart.

25. Tasman's Arch.

26. Spring River, Port Davey.

27. Russell Falls.

28. Mount Gould, Lake St. Clair.

30

29. Dilston Falls.

1899–1912.

PICTORIAL DESIGNS.

A. Recess-printed by Thos. De La Rue & Co., London.

1899 (Dec.)–**1900.** *W* **30.** *P* 14.

229	**22**	½d. deep green	0	6	0	6
230	**23**	1d. bright lake	0	4	0	1
231	**24**	2d. deep violet	0	9	0	2
232	**25**	2½d. indigo	2	6	2	6
233	**26**	3d. sepia	2	6	1	6
234	**27**	4d. deep orange-buff ..	3	6	1	3
235	**28**	5d. bright blue	6	0	3	0
236	**29**	6d. lake	5	0	3	0

B. Printed at the Government Printing Office Melbourne, Victoria.

I. *Wmk. V over Crown, Type* w. **10.**

1902–3. LITHOGRAPHED. *Transfers from London plates. Wmk. upright on* 1d. *P* 12½.

237	**22**	½d. green (1903)	0	3	0	3
		a. Perf. 11	4	0	1	0
		b. Perf. comp. of 12½ and 11 ..	17	6	17	6
238	**23**	1d. carmine-red	0	9	0	2
239	**24**	2d. violet	0	6	0	3
		a. Perf. 11	1	6	0	1
		b. Perf. comp. of 12½ and 11	30	0	12	6
		c. *Purple*	0	10	0	4
		ca. *Purple.* Perf. 11	1	9	0	1

As the V and Crown paper was originally prepared for stamps of smaller size, portions of two or more watermarks appear on each stamp.

The ½d. and 2d. may be found with wmk. upright, the normal position in these values being sideways.

We only list the main groups of shades in this and the following issues. There are variations of shade in all values, particularly in the 2d. where there is a wide range, also in the 1d. in some issues.

1902–3. ELECTROTYPED. *Plates made at Govt. Printing Office. P* 12½.

(*a*) *Wmk. sideways* (Oct. 1902).

240	**23**	1d. pale red (to rose) ..	0	8	0	1
		a. Perf. 11	5	0	0	4
		b. Perf. 12½ comp. with 11 ..	50	0	10	0

Stamps from this printing, with wmk. upright, are scarce, especially perf. 11.

(*b*) *Wmk. upright* (April, 1903).

241 **23** 1d. rose-red 0 4 0 1
a. Perf. 11 .. .. .. 1 6 0 2
b. Perf. comp of 12½ and 11 35 0 17 6
c. *Deep carmine-red* 30 0 0 3
ca. *Deep carmine-red.* Perf. 11 — 6 6
cb. *Deep carmine-red.* Perf. comp. of 12½ and 11 ..

II. *Wmk. Crown over* A, *Type* w. 11 (*sideways on oblong stamps*).

1905 (Sept.)–**1912.** Lithographed. *Transfers from London plates. P* 12½.

242 **24** 2d. purple 2 0 0 3
a. Perf. 11 .. .. .. 2 0 0 2
b. Perf. comp. of 12½ and 11 7 6 3 0
c. Perf. comp. of 12½ and 12 — 10 0
d. Perf. comp. of 11 and 12 ..
e. *Dull purple* 1 9 0 3
ea. *Dull purple. Perf.* 11 .. 2 0 0 2
243 **26** 3d. brown 4 0 1 0
a. Perf. 11 .. .. .. 5 0 1 6
b. Perf. comp. of 12½ and 11 27 6
244 **27** 4d. orange-buff (1907) .. 5 0 2 0
a. Perf. 11 .. .. .. 3 0 1 0
b. Perf. comp. of 12½ and 11
c. *Brown-ochre* (wmk. sideways). Perf. 11 (1907) .. 10 0 3 6
d. *Orange-yellow* (1912) .. 4 6 2 0
da. *Orange-yellow.* Perf. 11 ('12) 3 0
245 **29** 6d. lake 9 0 6 0
a. Perf. 11 .. .. .. 5 0 2 6
b. Perf. comp. of 12½ and 11 50 0

Stamps with perf. compound of 12½ and 12 or 11 and 12 are found on sheets which were sent from Melbourne incompletely perforated. The line of perforation gauging 12 was done at the Government Printing Office, Hobart.

1905–11. Electrotyped. *Plates made at Govt. Printing Office. P* 12½.

246 **22** ½d. yellow-green (1909) .. 0 6 0 2
a. Perf. 11 (1908) 0 6 0 2
b. Perf. comp. of 12½ and 11 10 0
c. Perf. comp. of 11 and 12 ..
247 **23** 1d. rose-red 0 6 0 1
a. Perf. 11 .. .. .. 0 6 0 1
b. Perf. comp. of 12½ and 11 2 0 2 0
c. Perf. comp. of 12½ and 12 12 6 5 0
d. Perf. comp. of 11 and 12 .. 10 0
e. *Bright rose* .. .. — 0 1
ea. *Bright rose.* Perf. 11 .. 1 6 0 1
f. *Crimson* (1910) .. ..
fa. *Crimson.* Perf. 11 ..
fb. *Crimson.* Perf. comp. of 12½ and 12 .. ..
248 **24** 2d. purple 1 3 0 3
a. Perf. 11 .. .. .. 2 0 0 3
b. *Dull violet* 1 3 0 2
ba. *Dull violet.* Perf. 11 .. 1 3 0 2
bb. *Dull violet.* Perf. comp. of 12½ and 11 .. .. 3 6 3 6
bc. *Dull violet.* Perf. comp. of 12½ and 12 .. ..
bd. *Dull violet.* Perf. comp. of 11 and 12 .. 25 0
c. *Bright violet* (1910) .. 2 6 0 8
ca. *Bright violet.* Perf. 11 .. 2 6 0 4
249 **26** 3d. brown (1909) 2 0 0 10
a. Perf. 11 .. .. .. 2 9 1 3
b. Perf. comp. of 12½ and 11 35 0
250 **29** 6d. dull lake (1911) .. 5 0 2 6
a. Perf. 11 .. .. .. 3 6 2 0
b. Perf. comp. of 12½ and 11 25 0

The note after No. 245 re perfs. compound with perf. 12 also applies here.

The ½d. and 2d. are found with wmk. upright and the 1d. with wmk. sideways, each perf. 12½ or 11.

Stamps showing a blotchy or defective impression often with shading appearing as solid colour, formerly listed under Nos. 328 to 348 as "lithographed" are from worn electrotyped plates, with the exception of Nos. 332, 333, 338, 339, 345 and 346, which are grouped in the present list under Nos. 244d and 244da.

1911. *Electrotyped from new plate. P* 12½.

251 **24** 2d. bright violet 0 8 0 2
a. Perf. 11 .. .. .. 0 6 0 2
b. Perf. comp. of 12½ and 11 17 6

Stamps from this plate differ from Nos. 248c and 248ca in the width of the design, which ranges from 33 to 33¾ mm., against just over 32 mm., in the letters of "TASMANIA" which appear taller and bolder, in the slope of the mountain in the left background, which is clearly outlined in white, instead of merging into the clouds, and in the outer vertical frame-line at left, which appears to be bent and "wavy". Compare Nos. 252, etc., which are always from this plate.

ONE PENNY

(31)

1912 (Oct.). *Nos.* 251, *etc., surcharged with T* **31.** *P* 12½.

252 **24** 1d. on 2d. bright violet (R.) 0 4 0 3
a. Perf. 11 .. .. .. 0 4 0 3
b. Perf. comp. of 12½ and 11

1912 (Dec.). *Thin paper, white gum.* (*As Victoria,* 1912.) *P* 12½.

253 **23** 1d. crimson 3 6 0 4
a. Perf. 11 .. .. .. 3 0 0 5
b. Perf. comp. of 12½ and 11
254 **26** 3d. brown 5 0

QUEEN VICTORIA PORTRAIT DESIGNS.

I. *Wmk.* V *over Crown, Type* w. **10.**

1903–5. *P* 12½.

255 **11** 9d. blue 1 9 2 0
a. Perf. 11 .. .. .. 6 6 7 6
b. Perf. comp. of 12½ and 11 — £15
c. *Pale blue* 3 0 3 0
d. *Bright blue* 5 0 2 6
e. *Ultramarine* £15
f. *Indigo* £6
256 **20** 1s. rose and green 6 0 5 0
a. Perf. 11 .. .. .. 20 0

1½d.

(32)

1904 (29 Dec.). *No.* 218 (*W* **16**) *surch. with T* **32.**

257 **20** 1½d. on 5d. pale blue & brn. 0 5 0 5

Stamps with inverted surcharge or without surcharge *se tenant* with stamps with normal surcharge were obtained irregularly and were not issued for postal use.

II. *Wmk. Crown over A, Type* w. **11.**

1906–13. *P* 12½.

258 **11** 8d. purple-brown (1907) .. 5 0 5 0
a. Perf. 11 .. .. .. 5 0 3 6
259 ,, 9d. blue (1907) 4 6 4 6
a. Perf. 11 .. .. .. 3 6 3 6
b. Perf. comp. of 12½ and 11 (1909) 40 0
c. Perf. comp. of 12½ and 12 (1909) .. ..
d. Perf. comp. of 11 and 12 ..
260 **20** 1s. rose and green (1907) .. 3 0 1 9
a. Perf. 11 (1907) 5 0 5 0
b. Perf. comp. of 12½ and 11 15 0
c. Perf. comp. of 12½ and 12 35 0
261 ,, 10s. mauve & brown (1906) 35 0
a. Perf. 11 .. .. .. 95 0
b. Perf. comp. of 12½ and 12 70 0

The note after No. 245 re perfs. compound with perf. 12 also applies here.

DIFFERENCES BETWEEN LITHOGRAPHED AND ELECTROTYPED ISSUES.

LITHOGRAPHED.	ELECTROTYPED.
General appearance fine.	*Comparatively crude and coarse appearance*
½d. All "V over Crown" wmk.	All "Crown over A" wmk.
1d. The shading on the path on the right bank of the river consists of very fine dots. In printings from worn stones the dots hardly show.	The shading on the path is coarser, consisting of large dots and small patches of colour.
The shading on the white mountain is fine (or almost absent in many stamps).	The shading on the mountain is coarse, and clearly defined.
2d. Three rows of windows	Two rows of windows

in large building on shore at extreme left, against inner frame.

LITHOGRAPHED.	ELECTROTYPED.
3d. Clouds very white.	Clouds dark.
Stars in corner ornaments have long points.	Stars have short points.
Shading of corner ornaments is defined by a coloured outer line.	Shading of ornaments terminates against white background.
4d. Lithographed only.	—
6d. No coloured dots at base of waterfall.	Coloured dots at base of waterfall.
Outer frame of value tablets is formed by outer line of design.	Thick line of colour between value tablets and outer line.
	Small break in inner frame below second "A" of "TASMANIA".

POSTAL FISCALS.

Authorized for use in 1882.

51

52

53

54

(Printed by Alfred Bock, of Hobart.)

T **51** *to* **54.**

1863. *Wmk. double-lined* "1"; *T* **4.** *Imperf.*

401	3d. green	35 0	
402	2s. 6d. carmine	40 0	
403	5s. sage-green	12 6	
404	5s. brown	30 0	30 0
405	10s. salmon	10 0	
406	10s. orange	20 0	30 0

1864. *Wmk. double-lined* "1", *T* **4.** (*a*) *P* 10.

407	3d. green	15 0	20 0
408	2s. 6d. carmine	20 0	
409	5s. brown	20 0	
410	10s. orange	20 0	

(*b*) *P* 12.

411	3d. green	15 0	20 0
412	2s. 6d. carmine	10 0	10 0
413	5s. sage-green	7 6	10 0
414	5s. brown	20 0	
415	10s. salmon	15 0	15 0
416	10s. orange-brown	20 0	20 0

(*c*) *P* 12½, 13.

417	3d. green	25 0	
418	2s. 6d. carmine	25 0	
419	5s. brown	30 0	
420	10s. orange-brown	30 0	

(*d*) *P* 11½.

421	3d. green		
422	2s. 6d. lake	10 0	10 0
423	5s. sage-green	7 6	7 6
424	10s. salmon	12 6	12 6

In 1879 the 3d., 2s. 6d., 5s. (brown), and 10s. (orange) were reprinted on thin, tough, white paper, and are found with or without "REPRINT." In 1889 another reprint was made on white card, imperforate and perforated 12. These later impressions are also found with or without "REPRINT."

Wmk. T **16.** *P* 11½, 12.

425	**2s. 6d. lake**	5 0	5 0
	a. Imperf. between (horiz. pair) ..	£6	

55. Duck-billed Platypus.

(Engraved by Messrs. De La Rue & Co.)

1880. *T* **55.** *W* **16.** *P* 14.

426	1d. slate	1 3	0 5
427	3d. chestnut	0 10	0 4
428	6d. mauve	1 9	0 9
429	1s. rose-pink	3 0	2 6

All values are known imperf., but not used.

Reprints are known of the 1d. in *deep blue* and the 6d. in lilac. The former is on yellowish white, the latter on white card. Both values also exist on wove paper and perf. 12, and have the word "REPRINT."

REVENUE

(56)

1900 (Nov.). *Optd.* "REVENUE", *T* **56.**

A. *T* **52** *and* **54.** *W* **16.**

430	2s. 6d. carmine (*imperf.*) ..	110 0	
431	2s. 6d. carmine (*perf.* 12) ..	80 0	80 0
432	10s. salmon (*perf.* 12) ..		
433	10s. salmon (*W* 4, *perf.* 12).		

Varieties. (i) " REVFNUE ".

No.	Stamp	Unused	Used
434	2s. 6d. carmine (*imperf.*) ..		
435	2s. 6d. carmine (*perf.*) ..		
436	10s. salmon (*wmk.* " TAS ") ..		
437	10s. salmon (**W 4.**)		

(ii) *Overprint inverted.*

No.	Stamp	Unused	Used
438	2s. 6d. carmine (*perf.*) ..		
439	2s. 6d. carmine (*perf.*) (i) ..		

B. *T* **55** (*wmk. T* **16**).

No.	Stamp	Unused	Used
440	3d. chestnut (*perf.* 14) ..	2 6	2 0
	a. Double opt., one vertical ..		

C. *T* **55.** *Lithographed. P* 12.

(*a*) *Thin transparent paper. W* **15.**

No.	Stamp	Unused	Used
441	1d. blue	25 0	

(*b*) *Thick paper. W* **16.**

No.	Stamp	Unused	Used
442	1d. blue	7 6	7 6
	a. Imperf. between (horiz. pair)	80 0	
	b. " REVENUE " inverted ..	50 0	
	c. " REVENUE " double ..	80 0	
443	1d. pale blue..	1 9	2 6
444	2d. chestnut	2 6	
	a. No value	80 0	
	b. Value double	£6	
445	6d. mauve	6 0	
	a. Double print	60 0	
446	1s. pink	12 6	12 6

There is considerable doubt if Nos. 441 to 446 were authorized for postage, though some are known duly postmarked. No. 444 is somewhat different in design from T **55.**

D. *T* **20.** *W* **16.** *P* 14.

No.	Stamp	Unused	Used
447	£1 green and yellow ..	£6	£8
	a. Double opt., one vertical ..		

Tasmania now uses the stamps of AUSTRALIA.

TOBAGO.

1

(Typo. De La Rue & Co.)

1879 (1 AUG.). *T* **1.** *Fiscal stamps issued provisionally pending the arrival of the stamps inscribed* " POSTAGE." *Wmk. Crown CC. P* 14.

No.	Stamp	Unused	Used
1	1d. rose	32 6	30 0
2	3d. blue	47 6	32 6
3	6d. orange	40 0	30 0
4	1s. green	£10	60 0
	a. Bisected (6d.)		
5	5s. slate	£20	
6	£1 mauve	£80	

1880 (NOV.). *No.* 3 *divided vertically down the centre and surcharged with pen and ink, in black.*

No.	Stamp	Unused	Used
7	1d. on half of 6d. orange ..	£25	£15

The stamps of T **1**, watermark Crown CA, are fiscals which were never admitted to postal use.

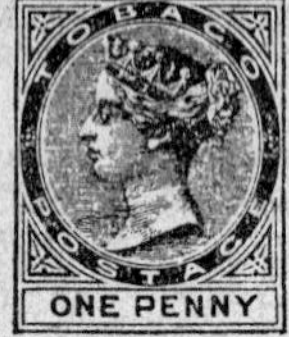

2

1880 (20 DEC.). *T* **2.** *Wmk. Crown CC. P* 14.

No.	Stamp	Unused	Used
8	½d. purple-brown	32 6	32 6
9	1d. Venetian red	42 6	42 6
	a. Bisected (½d.)		
10	4d. yellow-green	95 0	35 0
	a. Bisected (2d.)	—	£16
11	6d. stone	£10	£8
12	1s. yellow-ochre	20 0	20 0

2½ PENCE

(3)

1883 (APR.). *No.* 11 *surcharged with T* **3.**

No.	Stamp	Unused	Used
13	2½d. on 6d. stone	20 0	20 0
	a. Surcharge double		
	b. The large " 2 " with long tail	60 0	60 0

1882–84. *T* **2.** *Wmk. Crown CA. P* 14.

No.	Stamp	Unused	Used
14	½d. purple-brown (1883) ..	5 0	6 0
15	1d. Venetian red (1882) ..	8 0	7 6
	a. Bisected diagonally (½d.) ..		
16	2½d. dull blue (1883)	10 6	7 6
16*a*	2½d. bright blue	4 0	4 0
17	2½d. ultramarine (1883) ..	3 0	3 6
18	4d. yellow-green (1884) ..	£10	£6
	a. Malformed "CE" in "PENCE.		
19	6d. stone (1884)	£20	£16

1885–94. *T* **2.** *Colours changed. Wmk. Crown CA. P* 14.

No.	Stamp	Unused	Used
20	½d. dull green (1886)	1 0	1 0
21	1d. carmine (1886)	1 0	1 0
22	4d. grey (1885)	2 6	3 0
	a. Malformed "CE" in "PENCE."	35 0	
23	6d. orange-brown (1886) ..	5 0	6 0
24	1s. olive-yellow (1894) ..	7 6	12 6
25	1s. pale olive-yellow (1894) ..	7 6	8 0

Stamps of 1882–86 *surcharged.*

½ PENNY (4) **2½ PENCE** (5)

1886–89. *As T* **4.**

No.	Stamp	Unused	Used
26	½d. on 6d. stone	10 0	10 6
27	½d. on 2½d. dull blue	7 6	8 6
28	½d. on 6d. orange-brown ..	50 0	55 0
29	1d. on 2½d. dull blue	17 6	17

Varieties. (i) *Figure further from word.*

No.	Stamp	Unused	Used
30	½d. on 6d. stone	45 0	50 0
31	½d. on 2½d. dull blue	22 6	25 0
32	½d. on 6d. orange-brown ..	£16	
33	1d. on 2½d. dull blue	65 0	65

(ii) *Surcharge inverted.*

No.	Stamp	Unused	Used
34	½d. on 6d. stone	£45	

(iii) *Surcharge double.*

No.	Stamp	Unused	Used
34*a*	½d. on 2½d. blue	£20	
34*b*	½d. on 6d. stone	£35	
34*c*	½d. on 6d. orange-brown ..		

These are printed in groups of 12 stamps, in two rows of 6, repeated five times in each pane. In each group Nos. 7, 9 and 10 have a raised " P " in " PENNY ", and No. 10 also shows the wider spacing between figure and word.

1891–92. *With T 5 or 4.*

35	2½d. on 4d. grey	17 6	15 0
	a. Malformed "CE" in "PENCE"	£7	
36	½d. on 4d. grey	30 0	25 0
	a. Malformed "CE" in "PENCE"	£12	—

Varieties. Surcharge double.

36*b*	2½d. on 4d. grey	£28	
36*c*	½d. on 4d. grey	£25	

1896. *Error of colour. T 2. Wmk. Crown CA. P* 14.

37	1s. orange-brown	12 6	

½d

POSTAGE

(6)

Fiscal stamp (*T* 1, *value in second colour, wmk. Crown CA. P* 14) *surcharged with T* 6.

38	½d. on 4d. lilac and carmine..	8 0	7 0

Variety, "½" and "d" wider apart.

39	½d. on 4d. lilac and carmine	20 0	16 0

Trinidad stamps were subsequently used in Tobago until 1913, when a set appeared bearing the names of both islands.

TOGOLAND.

TOGO
Anglo-French
Occupation
(1)

I. Wide Printing. Lines 3 mm. apart.

Stamps of German Colonial issue Types A *and* B 1900 *and* 1909–14 (5 *pf. and* 10 *pf.*).

1914 (1 Oct.). *Optd. with T* 1.

1	3 pf. brown	30 0	30 0
2	5 pf. green	30 0	30 0
3	10 pf. carmine	42 6	42 6
	a. Opt. inverted	£50	£40
	b. Opt. tête-bêche in vert. pair	—	£100
4	20 pf. ultramarine	6 0	7 0
5	25 pf. black & red/*yellow* ..	15 0	17 6
6	30 pf. black & orange/*buff* ..	12 6	12 6
7	40 pf. black & carmine ..	70 0	70 0
8	50 pf. black & purple/*buff* ..	£150	£125
9	80 pf. black & carmine/*rose* ..	70 0	75 0
10	1 m. carmine	£55	£50
11	2 m. blue	£140	£125
	a. "Occupation" double ..	—	£175
	b. Overprint inverted ..	£175	

Half penny

(2)

1914 (1 Oct.). *As last, surcharged as T* 2.

12	½d. on 3 pf. brown	50 0	50 0
	a. Thin "y" in "penny" ..	£9	£9
13	1d. on 5 pf. green	50 0	50 0
	a. Thin "y" in "penny" ..	£9	£9

TOGO
Anglo-French
Occupation
(3)

II. Narrow Printing. Lines 2 mm. apart.

1914 (*end* Oct.). *With opt. T* 3, *only*.

14	3 pf. brown	£40	£30
	a. "Occupation" omitted ..	£80	
15	5 pf. green	£40	£35
16	10 pf. carmine	£60	£50
17	20 pf. ultramarine	7 6	7 6
	a. Error. "TOG"	£40	£40
18	25 pf. black and red/*yellow* ..	15 0	15 0
	a. Error. "TOG"	£125	
19	30 pf. black and orange/*buff* ..	10 6	10 6
20	40 pf. black and carmine ..	£25	£25
21	50 pf. black and purple/*buff* ..	£150	£125
22	80 pf. black and carmine/*rose*	£25	£25
23	1 m. carmine	£60	£60
24	2 m. blue	£160	£160
25	3 m. violet-black		
26	5 m. lake and black ..		

TOGO
Anglo-French
Occupation
Half penny
(4)

Narrow printing, but surcharged as T 4.

27	½d. on 3 pf. brown	10 0	10 0
	a. Error. "TOG"	£12	
	b. Thin "y" in "penny" ..	15 0	15 0
28	1d. on 5 pf. green	2 0	2 6
	a. Error. "TOG"	40 0	40 0
	b. Thin "y" in "penny" ..	4 0	4 0

Wide setting, 3 mm. apart.

The overprint used on the values 3 pf. to 80 pf. was set up in five rows of 10 stamps and repeated twice on each sheet. Owing to the shortage of type of a correct size there are many small varieties of interest to specialists.

In the 10 pf. there is an important and rare error. The upper part of the sheet (fifty stamps) was correctly printed, and then the sheet was turned round and the lower half had the overprint inverted. Therefore vertical pairs from the middle rows have the overprint *tête-bêche*.

In the 20 pf. another rare error occurs. One half of a sheet was overprinted with the wide setting (3 mm.), and the other half with the narrow setting (2 mm.), consequently vertical pairs from the middle of the sheet show the two varieties of the overprint.

Narrow setting, 2 mm. apart.

In the ½d. on 3 pf. brown, the 1d. on 5 pf. green, and the 20 pf. blue, the thirty-seventh stamp in each setting is the error "TOG".

The ½d. on 3 pf. brown and ½d. on 5 pf. green have the following varieties in each setting of fifty stamps :—

Thin dropped "y" with small serifs occurs on Nos. 1, 2, 11, 21, 31, 41, and 42.

In each sheet of 100 of these stamps there are

2 of the "TOG" error.
14 of the thin "y".
84 of the normal.

TOGO
Anglo-French
Occupation
(6)

TOGO
ANGLO-FRENCH
OCCUPATION
(7)

1915 (7 Jan.). *With opt. as T 8, the words "Anglo-French" measure 15 mm. instead of 16 mm. as T 3.*

No.	Description	Unused	Used
29	3 pf. brown	£50	£50
30	5 pf. green	20 0	20 0
31	10 pf. carmine	20 0	22 6
32	20 pf. ultramarine	£10	£10
33	50 pf. black and purple/*buff* ..	£125	£100

This is a printing upon another lot of German Togo stamps that was found at Sansane-Mangu, a small town in the North.

The setting in this printing is in groups of 25 (5 × 5), repeated four times on a sheet.

The fifth stamp in each setting has a broken second "o" in "TOGO", making it like a badly formed "U".

For German Colonial stamps optd. "Togo Occupation franco-anglaise", see Part II of this catalogue.

1915 (May). *Stamps of Gold Coast, T 9, 10, and 11, optd. locally with T 7 ("OCCUPATION" 14½ mm. long), in black.*

No.	Description	Unused	Used
34	½d. green	0 4	0 4
	g. Double overprint	80 0	£5
35	1d. red	0 6	0 6
	g. Double overprint	£5	
	h. Overprint inverted	80 0	£6
	ha. Ditto, "TOGO" omitted ..		
36	2d. greyish slate	0 9	1 3
37	2½d. bright blue	1 3	1 9
38	3d. purple/*yellow*	1 0	1 9
	g. White back	10 0	15 0
40	6d. dull and bright purple ..	2 0	3 0
41	1s. black/*green*	4 0	5 0
	g. Overprint double	£10	
42	2s. purple and blue/*blue* ..	8 6	12 0
43	2s. 6d. black and red/*blue* ..	10 0	15 0
44	5s. grn. & red/*yell.* (*white back*)	15 0	25 0
45	10s. green and red/*green* ..	22 6	32 6
46	20s. purple and black/*red* ..	55 0	65 0

Varieties (Nos. in brackets indicate positions in pane).

A. *Small* "F" *in* "FRENCH" (25, 58, *and* 59.)

B. *Thin* "G" *in* "TOGO" (24).

C. *No hyphen after* "ANGLO" (5).

D. *Two hyphens after* "ANGLO" (5).

E. "CUPATION" *for* "OCCUPATION" (33).

F. "CCUPATION" for "OCCUPATION" (57).

Prices are for unused. Used are worth rather more.

No.		A.	B.	C.	D.	E.	F.
34	½d. ..	1 9	7 6	3 6	†	£6	£6
35	1d. ..	2 6	10 0	4 0	†	†	£9
	b. Inv.	£100	£100	£100	†	†	†
36	2d. ..	4 0	15 0	†	30 0	†	£8
37	2½d. ..	5 0	18 6	50 0	50 0	†	£8
38	3d. ..	5 0	17 6	£6	†	†	£12
	g. W.b.	50 0	£5	†	†	†	†
40	6d. ..	7 0	15 0	†	†	†	£17
41	1s. ..	8 6	20 0	†	†	†	£8
42	2s. ..	22 6	42 6	£6	†	†	£20
43	2s. 6d.	27 6	52 6	£6	†	†	£16
44	5s. ..	42 6	82 6	£10	†	†	£16
45	10s. ..	60 0	£8	†	†	†	£30
46	20s. ..	£6	£12	†	†	†	£22

TOGO

Anglo-French

OCCUPATION

(8)

1916 (Apr.). *London opt. T 8* ("OCCUPATION" *15 mm. long*). *Heavy type and thicker letters showing through on back.*

No.	Description	Unused	Used
77	½d. green	0 3	0 3
78	1d. red	0 3	0 3
79	2d. greyish slate	0 6	0 6
80	2½d. bright blue	0 10	0 10
81	3d. purple/*yellow*	1 6	1 6
82	6d. dull and bright purple ..	1 9	1 9
83	1s. black/*green*	3 0	3 6
	a. On blue-green, olive back ..	12 6	17 6
	b. On emerald back	£12	
84	2s. purple and blue/*blue* ..	6 0	5 0
85	2s. 6d. black and red/*blue* ..	4 0	4 6
86	5s. green and red/*yellow* ..	9 0	10 0
	a. On orange-buff	8 6	10 0
87	10s. green and red/*green* ..	22 6	27 6
	a. On blue-green, olive back ..	15 0	27 6
88	20s. purple and black/*red* ..	52 6	60 0

TONGA.

(PROTECTORATE.)

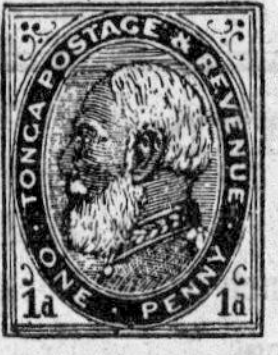

1. King George I. 2

Dies engraved by Messrs. Bock and Cousins. Plates and printing by Government Printing Office, Wellington, N.Z.)

1886-88. *W 2. P 12½ (line) or 12 × 11½ (comb).**

No.	Type	Description	Unused	Used
1	1	1d. carm. (27.8.86), *p.* 12½	65 0	4 6
		a. Perf. 12½ × 10 ..		
		b. Perf. 12 × 11½ (15.7.87) ..	2 0	2 6
		ba. Pale carmine (12 × 11½) ..	9 0	9 6
2	,,	2d. pale vio. (27.8.86), *p.* 12½	15 0	9 0
		a. Bright violet	17 6	8 0
		b. Perf. 12 × 11½ (15.7.87) ..	10 0	6 0
		ba. Bright violet (12 × 11½) ..	4 0	4 0
3	,,	6d. blue (9.10.86), *p.* 12½ ..	6 0	4 6
		a. Perf. 12 × 11½ (15.10.88) ..	5 0	3 0
		ab. Dull blue (12 × 11½) ..	6 0	6 6
4	,,	1s. pale grn. (9.10.86), *p.* 12½	25 0	7 0
		a. Deep green. p. 12½ ..	27 6	4 0
		b. Perf. 12 × 11½ (15.10.88) ..	7 6	5 6
		ba. Deep green (12 × 11½) ..	7 0	4 6

* See note after New Zealand, No. 186.

FOUR PENCE. (3)

EIGHT PENCE. (4)

(Surcharged by Messrs. Wilson & Horton, Auckland, N.Z.)

1891 (10 Nov.). *Nos. 1b and 2b surcharged.*

No.	Type	Description	Unused	Used
5	3	4d. on 1d. carmine	4 0	5 0
		a. No stop after "PENCE" ..	27 6	32 6
6	4	8d. on 2d. violet	7 0	7 6
		a. Short "T" in "EIGHT"	32 6	37 6

1891 (23 Nov.). *Optd. with stars in upper right and lower left corners.* P 12½.

7	1	1d. carmine ..	9 0	10 0
		a. Three stars	50 0	
		b. Four stars	£5	
		c. Five stars	£12	
		d. Perf. 12×11½	32 6	
		da. Three stars	£5	
		db. Four stars	£8	
		dc. Five stars	£12	
8	,,	2d. violet	15 0	16 0
		a. Perf. 12×11½	62 6	

1892 (15 Aug.). *W* 2. P 12×11½.

9	1	6d. yellow-orange ..	4 0	5 0

5. Arms of Tonga. 6. King George I.

(Dies engraved by A. E. Cousins. Typographed at Govt. Printing Office, Wellington, N.Z.)

1892 (10 Nov.). *Wmk. T* 2. P 12×11½.

10	5	1d. pale rose	4 6	5 0
		a. *Bright rose*	4 0	4 6
		b. Bisected diagonally (½d.)	—	32 6
11	6	2d. olive	3 6	4 0
12	5	4d. chestnut	12 0	15 0
13	6	8d. bright mauve	14 0	16 0
14	,,	1s. brown	10 6	12 6

½d. (7) 2½d. (8)

FIVE PENCE. (9) 7½d. (10)

1893. *Printed in new colours and surcharged.*

(*a*) *In carmine.* P 12½. (21 Aug.)

15	5	½d. on 1d. bright ultram.	7 0	8 6
		a. Surcharge omitted		
16	6	2½d. on 2d. green	6 0	7 0
17	5	5d. on 4d. orange	6 0	8 6
18	6	7½d. on 8d. carmine	12 0	15 0

(*b*) *In black.* P 12×11½. (Nov.)

19	5	½d. on 1d. dull blue	7 0	8 6
20	6	2½d. on 2d. green	5 6	7 0
		a. Surcharge double ..		

SURCHARGE. HALF-PENNY (11) SURCHARGE. 2½d. (12)

(Surcharged at the "Star" Office, Auckland, N.Z.)

1894 (June). *Surcharged with T* 11 *or* 12.

21	5	½d. on 4d. chestnut (No. 12) (B)	3 6	4 0
		a. "SURCHARCE."	7 6	9 0
22	6	½d. on 1s. brn. (No. 14) (Bk.)	4 0	6 0
		a. "SURCHARCE."	8 6	12 0
		b. Surcharge double	£10	
		c. Surcharge double with "SURCHARCE."		
23	,,	2½d. on 8d. bright mauve (No. 13) (Bk.)	4 0	6 0
		a. No stop after "SURCHARGE"	32 6	42 6
24	1	2½d. on 1s. grn. (No. 4*a*) (Bk.)	12 0	15 0
		a. No stop after "SURCHARGE"	82 6	
		b. Perf. 12×11½	6 0	7 6
		ba. No stop after "SURCHARGE"	42 6	

(Design resembling No. 11 lithographed and surcharged at "Star" Office, Auckland, N.Z.)

1895 (May). *As T* 6 *surcharged as T* 11 *and* 12. *No wmk.* P 12.

25	11	1d. on 2d. pale blue (C.)	5 0	6 6
26	12	1½d. on 2d. pale blue (C.)	17 6	22 6
		a. Perf. 12×11	15 0	17 6
27	,,	2½d. on 2d. pale blue (C.)*	15 0	17 6
		a. No stop after "SURCHARGE"	£5	
28	,,	7½d. on 2d. pale blue (C.)	£5	
		a. Perf. 12×11	35 0	40 0

* The 2½d. on 2d. is the only value which normally has a stop after the word "SURCHARGE."

13. King George II.

(Lithographed at "Star" Office, Auckland, N.Z.)

1895 (16 Aug.). *No wmk.* P 12.

29	13	1d. olive-green	8 0	9 0
		a. Bisected diagonally (½d.)	—	22 6
		b. Imperf. between (pair)		
30	,,	2½d. rose	4 0	5 6
		a. Stop (flaw) after "POSTAGE."	52 6	
31	,,	5d. blue	10 0	12 6
		a. Perf. 12×11	5 0	7 0
		b. Perf. 11	£16	
32	,,	7½d. orange-yellow	7 0	9 0
		a. *Yellow*	7 0	8 0

1895 (Sept.). *T* 13 *redrawn and surcharged. No wmk.* P 12.

33	11	½d. on 2½d. vermilion	10 0	12 6
		a. "SURCHARCE"	40 0	
		b. Stop after "POSTAGE."	82 6	
34	,,	1d. on 2½d. vermilion	5 0	6 6
		a. Stop after "POSTAGE."	60 0	
35	12	7½d. on 2½d. vermilion	12 6	15 0
		a. Stop after "POSTAGE."	90 0	

In the ½d. surcharge there is a stop after "SURCHARGE" and not after "PENNY." In the 1d. and 7½d. the stop is after the value only.

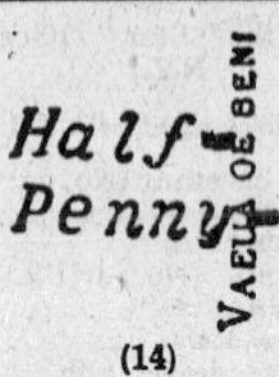

(14)

1896 (May). *Nos. 26a and 28a with typewritten surcharge* " Half-Penny-" *in violet, and Tongan surcharge in black.*

(A) *Tongan inscription reading downwards.*

(B) *Tongan inscription reading upwards.*

			A.	B.
36	**6**	½d. on 1½d. on 2d.	£5	£8
		a. Perf. 12	£12	£12
		ab. "Haalf" (*p.* 12) ..	†	£25

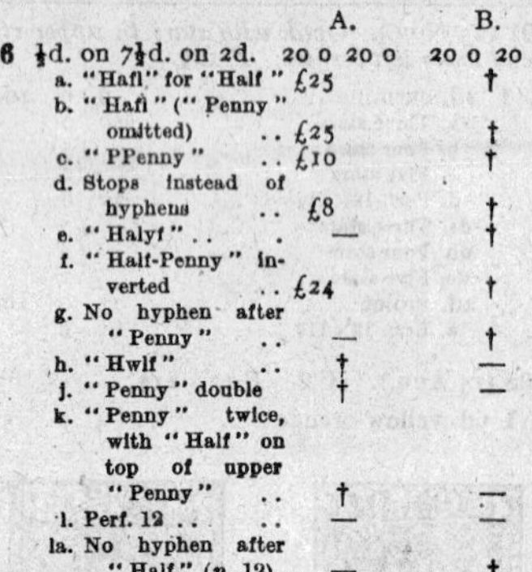

			A.		B.	
37	**6**	½d. on 7½d. on 2d.	20 0	20 0	20 0	20 0
		a. "Hafl" for "Half"	£25		†	
		b. "Hafl" ("Penny" omitted) ..	£25		†	
		c. "PPenny" ..	£10		†	
		d. Stops instead of hyphens ..	£8		†	
		e. "Halyf" .. .	—		†	
		f. "Half-Penny" inverted ..	£24		†	
		g. No hyphen after "Penny" ..	—		†	
		h. "Hwlf" ..	†		—	
		j. "Penny" double	†		—	
		k. "Penny" twice, with "Half" on top of upper "Penny" ..	†		—	
		l. Perf. 12	—		—	
		la. No hyphen after "Half" (*p.* 12)	—		†	

There are variations in the relative positions of the words " Half " and " Penny," both vertically and horizontally.

15. Arms.

16. Ovava tree, Kana-Kubolu.

17. Kink George II.

18. Prehistoric trilith at Haamonga. (29 × 24 mm.)

19. Bread fruit. (29 × 24 mm.)

20. Coral. (23 × 29mm.)

21. View of Haapai. (35 × 24 mm.)

22. Kaka, or Hawk-billed Parrot. (24 × 35 mm.)

23. View of Vavau harbour. (35 × 24 mm.)

I. No sword hilt.

24. Tortoises.

II. Top of hilt showing.

(Recess. De La Rue & Co.)

1897 (June). *T* **15** *to* **23** (*various designs*). *W* **24.** *P* 14.

38	**15**	½d. indigo	0	6	0	6
39	**16**	1d. black and scarlet ..	0	4	0	4
40	**17**	2d. sepia and bistre (I) ..	5	0	5	0
41	„	2d. grey and bistre (I) ..	8	0	3	6
42	„	2d. sepia and bistre (II) ..	3	0	3	0
43	„	2½d. black and blue ..	2	6	3	0
		a. No fraction bar in "½" ..	32	6	32	6
44	**18**	3d. black & yellow-green ..	1	3	1	6
45	**19**	4d. green and purple ..	6	0	6	6
46	**17**	5d. black and orange ..	6	0	6	0
47	**20**	6d. red	2	0	2	6
48	**17**	7½d. black and green ..	7	6	7	6
		a. Centre inverted	£70			
49	„	10d. black and lake ..	7	6	8	0
50	„	1s. black and red-brown ..	6	0	6	6
		a. No hyphen before "TAHA"	£6			
51	**21**	2s. black and ultramarine	10	6	12	6
52	**22**	2s. 6d. deep purple ..	8	6	10	6
53	**23**	5s. black and brown-red	17	6	20	0

The 1d., 3d., and 4d. are known bisected and used for half their value.

T - L

1 June, 1899.

(25)

1899 (1 June). *Royql Wedding. Overprinted with T* **25** *at* " Star " *Office, Auckland, N.Z.*

54	**16**	1d. black and scarlet ..	12	6	15	0
		a. "1889" for "1899" ..	£8		£8	

The letters " T L " stand for Taufa'ahau, the King's family name, and Lavinia, the bride's name.

26. Queen Salote.

(Recess. De La Rue & Co.)

1920 21. *W* **24.** *P* 14.

55 **26** 2d. brown-purple & violet 1 9 1 3
a. Black and dull purple .. 0 10 1 0
56 „ 2½d. black and blue .. 2 0 3 0
57 „ 5d. black & orange-verm. . 1 9 2 0
58 „ 7½d. black & yellow-green .. 2 6 3 0
59 „ 10d. black and lake .. 3 6 4 0
60 „ 1s. black and red-brown . 3 6 4 6

TWO PENCE

TWO PENCE

PENI-E-UA PENI-E-UA
(27) (28)

1923 (20 Oct.)–**1924.** *Nos.* 46 *and* 48 *to* 53 *surcharged as T* **27** (*vertical stamps*) *or* **28** (*oblong stamps*).

61 2d. on 5d. blk. & orge. (B.) .. 3 0 3 6
62 2d. on 7½d. blk. & green (B.) 16 0 17 6
63 2d. on 10d. blk. & lake (B.) 17 6 15 0
64 2d. on 1s. blk. & red-brn. (B.) 25 0 17 6
a. No hyphen before "TAHA" .. £22
65 2d. on 2s. blk. & ultram. (R.) 8 0 9 6
66 2d. on 2s. 6d. dp. purple (R.) 6 0 7 0
67 2d. on 5s. blk. & brn.-red (R.) 5 0 6 0

1934–35. *New colours.* *W* **24.** *P* 14.

68 **15** ½d. yellow-green .. 0 2 0 3
69 **26** 1½d. grey-black ('35) .. 0 4 0 8
70 „ 2½d. bright ultramarine .. 1 0 1 3

For T **15** to **26**, wmk. Mult. Script CA, see King George VI Catalogue.

OFFICIAL STAMPS.

G.F.B.

(O 1) (O 2)

(G.F.B.=Gaue Faka Buleaga=On Government Service.)

1893 (13 Feb.). *Overprinted with Type* O **1.** *W* **2.** *P* 12×11½.

O1 **5** 1d. ultramarine (C) .. 6 0 6 6
a. Bisected diagonally (½d.) ..
O2 **6** 2d. ultramarine (C) .. 8 6 10 0
O3 **5** 4d. ultramarine (C) .. 30 0 35 0
O4 **6** 8d. ultramarine (C) .. 60 0 70 0
O5 „ 1s. ultramarine (C) .. 70 0 80 0

Above prices are for stamps in good condition and colour. Faded and stained stamps from the remainders are worth much less.

1893 (Dec.). *Nos.* O1 *to* O5 *variously surcharged with new value, sideways as Type* O **2.**

O6 **5** ½d. on 1d. ultramarine .. 6 0 7 6
O7 **6** 2½d on 2d. ultramarine .. 5 0 6 0
O8 **5** 5d. on 4d. ultramarine .. 7 6 7 6
O9 **6** 7½d. on 8d. ultramarine .. 10 0 10 0
a. "D" of "7½D." omitted ..
b. Surcharge double ..
O10 „ 10d. on 1s. ultramarine .. 10 0 10 0

TRANSJORDAN.

(*The issues of Transjordan, an independent sovereign State, are included in this volume as a matter of convenience to collectors.*)

(A) BRITISH MANDATE.

شرقي الاردن شرقي الاردن

("East of Jordan.")

(1) (1*a*)

(Overprinted at the Greek Orthodox Convent, Jerusalem.)

1920 (Nov.). *T* **3** *of Palestine optd. with T* **1.**

(*a*) *P* 15×14.

1 **1** 1 m. sepia 0 3 0 6
a. Overprint inverted .. £6
2 „ 2 m. blue-green .. 7 6 15 0
3 „ 3 m. yellow-brown .. 0 6 1 0
4 „ 4 m. scarlet .. 0 6 1 0
5 „ 5 m. yellow-orange .. 1 0 2 0
6 „ 2 p. olive 4 6 8 6
a. Overprint Type 1a .. £40
7 „ 5 p. deep purple 25 0 32 6
8 „ 9 p. ochre £65

(*b*) *P* 14.

9 **1** 1 m. sepia 0 3 0 6
a. Overprint inverted .. £12
10 „ 2 m. blue-green .. 0 3 0 6
11 „ 3 m. yellow-brown .. 10 0 15 0
12 „ 4 m. scarlet .. 20 0 32 6
13 „ 5 m. orange .. 1 0 1 3
14 „ 1 p. deep indigo (silver) .. 1 3 1 6
15 „ 2 p. deep olive .. 1 9 4 6
16 „ 5 p. purple 4 0 10 0
17 „ 9 p. ochre 7 6 37 6
18 „ 10 p. ultramarine .. 8 6 30 0
19 „ 20 p. pale grey .. 20 0 45 0

عشر القرش القرش

("Tenth of a piastre.") ("Piastre.")

(2) (3)

1922 (Nov.). *Stamps of Transjordan,* 1920, *handstamped with a steel die as T* **2** (*millieme values*) *or* **3** (*piastre values*), *in black, red, or violet.* (*a*) *P* 15×14.

20 **2** 1 m. sepia (Bk.) 22 6 25 0
a. Red surcharge 55 0 55 0
b. Violet surcharge 55 0 55 0
21 „ 2 m. blue-green (Bk.) .. 22 6 22 6
a. Error. Surch. "$\frac{3}{10}$" for "$\frac{2}{10}$" 70 0
b. Red surcharge 55 0 55 0
c. Violet surcharge .. 55 0 55 0
22 „ 3 m. yellow-brown (Bk.) .. 10 0 10 0
a. Violet surcharge .. ..
23 „ 4 m. scarlet (Bk.) .. 32 6 37 6
24 „ 5 m. yellow-orange (Bk.) .. 110 0 20 0
a. Violet surcharge .. £8
25 **3** 2 p. olive (Bk.) .. £8 45 0
a. Red surcharge .. £8 55 0
26 „ 5 p. deep purple (Bk.) .. 37 6 50 0
27 „ 9 p. ochre (Bk.) .. £8 £8
a. Red surcharge .. 60 0 70 0

(*b*) *P* 14.

28 **2** 1 m. sepia (Bk.) .. 20 0 22 6
a. Surcharge omitted (in pair) £25
b. Red surcharge .. 45 0 50 0
29 „ 2 m. blue-green (Bk.) .. 22 6 22 6
a. Error. Surch. "$\frac{3}{10}$" for "$\frac{2}{10}$" 55 0
b. Red surcharge .. 75 0 25 0
c. Violet surcharge .. 55 0 65 0
30 „ 5 m. orange (Bk.) .. £6 27 6

31 **3** 1 p. deep indigo (R.) .. £7 25 0
  a. Violet surcharge .. ..
32 „ 9 p. ochre (R.) £25 £25
33 „ 10 p. ultramarine (Bk.) .. £35 £45
34 „ 20 p. pale grey (Bk.) .. £24 £30

T 3 of Palestine (perf. 15 × 14) similarly surch.

35 **3** 10 p. ultramarine .. £150
36 „ 20 p. pale grey £100

T **2** reads "tenth of a piastre" with Arabic figures below. T **3** reads "the piastre." These surcharges were supplied in order to translate the Egyptian face values of the stamps into terms intelligible to the local population, *i.e.* tenths of a piastre (=milliemes) and piastres of the Turkish gold pound; but the actual face value of the stamps remained unchanged. Being handstamped the surcharge may be found either at the top or bottom of the stamp, and exists double on most values.

("Government of Eastern Arabia, April, 1921.")
(4)

1922 (DEC.). *Stamps of Transjordan,* 1920, *handstamped with a steel die as T* **4**, *in red-purple, violet, or black.** (*a*) *P* 15 × 14.

37 **4** 1 m. sepia (R.P.) 22 6 22 6
  a. Violet overprint .. 25 0 25 0
  b. Black overprint 17 6 17 6
38 „ 2 m. blue-green (R.P.) .. 17 6 17 6
  a. Violet overprint .. 15 0 15 0
  b. Black overprint 10 0 10 0
39 „ 3 m. yellow-brown (R.P.) 20 0 20 0
  a. Violet overprint .. 3 6 3 6
  b. Black overprint .. 4 0 4 0
40 „ 4 m. scarlet (R.P.) .. 35 0 35 0
  a. Violet overprint 35 0 35 0
  b. Black overprint 35 0 35 0
41 „ 5 m. yellow-orange (R.P.) 25 0 10 0
  a. Violet overprint .. 10 0 8 6
42 „ 2 p. olive (No. 6) (R.P.) .. 50 0 50 0
  a. Violet overprint .. 20 0 17 6
  b. Black overprint 10 0 10 0
  c. On No. 6*a* (R.P.)
  d. On No. 6*a* (V) .. ..
43 „ 5 p. deep purple (R.P.) .. 65 0 80 0
  a. Violet overprint 40 0 50 0
44 „ 9 p. ochre (R.P.) £15 £22
  a. Violet overprint £7 £10
  b. Black overprint 45 0 55 0

(*b*) *P* 14.

45 **4** 1 m. sepia (R.P.) 7 6 8 6
  a. Violet overprint 25 0 17 6
  b. Black overprint 17 6 17 6
46 „ 2 m. blue-green (R.P.) .. 20 0 25 0
  a. Violet overprint .. 3 6 3 6
  b. Black overprint .. 4 0 4 0
47 „ 5 m. orange (R.P.) .. £8 30 0
  a. Violet overprint .. 15 0 10 0
48 „ 1 p. deep indigo (R.P.) .. 17 6 10 0
  a. Violet overprint .. 8 6 7 6
49 „ 2 p. olive (V.) 70 0 80 0
50 „ 5 p. purple (R.P.) 80 0 85 0
  a. Violet overprint 90 0 £5
51 „ 9 p. ochre (V.) £15 £17
52 „ 10 p. ultramarine (R.P.) .. £35 £40
  a. Violet overprint £30 £35
53 „ 20 p. pale grey (R.P.) .. £45 £50
  a. Violet overprint £42 £45

* The ink of the "black" overprint is not a true black, but is caused by a mixture of inks from different ink-pads. The colour is, however, very distinct from either of the others. Other values may exist with "black" overprint.

Most values are known with inverted and/or double overprints.

حكومة الشرق
العربية
نيسان سنة ١٩٢١

("Government of Eastern Arabia, April, 1921.")
(5)

1923 (1 MAR.). *Stamps of Transjordan,* 1920, *with typographed overprint,* T **5**, *in black or gold.* (G.) (*a*) *P* 15 × 14.

54 **5** 1 m. sepia (G.) £70 £70
55 „ 2 m. blue-green (G.) .. 17 6 20 0
56 „ 3 m. yellow-brown (G.) .. 10 0 12 6
  a. Black overprint 50 0 60 0
57 „ 4 m. scarlet (Bk.) 6 6 8 0
58 „ 5 m. yellow-orange (Bk.) .. 40 0 35 0
59 „ 2 p. olive (No. 6) (G.) .. 12 6 15 0
  a. Black overprint .. £5
  b. On No. 6*a* (G.) ..
60 „ 5 p. deep purple (G.) .. 30 0 40 0
  a. Overprint inverted .. £10
61 „ 9 p. ochre (Bk.) .. ..

(*b*) *P* 14.

62 **5** 1 m. sepia (G.) 17 6 25 0
63 „ 2 m. blue-green (G.) .. 10 0 15 0
  a. Overprint inverted .. £25
  b. Overprint double .. £12
64 „ 5 m. orange (Bk.) 7 6 7 6
65 „ 1 p. deep indigo (G.) 10 0 12 6
  a. Overprint double (G.) .. £35 £40
  b. Black overprint £35 £40
66 „ 9 p. ochre (Bk.) 37 6 45 0
67 „ 10 p. ultramarine (G.) .. 60 0 70 0
68 „ 20 p. pale grey (G.) 45 0 70 0
  a. Overprint inverted .. £15
  b. Overprint double .. £25
  c. Overprint double, one gold, one black, latter inverted £25
  d. Overprint double, in gold, one inverted £25

There are numerous constant minor varieties in this overprint in all values.

Same overprint on stamp of Palestine, T **3**.

69 **5** 5 m. orange £15

In this variety the overprint, T **1** of Transjordan, has been applied to the stamp, but is not inked, so that it is hardly perceptible.

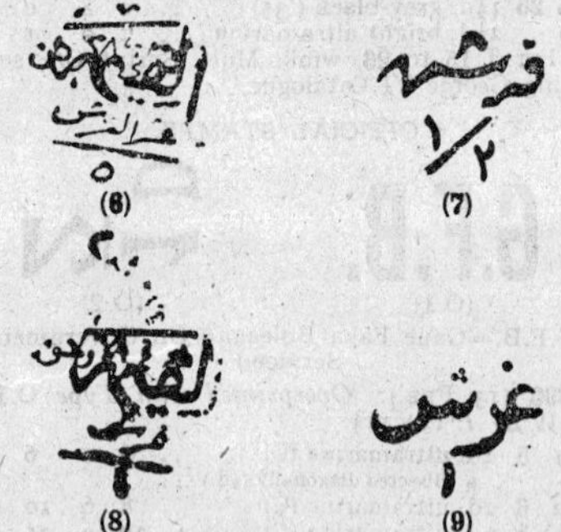

(6) (7) (8) (9)

1923 (APRIL–OCT.). *Stamps of the preceding issues further surcharged in black or violet.*

(*a*) *Issue of Nov.,* 1920.

70 – 2½/10ths p. on 5 m. (No. 13) (B.-Bk.) £8 £8
  a. Black surcharge .. £8 £8
  b. Violet surcharge .. £7 £7

(*b*) *Stamp of Palestine.*

71 **6** $\frac{5}{10}$ p. on 3 m. (No. 7) ..

(c) Issue of Nov., 1922.

72 **6** $\frac{5}{10}$ p. on 3 m. (No. 22) ..
73 ,, $\frac{5}{10}$ on 5 p.(N o. 26) .. 60 0 70 0
a. Surcharge double £8 £10
73*b* ,, $\frac{5}{10}$ p. on 9 p. (No. 27*a*) .. £12
74 **7** $\frac{1}{2}$ p. on 5 p. (No. 26) .. 45 0 70 0
a. Surcharge inverted .. £5
75 ,, $\frac{1}{2}$ p. on 9 p. (No. 27) ..
a. On No. 27*a* £10 £12
b. On No. 27*a*. Surch. inverted £12 £12
76 ,, $\frac{1}{2}$ p. on 9 p. (No. 32) ..
77 **8** 1 p. on 5 p. (No. 26) .. 60 0 70 0
a. Surcharge double .. £6
b. Surcharge treble .. £12

(d) Issue of Dec., 1922.

78 **6** $\frac{5}{10}$ p. on 3 m. (No. 39) .. 80 0
a. On No. 39*a* 27 6 35 0
b. On No. 39*a*. Surch. double £5
c. On No. 39*a*. Surch. inverted £5
d. Without numeral of value £5
79 ,, $\frac{5}{10}$ p. on 5 p. (No. 43*a*) .. 4 6 10 0
a. Surcharge inverted .. 70 0
b. Surcharge double £5
c. Surcharge omitted (in pair) £10
79*d* ,, $\frac{5}{10}$ p. on 9 p. (No. 44*b*) .. — £6
80 **7** $\frac{1}{2}$ p. on 2 p. (No. 42) .. 80 0 £5
a. Surch. inverted (No. 42) .. £5
b. On No. 42*a* 40 0
c. On No. 42*b* 40 0
d. On No. 42*b*. Surch. invrtd. 80 0
e. On No. 42*b*. Surcharge omitted (in pair) .. £20
f. On No. 42 .. ..
81 ,, $\frac{1}{2}$ p. on 5 p. (No. 43*a*) .. £60
82 ,, $\frac{1}{2}$ p. on 5 p. (No. 50) .. £40
83 **8** 1 p. on 5 p. (No. 43) ..
a. Surcharge inverted .. £80
b. On No. 43*a* .. £50
c. On No. 43*a*. Surch. double £100

(e) Issue of 1 March, 1923.

84 **6** $\frac{5}{10}$ p. on 3 m. (No. 56) .. 20 0 25 0
85 **7** $\frac{1}{2}$ p. on 9 p. (No. 61) .. £5 £8
a. Surcharge inverted ..
86 ,, $\frac{1}{2}$ p. on 9 p. (No. 66) .. £7
87 **9** 1 p. on 10 p. (No. 67) .. £45 £50
a. Surcharge inverted .. £60
88 ,, 2 p. on 20 p. (No. 68) .. 45 0 60 0
a. Surcharge inverted £5
b. Surcharge double .. £12

The surcharge on No. 88 has, of course, the Arabic "2" in place of the "1" shown in our illustration.

حكومة

الشرق العربية

٩ شعبان ١٣٤١

("Government of Eastern Arabia, 9 April, 1921.")

(10)

1923 (April). *Stamps of Saudi Arabia, T* 11, *with typographed overprint T* 10.

89 **10** $\frac{1}{8}$ p. chestnut 1 6 1 0
a. Overprint double .. £7
90 ,, $\frac{1}{2}$ p. scarlet 2 0 1 6
91 ,, 1 p. indigo 1 0 0 8
a. Overprint inverted .. £10
92 ,, 1$\frac{1}{2}$ p. mauve 1 6 2 0
a. Overprint double .. £7
93 ,, 2 p. orange 2 0 3 6
94 ,, 3 p. brown 3 0 6 6
a. Overprint inverted .. £12
b. Overprint double .. £18
c. Overprint omitted (in pair) £35
95 ,, 5 p. olive 6 6 10 0

On same stamps, surcharged with new values (Saudi Arabia, Nos. 41 *and* 42).

96 **10** $\frac{1}{4}$ on $\frac{1}{8}$ p. chestnut .. 2 0 2 6
a. Overprint and surcharge inverted £6
97 ,, 10 on 5 p. olive 15 0 30 0

In this setting, the first line of the overprint measures 9 mm., the second 18$\frac{1}{2}$–19$\frac{1}{2}$ mm., and the third, 19–21 mm. On 35 stamps out of the setting of 36 the Arabic "9" (right-hand character in bottom line) is widely spaced from the rest of the inscription.

Minor varieties of this setting exist on all values.

For later setting, varying from the above, see Nos. 121 to 124.

ح. ش. ع

تذكار استقلال

٢٥ شعبان ١٣٤١

("Government of Eastern Arabia. Souvenir of Independence, 25 May, 1923.")

(11)

1923 (25 May). *T* 3 *of Palestine optd. with T* 11, *reading up or down, in black or gold.*

A. *Reading downwards.* B. *Reading upwards.*

(*It should be noted that as Arabic is read from right to left, the overprint described as reading downwards appears to the English reader as though reading upwards.* Our illustration shows the overprint reading downwards.)

		A.		B.	
98 **11**	1 m. (Bk.)	22 6	22 6	£5	£6
	a. Opt. double, one inverted (Bk.)	£25	—	†	
	b. Gold opt.	£5	£5	£6	£8
	c. Opt. double, one inverted (G.)	£25	—	†	
	d. Opt. double (Bk. and G.)	£25	—	†	
99 ,,	2 m. (Bk.)	32 6	32 6	55 0	60 0
100 ,,	3 m. (Bk.)	10 0	12 6	£5	£6
101 ,,	4 m. (Bk.)	10 0	12 6	30 0	35 0
102 ,,	5 m. (Bk.)	55 0	60 0	†	
103 ,,	1 p. (G.)	†		60 0	60 0
	a. Overprint double	£30	—	†	
104 ,,	2 p. (Bk.)	55 0	60 0	†	
105 ,,	5 p. (G.)	60 0	70 0	£25	£25
	a. Overprint double	£25	—	†	
106 ,,	9 p. (Bk.)	95 0	£5	55 0	55 0
107 ,,	10 p. (Bk.)	55 0	65 0	£10	—
108 ,,	20 p. (Bk.)	£12	—	60 0	60 0

The 9 and 10 p. are perf. 14, all the other values being perf. 15 × 14.

An error reading "933" instead of "923" occurs as No. 2 in the setting of 24, on all values.

No. 107 A *surcharged with T* 9.

109 **9** 1 p. on 10 p. £120 £120

نصف قرش

(12)

1923 (Sept.). *No.* 92 *surcharged with T* 12.

(a) Handstamped.

110 **12** $\frac{1}{2}$ p. on 1$\frac{1}{2}$ p. mauve .. 2 6 3 6
a. Surcharge and overprint inverted 75 0

This handstamp is known inverted; double; double, one inverted; and omitted in pair with normal.

(*b*) *Typographed.*

111 **12** ½ p. on 1½ p. mauve .. 25 0 30 0
 a. Surcharge inverted ..

حكومة حكومة

الشرق العربية الشرق العربية

٩ شعبان ١٣٤١ ٩ شعبان ١٣٤١

(**12a**) (**12b**)

1923 (Oct.). *T* **11** *of Saudi Arabia handstamped as T* **12a** *or* **12b**.

112 **12a** ½ p. scarlet 2 0 2 6
 a. Overprint double .. £7
113 **12b** ½ p. scarlet 3 0 3 6
 a. Overprint inverted ..

The two types differ in the spacing of the characters and in the position of the bottom line which is to the left of the middle line in T **12a** and centrally placed in T **12b**.

حكومة الشرق العربية

(" Government of Eastern Arabia.")

(**13**)

1924 (Jan.). *T* **11** *of Saudi Arabia with typographed opt. T* **13**.

114 **13** ½ p. scarlet.. .. .. 7 6 10 0
 a. Overprint inverted .. £10
115 ,, 1 p. ultramarine £5 £8
 a. *Indigo* £7
116 ,, 1½ p. mauve £7

The ½ p. exists with thick, brown gum, which tints the paper, and with white gum and paper.

ذ ٠ ق ٠ ج

ملك العرب

ا ج ٠ ث ٣٤٢

(" Commemorating the coming of His Majesty the King of the Arabs " and date.)

(**14**)

1924 (18 Jan.). *T* **11** *of Saudi Arabia optd. with T* **13** *and with further typographed opt. T* **14**, A. *In Black*. B. *In Gold.*

A. B.

117 **14** ½ p. scarlet 1 0 2 0 1 0 2 0
 a. Type 13 omitted .. £18 — †
 b. Imperf. .. .. † —
 c. Imperf. between (pr.) † —
118 **14** 1 p. indigo 1 9 3 0 1 9 3 0
 a. Type 13 omitted .. £18 — †
 b. Both opts. inverted † £22 —
 c. *Ultramarine* .. 1 9 3 0 1 9 3 0
 d. Imperf. between (pr.) † —
119 ,, 1½ p. mauve 2 6 4 0 2 6 4 0
 a. Type 13 inverted .. † £12 —
120 ,, 2 p. orange 3 6 6 0 3 6 6 0

The above set commemorates the visit of King Hussein. The spacing of the lines of the overprint varies considerably, and a variety dated " 432 " for " 342 " occurs on the twelfth stamp in each sheet.

1924 (Mar.–May). *T* **11** *of Saudi Arabia optd as T* **10** (*new setting*).*

121 – ½ p. scarlet.. .. .. 2 6 1 0
 a. Overprint inverted .. £9
122 – ½ p. marone 7 6 2 0
 a. Overprint inverted .. £12
123 – 1 p. indigo 4 0 1 0
 a. Overprint double .. £8
124 – 1½ p. mauve 7 6 12 6

* This setting is from fresh type, the first line measuring 8¾ mm., the second nearly 20 mm. and the third 18½ mm.

On all stamps in this setting (except Nos. 1, 9, 32 and 33) the Arabic " 9 " is close to the rest of the inscription.

The dots on the character " Y " (the second character from the left in the second line) are on many stamps vertical (:) instead of horizontal (..).

There are many errors. In the third line, No. 24 of the setting reads " Shabál," and No. 27 reads " Shabn " (instead of " Shab'an ").

On some sheets of the ½ p. (both colours), the right hand character, " H ", in the first line, was omitted from the second stamp in the first row of the sheet.

حكومة الشرق

العربي

١٣٤٢

(" Government of the Eastern Arabs, 1924.")

(**15**)

1924 (Sept.–Nov.). *T* **11** *of Saudi Arabia with typographed opt. T* **15**.

125 **15** ⅛ p. chestnut 0 4 0 4
126 ,, ¼ p. apple-green 0 4 0 3
 a. Tête-bêche (pair) .. 6 0 8 6
127 ,, ½ p. scarlet.. .. .. 0 5 0 4
128 ,, ½ p. marone 2 6 0 8
129 ,, 1 p. indigo 4 0 0 8
130 ,, 1½ p. mauve 1 6 3 6
131 ,, 2 p. orange 1 9 3 0
132 ,, 3 p. red-brown 2 6 4 0
133 ,, 5 p. olive 3 0 5 0
134 ,, 10 p. black-brn. & mve. (R.) 5 0 12 6

Varieties may be found with dates " 1242 " or " 1343 ", with " 1 " or " 2 " inverted, and other errors exist.

سنة ١٣٤٣

(" Government of the Eastern Arabs, year 1925.")

(**16**)

1925 (Aug.). *T* **20** *to* **22** *of Saudi Arabia with lithographed opt. T* **16**.

135 **16** ⅛ p. chocolate 0 4 0 4
 a. Imperf. between (horiz. pr.) 65 0
136 ,, ¼ p. ultramarine 0 5 0 5
137 ,, ½ p. carmine 0 6 0 6
138 ,, 1 p. green 0 7 1 0
139 ,, 1½ p. orange 1 0 3 0
140 ,, 2 p. blue 1 3 4 0
141 ,, 3 p. sage-green (R.) .. 1 6 5 0
 a. Imperf. between (horiz. pr.) 75 0
 b. Overprint in black .. £7
142 ,, 5 p. chestnut 2 6 7 6

The whole series exists imperf. and (except the 1 and 2 p.) with inverted overprint, both perf. and imperf. The 2 p. is known with treble overprint.

شرق
الاردن

(" Eastern Jordan.")

(17)

(Overprinted typographically by Waterlow & Sons, Ltd.)

1925 (1 Nov.). *Stamps of Palestine*, 1922 (*without the three-line Palestine opt.*), *optd. with* T **17**. *Wmk. Mult. Script CA.* (*a*) *P* 14.

No.	Type	Description	s.	d.	s.	d.
143	**17**	1 m. deep brown	0	2	0	2
144	,,	2 m. yellow	0	2	0	2
145	,,	3 m. greenish blue ..	0	3	0	3
146	,,	4 m. carmine-pink ..	0	4	0	4
147	,,	5 m. orange	0	5	0	5
148	,,	6 m. blue-green	0	5	0	5
149	,,	7 m. yellow-brown ..	0	8	0	9
150	,,	8 m. scarlet	0	7	0	6
151	,,	13 m. ultramarine	1	6	3	6
152	,,	1 p. grey	0	8	0	7
153	,,	2 p. olive	1	3	2	0
		a. *Olive-green*	—		3	6
154	,,	5 p. deep purple	3	0	4	6
155	,,	9 p. ochre	5	0	8	6
156	,,	10 p. light blue	6	6	10	0
		a. Error. "E.F.F." in bottom panel ..	£10			
157	,,	20 p. bright violet ..	15	0	20	0
		(*b*) *P* 15×14.				
157*a*	**17**	9 p. ochre				
158	,,	10 p. blue	80	0	80	0
158*a*	,,	20 p. bright violet ..	£60		£60	

18. Emir Abdullah. **19**

(Recess. Perkins Bacon & Co., Ltd.)

1927–29. *Wmk. Mult. Script CA.* *P* 14.

No.	Type	Description	s.	d.	s.	d.
159	**18**	2 m. greenish blue ..	0	6	0	3
160	,,	3 m. carmine-pink ..	0	8	0	3
161	,,	4 m. green	1	6	1	0
162	,,	5 m. orange	1	0	0	6
163	,,	10 m. scarlet	1	3	0	8
164	,,	15 m. ultramarine ..	1	9	0	8
165	,,	20 m. olive-green ..	2	0	3	0
166	**19**	50 m. purple	12	6	17	6
167	,,	90 m. bistre	17	6	25	0
168	,,	100 m. blue	20	0	27	6
169	,,	200 m. violet	35	0	45	0
170	,,	500 m. brown ('29) ..	£8		£10	
171	,,	1000 m. slate-grey ('29) ..	£12		£17	

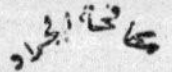

(20) (21)

(Overprinted at Cairo.)

1928 (1 Sept.). T **18** *and* **19** *optd. with* T **20**, *signifying* " Constitution."

No.	Type	Description	s.	d.	s.	d.
172	**18**	2 m. greenish blue ..	1	9	3	0
173	,,	3 m. carmine-pink ..	3	0	3	6
174	,,	4 m. green	3	0	3	6
175	,,	5 m. orange	2	0	2	6
176	,,	10 m. scarlet	3	0	4	0
177	,,	15 m. ultramarine ..	3	6	4	0
178	,,	20 m. olive-green ..	12	6	17	6
179	**19**	50 m. purple	12	6	17	6
180	,,	90 m. bistre	20	0	25	0
181	,,	100 m. blue	20	0	25	0
182	,,	200 m. violet	50	0	60	0

(Overprinted at Alexandria by Whitehead Morris & Co.)

1930 (1 Apr.). " *Locust Campaign*," *T* **18** *and* **19** *optd. as T* **21**.

No.	Type	Description	s.	d.	s.	d.
183	**18**	2 m. greenish blue ..	0	10	0	10
184	,,	3 m. carmine-pink ..	1	0	1	3
185	,,	4 m. green	0	10	1	0
186	,,	5 m. orange	12	6	17	6
		a. Overprint double ..	£35			
187	,,	10 m. scarlet	1	6	1	9
188	,,	15 m. ultramarine ..	1	6	1	9
		a. Overprint inverted ..	£25			
189	,,	20 m. olive-green ..	2	6	3	6
190	**19**	50 m. purple	6	0	8	6
191	,,	90 m. bistre	12	6	17	6
192	,,	100 m. blue	12	6	17	6
193	,,	200 m. violet	30	0	40	0
194	,,	500 m. brown	80	0	£5	
		a. "C" of "LOCUST" missing	£30			

22 **23**

(Re-engraved with figures of value at left only. Recess. Perkins Bacon & Co., Ltd.)

1930–36. *Wmk. Mult. Script CA.* *P* 14.

No.	Type	Description	s.	d.	s.	d.
194*b*	**22**	1 m. red-brown (6.2.34)	0	4	0	4
195	,,	2 m. greenish blue ..	0	4	0	5
196	,,	3 m. carmine-pink ..	0	9	1	0
196*a*	,,	3 m. green (6.2.34) ..	1	0	1	0
197	,,	4 m. green	1	0	1	6
197*a*	,,	4 m. carm.-pink (6.2.34)	2	6	1	3
198	,,	5 m. orange	1	0	1	6
		a. From coils. P 13½×14 ('36) ..	1	6	2	0
199	,,	10 m. scarlet	1	3	1	6
200	,,	15 m. ultramarine ..	2	6	2	6
		a. From coils. P 13½×14 ('36) ..	2	6	3	6
201	,,	20 m. olive-green ..	2	0	2	0
202	**23**	50 m. purple	3	0	3	6
203	,,	90 m. bistre	5	0	6	0
204	,,	100 m. blue	6	0	7	0
205	,,	200 m. violet	10	6	12	6
206	,,	500 m. brown	30	0	35	0
207	,,	£P 1 slate-grey	60	0	70	0

For stamps perf. 12 see Nos. 230 to 243, and for T **22** lithographed, perf. 13½, see Nos. 222 to 229 in King George VI Catalogue.

24. Mushetta.
25. The Nymphæum, Jerash.
26. Kasr Kharana. **27.** Kerak Castle.
28. Temple of Artemis, Jerash.
29. Ajlun Castle.
30. Allenby Bridge over the Jordan.
31. A threshing scene (33×24 mm.).

32. The Khazneh at Petra.

33. H.H. the Emir Abdullah.

(Vignettes copied from photographs; frames designed by Yacoub Sukker. Recess-printed by Messrs. Bradbury, Wilkinson & Co., Ltd.)

1933. *T* **24** *to* **33** (*various horiz.* (*T* **24** *to* **31**) *or vert. designs*). *Wmk. Mult. Script CA.* *P* 12.

No.	Type	Description	Unused		Used	
208	**24**	1 m. black and marone	1	0	1	3
209	**25**	2 m. black and claret ..	1	6	2	0
210	**26**	3 m. blue-green ..	1	9	2	3
211	**27**	4 m. black and brown ..	3	0	3	6
212	**28**	5 m. black and orange ..	3	6	4	0
213	**29**	10 m. carmine	4	0	4	6
214	**32**	15 m. blue	6	6	6	0
215	**30**	20 m. black & sage-green	6	0	7	0
216	**31**	50 m. black and purple	7	6	8	6
217	**26**	90 m. black and yellow ..	12	0	14	0
218	**28**	100 m. black and blue	17	6	22	6
219	**29**	200 m. black and violet ..	95	0	£5	
220	**32**	500 m. scarlet & red-brown	£10		£12	
221	**33**	£P 1 black & yellow-grn.	£27		£30	

The 90 m., 100 m., 200 m. and 500 m. are similar to the 3 m., 5 m., 10 m. and 15 m. respectively, but are larger in size.

POSTAGE DUE STAMPS.

مستحق

("Due.")

(D 1)

1923 (Sept.). *Issue of April,* 1923, *with opt. T* **10** *with further typographed opt. Type* D **1**. (*The* 3 *p. with hand-stamped surcharge as T* **12** *at top of stamp.*)

No.	Type	Description	Unused		Used	
D1	D **1**	½ p. on 3 p. brown ..	10	6		
		a. "Due" inverted ..	50	0	52	6
		b. "Due" double ..	60	0		
		c. Arabic "t" and "h" transposed	£5			
		d. Surcharge at foot of stamp	60	0		
		e. Surcharge omitted ..	60	0		
		f. Surcharge double ..	£5			
D2	,,	1 p. indigo	6	0		
		a. Type 10 inverted ..	£5			
		b. "Due" inverted ..	30	0	35	0
		c. "Due" double ..	50	0		
		d. "Due" double, one inverted	£12			
		e. Arabic "t" and "h" transposed	£5			
		f. "Due" omitted (in vertical pair) ..	£22			
D3	,,	1½ p. mauve	6	0		
		a. "Due" inverted ..	30	0	35	0
		b. "Due" double ..	50	0		
		c. Arabic "t" and "h" transposed	£5			
		d. "Due" omitted (in pair)	£22			
D4	D **1**	2 p. orange	7	6		
		a. "Due" inverted ..	35	0	50	0
		b. "Due" double ..	50	0		
		c. "Due" treble ..	£20			
		d. Arabic "t" and "h" transposed	£5			
		e. Arabic "h" omitted ..	£6			

The variety, Arabic "t" and "h" transposed, occurred on No. 2 in the first row of all values in the first batch of sheets printed.

The variety, Arabic "h" omitted, occurred on every stamp in the first three rows of at least three sheets of the 2 p.

حكومة
مستحق
الشرق العربية
٩ شعبان ١٣٤١

(D 2)

حكومة
الشرق العربية
مستحق
٩ شعبان ١٣٤١

(D 3)

Handstamped in four lines as Type D **2**, *and surcharged as on No.* D1.

No.	Type	Description	Unused	
D5	D **2**	½ p. on 3 p. brown ..	12	6
		a. Overprint and surcharge inverted ..	70	0
		b. Overprint double ..		
		c. Surcharge omitted ..	60	0
		d. Overprint inverted. Surcharge normal, but at foot of stamp ..	55	0
		e. Overprint omitted and overprint inverted (pr.)	£10	

1923 (Oct.). *T* **11** *of Saudi Arabia handstamped with Type* D **3**.

No.	Type	Description	Unused	
D 6	D **3**	½ p. scarlet	0	6
D 7	,,	1 p. indigo	0	10
D 8	,,	1½ p. mauve	1	3
D 9	,,	2 p. orange	1	9
D10	,,	3 p. brown	3	0
D11	,,	5 p. olive	4	6

The ½, 1½ and 3 p. are known with overprint double, and the 1½ p. with overprint inverted.

There are three types of this overprint, differing in some of the Arabic characters.

1923 (Nov.). *T* **11** *of Saudi Arabia with overprint similar to Type* D **3**, *but first three lines typographed and fourth handstruck.*

No.	Type	Description	Unused	
D12	D **3**	1 p. ultramarine ..	25	0
D14	,,	5 p. olive	4	0

مستحق
شرق الاردن

("Due. Eastern Jordan.")

(D 4)

(Overprinted typographically by Waterlow & Sons, Ltd.)

1925 (Nov.). *Stamps of Palestine,* 1922 (*without the three-line Palestine overprint*), *overprinted with Type* D **4**. *P* 14.

No.	Type	Description	Unused	
D15	D **4**	1 m. deep brown ..	0	3
D16	,,	2 m. yellow ..	0	4
D17	,,	4 m. carmine-pink ..	0	6
D18	,,	8 m. scarlet ..	0	9
D19	,,	13 m. ultramarine ..	1	0
D20	,,	5 p. deep purple ..	4	0
		a. Perf. 15×14	25	0

مستحق

١ مليم	٢ مليم	٤ مليم
(1 m.)	(2 m.)	(4 m.)
(D 5)		
٨ مليم	١٣ مليم	٥ قروش
(8 m.)	(13 m.)	(5 p.)

(Surcharged typographically at Jerusalem.)

1926. *Postage stamps of 1 Nov., 1925, surcharged "Due" and new value as Type* D **5**. *Bottom line of surcharge differs for each value as illustrated.*

D21	D **5**	1 m. on 1 m. deep brn.	2	0
D22	„	2 m. on 1 m. deep brn.	2	0
D23	„	4 m. on 3 m. gr'nish blue	3	0
D24	„	8 m. on 3 m. gr'nish blue	3	0
D25	„	13 m. on 13 m. ultramarine	3	6
D26	„	5 p. on 13 m. ultram. ..	3	6

("Due.")
(D 6)   D **7**

(Surcharged at Cairo.)

1929. *T* **18** *and* **19** *overprinted only or surcharged in addition as Type* D **6**.

D27	1 m. on 3 m. carmine-pink	1	0	1	0
D28	2 m. greenish blue	1	0	1	0
	a. Pr one stamp without surch.	£20			
D29	4 m. on 15 m. ultramarine..	1	6	2	0
D30	10 m. scarlet	2	6	3	6
D31	20 m. on 100 m. blue ..	3	6	5	0
	a. Vert. pr. one stamp no surch.	£35			
D32	50 m. purple	5	0	10	0

(Recess. Perkins Bacon & Co., Ltd.)

1929 (1 Apr.). *Wmk. Mult. Script CA. P* 14.

D33	D **7**	1 m. red-brown ..	0	6	1	0
D34	„	2 m. orange-yellow ..	0	6	1	0
D35	„	4 m. green	0	9	1	6
D36	„	10 m. scarlet	1	6	2	6
D37	„	20 m. olive-green ..	2	0	3	0
D38	„	50 m. blue	2	6	5	0

For similar stamps, perf. 13½ or 12, see King George VI Catalogue.

TRANSVAAL.

Late SOUTH AFRICAN REPUBLIC.

SIMPLIFICATION (see p. xii)

Nos. 1 to 85.

Simplest. 64, 22, 7, 30, 38, 31.

More advanced (distinguishing between imperf., perf. and roulette and including very distinct shades) :—

28, 64, 21, 53, 36, 72, 76, 14.
4b. 18a, 24, 35, 7, 29, 5, 19, 23, 30, 38, 20, 31. 39, 40.

Nos. 86 to 155.

Red opt. (*omit if desired*) : 87, 88, 89. 90, 91, 92.

Black opt. 98, 101, 102, 103*e*, 104. 113.
99, 106, 107, 108. 114a.
116, 117, 118, 139, 119, 120. 121, 122, 123, 140, 124, 125.
130, 131, 142, 132. 133, 134, 143, 135.
145b, 146, 147. 148, 149, 150.

I. FIRST REPUBLIC.

Note.—For the 1d., 3d., 6d., and 1s. stamps, T **1** and **2**, two plates of each value were made, each plate consisting of forty stamp blocks, arranged in five rows of eight in a row.

The two plates of a value were sometimes, but not always, used together, producing a sheet of eighty stamps in two panes of forty each.

One block was inverted in the original left-hand plate of the 6d. and also of the 1s. In the panes of the printed stamps this was No. 25 on the right-hand pane in the 6d., and No. 1 on the right pane of the 1s. From this cause arose the *tête-bêche* varieties of these two values in some of the printings; and later, when these stamps were overprinted, an inverted surcharge is found whenever these panes were so treated. In addition to this, in the case of the 1d., 3d., 6d., and 1s. stamps it is known that at least one sheet of each of these values must have been printed with the whole surcharge inverted.

Many unauthorised imitations of these three values were made in Germany, but, with the exception of certain impressions of the 1s. value, in yellow-green on soft medium paper, they all differ from the originals in some parts of the design, particularly in the eagle and the ribbon bearing the motto under the coat of arms. To this class belong forgeries of the 1d., in red or black, in which the numerals in the top corners are enclosed in a white frame.

The exception—the 1s., in yellow-green, above mentioned—was once regarded as genuine and catalogued, but it has been proved by Mr. J. N. Luff (see his articles, "Otto's Printings," in Vols. XXXIII and XXXIV of the *Philatelic Record*; it is his "surreptitious printing J") that these were printed from an unauthorised small plate of four subjects, on each of which were certain flaws that can be easily identified in the impressions. They somewhat resemble the 1s. stamps of 1876–7, but the paper is smoother and firmer and the printing clearer.

1

2

(T **1** printed by Adolph Otto in Gustrow, Mecklenburg-Schwerin.)

1869. *Thin paper, clear and distinct impressions.*

(*a*) *Imperf.*

1	**1**	1d. brown-lake	£9	
		a. *Orange-red*	£12	
2	„	6d. bright ultramarine ..	£6	
		a. *Pale ultramarine*	£5	
3	„	1s. deep green	£18	
		a. Tête-bêche (pair).. ..		

(*b*) *Fine roulette,* 15½ *to* 16.

4	**1**	1d. brown-lake	50	0
		a. *Brick-red*	37	6
		b. *Orange-red*	30	0
		c. *Vermilion*	32	6
5	„	6d. bright ultramarine ..	30	0
		a. *Pale ultramarine*	30	0
6	„	1s. deep green	60	0
		a. *Yellow-green*	50	0
		b. *Emerald-green*	50	0

Stamps of this issue, genuinely used for postal purposes, are scarce.

These stamps were printed from two sets of plates, one with the stamps spaced 1¼ to 1½ mm. apart, the other with the stamps spaced 2½ to 3½ mm. apart. The former are rouletted close to the design on all the four sides, and on the 1d. of that printing the outer frame-lines do not join at the right lower corner.

(T 2 printed as last in Germany.)

1871 (July). *Thin paper, clear and distinct impressions.*

Fine roulette, 15½ to 16.

7 **2** 3d. pale reddish lilac .. 30 0 30 0
a. Deep lilac 35 0 30 0

These fine rouletted stamps and all subsequent printings are from the plates which were subsequently sent to South Africa.

Imperf. specimens of the 3d. pale reddish lilac, which are also found in *tête-à-tête* pairs, were sent out to South Africa, but there is no evidence to show that they were issued for postal use.

These imperf. stamps are without the small dot on the left leg of the eagle which is always found in the issued stamps.

(Printed by M. J. Viljoen at Pretoria.)

1870 (4 April). *Printed on thin gummed paper sent out from Germany. Impressions coarse and defective.*

(*a*) *Imperf.*

8 **1** 1d. dull rose-red 30 0
a. Reddish pink 30 0
b. Carmine-red 25 0
9 „ 6d. dull ultramarine .. £8
a. Tête-bêche (pair) .. ..

(*b*) *Fine roulette, 15½ to 16.*

10 **1** 1d. carmine-red £25 £10
11 „ 6d. dull ultramarine .. £10 90 0

(*c*) *Wide roulette, 6½.*

12 **1** 1d. carmine-red .. .. — £40

1870 (26 April). *Thick, hard paper, yellow streaky gum.*

(*a*) *Imperf.*

13 **1** 1d. pale rose-red 25 0
a. Carmine-red 25 0 35 0
14 „ 1s. yellow-green 60 0 50 0
a. Tête-bêche (pair) .. ..

(*b*) *Fine roulette, 15½ to 16.* (10 May, 1870.)

15 **1** 6d. ultramarine 50 0 50 0
a. Tête-bêche (pair) £150
16 „ 1s. yellow-green £20 £25

1870 (24 May). *Thick hard paper, thin yellow, smooth gum. Fine roulette, 15½ to 16.*

17 **1** 1d. carmine-red 75 0

1870 (4 July). *Medium paper, blotchy heavy printing and whitish gum.*

Fine roulette, 15½ to 16.

18 **1** 1d. rose-red 25 0 25 0
a. Carmine-red 25 0 25 0
b. Crimson. From over-inked plate 80 0
19 „ 6d. ultramarine 50 0 50 0
a. Tête-bêche (pair) .. ..
b. Deep ult. From over-inked pl. £15 £6
20 „ 1s. deep green 80 0 45 0
a. From over-inked plate .. £15 £5

Nos. 18b, 19b and 20a were printed from over-inked plates giving heavy, blobby impressions.

(Printed by J. P. Borrius, at Potchefstroom.)

1870 (Sept.).

I. *Stout paper, but with colour often showing through, whitish gum.*

(*a*) *Imperf.*

21 **1** 1d. black £5 £5

(*b*) *Fine roulette, 15½ to 16.*

22 **1** 1d. black 10 0 15 0
a. Grey-black 10 0 15 0
23 „ 6d. blackish blue £5 40 0
a. Dull blue 80 0 30 0

II. *Thin transparent paper.*
Fine roulette, 15½ to 16.

24 **1** 1d. bright carmine .. £8 40 0
25 „ 1d. black £8 £40
26 „ 6d. ultramarine 80 0 30 0
27 „ 1s. green 65 0 30 0

1872 (Dec.).

I. *Thinnish opaque paper, clear printing.*
Fine roulette, 15½ to 16.

28 **1** 1d. reddish pink 50 0 30 0
a. Carmine-red 60 0 30 0
29 **2** 3d. grey-lilac 80 0 30 0
30 **1** 6d. ultramarine 45 0 14 0
a. Pale ultramarine 60 0 17 6
31 „ 1s. yellow-green 45 0 17 6
a. Green 45 0 20 0
aa. Bisected .. ..

II. *Thickish wove paper.*

(*a*) *Fine roulette, 15½ to 16.*

32 **1** 1d. dull rose £20 60 0
a. Brownish rose £30 80 0
b. Printed on both sides ..
33 „ 6d. milky blue £7 32 6
a. Deep dull blue 80 0 27 6
aa. Imperf. £18

(*b*) *Wide roulette, 6½.*

34 **1** 6d. dull blue .. ..

III. *Very thick dense paper.*
Fine roulette, 15½ to 16.

35 **1** 1d. dull rose £30 £6
a. Brownish rose .. .. — £5
36 „ 6d. dull ultramarine .. £10 50 0
a. Bright ultramarine .. £12 50 0
37 „ 1s. yellow-green .. £50 £50

3

(Printed in Germany from a new plate made by A. Otto at Gustrow.)

1874 (30 Sept.). *Thin smooth paper, clearly printed Fine roulette, 15½ to 16.*

38 **3** 6d. bright ultramarine .. 50 0 15 0
a. Bisected (3d.) .. ..

Reprints of this stamp, both unused and with forged postmarks, are in a *duller* shade of colour than the originals, and the paper is rather thicker. Reprints also exist in fancy colours.

(Printed by P. Davis & Son, Pietermaritzburg.)

1874 (Sept.). *T* 1. *P* 12½.

(*a*) *Thin transparent paper.*

39 **1** 1d. pale brick-red 70 0 40 0
a. Brownish red 80 0 40 0
40 „ 6d. deep blue £5 35 0

(*b*) *Thicker opaque paper.*

41 **1** 1d. pale red £8 80 0
42 „ 6d. blue £6 50 0
a. Imperf. between (pair) ..
b. Deep blue £6 50 0

(Printed by " The Stamp Commission " at Pretoria.)

I. **1875** (29 April). *Very thin soft opaque paper (semi-pelure).*

(a) Imperf.

43	1	1d. orange-red	£8	50 0
		a. Pin-perf.		
44	2	3d. lilac	£5	45 0
45	1	6d. blue	80 0	30 0
		a. *Milky blue*	£8	25 0
		aa. Tête-bêche (pair)		
		ab. Pin-perf.		

(b) Fine roulette, 15½ to 16.

46	1	1d. orange-red	£20	£8
47	2	3d. lilac	£20	£10
48	1	6d. blue	£25	£6

(c) Wide roulette, 6½.

49	1	1d. orange-red	—	£10
50	2	3d. lilac	—	£12
51	1	6d. blue	—	£5
		a. *Bright blue*	—	£5
		b. *Milky blue*		

II. **1876** (?). *Very thin hard transparent paper (pelure).*

(a) Imperf.

52	1	1d. brownish red	50 0	25 0
		a. *Orange-red*	37 6	17 6
		b. *Dull red*	37 6	40 0
53	2	3d. lilac	50 0	32 6
		a. *Deep lilac*	60 0	37 6
54	1	6d. pale blue	47 6	37 6
		a. *Blue*	32 6	20 0
		aa. Tête-bêche (pair)		
		b. *Deep blue*	42 6	20 0

(b) Fine roulette 15½ to 16.

55	1	1d orange-red	£20	£10
		a. *Brown-red*	£20	£10
56	2	3d. lilac	£25	£8
57	1	6d blue	£12	£6
		a. *Deep blue*	£12	£8

(c) Wide roulette, 6½.

58	1	1d. orange-red	£30	£8
		a. *Bright red*	—	£10
59	2	3d. lilac	—	£15
60	1	6d. deep blue	£20	£5

(d) Pin-perf.

61	1	1d. dull red	£25	£15
62	2	3d. lilac	—	£15
63	1	6d. blue	—	£10

1876. *Stout hard-surfaced paper.*

I. *Smooth, nearly white, gum.*

(a) Imperf.

64	1	1d. bright red	20 0	17 6
65	2	3d. lilac		
66	1	6d. bright blue	£6	22 6
		a. Tête-bêche (pair)		
		b. *Pale blue*	£6	22 6

(b) Fine roulette, 15½ to 16.

67	1	1d. bright red	£25	£10
68	2	3d. lilac	£15	
69	1	6d. bright blue	—	£10

(c) Wide roulette, 6½.

70	1	1d. bright red	£30	£10
71	,,	6d. pale blue	—	£12

II. *Deep brown gum, staining the paper.*

72	1	6d. deep blue (*imperf.*)	60 0	15 0
		a. Tête-bêche (pair)		
73	,,	6d. deep blue (*fine roulette*)	—	£25
74	,,	6d. deep blue (*wide roulette*)	£30	£10

1876–77.

I. *Coarse soft white paper, printed in the colours that were overprinted in July, 1877.*

(a) Imperf.

75	1	1d. brick-red	£5	40 0
76	,,	6d. deep blue	£8	40 0
		a. *Milky blue*	£20	£5
77	,,	1s. yellow-green	£12	£6

(b) Fine roulette, 15½ to 16.

78	1	1d. brick-red	—	£20
79	,,	6d. deep blue	—	£8
80	,,	1s. yellow-green	£30	£15

(c) Wide roulette, 6½.

81	1	1d. brick-red	—	£20
81*a*	,,	6d. deep blue		
82	,,	1s. yellow-green		

(d) Fine × wide roulette.

83	1	1d. brick-red	£35	£20

II. *Hard thick coarse yellowish paper.*

84	1	1d. brick-red (*imperf.*)		
85	,,	1d. brick-red (*wide roulette*)		

II. FIRST BRITISH OCCUPATION.

V. R. V. R.

TRANSVAAL. TRANSVAAL.

(4) (5)

T 4 is the normal overprint, but in some printings No. 11 on the pane has a wider-spaced overprint, as T 5.

T 1 and 2 (3d.) overprinted with T 4.

1877 (July). (A) *Opt. in red.*

(a) Imperf.

86	3d. lilac (semi-pelure)	£60	£12
	a. Overprint Type 5		
87	3d. lilac (pelure)	£50	£9
	a. Overprint Type 5		
	b. Overprint on back	£80	
	c. Opt. double, in red and in black		
88	6d. blue	£60	£9
	a. Opt. inverted or tête-bêche pair		
	b. Overprint double		
	c. Overprint Type 5		
	d. *Deep blue*	—	£13
89	1s. yellow-green	£20	90 0
	a. Bisected	—	£40
	b. Opt. inverted or tête-bêche pair		
	c. Overprint Type 5	£100	

(b) Fine roulette, 15½ to 16.

90	3d. lilac (pelure)	—	£50
91	6d. blue	—	£50
92	1s. yellow-green	£75	£22
	a. Overprint Type 5		

(c) Wide roulette, 6½.

93	3d. lilac (pelure)	—	£50
	a. Overprint Type 5		
94	6d. blue	—	£50
	a. Overprint Type 5		
95	1s. yellow green	£70	£30
	a. Opt. inverted or tête-bêche pair		

In the above, the stamps overprinted are the 3d. of the issues of April, 1875 and 1876 and the 6d. and 1s. of 1876–77.

1877. (B) *Opt. in black.*

I. *Pelure paper.*

96	1d. orange-red (*imperf.*)	£12	£5
97	1d. orange-red (*fine roulette*)	—	£40

II. *Hard-surfaced paper.*

No.	Description	Unused	Used
98	1d. bright red (*imperf.*)	15 0	15 0
	a. Overprint inverted	£40	£15
	b. Overprint Type 5	£50	£45
99	1d. bright red (*fine roulette*)	£7	50 0
	a. Overprint inverted		
	b. Overprint double		
100	1d. bright red (*wide roulette*)	£25	£8

III. *Coarse soft paper.*

(*a*) *Imperf.*

No.	Description	Unused	Used
101	1d. brick-red	10 0	10 0
	a. Overprint double	—	£65
	b. Overprint Type 5		
102	3d. lilac	65 0	20 0
	a. Overprint inverted		
	b. Deep lilac	£8	85 0
103	6d. dull blue	£5	35 0
	a. Overprint double		
	b. Overprint inverted	£60	£10
	c. Tête-bêche (pair)		
	d. Overprint Type 5	—	£50
	da. Overprint Type 5, inverted		
	e. Blue (bright to deep)	£8	30 0
	ea. Bright blue, overprint inverted		
	f. Pin-perf.		
104	1s. yellow-green	75 0	35 0
	a. Overprint inverted	£50	£10
	b. Tête-bêche (pair)		
	c. Overprint Type 5	—	£40
	d. Bisected	—	£20

(*b*) *Fine roulette*, 15½ *to* 16.

No.	Description	Unused	Used
105	1d. brick-red	80 0	65 0
106	3d. lilac	£8	65 0
107	6d. dull blue	£10	90 0
	a. Overprint inverted	—	£25
	b. Overprint Type 5		
108	1s. yellow-green	£7	65 0
	a. Overprint inverted	£45	£20
	b. Overprint Type 5	—	£60

(*c*) *Wide roulette*, 6½.

No.	Description	Unused	Used
109	1d. brick-red	£30	£8
110	3d. lilac	—	£15
111	6d. dull blue	—	£25
	a. Overprint inverted		
112	1s. yellow-green	£15	£6
	a. Overprint inverted	£80	£20

1877 (31 Aug.). *T* **1** *optd. with T* **4** *in black.*

No.	Description	Unused	Used
113	6d. blue/*rose* (*imperf.*)	55 0	18 6
	a. Bisected (3d.)		
	b. Overprint inverted	55 0	18 6
	c. Tête-bêche (pair)		
	d. Overprint omitted		
114	6d. blue/*rose* (*fine roulette*)	£10	50 0
	a. Overprint inverted	£20	40 0
	b. Tête-bêche (pair)		
	c. Overprint omitted		
115	6d. blue/*rose* (*wide roulette*)		
	a. Overprint inverted		
	b. Overprint omitted		

V. R.   *V. R.*

Transvaal (6)   Transvaal (7)

1877 (Oct.). *T* **1** *and* **2** (3d.) *optd. with T* **6** *in black.*

(*a*) *Imperf.*

No.	Description	Unused	Used
116	1d. red/*blue*	50 0	25 0
	a. "Transvral"	—	£60
	b. Overprint double		
	c. Overprint inverted	£40	£15
117	1d. red/*orange*	10 0	12 6
	a. Pin-perf.		
	b. Printed both sides		
118	3d. mauve/*buff*	25 0	15 0
	a. Overprint inverted	—	£30
	b. Pin-perf.		
119	6d. blue/*green*	80 0	20 0
	a. Deep blue-green	£5	40 0
	b. Broken "Y" for "V" in "V.R."		
	c. Small "v" in "Transvaal"		
	d. Stop in front of "R" (=V. . R.)	—	£60
	e. Tête-bêche (pair)		
	f. Overprint inverted	—	£25
	g. Pin-perf.		
120	6d. blue/*blue*	50 0	20 0
	a. Tête-bêche (pair)		
	b. Overprint inverted	—	£25
	c. Overprint omitted	—	£75
	d. Overprint double	—	£85
	e. Pin-perf.		
	f. Bisected (3d.)	—	£10

(*b*) *Fine roulette*, 15½ *to* 16.

No.	Description	Unused	Used
121	1d. red/*blue*	95 0	35 0
	a. "Transvral"	—	£85
122	1d. red/*orange*	25 0	25 0
	a. Imperf. between (pair)		
123	3d. mauve/*buff*	£5	25 0
	a. Imperf. between (pair)		
	b. Overprint inverted	—	£100
124	6d. blue/*green*	60 0	20 0
	a. Bisected (3d.)	—	£10
	b. Tête-bêche (pair)		
	c. Overprint inverted	—	£25
	d. Overprint omitted	—	£110
	e. Stop in front of "R" (=V. . R.)	—	£80
125	6d. blue/*blue*	£15	45 0
	a. Bisected (3d.)	—	£10
	b. Imperf. between (pair)		
	c. Overprint inverted	—	£40
	d. Overprint omitted	—	£85

(*c*) *Wide roulette*, 6½.

No.	Description	Unused	Used
126	1d. red/*orange*	£12	£8
127	3d. mauve/*buff*	—	£8
128	6d. blue/*green*	—	£35
129	6d. blue/*blue*	—	£16
	a. Overprint inverted		

T **1** *and* **2** (3d.) *optd. with T* **7** *in black.*

(*a*) *Imperf.*

No.	Description	Unused	Used
130	1d. red/*orange*	45 0	35 0
131	3d. mauve/*buff*	45 0	25 0
	a. Pin-perf. about 9	—	£40
132	6d. blue/*blue*	£6	27 6
	a. Tête-bêche (pair)		
	b. Overprint inverted	—	£20

(*b*) *Fine roulette*, 15½ *to* 16.

No.	Description	Unused	Used
133	1d. red/*orange*	—	£10
134	3d. mauve/*buff*	£10	£7
	a. Imperf. between (pair)		
135	6d. blue/*blue*	—	£7
	a. Overprint inverted	—	£35

(*c*) *Wide roulette*, 6½.

No.	Description	Unused	Used
136	1d. red/*orange*	—	£14
137	3d. mauve/*buff*	—	£15
138	6d. blue/*blue*	—	£15
	a. Overprint inverted		

1879 (18 April). *T* **2**.

a) *Imperf.* (*b*) *Fine roulette.* (*c*) *Wide roulette*

I. *Optd. with T* **6** *in black.*

No.	Description	Unused	Used
139	3d. mauve/*green* (*a*)	£8	20 0
	a. Pin-perf.		
	b. Overprint inverted	—	£50
	c. Overprint double		
140	3d. mauve/*green* (*b*)	£40	£10
141	3d. mauve/*green* (*c*)	—	£15

II. *Optd. with T 7 in black.*

142	3d. mauve/*green* (*a*)	£5	16 0
	a. Overprint inverted	—	£50
	b. Overprint omitted	—	£65
143	3d. mauve/*green* (*b*)	£30	£12
144	3d. mauve/*green* (*c*)	—	£20

V. R. **V. R.**

Transvaal (8) **Transvaal** (8*a*)

1879 (Aug.–Sept.). *T* **1** *and* **2** (*3d.*) *optd. with T* **8** *in black.*

(*a*) *Imperf.*

145	1d. red/*yellow*	27 6	25 0
	a. Small "T", Type 8a ..	£14	£12
	b. Red/orange	22 6	20 0
	ba. Small "T", Type 8a ..	£12	£12
146	3d. mauve/*green*	22 6	15 0
	a. Small "T", Type 8a ..	£18	£8
147	3d. mauve/*blue*	30 0	20 0
	a. Small "T", Type 8a ..	£12	£5

(*b*) *Fine roulette,* 15½ *to* 16.

148	1d. red/*yellow*	—	£15
	a. Small "T", Type 8a ..	£40	£30
	b. Red/orange	—	£16
	ba. Small "T", Type 8a ..		
149	3d. mauve/*green*	—	£14
	a. Small "T", Type 8a		
150	3d. mauve/*blue*	—	£12
	a. Small "T", Type 8a ..	—	£30

(*c*) *Wide roulette,* 6½.

151	1d. red/*yellow*		
	a. Small "T", Type 8a ..		
	b. Red-orange		
152	3d. mauve/*green*		
	a. Small "T", Type 8a ..		
153	3d. mauve/*blue*		

(*d*) *Pin-perf., about* 17.

154	1d. red/*yellow*	—	£30
	a. Small "T", Type 8a ..		
155	3d. mauve/*blue*		

9

(Recess. Bradbury, Wilkinson & Co.)

1878 (26 Aug.)–**1880**. *P* 14, 14½.

156	9	½d. vermilion (1880) ..	12 6	22 6
157	,,	1d. pale red-brown ..	6 0	4 0
		a. Brown-red	5 0	3 6
158	,,	3d. dull rose	6 6	2 6
		a. Claret	7 6	2 6
159	,,	4d. sage-green ..	12 6	10 0
160	,,	6d. olive-black ..	6 0	4 0
		a. Black-brown ..	7 6	2 9
161	,,	1s. green	40 0	27 6
162	,,	2s. blue	60 0	25 0

The above prices are for specimens perforated on all four sides. Stamps from margins of sheets, with perforations absent on one or two sides, can be supplied for about 30% less.

1 Penny (10)

1 Penny (11) 1 Penny (12)

1 Penny (13) 1 Penny (14)

1 PENNY (15) *1 Penny* (16)

1879 (22 April). *No.* 160*a surch. with T* **10** *to* **16**.

(A) *In black.* (B) *In red.*

			A.		B.	
163	**10**	1d. on 6d. ..	£8	75 0	£20	£12
164	**11**	1d. on 6d. ..	60 0	40 0	£8	£6
165	**12**	1d. on 6d. ..	£8	75 0	£20	£12
166	**13**	1d. on 6d. ..	80 0	35 0	£9	£7
167	**14**	1d. on 6d. ..	£16	£8	—	—
168	**15**	1d. on 6d. ..	35 0	25 0	£4	60 0
169	**16**	1d. on 6d. ..	£9	65 0	£16	£10

III. SECOND REPUBLIC.

Een Penny (17)

1882. *No.* 159 *surch. with T* **17**.

170	1d. on 4d. sage-green ..	4 0	4 0
	a. Surcharge inverted ..	£10	

1883. *Re-issue of T* **1** *and* **2** (3d.). *P* 12.

171	1d. grey (to black) ..	2 0	1 6
172	3d. grey-black (to black)/*rose*	7 6	6 6
	a. Bisected (1d.)	—	£10
173	3d. pale red	5 0	2 0
	a. Bisected (1d.)		
	b. Chestnut	30 0	3 6
	c. Vermilion	20 0	6 6
174	1s. green (to deep) ..	10 0	3 6
	a. Bisected (6d.)	—	60 0
	b. Tête-bêche (pair) ..	£10	55 0

Reprints are known of Nos. 172, 173, 173*b* and 173*c*. The paper of the first is bright rose in place of dull rose, and the impression is brownish black in place of grey-black to deep black. The reprints on white paper have the paper thinner than the originals, and the gum yellowish instead of white. The colour is a dull deep orange-red.

18

(Des. J. Vurtheim. Typo. Enschedé & Son, Haarlem.)

REPRINTS. Reprints of the general issues, 1885–93, 1894–95, 1895–96 and 1896–97 exist in large quantities. They cannot readily be distinguished from genuine originals except by comparison with used stamps, but the following general characteristics may be noted. The reprints are all perf. 12½, large holes; the paper is whiter than that usually employed for the originals and their colours lack the lustre of those of the genuine stamps.

Forged surcharges have been made on these reprints.

1885 (13 Mar.)–**1893**. *P* 12½.

175	**18**	½d. grey	0 2	0 1
		a. Perf. 13½	5 0	10 0
		b. Perf. 12½×12	1 6	0 4
		ba. Var. Perf. 11½×12 ..		

No.	Type	Description	Unused	Used
176	18	1d. carmine	0 6	0 1
		a. Perf. 12½×12	0 9	0 4
		aa. Var. Perf. 11½×12 ..	10 0	7 6
		b. Rose	0 3	0 1
		ba. Perf. 12½×12	0 6	0 2
177	„	2d. brown-pur. (p. 12½×12)	0 9	0 6
178	„	2d. olive-bistre (1887)	0 8	0 1
		a. Perf. 12½×12	3 6	0 4
179	„	2½d. mauve (to bright) ('93)	1 6	0 8
180	„	3d. mauve (to bright) ..	1 6	1 6
		a. Perf. 12½×12	8 6	2 6
		aa. Var. Perf. 11½×12 ..	30 0	15 0
181	„	4d. bronze-green	3 0	0 8
		a. Perf. 13½	4 6	1 6
		b. Perf. 12½×12	20 0	2 0
		ba. Var. Perf. 11½×12 ..	£15	£5
182	„	6d. pale dull blue ..	1 6	0 9
		a. Perf. 13½	7 6	2 0
		b. Perf. 12½×12	8 6	1 0
		ba. Var. Perf. 11½×12		
183	„	1s. yell.-green	5 0	0 8
		a. Perf. 13½	30 0	10 0
		b. Perf. 12½×12	12 6	1 0
184	„	2s. 6d. orange-buff (to buff)	9 0	3 6
		a. Perf. 12½×12	15 0	8 6
185	„	5s. slate	10 0	4 0
		a. Perf. 12½×12	15 0	4 0
186	„	10s. fawn	30 0	4 0
187	„	£5 deep green (1892) ..		

The variety, perf. 11½×12 in the 1d., 3d., 4d. and 6d. is from sheets perforated with the 12½×12 machine. (See note after Holland, No. 109.)

HALVE PENNY

(19)

HALVE PENNY

(20)

1885. *Surch. with* **T 19** *or* **20** (*½d. on 3d. mauve*).

A. *Reading down.* B. *Reading up.*

No.	Type	Description	A.		B.	
188	2	½d. on 3d. (No. 173)	3 0	3 0	3 0	3 0
189	18	½d. on 3d. (No. 180*a*)	3 0	3 0	†	
		a. "PENNY" for "PENNY" ..	40 0		†	
		b. Second "N" in "PENNY" invert.	£6		†	
		c. Var. Perf. 11½×12 ..	10 0		†	
190	1	½d. on 1s. (No. 174)	10 0	15 0	10 0	15 0
		a. Tête-bêche (pair) ..	†		£8	

No. 188 was issued on May 22, No. 189 on Sept. 28 and No. 190 in August.

In sheets of Nos. 188 and 190 one half-sheet had the surch. reading upwards and the other half-sheet downwards.

HALVE PENNY Z. A. R.

(21)

TWEE PENCE Z. A. R.

(22)

1885 (1 Sept.). *No. 160a surcharged in red.*

No.	Type	Description	Unused	Used
191	21	½d. on 6d. black-brown	30 0	35 0
192	22	2d. on 6d. black-brown	5 0	5 0

2d

(23)

2d

(24)

1887 (15 Jan.). **T 18** *surch.* *P* 12½×12.

No.	Type	Description	Unused	Used
193	23	2d. on 3d. mauve	4 0	4 0
		a. Surch. double	—	£15
		b. Var. Perf. 11½×12 ..	10 0	
194	24	2d. on 3d. mauve	2 0	2 0
		a. Surch. double	—	£18
		b. Var. Perf. 11½×12 ..	7 6	6 0
		ba. Ditto. Surch. double ..		

Halve Penny

(25)

1 Penny

(26)

2½ Pence

(27)

2½ Pence

(28)

1893. **T 18** *surcharged.* *P* 12½.

Two varieties of surcharge:

(A) *Vertical distance between bars* 12½ *mm.*
(B) *Distance* 13½ *mm.*

(1) *In red.*

No.	Type	Description	Unused	Used
195	25	½d. on 2d. olive-bistre (A) (27 May)	1 0	1 0
		a. Surcharge inverted (A) ..	5 0	5 0
		b. Variety B	3 6	3 6
		ba. Variety B, inverted ..	15 0	

(2) *In black.*

No.	Type	Description	Unused	Used
196	25	½d. on 2d. olive-bistre (A) (2 July)	1 0	1 0
		a. Surcharge inverted (A) ..	8 6	8 6
		b. Extra surcharge on back inverted (A)	£10	
		c. Variety B	3 0	3 0
		ca. Variety B, inverted ..	—	20 0
		cb. Extra surcharge on back inverted (B)		
197	26	1d. on 6d. blue (A) (26 Jan)	0 6	0 6
		a. Surcharge double (A) ..	80 0	50 0
		b. Surcharge inverted (A) ..	3 0	4 0
		c. Variety B	1 0	1 0
		ca. Variety B inverted ..	10 0	10 0
		cb. Variety B double ..	—	£7
		d. Pair, with and without sur.	£8	
198	27	2½d. on 1s. green (A)(2 Jan.)	1 3	1 6
		a. "2/1½" for "2½" ..	50 0	50 0
		b. Surcharge inverted (A) ..	5 0	6 6
		ba. Surcharge inverted and "2/1½" for "2½" ..	£15	
		c. Extra surcharge on back inverted (A)		
		d. Variety B	3 6	5 0
		da. Variety B, inverted ..	15 0	20 0
199	28	2½d. on 1s. grn. (A) (24 June)	4 0	3 6
		a. Surcharge double (A) ..	60 0	60 0
		b. Surcharge inverted (A) ..	12 6	12 6
		c. Variety B	10 0	10 0
		ca. Variety B, double ..		
		cb. Variety B, inverted ..		

29

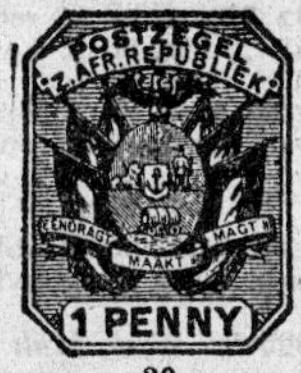

30

1894–95. *Waggon with shafts.* *P* 12½.

No.	Type	Description	Unused	Used
200	29	½d. grey	0 6	0 6
201	,,	1d. carmine	0 6	0 3
202	,,	2d. olive-bistre	0 6	0 6
203	,,	6d. pale dull blue ..	1 6	1 6
204	,,	1s. yellow-green	10 0	10 0

For note *re* reprints, see below T **18**.

1895–96. *Waggon with pole.* *P* 12½.

No.	Type	Description	Unused	Used
205	30	½d. pearl-grey	0 4	0 2
		a. *Lilac-grey*	0 4	0 2
206	,,	1d. rose-red	0 2	0 1
207	,,	2d. olive-bistre	0 4	0 2
208	,,	3d. mauve	1 0	0 9
209	,,	4d. olive-black	2 6	2 6
210	,,	6d. pale dull blue ..	1 6	0 9
211	,,	1s. yellow-green	3 6	3 0
212	,,	5s. slate	10 0	10 0
212*a*	,,	10s. pale chestnut	12 6	4 0

For note *re* reprints, see below T **18**.

Halve
Penny

(31)

1d.   1d.

(32)   (32*a*)

1895 (July–Aug.). *Nos.* 211 *and* 179 *surch.*

No.	Type	Description	Unused	Used
213	31	½d. on 1s. green (R.) ..	0 2	0 3
		a. " Pennij " for " Penny " ..	60 0	
		b. Surcharge inverted ..	8 6	8 6
		c. Surcharge double ..	50 0	
214	32	1d. on 2½d. brt. mve. (G.)	0 3	0 3
		a. Surcharge inverted ..	15 0	15 0
		b. Surcharge double		
		c. Surcharge on back only ..		
		d. Type 32*a*	3 6	3 6
		da. Type 32*a*, inverted ..	80 0	

Copies of the ½d. may be found in which one or both of the bars have failed to print.

T **32***a* differs from T **32** in the space between the " 1 " and " *d.*"

33

1895 (Aug.). *Fiscal stamp overprinted* " POSTZEGEL," *in green.* *P* 11½.

No.	Type	Description	Unused	Used
215	33	6d. bright rose	1 6	1 6
		a. Imperf. between (pair) ..		

1896–97. *P* 12½.

No.	Type	Description	Unused	Used
216	30	½d. green	0 1	0 1
217	,,	1d. rose-red and green ..	0 1	0 1
218	,,	2d. brown and green ..	0 1	0 4
219	,,	2½d. dull blue and green ..	0 6	0 4
220	,,	3d. purple and green ..	0 3	0 9
221	,,	4d. sage-green and green	0 3	1 0
222	,,	6d. lilac and green ..	0 8	0 8
223	,,	1s. ochre and green ..	1 0	0 6
224	,,	2s. 6d. dull violet & green	2 6	2 6

For note *re* reprints, see below T **18**.

34

(Litho. Printing Press and Publishing Co., Pretoria.)

1895 (6 Sept.). *Introduction of Penny Postage.* *P* 11.

No.	Type	Description	Unused	Used
225	34	1d. red (pale to deep) ..	0 4	0 5
		a. Imperf. between (pair) ..	10 0	6 0

This stamp is reported to exist *imperf.*, and it is said that a block of eight is known in this condition postally used, but there is no evidence that such stamps were officially issued.

IV. SECOND BRITISH OCCUPATION.

V. R. I.

(35)

FORGERIES. The forgeries of the " V.R.I." and " E.R.I." overprints most often met with can be recognised by the fact that the type used is perfect and the three stops are always in alignment with the bottom of the letters. In the genuine overprints, which were made from old type, it is impossible to find all three letters perfect and all three stops perfect and in exact alignment with the bottom of the letters.

1900 (18 June). *Overprinted with T* **35.**

No.	Type	Description	Unused	Used
226	30	½d. green	0 2	0 2
		f. " V.I.R."		
227	,,	1d. rose-red and green ..	0 2	0 2
		f. No stop after " R " and " I"	£5	£5
228	,,	2d. brown and green ..	0 3	0 3
		f. " V.I.R."		
229	,,	2½d. dull blue and green ..	0 6	0 6
230	,,	3d. purple and green ..	0 6	0 6
231	,,	4d. sage-green and green	0 9	0 9
		f. " V.I.R."		
232	,,	6d. lilac and green ..	1 0	1 0
233	,,	1s. ochre and green ..	1 9	1 9
234	,,	2s. 6d. dull violet & green	3 0	3 0
235	,,	5s. slate	7 6	10 0
236	,,	10s. pale chestnut	10 0	12 6
237	18	£5 green		

The error " V.I.R." occurred on stamp No. 34 in the first batch of stamps to be overprinted—a few sheets of the ½d., 2d. and 4d. The error was then corrected and stamps showing it are very rare.

Varieties.

A. No stop after " V ". B. No stop after "R".
C. No stop after " I ". D. Overprint inverted.
E. Overprint double.

No.	Value	A	B	C	D	E
226	½d.	40 0	20 0	10 0	10 0	—
227	1d.	40 0	20 0	7 6	10 0	£5
228	2d.	60 0	†	70 0	20 0	—
229	2½d.	50 0	—	20 0	10 0	†

No.		A	B	C	D	E
230	3d.	60 0	80 0	60 0	£6	†
231	4d.	80 0	£5	50 0	50 0	†
232	6d.	30 0	60 0	40 0	40 0	†
233	1s.	30 0	—	60 0	50 0	£5
234	2s. 6d.	45 0	£5	†	†	†
235	5s.	—	†	†	†	†
236	10s.	£5	†	£5	†	†
237	£5	—	†	†	†	†

The above prices are for unused. Used are worth the same, or rather more in some cases.

E. R. I. (36)

E. R. I. Half Penny (37)

FORGERIES. See note below T 35.

1901–2. *Overprinted with T* **36.**

No.	Type	Description	Unused	Used
238	30	½d. green (July, '01) ..	0 4	0 5
239	,,	1d. rose-red & grn. (20.3.01)	0 4	0 4
		a. "E" of opt. omitted ..	£5	
240	,,	3d. purple & green (6.02)	2 0	2 6
241	,,	4d. sage-green & grn. (6.02)	2 6	3 0
242	,,	2s. 6d. dull violet & green (10.02)	10 0	12 6

1901 (July). *Surch. with T* **37.**

No.	Type	Description	Unused	Used
243	30	½d. on 2d. brown and green	0 2	0 2
		a. No stop after "E"	85 0	

38 (Postage Revenue). **39** (Postage Postage).

(Typo. De La Rue & Co.)

1902 (1 April)–**1903.** *Wmk. Crown CA. P* 14.

No.	Type	Description	Unused	Used
244	38	½d. black and bluish green	0 5	0 3
245	,,	1d. black and carmine ..	0 5	0 3
246	,,	2d. black and purple ..	0 8	0 6
247	,,	2½d. black and blue ..	1 9	1 9
248	,,	3d. black & sage-grn. ('03)	1 6	1 3
249	,,	4d. black and brown ('03)	2 6	2 0
250	,,	6d. black and orange-brown	2 6	1 6
251	,,	1s. black and sage-green	5 6	5 6
252	..	2s. black and brown ..	18 6	18 6
253	39	2s. 6d. magenta & black ..	8 0	5 0
254	,,	5s. black & purple/*yellow*	12 6	12 6
255	,,	10s. black and purple/*red* ..	25 0	25 0

The colour of the "black" centres varies from brownish grey or grey to black.

1903. *Wmk. Crown CA. P* 14.

No.	Type	Description	Unused	Used
256	39	1s. grey-black & red-brn.	3 6	2 6
257	,,	2s. grey-black & yellow ..	10 0	10 0
258	,,	£1 green and violet ..	57 6	50 0
259	,,	£5 orange-brown & violet	£45	

1904–9. *Wmk. Mult. Crown CA. P* 14.

No.	Type	Description	Unused	Used
260	38	½d. blk. & bluish grn., O ('04)	1 3	1 0
261	,,	1d. black & car., O ('04) ..	1 3	0 3
262	,,	2d. blk. & purple, C ('06)	1 9	0 8
263	,,	2½d. blk. & blue, O ('05) ..	2 0	1 0
		a. On chalky paper	2 6	1 3
264	,,	3d. blk. & sage-grn., C ('06)	1 3	0 7
265	,,	4d. black & brown, C ('06)	1 6	0 6
266	,,	6d. black & orge., O ('05) ..	2 6	0 5
		a. Black and brown-orange (chalky paper) ..	2 0	0 8
267	39	1s. blk. & red-brn., O ('05)	2 9	0 5
268	,,	2s. black & yellow, O ('06)	8 0	1 6
269	,,	2s. 6d. mag. & blk., O ('09)	10 0	3 6
270	,,	5s. black & pur./*yellow*, O	17 6	2 6
271	,,	10s. blk. & pur./*red*, O ('07)	22 6	4 0
272	,,	£1 green & violet, O ('08)	52 6	10 0
		a. On chalky paper ..	50 0	10 0

There is considerable variation in the "black" centres as in the previous issue.

1905–9. *Wmk. Mult. Crown CA. P* 14.

No.	Type	Description	Unused	Used
273	38	½d. yellow-green	0 6	0 2
		a. *Deep green* (1908) ..	0 6	0 2
274	,,	1d. scarlet	0 3	0 1
		a. Error. Wmk. cabled anchor, T 13 of Cape of Good Hope	—	£25
275	,,	2d. purple (1909) ..	1 3	0 3
276	,,	2½d. bright blue (1909) ..	4 0	2 6

The monocoloured ½d. and 1d. are printed from new combined plates. These show a slight alteration in that the frame does not touch the crown.

Many of the King's Head stamps are found overprinted or perforated "C.S.A.R.", for use on the Central South African Railways.

Fiscals with Postal Cancellations.

Various fiscal stamps are found apparently postally used, but these were used on telegrams not on postal matter.

POSTAGE DUE STAMPS.

D 1

(Typo. De La Rue & Co.)

1907. *Wmk. Mult. Crown CA. P* 14.

No.	Type	Description	Unused	Used
D1	D 1	½d. black and blue-green ..	0 4	0 4
D2	,,	1d. black and scarlet ..	0 8	0 3
D3	,,	2d. brown-orange ..	0 9	0 4
D4	,,	3d. black and blue ..	2 0	1 3
D5	,,	5d. black and violet ..	1 3	1 6
D6	,,	6d. black and red-brown ..	1 6	1 9
D7	,,	1s. scarlet and black ..	4 6	4 6

Transvaal now uses the stamps of South Africa.

PIETERSBURG.

These stamps were an unofficial issue of the Transvaal Government, made under President Kruger's authority while he was still in office.

(i.) (ii.)

(iii.)

1901 (March).

Printed at Pietersburg, at the office of "De Zoutpansberg Wachter," and issued from middle of March, 1901, until 9th April, when the British troops occupied that district.

Type-set and printed in sheets of 24 (4 *rows of* 6); *the first two rows have* (i.) *large* "P" *in* "Postzegel" *and large date; the third row has* (ii.) *large* "P" *in* "Postzegel" *and small date; the fourth row has* (iii.) *small* "p" *in* "postzegel" *and small date. Black impression on coloured paper. Initialled by the Controller, in black.*

(*a*) *Imperf.*

			s.	d.
1	½d. *green*	(i.)	10	0
	a. Controller's initials in red		10	0
	b. Controller's initials omitted		15	0
2	½d. *green*	(ii.)	15	0
	a. Controller's initials in red		12	6
	b. Controller's initials omitted		15	0
3	½d. *green*	(iii.)	15	0
	a. Controller's initials in red		12	6
	b. Controller's initials omitted		15	0
4	1d. *rose*	(i.)	2	6
5	1d. *rose*	(ii)	5	0
6	1d. *rose*	(iii).	5	0
7	2d. *orange*	(i.)	6	0
8	2d. *orange*	(ii.)	10	0
9	2d. *orange*	(iii.)		
10	4d. *blue*	(i.)	10	0
11	4d. *blue*	(ii.)	15	0
12	4d. *blue*	(iii.)	15	0
13	6d. *green*	(i.)	10	0
14	6d. *green*	(ii.)	15	0
15	6d. *green*	(iii.)	15	0
16	1s. *yellow*	(i.)	10	0
17	1s. *yellow*	(ii.)	15	0
18	1s. *yellow*	(iii.)	15	0

Nos. 1*b*, 2*b*, and 3*b* were issued in error, three sheets having stuck together; other values without initials are only incomplete stamps and *were not issued.*

Errors and varieties.

The following exist; the numbers in brackets being the numbers of the positions of the stamps on the sheet. Prices from 10s. upwards.

1. "Postzfgel" (No. 5): 1d. (i.), 4d. (i.), 6d. (i.)
2. "Postzeoel" (No. 9): 1d. (i.) 4d. (i.) 6d. (i.).
3. "Postzegfl" (No. 18): 4d. (ii.), 6d. (ii.).
4. "Postzegfl", and no stop after "afr" on right (No. 18): 1d. (ii.)
5. "Postzegei" (No. 21): 1d. (iii.), 4d. (iii.), 6d. (iii.).
6. "Postzegei," and no stop after "z" on left (No. 16): ½d. (ii.), 1s. (ii.).
7. "Postzecel" and "aer" on left (No. 23): ½d. (iii.).
8. "aer" on left (No. 23): 4d. (iii.), 6d. (iii.), 1s. (iii.).
9. "aer" on left, and with "4" in left upper corner (No. 23): 2d. (iii.).
10. "aer" on right (No. 10): 1d. (i.), 4d. (i.), 6d. (i.).
11. "afb" on left: ½d. (ii.) (No. 15), 2d. (i.), (No. 8), 4d. (i.) (No. 8), 6d. (i.) (No. 8).
12. "afb" on right (No. 6): 1d. (i.), 4d. (i.), 6d. (i.)
13. "bep" on left (No. 8): 1d. (i.)
14. "bep" on left and no stop after 1901" (No. 11): ½d. (i.).
15. "reb" on left (No. 7): 1d. (i.), 4d. (i.), 6d. (i.).
16. Floreate ornament in left corner inverted (Nos. 20 and 24): 1d. (iii.), 4d. (iii.), 6d. (iii.).
17. Floreate ornament in right corner inverted (No. 14): 1d. (ii.), 2d. (ii.), 4d. (ii.), 6d. (ii.).
18. Wider figure in centre and floreate ornament in left corner inverted (No. 20): 4d. (iii.), 6d. (iii.).
19. Wider figure in centre: 2d. (iii.) (No. 20), 4d. (iii.) (Nos. 19 and 20), 6d. (iii.) (Nos. 19 and 20).
20. Wider figure in centre and no stop after "afr" on right (No. 19): 2d. (iii.), 4d. (iii.), 6d. (iii.).
21. No stop after "afr" on left (No. 2): ½d. (i.), 2d. (i.), 4d. (i.), 6d. (i.), 1s. (i.).
22. No stop after "afr" on right: ½d. (ii.) (No. 18), (iii.) (No. 19), 1d. (ii.) (No. 18), (iii.) (No. 19), 2d. (ii.) (No. 18), (iii.) (No. 19), 1s. (iii.) (No. 19).
23. ½ inverted in upper left-hand corner and no stop after "afr" on right: ½d. (i.).
24. No stop after "rep" on left (No. 7): 6d. (i.).
25. No stop after "z" on left (No. 16): 1d. (ii.), 4d. (ii.), 6d. (ii.).
26. No stop after "z" on left and no bar below figure in right upper corner (No. 22): ½d. (iii.).
27. No stop after "1901" (No. 11): ½d. (i.), 1d. (i.), 4d. (i.), 6d. (i.), 1s. (i.).
28. No bar under figure in left upper corner (No. 3): 1d. (i.).
29. No bar under figure in right upper corner (No. 22): ½d. (iii.), 1d. (iii.), 2d. (iii.), 4d. (iii.), 6d. (iii.), 1s. (iii.).
30. No bar over figure in left lower corner (No. 15): 1d. (ii.), 4d. (ii.).
31. No bar over figure in right lower corner: ½d. (ii.) (No. 18), 1d. (i.) (No. 4), 2d. (i.), 4d. (i.) (No. 3), 6d. (i.) (No. 3), 1s. (i.) (No. 3).
32. Figure in left lower corner inverted (No. 2): 1d. (i.).
33. "⅓" for "½" in left upper corner (No. 3): ½d. (i.).
34. No stop after "afr" on right: ½d. (i.) (No. 4), (ii.) (No. 18).
35. No stop after "penny": 1d. (i.).
36. "afr–rep" on right (No. 24): ½d. (iii.).
37. Figures in centre level (No. 17): ½d. (ii.).

(*b*) *P* 11½.

Controller's initials in red on the ½d.*, in black on the others.*

			s.	d.	s.	d.
19	½d. *green*	(i.)	5	0		
20	½d. *green*	(ii.)	7	6		
21	½d. *green*	(iii.)	7	6		
22	1d. *rose*	(i.)	2	6		
	a. Imperf. between (pair)		5	0		
23	1d. *rose*	(ii.)	4	0	4	0
	a. Imperf. between (pair)		8	0		
24	1d. *rose*	(iii.)	4	0	4	0
	a. Imperf. between (pair)		8	0		
25	2d. *orange*	(i.)	5	0		
26	2d. *orange*	(ii.)	7	6		
27	2d. *orange*	(iii.)	7	6		

Errors and varieties.

Prices from 7s. 6d. upwards.

1. "Postzfgel" (No. 5): 1d. (i.).
2. "Postzeoel" (No. 9): 1d. (i.).
3. "Postzegfl", and no stop after "afr" on right (No. 18): 1d. (ii.).

4. "POSTZEGEI" (No. 21) : 1d. (iii.).
5. "AER" on right (No. 10) : 1d. (i.).
6. "AFR" on right (No. 6) : 1d. (i.).
7. "BEP" on left (No. 8) : 1d. (i.).
8. "BEP" on right : 1d. (ii.).
9. "REB" on left (No. 7) : 1d. (i.).
10. Floreate ornament in left corner inverted (Nos. 20 and 24) : 1d. (iii.).
11. Floreate ornament in right corner inverted (No. 14) : 1d. (ii.).
12. Wider figure in centre (No. 20) : 2d. (iii.).
13. Wider figure in centre, and no stop after "AFR" on right (No. 19) : 2d. (iii.).
14. No stop after "AFR" on left : 2d. (i.) (No. 2), (iii.) (No. 24).
15. No stop after "AFR" on right : ½d. (i.) (No. 4), (ii.) (No. 18), 1d. (ii.) (No. 18), (iii.) (No. 19), 2d. (ii.) (No. 18).
16. No stop after "REP" on left (No. 7) : 2d. (i.).
17. No stop after "Z" on left (No. 16) : 1d. (ii.).
18. No stop after "1901" (No. 11) : 1d. (i.), 2d. (i.).
19. No bar under figure in left upper corner (No. 3) : 1d. (i.).
20. No bar under figure in right upper corner (No. 22) : 1d. (iii.).
21. No bar over figure in left lower corner (No. 15) : 1d. (ii.).
22. No bar over figure in right lower corner (No. 4) : 1d. (i.).
23. Figure in left lower corner inverted (No. 2) : 1d. (i.).
24. No stop after "PENNY" : 1d. (i.).
25. "AFR-REP" on right (No. 24) : ½d. (iii.).
26. Figures in centre level (No. 17) : ½d. (ii.).
27. "4" in right lower corner (No. 17) : 2d. (ii.).

Varieties in which either of the figures of the "½" in the corners is omitted are due to imperfect printing and not to the absence of type.

LOCAL ISSUES DURING THE WAR 1900–2.

Stamps of the Transvaal Republic variously overprinted or surcharged.

LYDENBURG.

1900 (SEPT.). *Commemorative stamp, T 34 surch.* "V.R.I. 1d.".

1	**34**	1d. red	£12	£10

V.R.I.
3d.
(L 1)

Optd. "V.R.I." *as in Type* L 1 (*the* 3d. *formed by a surcharge, Type* L 1, *on the* 1d.).

2	**30**	½d. green	22 6	22 6
3	„	1d. rose-red and green ..	15 0	15 0
4	„	2d. brown and green ..	£6	£6
5	„	2½d. blue and green	—	90 0
6	„	3d. on 1d. rose-red & green	15 0	15 0
7	„	4d. sage-green and green ..	£7	
8	„	6d. lilac and green	£9	110 0
9	„	1s. ochre and green ..	£20	

RUSTENBURG.

1900 (23 JUNE). *Stamps of* 1896–97 *handstamped*

V.R. *in violet.*

1	**30**	½d. green	22 6	20 0
2	„	1d. rose-red and green ..	10 0	11 0
3	„	2d. brown and green ..	42 6	37 6
4	„	2½d. blue and green	17 6	17 6
5	„	3d. purple and green ..	32 0	35 0
6	„	6d. lilac and green	42 0	42 0
7	„	1s. ochre and green ..	87 6	57 6
8	„	2s. 6d. dull violet and green		

SCHWEIZER RENECKE.

On 19th August, 1900, on the occupation of this place, certain stamps were overprinted "BESIEGED" with a handstamp in violet, and also with the Post Office obliterating stamp, which gave "SCHWEIZER RENECKE, Z.A.R.", in a circle, with date in centre. Other values were similarly treated between the above date and 21 October, 1900. This defacing of the stamps does not, in our opinion, constitute them a particular issue, such as those given in this Catalogue.

The stamps so treated were the current Cape of Good Hope ½d. and 1d. and the Transvaal ½d., 1d., 2d. and 6d.

VOLKSRUST.

1902 (MAR.). *Fiscal stamps, T* **33**, *optd.* "V.R.I." *T* **35**. *P* 12.

1	1d. pale blue	1 6	1 9
2	6d. dull carmine	10 0	7 6
3	1s. olive-bistre	8 6	9 6
4	1s. 6d. brown	16 0	15 6
5	2s. 6d. dull purple	16 0	15 6

WOLMARANSTAD.

Cancelled V-R-I. (L 3) Cancelled V-R-I. (L 4)

1900 (JUNE). *Optd. with Type* L 3.

1	**30**	½d. green (B)	16 0	
		a. Opt. inverted		
2	„	1d. rose-red and green (B)	12 6	12 6
3	„	2d. brown and green (B) ..	—	£6
4	„	2½d. blue and green (R) ..	62 6	
		a. Opt. in blue		
5	„	3d. purple and green (B) ..		
6	„	4d. sage-green & green (B) ..		
7	„	6d. lilac and green (B) ..		
8	„	1s. ochre and green (B) ..		

1900 (JULY). *Commemorative stamp, optd. with Type* L **4**.

9	**34**	1d. red (B)	22 0	22 0

TRINIDAD.

SIMPLIFICATION (see p. xii)

Nos. 1 to 85.

2, 3, 5, 8, 9, 11.
16, 21, 22, 24.
25, 27, 29 : 39, 40, 42, 44.
52, 55, 57, 58.
60, 64, 61, 62, 65, 63, 67.
69, 70, 71, 72, 73, 74, 80, 81, 84, 85.

1

1847 (24 Apr.). *T* **1.** *Imperf.*

No.	Description	Unused	Used
1	(5 c.) blue	£300	£75 *to* £200

The "Lady McLeod" stamps were issued in April, 1847, by David Bryce, owner of the s.s. *Lady McLeod*, and sold at five cents each for the prepayment of the carriage of letters by his vessel between Port of Spain and San Fernando.

2. Britannia. **3**

(Recess. Perkins, Bacon & Co.)

1851 (11 Apr.)–**1853.** *T* **2.** *No value expressed. Imperf. Blued paper.*

No.	Description	Unused	Used
2	(1d.) purple-brown (1851) ..	10 0	30 0
3	(1d.) blue (1851)	10 0	30 0
4	(1d.) deep blue (1851) ..	22 6	30 0
5	(1d.) grey (1851)	55 0	60 0
6	(1d.) brownish grey (1851) ..	35 0	40 0
7	(1d.) brick-red (1853) ..	£6	40 0
8	(1d.) brownish red (1853) ..	95 0	40 0

1854-57. *As T* **2.** *Imperf. White paper.*

No.	Description	Unused	Used
9	(1d.) deep purple (1854) ..	10 0	45 0
10	(1d.) dark grey (1854) ..	25 0	65 0
11	(1d.) rose-red (1857)	£20	45 0

The prices quoted for the unused of the above issues are for "remainders" with original gum that were found in London in large quantities about 1889. Old colours that have been out to Trinidad are rare and of much greater value.

Engraved by Mr. Charles Pétit, and lithographed in the colony.)

T **3.** *No value expressed. Imperf.*

1852 (Oct.). *Yellowish paper. Fine impression lines of background clear and distinct.*

No.	Description	Unused	Used
12	(1d.) blue	—	£28 *to* £120
13	(1d.) deep blue	—	£28 *to* £140

1853. *Similar, but on bluish cartridge paper.*

No.	Description	Unused	Used
14	(1d.) blue	—	£28 *to* £140
15	(1d.) deep blue	—	£32 *to* £150

1855. *Thin paper. Impression less distinct than the former.*

No.	Description	Unused	Used
16	(1d.) blue	—	£10 *to* £40
17	(1d.) deep blue	—	£10 *to* £45
18	(1d.) greenish blue ..	—	£10 *to* £40

1856. *Impression less distinct still: only faint traces of lines of background.*

No.	Description	Unused	Used
19	(1d.) blue	—	£7 *to* £30
20	(1d.) deep blue	—	£8 *to* £35
20*a*	(1d.) grey-blue	—	£7 *to* £30

1860. *Impression shows none or hardly any lines of the background.*

No.	Description	Unused	Used
21	(1d.) grey-blue	£50	80 0 *to* £20
22	(1d.) slate	£50	£5 *to* £25
23	(1d.) dull red	37 6	50 0 *to* £8
24	(1d.) red	35 0	50 0 *to* £8
24*a*	(1d.) bright red ..	50 0	50 0 *to* £8

4. Britannia.

(Recess. Perkins, Bacon & Co.)

T **2** *for the* 1*d.* *T* **4** *other values.*

1859 (9 May). *Imperf.*

No.	Description	Unused	Used
25	4d. grey-lilac	£6	70 0 *to* £12
26	4d. dull purple ..	—	£18
27	6d. yellow-green ..	£75	£5 *to* £25
28	6d. deep green	£75	£5 *to* £25
29	1s. indigo	£8	60 0 *to* £15
30	1s. purple-slate ..	£30	

1859 (Sept.). *T* **2** *and* **4.**

(*a*) *Pin-perf.* 12½.

No.	Description	Unused	Used
31	(1d.) rose-red	£20	80 0
32	(1d.) carmine-lake	£26	80 0
33	4d. dull lilac	—	£20
34	4d. dull purple	—	£35
35	6d. yellow-green	—	£10
36	6d. deep green	—	£8
37	1s. purple-slate	£125	£40

(*b*) *Pin-perf.* 13½–14.

No.	Description	Unused	Used
38	(1d.) rose-red	£6	42 6
39	(1d.) carmine-lake	£8	35 0
40	4d. dull lilac	£6	£7
41	4d. dull purple	£12	£7
42	6d. yellow-green	£8	80 0
	a. Imperf. between (pair) ..	£60	
43	6d. deep green	—	90 0
44	1s. purple-slate	—	£20
45	1s. indigo	—	£30

NOTE. *Nos.* 31 *to* 45 *are very scarce with perforations on all sides and are worth much more than the prices quoted above, which are for good average specimens.*

1860 (Aug.). *T* **2** *and* **4.** *Clean-cut perf.* 14–16½.

No.	Description	Unused	Used
46	(1d.) rose-red	95 0	47 6
	a. Imperf. between (horiz. pair) ..	£20	
47	4d. brownish lilac	£6	80 0
48	4d. lilac	—	£12
49	6d. yellow-green	£8	£6
50	6d. deep green	—	95 0

T **4.** *Intermediate perf. between the clean-cut and the rough.*

No.	Description	Unused	Used
51	1s. indigo	—	£35

1861 (June). *Rough perf.* 14–16½.

No.	Description	Unused	Used
52	(1d.) rose-red	85 0	25 0
53	(1d.) rose	85 0	25 0
54	4d. brownish lilac	£12	60 0
55	4d. lilac	£26	55 0
	a. Imperf.		
56	6d. yellow-green	£12	95 0
57	6d. deep green	£25	55 0
58	1s. indigo	£35	£15
59	1s. deep bluish purple ..	£40	£15

(Recess. De La Rue & Co.)

Thick paper.

1862. (*a*) *P* 11½, 12.

No.	Description	Unused	Used
60	(1d.) crimson-lake	80 0	32 6
61	4d. deep purple	95 0	55 0
62	6d. deep green	£35	60 0
63	1s. bluish slate	£30	85 0

(b) P 11½, 12, compound with 11.

63*a* (1d.) crimson-lake .. ..

1863. *(c) P* 13.

64 (1d.) lake 42 6 20 0
65 6d. emerald-green £20 50 0
67 1s. bright mauve £125 £8

1863. *(d) P* 12½.

68 (1d.) lake 27 6 37 6

1863–75. *Wmk. Crown CC. P* 12½.

69 (1d.) lake 47 6 12 6
a. Wmk. sideways 72 6 27 6
70 (1d.) rose 37 6 6 0
a. Impert. £10
71 (1d.) scarlet 32 6 5 0
72 (1d.) carmine 32 6 5 0
73 4d. bright violet 90 0 15 0
74 4d. pale mauve £12 22 6
75 4d. dull lilac 45 0 17 6
77 6d. emerald-green 65 0 17 6
78 6d. deep green.. .. .. £17 15 0
80 6d. yellow-green 70 0 10 0
81 6d. apple-green 45 0 12 6
82 6d. blue-green 60 0 7 6
83 1s. bright deep mauve .. £10 17 6
84 1s. lilac-rose £8 15 0
85 1s. mauve (aniline) 95 0 17 6

The 1s. in a purple-slate shade is a colour changeling.

5

(Typo. De La Rue & Co.)

1869. *T* **5.** *Wmk. Crown CC. P* 12½.

87 5s. rose-lake 65 0 50 0

1872. *T* **4.** *Colours changed. Wmk. Crown CC. P* 12½.

88 4d. grey 50 0 7 6
89 4d. bluish grey 50 0 8 0
90 1s. chrome-yellow 75 0 6 6

1876. *T* **2** *and* **4.** *Wmk. Crown CC. P* 14.

91 (1d.) lake 8 0 2 0
a. Bisected (½d.) .. .. — 15 0
92 (1d.) rose-carmine 12 6 4 6
93 (1d.) scarlet 22 6 4 0
94 4d. bluish grey 47 6 5 0
95 6d. bright yellow-green .. 30 0 5 0
96 6d. deep yellow-green .. 27 6 4 6
a. Bisected (3d.) .. ..
97 1s. chrome-yellow 55 0 12 6

P 14×12½.

97*a* 6d. yellow-green .. .. — £250

HALFPENNY (6) **ONE PENNY** (7)

1879–82. *Surch. with T* **6** *or* **7** *in black. P* 14.

(a) Wmk. Crown CC. (June 1879.)

98 **2** ½d. lilac 6 0 6 6
99 ,, ½d. mauve 15 0 15 0
a. Wmk. sideways 27 6 27 6

(b) Wmk. Crown CA. (1882.)

100 **2** ½d. lilac £6 37 6
101 ,, 1d. rosy carmine 17 6 3 0
a. Bisected (½d.) .. .. — 35 0

1882. *T* **4.** *Wmk. Crown CA. P* 14.

102 4d. bluish grey 80 0 12 6

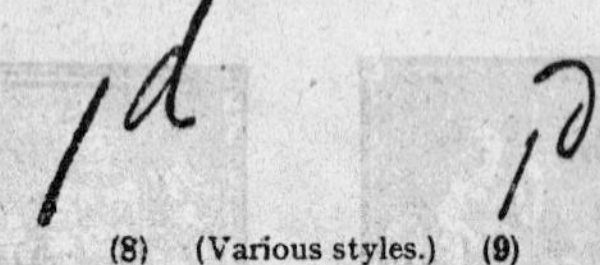

(8) (Various styles.) (9)

1882 (9 May). *Surcharged by hand in red or black ink and the original value obliterated by a thick or thin bar or bars of the same colour.*

103 **8** 1d. in *black*, on 6d. (No. 95) — £32
104 **9** 1d. in *red*, on 6d. (No. 95).. 8 6 8 6
105 **8** 1d. in *red*, on 6d. (No. 96).. 9 0 7 6
a. Bisected (½d.) .. .. — 50 0

10

(Typo. De La Rue & Co.)

1883–4. *T* **10.** *Wmk. Crown CA. P* 14.

106 ½d. dull green 0 8 0 4
107 1d. carmine 0 6 0 3
a. Bisected (½d.) .. ..
108 2½d. bright blue 8 0 2 0
109 2½d. ultramarine 4 0 0 6
110 4d. grey 1 6 1 0
111 6d. olive-black (1884) .. 3 6 4 6
112 1s. orange-brown (1884) .. 6 0 7 6

1894. *T* **5.** *Colour changed. Wmk. Crown CC. P* 14.

113 5s. marone 20 0 27 6

11. Britannia.

ONE PENNY *(a)* (round "o") **ONE PENNY** *(b)* (oval "o")

(Typo. De La Rue & Co.)

1896–1900. *T* **11.** *Two varieties (a) and (b), of inscription on 1d. Wmk. Crown CA. P* 14.

114 ½d. dull purple and green .. 0 2 0 2
115 1d. dull purple and rose *(a)* 0 3 0 2
116 1d. dull pur. & rose *(b)* (1900) 30 0 2 0
117 2½d. dull purple and blue .. 2 0 0 8
118 4d. dull purple and orange .. 5 0 5 0
119 5d. dull purple and mauve .. 7 6 7 6
120 6d. dull purple and black .. 6 0 5 0
121 1s. green and brown .. 10 0 8 6

12. Britannia.

(Typo. De La Rue & Co.)

T **12.** *Wmk. CA over Crown.* *P* 14.

122 5s. green and brown, O .. 45 0 22 6
123 10s. green and ultramarine, O £7 £7
124 £1 green and carmine, OC £6 £6

Collectors are warned against apparently postally used copies of these three stamps which bear "REGISTRAR-GENERAL" obliterations and are of very little value.

13. Landing of Columbus.

(Recess. De La Rue & Co.)

1898. *Stamp commemorative of the discovery of Trinidad.* *T* **13.** *Wmk. Crown CC.* *P* 14.

125 2d. brown and dull violet .. 3 0 3 0

1901–6. *T* **11** *and* **12.** *Colours changed.* *Wmk. Crown CA or CA over Crown* (5*s.*). *P* 14.

126 1d. black/*red*, O (*b*) 0 8 0 2
127 5s. lilac and mauve, O .. 50 0 55 0
128 5s. dp. pur. & mve., OC ('06) 42 6 45 0

Error. Value omitted.

129 (–) black/*red* .. .. ..

A pane of sixty stamps of this error was found in a post office in Trinidad, and one or more copies were issued and the rest withdrawn.

1902–3. *T* **11.** *Colours changed.* *Wmk. Crown CA.* *P* 14.

130 ½d. grey-green, O 0 6 0 6
131 2½d. purple and blue/*blue*, O 6 0 2 0
132 4d. green and blue/*buff*, OC 3 6 4 0
133 1s. black & blue/*yellow*, O ('03) 8 0 6 6

1904–5. *T* **11.** *Wmk. Mult. Crown CA.* *P* 14.

134 ½d. grey-green, OC 0 6 0 2
135 1d. black/*red*, OC (*b*) .. 0 8 0 3
136 2½d. purple & blue/*blue*, C 10 0 6 6
137 6d. dull purple & blk., C ('05) 8 0 6 6
138 1s. black & blue/*yellow*, C .. 17 6 12 6
139 1s. pur. & blue/*golden*-yell., C 12 6 15 0

1906–9. *T* **11.** *Wmk. Mult. Crown CA.* *P* 14.

139*a* ½d. blue-green, O 0 8 0 2
140 1d. rose-red, O (1907) .. 1 0 0 2
141 2½d. blue, O (1906) 3 6 1 6
142 4d. grey and red/*yellow*, C .. 6 6 7 6
143 4d. black & red/*yellow*, C .. 8 6 6 6
144 6d. dull & bright purple, C .. 8 6 6 0
145 1s. black/*green*, C 4 6 5 0

No. 140 is from a new die, the letters of "ONE PENNY" being short and thick, while the point of Britannia's spear breaks the uppermost horizontal line of shading in the background.

1907. *T* **12.** *Wmk. Mult. Crown CA.* *P* 14.

146 5s. deep purple & mauve, C 40 0 40 0
147 £1 green and carmine, C .. £10 £10

14

15

16

(Typo. De La Rue & Co.)

1909. *T* **14** *to* **16.** *Wmk. Mult. Crown CA.* *P* 14.

148 ½d. green, O 0 6 0 3
149 1d. rose-red, O 0 8 0 2
150 2½d. blue, O 7 6 6 0

The 1913 issue of postage stamps bears the names of both Trinidad and Tobago. We therefore list them under that heading (v. inf.).

TRINIDAD AND TOBAGO.

17

(Typo. De La Rue & Co.)

1913–23. *T* **17.** *Wmk. Mult. Crown CA.* *P* 14.

151 ½d. green, O ('13) 0 2 0 1
152 ½d. yellow-green, O ('15) .. 0 4 0 1
153 ½d. blue-green, O ('17) .. 0 4 0 1
154 ½d. blue-green/*bluish*, O (3.18) 0 6 0 3
155 1d. bright red, O ('13) .. 0 8 0 3
156 1d. red on *thick paper*, O ('16) 0 6 0 1
157 1d. pink, O ('18) .. .. — 0 6
158 1d. carmine-red, O (5.18) .. 0 6 0 1
159 2½d. ultramarine, O ('13) .. 2 6 1 3
160 2½d. bright blue on *thick paper* O ('16) 2 6 2 0
161 2½d. bright blue on *thin paper*, O ('18) 3 6 2 0
162 4d. blk. & red/*yellow*, OC ('13) 3 6 3 6
a. White back (12.13) .. 7 6 5 0
b. On lemon ('17) 10 0
c. On pale yellow ('23) .. 5 0 4 0
163 6d. dull purple and reddish purple, C ('13) 5 0 3 0

164 6d. dull purple and deep pur., C ('18) 5 0 3 0
165 6d. dull pur. & mve., C (2.18) 5 0 3 0
166 1s. black/*green*, O ('13) .. 6 0 5 0
a. White back 5 0 6 0
b. On blue-green, olive back .. 10 0 7 6
c. On emerald back 5 0 5 0

18

(Typo. De La Rue & Co.)

1914–18. *T* **18.** *Wmk. Mult. Crown CA. P.* 14

167 5s. dull pur. & mve., C ('14) 25 0
168 5s. deep pur. & mve., C ('18) 27 6
169 5s. lilac and violet, C .. 27 6
170 5s. dull purple & violet, C .. 37 6
171 5s. brown-pur. & violet, C .. 30 0
172 £1 grey-grn. & carm., C ('14) £6
173 £1 deep yellow-grn. & carm., C ('18) £5

The last £1 stamp is from a plate showing the lines in background much worn away.

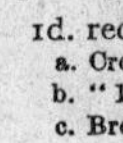

21. 10. 15.

(19)

19. 10. 16.

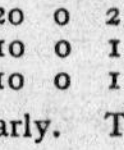

(19*a*)

1915 (21 Oct.). *T* **17** *optd. with T* **19.** *Cross in deep red with outline and date in black.*

174 1d. red 1 6 2 0
a. Cross 2 mm. to right .. 20 0 25 0
b. "1" of "15" forked foot .. 10 0 12 6
c. Broken "0" in "10" .. 10 0 12 6

These plate errors occur regularly. Their positions are :—

a. No. 11 on pane.
b. No. 84 „
c. No. 87 „

Variety *a* is only found on the right-hand pane.

1916 (19 Oct.). *T* **17** *optd. with T* **19*a*.** *Cross in scarlet with outline and date in black.*

175 1d. scarlet 0 5 0 7
a. No stop after "16" .. 8 6 10 0
b. "19.10.16" omitted ..

No. 175*a* appears on stamp No. 36 on the right-hand pane only.

A variety in the colour of the cross has been reported, but this is only caused by printing on greasy paper.

> Note. Numerous forgeries of the various "WAR TAX" errors listed below and other unlisted errors which are purely fakes, are offered in Trinidad and tourists and collectors buying by post should be on their guard. Many of these fakes have reached England.

1917 (2 Apr.). *T* **17** *optd.*

WAR TAX *in one line.*

176 1d. red/*thick p., white gum* .. 0 9 1 0
a. Inverted £12
177 1d. scarlet/*thin p., yellow gum* 1 0 1 0

WAR
TAX
(20)

.WAR
TAX
(21)

1917 (May). *T* **17** *optd. with T* **20.**

(*a*) *Thin paper, yellow gum.*

178 ½d. green 1 3 1 3
a. Without opt. in pair w. norm. £12
179 1d. red 1 0 0 7
a. Without opt. in pair w. norm. £10
180 1d. scarlet 0 10 0 6
a. Double opt. £6

The varieties without overprint were caused by the latter being shifted over towards the left so that one stamp in the lowest row of each pane escaped.

(*b*) *Thick paper, white gum.*

181 ½d. deep green 0 2 0 6
182 1d. red 0 4 0 4

1917 (21 June). *Optd. with T* **21.**

(*a*) *Thin paper, yellow gum.*

183 ½d. yellow-green 1 0 1
184 ½d. pale green 2 6 3
185 1d. red 0 8 0

(*b*) *Thick paper, white gum.*

186 ½d. deep green 1 0 1
187 ½d. pale green 1 6 2
188 1d. red 0 6 0

Pairs are known of the 1d. stamps, one stamp without the overprint. This was caused by a shifting of the type to the left-hand side, but only a few stamps on the right-hand vertical row escaped the overprint and such pairs are very rare.

WAR
TAX
(22)

WAR
TAX
(23)

1917 (21 July). *Optd. with T* **22.**

(*a*) *Thin paper.*

189 ½d. yellow-green 2 0 2
190 ½d. deep green 3 6 4

(*b*) *Thick paper.*

191 ½d. deep green 0 3 0
192 1d. red (Sept.) 0 4 0

1917 (1 Sept.). *Optd. with T* **23,** *in black (close spacing between lines of opt.). Thick paper.*

193 ½d. deep green 0 2 0
194 ½d. pale yellow-green .. ..
195 1d. red 11 0 12

WAR
TAX
(24)

WAR
TAX
(25)

War
Tax
(26)

1917 (31 Oct.). *Optd. with* **T 24.**

196	1d. scarlet/*thin paper* ..	0	6	0	7
	a. Inverted	£5			
197	1d. scarlet/*thick paper* ..	0	6	0	6

1918 (7 Jan.). *Optd. with* **T 25.**

198	1d. scarlet/*thin paper* ..	0	3	0	4
199	1d. scarlet/*thick paper* ..	1	3	1	0
	a. Double	£12			
	b. Inverted	£8			

1918 (13 Feb.). *Optd. with* **T 26**, *in black.*

200	½d. blue-green/*thin paper* ..	0	3	0	4
201	½d. bluish green/*thick bluish paper* (26 Mar.) ..	0	2	0	3
	a. Without opt., in pair with normal	£30			
202	1d. scarlet/*thick paper* (13.2)	0	2	0	2
	a. Overprint double	£6			
203	1d. rose-red/*thick bluish p.* (1.5)	0	4	0	2
204	1d. rose-red/*thin bluish p.* (1.5)	0	4	0	2

1918 (14 Sept.). *New printing as* **T 26**, *but* 16 *stamps on each sheet have the letters of the word* "Tax" *wider spaced, the* "x" *being to the right of* "r" *of* "War" *instead of under it.*

Thick bluish paper.

205	1d. scarlet ("Tax" spaced)	3	0	1	6
	a. Overprint double	£12			

1921–22. *T* **17** *and* **18.** *Wmk. Mult. Script CA. P* 14.

206	½d. green, O	0	4	0	2
207	1d. scarlet, O	0	8	0	4
208	2½d. bright blue, O	2	0	2	6
209	6d. dull & bright purple, C..	4	0	4	6
210	5s. dull pur. & pur., C ('21)	65	0	70	0
211	5s. deep pur. & pur., C ('22)	60	0	65	0
212	£1 green and carmine, C ..	£6		£7	

1922. *T* **17.** *Colours changed and new values.*

213	1d. brown, O	0	6	0	4
214	2d. grey, O	1	6	1	6
215	3d. bright blue, O	3	6	4	0

27

(Typo. De La Rue & Co.)

1922–8. *T* **27.** *Portrait in first colour. P* 14.

(a) Wmk. Mult. Crown CA.

216	4d. black & red/*pale yell.*, C	2	0	1	9
217	1s. black/*emerald*, C.. ..	6	0	6	6

(b) Wmk. Mult. Script CA.

218	½d. green, O	0	5	0	3
219	1d. brown, O	0	5	0	3
220	1½d. bright rose, O	1	6	0	6
221	1½d. scarlet, O	0	10	0	6
222	2d. grey, O	1	9	1	0
223	3d. blue, O	2	6	2	6
224	4d. blk. & red/*pale yell.*, C ('28)	4	6	3	6
225	6d. dull pur. & brt. mag., C..	15	0	12	6
226	6d. grn. & red/*emer.*, C ('24)	12	6	10	6
227	1s. black/*emerald*, C.. ..	12	6	9	0
228	5s. dull purple and mauve, C	60	0	60	0
229	£1 green and bright rose, C..	£7		£8	

New currency. 100 cents = $1.

28. First Boca.

29. Imperial College of Tropical Agriculture.

30. Mt. Irvine Bay, Tobago.

31. Discovery of Lake Asphalt.

32. Queen's Park, Savannah.

33. Town Hall, San Fernando.

34. Government House.

35. Memorial Park. **36.** Blue Basin.

(*Types* **29** *to* **36** *are same size as T* **28.**)

(Recess. Bradbury Wilkinson & Co.)

1935–37 (1 Feb.). *T* **28** *to* **36** *(various pictorial designs). Wmk. Mult. Script CA. P* 12.

230	**28**	1 c. blue and green ..	1	6	0	2
		a. Perf. 12½ ('36)	0	2	0	2
231	**29**	2 c. ultram. & yellow-brn.	3	0	0	3
		a. Perf. 12½ ('36)	0	4	0	2
232	**30**	3 c. black and scarlet ..	0	6	0	2
		a. Perf. 12½ ('36)	0	9	0	2
233	**31**	6 c. sepia and blue ..	2	0	1	3
		a. Perf. 12½ ('37)	1	3	1	0
234	**32**	8 c. sage-green & verm..	3	0	2	6
235	**33**	12 c. black and violet ..	3	6	3	0
		a. Perf. 12½ ('37)	4	6	2	6
236	**34**	24 c. black and olive-green	7	6	3	6
		a. Perf. 12½ ('37)	7	6	2	6
237	**35**	48 c. deep green ..	12	6	12	6
238	**36**	72 c. myrtle-green & carm.	25	0	25	0

1935 (6 May). *Silver Jubilee. As T* **13** *of Antigua, inscribed* "TRINIDAD & TOBAGO". *Recess. B. W. & Co. Wmk. Mult. Script CA. P* 11×12.

239	2 c. ultramarine & grey-black	0	4	0	10
240	3 c. deep blue and scarlet ..	1	0	1	6
241	6 c. brown and deep blue ..	3	6	4	0
242	24 c. slate and purple ..	10	0	12	6

All values exist with "double flagstaff" variety.

POSTAGE DUE STAMPS.

TRINIDAD.

D 1

(Typo. De La Rue & Co.)

1885 (1 Jan.). *Type* D **1.** *Wmk. Crown CA. P* 14.

D1	½d. slate-black	3	0	3	0
D2	1d. slate-black	1	0	0	4
D3	2d. slate-black	3	6	0	9
D4	3d. slate-black	7	6	1	6
D5	4d. slate-black	8	6	5	0
D6	5d. slate-black	8	6	1	6
D7	6d. slate-black	7	6	7	6
D8	8d. slate-black	8	6	5	0
D9	1s. slate-black	12	6	10	0

1905–6. *Type* D 1. *Wmk. Mult. Crown CA. P* 14.

D10	1d. slate-black	0 6	0 3
D11	2d. slate-black	1 0	0 6
D12	3d. slate-black	0 9	1 0
D13	4d. slate-black	1 0	1 0
D14	5d. slate-black	0 7	0 9
D15	6d. slate-black	0 8	0 10
D16	8d. slate-black	0 11	1 2
D17	1s. slate-black	1 4	1 6

TRINIDAD AND TOBAGO.

1923–29. *Type* D 1 (*still inscribed* " Trinidad "), *Wmk. Mult. Script CA. P* 14.

D18	1d. black	0 2	0 3
D19	2d. black	0 3	0 3
D20	3d. black ('25)	0 5	0 6
D21	4d. black ('29)	0 6	0 8

" Too Late " Stamps.

A handstamp with the words " too late " was used upon letters on which a too-late fee had been paid, and was sometimes used for cancelling the stamps on such letters.

OFFICIAL STAMPS.

TRINIDAD.

O S

(S 1)

1894. *Overprinted with Type* S 1, *in black.*

A. *T* 10. *Wmk. Crown CA. P* 14.

S1	½d. dull green	15 0	15 0
S2	1d. carmine	15 0	15 0
S3	2½d. ultramarine	17 6	17 6
S4	4d. grey	22 6	22 6
S5	6d. olive-black	30 0	30 0
S6	1s. orange-brown	45 0	45 0

B. *T* 5. *Wmk. Crown CC. P* 12½.

S7	5s. rose-lake	90 0	£6

OFFICIAL

(S 2)

1909. *T* 11 *overprinted with Type* S 2, *in black. Wmk. Multiple Crown CA. P* 14.

S8	½d. green, O	1 6	2 0
S9	1d. rose-red, O	0 3	0 4
	a. Double overprint		
	b. Vertical	60 0	
	c. Inverted	—	£10

1910. *T* 14 *overprinted with Type* S 2. *Wmk. Mult. Crown CA. P* 14.

S10	½d. green, O	0 3	0 4

TRINIDAD AND TOBAGO.

OFFICIAL (S 3) OFFICIAL (S 4)

1913. *T* 17, *wmk. Mult. Crown CA, optd.*

(*a*) *With Type* S 3, *in black.*

S11	½d. green, O	0 6	0 8
	a. Overprint vertical		

1914. (*b*) *With Type* S 4.

S12	½d. green, O	0 6	0 8

OFFICIAL (S 5) OFFICIAL. (S 6)

(*c*) *With Type* S 5 (*without stop*).

S13	½d. green	0 8	0 10
S14	½d. blue-grn./*thick paper* ('17)	1 6	2 0

1916–17. (*d*) *With Type* S 6 (*with stop*).

S15	½d. yellow-green, O	0 8	0 10
	a. Overprint double	25 0	

OFFICIAL

(S 7)

1917 (22 Aug.). (*e*) *With Type* S 7, *in black.*

S16	½d. green/*thin paper* ..	0 2	0 3
S17	½d. yellow-green/*thin paper* ..	0 9	1 0
S18	½d. blue-green/*thick paper* ..	0 2	0 3

TURKS ISLANDS.

1

(Recess. Perkins, Bacon & Co.)

1867 (4 April). *T* 1. *No wmk. P* 11–12.

1	1d. dull rose	27 6	25 0
2	6d. black	60 0	60 0
3	1s. dull blue	60 0	55 0

1873–79. *Wmk. Small Star, Type* w. 2. *P* 11–12×14½–15½.

4	1d. dull rose-lake (July, '73) ..	22 6	20 0
5	1d. dull red (Jan., 1879) ..	30 0	25 0
	a. Imperf. between (pair) ..	£46	
	b. Perf. 11–12		
6	1s. lilac	£150	£75

1881 (1 Jan.). *Stamps of the preceding issues surcharged locally, in black.*

There are twelve different settings of the ½d., nine settings of the 2½d., and six settings of the 4d.

The halfpenny provisionals.

½ (2) ½ (3)

Setting 1. *T* 2. *Long fraction bar. Two varieties repeated fifteen times in the sheet.*

7	½ on 6d. black	£6	

Setting 2. *T* 3. *Short fraction bar. Three varieties in a vertical strip repeated ten times in sheet.*

Setting 3. *Similar to setting* 2, *but the middle stamp of the three varieties has a longer bar.*

8	½ on 6d. black	75 0	
9	½ on 1s. dull blue	75 0	
	a. Double surcharge	£35	

½ (4) ½ (5) ½ (6)

Setting 4. *T* 4 *and* 5. *Three varieties repeated ten times in sheet. One is T* 4 *and two and three are T* 5.

Setting 5. *As last, but No.* 1 *is T* 6 (*without bar*).

Setting 6. *As* 4, *but No.* 3 *is T* 5 *without bar.*

Setting 7. *As* 4, *but No.* 1 *with long fraction bar, and No.* 2 *with sloping serif to* " 1."

10	½ on 1d. dull red (S. 7 *only*) ..	£42	
11	½ on 1s. slate-blue (S. 6 *and* 7)	£32	
12	½ on 1s. lilac (T 4)	50 0	
13	½ on 1s. lilac (T 5)	40 0	45 0
14	½ on 1s. lilac (T 6)	50 0	

(7)  (8)

Setting 8. *T* 7. *Three varieties in a vertical strip. All have very short bar.*

15 ½ on 1d. dull red 30 0

Setting 9. *T* 8. *Three varieties in a vertical strip. Bars long and thick and "1" leaning little to left.*

16 ½ on 1d. dull red £7
a. Double surcharge .. ..

(9)  (10)

Setting 10. *T* 9 *and* 10. *Fifteen varieties repeated twice on a sheet. Ten are of T* 9, *five of T* 10.

17 ½ on 1d. dull red (T 9) .. 20 0 22 6
18 ½ on 1d. dull red (T 10) .. 35 0 32 6
19 ½ on 1s. lilac (T 9) 50 0 60 0
20 ½ on 1s. lilac (T 10) 80 0 80 0

(11)  (12)  (13)  (14)

Setting 11. *T* 11 *to* 14. *Fifteen varieties repeated twice in a sheet. Ten of T* 11, *three of T* 12, *and one each of T* 13 *and* 14.

Setting 12. *Similar to last, but T* 13 *replaced by another T* 12.

21 ½ on 1d. dull red (T 11) .. 25 0
22 ½ on 1d. dull red (T 12) .. 60 0
23 ½ on 1d. dull red (T 13) .. £8
24 ½ on 1d. dull red (T 14) .. £8
24*a* ½ on 1s. slate-blue (T 11) .. £250

The twopence-halfpenny provisionals.

(15) 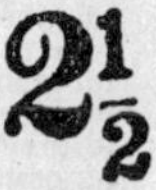 (16)

Setting 1. *T* 15. *Fraction in very small type.*

25 2½ on 6d. black £250

Setting 2. *T* 16. *Large "2" on level with top of the "1", long thin bar.*

26 2½ on 6d. black £25
a. Imperf. between (pair) ..
b. Double surcharge .. ..

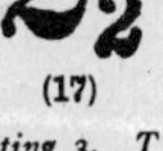

(17) 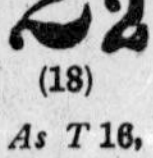 (18) 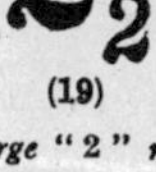 (19)

Setting 3. *T* 17. *As T* 16, *but large "2" not so high.*

27 2½ on 1s. lilac £45

Setting 4. *T* 18. *Three varieties in a vertical strip repeated ten times in sheet. Large "2" placed lower and small bar.*

28 2½ on 6d. black £8 £8

Setting 5. *T* 19. *Three varieties in a vertical strip repeated ten times in sheet. "2" further from "½", small fraction bar.*

29 2½ on 1s. lilac £22 £22

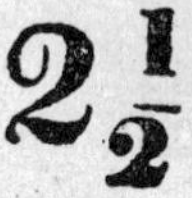

(20) 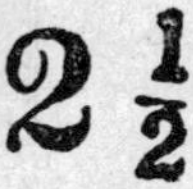 (21)

Setting 6. *T* 20 *and* 21. *Fifteen varieties. Ten of T* 20 *and five of T* 21.

30 2½ on 1s. lilac (T 20) £70
31 2½ on 1s. lilac (T 21) £85

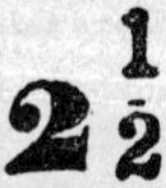

(22) 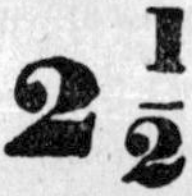 (23) 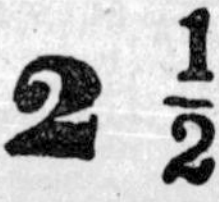 (24)

Setting 7. *T* 22. *Three varieties in a vertical strip.*

32 2½ on 6d. black £250
33 2½ on 1s. slate-blue £250

Setting 8. *T* 23 *and* 24. *Fifteen varieties. Ten of T* 23 *and five of T* 24.

34 2½ on 1d. dull red (T 23) .. £20
35 2½ on 1d. dull red (T 24) .. £28
36 2½ on 1s. lilac (T 23) £18
37 2½ on 1s. lilac (T 24) £25

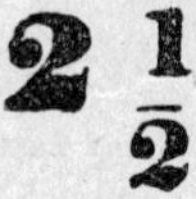

(25) 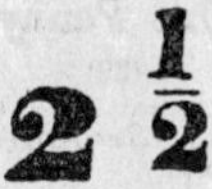 (26) 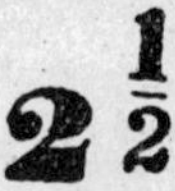 (27)

Setting 9. *T* 25, 26, *and* 27. *Fifteen varieties. Ten of T* 25, *three of T* 26, *one of T* 26 *without bar, and one of T* 27.

38 2½ on 1s. slate-blue (T 25) .. £35
39 2½ on 1s. slate-blue (T 26) .. £90
40 2½ on 1s. slate-blue (T 26) (without bar) £170
41 2½ on 1s. slate-blue (T 27) .. £230

The fourpenny provisionals.

(28)  (29)  (30)

Setting 1. *T* 28. *"4" 8 mm. high, pointed top.*

42 4 on 6d. black £15 £13

This variety is often forged from a genuine T 29 by painting in a pointed top.

T 29 *and* 30. *There are five other settings of these stamps which can only be distinguished when in blocks.*

[For particulars see Sir Edward Bacon's Handbook on this country.]

43 4 on 6d. black (T 29) .. 75 0
44 4 on 6d. black (T 30) .. £10
45 4 on 1s. lilac (T 29) £15

46 4 on 1s. lilac (T 30) £35
47 4 on 1d. dull red (T 29) £15 £15
48 4 on 1d. dull red (T 28) £20
a. Inverted £70

31

(Typo. De La Rue & Co.)

1881. *T* **1** *and* **31** (4*d*.). *Wmk. Crown CC. P* 14.

49 1d. brown-red (Oct.) 17 6 20 0
50 4d. ultram., Die I. (Aug.). .. 45 0 40 0
51 6d. olive-black (Oct.) .. 75 0 80 0
52 1s. slate-green (Oct.) .. £8 £8

1882–84. *T* **1** (1*d*.) *and* **31**. *Wmk. Crown CA. P* 14.

53 ½d. blue-grn. Die I. (2.82) .. 5 0 6 0
54 ½d. pale green, Die I. ('84) .. 3 6 4 0
55 1d. orange-brown (10.83) .. 25 0 27 6
a. Bisected (½d.) .. .. — £10
56 2½d. red-brown, Die I. (2.82) .. 10 0 12 6
57 4d. grey, Die I. (10.84) .. 6 0 7 6
a. Bisected (2d.) .. ..

1887 (July). *T* **1**. *Wmk. Crown CA.*

(*a*) *P* 12.

58 1d. crimson-lake 10 0 10 6
a. Imperf. between (pair) ..

(*b*) *P* 14.

59 6d. yellow-brown 5 0 6 0
60 1s. sepia 6 6 6 6

One Penny

(32)

1889 (May). *T* **31**. *Surcharged at Grand Turk with T* **32** *in black.*

61 1d. on 2½d. red-brown .. 15 0 15 0

1889–93. *T* **1** *and* **31** (2½*d*.). *Wmk. Crown CA. P* 14.

62 1d. crimson-lake (7.89) .. 5 0 6 0
63 1d. lake 3 0 3 6
64 1d. pale rosy lake 2 0 2 6
65 2½d. ultram., Die II. (4.93) .. 3 0 3 6

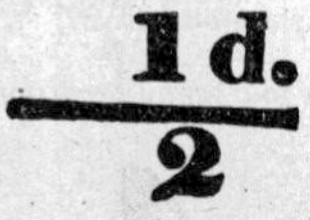

(33)

1893 (June). *No.* 57, *surcharged at Grand Turk with T* **33**, *in black.*

Setting 1. *Bars between "1d." and "2" separate instead of continuous across the row of stamps.*

66 ½d. on 4d. grey £16 £12

Setting 2. *Continuous bars. Thin and thick bar* 10¾ *mm. apart. "2" under the "1."*

67 ½d. on 4d. grey 95 0 80 0

Setting 3. *As last, but bars* 11½ *mm. apart.*

68 ½d. on 4d. grey £7 £7

Setting 4. *Bars* 11 *mm. apart. Five out of the six varieties in the strip have the "2" below the space between the "1" and "d."*

69 ½d. on 4d. grey £7

There is a fifth setting, but in a minor variety only.

34

(Typo. De La Rue & Co.)

1894–95. *T* **31** *and* **34** (5d.). *Wmk. Crown CA. P* 14.

70 ½d. dull green, Die II (1894) 0 6 1 0
71 4d. dull purple and ultramarine, Die II (May, 1895) .. 4 6 5 6
72 5d. olive-green & car. (6.94) .. 5 0 6 6
a. Bisected (2½d.) .. ..

TURKS AND CAICOS ISLANDS

35. Salt raking. **36.**

(Recess. De La Rue & Co.)

The dates on the stamps have reference to the political separation from Bahamas.

1900. *T* **35**, *wmk. Crown CA and T* **36**, *wmk. Crown CC. P* 14.

101 **35** ½d. green 2 0 2 6
102 „ 1d. red 1 6 1 9
103 „ 2d. sepia 2 9 2 6
104 „ 2½d. blue 12 6 15 0
104*a* „ 2½d. greyish blue 4 6 6 0
105 „ 4d. orange 6 0 7 0
106 „ 6d. dull mauve 5 6 6 0
107 „ 1s. purple-brown .. 8 0 8 6
108 **36** 2s. purple 90 0 90 0
109 „ 3s. lake 55 0 55 0

1905. *Wmk. Mult. Crown CA. P* 14.

110 **35** ½d. green 1 6 1 9
111 „ 1d. red 6 6 6 6
114 „ 3d. purple/*yellow* .. 12 0 15 0

37

(Recess. De La Rue & Co.)

1909 (Sept.). *T* **37**. *Wmk. Mult. Crown CA. P* 14.

No.	Description	Unused	Used
117	½d. yellow-green	0 9	1 0
118	1d. red	1 0	1 3
119	2d. greyish slate	4 6	5 0
120	2½d. blue	10 6	10 6
121	3d. purple/*yellow*	5 0	5 6
122	4d. red/*yellow*	12 6	15 0
123	6d. purple	8 0	9 0
124	1s. black/*green*	12 0	12 6
125	2s. red/*green*	25 0	27 6
126	3s. black/*red*	30 0	32 6

38. Melocactus Communis. **39**

(Recess. De La Rue & Co.)

1910. *T* **38.** *Wmk. Mult. Crown CA. P* 14.

No.	Description	Unused	Used
127	½d. rosy mauve	0 6	0 8
128	½d. red	0 4	0 6

1913–18. *T* **39.** *Wmk. Mult. Crown CA. P* 14.

No.	Description	Unused	Used
129	½d. green	0 3	0 4
130	1d. red	1 6	1 3
130*a*	1d. bright scarlet	1 0	1 3
130*b*	1d. rose-carmine (1918) ..	0 7	0 9
131	2d. greyish slate	1 6	1 9
132	2½d. ultramarine	3 0	3 6
132*a*	2½d. bright blue (1918) ..	3 0	3 6
133	3d. purple/*yellow*	2 9	3 3
	a. On lemon	12 6	
	b. On yellow-buff	4 0	
	c. On orange-buff	4 0	
	d. On pale yellow	3 6	4 0
134	4d. red/*yellow*	5 0	5 0
	a. On orange-buff	6 0	7 0
	b. Carmine on pale yellow ..	6 0	7 6
135	5d. pale olive-green (1916)	5 0	6 0
135*a*	6d. dull purple	5 0	6 0
136	1s. brown-orange	6 0	7 6
137	2s. red/*blue-green*	12 6	15 0
	a. On greenish white	£10	
	b. On emerald	12 6	15 0
138	3s. black/*red*	17 6	20 0

WAR TAX

(40)

1917 (3 Jan.). *T* **39** *overprinted with T* **40**, *in black, at bottom of stamp.*

No.	Description	Unused	Used
139	1d. red	0 6	2 6
	a. Overprint double	£12	
	b. "TAX" omitted		
	c. Inverted overprint at top ..	£12	
140	3d. purple /*yellow-buff* ..	1 6	3 6
	a. Overprint double ..	50 0	
141	3d. purple/*lemon*	1 0	3 6
	a. Overprint double	55 0	

In both values of the first printings the stamp in the bottom left-hand corner of the sheet has a long "T" in "TAX," and the first stamp on the sixth row has "TAI" for "TAX."

One sheet of the 1d. red has been found having the overprint double on the sixth vertical row (10 stamps).

1917 (Oct.). *Second printing with overprint at top or in middle of stamp.*

No.	Description	Unused	Used
142	1d. red	0 4	0 5
	a. Inverted opt. at bottom or centre	20 0	
	c. Overprint omitted, in pair with normal	£12	
	d. Double overprint, one at top, one at bottom	40 0	
	e. As d., but additional overprint in top margin	£6	
	f. Vertical pair, one as d., the other normal	£15	
	g. Pair, one overprint inverted, one normal	£25	
	h. Double overprint at top (in pair with normal)	£25	
	k. Horizontal pair, one double, one normal	£25	
	l. Overprint double	20 0	
144	3d. purple/*yellow*	1 3	1 9
	a. Double	12 6	
	b. Double, one inverted ..	40 0	

1918. *Overprinted with T* **40**, *in red.*

No.	Description	Unused	Used
145	3d. purple/*yellow*	5 0	7 6

WAR

TAX

(41)

1918. *Overprinted with T* **41**, *in black.*

No.	Description	Unused	Used
146	1d. rose-carmine	0 8	0 10
146*a*	1d. bright rose-scarlet ..	0 4	0 6
147	3d. purple/*yellow*	1 0	1 6

1919. *Optd. with T* **41**, *in red.*

No.	Description	Unused	Used
148	3d. purple/*orange-buff* ..	1 3	1 6

1919. *Local overprint. T* **40**, *in violet.*

No.	Description	Unused	Used
149	1d. bright rose-scarlet ..	0 8	1 0
	a. "WAR" omitted	£5	
	b. Overprint double	25 0	
	c. Overprint double in pair with normal	£5	
149*d*	1d. rose-carmine	2 6	3 0

WAR **TAX**

(42)

WAR

TAX

(43)

1919. *T* **39**, *overprinted with T* **42.**

No.	Description	Unused	Used
150	1d. scarlet	0 3	0 6
	a. Overprint double	£5	£5
151	3d. purple/*orange-buff* ..	1 0	1 6

1919 (17 Dec.). *T* **39** *optd. with T* **43.**

No.	Description	Unused	Used
152	1d. scarlet	0 3	0 3
153	3d. purple/*yellow*	0 8	1 0

The two bottom rows of this setting have the words "WAR" and "TAX" about 1 mm. further apart.

1921 (23 April). *T* **38** (½*d.*) *and* **39.** *Wmk. Mult. Script CA. P* 14.

No.	Description	Unused	Used
154	¼d. rose-red	0 4	0 6
155	½d. green	0 4	0 9
156	1d. carmine-red	0 8	1 0
157	2d. slate-grey	2 0	2 6

158	2½d. bright blue	5 0	6 0
159	5d. sage-green	11 0	13 6
160	6d. purple	16 0	18 6
161	1s. brown-orange	47 6	52 6

44 45

(Recess. De La Rue & Co.)

1922–26. *T* **38** (*½d.*) *and* **44.** *P* 14.

(*a*) *Wmk. Mult. Script CA.*

162*a*	½d. black (1926)	0 1	0 2
163	½d. yellow-green	0 3	0 4
163*a*	½d. bright green	0 6	0 6
163*b*	½d. apple-green	0 10	1 0
164	1d. brown	0 6	0 6
165	1½d. scarlet (1925)	1 0	1 3
166	2d. slate	1 0	1 3
167	2½d. purple/*pale yellow*	1 3	1 6
168	3d. bright blue	1 6	1 9
169	4d. red/*pale yellow*	1 6	1 9
169*a*	4d. carmine/*pale yellow*	6 0	7 0
170	5d. sage-green	2 6	3 0
171	6d. purple	3 0	3 6
172	1s. brown-orange	6 0	7 0
173	2s. red/*emerald* (1925)	15 0	17 6

(*b*) *Wmk. Mult. Crown CA.*

174	2s. red/*emerald*	70 0	75 0
175	3s. black/*red*	15 0	17 6

1928. *T* **45** (*inscribed* "POSTAGE & REVENUE"). *Wmk. Mult. Script CA. P* 14.

176	½d. green	0 2	0 3
177	1d. brown	0 4	0 6
178	1½d. scarlet	0 8	1 0
179	2d. grey	0 9	1 0
180	2½d. purple/*yellow*	1 3	1 6
181	3d. bright blue	1 3	1 6
182	6d. purple	2 0	2 6
183	1s. brown-orange	5 0	6 0
184	2s. red/*emerald*	9 0	10 6
185	5s. green/*yellow*	30 0	32 6
186	10s. purple/*blue*	45 0	50 0

1935 (6 May). *Silver Jubilee. As T* **13** *of Antigua, inscribed* "TURKS AND CAICOS ISLANDS". *Recess. W'low & Sons. Wmk. Mult. Script CA. P* 11×12.

187	½d. black and green	0 3	0 6
188	3d. brown and deep blue	3 0	3 6
189	6d. light blue and olive-grn.	4 6	5 0
190	1s. slate and purple	10 0	10 6

UGANDA PROTECTORATE

U G
50

T **1**, *type-written by Rev. E. Millar at Mengo, wide letters. Thin laid paper. Imperf.*

1895 (20 Mar.). A. *Wide stamps,* 20 *to* 26 *mm. wide.*

1	5 (cowries), black		
2	10 (cowries), black	£10	
3	15 (cowries), black		
4	20 (cowries), black	—	£8
5	25 (cowries), black		
6	30 (cowries), black	£8	£8
7	40 (cowries), black	£15	
8	50 (cowries), black	£5	
9	60 (cowries), black	£18	

1895 (May). *Provisionals. Pen-written surcharges, in black.*

10	10 on 50 (c.) black		
11	15 on 10 (c.) black	—	£16
12	15 on 20 (c.) black		
13	15 on 40 (c.) black	—	£20
14	15 on 50 (c.) black		
15	25 on 50 (c.) black		
16	50 on 60 (c.) black		

1895 (April). B. *Narrow stamps,* 16 *to* 18 *mm. wide.*

17	5 (c.) black	—	£10
18	10 (c.) black	—	£12
19	15 (c.) black	—	£8
20	20 (c.) black	£7	£7
21	25 (c.) black	—	£10
22	30 (c.) black	£9	£8
23	40 (c.) black	£10	
24	50 (c.) black	£14	
25	60 (c.) black	£18	

U G
20

2

V.96.R
25
Uganda

3

1895 (May). *T* **2**, *narrow letters. Narrow stamps,* 16 *to* 18 *mm. wide.*

26	5 (c.) black	67 6	
27	10 (c.) black	67 6	
28	15 (c.) black	27 6	
29	20 (c.) black	30 0	
30	25 (c.) black	77 6	
31	30 (c.) black	77 6	
32	40 (c.) black	77 6	
33	50 (c.) black	77 6	
34	60 (c.) black	95 0	

End of 1895. *Change of colour.*

35	5 (c.) violet	67 6	67 6
36	10 (c.) violet	67 6	57 6
37	15 (c.) violet	67 6	57 6
38	20 (c.) violet	25 0	25 0
	a. "G U" for "U G"		
39	25 (c.) violet	67 6	
40	30 (c.) violet	77 6	
41	40 (c.) violet	77 6	
42	50 (c.) violet	77 6	
43	100 (c.) violet	92 6	

Stamps of 35 (c.) and 45 (c.) have been chronicled in both colours. They were never prepared for postal use, and did not represent a postal rate, but were type-written to oblige a local collector.

1896 (June). *T* **3.** *Type-written.*

44	5 (c.) violet	47	6	35	0
45	10 (c.) violet	57	6		
46	15 (c.) violet	57	6		
47	20 (c.) violet	25	0	25	0
48	25 (c.) violet	87	6		
49	30 (c.) violet	87	6		
50	40 (c.) violet	87	6		
51	50 (c.) violet	87	6		
52	60 (c.) violet	87	6		
53	100 (c.) violet	£6			

Many of the values of the above are known tête-bêche.

UGANDA
POSTAGE
V†R
1 ANNA
PROTECTORATE

4

UGANDA
POSTAGE
V†R
1 ANNA
PROTECTORATE

5

UGANDA
POSTAGE
V†R
4 ANNAS
PROTECTORATE

6

(Printed by the Rev. F. Rowling at Luba's, in Usoga.)

1896 (7 Nov.). *T* **4** (*thin* "1"), **5** (*thick* "**1**"), *and* **6** (*other values*).

54	1 anna, black (T **4**)	25	0	20	0
55	1 anna, black (T **5**)	3	6	3	6
56	2 annas, black	6	0	6	0
57	3 annas, black	7	0	6	0
58	4 annas, black	7	6	7	6
59	8 annas, black	12	6	12	6
60	1 rupee, black	30	0	30	0
61	5 rupees, black	70	0	75	0

The position of the stars and/or the type of ornament between the letters "VR" varies in each value.

The three higher values are on yellowish paper.

Varieties. Small "o" *in* "POSTAGE".

62	1 anna, black (T **4**)	65	0	65	0
63	1 anna, black (T **5**)	17	6	17	6
64	2 annas, black	17	6	18	0
65	3 annas, black	25	0	25	0
66	4 annas, black	20	0	20	0
67	8 annas, black	40	0	40	0
68	1 rupee, black	£5		£5	
69	5 rupees, black	£10		£10	

7

T **4** (1 *a.*) *and* **6** *overprinted with* "L," *in black, as in T* **7**, *by the Collector at Kampala.*

70	1 anna, black	25	0	30	0
71	2 annas, black	25	0	30	0
72	3 annas, black	40	0	45	0
73	4 annas, black	30	0	35	0
74	8 annas, black	50	0	55	0
75	1 rupee, black	70	0	80	0

Varieties. Small "o" *in* "POSTAGE".

77	1 anna, black				
78	2 annas, black	50	0	60	0
79	3 annas, black				
80	4 annas, black	65	0		
81	8 annas, black	150	0		
82	1 rupee, black	£10			
83	5 rupees, black				

Tête-bêche pairs of all values may be found owing to the settings being printed side by side or above one another.

8

9

(Recess. De La Rue & Co.)

1898. *P* 14.

T **8.** *Wmk. Crown CA.*

84	1 a. scarlet	0	6	0	8
85	2 a. red-brown	1	0	1	3
86	3 a. pale grey	2	0	2	0
87	3 a. bluish grey	2	0	2	0
88	4 a. deep green	2	0	2	0
89	8 a. pale olive	2	6	3	0
89*a*	8 a. grey-green	2	0	3	0

T **9.** *Wmk. Crown CC.*

90	1 r. dull blue	5	0	6	6
90*a*	1 r. bright blue	12	6	12	6
91	5 r. brown	17	6	20	0

UGANDA

(10)

1902. *T* **11** *of British East Africa overprinted with T* **10.**

92	½ a. yellow-green	0	9	1	0
	a. Overprint omitted (*pair*)	£25			
	b. Overprint inverted (at foot)	£10			
	c. Overprint double	£20			
93	2½ a. deep blue (R.)	0	9	1	0
	a. Overprint double	£25			

1902. *T* **8.** *Wmk. Crown CA.* *P* 14.

94	1 a. carmine-rose	0	8	0	9

The stamps inscribed as above were superseded by those inscribed "EAST AFRICA AND UGANDA PROTECTORATES," for which see KENYA, UGANDA AND TANGANYIKA.

UNION OF SOUTH AFRICA.

See SOUTH AFRICA.

VICTORIA.

SIMPLIFICATION (see p. xii)

Nos. 1 to 101.

16, 17, 22, 42, 45, 46, 48, 70, 87 : 83. 90, 93, 98.

Nos. 102 to 335.

102, 106. 109, 110. 112, 115. 120. 121, 122, 123. 124. 128, 128a. 129.
130, 139, 132, 134. 143, 145 : 147, 149. 152 : 155, 157. 160, 163 : 165, 167. 169 : 170, 172, 175, 176, 177 : 180. 181, 184.
185, 189. 191, 192, 193, 195, 197, 198. 199, 200.
206, 207, 208. 209, 210 : 211, 212.
219, 225, 227, 232, 235. (Also selection of 236 to 256 if desired.) 259, 263, 264, 266, 269, 273, 274, 276, 278. 280.
283, 284. 285, 288, 291.
293. (Select from 295 to 300a if desired.) 302, 309. 310, 311, 313.
315, 318. 320. 322, 323, 324 : 325. 327, 328. 332, 334. 335.

Nos. 336 to 591.

These issues can be greatly simplified by omitting minor shades, disregarding dies and perforations and by treating Wmks. 64a and 64b as the same.

Postage Dues.

The colour groups listed are in most cases very distinct and the catalogue list cannot be seriously reduced.

1

(Lithographed by Mr. Thomas Ham, of Melbourne, who engraved the steel die.)

(Earliest known postmark dates are within brackets.)

1850 (5 Jan.). *T* **1.** *Imperf.*

(1) *No frame-lines, stamps* 1 *to* 1½ *mm. apart, design always sharp and distinct, colours clear. Ham's* 1st *setting, in two right and left panes of* 60 *transfers each,* 6 × 10.

1	1d. vermilion (10.1.50) ..		
2	1d. red-brown (27.2.50)	£225	£10 *to* £40
3	1d. orge.-brown (16.3.50)	£250	£10 *to* £45
4	1d. deep brn.-red (4.3.50)	£225	£10 *to* £45

(2) *With frame-lines, stamps about* ½ *mm. apart, though sometimes touching. Design indistinct owing to the dull colour used, veil always heavily shaded, with no distinction between hair and veil at sides of head. Ham's* 2nd *setting, in four panes of* 30 *transfers each,* 6 × 5.

5	1d. dull red (7.11.50)	—	80 0 *to* £12
6	1d. dull orange-vermilion (24.4.51)	—	£5 *to* £15
7	1d. dark red	£150	£8 *to* £25

(3) *With frame-lines, stamps close, often touching each other, impressions generally indistinct, but colour is brighter than in second setting. Only the very earliest impressions of this setting show the veil at sides of head heavily shaded, the great majority of specimens showing the hair sharply defined against a "white veil," a feature at once identifying the specimen as belonging to this setting. Ham's* 3rd *setting, in two right and left panes each composed of five groups of* 12 *transfers each,* 6 × 2.

(*a*) *Early impressions, veil shaded.*

8	1d. brown-red	—	80 0 *to* £16
9	1d. dull red (8.5.51) ..	£30	60 0 *to* £12

(*b*) *Later impressions, hair distinct against white veil.*

10	1d. dull red (5.10.51) ..	£20	50 0 *to* £10
11	1d. bright red (3.6.51)	—	50 0 *to* £12
12	1d. brown-red (22.12.51)	—	80 0 *to* £15

Variety. Rouletted about 12.

13	1d. bright red	—	£65

(Lithographed by Messrs. J. S. Campbell & Company of Melbourne, from transfers made from Ham's original die.)

1854 (Feb.).

(4) *With outer frame-lines; stamps* 2 *to* 3 *mm. apart horizontally (late impressions have the frame-lines barely discernible), printed from new transfers in four groups of* 24 *subjects each,* 6 × 4, *later printings were from stones with* 120 *subjects in various arrangements, impressions generally clear.*

14	1d. orange-red (6.3.54) ..	£20	80 0 *to* £14
15	1d. dull lake (9.5.54) ..	£17	40 0 *to* £8
16	1d. brick-red (26.5.54) ..	—	60 0 *to* £9
17	1d. dull red (3.5.55) ..	£17	40 0 *to* £8
18	1d. deep red	—	80 0 *to* £14

Variety. Retouched.

19	1d. brick-red (14.11.55) ..	—	£22

(Lithographed by Messrs. Campbell & Fergusson, as successors to the firm of J. S. Campbell & Co.)

1854 (July).

(5) *Same as* (4) *but colours changed; impressions not as clear.* (*In one printing right and left panes were printed almost touching so that horizontal pairs of one stamp from right pane and one stamp from left pane are sometimes mistaken for pairs of Ham's* 3rd *setting.*)

20	1d. rose-red (30.4.56) ..	£12	30 0 *to* 85 0
21	1d. dull rose (24.10.54) ..	£12	20 0 *to* 75 0
22	1d. pink	£14	20 0 *to* 75 0
23	1d. rose-lilac	£16	35 0 *to* £6
24	1d. bright rose (3.4.55)	£14	30 0 *to* 85 0

Varieties. (*a*) *Late impression, much worn.*

25	1d. bright rose (7.7.55) ..	—	35 0 *to* £5
25*a*	1d. carmine		

(*b*) *Retouched.*

26	1d. bright rose	£40	£22

1850 (3 Jan.). *T* **2.** *Imperf.*

(1) *Fine background and fine border, stamps* 1 *to* 1½ *mm. apart, usually no traces of a frame, design always sharp and distinct. Ham's* 1*st setting, probably in two right and left panes of* 60 *transfers each,* 6 × 10.

27	2d. deep lilac (19.1.50) ..		
28	2d. pale lilac (20.5.50) ..	£150	£7 *to* £35
29	2d. brown-lilac (13.2.50)	£150	£7 *to* £35
30	2d. grey-lilac	£150	£7 *to* £35
31	2d. dark brown-lilac ..	£150	£10 *to* £35

1850 (27 Jan.).

(2) *Coarse background and fine border, stamps* 1 *to* 1½ *mm. apart, usually no traces of a frame, impressions not so clear as first setting. Ham's* 2*nd setting, in four groups of* 30 *transfers each,* 5 × 6.

32	2d. dull lilac (27.1.50) ..	—	£3 *to* £10
33	2d. grey-lilac (18.4.50) ..	£30	£2 *to* £8
34	2d. dull grey (24.4.50) ..	£30	£2 *to* £8
35	2d. brown-lilac (29.5.50)	—	£3 *to* £10

(3) *Coarse background and fine border, stamps close together, nearly touching, with frame lines. Ham's* 3*rd setting, in two right and left panes, each composed of five groups of* 12 *transfers each,* 6 × 2.

36	2d. grey-lilac (19.4.50) ..	£25	£2 *to* £8
37	2d. brown-lilac (30.1.51)	£28	£2 *to* £9
38	2d. grey	£25	£2 *to* £7
39	2d. olive-grey	—	50 0 *to* £9
40	2d. red-lilac		

Variety. "*White veil*" *showing.*

41	2d. lilac	—	£4 *to* £12

(4) *Coarse background and coarse border, stamps close together, with frame lines: impressions poor with all details indistinct. Ham's* 4*th setting, in four panes of* 30 *transfers each,* 6 × 5.

42	2d. brown-lilac (14.4.50)	£15	20 0 *to* £5
43	2d. lilac (17.9.50) ..	£15	20 0 *to* £5
44	2d. grey-lilac (14.1.51) ..	£12	20 0 *to* £6
45	2d. grey	£12	20 0 *to* £7
46	2d. red-lilac (3.6.50) ..		
47	2d. red-lilac (*retouched*) ..	—	£12 *to* £30
48	2d. cinnamon (12.2.50) ..	£10	17 6 *to* £4

Variety. Retouched lower label, etc. (*value omitted*).

49	2d. brown-lilac		
50	2d. lilac	—	£150
51	2d. grey-lilac		
52	2d. red-lilac		

3

1850 (5 Jan.). *As T* **3.** *Imperf.*

(1) *Without frame lines: band about orb incomplete, stamps* 1 *mm. apart, design always distinct, colours clear. Ham's* 1*st setting, in two right and left panes of* 60 *transfers each,* 6 × 10.

53	3d. bright blue (17.1.50)	£35	40 0 *to* £8
54	3d. dark blue	—	45 0 *to* £8
55	3d. dull blue (28.6.50) ..	—	35 0 *to* £8
56	3d. pale blue (10.1.50) ..	—	35 0 *to* £8

4

(2) *Without frame lines, band about orb complete as in T* **4.** *Stamps* 1 *mm. apart, design not as distinct as in* 1*st setting. Ham's* 2*nd setting, presumably in four groups of* 30 *transfers each,* 6 × 5. *The veil is always heavily shaded, with no distinction between hair and veil at sides of head.*

57	3d. pale blue (6.10.51) ..	£50	£3 to £12
58	3d. bright blue (2.2.52) ..	—	£4 *to* £14
59	3d. deep blue (31.3.52) ..	—	£6 *to* £15
60	3d. slate-blue		
61	3d. blue (*retouched*) ..		

(3) *As last, with frame lines, stamps close, often touching each other, impressions duller and colour more variable than in earlier settings. Only the very earliest impressions of this setting show the veil at sides of head heavily shaded, the majority of specimens showing the hair sharply defined against a "white veil," a feature at once identifying the specimen as belonging to this setting. Ham's* 3*rd setting, in two right and left panes, each composed of five groups of* 12 *transfers each,* 6 × 2.

(*a*) *Early impressions, veil shaded.*

62	3d. pale blue (5.5.53) ..	—	40 0 *to* £6
63	3d. blue (6.4.53)	—	40 0 *to* £6
64	3d. deep blue (20.5.53) ..	—	50 0 *to* £7

(*b*) *Later impressions, hair distinct against white veil.*

65	3d. pale blue (26.5.54) ..	—	25 0 *to* 90 0
66	3d. blue (24.5.54) ..	£15	25 0 *to* 90 0
66*a*	3d. blue (*retouched*) (7.12.52)		
67	3d. greenish blue (25.4.53)	£15	30 0 *to* 95 0
68	3d. dark blue (26.10.53)	—	35 0 *to* £5
69	3d. dark blue (*retouched*) (May, '54)		

(Lithographed by Messrs. J. S. Campbell & Co.)

1854 (June). *T* **4.**

(4) *With frame-lines, stamps* 1½ *to* 2 *mm. apart horizontally, printed from new transfers in four groups of* 24 *subjects each,* 6 × 4. *Later printings were undoubtedly from stones having* 120 *subjects. Impressions generally clear.*

(*a*) *Imperf.*

70	3d. pale blue (24.10.54) ..	£12	20 0 *to* 60 0
71	3d. blue (3.7.54)	£12	20 0 *to* 60 0
72	3d. greenish blue (10.10.58)	—	30 0 *to* 80 0
73	3d. deep blue	—	25 0 *to* 70 0
74	3d. dull blue (17.5.59) ..	£14	25 0 *to* 70 0
75	3d. ultramarine		
76	3d. Prussian blue (14.11.56)	—	£3 *to* £8
77	3d. blue (*retouched*) ..	—	£5 *to* £20

(*b*). *Rouletted* 7½–9 (4 Oct., 1858).

78	3d. dull blue	—	£10
79	3d. greenish blue ..	—	£12

A specimen in dull blue, gauge about 7, dated 3 Aug., 1854, has been recorded. This must be of unofficial origin.

(*c*) *P* 12.

80	3d. pale blue	£35	35 0 *to* £5
81	3d. dull greenish blue (17.5.59)	—	45 0 *to* £8
82	3d. blue (16.4.59) ..	—	35 0 *to* £5
83	3d. deep blue (*retouched*)	—	50 0 *to* £10

(Lithographed by Messrs. Campbell & Fergusson.)

1855 (Jan.). *T* **4.** *Imperf.*

(5) *With frame-lines, stamps* 2 *to* 2½ *mm. apart, in four panes of* 24 *subjects each,* 6 × 4. *Later printings from stones having* 120 *subjects.*

85	3d. dull greenish blue (30.12.56)	—	30 0 *to* 90 0
86	3d. dull blue (3.5.55) ..	£12	30 0 *to* 90 0

87	3d. deep blue (3.9.55) ..	£7	15 0 *to* 50 0
88	3d. Prussian blue ..	£6	15 0 *to* 55 0
89	3d. indigo (8.11.55) ..	£7	15 0 *to* 50 0

For reprints of the above and subsequent types see note after No. 385.

5. Queen on throne.

T 5. *Imperf.*

1852 (Dec.). *Printed by Mr. Thomas Ham from a steel plate engraved by him; 50 varieties of type.*

90	2d. reddish brn. (10.10.53)	£6	20 0 *to* 50 0
91	2d. purple-brown (13.1.53)	—	20 0 *to* 50 0

1854–55. *Stamps in early colours lithographed by Messrs. Campbell & Co., the later ones by Messrs. Campbell & Fergusson. Imperf.*

92	2d. brown-violet (2.11.53)	—	10 0 *to* 35 0
93	2d. grey-lilac (6.3.54) ..	£8	10 0 *to* 30 0
94	2d. brown-lilac (17.2.54)	—	10 0 *to* 30 0
95	2d. reddish lilac (9.5.55)	£8	10 0 *to* 25 0
	a. Variety "TVO" ..	—	£35
96	2d. reddish pur. (10.7.55)	£8	10 0 *to* 25 0
97	2d. brown		

Late worn impressions; little or no shading behind throne.

98	2d. claret ..	£8	10 0 *to* 20 0
99	2d. bright lilac-rose ..	—	10 0 *to* 20 0
100	2d. dull lilac	£8	10 0 *to* 20 0
101	2d. grey-lilac		

There are many interesting varieties in this issue, such as creases in the transfers, and new transfers in wrong positions giving errors in the corner lettering. Vertical pairs may be found with wide distances between the stamps, due to two panes, of 50 stamps each, being laid down on the stones at a considerable distance apart.

6

(Engraved and lithographed by Messrs. Campbell & Fergusson.)

1854–59. *T* 6. (*a*) *Imperf.*

102	1s. greenish blue (1.8.54)	£6	12 6 *to* 50 0
103	1s. bright blue (2.9.54)..	£7	15 0 *to* 50 0
104	1s. dark blue (18.7.54)..	£8	15 0 *to* 65 0

(*b*) *Rouletted* 7 *to* 8½.

105	1s. greenish blue (27.8.57)	—	£8
105*a*	1s. blue		

(*c*) *P* 12.

106	1s. greenish blue (15.5.59)	70 0	15 0
107	1s. bright blue (17.6.59)	80 0	17 6
108	1s. dark blue	90 0	20 0

Varieties with creased or retouched transfers exist.

7. Queen on throne.

(Eng. and printed by Perkins Bacon & Co.)

1856 (Oct.). *T* 7. *Wmk. Large Star. Type* w. 1. *Imperf.*

109	1d. green	£5	20 0 *to* 80 0

1858 (Nov.). *T* 7. *Wmk. Large Star. Rouletted* 5½, 6½ *by Mr. F. W. Robinson, Melbourne.*

110	6d. bright blue	65 0	2 0 *to* 6 0
111	6d. light blue	60 0	2 0 *to* 6 0

8

Printed from a plate engraved by Mr. S. Calvert, comprising 100 *woodblocks, all differing, but of two main types:—*

A. *Small white mark after* "VICTORIA" *like an apostrophe, and ornaments to right of* "POS" *and* "STA" *each contain two dividing lines.*

B. *No white mark after* "VICTORIA", *and only one dividing line in the ornaments.*

1854–58. *T* 8. (*a*) *Imperf.*

112	6d. yellow-orge. (18.2.54)	75 0	5 0 *to* 15 0
113	6d. red-orange (20.11.54)	£6	6 0 *to* 30 0
114	6d. yellow (April, '58) ..	75 0	5 0 *to* 15 0

(*b*) *Rouletted* 7 *to* 9.

115	6d. yellow-orge. (1.5.56)	—	£2 *to* £5
116	6d. red-orange (1856 ?)	—	50 0 *to* £8

(*c*) *Serpentine roulette*, 10½.

117	6d. yellow-orange (1855)	—	50 0 *to* £6

(*d*) *Serrated* 18, 19 × *serpentine* 10½.

118	6d. yellow-orge. (10.57)	—	60 0 *to* £9

(*e*) *Serrated* 18, 19.

119	6d. yellow-orge. (18.9.55)	£25	50 0 *to* £6

(*f*) *Pin-perf. about* 10.

119*a*	6d. yellow-orge. (4.56) ..		

1861 (June). *Printed by the Government printer, Mr. F. W. Robinson, from the old plate, with slight alteration in the arrangement of the blocks.*

T 8. *Wmk.* "SIX PENCE," *in single lined frame. P* 12.

120	6d. black (25.6.61) ..	£8	25 0 *to* 60 0

1854–60. *T* **8.** ***Printed by Mr. S. Calvert from a plate of* 50 *woodblocks.***

(*a*) *Imperf.*

121 2s. bluish green (2.9.54) £48 £4 *to* £10

(*b*) *Rouletted,* 7, 7½.

122 2s. bluish grn. (4.58) .. £165 £12 *to* £25

(*c*) *P* 12.

123 2s. bluish grn. (18.11.59) £10 15 0 *to* 40 0

1864–5. *T* **8.** *Printed by Mr. F. W. Robinson from a plate consisting of* 18 *of the original woodblocks and* 12 *electros. Wmk. single-lined* "**2**", *T* **14.**

(*a*) *P* 12.

124 2s. blue/*green* (11.64) .. £8 5 0 *to* 10 0
125 2s. deep blue/*green* .. — 5 0 *to* 15 0

(*b*) *P* 13.

126 2s. blue/*green* (26.11.64) 90 0 5 0 *to* 10 0
127 2s. deep blue/*green* .. £5 5 0 *to* 10 0

9

10

(Printed partly from metal plates and partly from woodblocks engraved by Mr. S. Calvert.)

1854 (1 Dec.). Registration stamp. *T* **9.**

(*a*) *Imperf.*

128 1s. rose and blue .. £32 30 0 *to* £6

(*b*) *Rouletted* 7, 7½.

128*a* 1s. rose and blue (4.3.57) £160 £12

1855 (1 Jan.). "Too late" stamp. *T* **10.** *Imperf.*

129 6d. lilac and green .. £17 40 0 *to* £8

11. Emblems in corners.

T **11.** *Printed from electrotyped plates.*

1857.

I. Printed by Messrs. Calvert Brothers.

(i) *Wmk. Large Star, Type* w. 1.

(*a*) *Imperf.*

130 1d. yellow-green (2.57).. 50 0 10 0 *to* 30 0
a. Printed on both sides ..
131 1d. deep green .. .. 80 0 12 6 *to* 35 0
132 4d. vermilion (7.2.57) .. £10 6 0 *to* 12 6
133 4d. dull red .. .. — 6 0 *to* 12 6
134 4d. dull rose (July, '57) £8 6 0 *to* 12 6

(*b*) *Rouletted* 7 *to* 9 (*sometimes on only two sides*).

135 1d. yellow-green .. £30 £10
136 4d. dull red .. .. — £8
137 4d. rose-red .. .. — 60 0

(*c*) *P* 12.

138 1d. yellow-green .. — £50

(ii) *No wmk. Medium paper of good quality.*

(*a*) *Imperf.*

139 2d. lilac (May, '57) .. £12 10 0 *to* 20 0

(*b*) *Rouletted* 7 *to* 9 (*sometimes on only two sides*).

140 2d. lilac (10.6.57) .. — 90 0

(*c*) *P* 12.

141 2d. lilac .. .. .. — £15

(*d*) *Serrated* 19.

142 2d. lilac £50

This variety is so far only known unused.

1858.

II. Printed by Mr. S. Calvert, on white unwatermarked paper of good quality.

(*a*) *Imperf.*

143 1d. pale emerald (1.58) £15 15 0 *to* 35 0
144 1d. deep emerald .. — 20 0 *to* 45 0
145 4d. pink (1.58) .. .. — 30 0 *to* 75 0
146 4d. carmine .. .. £30 25 0 *to* 60 0

Remainders or "printer's waste" of the 4d. are quite common; they are on thinner paper and are in dull red or dull carmine.

(*b*) *Rouletted* 8 *to* 9 (*usually fine points*).

147 1d. emerald-green (24.2.58).. £20 30 0
a. Rouletted only horizontally ..
148 1d. deep emerald-green .. £30 40 0
149 4d. pink (18.1.58) .. .. — 7 6
150 4d. carmine £18 10 0
a. Rouletted only horizontally ..

(*c*) *P* 12.

151 1d. emerald-green .. ..
a. Imperf. between (pair) ..

1858.

III. Printed by Mr. F. W. Robinson, at first as a contractor and afterwards as Government Printer.

(i) *On vertically laid paper.*

(*a*) *Imperf.*

152 4d. pale rose (20.5.58) .. — 15 0 *to* 40 0
153 4d. dull rose .. .. £40 15 0 *to* 40 0
154 4d. pink .. .. .. — 15 0 *to* 50 0

(*b*) *Rouletted* 5½, 6½.

155 2d. brown-lilac (21.9.58) .. £15 17 6
156 4d. dull rose (5.5.58) .. £8 6 0
157 4d. pale rose .. .. .. — 6 0
158 4d. pink .. .. .. — 7 6

(*c*) *P* 12.

159 4d. carmine (12.2.59) .. — £45

(*d*) *Serrated* 19.

159*a* 4d. dull rose .. .. ..

The separation of this stamp differs from that of Nos. 118, 119 and 142, being by oblique straight cuts instead of by curves.

(ii) *On horizontally laid paper.*

(*a*) *Rouletted* 5½, 6½.

160 2d. brown-lilac (14.7.58) .. £2 7 6
161 2d. dull lilac (3.3.64) .. £7 7 6
162 2d. pale violet (4.4.59) .. £6 8 6
163 2d. deep violet (27.7.59) .. £8 10 0
163*a* 4d. dull rose .. .. ..

(*b*) *P* 12.

164 1d. green (18.7.59) £15 25 0
165 1d. yellowish green (16.5.59) £12 20 0
166 4d. pink (22.4.59) .. .. — 6 0
167 4d. rose (16.4.59) £8 5 0
168 4d. carmine (12.6.60) .. — 5 0

(iii) *On wove paper, usually webbed.*

(*a*) *Rouletted* 5½, 6½

169 1d. yellow-green (24.12.58) .. £30 45 0

(*b*) *P* 12.

170 1d. yellow-green (14.1.59) .. £12 35 0
 a. Pair, imperf. × perf. ..
171 1d. green (10.11.59) £10 25 0
172 4d. pale rose (18.2.59) .. £10 5 0
173 4d. carmine (17.6.59) .. — 6 0

(*c*) *Thin, surfaced paper.* *P* 12.

174 1d. yellow-green (21.6.60) .. — £5
174*a* 1d. bright green .. .. — £5

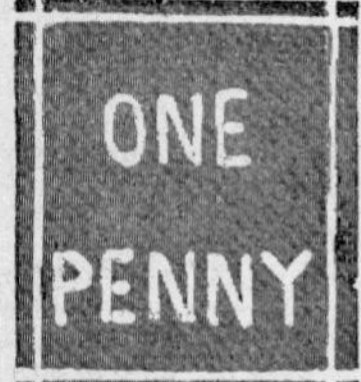

12

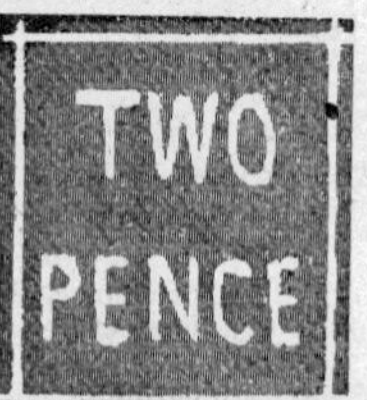

13

1860–63.

(iv) *Wmk. value in words as T* **12** *and* **13.** *P* 12.

175 1d. yellowish green (23.7.60) 65 0 15 0
 a. Error. Wmk. "FOUR PENCE" .. .. — £150
176 2d. brown-lilac (22.7.61) .. — 60 0
177 2d. bluish slate (2.7.61) .. £6 10 0
178 2d. dull lilac (28.9.61) .. £5 10 0

Variety. Wmk. "THREE PENCE".

179 2d. pale slate (3.1.63) .. £8 25 0
180 2d. lilac-grey (1.3.63) .. £10 25 0

14

1863–64.

(v) *Wmk. numerals as T* **14.** *P* 12.

181 2d. reddish lilac (25.5.63) .. £8 20 0
182 2d. deep purple £10 25 0
183 2d. slate (12.11.63) .. .. — 30 0
184 2d. grey-violet (18.7.63) .. £10 25 0
 a. Error. Wmk. "**6**" ..

Most of the shades exist without any shading to the letters "VICTORIA".

16

(Printed by Mr. F. W. Robinson from electrotyped plates, constructed by him from dies engraved by Mr. F. Grosse of Melbourne.)

1860. *T* **16.** *P* 12.

(*a*) *On horizontally laid paper.*

185 3d. deep blue (31.1.60) .. £30 60 0
186 3d. light blue.. .. .. £150 £15

(*b*) *No wmk. Thin surfaced wove paper.*

187 4d. lilac-rose (20.4.60) .. — 30 0
188 4d. rose (16.6.63) £30 15 0

(*c*) *No wmk. Stout rough paper.*

189 4d. rose (11.8.60) £25 12 6

1860–66. *T* **16.** *Wmk. value in words in single-lined frame as T* **12.** *P* 12.

190 3d. pale blue (Jan., '61) .. 60 0 15 0
191 3d. blue (15.10.60) 60 0 15 0
192 3d. marone (Feb., '66) .. 75 0 45 0
 a. Perf. 13 (26.3.66) £5 45 0
193 4d. pink (July, '60) .. .. — 4 6
194 4d. rose (31.7.60) 70 0 2 6
195 4d. carmine .. .. .. — 12 6
197 6d. orange (20.9.60) .. £110 £7 *to* £20
198 6d. black (19.6.61) £4 8 6

17

1862 (11 SEPT.). *T* **16.** *W* **17.** *P* 12.

199 4d. carmine £55 40 0

1862–63. *T* **16.** *Wmk. single-lined* "**4**".

200 4d. rose (*perf.* 12) (15.10.62) £5 5 6
201 4d. pink (*perf.* 12) (26.6.63).. — 6 0
204 4d. pink (*imperf.*) (8.6.63) .. £50 £6
205 4d. pink (*rouletted* 8) (28.7.63) £135 £12

19

(Printed from an electrotyped plate made from a die engraved by Messrs. Gruchy and Leigh, of Melbourne.)

1861. *T* **19.** *W* **12.** *P* 12.

206 1d. yellow-green (17 May) .. 90 0 16 6

1863 (JAN.). *T* **19.** *Wmk. single-lined* "**1**". *P* 12.

207 1d. yellow-green (16.6.63) .. 25 0 7 6

1863. *T* **19**, *but printed on Tasmania paper, with wmk. double-lined* "**1**". *P* 12.

208 1d. yellow-green (23 Feb.) .. £6 30 0
 a. Imperf. between (pair) ..

22

1862-65. *T* **22.** *Many of these stamps are defective, particularly in the background round the head, due to faulty construction of the clichés.*

(*a*) *Wmk.* "SIX PENCE", *as T* **13.** *P* 12.

(April, 1862.)

No.	Description	Unused	Used
209	6d. jet-black	60 0	5 0
210	6d. black	50 0	5 0

(*b*) *Wmk. single-lined* "**6**".

(i) *P* 12. (June, 1863.)

No.	Description	Unused	Used
211	6d. jet-black	50 0	4 6
212	6d. black	40 0	4 6

(ii) *P* 13.

No.	Description	Unused	Used
213	6d. jet-black (3.3.64) ..	—	6 0
214	6d. black	50 0	5 0
	a. Imperf.	—	£15

23

(Several plates were used for some values, and many clichés are defective. Some have parts of frames missing, the word "VICTORIA" double, the profile double, etc.)

1863-67. *T* **23.** *Wmk. single-lined numerals as T* **14.**

No.	Description	Unused	Used
215	1d. pale emer.-grn. (*perf.* 12)	30 0	7 6
216	1d. pale emer.-grn. (*perf.* 13)	15 0	7 6
217	1d. pale emer.-grn. (*p.* 12×13)	50 0	15 0
218	1d. green (*perf.* 12) ..	20 0	6 0
219	1d. green (*perf.* 13) ..	15 0	5 0
220	1d. green (*perf.* 12×13) ..	—	15 0
221	2d. slate-mauve (*perf.* 12) ..	30 0	3 0
222	2d. slate-mauve (*perf.* 13) ..	30 0	2 6
223	2d. slate-mauve (*perf.* 12×13)		
224	2d. dull lilac (*perf.* 12) ..	25 0	4 0
225	2d. dull lilac (*perf.* 13) ..	25 0	2 0
226	2d. dull purple (*perf.* 12) ..		
227	2d. dull purple (*perf.* 13) ..	25 0	7 6
228	2d. dull purple (*perf.* 12×13)	50 0	7 6
229	4d. pink (*perf.* 12)	40 0	3 6
230	4d. pink (*perf.* 13)	30 0	4 0
231	4d. pink (*perf.* 12×13) ..	—	10 0
232	4d. rose-red (*perf.* 12) ..	35 0	3 6
233	4d. rose-red (*perf.* 13) ..	30 0	3 6
234	4d. rose-red (*perf.* 12×13) ..	40 0	4 0
235	8d. orange-yellow (*perf.* 13)	60 0	25 0

N.B.—Perforations gauging between 11½ and 12 are classed as p. 12, and those gauging between 12½ and 13 as p. 13.

PRINTED ON VARIOUS PAPERS BORROWED FROM TASMANIA AND ON OLD VICTORIAN PAPER.

1864-68. *T* **23.** *Wmk. double-lined numerals.*

No.	Description	Unused	Used
236	1d. yellow-green (**1**, *perf.* 13)	20 0	7 6
237	1d. green (**1**, *perf.* 13) ..	20 0	7 6
238	1d. green (**4**, *perf.* 13) ..	—	£8
239	2d. grey-lilac (**1**, *perf.* 13) ..	£10	8 6
240	2d. pale mauve (**1**, *perf.* 13)	£10	8 6
241	2d. grey-lilac (**4**, *perf.* 13) ..	£9	4 0
242	2d. dull mauve (**4**, *perf.* 13)	£8	4 0
243	4d. carmine (**4**, *perf.* 12) ..	80 0	7 6
244	4d. carmine (**4**, *perf.* 13) ..	—	7 6
245	4d. carmine (**4**, *perf.* 12×13)	—	15 0
246	4d. dull rose (**4**, *perf.* 12) ..	—	6 0
247	4d. dull rose (**4**, *perf.* 13) ..	£5	4 0
248	4d. dull rose (**4**, *perf.* 12×13)	—	15 0

1867. *Wmk. single-lined numerals* (*except No.* 252, *as T* **13**).

No.	Description	Unused	Used
249	1d. green (**4**, *perf.* 13) ..	50 0	20 0
250	1d. green (**6**, *perf.* 13) ..	£8	35 0
251	1d. green (**8**, *perf.* 13) ..	£10	30 0
252	1d. green (SIX PENCE, *p.* 13)	£40	60 0
253	2d. grey-lilac (**4**, *perf.* 13) ..	£4	5 0
253*a*	2d. grey-lilac ((? SIX) PENCE, *perf.* 13)	£4	6 0
254	2d. slate-mauve (**4**, *perf.* 13)	£4	6 0
255	2d. slate-mauve (**6**, *perf.* 13)	£12	12 6
256	2d. slate-mauve (**8**, *perf.* 13)	£8	6 0

Stamps may be frequently found without watermark, but these are from margins of sheets of the watermarked papers.

26

☞ *Many stamps watermarked V and Crown may be found with watermark inverted or sideways. We do not list these as separate varieties, but copies can be supplied if in stock.*

1867-81. *T* **23.** *W* **26.**

No.	Description	Unused	Used
258	1d. yellow-green (*perf.* 13) ..	17 6	3 6
259	1d. bluish green (*perf.* 13) ..	12 6	2 6
260	1d. bluish green (*perf.* 12) ..	12 6	3 0
261	1d. dull blue-green (*perf.* 13)	12 6	2 6
262	1d. dull blue-green (*perf.* 12)	15 0	2 6
263	2d. slate-mauve (*perf.* 13) ..	15 0	2 0
264	2d. rosy lilac (*perf.* 13) ..	15 0	1 9
265	2d. mauve (*perf.* 13)	15 0	2 3
266	2d. mauve/*lilac* (*perf.* 13) ..	25 0	10 0
267	2d. purple (*perf.* 13) ..	20 0	4 0
268	4d. rose (*perf.* 13)	30 0	4 6
269	4d. rose (*perf.* 12)	40 0	4 6
270	4d. rose (*perf.* 12×13) ..		
271	4d. carmine (*perf.* 13) ..	—	5 0
272	4d. pink (*perf.* 12)	40 0	4 6
273	4d. pink (*perf.* 13)	—	4 6
274	4d. aniline-rosine (*perf.* 12) ..	£5	6 6
275	4d. aniline-rosine (*perf.* 13)	—	15 0
276	8d. red-brn./*rose* (*perf.* 13) ..	30 0	5 0
277	8d. dark vio.-brn./*rose* (*p.* 13)	—	6 0
278	8d. aniline-brown/*rose* (*p.* 12)	35 0	10 6

1879-80. *T* **23.** *Wmk. single-lined* "**10**".

No.	Description	Unused	Used
279	8d. red-brown/*rose* (*perf.* 12)	—	25 0
280	8d. red-brown/*rose* (*perf.* 13)	50 0	10 0
281	8d. red-brown/*rose* (*p.* 13×12)	—	30 0
282	8d. dark vio.-brn./*rose* (*p.* 13)	80 0	15 0

N.B.—From 1869 a new single-line perforating machine was used gauging between 12¼ and 12½, and was in use up to 1910. The old machines gauging 12 and 13 ceased to be used in about 1881.

28

29

1866 (29 OCT.). *T* **28.** *Wmk. single-lined* "**8**". *P* 13.

No.	Description	Unused	Used
283	3d. rosy lilac	45 0	40 0

1868 (8 Dec.). *T* **28.** *Wmk. double-lined* "**1**". *P* 13.

284 3d. grey-lilac £12 £4

1867–81. *T* **28.** *Wmk. V and Crown, T* **26.**

285 3d. red-lilac (*p.* 13) (28.9.67) 60 0 50 0
286 3d. grey-lilac (*p.* 13) (15.8.68) 80 0 50 0
287 3d. orange (*perf.* 12) (15.7.73) 20 0 4 0
288 3d. orange (*perf.* 13) (23.8.69) 12 6 3 6
289 3d. orge.-yell. (*p.* 12) (30.1.71) 30 0 15 0
290 3d. orge.-yell. (*p.* 13) (1.2.72) 20 0 7 6
291 3d. light yellow (*perf.* 12) .. 30 0 7 6
291*a* 3d. light yell (*p.* 13) (22.8.81) — 12 6

PERFORATIONS

N.B.—Some of the apparent compound perforations found on certain of the 3d. and the 6d., T **29**, were made by comb machines, and may be separately collected by a specialist, but we do not think it necessary to include them in this catalogue. We may mention that comb machines were first used about 1873. They were of various gauges—such as 12¾ × 12½, 13 × 12½, and 12 to 12½ × 12½ to 12½, and were extensively used for the stamps of ordinary size and spacing described below as "Perf. 12½" or "Perf. 12½ or 12 × 12½"; also for the small ½d., T **37** or **68**, a horizontal pair for this purpose being equivalent to one ordinary sized stamp, but in this case a second perforation by a single-line machine was necessary to separate the pairs of ½d. stamps. The combs were never used for the large "Stamp Duty" postal fiscals or for any of the laureated types except T **28** and **29**. Further, the old single-line machines which we have called 12 (really 11½–12) and 13 (really 12½–13) were laid aside about 1881, but new machines of the same description gauging about 12¼ to 12½ (which we call 12½) were obtained about 1869, and thenceforth used extensively down to the close of the issue of separate Victorian stamps. Other details of interest to specialists are the sizes of the holes made by the several machines (combs as well as single line) at different stages of their history. In 1910–13 a new kind of comb machine was employed for some of the 1d. stamps. They gauged 11½ × 12½.

1866 (14 Apr.). *T* **29.** *Wmk. single-lined* "**6**".

292 6d. Prussian blue (*perf.* 12).. 40 0 5 0
a. Imperf. between (pair) .. — £25
293 6d. Prussian blue (*perf.* 13).. 25 0 2 6
294 6d. Prussian blue (*p.* 12 × 13) 25 0 3 0

1867–70. *T* **29.** *Various old wmks. P* 13.

295 6d. Prussian blue ("THREE PENCE") £16 17 6
296 6d. Prussian blue ("FOUR PENCE") £40 50 0
297 6d. Prussian blue ("SIX PENCE") £25 30 0
298 6d. Prussian blue (**4**) .. — £100
299 6d. Prussian blue (**1**) .. £6 10 0
300 6d. Prussian blue (**2**) .. — £100
300*a* 6d. Prussian blue (**4**) (17.7.68) £25 52 6

No. 298 *has a single-lined* "**4**" *wmk. Nos.* 299–300*a have double-lined numeral wmks.*

1867–79. *T* **29.** *Wmk. V and Crown, T* **26.**

301 6d. Prussian blue (*perf.* 12).. 20 0 1 0
302 6d. Prussian blue (*perf.* 13).. 10 0 0 9
302*a* 6d. Prussian blue (*p.* 12 × 13) — 20 0
303 6d. bright blue (*perf.* 12) .. 12 0 1 0
304 6d. bright blue (*perf.* 13) .. 10 0 1 0
305 6d. bright blue (*perf.* 12 × 13) 20 0 3 0
306 6d. dull ultram. (*perf.* 12) .. 30 0 2 6
307 6d. dull ultram. (*perf.* 13) .. 20 0 1 0
308 6d. ultramarine (*perf.* 12) ..
309 6d. ultramarine (*perf.* 13) .. 25 0 2 6

1865 (2 Oct.). *T* **29.** *Wmk. single-lined* "**8**". *P* 13.

310 10d. slate £8 £4

1866 (Apr.). *T* **29.** *Wmk. single-lined* "**10**".

311 10d. brown/*rose* (*perf.* 13) .. 30 0 4 6
312 10d. brown/*rose* (*perf.* 12 × 13) 40 0 10 0

9 9

NINEPENCE

(30)

31

1871 (May). *T* **29,** *surch. as T* **30,** *in blue.*

313 9d. on 10d. brown/*rose* (*p.* 13) £6 15 0
314 9d. on 10d. brown/*rose* (*perf.* 12 × 13) .. .. ..
a. Double surcharge .. ..

1865 (10 Apr.). *T* **31.** *Wmk. single-lined* "**1**."

315 1s. blue/*blue* (*perf.* 13) .. 50 0 5 0
316 1s. blue/*blue* (*perf.* 12) .. 60 0 7 0
317 1s. blue/*blue* (*perf.* 12 × 13) .. 50 0 8 6
a. Imperf. between (pair) ..

Stamps perf. 12 and perf. 13 have both been seen with the wmk. sideways.

1875 (18 May). *T* **31.** *Wmk. V and Crown, T* **26**

318 1s. blue/*blue* (*perf.* 13) .. £6 20 0
319 1s. blue/*blue* (*perf.* 12) .. — 20 0

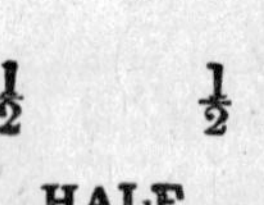

(32)

33

1873 (19 July). *T* **23** *surch. as T* **32,** *in red.*

320 ½d. on 1d. green (*perf.* 13) .. 15 0 11 0
321 ½d. on 1d. green (*perf.* 12) .. 25 0 15 0

1868 (31 Mar.). *T* **33.** *Printed from a single plate. Wmk. V and Crown, T* **26.** *P* 13.

322 5s. blue/*yellow* .. £25 £8 *to* £18

1868 (Sept.). *T* **33,** *but printed from two plates. W* **26** *and P* 13, *unless otherwise stated.*

Type I. With a coloured line under the Crown.

323 5s. Prussian blue and rose-red £5 15 0
324 5s. lavender & carm. (3.7.77) £8 20 0

Type II. Without the coloured line under the Crown.

325 5s. aniline-blue and scarlet (21.12.81) £5 20 0
326 5s. aniline-blue and scarlet (*perf.* 12) (12.12.82) .. 80 0 20 0

34

35

(Printed from electrotypes engraved by Messrs. De La Rue & Co.)

1870 (2 Mar.). *T* **34**. *Wmk. V and Crown, T* **26**.

327	2d. brownish lilac (*perf.* 13)	20 0	1 9
328	2d. bright mauve (*perf.* 13)..	15 0	1 0
329	2d. bright mauve (*perf.* 12)..	25 0	1 0
330	2d. lilac (*perf.* 13)	15 0	2 0
331	2d. lilac (*perf.* 12)		

1873 (Mar.). *T* **35**. *Wmk. single-lined* "**10**."

332	9d. brown/*rose* (*perf.* 13) ..	35 0	7 0
333	9d. brown/*rose* (*perf.* 12) ..	65 0	20 0

1875 (Dec.). *T* **35**. *Wmk. V and Crown, T* **26** *P* 12.

334	9d. brown/*rose*	80 0	22 6

8d **8d**

EIGHTPENCE

(36)

1876 (July). *No.* 334 *surch. with T* **36**.

335	8d. on 9d. brown/*rose* (B.) ..	100 0	25 0

37

38

39

40

41

42

1873–83. *T* **37** *to* **40**. *The* 2*d. has single-lined outer oval as T* **41**. *Wmk. V and Crown, T* **26**.

336	½d. pale rose (*perf.* 13) ..	2 6	2 0
	a. Perf. 12	15 0	2 6
337	½d. deep rose (*perf.* 13) ..	2 6	1 9
	a. Perf. 12	4 0	1 6
	b. Perf. 12×13	—	15 0
338	½d. rose/*rose* (*perf.* 13) ..	11 6	6 6
339	½d. rosine (*perf.* 13)	2 6	1 0
	a. Perf. 12	3 0	0 8
	b. Perf. 12×13	22 6	
340	½d. scarlet (*perf.* 13) ..	—	1 0
	a. Perf. 12	5 0	0 8
341	1d. yellow-green (*perf.* 13)	6 0	4 0
	a. Perf. 12	12 6	5 0
342	1d. pale green (*perf.* 13) ..	7 6	0 9
	a. Perf. 12	6 0	1 3
343	1d. green/*yellow* (*perf.* 13) ..	30 0	16 6
344	1d. green/*drab* (*perf.* 13) ..	45 0	37 6
345	2d. dull mauve (*perf.* 13) ..	5 0	0 6
	a. Perf. 12	25 0	2 6
346	2d. deep mauve (*perf.* 13) ..	7 6	0 9
	a. Perf. 12	—	5 0
347	2d. bright mauve (*perf.* 13)..	5 0	0 9
348	2d. mauve/*green* (*perf.* 13) ..	45 0	8 6
349	2d. mauve/*buff* (*perf.* 13) ..	40 0	11 0
350	2d. mauve/*lilac* (*perf.* 13) ..		
	a. Perf. 12×13		
351	1s. bright blue/*blue* (*p.* 13) ..	20 0	3 6
	a. Perf. 12	—	10 0
352	1s. deep blue/*blue* (*perf.* 13)	20 0	4 0
	a. Perf. 12	—	7 6

Many ½d. stamps were perforated by the new 12¼, 12½ single line machine. The pins in the 12 machine were altered to make large holes from 1879 to 1881. The 13 machine was altered to give large holes in 1873, and used thus up to 1881 also.

1876. *T* **39** *with double-lined outer oval, as T* **42**. *Wmk. T* **26**.

353	2d. mauve (*perf.* 13).. ..	10 0	0 6
	a. Perf. 12	15 0	2 0
	b. Perf. 12×13	—	4 0
	c. Imperf.		
	d. Imperf. between (pair) ..		

43

44

45

1881. *T* **43** *to* **45**. *W* **26**. *P* 12½.

354	2d. brown	3 0	0 4
	a. Perf. 12		
355	2d. chocolate	3 6	0 4
356	2d. mauve	6 6	0 5
357	4d. carmine	12 6	4 6
358	2s. blue/*green*	35 0	17 6
359	2s. deep blue/*green*	35 0	15 0

46

1883. *T* **46**. *W* **26**. *P* 12½.

360	1d. pale green	7 0	1 0
361	1d. yellow-green	7 0	1 0

47 48 49 50 51 52

52a

1884–86. *W* 26. *P* 12½.

No.	Type					
362	47	½d. salmon	4	6	3	6
363	,,	½d. pale rosine	3	0	1	0
364	,,	½d. deep rosine ..	3	6	2	6
365	48	1d. pale yellow-green ..	12	0	5	0
366	,,	1d. green	2	6	0	6
367	49	2d. mauve (Jan. 1885) ..	4	0	0	5
368	,,	2d. rose-lilac (1886) ..	6	0	1	0
369	,,	2d. lilac-rose	5	0	0	6
370	48	3d. pale brown	4	0	1	6
371	,,	3d. brown	3	6	0	10
372	,,	3d. yellow-brown ..	3	6	0	8
372*a*	,,	3d. olive-brown	6	6	2	6
373	50	4d. magenta	12	6	5	0
374	48	6d. ultramarine	20	0	5	0
375	,,	6d. pale dull blue ..	20	0	5	0
376	51	8d. rosine/*rose*	8	0	5	0
377	,,	8d. scarlet/*rose*	8	6	6	0
378	52	1s. blue/*pale lemon* ..	22	6	6	0
379	,,	1s. blue/*yellow*	25	0	6	0
380	51	2s. olive/*grn.** (July, '86)	10	0	4	0
381	,,	2s. apple-green/*white* (Aug. 1895)	8	6	8	6
382	,,	2s. emerald/*white* (11.95)	8	6	6	0
383	52*a*	2s. 6d. orange (Oct. 1884)	7	6	5	0
384	,,	2s. 6d. orge.-yell. (1889)	8	6	4	0
		Error: 4d. *in colour of the* 2d.				
385	50	4d. mauve† ..	£200			

* The paper was first a bluish green; later printings were on a yellowish green paper with the same watermark.

† Specimens of the 4d. in a dull shade of mauve are probably colour-changelings. Mr. W. R. Rundell in his notes on this error in the *Monthly Journal* of 31st January, 1914, stated that fifty sheets were printed in violet by mistake, and that so far as he was aware only seven specimens were then in existence, "all unused."

[NOTE.—As from the 1st January, 1884, all distinction between postage stamps and fiscal stamps was abolished (except as to a few specified fiscal stamps), and accordingly all stamps of either description which had theretofore been issued were made available for postage or fiscal purposes. This arrangement, however, came to an end shortly after Federation; from 1st April, 1901, the postal and telegraph services of all the States were transferred to the Commonwealth, but the States were authorized to impose fiscal duties for their own use; nevertheless the use of the States' stamps for postage was permitted down to the 30th June, 1901. During the period 1st January, 1884–30th June, 1901, all the new types of stamps issued, with the exception of the 1½d., were inscribed "STAMP DUTY"—while many of the large fiscal stamps with the same inscription, described below under Postal Fiscals, were continued in use—sometimes in new colours or with new watermarks. For the 5s. value the old laureated type was withdrawn and replaced by the large fiscal. The 9d., T **35**, however, was reissued in November, 1892, but in green or rose on white paper.]

In 1891 reprints were made of Nos. 6, 29, 53, 90, 106, 109, 110, 191, 192, 206, 210, 235, 258, 261, 266, 290, 309, 313, 318, 326, 334, 339, 341, 345, 351, 354, 357, 358, 360, 362, 365, 367, 373, 374, and 378. These are on paper wmk. V and Crown, T **26**, and are perf. 12, 12½; they are usually found with the word "REPRINT," but some, if not all, may be found without it.

STAMP DUTY

(53)

1885. *Overprinted with T* **53**. *W* **26**. *P* 12½.

(*a*) *In blue.*

No.	Type					
386	28	3d. orange	17	6	12	6
387	44	4d. rose-carmine	17	6	10	0
388	40	1s. blue/*pale blue* ..	—		£15	
		(*b*) *In black.*				
389	40	1s. blue/*pale blue* ..	25	0	20	0
390	45	2s. blue/*gree*	20	0	15	0

54

55

56

57

58

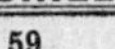
59

60

1886-88. *W* **26.** *P* 12½.

391	**54**	½d. grey-lilac (Oct. 1886) ..	3	6	2	3
392	„	½d. pink (April, 1887) ..	3	0	1	3
393	„	½d. rosine	2	0	0	8
394	„	½d. scarlet	0	10	0	3
394*a*	„	½d. red				
395	**55**	1d. green (Nov., 1886) ..	3	0	0	4
396	„	1d. yellow-green ..	2	6	0	3
397	**56**	2d. lilac	1	0	0	2
398	„	2d. violet	0	8	0	2
399	„	2d. lilac-rose	1	6	0	2
400	**57**	4d. rose-carmine	5	6	1	3
401	**58**	6d. pale ultram. (20.3.86) ..	4	0	0	6
402	„	6d. blue (10.3.90)	5	0	0	5
403	„	6d. bright ultramarine ..	2	0	0	3
404	**59**	1s. purple-brown	15	0	2	6
405	„	1s. lake-brown	20	0	5	0
406	„	1s. carmine-lake	6	0	1	6
407	„	1s. brownish red	6	0	1	6
408	**60**	1s. 6d. blue	25	0	25	0
409	„	1s. 6d. orange	6	0	4	0
409*a*	„	1s. 6d. red-orange ..	6	0	5	0

Variety. Imperf.

410 **56** 2d. lilac .. .. ..

A horizontal imperforate pair is described in the *Monthly Journal* of 29th Nov., 1902, page 101. See a later reference in the *Monthly Journal* of 31st August, 1904, from which it appears that an imperforate sheet was on sale at the Mortlake, Victoria, Post Office in 1890.

Nos. 391 and 408 were reprinted in 1895.

60*a*

1888-92. *Designs differing for each value in detail, but substantially as T* **60***a. Medallion and spandrels in first colour. Wmk. V and Crown T* **26.** *P* 12½.

410*b*	£5 pale blue & brn.-pur. (2.12.92)	£7	25	0
410*c*	£6 orge. & pale blue (25.1.92)	£10	30	0
410*d*	£7 rosine & blk. (15.10.89)	£12	35	0
410*e*	£8 lilac and orange ..	£15	40	0
410*f*	£9 pale green and rosine .	£20	50	0

The used prices quoted above are for stamps postmarked to order by the Victorian postal authorities for sale in sets.

61

62

63

1890-92. *W* **26.** *P* 12½.

411	**61**	1d. Venetian red (1.90) ..	2	6	0	6
412	„	1d. oran.-brn. (5.91)	0	10	0	1
413	„	1d. brn./*rose* (7.91) ..	1	6	0	6
414	„	1d. dull yellow (12.93) ..	1	3	0	1
415	„	1d. bright orange (5.94)..	0	9	0	1
416	„	1d. brown-red (11.94) ..	1	6	0	2
417	**62**	2½d. brown-red/*lemon* ..	2	0	0	6
418	„	2½d. pale brown-red/*yell.*	2	6	0	5
419	„	2½d. red/*orange-yellow* ..	3	0	0	5
420	**63**	5d. chocolate (1.91) ..	3	0	0	6
421	„	5d. reddish brn. (10.95)	2	6	0	8
422	**35**	9d. yell.-green (11.92) ..	12	6	8	6
423	„	9d. rose-pink (1895) ..	7	6	2	9
424	„	9d. aniline scar. (23.9.96)	10	0	4	6
425	„	9d. rose-carmine ..	6	6	2	6

64

64*a*

64*b*

¶ (For note *re* inverted and sideways wmks. see below **T 26.**)

1896–99. *Wmk. V and Crown, T* **64***a*. *P* 12½.

[Note.—The new white paper with V and Crown of designs **64***a* or **64***b* differs considerably from that of the first V and Crown design—it is smooth and thicker and of a purer white than that of the first design; further, it is nearly always webbed in texture, while the earlier paper rarely shows any grain, and was presumably more heavily pressed or rolled in the course of manufacture. The white paper of T **64***a* was apparently first used in 1896, and was replaced in 1899 by the paper watermarked T **64***b*. The stocks of the yellow and rose V and Crown papers of the early design lasted somewhat longer, but on exhaustion were replaced by similarly coloured papers with the new designs of the watermarks, as appears below.]

426	**54**	½d. scarlet	1	6	0	4
427	,,	½d. rosine	2	9	0	4
428	,,	½d. green (Sept., 1899) ..	2	0	0	5
429	**61**	1d. brown-red	1	0	0	1
430	,,	1d. brown-orange ..	1	0	0	1
431	**64**	1½d. green (Oct. 1897) ..	1	3	1	6
434	**56**	2d. violet (1898) ..	2	6	0	6
435	**62**	2½d. blue (Aug., 1899) ..	2	0	1	0
436	**48**	3d. yellow-brown ..	6	0	0	8
437	,,	3d. dull yellow	8	0	1	9
438	**57**	4d. rose-red	5	0	0	9
439	,,	4d. rose	3	6	0	7
440	**63**	5d. red-brown	12	6	1	6
442	**58**	6d. dull ultramarine ..	2	6	0	5
443	**35**	9d. pink (17.3.96) ..	8	6	2	6
444	,,	9d. red-rose	7	6	2	6
445	,,	9d. aniline scarlet (3.2.97)	15	0	4	6
446	**59**	1s. brownish red (27.8.97)	7	0	1	9
447	**60**	1s. 6d. pale red-orange	15	0	12	6
448	**51**	2s. emerald	25	0	15	0
449	**52***a*	2s. 6d. yellow	25	0	25	0

Specimens of the 5d., wmk. either T **26** or **64***a*, in *dull brown*, are probably colour changelings.

Change of colour. Wmk. V and Crown, T **26**. *P* 12½.

450	**64**	1½d. red/*yellow*	1	6	1	3

* **64***c*

* **64***d*

1897. *Charity stamps. T* **64***c and* **64***d*. *W* **64***a*. *P* 12½.

450*a*	1d. (1s.), blue	3	6	4	6
450*b*	2½d. (2s. 6d.), red-brown ..	17	6	17	6

These stamps, sold at 1s. and 2s. 6d. respectively, paid postage as 1d. and 2½d. stamps only, the difference being given to a Hospital Fund.

1899–00. *Wmk. V and Crown, T* **64***b*. *P* 12½.

451	**54**	½d. green (Aug., 1899) ..	0	6	0	3
452	**61**	1d. rosine	0	6	0	1
453	**56**	2d. mauve	5	0	1	0
454	**62**	2½d. blue	1	3	0	9
455	**48**	3d. pale olive-yellow ..				
456	,,	3d. pale brownish yellow	3	0	0	8
457	**57**	4d. dull rose	2	6	0	6
458	**63**	5d. red-brown	3	0	0	9
459	**58**	6d. ultramarine	4	6	0	9
460	**35**	9d. red-rose	2	6	1	9
462	**59**	1s. brownish red ..	7	6	2	0
463	**60**	1s. 6d. yellow-orange ..	6	6	7	6
464	**51**	2s. emerald (18.9.00) ..	7	6	15	0
465	**52***a*	2s. 6d. yellow	6	6	3	6

* **64***e*

* **64***f*

1900. *Charity stamps. T* **64***e and* **64***f*. *W* **64***b*. *P* 12½.

465*a*	1d. (1s.), olive-brown ..	12	6	12	6
465*b*	2d. (2s.), emerald-green ..	17	6	17	6

These stamps were sold on a similar basis to Nos. 450*a* and 450*b*, for the benefit of a Patriotic Fund.

* Blocks reduced in size.

AFTER FEDERATION (1st January, 1901).

65

66

67

1901 (29 Jan.). *Wmk. V and Crown, T* **64***b* (*except* 2*s*., *W* **64***a*). *P* 12½ *or* 12 × 12½.

466	**37**	½d. emerald	0	3	0	2
467	,,	½d. emerald ("VICTCRIA")	40	0	40	0
468	**65**	1d. rose-red (Die I) ..	0	4	0	1
469	,,	1d. rose (Die I)	0	4	0	1
470	,,	1d. rose-car. (Die II) ..	0	6	0	2
471	,,	1d. rose-red (Die II) ..	0	4	0	1
472	,,	1d. brick-red (Die II) ..	0	8	0	2
472*a*	,,	1d. rose-carm. (Die III) ..	2	6	0	6
473	**43**	2d. bright mauve ..	0	8	0	3
474	**66**	2½d. deep blue	1	0	0	3
475	,,	2½d. blue	0	10	0	3
476	**28**	3d. orange-brown ..	3	0	2	0
477	**44**	4d. yellow-bistre ..	3	6	2	0
478	**67**	5d. red-brown	2	6	0	3
479	,,	5d. chocolate	6	0	0	10
480	**29**	6d. bright green	3	6	3	0
481	**40**	1s. orange-yellow ..	3	6	3	0
482	**45**	2s. blue/*rose*	10	0	8	6
483	**33**	5s. scarlet and blue ..	20	0	17	6

Three dies of the 1d. :—

I. As 1d. green, T **46**, except for label "POSTAGE." Background behind head graduated from thick lines at top to thin at bottom.

II. Background lines of uniform thickness. Stop after "1d." at left just touches the circle. **Faint line across bridge of nose.**

III. Background lines of uniform thickness. Clear space between stop and circle. Heavy line joining the eyebrows.

The above perforations are not easy to distinguish from single specimens. They are made by two separate machines, one a single cutter gauging 12½ (which alone was used for the 5s.) and the other a comb machine gauging 12 × 12½.

1901 (May). *W* **64***b*. *P* 12½ *or* 12 × 12½.

484	**61**	1d. olive	5 0	4 0

1901 (20 June). *W* **64***b*. *P* 12½ *or* 12 × 12½.

485	**48**	3d. slate-green	7 6	10 0

These two stamps were only available for postal use until the 30th June; afterwards for fiscal purposes only.

68

69

70

71

72

73

74

75

76

77

1901 (June). *T* **68** *to* **77.** *Similar to former types, but* "POSTAGE" *inserted in design. All watermarked V and Crown, T* **64***b*. *P* 12½ *or* 12 × 12½.

486	½d. green	0 3	0 3
487	1½d. red/*yellow*	1 3	0 5
488	1½d. marone/*yellow*	1 0	0 5
489	2d. mauve	0 6	0 2
490	2d. bright mauve	0 9	0 4
491	2d. violet-mauve	1 0	0 4
492	3d. orange-brown	2 0	0 4
493	3d. pale orange-brown ..	1 9	0 4
494	4d. yellow-bistre	1 3	0 8
495	4d. olive-bistre	2 6	0 9
496	6d. bright green	2 6	0 8
497	6d. dull green	6 0	2 6
498	9d. rose	5 0	3 0
499	9d. red-rose	8 6	2 6
500	1s. orange-yellow	3 6	1 9
501	1s. orange	3 0	2 0
502	2s. blue/*rose*	3 6	1 9
503	5s. rose-red and pale blue ..	15 0	15 0
504	5s. bright red and indigo ..	17 6	15 0

78

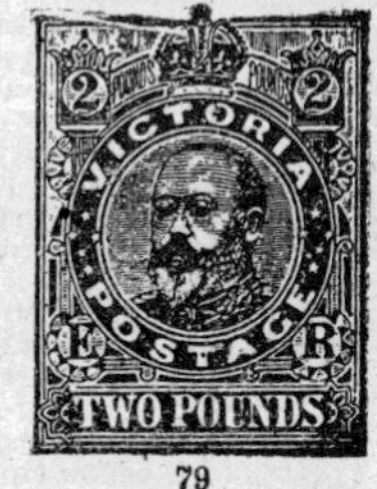

79

1901-2. *T* **78** *and* **79.** *W* **64***b*. *P* 12½.

505	£1 carmine	85 0	50 0
506	£2 deep blue	£7	90 0

These large stamps were always perforated by single-line machines. A new single-line machine gauging 11 was used in and after 1902.

80

1903. *T* **80** (*T* **75** *redrawn*). *W* **64***b*. *P* 12½ *or* 12 × 12½.

507	1s. orange-yellow	7 6	4 0
508	1s. orange	6 6	2 6

A good test to distinguish the redrawn type from the original is to compare the words "POSTAGE," more particularly the "POS" of word on right and "AGE" of word on left.

1902. *W* **64***b*. (*a*) *P* 11.

509	**68**	½d. green	0 10	0 8
509*a*	**65**	1d. rose-red (Die I) ..	—	60 0
510	,,	1d. rose-red (Die II) ..	2 6	2 6
510*a*	,,	1d. rose-red (Die III) ..	£5	80 0
511	**69**	1½d. marone/*yellow* ..	80 0	
512	**70**	2d. mauve	—	£30
513	**71**	3d. orange-brown ..	7 6	7 6
514	**73**	6d. bright green ..	10 0	10 0
514*a*	**74**	9d. red-rose		
515	**78**	£1 carmine	£6	
516	**79**	£2 deep blue	£40	

(b) Perf. compound of 12½ or 12 × 12½ with 11.

No.	Type	Description	Unused	Used
517	**68**	½d. green	10 0	10 0
518	**65**	1d. rose-red (Die II) ..	—	£7
519	**69**	1½d. marone/*yellow* ..		
520	**71**	3d. orange-brown ..	—	£38
521	**73**	6d. bright green ..	—	£40

In the case of the ½d. the compound perf. can be found (i.) compound of the single-line machine 12½ and the single-line machine 11, or (ii.) compound of the comb-machine 12 × 12½ with the single-line 11.

1905–11. *Wmk. Crown over A, Type* **w. 11**

(a) P 12½ or 12 × 12½.

No.	Type	Description	Unused	Used
522	**68**	½d. green	0 10	0 6
523	**65**	1d. rose-red (Die III) ..	0 3	0 1
524	,,	1d. rose (Die III) ..	0 3	0 1
525	,,	1d. brt. rose (Die III) ('11)	0 4	0 1
526	**70**	2d. rosy lilac	2 0	0 1
527	,,	2d. mauve (1908) ..	2 0	0 1
528	,,	2d. violet-mauve (1910)	1 0	0 1
529	**66**	2½d. blue (1908)	1 9	1 0
530	,,	2½d. deep blue	1 9	1 0
531	**71**	3d. brown-orange ..	2 0	0 10
532	,,	3d. orange (1907) ..	3 0	0 10
533	,,	3d. orange-yellow ..	4 0	0 9
534	,,	3d. pale orge.-yell. (1908)	4 0	1 0
535	**72**	4d. yellow-bistre (1906)	3 6	0 6
536	,,	4d. olive	3 0	0 6
537	**67**	5d. chocolate (1906) ..	3 0	1 3
538	,,	5d. pale chocolate ..	2 6	0 10
539	**73**	6d. green	4 0	0 6
540	,,	6d. pale green (1910)	4 0	0 4
541	**74**	9d. brownish rose ..	5 0	1 9
542	,,	9d. dull red (1907) ..	5 6	1 9
543	,,	9d. carmine-red (1910) ..	5 0	2 0
544	**80**	1s. orange (1906) ..	3 0	0 10
545	,,	1s. yellow (1908) ..	3 0	0 10
546	,,	1s. golden orange (1910)	7 6	0 9
547	**77**	5s. rose-red & ultram. (1908)	25 0	12 6
548	,,	5s. red and indigo ..	30 0	15 0
549	**78**	£1 rose (1907)	£6	
550	,,	£1 salmon (1910) ..	£6	
551	**79**	£2 deep blue (1907) ..	£12	

(b) P 11.

No.	Type	Description	Unused	Used
552	**68**	½d. green	0 5	0 5
553	**65**	1d. rose-red (Die III) ..	1 6	0 6
554	,,	1d. rose (Die III) ..	1 3	0 6
555	,,	1d. rose-car. (Die III) ('11)	3 0	
556	**70**	2d. mauve	35 0	20 0
557	**66**	2½d. blue	10 0	
558	,,	2½d. deep blue ..	7 6	
559	**71**	3d. orange-brown ..	10 0	
560	,,	3d. orange-buff ..	6 0	
561	**72**	4d. yellow-bistre (1909)	7 6	
562	,,	4d. olive	6 0	6 0
563	**67**	5d. chocolate		
564	**73**	6d. green	4 6	
565	**80**	1s. orange (1907) ..	£30	£30
566	**77**	5s. rose-red & ultram. (1907)	17 6	15 0
567	**78**	£1 salmon	85 0	
568	**79**	£2 deep blue	£10	

(c) Perf. compound of 12½ or 12 × 12½ with 11.

No.	Type	Description	Unused	Used
569	**68**	½d. green	35 0	
570	**65**	1d. rose-red (Die III) ('10)	75 0	£5
571	**70**	2d. violet	—	£20
572	**71**	3d. orange-brown ..		
573	**72**	4d. olive-bistre		
573*a*	**73**	6d. green	—	£30
574	**74**	9d. carmine-red	—	80 0

(d) Perf. by rotary comb machines gauging 11½ × 12¼.

No.	Type	Description	Unused	Used
575	**65**	1d. rose-red (Die III) ..	3 0	1 0
575*a*	**70**	2d. violet	8 6	3 0

1912. *Thin paper, white gum. (a) P 12 or 12 × 12½.*

No.	Type	Description	Unused	Used
576	**68**	½d. green	6 0	3 6
577	**65**	1d. carmine (Die III) ..	8 6	1 6
578	,,	1d. rose-red (Die III) ..	10 0	2 0
579	**70**	2d. violet	15 0	5 0
580	**67**	5d. chocolate	10 0	5 0
581	**73**	6d. green	17 6	7 6
582	**80**	1s. orange	15 0	7 6
582*a*	,,	1s. yellow	17 6	7 6

(b) P 11.

No.	Type	Description	Unused	Used
583	**68**	½d. green	25 0	20 0
583*a*	**65**	1d. rose-red (Die III) ..	10 0	5 0

(c) Perf. by rotary comb machines gauging 11½ × 12¼.

No.	Type	Description	Unused	Used
584	**65**	1d. rose-red (Die III) ..	2 6	0 5

Reissue on "Stamp Duty" paper watermarked V and Crown. (a) P 12½ or 12 × 12½.

No.	Type	Description	Unused	Used
585	**68**	½d. green	4 6	3 0
586	**65**	1d. carmine-red (Die III)	3 6	1 0
587	**70**	2d. violet	7 6	3 6
587*a*	,,	2d. bright violet ..	7 6	3 6
588	**74**	9d. carmine-rose ..	6 6	5 0

(b) P 11.

No.	Type	Description	Unused	Used
588*a*	**68**	½d. green	25 0	20 0
589	**65**	1d. carm.-red (Die III)	45 0	30 0
590	**74**	9d. carmine-rose ..	12 6	7 6

The watermark of this paper varies considerably and does not agree exactly with either T **64***a* or **64***b*. The shades are usually distinctive, but collectors should, if possible, take specimens with margin attached, showing the wmk. "VICTORIA DUTY".

ONE PENNY

(82)

1912. *T* **70** *surcharged with T* **82**, *in red. Wmk. Crown over A. P 11½ × 12¼.*

No.	Description	Unused	Used
591	1d. on 2d. violet (No. 575*a*) ..	0 9	0 8

Postal Fiscals

Strictly this group should contain only those stamps which were actually issued for fiscal purposes before the 1st January, 1884, on which date all distinction between fiscal stamps and postage stamps was abolished. For convenience we have included in this group all stamps inscribed "STAMP DUTY" and of designs in existence before the 1st January, 1884, but which were printed after that date. These later printings were in many cases in new colours, and in a few instances on the later V and Crown papers.

The stamps were all of large size—rectangular or oblong—and were perforated only by the single-line machines to which we have already referred in the main group of stamps, namely, those gauging 11½, 12 (12), 12½, 13 (13), and 12¼, 12½ (12½). The first can easily be identified. A simple test which is almost infallible for distinguishing the (13) and (12½) gauges is this: if the perforation gauges even slightly under 12½, it is the (12½) gauge, but if it gauges even slightly over 12½, then it is the (13) gauge. Specialists in the history or stages of the perforating machines will notice the same variations in the clearness or roughness of the punctures and the sizes of the holes as they observe in the perforations of the postage and ordinary smaller "STAMP DUTY" stamps of the same dates.

Undoubtedly heavy parcels were forwarded from Victoria by registered post, such as ledgers and account books, especially in the 'eighties of the last century. The £5 and £10 values were frequently used for this purpose, and even the £25 stamp has been genuinely used in this way, but probably that value is the practical limit. All the stamps of this group were surface-printed, unless it is otherwise stated.

F 1

F 2

A. *Inscribed* "STAMP STATUTE."

1870–98. *Large rectangular stamps of various sizes and designs (such as Types* F 1 *and* F 2*).*

(The central design of the 3*d. is a coin, and of the* 2*s.* 6*d. the Royal Arms.)*

I. *Watermarked single-line numerals as* **14** *which are sometimes sideways.*

F 1	1s. blue/*blue*, *wmk.* **1**, *p.* 12 ..		
	a. Perf. 13	10 0	15 0
F 2	2s. blue/*green*, *wmk.* **2**, *p.* 12	50 0	60 0
	a. Perf. 13	30 0	40 0
F 3	10s. brn./*rose*, *wmk.* **10**, *p.* 12		
	a. Perf. 13	—	40 0
	b. Perf. 12½		
F 4	10s. red-brown/*rose*, *p.* 13 ..		

II. *Wmk. V and Crown, T* **26**.

F 5	1d. green, *perf.* 13 ..	3 6	4 0
F 6	1d. bluish green, *perf.* 13 ..	—	10 0
	a. Perf. 12½		
F 7	3d. lilac, *perf.* 13 (1880) ..	10 0	10 0
F 8	4d. rose, *perf.* 13	10 0	10 0
F 9	6d. Prussian blue, *perf.* 13 (24.12.71)	5 0	
F10	6d. dull blue, *perf.* 12 (6.3.27)		
F11	6d. pale ultram., *perf.* 13 ..	4 0	4 0
	a. Perf. 12 (June, 1884) ..		
	b. Perf. 12½ (21.2.80)		
F12	1s. blue/*blue*, *perf.* 12 ..	15 0	
	a. Perf. 12½	7 6	7 6
	b. Perf. 13	7 6	7 6
F13	1s. dark blue/*blue*, *perf.* 13		
	a. Perf. 12½	10 0	10 0
F14	2s. blue/*yellow*, *perf.* 13 ..	—	40 0
	a. Perf. 12		
F15	2s. blue/*green*, *perf.* 13 ..		
	a. Perf. 12	30 0	30 0
F16	2s. 6d. orange, *perf.* 13 ..	20 0	50 0
	a. Perf. 12½	20 0	50 0
F17	2s. 6d. yellow, *perf.* 13 ..	20 0	50 0
	a. Perf. 12		
	b. Perf. 12½		
F18	5s. blue/*yellow*, *perf.* 12 ..	—	40 0
	a. Perf. 13		
F19	10s. pale brown/*rose*, *perf.* 13		
F20	10s. dark brown/*rose*, *perf.* 12		
	a. Perf. 13		
F21	£1 lilac/*yellow*, *perf.* 12½ ..		
	a. Perf. 12	90 0	60 0
F22	£1 dull violet/*yell.*, *perf.* 13	£5	70 0
F23	£5 black & green, *perf.* 13..	—	50 0‡
	a. Perf. 12		

Surcharged "½d. HALF" *in red on No.* F5.

F24	½d. on 1d. green, *perf.* 13 ..	7 6	10 0

F 3

F 4

F 5

B. *Inscribed* "STAMP DUTY."

I. *Types* F 3, F 4, *and similar portraits, or arms and devices such as Type* F 5, *surface-printed* (*) *or lithographed* (†).

(*a*) *Wmk. V and Crown, T* **26**.

F25	1d. yell.-grn. (Type F 3),* *p.*12	5 0	7 6
	a. Perf. 13	3 6	5 0
	b. Perf. 12½	3 0	5 0
F26	1d. blue-grn.(Type F 3),† *p.*12		
	a. Perf. 13	3 6	5 0
	b. Perf. 12½		
F27	1d. light brn.(Type F 4),**p.*12	0 6	0 9
	a. Perf. 13	0 9	1 0
	b. Perf. 12½		
	c. Perf. comp. 12 and 13 ..		

(The stamps of this type in yellow are believed to be changelings.)

F28	6d. ultramarine,* *perf.* 12 ..	2 6	2 6
F29	6d. dull blue,* *perf.* 12 ..	2 6	2 6
	a. Perf. 13		
	b. Perf. 12½		
F30	1s. deep blue/*blue*,* *perf.* 12	4 0	1 6
	a. Perf. 13	6 0	2 6
	b. Perf. 12½	4 0	1 6
F31	1s. blue/*pale yell.* (1885)* *perf.* 12½	3 0	1 0
F32	1s. 6d. pink,* *perf.* 12½ ..		
	a. Perf. 13	5 0	2 0
F33	1s. 6d. carmine,* *perf.* 12½	5 0	2 6
F33*a*	1s. 6d. rosine,† *perf.* 12 ..		
	b. Perf. 13		
F34	2s. blue/*green*,* *perf.* 12 ..	5 0	5 0
	a. Perf. 13		
F35	3s. purple/*blue*,* *perf.* 12½..	7 6	3 6
F35*a*	3s. dull pur./*blue*,† *p.* 12½ ..	5 0	3 0
	b. Perf. 13	5 0	3 0
F36	3s. drab/*white*,* *perf.* 12½ ..	4 0	1 6
F36*a*	3s. olive/*white* (1895)* ..	10 0	3 6
F37	4s. vermilion,† *perf.* 12 ..	7 6	
	a. Perf. 13		
	b. Perf. 12½		
F38	4s. orge.-verm.,† *perf.* 12½	5 0	2 0
	a. Perf. 13		
F39	4s. orange,* *perf.* 12½ ..	7 6	3 0
F40	5s. claret/*yellow*,* *perf.* 12		
	a. Perf. 13		
	b. Perf. 12½	5 0	1 0
F41	5s. carm./*yell.*,*('96) *p.* 12½	7 6	4 0
F42	5s. scarlet (aniline)/*white* (1896),* *perf.* 12½ ..	7 6	4 0

F43 6s. yellow-green,* *perf.* 13 .. 8 6 5 0
a. Perf. 12½ .. .. ..
F43*b* 6s. pale yell.-green.† *p.* 12
c. Perf. 13 .. .. ..
F44 10s. brown/*rose*,* *perf.* 12 .. — 10 0
a. Perf. 12½ .. .. .. — 10 0
F44*b* 10s. pale yell.-brn./*rose*,† *p.* 12
c. Perf. 13 .. .. ..
F45 10s. dull greyish grn.,* *p.* 12½ — 2 6
F46 15s. pale mauve, *perf.* 13 ..
a. Perf. 12½ .. .. .. — £5
F47 15s. fawn (1891),* *perf.* 12½ .. 20 0 10 0
F48 £1 red-oran./*yell.*,† *p.* 12 ..
a. Perf. 12½ .. .. .. — 5 0
b. Perf. 13 .. .. ..
F49 £1 orge.-yel./*yellow*, *p.* 12½ 30 0 5 0
F50 £1 orange/*white*, *perf.* 12½ — 10 0
F51 £1 5s. pale rose,* *perf.* 13
F51*a* £1 5s. pink, † *perf.* 13 ..
F52 £1 10s. bronze, *perf.* 13 ..
a. Perf. 12½ 40 0 15 0
F53 £1 10s. deep slate-green (2.11.87), *perf.* 12½ .. 40 0 15 0
F54 £1 10s. pale olive-brown (21.11.89), *perf.* 12½
F55 £1 15s. dull purple,† *p.* 12½
F56 £2 blue, *perf.* 13 .. ..
a. Perf. 12½ 50 0 15 0
b. Perf. 12 .. .. ..
F57 £2 deep blue,* *perf.* 12½ .. — 15 0
F58 £2 pale blue (28.10.89),* *perf.* 12½ .. .. — 20 0
F58*a* £2 5s. grey-lilac, *perf.* 13
F59 £2 5s., dull lilac, *perf.* 13 — 40 0
a. Perf. 12½ ..
F60 £5 pink, *perf.* 12½ .. .. — 60 0
F61 £5 rosine, *perf.* 12 .. — 75 0
a. Perf. 13 .. .. ..
F62 £6 blue/*rose*, *perf.* 12½ .. — £7
F63 £7 purple/*blue*, *perf.* 13 .. — £8
F64 £8 vermilion/*yell.*, *perf.* 13
F65 £9 green/*green*, *perf.* 13 ..
F66 £10 (large oblong), lilac,* *p.* 12 .. .. .. — 50 0
a. Perf. 13 (26.2.90) ..
b. Perf. 12½ (7.5.90) .. ..
F67 £10 (large oblong), purple (11.6.84),* *perf.* 12 .. — 60 0

Of the values against which we have not indicated the method of printing the £1, £1 10s., £1 15s., £5, £6, £7, £8, and £9 are known to have been lithographed, but we are so far without information as to the distinctive shades, etc., of this printing. The 3d. and 2s. 6d. "STAMP STATUTE" are also known to have been lithographed and the same remark applies.

II. *Printed from line-engraved dies* (*large oblong stamps*).

F68 £25 yellow-green, *perf.* 12½ ..
F69 £50 violet, *perf.* 12½ .. ..
F70 £50 purple, *perf.* 13 ..
F71 £100 carmine, *perf.* 12½ ..

III. *Printed from lithographic transfers from the line-engraved dies.*

F72 £25 emerald-green, *perf.* 12½ — 50 0‡
F73 £50 deep violet, *perf.* 12½ ..
F74 £50 dull purple, *perf.* 12½ .. — 60 0‡
F75 £100 scarlet, *perf.* 12½ .. — 80 0‡

(*b*) *Wmk. V and Crown, T* **64*a*.** *Perf.* 12½.

F76 3s. pale olive-brown (1898) — 2 0
F77 4s. orange 5 0 2 0
F78 5s. rosine/*white* 6 0 1 6
F79 6s. yellow-green 10 0 6 6
F80 10s. dull greyish green .. — 2 6
F80*a* 10s. bright green .. ..
F81 15s. light brown .. ..

(*c*) *Wmk. V and Crown, T* **64*b*.** *Perf.* 12½.

F82 3s. pale olive-brown .. 6 0 2 6
F83 5s. carmine/*white* .. — 2 0
F84 10s. dull greyish green ..

Prices marked (‡) are for stamps postmarked to order by the Victorian postal authorities for sale in sets.

NOTE.—All the "Stamp Statute" series, except the 2s. on yellow paper, were reprinted in 1891 on paper watermarked V and Crown, T **26**, and perforated (12½). They are mostly overprinted "Reprint." There were also some printings of some of the large "Stamp Duty" stamps made in the 'nineties of the last century and in 1900, probably to complete sets of current stamps which were sold by the Post Office cancelled. These impressions are well known to collectors. They usually have full gum, but are obliterated with a neat circular postmark. It was once thought that all the lithographic transfers of the values £25, £50, and £100 were reprints, but that view is no longer accepted, as many of such lithographs were used fiscally. However, certain impressions in particular shades described in the *Monthly Journal* of the 30th June, 1906, may have been made to complete the sets of cancelled stamps above-mentioned.

POSTAGE DUE STAMPS

1

1890. *Type* D **1.** *Wmk. V and Crown, T* **26.** *P* 12 × 12½.

D 1 ½d. pale blue & brown-lake 2 0 2 0
D 2 1d. pale blue & brown-lake 2 0 1 9
D 3 2d. pale blue & brown-lake 2 6 1 9
D 4 4d. pale blue & brown-lake 2 6 1 0
D 5 5d. pale blue & brown-lake 3 0 2 0
D 6 6d. pale blue & brown-lake 2 6 1 6
D 7 10d. pale blue & brown-lake 5 0 5 0
D 8 1s. pale blue & brown-lake 4 0 3 0
D 9 2s. pale blue & brown-lake 10 0 7 6
D10 5s. pale blue & brown-lake 15 0 10 0

1890–94. *W* **26.** *P* 12 × 12½.

D11 ½d. ultram. & claret (11.90) 0 9 0 9
D12 1d. ultram. & brownish red 0 8 0 6
D13 2d. ultram. & brownish red 2 6 1 0
D14 4d. ultram. & claret (8.94) 5 0 3 0

1894. *Colours changed.* *W* **26.** *P* 12 × 12½.

D15 ½d. rosine and blue-green .. 0 6 0 6
D16 1d. rosine and blue-green .. 0 9 0 6
D17 2d. rosine and blue-green .. 0 9 0 6
D18 4d. rosine and blue-green .. 1 6 0 6
D19 5d. rosine and blue-green .. 3 6 2 0
D20 6d. rosine and blue-green .. 2 6 2 0
D21 10d. rosine and blue-green .. 3 0 2 0
D22 1s. rosine and blue-green .. 3 6 1 6
D23 2s. rosine and green .. 15 0
D24 5s. rosine and green .. — 20 0

1896–99. *Colours changed.* *W* **26.** *P* 12 × 12½.

D25 ½d. rosine and yellow-green 0 7 0 5
D26 1d. rosine and yellow-green 0 6 0 4
D27 2d. rosine and yellow-green 1 0 0 6
D28 4d. rosine and yellow-green 3 0 0 9
D29 5d. rosine & yell.-grn. (12.96) 2 0 1 0
D30 6d. rosine and yellow-green 2 6 1 6
D31 1s. rosine and yellow-green 10 0
D32 2s. rosine and pale green .. 6 0 2 0
D33 5s. rosine and pale green .. 10 0 7 6

1898. *Wmk. V and Crown, T* **64*a*.** *P* 12 × 12½.

D34 ½d. scarlet & yellowish grn. 0 10 0 8
D35 ½d. scarlet & bluish green (19.2.00) .. ..
D36 1d. scarlet & yellow-green .. 0 9 0 6
D37 1d. scarlet and green ..

D37*a*	2d. scarlet & yellow-green . .		
D38	2d. scarlet and green . .	1 0	0 6
D39	4d. scarlet and yellow-green (2.11.98)		
D40	4d. scarlet and green . .	3 0	2 6
D41	5d. scarlet and green . .	4 0	3 0
D42	6d. scarlet and yellow-green	4 0	3 0

1902–04. *Wmk. V and Crown, T* **64***b*. *P* 12 × 12½.

D43	½d. scarlet and green . .	0 9	0 6
D44	1d. scarlet & grn. (13.10.04)	0 9	0 6
D45	2d. scarlet & grn. (13.3.02) . .	1 0	0 4
D46	4d. scarlet and green . .	3 0	2 6
D47	5d. scarlet and green . .	4 0	3 0
D48	1s. scarlet and green . .	5 0	2 0
D49	2s. scarlet and green . .		
D50	5s. scarlet and green . .		

1906–07. *Type* D **1**. *Wmk. Crown and A, Type* w. **11**. (*a*) *P* 12½ *or* 12 × 12½.

D51	½d. scarlet & yell.-grn.(1907)	0 4	0 4
D52	½d. scarlet & bluish green . .	1 0	1 0
D53	1d. scarlet & yellow-green . .	0 6	0 6
D53*a*	1d. scarlet & bluish green . .	2 0	2 0
D54	2d. scarlet & yellow-green . .	2 0	1 0
D55	4d. scarlet & yellow-green . .	10 0	

(*b*) *Perf. compound of* 12½ (*comb*) *and* 11.

D56	½d. scarlet & yellow-green . .	60 0	60 0

Victoria now uses the stamps of AUSTRALIA.

VIRGIN ISLANDS.

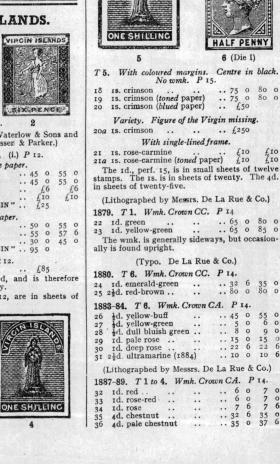

1 St. Ursula. 2

(Lithographed by Messrs. Waterlow & Sons and supplied by Messrs. Nissen & Parker.)

1866. *T* **1** *and* **2**. *No wmk.* (i.) *P* 12.

(*a*) *White wove paper.*

1	1d. green	45 0	55 0
2	1d. deep green	45 0	55 0
3	6d. rose	£6	£6
4	6d. deep rose	£10	£10
	a. Large "V" in "VIRGIN" . .	£25	

(*b*) *Toned paper.*

5	1d. green	50 0	55 0
6	1d. deep green	55 0	57 6
7	6d. rose-red	30 0	45 0
	a. Large "V" in "VIRGIN" . .	95 0	

(ii.) *P* 15 × 12.

7*b*	1d. green	£85	

This is now known used, and is therefore included as an issued variety.

The 1d. and 6d. perf. 12, are in sheets of twenty-five.

3

4

1867–68. *T* **1** *to* **4**. *No wmk.* *P* 15.

The central figure in the 1s. *is in black.*

(*a*) *White wove paper.*

8	1d. blue-green	40 0	47 6
9	1d. yellow-green	50 0	50 0
10	6d. pale rose	£20	£20
11	1s. rose-carmine	£15	£16

(*b*) *Toned paper.*

12	1d. yellow-green	42 6	47 6
13	6d. dull rose	£20	£20
14	1s. rose-carmine (*blued*) . .	£30	£28

(*c*) *Pale rose paper.*

15	4d. lake-red	50 0	60 0

(*d*) *Buff paper.*

16	4d. lake-red	35 0	40 0
17	4d. lake-brown	35 0	40 0

Nos. 11 and 14 have the double-lined frame.

5

6 (Die I)

T 5. *With coloured margins. Centre in black. No wmk.* *P* 15.

18	1s. crimson	75 0	80 0
19	1s. crimson (*toned* paper) . .	75 0	80 0
20	1s. crimson (*blued* paper) . .	£50	

Variety. Figure of the Virgin missing.

20*a*	1s. crimson	£250	

With single-lined frame.

21	1s. rose-carmine	£10	£10
21*a*	1s. rose-carmine (*toned* paper)	£10	£10

The 1d., perf. 15, is in small sheets of twelve stamps. The 1s. is in sheets of twenty. The 4d. in sheets of twenty-five.

(Lithographed by Messrs. De La Rue & Co.)

1879. *T* **1**. *Wmk. Crown CC.* *P* 14

22	1d. green	65 0	80 0
23	1d. yellow-green	65 0	85 0

The wmk. is generally sideways, but occasionally is found upright.

(Typo. De La Rue & Co.)

1880. *T* **6**. *Wmk. Crown CC.* *P* 14.

24	1d. emerald-green	32 6	35 0
25	2½d. red-brown	80 0	80 0

1883–84. *T* **6**. *Wmk. Crown CA.* *P* 14.

26	½d. yellow-buff	45 0	55 0
27	½d. yellow-green	5 0	6 0
28	½d. dull bluish green	8 0	9 0
29	1d. pale rose	15 0	15 0
30	1d. deep rose	22 6	22 6
31	2½d. ultramarine (1884) . .	10 0	10 6

(Lithographed by Messrs. De La Rue & Co.)

1887–89. *T* **1** *to* **4**. *Wmk. Crown CA.* *P* 14.

32	1d. red	6 0	7 0
33	1d. rose-red	6 0	7 0
34	1d. rose	7 6	7 6
35	4d. chestnut	32 6	35 0
36	4d. pale chestnut	35 0	37 6

37	4d. brown-red	35	0	32	6
38	6d. dull violet	27	6	37	6
39	6d. deep violet	25	0	37	6
40	1s. sepia	40	0	60	0
41	1s. brown	35	0	60	0

The De La Rue transfers of T **1** to **4** are new transfers and differ from those of Messrs. Nissen and Parker.

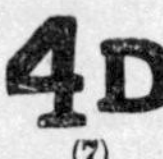

(7)

1888 (July). *No.* 19 *surch. with T* **7**, *in violet.*

42	4d. on 1s. black and crimson	90	0	95	0

Variety. Surcharge double.

42*a*	4d. on 1s. black and crimson	£70

The special issues for Virgin Islands were superseded on 31st Oct., 1890, by the general issue for Leeward Islands. In 1899, however, a new special issue (given below) was brought out; these stamps did not supersede the general issue for Leeward Islands, but were used concurrently, as have been all subsequent issues.

8

(Recess. De La Rue & Co.)

1899. *T* **8**. *Wmk. Crown CA. P* 14.

43	½d. yellow-green	1	3	1	6
44	1d. brick-red	2	0	2	0
45	2½d. ultramarine	15	0	12	6
46	4d. brown	15	0	15	0
47	6d. dull violet	15	0	15	0
48	7d. deep green	15	0	15	0
49	1s. brown-yellow	22	6	22	6
50	5s. indigo	60	0	60	0

Errors.

51	HALFPFNNY, yellow-green ..	60	0	65	0
52	HALΓPENNY, yellow-green ..	60	0	65	0
53	FOURPENCF, brown	£35		£35	

9

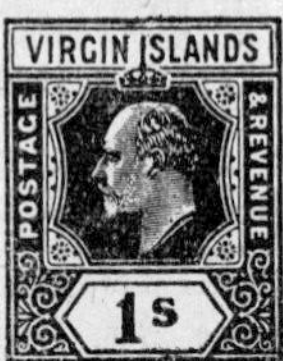

10

(Typo. De La Rue Co.)

1904 (1 June). *T* **9** *and* **10** (*2d., 3d., 1s. and 2s. 6d.*). *Wmk. Mult. Crown CA. P* 14.

54	½d. dull purple and green ..	1	6	1	6
55	1d. dull purple and scarlet ..	4	0	4	6
56	2d. dull purple and ochre ..	15	0	17	6
57	2½d. dull purple and ultram. ..	7	6	8	0
58	3d. dull purple and black ..	10	0	10	6
59	6d. dull purple and brown ..	10	0	10	6
60	1s. green and scarlet	17	6	18	0
61	2s. 6d. green and black ..	25	0	25	0
62	5s. green and blue	60	0	60	0

11

12

(Typo. De La Rue & Co.)

1913–19. *T* **11** *and* **12** (*2d., 3d., 1s. and 2s. 6d.*). *Wmk. Mult. Crown CA. P* 14.

63	½d. green, O	0	7	0	9
64	½d. yellow-green, O (1916) ..	0	7	0	9
65	½d. blue-grn. & dp. grn., O ('19)	0	6	0	8
66	1d. deep red, O	4	6	5	0
67	1d. deep red & carmine, O ..	4	0	4	6
68	1d. scarlet, O (1917)	2	0	2	3
69	1d. carmine-red, O (1919) ..	1	0	1	3
70	2d. grey, O	3	0	3	6
71	2d. slate-grey, O (1919) ..	3	6	4	0
72	2½d. bright blue, O	3	6	4	0
73	3d. purple/*yellow*, C ..	4	0	4	6
74	6d. dull & bright purple, C ..	5	6	6	0
75	1s. black/*green*, C	10	0	12	6
76	2s. 6d. black and red/*blue*, C	20	0	22	6
77	5s. green and red/*yellow*, C ..	40	0	42	6

WAR STAMP

(13)

1917. *T* **11** *and* **12** *optd. with T* **13**.

78	1d. carmine	2	6	3	0
79	1d. pale red/*bluish*	0	4	0	6
80	1d. scarlet	0	8	1	0
81	3d. purple/*yellow*	1	0	1	3
82	3d. purple/*lemon*	3	6	4	0
83	3d. purple/*pale yellow* ..	0	9	1	0

1921. *As* 1913–19, *but wmk. Mult. Script CA.*

84	½d. green, O	0	10	1	0
85	1d. scarlet & deep carmine, O	0	10	1	0

14

(Typo. De La Rue & Co.)

1922–28. *T* **14**. *P* 14.

(*a*) *Wmk. Mult. Crown CA.*

86	3d. purple/*pale yellow*, C ..	1	3	1	6
87	1s. black/*emerald*, C	5	0	5	6
88	2s. 6d. black & red/*blue*, C ..	12	6	15	0
89	5s. green & red/*pale yellow*, C	55	0	65	0

(*b*) *Wmk. Mult. Script CA.*

90	½d. dull green, O	0	2	0	4
91	1d. rose-carmine, O	0	7	0	8
92	2d. grey, O	0	9	1	0
93	2½d. pale bright blue, O (1922)	7	6	8	0
93*a*	2½d. bright blue, O (1927) ..	1	6	1	9
93*b*	3d. purple/*pale yellow*, C ..	1	6	1	9
94	5d. dull purple and olive, C ..	20	0	22	6
95	6d. dull & bright purple, C ..	2	6	3	0
96	1s. black/*emerald*, C	5	0	6	0
96*a*	2s. 6d. black & red/*blue*, C	15	0	17	6
97	5s. green and red/*yellow*, C ..	25	0	30	0

1923–29. *T* **14.** *Colours changed, etc. Wmk. Mult. Script CA. P* 14.

98	1d. bright violet, O (1927)	5 0	6 0
99	1d. scarlet, O (1929) ..	0 6	0 8
100	1½d. carmine-red, O (1927) ..	6 6	8 0
101	1½d. Venetian red, O (1928)	0 10	1 0
102	2½d. dull orange, O (1923) ..	3 0	3 6

In the 1½d. stamps the value is in colour on a white ground.

1935 (6 May). *Silver Jubilee. As T* **13** *of Antigua inscribed* " VIRGIN ISLANDS ". *Recess. W'low & Sons. Wmk. Mult. Script CA. P* 11 × 12.

103	1d. deep blue and scarlet ..	0 4	0 10
104	1½d. ultramarine and grey ..	0 8	1 3
105	2½d. brown and deep blue ..	5 0	6 0
106	1s. slate and purple ..	15 0	20 0

WESTERN AUSTRALIA.

SIMPLIFICATION (see p. xii)

Nos. 1 to 51a.

1, 2, 4, 5, 7. 15, 17a, 18.
25, 27, 28. 41, 33, 46, 34, 35. 49, 51.

Later Issues

Omit less distinct shades. Disregard perfs.

1

2

3

4

(Eng. and printed by Perkins Bacon & Co.)

1854 (1 Aug.). *T* **1.** *Wmk. Swan, T* **4.** *Imperf.*

1	1d. black	60 0	15 0 *to* 40 0

(Lithographed by M. Sanson, Government printer in the Colony.)

1854. *T* **1** *to* **3.** *W* **4.**

(a) Imperf.

2	4d. pale blue	45 0	20 0 *to* 60 0
3	4d. blue ..	45 0	20 0 *to* 60 0
3a	4d. deep dull blue ..	£25	£6 *to* £17
4	4d. slate-blue	£17	£4 *to* £15
5	1s. pale brown ..	£6	50 0 *to* £8
6	1s. grey-brown ..	£10	60 0 *to* £10
7	1s. deep red-brown ..	£17	£5 *to* £15
8	1s. salmon	—	£20 *to* £60

Transfer varieties of the 4d. blue.

[The numbers in brackets show the position on the sheets.]

3 a. Frame inverted .. .. *used* £350 *to* £1,000

b. Top of letters of " AUSTRALIA " cut off so that they are barely 1 mm in height .. .. ..

These two errors were quickly corrected on the stone, but the following varieties appeared throughout all the printings :—

c.	" WEST " in squeezed-down letters and " F " of " FOUR " has pointed foot (No. 37)	£25	£25
d.	" ESTERN " in squeezed-down letters, and " U " of " FOUR " squeezed up (No. 57)	£50	£50
e.	Small " S " in " POSTAGE " (No. 77)	£25	£25
f.	" EN " of " PENCE " shorter (No. 104)	£15	£15
g.	" N " of " PENCE " has the first downstroke thinner and the letter slants to the right (No. 116) ..	£18	£18
h.	The water and part of swan damaged above " ENCE " (No. 120)	£20	£20
i.	" T " of " POSTAGE " shaved off to a point at foot (No. 125) ..	£15	£15
j.	" F " of " FOUR " slanting to left (No. 137)	£15	£15
k.	Coloured line above " AGE " of " POSTAGE " (No. 146) ..	£15	£15
l.	No outer line above " GE " of " POSTAGE " and a coloured line under " FOU " of " FOUR " (No. 151)	£15	£15
m.	" WESTERN " in squeezed-down letters, only 1½ mm. in height (No. 157)	£25	£25
n.	" P " of " PENCE " small head (No. 175)	£15	£15
o.	" RALIA " in squeezed-down letters only 1½ mm. in height (No. 176)	£25	£25
p.	" PE " of " PENCE " close together (No. 195)	£15	£15
q.	" N " of " PENCE " narrow (No. 196)	£15	£15
r.	Part of the right cross-stroke and down-stroke of " T " of " POSTAGE " is cut off (No. 215)	£15	£15
s.	Defective " A " in " POSTAGE ", the right limb being very thin (No. 216)	£15	£15

These varieties may be found in all shades of the blue stamps, being rare in the slate-blue. They also occur in the rouletted stamps. The stamp with " inverted frame " is only found in one shade.

(b) Rouletted 8 *to* 14 *and compound.*

10	1d. black	£16	£6
11	4d. pale blue	£16	£8
12	4d. blue	—	£8
12a	4d. slate-blue	—	£25
13	1s. pale brown	£38	£15
14	1s. grey-brown	£48	£20

5

(Litho. by A. Hillman, Government printer.)

1857. *T* **5.** *W* **4.** *(a) Imperf.*

		Un.	*Used.*
15	2d. brown-black/*red*	£15 *to* £40	£7 *to* £25
16	2d. brn.-blk./*Indian red*	—	£10 *to* £30
17	6d. black-bronze ..	£20 *to* £50	£8 *to* £25
17a	6d. grey-black ..	£20 *to* £50	£6 *to* £20
18	6d. golden bronze	£50 *to* £110	£25 *to* £80

Variety. Printed both sides.

19 2d. brown-black/*red* £25 *to* £55 £7 *to* £25
19*a* 2d. blk.-brn./*Indian red* .. .. — £10 *to* £30

(*b*) *Rouletted* 9 *to* 14 *and compound.*

20 2d. brown-black/*red* £75 £35
20*a* 2d. brown-black/*Indian red* .. — £50
21 6d. black-bronze £70 £25
21*a* 6d. grey-black .. ..

Variety. Printed both sides.

22 2d. brown-black/*red* .. ..

The 1d., 2d., 6d., and 1s. are occasionally met with *pin-perf.*

(Printed in the colony from Messrs. Perkins, Bacon & Co.'s plates.)

1860. *T* **1.** *W* **4.** (*a*) *Imperf.*

24 2d. pale orange .. 32 6 30 0 *to* 50 0
25 2d. orange-vermilion 25 0 15 0 *to* 35 0
25*a* 2d. deep vermilion £8 70 0 *to* £10
26 4d. blue £5 £22
27 4d. deep blue .. £6 £30
28 6d. sage-green .. £12 *to* £30 £3 *to* £9
28*a* 6d. deep sage-green — £15

(*b*) *Rouletted* 7½ *to* 14.

29 2d. pale orange £10 80 0
30 2d. orange-vermilion £12 80 0
31 4d. deep blue £50
32 6d. sage-green .. .. — £10

(Printed by Messrs. Perkins, Bacon & Co.)

1861. *T* **1.** *Wmk* **4.**

(*a*) *Perf. clean-cut* 14–16.

33 2d. blue 30 0 17 6
a. Imperf. between (pair) ..
34 6d. purple-brown 60 0 20 0
35 1s. yellow-green £7 32 6

(*b*) *Intermediate perf.* 14–16.

36 1d. rose £10 60 0
37 2d. blue 80 0 25 0
38 4d. vermilion £10 £6
39 6d. purple-brown £10 35 0
40 1s. yellow-green £15 70 0

(*c*) *P* 14–16 *very rough.* (JULY.)

41 1d. rose-carmine 80 0 22 6
41*a* 2d. deep blue .. .. .. — £12
42 6d. purple/*blued* £16 85 0
43 1s. deep green £30 £8

(*d*) *P* 14.

44 1d. rose 57 6 35 0
45 2d. blue 25 0 25 0
46 4d. vermilion 90 0 67 6

The 6d. purple-brown and 1s. yellow-green are known, perf. 14, with "SPECIMEN" overprint.

(Printed by Messrs. De La Rue & Co.)

1864. *T* **1.** *No wmk.* *P* 13.

49 1d. carmine-rose 17 6 5 0
50 1d. lake 17 6 5 0
51 6d. deep lilac 50 0 20 0
51*a* 6d. dull violet 60 0 30 0

Both values exist on thin and on thick papers the former being the scarcer.

Several varieties, both with wmk. (Swan) and without wmk., are to be found *imperf.*, but the majority of these were probably never issued.

1865. *T* **1.** *Wmk. Crown CC.* *P* 12½.

52 1d. bistre 10 6 2 6
53 1d. yellow-ochre 22 6 5 0
54 2d. chrome-yellow 15 0 0 8
55 2d. yellow 12 6 1 0
56 4d. carmine 15 0 5 6
a. Doubly printed .. ..
57 6d. lilac 75 0 8 6
58 6d. mauve 55 0 7 6
59 6d. violet 45 0 7 6
a. Doubly printed .. ..
60 6d. indigo-violet £7 40 0
61 1s. bright green 32 6 7 6
62 1s. sage-green £6 17 6

Error of colour.

65 2d. mauve (1879) £70 £55

ONE PENNY

(7)

1875 (FEB.). *No.* 55 *surch. with T* **7**, *in green.*

67 1d. on 2d. yellow 57 6 15 0
a. Pair, one stamp no surcharge ..
b. Surcharged three times .. — £20
c. "O" of "ONE" omitted ..

Forged surcharges of T 7 are known on stamps wmk. Crown CC, perf. 14, and on Crown CA, perf. 12 and 14.

8

T **1** *and* **8** (3*d.*).

1872–78. *Wmk. Crown CC.* *P* 14.

68 1d. bistre 22 6 2 6
69 1d. ochre 20 0 0 8
70 1d. yellow-ochre 15 0 1 0
71 2d. chrome-yellow 18 6 0 8
72 3d. pale brown 6 0 4 0
73 3d. cinnamon 5 0 3 6
74 4d. carmine 80 0 45 0
75 6d. lilac 35 0 4 0
75*a* 6d. reddish lilac 40 0 5 0

1882–90. *Wmk. Crown CA.* (*a*) *P* 12.

76 1d. yellow-ochre 26 6 1 9
77 2d. chrome-yellow 40 0 1 6
a. Imperf. between (pair) ..
78 4d. carmine 60 0 22 6
79 6d. lilac 90 0 12 6

(*b*) *P* 14.

81 1d. yellow-ochre 3 6 0 6
82 2d. chrome-yellow 5 0 0 6
83 3d. pale brown 3 0 1 0
84 3d. red-brown 2 0 0 6
85 4d. carmine 15 0 10 0
86 6d. lilac 20 0 3 0
87 6d. reddish lilac 17 6 3 0

(*c*) *P* 12×14.

88 1d. yellow-ochre (1883) .. £25 22 6

The 3d. sage-green, wmk. Crown CA, perf. 12, is known unused, but was never issued.

½ **1d.** **1d.**

(9) (10) (11)

1884. *T* **1** *surcharged with T* **9**, *in red.*

89 ½ on 1d. yellow-ochre (No. 76) 3 6 4 0
90 ½ on 1d. yellow-ochre (No. 81) 7 6 7 6

Variety. Thin bar.

90*a* ½ on 1d. yellow-ochre (No. 76) 25 0 20 0
90*b* ½ on 1d. yellow-ochre (No. 81) 45 0 30 0

Varieties with inverted or double surcharges are forgeries made in London about 1886.

1885. *T* **8** *surcharged in green.* *Wmk. Crown CC.* *P* 14.

(*a*) *Thick* "**1**" *with slanting top, T* **10.**

91 1d. on 3d. pale brown .. 10 0 7 6
92 1d. on 3d. cinnamon 6 6 6 6

(b) Thin "1" with straight top, T **11.**

93	1d. on 3d. pale brown ..	20	0	10	0
94	1d. on 3d. cinnamon	10	0	10	0

1888. *T* **1.** *Wmk. Crown CA. P* 14.

95	1d. carmine-pink	3	6	1	0
96	2d. grey	6	0	2	0
97	4d. red-brown	50	0	20	0

12  13

14  15

1885–93. *T* **12** *to* **14**, *and* **15** (2½*d. and higher values*). *Wmk. Crown CA. P* 14.

98	½d. yellow-green	0	4	0	2
98*a*	½d. green	0	4	0	2
99	1d. carmine	0	9	0	1
100	2d. bluish grey	1	0	0	1
100*a*	2d. grey	0	8	0	1
101	2½d. deep blue	3	0	0	6
101*a*	2½d. blue	3	0	0	6
102	4d. chestnut	3	0	0	6
103	5d. bistre	3	6	1	0
104	6d. bright violet	3	6	0	8
105	1s. pale olive-green ..	5	0	1	0
106	1s. olive-green	2	6	0	8

ONE PENNY (16)

Half-penny (17)

1893. *T* **8** *surcharged with T* **16**, *in green.*

107	1d. on 3d. pale brown (No. 72)	5	0	3	6
108	1d. on 3d. cinnamon (No. 73)	5	6	4	6
	a. Double surcharge	£10			
109	1d. on 3d. brown (No. 83) ..	10	0	5	0

1895. *T* **8** *surcharged with T* **17**, *in green.*

110	½d. on 3d. pale brown (No. 72)	4	0	4	6
110*a*	½d. on 3d. cinnamon (No. 73)	2	0	3	0
	b. Double surcharge				

Variety. Surcharged in red and in green.

111	½d. on 3d. cinnamon (No. 73)	27	6

The double surcharge is also found on the 3d. Crown CA, but this was printed off specially to supply a local philatelic (!) demand, and is therefore a reprint.

18  19

1899–1901. *T* **13, 14** *and* **19.**

Wmk. W Crown A, T **18.** *P* 14.

112	1d. carmine	0	6	0	1
	a. Imperf.				
113	2d. bright yellow	0	8	0	1
	a. Imperf.				
114	2½d. blue	1	6	0	3

19*a*  20

21  22

23  24

25  26

27  28

29 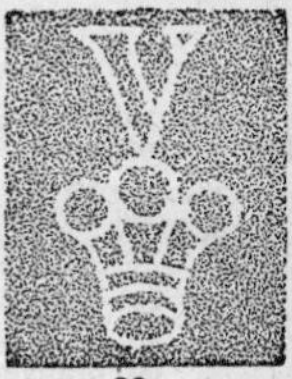 30

(Printed in Melbourne, Victoria.)

1902–11. *Wmk. V and Crown, T* **30.**

(*a*) *P* 12½ *or* 12×12½.

115	**19a**	1d. carmine-rose	0	4	0	1
116	**20**	2d. yellow	0	10	0	1
117	**21**	4d. chestnut	2	0	0	6
117a	**15**	5d. bistre (1905)	17	6	12	6
118	**22**	8d. apple-green	4	6	4	0
119	**23**	9d. yellow-orange	6	0	5	0
119a	,,	9d. red-orange	6	6	6	0
120	**24**	10d. red	10	0	6	6
121	**25**	2s. red/*yellow*	12	6	12	6
121a	,,	2s. orange/*yellow*	15	0	7	6
122	**26**	2s. 6d. deep blue/*rose*	8	6	8	6
123	**27**	5s. emerald-green	15	0	15	0
124	**28**	10s. deep mauve	25	0	15	0
124a	,,	10s. bright purple (1911)	30	0	20	0
125	**29**	£1 orange-brown	60	0	35	0
125a	,,	£1 orange (1911)	£5		60	0

(*b*) *P* 11.

126	**19a**	1d. carmine-rose	30	0	5	0
127	**20**	2d. yellow	40	0	4	0
128	**21**	4d. chestnut	£6		60	0
129	**15**	5d. bistre (1905)	15	0	10	0
130	**23**	9d. orange (1906)	20	0	15	0
132	**25**	2s. red/*yellow*	25	0	25	0

(*c*) *Perf. compound of* 12½ *and* 11.

133	**19a**	1d. carmine-rose	—		70	0
134	**20**	2d. yellow	—		85	0

Type **19a** is similar to Type **13** but larger

The wmk. is generally sideways, except on the 2s. 6d., and 10s., which have the wmk. upright It is known upright on the 1d., 2d., 4d., and 9d., perf. 12½, and on the 2d., perf. 11. On the 2s., perf. 12½, the upright wmk. is the commoner.

31

32

1905–12. *Wmk. Crown and A, T* **31** (*sideways*).

(*a*) *P* 12½ *or* 12×12½.

138	**12**	½d. green (1910)	0	8	0	8
139	**19a**	1d. rose-pink	0	8	0	2
139a	,,	1d. carmine (1910)	0	10	0	1
139b	,,	1d. carmine-red (1912)	0	8	0	1
140	**20**	2d. yellow	0	10	0	1
141	**8**	3d. brown	1	9	0	6
142	**21**	4d. bistre-brown	2	6	0	8
142a	,,	4d. pale chestnut	5	0	0	8
142b	,,	4d. bright brown-red	3	6	0	8
143	**15**	5d. pale olive-green	3	0	1	6
143a	,,	5d. olive-bistre	3	0	1	6
143b	**22**	8d. apple-green (1912)	5	0	4	6
144	**23**	9d. orange	5	0	2	0
144a	,,	9d. red-orange	6	0	2	6
145	**24**	10d. rose-orange	8	6	6	0
148	**27**	5s. emerald-green	20	0	15	0

(*b*) *P* 11.

151	**19a**	1d. rose-pink	2	6	1	6
151a	,,	1d. carmine-red	2	6	1	6
152	**20**	2d. yellow	3	0	2	6
153	**8**	3d. brown	2	6	2	6
154	**21**	4d. yellow-brown	£15		80	0
155	**15**	5d. olive	12	6	5	0
156	,,	5d. pale greenish yellow	17	6	12	6
156a	,,	5d. olive-bistre	4	6	3	6
157	**23**	9d. orange	35	0	35	0
157a	,,	9d. red-orange	—		25	0

(*c*) *Perf. compound of* 12½ *and* 11.

161	**19a**	1d. rose-pink	90	0	50	0
162	**20**	2d. yellow	£5		60	0
163	**15**	3d. brown	£6		80	0

Nos. 139*b* and 140 are known with upright watermark.

33

34

(Typo. De La Rue & Co.)

1906–7. *T* **33** *and* **34.** *Wmk. W Crown A, T* **18.** *P* 14.

164	6d. bright violet	2	6	1	3
165	1s. olive-green	7	0	3	0

1912. *T* **33** *and* **34.** *Wmk. Crown and A, T* **32** *P* 11½×12.

168	6d. bright violet	2	0	2	0
169	1s. sage-green	8	0	4	0
	a. Perf. 12½ (single line)	..			

ONE PENNY

(35)

Nos. 140 *and* 162 *surcharged with T* **35**, *in black.*

(*a*) *P* 12½ *or* 12×12½.

170	1d. on 2d. yellow	0	8	0	8

(*b*) *Perf. compound of* 12½ *and* 11.

171	1d. on 2d. yellow	£8			

No. 170 comes with upright or with sideways watermark.

1912. *T* **8.** *W* **31** (*upright or sideways*). *Thin paper and white gum* (*as Victoria*).

172	3d. brown (*perf.* 12½)	12	6	7	6
173	3d. brown (*perf.* 11)	80	0	80	0

POSTAL FISCALS

51

1893. *T* **51.** *Wmk. CA over Crown.* *P* 14.

201	1d. dull purple	1	0	0	6
202	2d. dull purple	5	0	4	0
203	3d. dull purple	6	0	1	0
204	6d. dull purple	6	0	3	0
205	1s. dull purple	8	6	3	6
206	2s. 6d. dull purple	40	0	40	0
207	3s. dull purple	£7		£5	
208	5s. dull purple	50	0	50	0

I. R.

TWO PENCE

(52)

T 8 (*wmk. Crown CC*) *surcharged as T* 52. *in black. P* 14.

No.	Description	Unused	Used
209	1d. on 3d. lilac	70 0	70 0
210	2d. on 3d. lilac	3 6	3 6
211	3d. on 3d. lilac	8 0	8 0
212	6d. on 3d. lilac	60 0	60 0
213	1s. on 3d. lilac	£8	£9

1899. *T* **51.** *Wmk. W Crown A, T* **18.** *P* 14.

No.	Description	Unused	Used
214	1d. dull purple	1 3	0 6
215	3d. dull purple	2 0	0 9
216	6d. dull purple	3 6	1 6
217	1s. dull purple	4 0	2 6
218	2s. 6d. dull purple	30 0	30 0
219	3s. dull purple	60 0	60 0
220	5s. dull purple	110 0	110 0

I R

(53)

Various stamps are known with the overprint T **53**, most of which are forgeries, although the 1d. and 2d., wmk. Crown CC, perf. 14, were so overprinted, but purely for fiscal purposes.

TELEGRAPH STAMPS USED FOR POSTAGE.

61

1886. *T* **61.** *Wmk. Crown CC.*

No.	Description	Unused	Used
301	1d. bistre (*perf.* 12½)	3 6	1 6
	a. Imperf.		
302	1d. bistre (*perf.* 14)	5 0	3 6
303	6d. lilac (*perf.* 14)	8 6	7 6

OFFICIAL STAMPS

Stamps of the various issues from 1854–85 are found with a circular hole punched out, the earlier size being about 3 mm. in diameter, and the later 4 mm. These were used on official correspondence. This system of punching ceased in 1886. Any in stock will be supplied at the same price as similar stamps without the hole. Stamps from No. 98 onward exist punctured "O S".

Western Australia now uses the stamps of AUSTRALIA.

WESTERN SAMOA.

(*See* SAMOA.)

ZANZIBAR.

(BRITISH PROTECTORATE.)

Zanzibar

(1)

1895 (10 Nov.). *Contemporary stamps of India optd. with T* 1.

A. *In blue.*

No.	Description	Unused	Used
1	½ a. blue-green	£18	£12
2	1 a. plum	£6	95 0
	a. "Zanzidar"		

Most of the varieties found on the same values with black overprint exist on the above.

B. *In black.*

No.	Description	Unused	Used
3	½ a. blue-green	2 6	2 6
	a. "Zanzidar"	£6	80 0
	b. "Zanibar"	£7	£6
4	1 a. plum	2 6	2 6
	a. "Zanzidar"	£12	£9
	b. "Zanibar"	£7	£6
5	1½ a. sepia	4 0	4 0
	a. "Zanzidar"	£14	£9
	b. "Zanibar"	£9	£8
	c. "Zanizbar"	£18	
6	2 a. pale blue	3 6	3 6
	a. Blue	4 0	4 0
	b. Opt. double	85 0	
	c. "Zanzidar"	£18	
	d. "Zanibar"	£12	
7	2½ a. yellow-green	3 6	3 6
	a. "Zanzidar"	£8	£8
	b. "Zanibar"	£6	£6
	c. "Zapzibar"		
8	3 a. orange	4 0	4 0
	a. Brown-orange	4 0	4 0
	b. "Zanzidar"	£6	
	c. "Zanizbar"	£30	
9	4 a. olive-green	6 0	6 0
	a. Slate-green	5 0	5 0
	b. "Zanzidar"		
10	6 a. pale brown	6 0	6 0
	a. Opt. double		
	b. "Zanzidar"	£16	£16
	c. "Zanibar"	£10	
	d. "Zanzibarr"	£20	
11	8 a. dull mauve	10 0	10 0
	a. Magenta	6 0	6 0
	b. "Zanzidar"		
12	12 a. purple/*red*	8 0	8 0
	a. "Zanzidar"	£24	£24
13	1 r. slate	57 6	57 6
	a. "Zanzidar"	—	£30
14	1 r. green and carmine	15 0	15 0
	a. Opt. vert. downwards	£6	
15	2 r. carm. & yellow-brown	20 0	20 0
	a. "r" omitted	£15	
	b. Inverted "r"	£10	£10
16	3 r. brown and green	22 6	22 6
	a. "r" omitted	£15	
	b. Inverted "r"	£11	£11
17	5 r. ultramarine and violet	27 6	27 6
	a. Opt double, one inverted	£10	
	b. "r" omitted	£15	
	c. Inverted "r"	—	£12

Many forgeries of the "Zanzibar" overprint exist, also bogus errors.

Varieties of printer's type.

The following varieties exist on all values to the 5r. including both types of the 1 r:—

(i) Tall second "z".
(ii) First "z" antique.

The following exist on all values to the 1 r. (both types):—

(iii) Inverted "q" for "b".
(iv) "p" with tail broken off for "n".
(v) "i" without dot.
(vi) Small second "z".
(vii) Inverted "q" for "b" and small second "z".

The following exists on the ½ a., 1½ a., 2 a. and ½ a.:—

(viii) "ā" with diæresis for last "a".

The following exists on the 2½ a.:—

(ix) Second "z" italic.

1895–96. Provisionals.

I. *Stamps used for postal purposes.*

2½
(2)

1895 (Dec.).

No. 5 surcharged with T 2 in red.

119	2½ on 1½ a. sepia	..	15 0	12 6
	a. "Zanizbar"	..	£17	£13
	b. "Zanzidar"	..	£14	£14
	c. Inverted "1" in "½"	..	£9	£9

2½ (3) 2½ (4) 2½ (5)

1896 (11 May). *No. 4 surcharged in black.*

123	3 2½ on 1 a. plum	..	30 0	30 0
124	4 2½ on 1 a. plum	..	65 0	65 0
125	5 2½ on 1 a. plum	..	22 6	22 6

2½ (6) 2½ (7) 2½ (8)

1896 (15 Aug.). *No. 6 surcharged in red.*

126	6 2½ on 2 a. pale blue	..	15 0	15 0
	a. "1" of "½" inverted	..	55 0	55 0
	b. Roman "I" in "½"	..	£6	90 0
127	7 2½ on 2 a. pale blue	..	40 0	40 0
	a. Roman "I" in "½"	..		
	b. "2¹" for "2½"	..	£18	
	c. "2⅔" for "2½"	..		
	d. "2₂" for "2½"	..		
128	8 2½ on 2 a. pale blue	..	90 0	£5

1896 (15 Nov.). *No. 5 surcharged in red.*

135	6 2½ on 1½ a. sepia	..	35 0	35 0
	a. "1" of "½" inverted	..	£7	£7
	b. Roman "I" in "½"	..	£7	
136	7 2½ on 1½ a. sepia	..	80 0	
137	8 2½ on 1½ a. sepia	..	£6	

II. *Stamps prepared for official purposes, but it is doubtful whether they were issued to the public.* (*Nos.* 140–148.)

1898 (Jan.). *Surcharged as before in red.*

140	3 2½ on 1 a. plum	..	75 0	
141	4 2½ on 1 a. plum	..	£6	
142	5 2½ on 1 a. plum	..	90 0	90 0
143	3 2½ on 1½ a. sepia	..	35 0	35 0
144	4 2½ on 1½ a. sepia	..	45 0	45 0
145	5 2½ on 1½ a. sepia	..	32 6	32 6
146	3 2½ on 2 a. dull blue	..	35 0	35 0
147	4 2½ on 2 a. dull blue	..	45 0	
148	5 2½ on 2 a. dull blue	..	40 0	40 0

All the varieties of printer's type of the overprint found on the general issue can, of course, be found on the surcharged stamps.

1896. *Stamps of British East Africa, T 11, overprinted with T 1, in black, except the 2½ a., which is in red.*

149	½ a. yellow-green (1 June)	25 0	17 6
150	1 a. carmine-rose (1 June)	25 0	17 6
	a. Overprint double	£12	£7
151	2½ a. deep blue (1 June)	25 0	22 6
152	4½ a. orange-yellow (12 Aug.)	25 0	22 6
153	5 a. olive-bistre (12 Aug.)	25 0	25 0
154	7½ a. mauve (12 Aug.)	25 0	25 0

The same varieties of printer's type of the overprint can be found on the above.

12

Sultan Seyyid Hamed-bin-Thwain.
13

(Recess. De La Rue & Co.)

1896 (20 Sept.). *W* **12.** *P* 14. *Flags in red on all values.*

Type **13.**

156	½ a. yellow-green	1 0	1 0
157	1 a. indigo	1 9	1 9
158	1 a. violet-blue	2 0	2 0
159	2 a. red-brown	1 6	1 6
160	2½ a. bright blue	1 9	1 3
161	2½ a. pale blue	1 9	1 3
162	3 a. grey	3 6	3 6
163	3 a. bluish grey	4 0	3 6
164	4 a. myrtle-green	3 6	4 0
165	4½ a. orange	4 0	4 0
166	5 a. bistre	4 0	4 0
	a. Bisected (2½ a.)	—	40 0
167	7½ a. mauve	4 0	4 0
168	8 a. grey-olive	4 0	4 0

Similar type, but larger.

169	1 r. blue	8 0	8 0
170	1 r. deep blue	7 0	7 0
171	2 r. green	8 6	8 6
172	3 r. dull purple	14 0	14 0
173	4 r. lake	15 0	15 0
174	5 r. sepia	18 6	17 6

The ½, 1, 2, 2½ and 8 a. are known without wmk., these being from edges of the sheets.

1897 (5 Jan.). *No.* 164 *surcharged as before in red.*

175	3 2½ on 4 a. myrtle-green	22 6	22 6
176	4 2½ on 4 a. myrtle-green	35 0	35 0
177	5 2½ on 4 a. myrtle-green	22 6	22 6

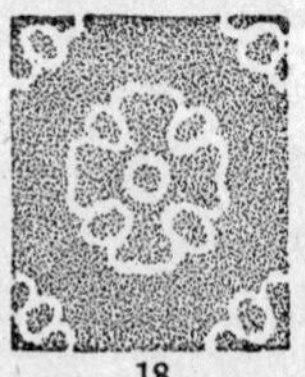

18

19

Sultan Seyyid Hamoud-bin-Mahommed bin Said.

1898 (May). *T* **13.** *Wmk. Mult. Rosettes, T* **18.** *P* 14.

178	½ a. yellow-green	0 9	0 9
179	1 a. indigo	1 3	1 3
179*a*	1 a. greenish black	1 9	1 6
180	2 a. red-brown	1 6	1 9
180*a*	2 a. deep brown	1 6	1 6
181	2½ a. bright blue	1 3	1 0
182	3 a. grey	2 6	2 6
183	4 a. myrtle-green	2 6	2 6
184	4½ a. orange	3 6	3 6

185	5 a. bistre	4 0	4 0
185a	5 a. pale bistre	3 6	3 6
186	7½ a. mauve	4 0	3 6
187	8 a. grey-olive	4 0	4 0

(Recess. De La Rue & Co.)

1899 (Sept.). *Flags in red as before.* *P* 14.

T 19. *W*. 18.

188	½ a. yellow-green	0 6	0 8
189	1 a. indigo	1 0	0 10
190	2 a. red-brown	1 0	1 0
191	2½ a. bright blue	1 3	1 3
192	3 a. grey	2 6	2 6
193	4 a. myrtle-green	2 6	2 6
194	4½ a. orange	3 0	3 0
195	5 a. bistre	3 0	3 0
196	7½ a. mauve	3 6	3 6
197	8 a. grey-olive	3 6	3 6

Similar type, but larger. *W* 12

198	1 r. blue	10 0	10 0
199	2 r. green	18 6	18 6
200	3 r. dull purple	27 6	27 6
201	4 r. lake	40 0	40 0
202	5 r. sepia	42 6	45 0

1901. *Colours changed.* *W* 18. *P* 14.

203	1 a. carmine	0 6	0 4
204	4½ a. blue-black	4 0	3 6

One
(21)

Two
&
Half
(22)

1904. *Provisionals. Stamps of* 1899 *and* 1901 *surcharged* "One," "Two," *or* "Two & Half," *as T* 21 *and* 22, *in black* (B.), *or lake* (L.).

205	1 on 4½ a. orange (B.)	4 6	5 0
206	1 on 4½ a. blue-black (L.)	4 6	5 0
207	2 on 4 a. myrtle-green (L.)	10 0	12 6
208	2½ on 7½ a. mauve (B.)	12 0	15 0
209	2½ on 8 a. grey-olive (B.)	15 0	17 6

Two
&
Half
(22a)

Two
&
Half
(22b)

Varieties. (i.) *Thin, open* "w," *as in T* 22a.

209a	2½ on 7½ a. mauve	80 0	£5
	b. Serif to foot of "f" (T 22b)	60 0	75 0
	c. "Hlaf" for "Half"		
209d	2½ on 8 a. grey-olive	80 0	£5
	e. Serif to foot of "f" (T 22b)	60 0	75 0
	f. "Hlaf" for "Half"		£25

23 24
Monogram of Sultan Seyyid Ali bin Hamoud bin Naherud.

(Typo. De La Rue & Co.)

1904 (8 June). *Multiple wmk., T* 18. *P* 14.

T 23.

210	½ a. green	0 6	0 6
211	1 a. rose-red	0 8	0 4
212	2 a. brown	1 9	2 0
213	2½ a. blue	1 9	1 6
214	3 a. grey	3 6	4 0
215	4 a. deep green	5 0	6 0
216	4½ a. black	6 0	6 6
217	5 a. yellow-brown	4 6	5 0
218	7½ a. purple	7 0	7 6
219	8 a. olive-green	6 6	7 0

T 24.

Background of centre in second colour.

220	1 r. blue and red	17 6	18 6
221	2 r. green and red	35 0	37 6
222	3 r. violet and red	42 6	45 0
223	4 r. claret and red	50 0	52 6
224	5 r. olive-brown and red	70 0	72 6

25 26

27. Sultan Ali bin Hamoud.

28. View of Port.

(Recess. De La Rue & Co.)

1908 (May)–**1909.** T 25 (1 *c. to* 12 *c.*), 26 (15 *c. to* 75 *c.*), 27 (1 *r. to* 5 *r.*), *and* 28 (*higher values*). *Centres in first colour.* *Mult. wmk.*, *T* 18. *P* 14.

225	1 c. pearl-grey (Oct., '09)	0 3	0 3
226	3 c. yellow-green	0 7	0 3
227	6 c. rose-carmine	0 10	0 3
228	10 c. brown (Oct., '09)	2 0	2 3
229	12 c. violet	2 0	1 6
230	15 c. ultramarine	2 0	1 3
231	25 c. sepia	3 0	2 3
232	50 c. blue-green	4 0	4 6
233	75 c. grey-black (Oct., '09)	6 0	6 6
234	1 r. yellow-green	8 6	8 6
235	2 r. violet	17 6	17 6
236	3 r. orange-bistre	25 0	25 0
237	4 r. vermilion	40 0	40 0
238	5 r. Antwerp blue	42 6	42 6

No.	Value	Description	Unused	Used
239	10 r.	blue-green and brown..	£8	£7
240	20 r.	black and yellow-green	£16	
241	30 r.	black and sepia ..	£28	
242	40 r.	black and orange-brown	£40	
243	50 r.	black and mauve ..	£55	
244	100 r.	black & Antwerp blue	£80	
245	200 r.	brown and greenish blk.	£150	

29. Sultan Kalif bin Harub.

30. Native Craft.

31

(Recess. De La Rue & Co.)

1913. *T* **29**, **30** (1 *r. to* 5 *r.*) *and* **31** (10 *r. to* 200 *r.*). *W* **18.** *P* 14.

No.	Value	Description	Unused	Used
246	1 c.	grey	0 3	0 4
247	3 c.	yellow-green	0 6	0 4
248	6 c.	rose-carmine ..	0 10	0 5
249	10 c.	brown	1 6	1 3
250	12 c.	violet	1 3	0 6
251	15 c.	blue	1 9	0 9
252	25 c.	sepia	2 6	1 6
253	50 c.	blue-green	7 0	6 0
254	75 c.	grey-black	6 6	6 6
255	1 r.	yellow-green	8 6	5 0
256	2 r.	violet	15 0	15 0
257	3 r.	orange-bistre	22 6	22 6
258	4 r.	scarlet	27 6	27 6
259	5 r.	Antwerp blue ..	37 6	37 6
260	10 r.	green and brown ..	85 0	85 0
260*a*	20 r.	black and green ..	£10	£10
260*b*	30 r.	black and brown ..	£9	£9
260*c*	40 r.	black and vermilion ..	£9	£9
260*d*	50 r.	black and purple	£12	£12
260*e*	100 r.	black and blue ..	£20	£20
260*f*	200 r.	brown and black ..	£35	£35

1914. *As last, but wmk. Multiple Crown CA.*

No.	Value	Description	Unused	Used
261	1 c.	grey	0 2	0 2
262	3 c.	yellow-green	0 6	0 4
263	3 c.	dull green	0 6	0 4
264	6 c.	deep carmine	0 9	0 4
265	6 c.	bright rose-carmine ..	0 6	0 3
266	15 c.	deep ultramarine ..	1 3	1 3
268	50 c.	blue-green	3 0	3 0
269	75 c.	grey-black	4 0	4 0
270	1 r.	yellow-green	6 0	3 0
271	2 r.	violet	12 6	12 6
272	3 r.	orange-bistre	15 0	15 0
273	4 r.	scarlet	25 0	25 0
274	5 r.	Antwerp blue	37 6	37 6
275	10 r.	green and brown ..	85 0	90 0

1921–29. *As last. Wmk. Mult. Script CA.*

No.	Value	Description	Unused	Used
276	1 c.	slate-grey	0 3	0 3
277	3 c.	yellow-green	0 5	0 5
278	6 c.	carmine-red	0 6	0 4
279	10 c.	brown	1 3	0 8
280	12 c.	violet	1 3	0 10
281	15 c.	blue	1 6	1 6
282	25 c.	sepia	2 6	2 6
283	50 c.	myrtle-green	3 0	3 6
284	75 c.	slate	4 0	4 6
285	1 r.	yellow-green	3 0	3 0
286	2 r.	deep violet	6 0	6 6
287	3 r.	orange-bistre	8 6	8 6
288	4 r.	scarlet	15 0	17 6
289	5 r.	Prussian blue	17 6	20 0
290	10 r.	green and brown ..	35 0	37 6
291	20 r.	black and green ..	£5	110 0
291*a*	30 r.	black and brown ('29)	£9	£10

1922. *Types and perf. as last. Colours changed and new values.*

(*a*) *Wmk. Mult. Crown CA.*

No.	Value	Description	Unused	Used
292	8 c.	purple/*pale yellow* ..	0 10	0 10
293	10 c.	myrtle/*pale yellow* ..	0 10	0 9

(*b*) *Wmk. Mult. Script CA.*

No.	Value	Description	Unused	Used
294	3 c.	yellow	0 5	0 4
295	4 c.	green	0 7	0 8
296	6 c.	purple/*blue*	0 9	0 5
297	12 c.	carmine-red	1 3	1 3
298	20 c.	indigo	2 0	2 0

32. Sultan Kalif bin Harub.

(Recess. De La Rue & Co.)

1926–27. *T* **32** ("CENTS" *in seriffed capitals*). *Wmk. Mult. Script CA. P* 14.

No.	Value	Description	Unused	Used
299	1 c.	brown	0 4	0 4
300	3 c.	yellow-orange	0 5	0 5
301	4 c.	deep dull green	1 3	1 0
302	6 c.	violet	0 8	0 4
303	8 c.	slate	0 10	0 10
304	10 c.	olive-green	0 10	0 10
305	12 c.	carmine-red	1 0	0 10
306	20 c.	bright blue	1 6	1 0
307	25 c.	purple/*yellow*	2 6	2 6
308	50 c.	claret	3 0	3 0
309	75 c.	sepia	3 6	3 6

(*Currency.* 100 *cents* = 1 *shilling.*)

33. Sultan Kalif bin Harub.

(Recess. De La Rue & Co., Ltd.)

1936 (1 Jan.). *T* **33** ("cents" *in sans-serif capitals*), *and T* **30/1**, *but values in shillings. Wmk. Mult. Script CA.* *P* 14×13½–14.

No.	Type	Description	Unused	Used
310	33	5 c. green	0 2	0 2
311	„	10 c. black	0 3	0 2
312	„	15 c. carmine-red	0 3	0 3
313	„	20 c. orange	0 4	0 3
314	„	25 c. purple/*yellow*	0 5	0 6
315	„	30 c. ultramarine	0 6	0 6
316	„	40 c. sepia	0 7	1 0
317	„	50 c. claret	0 8	0 8
318	30	1s. yellow-green	1 4	1 6
319	„	2s. slate-violet	2 8	4 0
320	„	5s. scarlet	6 6	10 0
321	„	7.50s. light blue	10 0	15 0
322	31	10s. green and brown	12 6	20 0

36. Sultan Kalif bin Harub.

(Recess. De La Rue & Co., Ltd.)

1936 (9 Dec.). *Silver Jubilee of Sultan. Wmk. Mult. Script CA.* *P* 14.

No.	Type	Description	Unused	Used
323	36	10 c. black and olive-green	0 9	0 6
324	„	20 c. black & bright purple	1 6	1 9
325	„	30 c. black & deep ultram.	1 6	1 9
326	„	50 c. black & orange-verm.	2 0	2 6

POSTAGE DUE STAMPS.

Insufficiently prepaid.
Postage due.
1 cent.

D 1

(Types D 1 and D 2 typo. by the Government Printer.)

1930–33.

(*a*) *Rouletted* 10, *with imperf. sheet edges. No gum.*

No.	Type	Description	Unused	Used
D 1	D 1	1 c. black/*orange*	1 0	
D 2	„	2 c. black/*orange*	1 0	
D 3	„	3 c. black/*orange*	0 6	
		a. "cent.s" for "cents."	4 0	
D 4	„	6 c. black/*orange*	..	
		a. "cent.s" for "cents."		
D 5	„	9 c. black/*orange*	1 0	
		a. "cent.s" for "cents."	8 6	10 0
D 6	„	12 c. black/*orange*	..	
		a. "cent.s" for "cents."		
D 7	„	12 c. black/*green*	—	17 6
D 8	„	15 c. black/*orange*	1 0	
		a. "cent.s" for "cents."	8 6	10 0
D 9	„	18 c. black/*salmon*	6 6	10 0
		a. "cent.s" for "cents."	17 6	20 0
D10	D 1	18 c. black/*orange*	1 6	
		a. "cent.s" for "cents."	10 0	12 6
D11	„	20 c. black/*orange*	1 9	
		a. "cent.s" for "cents."	15 0	
D12	„	21 c. black/*orange*	1 9	
		a. "cent.s" for "cents."	15 0	17 6
D13	„	25 c. black/*magenta*	..	
		a. "cent.s" for "cents."		
D14	„	25 c. black/*orange*	..	
D15	„	31 c. black/*orange*	5 0	
		a. "cent.s" for "cents."	35 0	
D16	„	50 c. black/*orange*	12 6	
		a. "cent.s" for "cents."	£5	
D17	„	75 c. black/*orange*	18 6	
		a. "cent.s" for "cents"		

Sheets of the first printings of all values except the 1 c. and 2 c. contained one stamp showing the error "cent.s" for "cents."

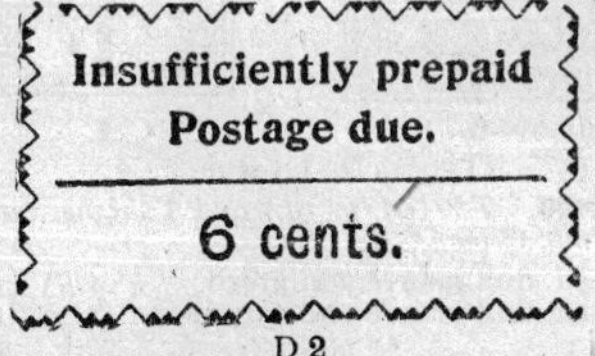

D 2

(*b*) *Rouletted* 5. *No gum.*

No.	Type	Description	Unused	Used
D18	D 2	2 c. black/*salmon*	0 9	
D19	„	3 c. black/*rose*	2 6	3 6
D21	„	6 c. black/*yellow*	1 0	
D22	„	12 c. black/*blue*	1 6	
D23	„	25 c. black/*rose*	6 0	
D24	„	25 c. black/*lilac*	2 6	

D 3

(Typo. De La Rue & Co., Ltd.)

1936 (1 Jan.). *Wmk. Mult. Script CA.* *P* 14.

No.	Type	Description	Unused	Used
D25	D 3	5 c. violet	0 2	
D26	„	10 c. scarlet	0 3	
D27	„	20 c. green	0 4	
D28	„	30 c. brown	0 6	
D29	„	40 c. ultramarine	0 7	
D30	„	1s. grey	1 4	

ZULULAND.

ZULULAND (1) ZULULAND. (2)

1888–93. *Stamps of Great Britain (wmk. Imperial Crown, the* 5*s. wmk. Anchor, P* 14), *overprinted with T* 1, *in black.*

No.	Description	Unused	Used
1	½d. vermilion	1 3	1 6
2	1d. dull purple	4 0	4 0
3	2d. green and carmine	6 0	6 0
4	2½d. purple/*blue*	12 6	10 6
5	3d. purple/*yellow*	15 0	12 6
6	4d. green and brown	12 6	12 6
7	5d. dull purple and blue ('93)	32 6	32 6
8	6d. purple/*rose-red*	20 0	20 0
9	9d. dull purple and blue	37 6	37 6
10	1s. green	37 6	37 6
11	5s. rose	£8	£8

Postage stamp of Natal (*T* **23**, *wmk. Crown CA, P* 14) *optd. with T* **2**, *in black.*

12	½d. green	8	6	9	6
	a. Overprint double	£6			
	b. Overprint inverted	£10			
	c. Without stop	12	6	12	6
	d. Overprint omitted (pair) ..				

1894 (Jan.). *Postage stamp of Natal* (*T* **15**, *wmk. Crown CA, P* 14) *optd. with T* **1**, *in black.*

16	6d. mauve	22	6	22	6

8 4

(Typo. De La Rue & Co.)

1894–96. *T* **3** (½*d. to* 3*d.*) *and* **4** (*higher values*). *Wmk. Crown CA. P* 14.

20	½d. dull mauve and green ..	1	3	1	3
21	1d. dull mauve and carmine	1	3	1	3
22	2½d. dull mauve and ultram. ..	4	0	3	6
23	3d. dull mauve and olive-brn.	5	0	4	6
24	6d. dull mauve and black ..	4	6	5	0
25	1s. green	6	0	7	0
26	2s. 6d. green and black ..	25	0	25	0
27	4s. green and carmine ..	35	0	37	6
28	£1 purple/*red*	£10		£8	
29	£5 purple and black/*red* ..	£45		£20	

Dangerous forgeries exist of the £1 and £5.

FISCAL STAMPS USED FOR POSTAGE

Fiscal stamps of Natal (*T* **41**, *name and value in second colour, wmk. Crown CA, P* 14) *optd. with T* **1**, *in black.*

51	1d. dull mauve	3	6	3	0
52	1s. mauve and carmine ..	55	0	55	0
54	5s. mauve and carmine ..	£8		£8	
55	9s. mauve and carmine ..	£8		£8	
56	£1 green	£9		£7	
57	£5 green and red	£28		£22	
58	£20 green and black	£75		£55	

The issue of Zululand stamps ceased on June 30, 1898, the territory having been annexed to Natal on December 31, 1897.

THE END